PETROLEUM
REFINERY ENGINEERING

THE SERIES

PETROLEUM
REFINERY ENGINEERING

W. L. Nelson

Consulting Petroleum and Chemical Engineer
Professor of Petroleum Refining
University of Tulsa

Fourth Edition

McGRAW-HILL BOOK COMPANY

NEW YORK   ST. LOUIS   SAN FRANCISCO   LONDON   SYDNEY
TORONTO   MEXICO   PANAMA

Lovingly dedicated to
Marian, my wife

PREFACE

When first published (1936) a main purpose of this book was the introduction of the principles of chemical engineering to the petroleum refining industry. The situation is now reversed. The chemical industry now looks to petroleum refiners for leadership in the development of many phases of chemical engineering especially those related to the large-scale processing of fluids and to the application of catalysts. Refinery engineering organizations made vital contributions in original commercial preparation of uranium or atomic fuels.

Although conceived originally as a textbook, it rapidly became apparent that industry also wanted or needed the book. Accordingly succeeding editions have been aimed more and more toward providing a survey of the industry's engineering practices. International interest is being recognized in the Fourth Edition by the introduction of more information on foreign crude oils and more complete information on the evaluation of oils. Crude oil is being shipped in increasing quantities from Venezuela, the Middle East, and Canada, and the refiner must be familiar with foreign oils as well as his local varieties not only because the properties and specifications of the products are affected but because the economy of the entire industry is influenced. New Appendix B of the Fourth Edition introduces the analyses of over 70 foreign crude oils as well as about 90 representative United States oils for comparison.

When the First Edition was written, much of the information on design computations had not theretofore been published, and such methods were new to much of the industry. This situation has also been reversed. Computation methods now flow from the industry at a rate that cannot be accommodated in new editions.

At least twelve major books or series of books relating to petroleum refining were published prior to 1939, but only a few of these have been revised and scarcely any new publications have appeared. Undoubtedly the rapidly growing complexity of the industry and the enormity of the current literature have been a discouragement to authors. To properly explore the current literature would require the continuous services of an entire staff of engineers and the publishing of editions at two- or three-year intervals. Important engineering material could not be included in the First Edition, and the situation has become more unsatisfactory with each succeeding edition. Growth during the last decade has been especially rapid, and in addition an entirely new chemical industry based upon petroleum as the raw stock is emerging. Chemical developments have been recognized throughout the entire Fourth Edition but especially in the chapters pertaining to processing, chemical and solvent treatment, thermal decomposition, and, of course, the conversion of gaseous hydrocarbons. Catalytic cracking and catalytic reforming are now practiced in nearly all refineries. Hydrocracking and hydrodesulfurization processes have been thoroughly explored, and they, too, may find extensive application. The status of atomic treatments does not, at the moment, warrant incorporation into the Fourth Edition. The long lists of references at the ends of chapters of earlier editions have been deleted in the Fourth Edition.

The following statements from the First Edition are still pertinent:

Engineering involves the practical application of scientific knowledge, and hence I have made a conscious effort to emphasize the practical phases of engineering work. In so doing it has often been necessary to resort to empirical relationships. No apology is necessary for such a treatment because engineers must build and operate plants regardless of inadequate information. In fact the history of industrial development shows that commercial plants are usually built before the theory of the process is fully understood. Scientific study follows the empirical development, and science finally administers those fine improvements which stamp the new process as truly great. The process of empirical growth will always be the lot of the practical scientist or engineer.

For the same reasons some handbook information has been introduced. Although such information is not profound, it is the tool by which theory can be put into action. Such information is also necessary in the solution of illustrative problems, and I believe that no method of engineering study is more effective than detailed examples. Furthermore an engineer must spend more time applying information than deriving or finding it, and hence handbook information and comprehensive references are provided. The current literature contains much that is useful, but the literature is so voluminous that it may be useless to a busy engineer unless it is presented in an organized form. I have attempted to organize this contemporaneous literature, but I have refrained as far as possible from tiring the average reader with too many references and with conflicting opinions.

The author is greatly indebted to all of those who have contributed to the several editions.   In connection with the Fourth Edition, A. Paul Buthod, Chairman of the Department of Refinery and Chemical Engineering of the University of Tulsa, has been especially helpful throughout the entire book, and Chapter 17 on the subject of Heat Transfer is his particular contribution.

Wilbur L. Nelson

CONTENTS

CHAPTER 1

HISTORY AND DEVELOPMENT OF REFINING

Coal oil and sperm oil were the common burner fuels when the Drake discovery well was drilled in 1859. It has been estimated that 60 coal distillation plants operated between 1852 and 1859. Perhaps the first real petroleum refinery was that of William Barnsdall and William A. Abbott, built at Titusville, Pa., in 1860 at a cost of about $15,000, although records indicate that petroleum was distilled in Russia in 1735.[1]

Continuous Distillation. Early refiners employed batch systems of separation, but the essentials of continuous operation were being explored and patents were issued as early as 1860. Developments continued, but the first widely recognized continuous plants were those of M. J. Trumble (1912). These plants involved the use of both pipestills and continuous fractionators. Modern distillation plants are completely continuous, with the exception of coke stills which are operated either as batch or as semicontinuous operations. In modern plants several distillation units are often connected so that the hot product from one unit (usually the residue) is pumped directly to another. Also, several units may have a common heat-exchange system by which the charge stock for one unit is heated in other units. In other phases of refining, such as treating, dewaxing, compounding, and packaging, the processing is still partly batch or semicontinuous, but continuous operation is not of great value in these operations.

Cracking or Thermal Decomposition. Even the phenomenon of cracking is not a modern development. True, the large plants and the wholesale manufacture of decomposition products are new, but thermal decomposition was actually practiced in the distillation of coal and oil shale even before the days of the oil industry. During the first years of the petroleum industry a "cracking distillation," in addition to the customary distillation with steam, was practiced. The cracking distillation is reported to have been discovered accidentally in 1861. A distillation in a 16-bbl still had been half completed, and the stillman had built a strong fire. The stillman intended to be away an hour but was unable to return until

[1] Herodotus (450 B.C.) and other historians report petroleum and tar (by other names) at dates before 1735, but they fail to tell how the oil was refined.

1

4 hr later. He found that a light-colored distillate of a low specific gravity was being collected. The specific gravity was even lower than that of the product before he left. Upon investigation, it was found that a heavy oil was condensing on cooler parts of the equipment and dropping back into parts of the still that were at a temperature sufficiently high to cause decomposition of the heavy oil into lower-boiling-point products. In the early days of the industry, gasoline was of little value, and cracking was practiced for the purpose of producing more kerosene than could be obtained by steam or simple distillation. The first attempts to produce gasoline by cracking were by the decomposition of petroleum vapor. None of the early commercial attempts were successful until the Gyro process was developed in about 1925. Success was

TABLE 1-1

Refinery statistics	Jan., 1931	Jan., 1941	Jan., 1951	Jan., 1956
Operating capacity, U.S., 1,000 bbl/day[a]	3,707	4,181	6,702	8,381
Cracked-gasoline capacity, U.S., 1,000 bbl/day[a]	560[b]	1,103	1,853	2,777
Cracked gasoline, percentage of total refinery gasoline[b]	41.0	51.3	60	70.3
Average capacity of U.S. refineries, bbl/day	10,700	10,000	20,600	28,200
Number of operating refineries (U.S.)[a]	346	420	325	294
Foreign capacity, excluding U.S.S.R., 1,000 bbl/day[b]	1,577	2,588	4,300	7,244

[a] *U.S. Bur. Mines Inform. Circs.*
[b] Approximate.

attained by the elimination of traces of liquid from the vapor. The liquid particles had been wetting the walls of the heating tubes where they decomposed into coke which plugged the tubes. Modern thermal reforming and gas-cracking processes are possible because of the discovery of this principle.

The liquid-phase cracking processes were the first to be commercially applied, and the Burton process was the first to be practiced on a large scale. Development began in 1910; a patent was issued in 1912; recognition of Dr. Burton by the Willard Gibbs Medal was given in 1918; and by 1921 over 800 Burton stills were said to be in operation. Other early liquid-phase processes were the Fleming, Isom, and Emerson processes.

The importance of cracking in the modern refinery is emphasized by the statistics shown in Tables 1-1, 6-1, 6-2, and page 759.

The general scheme of processing is much the same in all modern thermal cracking plants. The advantage of cracking only those stocks which contain no cracked tar is recognized by everyone. A residual charge stock is often distilled in the cracking unit itself, and only the distilled part of the feedstock is exposed to severe cracking conditions. In most modern plants, residual stocks are introduced into the cracking plant through a high-temperature cracking coil which greatly increases the amount of distillable material in the residual feedstock.

Later developments in thermal cracking were "viscosity breaking" and "reforming." The mild decomposition known as viscosity breaking is conducted on residual or asphaltic feedstocks. Originally it was aimed at a reduction of viscosity and pour point, but it was soon learned that a large amount of partially cracked gas oil, which could then be processed in a conventional cracking plant, was also produced. Reforming units are cracking plants that operate on naphtha or low-octane-number gasoline for the production of a large yield of highly antiknock gasoline. These units were developed in response to the growing demand for antiknock gasoline and for larger and larger amounts of motor fuel.

High-boiling reactive polymers are formed during thermal cracking, and they are currently removed as residual fuel oil by distillation. Reaction or coking of the polymers is also prevented by diluting the material undergoing cracking with so-called "recycle stock." Difficulties with reactive polymers do not occur in the modern catalytic cracking processes because these processes employ adsorptive catalysts that remove the polymers in the form of coke on the surface of the catalyst. In such processes the cracking reactions can be much more complete, and the antiknock quality of the product is correspondingly high.

Fractionation. The term "fractionation" refers to the separation of a liquid mixture into several products of shorter boiling range by means of vaporization. In early refineries this separation was obtained by a series of distillations in which, first, an inaccurate separation was made and then the partly separated products were redistilled several times, if necessary, until finally the product met market requirements. The next development was to fractionate by partial condensation (i.e., a mixture of vapor was condensed in portions by successively cooling the vapor to lower and lower temperatures). An invention of this nature was that of Hugh L. Allen,[2] in which the vapor was successively cooled by means of a series of air-cooled condensers into several liquid products.

The modern era of refining dates from the adoption of pipestills and bubble towers. The name "bubble tower" has become common because the vapor in the tower bubbles through the liquid on the plates in the tower. In bubble-tower fractionation a mixture of ascending vapor is scrubbed by a descending flow of oil. Bubble towers have been so universally adopted, all within a few years, that no one can be accredited

[2] Eng. Pat. 117,277 (1918).

with invention. In fact the fundamentals of fractionation were borrowed directly from the chemical distillation industries. Today bubble towers are used in topping plants, rerun plants, vacuum plants, cracking plants, natural-gasoline stabilizers, absorption plants, and steam stripping operations.

Natural-gasoline Plants. Natural gasoline attracted little attention until about 1912, at which time the demand for motor fuels became acute. Today more than 10 per cent of all gasoline is manufactured from natural gas. The first widely used method of recovery was the compression process. As gas is compressed, the dew point is raised so that, upon cooling to the original temperature, a mixture of hydrocarbons condenses. The condensate contains a large percentage of volatile hydrocarbons, such as propane, which must be removed before the gasoline is a suitable motor fuel. The first method that was used to remove these hydrocarbons from the raw gasoline was called "weathering." Weathering was accomplished by allowing the "wild" gasoline to stand in an open vessel for a time. A large part of the gasoline was lost during weathering.

For a few years following World War I, the *adsorption* process received much attention, but since that time it has been almost abandoned. In this process the gasoline was adsorbed by charcoal and recovered from the charcoal by steaming.

In later processes, natural gas was passed through absorption chambers or packed columns, in which the gasoline was absorbed by naphtha. These naphtha columns finally developed into the *absorption* process of today. In this process the natural gasoline is absorbed by a low-boiling-range gas oil, and the gasoline is recovered from the rich gas oil by heating it and stripping the gasoline from it with steam. A high pressure assists absorption, but pressures above about 130 psi have been found uneconomical unless the gas happens to be available at a high pressure in the field. Weathering has been replaced by the use of high-pressure (150 psig) fractionators (stabilizers) which precisely separate the gaseous hydrocarbons from the stable natural gasoline.

Dewaxing. The filter-press method of dewaxing followed by sweating, as originally used in Scotland for shale oil before the development of the oil industry, is still a widely used method of dewaxing the lighter wax-bearing oils. Heavy residual wax-bearing stocks were first dewaxed by cold-settling. In this process the oil was chilled and allowed to stand in insulated tanks. The centrifuge process of dewaxing residual stocks was studied for many years before it was entirely successful. The difficulties had been the attainment of sufficiently high centrifuge speeds and the tendency of the petrolatum wax to stick to the bowl of the machine. In about 1921 warm water was suggested as a carrying liquid to be injected at the edge of the bowl. The use of warm water was successful, and the centrifuge method of today is essentially the same process as was then used.

Recently, solvent dewaxing methods have become important. An important advantage of these processes is the ability to handle both light and heavy wax stocks by a single process. Many different solvent processes are being practiced commercially, but the use of methyl ethyl ketone has been accepted almost to the exclusion of other solvents. It is also used for the deoiling of waxes.

Chemical Processing. Although Professor B. Silliman[3] recognized in his report of Apr. 16, 1855, the chemical possibilities of petroleum, no bulk chemical conversion of petroleum was practiced until cracking was introduced in 1912. The removal of small amounts of impurities by treatment with sulfuric acid, caustic soda, etc., has been and continues to be practiced. In 1927 the process of hydrogenation as developed by the Standard Development Company attracted attention. This process is essentially a thermal decomposition (cracking) process conducted at high pressures and in the presence of hydrogen. Although several large plants have been operated, the economic position of bulk-scale hydrogenation has not yet (1957) been established.

Although the usefulness of adsorptive earths and other materials had been known for many years, successful commercial operation of catalytic cracking processes did not appear until about 1937 with the advent of the Houdry catalytic cracking process. The catalyst acts primarily in adsorbing the reactive tarlike materials produced by thermal cracking, but it may also exert some influence on the cracking reaction. Since World War II some type of catalytic cracking plant has been employed by all major refiners.

A multitude of processes for utilizing the olefinic hydrocarbons of cracking-still gas have followed the development of polymerization processes in about 1935. Among these are processes of alkylation, hydrogenation of hydrocarbons, dehydrogenation, catalytic desulfurization, and the manufacture of many organic chemicals. Although the chemicals so manufactured are small in bulk compared with the regular distillation products of the industry, they are important because they foretell the cheap large-scale production of many heretofore somewhat scarce materials.

Chronology of Development. In the following outline no attempt has been made to set the date at which new processes were conceived. Developments are not mentioned until the time when they were generally accepted by the industry.

1860 to about 1885. The major refinery product was kerosene or burning oil. During this period disfavor was brought upon the industry by

[3] *Am. Chem.*, **2**, 18 (1871–1872).

the sale of burning oils that contained too much gasoline. Laws were enacted limiting their flash point.

1885–1900. Mineral lubricating oils gained favor with the public. Until this time vegetable oils were considered the best. Paraffin-base lubricating oils gained a favorable reputation which has been retained to this day.

1900–1914. Shortly after 1900 gasoline began to be valuable, and within a few years it had grown to be the most useful refinery product. The demand became so great that many new oil fields were discovered, and fundamental improvements in refining methods ensued. The compression process for the recovery of natural gasoline was developed, and experiments were conducted concerning cracking.

1914–1925. The ever-increasing demand for gasoline caused the refiner to turn to methods of recovering more of it from crude oil. The thermal cracking processes were brought to a high degree of perfection, and the fundamentals of heating, fractionation, heat transfer, and absorption were developed and applied commercially. Continuous processing systems using fractionating towers, pipe- or tubestill heaters, and heat exchangers were developed. Structural equipment was developed for high pressures and high temperatures. In 1920 a marked increase in the use of fuel oil for the generation of power was noted, and the tendency has continued until today.

1925–1929. During 1925–1935, the industry profited greatly by the application of chemical engineering practices, and the scarcely recognized young science of chemical engineering was able to establish itself firmly by practice in the petroleum industry. To this day, the petroleum industry is the major outlet for chemical engineers. During this period the large profits from lubricating-oil processing attracted attention, and vacuum distillation was developed. Until this time vacuum distillation had not been truly successful, because batch or shellstill heating had to be used. The newly acquired knowledge of pipestill and fractionating-tower design made the development of continuous vacuum-distilling systems a logical step. Low-cold-test oils were produced by direct expansion of ammonia rather than by the customary method of circulating brine. Continuous pipestill equipment was adapted to all distillation operations including the rerunning of pressure-distillate and lubricating-oil stocks. The Edeleanu method of solvent treating with sulfur dioxide proved to be commercially successful.

1929–1935. The demand for highly antiknock gasoline resulted in the development of vapor-phase cracking plants, gasoline-reforming units, and an ever-increasing use of cracking plants. The hydrogenation process was developed, but it has not been widely used because of unfavorable economic conditions. Several successful solvent-dewaxing and solvent-treating methods were developed. High Viscosity Index lubricating oils were produced by solvent-treating methods. Vacuum distillation was widely applied to the manufacture of road oil and asphalt. Tetraethyllead was adopted as a means of improving the antiknock properties of motor fuels.

1935–1941. Propane, butane, and the unsaturated hydrocarbons found in cracking-still gas were utilized for polymerization, dehydrogenation, and alkylation processes. Polymerization of olefins into "poly" gasoline was practiced at nearly all large cracking plants. The Houdry catalytic cracking process was introduced. Refiners delayed the formation of gum in cracked gasoline by the use of oxidation-inhibiting chemicals; colored gasolines were generally accepted by the public; and the properties of lubricating oils were enhanced by the use of additive agents for lowering the pour point, improving the Viscosity Index, and imparting extreme pressure properties. Ethylene and the gaseous olefins were obtained in high concentration by the vapor-phase cracking of ethane, propane, and the butanes. Large amounts of formaldehyde and alcohol were manufactured from natural gas. Lower-viscosity automotive engine oils were employed.

1941–1947. Heavy-duty lubricating oils were produced by the introduction of numerous chemical additive agents for improving pour point, Viscosity Index, detergent and suspensoid properties, oxidation stability, tendency to foam, and tendency toward corrosion. Large chemical manufacturers introduced the first nonpetroleum synthetic lubricating oils. The demand for diesel fuel oil and domestic distillate fuel oil increased rapidly. The urgency during World War II hastened the manufacture of high-melting-point microcrystalline waxes from petrolatum or crude-oil tank bottoms; and numerous chemicals were manufactured from petroleum on a large scale, including toluene, glycerol, butadiene, styrene, isopentane, and isooctane in the form of alkylate for aviation gasoline; and many petroleum hydrocarbons were separated on a commercial scale by superfractionation processes. Most synthetic tire rubber was derived from petroleum, and it was found that the coarser carbon black produced from oil rather than natural gas was superior for compounding with the new rubber. The Fischer-Tropsch process of producing gasoline, etc., from natural gas attracted wide attention. The Houdry, Thermofor, Fluid, or Hydroforming catalytic cracking processes were employed in all large refineries, and catalytic desulfurization of gasoline was widely used. The production of 100 octane aviation gasoline attained 500,000 bbl per day in 1945 but decreased rapidly after the war. Cooperative associations operated more than 11 refineries, and 2,327 local cooperatives handled oil products in 1944. Physical methods of analyzing the chemical structures of oil molecules were developed whereby chemists for the first time were enabled to apply extensively the science of chemistry to high-boiling oils.

1947–1957.   Petrochemical manufacture increased tremendously, and synthetic rubber was more widely used than natural rubber.   Sulfur from refinery and natural gases became a significant amount of total sulfur production.   Natural gasoline, liquefied petroleum gases, and natural gas were stored in natural underground reservoirs.   The shortage of cooling water in some areas hastened the development of air-cooled product coolers.   The development of jet and turbine aircraft engines caused a rapid increase in jet fuel manufacture so that the middle distillate portion of petroleum was in great demand for distillates, diesel fuel, jet fuel, and rocket fuel.   Air or flue-gas lift of catalyst as developed for the Thermofor and Houdriflow processes was the major contribution in catalytic cracking.   The first truly catalytic processes to be applied to the bulk-scale treatment of petroleum were introduced as Platforming or similar platinum catalyst reforming processes.   Starting from 1950, catalytic reforming increased by 1955 to nearly 1 million barrels per day, and nearly every refiner had installed a plant.   Adequate supplies of benzene and toluene are now assured because the platinum-refined gasolines are rich in aromatics.   Sweetening by means of inhibitors rather than chemical treatment was introduced.   Improvements in lubricating-oil manufacture led to the sale of such high Viscosity Index oils that a single grade of oil could be used during all seasons of the year.   The continual surplus of residual fuel oil at inland points led to a wider use of coking and the development of continuous coking processes.   Refrigeration was employed rather than pressure in the storage and transportation of volatile products such as propane and even liquefied natural gas.   The increasing percentage of sulfur in newly discovered oils led to the development of several hydrogenation methods of desulfurizing gas oil and distillate materials.   Premium gasoline of 100 Research octane number was first marketed in 1956, and many alkylation plants were installed in maintaining the so-called "octane race."   Room temperature dewaxing was accomplished on a commercial scale by the use of urea, which forms a complex with paraffin hydrocarbons.

CHAPTER 2

COMPOSITION OF PETROLEUM

Most of the compounds found in petroleum are composed of hydrogen and carbon. In addition to these materials, called hydrocarbons, other compounds containing small amounts of sulfur, oxygen, and nitrogen are also present. The physical operations of refining, such as vaporization, fractionation, and cooling, are governed to a large extent by the properties of the hydrocarbons because they constitute the bulk of the petroleum, but the chemical operations, such as treating and filtering, are governed by the presence of sulfur, oxygen, and nitrogen compounds and, to some extent, by the small amounts of reactive hydrocarbons that may be present. Russian crude oils[1] and certain naphthene-base oils contain relatively large amounts of oxygen. The oxygen is often combined in the form of naphthenic acids. Nitrogen is most often found in naphthene-base oils and is generally supposed to be in the form of basic compounds similar to the alkyl quinolines.[2] Sulfur may be present as dissolved free sulfur, hydrogen sulfide, or as organic compounds,[3] such as the thiophenes, sulfonic acids, mercaptans, alkyl sulfates, and alkyl sulfides. Some of these sulfur compounds are not found in crude petroleum, but they are produced from other compounds during distillation and refining. Sulfur compounds are particularly troublesome because they are usually foul smelling and some of them are corrosive. A few parts per million of metalloorganic compounds containing iron, nickel, vanadium, arsenic, etc., are found in some petroleum, and such amounts are poisonous to some catalysts.

Many series of hydrocarbons are found in crude petroleum, and still other series are produced by cracking and hydrogenation. Among the series that are said to have been identified in petroleum are those having the type formulas C_nH_{2n+2}, C_nH_{2n}, C_nH_{2n-2}, C_nH_{2n-4}, C_nH_{2n-6}, C_nH_{2n-8}, C_nH_{2n-10}, C_nH_{2n-14}, and C_nH_{2n-20}. Inasmuch as most of the higher members of these series have never been produced synthetically or prepared in sufficient quantity for study, we have few compounds with which to com-

---

[1] Vuistavkina, T., *Neftyanoe Khoz.*, **18**, 1000 (1930).

[2] Schulze, King, and Thompson, *J. Am. Chem. Soc.*, **52**, 1239 (1930).

[3] Egloff and Morrell, *Chem. Met. Eng.*, **28**, 633 (1923).

pare those which are isolated from petroleum. Furthermore, the isolation of pure compounds is extremely difficult because the properties of adjacent members of a series differ from one another only slightly and because constant-boiling mixtures, which cannot be separated by fractionation, are prevalent. These difficulties and the multitude of hydrocarbons that are present in petroleum[4] have discouraged the study of petroleum chemistry.

Hydrocarbon Series. Of the many hydrocarbon series present in petroleum, only a few have been studied thoroughly enough to guide commercial development. The best known series are the paraffin, olefin, naphthene, aromatic, diolefin, and acetylene (Figs. 2-1a to f are examples of the structural formulas of these types of compounds).

The *paraffin series* (type formula C_nH_{2n+2}) is characterized by great stability. The name of each member ends in -*ane*—meth*ane*, eth*ane*, hex*ane*, and hexadec*ane*. At room temperatures the members, with the exception of those containing a tertiary carbon atom, are not acted upon by fuming sulfuric acid, concentrated alkalies, nitric acid, or even the powerful oxidizer chromic acid. They react slowly with chlorine in sunlight and with both chlorine and bromine if a catalyst is present.[5] Reaction usually occurs by the *substitution* of an element or a chemical group for a hydrogen atom. The lower members have been identified in most crude petroleums, but Mabery[6] reports that Mahoning County, Ohio, crude oil contains no paraffin hydrocarbons. The higher members of the paraffin series are probably present in most petroleums, although crude oils that are entirely free from wax may contain no high-boiling paraffin hydrocarbons. Paraffin wax probably consists of straight- or branched-chain paraffin hydrocarbons.[7] Egloff, Schaad, and Lowry[8] have made a thorough study of the decomposition of paraffin hydrocarbons (Fig. 2-1a and f).

The *olefin* or *ethylene series* (type formula C_nH_{2n}) is composed of unsaturated hydrocarbons; i.e., the members of this series are capable of uniting directly with other materials such as chlorine, bromine, hydrochloric acid, and sulfuric acid, without displacing a hydrogen atom. The names of these hydrocarbons end in -*ene*, as eth*ene* (ethyl*ene*), prop*ene* (propyl*ene*), and but*ene* (butyl*ene*). Unsaturated compounds react with and dissolve in sulfuric acid and may thus be removed from petroleum oils. The low-boiling olefins are probably not present in crude petroleum, but they are

[4] Some authorities estimate that 3,000 compounds may be present in crude petroleum.

[5] Egloff, Schaad, and Lowry, The Halogenation of the Paraffin Hydrocarbons, *Chem. Rev.*, **8**, (1) (1931).

[6] *Ind. Eng. Chem.*, **6**, 101–107 (1914).

[7] Buchler and Graves, The Petroleum Waxes, *Ind. Eng. Chem.*, **19**, 718 (1927).

[8] The Decomposition of the Paraffin Hydrocarbons, *J. Phys. Chem.*, **34**, 1617 (1930).

‚ound in cracked products. Egloff, Schaad, and Lowry[9] have made an excellent study of the literature of the olefin hydrocarbons (Fig. 2-1*b*).

The *naphthene series* (type formula C_nH_{2n}) has the same type formula as the olefin series but has greatly different properties. The naphthenes are ring or cyclic compounds, whereas the olefins are straight-chain compounds in which a double bond connects two carbon atoms. The naphthenes are saturated compounds and the olefins are unsaturated. Unsaturated com-

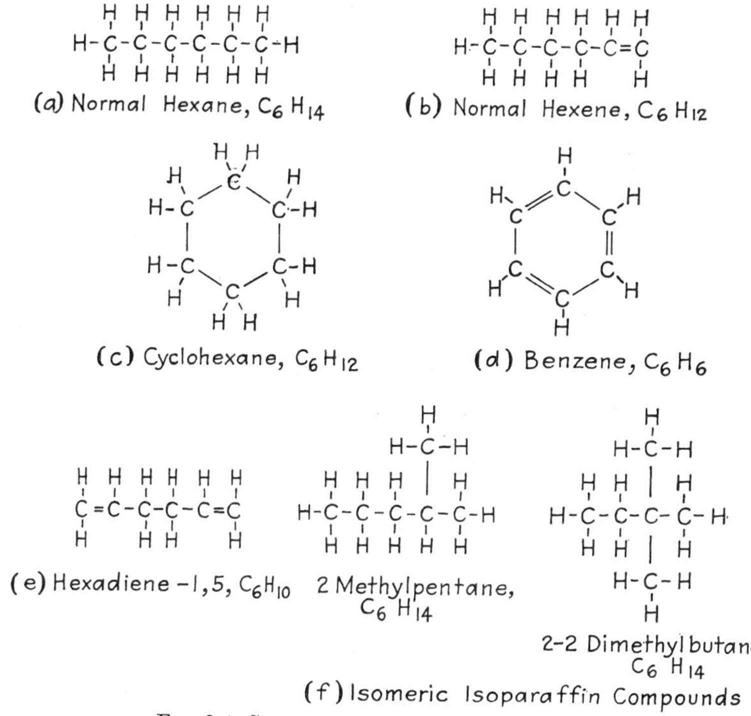

(a) Normal Hexane, C_6H_{14}

(b) Normal Hexene, C_6H_{12}

(c) Cyclohexane, C_6H_{12}

(d) Benzene, C_6H_6

(e) Hexadiene -1,5, C_6H_{10}

2 Methylpentane, C_6H_{14}

2-2 Dimethylbutane C_6H_{14}

(f) Isomeric Isoparaffin Compounds

FIG. 2-1. Structural formulas of hydrocarbons.

pounds can react by direct combination with other materials, but saturated compounds can react only by the displacement of hydrogen by another material. In the older chemistry texts the naphthenes are called methylenes, e.g., tetramethylene, pentamethylene, and hexamethylene, whereas the preferred names are now cyclobutane, cyclopentane, and cyclohexane. As an example of the relation of this series to other cyclic series, consider benzene and cyclohexane. Both compounds contain six carbon atoms per molecule, but six hydrogen atoms must be added to benzene to produce cyclohexane. The cyclohexane molecule is saturated, but the benzene molecule is highly unsaturated because it has three doubly

[9] The Decomposition and Polymerization of the Olefinic Hydrocarbons, *J. Phys. Chem.*, **35**, 1825 (1931).

combined carbon atoms (Fig. 2-1d).   The three double bonds are active so that benzene is an active material, but the cyclohexane contains no double bonds and does not react readily.   However, most of the reactions of benzene are by substitution rather than combination.   The naphthenes, unlike their isomers the olefins, are not easily soluble in sulfuric acid. They have been found in almost all crude oils, but again Mahoning County crude oil is an exception.[6]   This crude oil contained the hydrocarbons of the C_nH_{2n-2} and C_nH_{2n-4} series but no paraffins or simple naphthenes. Egloff, Bollman, and Levinson[10] have studied the reactions of the cyclo hydrocarbons (Fig. 2-1c).

The *aromatic series* (type formula C_nH_{2n-6}), often called the *benzene series*, is chemically active.   These hydrocarbons are particularly suscep-tible to oxidation with the formation of organic acids.   The aromatics may form either addition or substitution products, depending upon the condi-tions of the reaction.   Only a few petroleums contain more than a trace of the low-boiling aromatics such as benzene and toluene.   Mabery[11] found relatively large quantities of aromatics in Ventura, Coalinga, and Puente Hills, Calif., petroleums.   Some of the Sumatra and Borneo crude oils are rich in aromatics.   This series is found in catalytically reformed gasoline and is highly prized for its antiknock qualities (Fig. 2-1d).

The *diolefin series* (type formula C_nH_{2n-2}) is similar to the olefin series except that two hydrogen atoms are missing or two double bonds are present in each molecule.   These double bonds cause the series to be extremely active.   The diolefins tend to polymerize or combine with other unsaturated molecules forming high-molecular-weight gumlike solids.   The diolefins and the gums from them are found in untreated cracked gasoline,[12] but they are probably not present in crude petroleum. They are polymerized and removed by sulfuric acid (Fig. 2-1e).

The *cyclic series* such as those having type formulas C_nH_{2n-2}, C_nH_{2n-4}, C_nH_{2n-8}, etc., are not well known.   Nevertheless, the literature indicates that these series predominate in the higher boiling point oils, such as gas oil and lubricating oils.   Most of the hydrocarbons in lubricating oil are saturated, but Seyer[13] reports that about 20 per cent of a lubricating oil is soluble in sulfur dioxide.   Doubtless the 20 per cent consists largely of unsaturated hydrocarbons.

Isomeric Compounds.   Confusion often arises because different com-pounds may have the same molecular formula.   Isomeric compounds are those which have the same molecular formula but different internal struc-tures.   Compounds of the type formula C_nH_{2n} may be either saturated or

[10] Thermal Reactions of Cycloparaffins and Cycloölefins, *J. Phys. Chem.*, **35**, 3489 (1931).

[11] *Proc. Am. Acad. Arts Sci.*, **36**, 255 (1901).

[12] Bridgeman and Aldrich, *Oil Gas J.*, Jan. 29, 1931, p. 42.

[13] *Petroleum Equipment Exporter*, January, 1930, p. 65.

unsaturated. The formulas of the saturated compound cyclohexane and the unsaturated compound hexene-1 may be compared in Fig. 2-1b and c. Likewise the formulas of n-hexane, 2-methylpentane, and 2,2-dimethyl-butane, all having the type formula C_nH_{2n+2} or C_6H_{14}, may be compared in Fig. 2-1a and f. Groups of atoms such as the methyl groups in the compounds just referred to are called "alkyl groups" or "radicals." These terms refer to a group of carbon and hydrogen atoms that may be conveniently considered as a unit because they usually act as a unit in a chemical reaction. They may be defined as a monovalent hydrocarbon group having the general formula C_nH_{2n+1}. Common radicals are the methyl (CH_3), ethyl (C_2H_5), and propyl (C_3H_7) groups. Radicals are not individual compounds because they must always be attached to other radicals, elements, or groups of atoms.

There are two possible isomeric butanes, viz., n-butane and 2-methyl propane; three pentanes; five hexanes; and nine heptanes. The number of possible isomeric hydrocarbons increases rapidly as the number of carbon atoms increases. Compounds of the type formula C_nH_{2n-4} present even more possibilities of isomerism than the foregoing. As an example, the saturated series might consist of three doubly combined rings or combined rings with alkyl side chains; the unsaturated series might consist of numerous compounds having unsaturated carbon atoms in the rings, in the side chains, or in both; and other series might exist having combinations of saturated or unsaturated rings with saturated, unsaturated, or acetylene side chains. Consideration of the series that are even more deficient in hydrogen than the C_nH_{2n-4} series indicates that an enormous number of isomers is possible. Fortunately the number of unsaturated, high-molecular-weight hydrocarbons in petroleum are probably few, or the isolation of these complex compounds would prove an endless task. The number of possible aliphatic (C_nH_{2n+2}) isomeric hydrocarbons is

Carbon atoms	Isomers	Carbon atoms	Isomers
6	5	15	4,347
7	9	18	60,523
8	18	25	36,797,588
9	35	40	62,491,178,805,831
12	355		

Determination of Series. Although chemists have not yet determined procedures and reagents for the isolation of each chemical series, a start toward this goal has been made.[14] The proposed methods do not indicate the exact series of hydrocarbons that are present, but they do indicate groups of compounds that behave chemically in the same way as the lower

[14] Hill, J. B., *Ind. Eng. Chem.*, **45**, 1398 (1955).

members of the paraffin, olefin, aromatic, or naphthene series. With the exception of normal paraffins, no individual hydrocarbon beyond C_{12} has as yet been isolated from petroleum and identified.[14] All double-bonded hydrocarbons such as the olefins, diolefins, and double-bonded cyclics are classed together as one group, called "unsaturates." The unsaturated group may be absorbed or polymerized by sulfuric acid; the aromatics may be nitrated or absorbed by fuming sulfuric acid or dissolved by

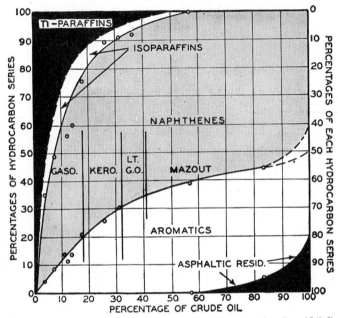

Fig. 2-2. Chemical composition of an aromatic-base crude oil. (*Oil Gas J.*)

dimethyl sulfate; the naphthenes may be determined by means of the aniline index; and the paraffins are found by difference. Such an analysis is perhaps just as valuable to the engineer as an exact one, because he is concerned with the retention or elimination of certain properties in the finished products rather than with a detailed knowledge of exactly what compounds are present. By means of the foregoing analysis of chemical properties and the physical constants of each series, a reliable estimate or check of the physical constants for any petroleum oil is possible. Such an analysis, to be of most value, should be made on each of, say, 10 fractions of a crude oil, so that the change in the percentage of each series can be followed throughout the entire boiling range of the oil. Kurtz et al.[15] present a triangular composition chart for percentage of paraffin, naphthene, and aromatic carbon atoms in lubricating oils. On the same chart they have plotted the relationship between viscosity-gravity-con-

[15] Kurtz, King, Stout, and Gilbert, Div. Pet. Chem., Am. Chem. Soc. Meeting, Minneapolis, Sept. 12, 1955.

stant and refractivity intercept so that these easily obtainable properties can be used to estimate chemical composition.

Figure 2-2 shows such an analysis of a Grozny wax-free (Russian) crude oil.[16] Vlugter, Waterman, and van Westen[17] were among the first to actively develop the so-called "ring analysis" whereby the percentage of aromatic and naphthenic rings per molecule can be determined as well as the percentage of paraffinic side chains. Chemists are becoming increas-

TABLE 2-1. CHEMICAL ANALYSES OF PETROLEUM, PER CENT

Fraction, °F	1. Grozny ("high paraffin"), 45.3 per cent at 572°F			2. Grozny ("paraffin-free upper level"), 40.9 per cent at 572°F			3. Oklahoma (Davenport), 64 per cent at 572°F			4. California (Huntington Beach), 34.2 per cent at 572°F		
	Aromatic	Naphthene	Paraffin	Aromatic	Naphthene	Paraffin	Aromatic	Naphthene	Paraffin	Aromatic	Naphthene	Paraffin
140–203	3	25	72	4	31	65	5	21	73	4	31	65
203–252	5	30	65	8	40	52	7	28	65	6	48	46
252–302	9	35	56	13	52	35	12	33	55	11	64	25
302–392	14	29	57	21	55	24	16	29	55	17	61	22
392–482	18	23	59	26	63	11	17	31	52	25	45	30
482–572	17	22	61	35	57	8	17	32	51	29	40	31

ingly aware that the structures of large petroleum hydrocarbon molecules are seldom totally aromatic, naphthenic, or paraffinic.

Physical methods of analyzing for the kinds of molecules in an oil are discussed by Schlesman and Hochgesang.[18] Among such methods are X-ray and electron diffraction; electron micrography; mass, emission, ultraviolet absorption, Raman, and infrared spectroscopy.

Composition of Petroleum. In the past, petroleum has often been considered as a solution of the paraffin hydrocarbons, but a survey of the literature indicates that such an assumption is not justified. The paraffins predominate in most gasolines[13,14] and probably in kerosenes from paraffin- and mixed-base petroleum; the naphthenes predominate in most gas oils and lubricating oils from all bases of crude oils; and the naphthenes, aromatics, and unsaturated hydrocarbons constitute the bulk of the highest-boiling or residual products. The only paraffins present in the higher-boiling products appear to be those occurring in the wax, and the amount of wax in even paraffin-base petroleum is relatively small. Sachanen and Wirabian[19] present analyses of several Russian and American oils (Table 2-1); and refer again to the more complete analysis given in Fig. 2-2.

[16] Nelson, W. L., Aromatic-base Crude Oils, *Oil Gas J.*, Oct. 28, 1944, p. 101.

[17] *J. Inst. Petroleum*, **18**, 735 (1932); **21**, 661 (1935); **21**, 701 (1935).

[18] *Oil Gas J.*, Jan. 13, 1944, p. 41.

[19] *Petroleum Z.*, **25**, 867 (1929).

TABLE 2-2. HYDROCARBON SERIES FOUND IN PETROLEUM

No. of carbon atoms	Pennsylvania	Mid Continent	California and Gulf Coast
5	C_nH_{2n+2}	C_nH_{2n+2}	C_nH_{2n} and C_nH_{2n+2}
10	C_nH_{2n+2}	C_nH_{2n+2} and C_nH_{2n}	C_nH_{2n} and C_nH_{2n-6}
15	C_nH_{2n+2}	C_nH_{2n-2}	C_nH_{2n-2}
20	C_nH_{2n}	C_nH_{2n-4}	C_nH_{2n-4}
25	C_nH_{2n} and C_nH_{2n-2}	C_nH_{2n-4}	C_nH_{2n-4}
30	C_nH_{2n} and C_nH_{2n-4}	C_nH_{2n-8}	C_nH_{2n-8}
35	C_nH_{2n-4} and C_nH_{2n-8}	C_nH_{2n-8} and C_nH_{2n-12}	C_nH_{2n-12}
40	C_nH_{2n-4} and C_nH_{2n-8}	C_nH_{2n-8} and C_nH_{2n-12}	C_nH_{2n-12} and C_nH_{2n-16}
50	C_nH_{2n-8}	C_nH_{2n-8} and C_nH_{2n-12}	C_nH_{2n-16}
80	C_nH_{2n-8}	C_nH_{2n-16}	C_nH_{2n-20}

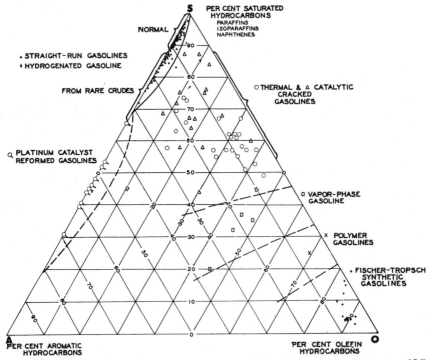

FIG. 2-3. Indication of the chemical composition of gasolines, weight per cent. (*Oil Gas J.*)

Figure 2-3 shows the composition of several gasolines. Table 2-2 indicates in a general way the series of hydrocarbons that have been found in Pennsylvania, Mid Continent, and California oils. The C_nH_{2n-8}, C_nH_{2n-12}, C_nH_{2n-16}, and C_nH_{2n-20} series were taken from Mabery's study of lubricant and asphaltic hydrocarbons.[20] The ultimate composition[21] of a few petroleums is listed in Table 2-3.

TABLE 2-3. ULTIMATE CHEMICAL ANALYSES OF PETROLEUM

Petroleum	Sp gr	At °C	Per cent C	Per cent H	Per cent N	Per cent O	Per cent S	Base
Pennsylvania pipeline..	0.862	15	85.5	14.2	....	...	....	Paraffin
Mecook, W.Va........	0.897	0	83.6	12.9	3.6			Paraffin
Humbolt, Kans........	0.912	...	85.6	12.4	....	...	0.37	Mixed
Healdton, Okla.......	.....	...	85.0	12.9	....	...	0.76	Mixed
Coalinga, Calif........	0.951	15	86.4	11.7	1.14	...	0.60	Naphthene
Beaumont, Tex........	0.91	...	85.7	11.0	2.61		0.70	Naphthene
Mexico...............	0.97	15	83.0	11.0	1.7		4.30	Naphthene
Baku, U.S.S.R........	0.897	...	86.5	12.0	....	1.5		
Colombia, South America............	0.948	20	85.62	11.91	0.54			

Sulfur Compounds. The common types of sulfur compounds are indicated in Fig. 2-4. Difficulties with oils that contain sulfur compounds arise in only three main ways—corrosion, odor, and poor explosion characteristics of gasoline fuels. Corrosion by finished products presents little difficulty because most products are used at low temperatures, temperatures at which only such compounds as hydrogen sulfide, free sulfur, and some of the lowest boiling sulfides, disulfides, and perhaps mercaptans are corrosive toward the main commercial metals. These low-boiling materials tend to be concentrated into the gasoline by distillation, and hence inherent corrosiveness is seldom encountered in higher-boiling products except occasionally in kerosene. Thus the main bulk of the corrosive sulfur compounds can be removed by treatment with alkalies or the "sweetening" treatments. In the presence of air and moisture, the sulfur gases produced during the burning of oils may cause corrosion, as in steel stacks, ducts, and engine exhaust pipes or mufflers. Corrosive or unstable sulfur derivatives of the sulfuric acid used in treating oils, such as alkyl sulfates and sulfonic acids, may also be present, but these can usually be eliminated by better plant control of treating. Real difficulties arise when high-sulfur oils are heated to temperatures of 300°F or higher

[20] *Ind. Eng. Chem.*, **15**, 1233 (1923).

[21] Int. Crit. Tables, **II**, 136–162 (1927).

for copper, or 400°F for steels. This may be illustrated by dibenzyl disulfide, a common gear-lube additive, which is noncorrosive to copper at 212°F but is corrosive at 300°F—must be corrosive if this type of lubricant is to function properly. The sulfides (mono- and di-) are generally considered to be thermally unstable, whereas cyclic compounds such as thiophene are stable. Straight-run gasolines contain primarily mercaptans, hydrogen sulfide, and the sulfides, whereas cracked gasoline usually contains only small amounts of the mono- and disulfides.

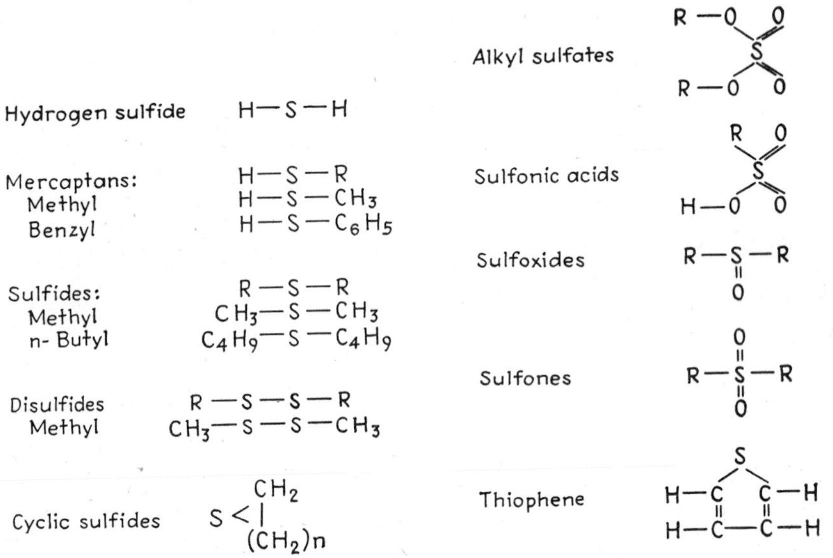

Fig. 2-4. Structural formulas of sulfur compounds. The symbol R refers to an alkyl radical, i.e., a group of carbon and hydrogen atoms.

Odor is most obnoxious with low-boiling or gaseous sulfur compounds, as hydrogen sulfide, sulfur dioxide in flue gases, mercaptans up to even six carbon atoms (boiling point of about 400°F), sulfides up to eight carbon atoms (about 350°F), and among disulfides only methyl disulfide (boiling point 243°F). Thus odor is not obnoxious in sweetened products except in certain extremely high-sulfur gasolines.

Susceptibility or responsiveness of gasolines to tetraethyllead is greatly harmed by small amounts of sulfur compounds (Tables 3-7 and 10-1), and the approximate effect of each type of compound can be estimated by the method outlined in Example 3-2. The distribution of mercaptans in typical gasolines is indicated in Table 10-2.

The percentage of sulfur in crude oils ranges from nearly zero for certain high-API-gravity crude oils to as high as 7.5 per cent in a few very heavy crude oils (see Appendix B). Such a high percentage of sulfur means that more than half of the compounds in the crude oil may contain sulfur.

CHAPTER 3

REFINERY PRODUCTS AND TEST METHODS

A complete discussion of the large number of routine tests that are practiced today could easily fill an entire book, and hence only the barest mention of test methods will be possible. Details of laboratory manipulation must be obtained from other sources, particularly "Petroleum Products and Lubricants,"[1] an annual publication of Committee D-2 of the American Society for Testing Materials.

A voluminous but much less satisfactory literature is available concerning the relation of routine test results and the performance characteristics of petroleum products. This is unfortunate, because to a large extent refinery operations should be governed or regulated by the performance of the products.

ROUTINE LABORATORY TESTS

In general, these tests have been adopted because they can be (1) performed quickly, (2) easily duplicated by ordinary laboratory technicians, and (3) interpreted as a function of the performance of the product while in use. They are not usually scientifically exact, and hence the procedures for the tests are carefully specified and must be faithfully followed if the results are to be dependable.[2] Routine tests are universally used for controlling refinery operations. Tests may be conducted at 2-hr intervals during the initial operation of a plant, and very quickly the test results assume importance as a criterion of plant operation. Not only are the raw and intermediate plant products examined, but the finished products are tested repeatedly as they progress from the unit into run-down storage, finished storage, tank cars, trucks, pipelines, ocean tankers, and filling-station or consumer storage.

Temperatures at which samples may be opened or poured[3] without materially altering the composition of the sample are indicated in Table 3-1.[4] Safe pouring temperatures from the standpoint of fire are even

[1] *Report of Committee* D-2, ASTM, Philadelphia, Pa., yearly.

[2] Mapstone, G. E., *Pet. Refiner*, October, 1950, p. 114.

[3] API, New York, Code 50-B.

[4] Nelson, W. L., *Oil Gas J.*, May 20, 1948, p. 239.

lower than those of Table 3-1, being about 30°F below the flash point. The term "wide boiling" used in Table 3-1 refers to materials that contain small amounts of relatively low-boiling material, such as natural gasoline that contains propane, gassy or unexposed crude oil, unstripped refinery products, and asphalts that have been cut back with lighter materials.

TABLE 3-1. APPROXIMATE RELATIONSHIP BETWEEN POURING TEMPERATURE AND SUCH PROPERTIES AS VAPOR PRESSURE, FLASH POINT, AND BOILING POINT[a]

Reid v.p., psia	Flash point, °F	Approx. 0–10% boiling range, °F	Illustrative materials		Pouring temp., °F	
			Fractioned	Wide boiling	Fractionated	Wide boiling
45	...	.....	Nat. gaso.	Wild nat. gaso.	12	−11
40	...	.....	Nat. gaso.	Wild nat. gaso.	20	− 5
35	...	.....	Nat. gaso.	Wild nat. gaso.	28	2
30	...	.....	Nat. gaso.	Wild nat. gaso.	38	9
25	...	.....	Nat. gaso.	Wild nat. gaso.	48	18
20	...	80	C_3-free nat. gaso.	Contains C_3	60	26
15	...	95	C_3-free nat. gaso.	Contains C_3	77	36
10	...	115	C_3-free nat. gaso.	Contains C_3	100	48
8	...	125	Stable gaso.	Crude oil	112	57
6	...	140	Stable gaso.	Crude oil	123	67
4	...	160	Stable gaso.	Crude oil	140	86
2	...	190	Solvents	Unstripped	178	125
	30	215	Solvents	Unstripped	195	135
	50	245	Solvents	Unstripped	225	165
	70	275	Solvents	Unstripped	245	185
	90	305	Solvents	Unstripped	270	210
	110	335	Kerosene	Unstripped	305	240
	150	395	Distillates	Gas oil	365	280
	200	475	Distillates	Fuel oil	440	330
	250	550	Gas oil	Cutbacks	515	380
	300	625	Fuel oil	Asphalts	585	430
	350	700	Lube oil	Cutback asphalts	660[b]	490
	400	780	Lube oil	Cutback asphalts	660[b]	540
	500	930	Lube oil	Cutback asphalts	660[b]	640
	...	1,000	Asphalts	Cutback asphalts	660[b]	660[b]

[a] Nelson, W. L., *Oil Gas J.*, May 20, 1948, p. 239.
[b] Decomposition occurs at higher temperatures.

API Gravity and Specific Gravity. Specific gravity and API (American Petroleum Institute) gravity are expressions of the density or weight of a unit volume of material. The specific gravity is the ratio of the weight of a unit volume of oil to the weight of the same volume of water at a standard temperature. Unless otherwise stated, both specific gravity and API gravity refer to these constants at 60°F. An exception is the use of 77°F (25°C) in connection with asphalts and road oils.

$$\text{Deg. API} = \frac{141.5}{\text{sp gr}} - 131.5 \quad \text{or} \quad \text{sp gr} = \frac{141.5}{\text{API} + 131.5} \quad (3\text{-}1)$$

Corresponding values of API gravity (0 to 100), specific gravity, and pounds per gallon are given in Appendix A, as well as pounds per barrel, barrels or cubic meters per long ton, etc.

The Baumé scale of gravity for liquids lighter than water, used previously by the industry, differs slightly from API gravity by the use of constants of 140 and 130 rather than 141.5 and 131.5.

Specific gravity or API gravity is measured by means of hydrometers[1] (D287), pycnometers[1] (D941 and D1217), or the chainomatic specific-gravity balance if very many small samples (15 cc) must be tested. For viscous oils or semisolid bitumens, a pycnometer (D70) or weighing bottle may be used, for solids an analytical balance (D71) equipped with a pan straddle.

Most products are sold on a basis of volume delivered corrected to 60°F by means of standard tables of volume corrections.[5] Weight is important in determining freight rates, tanker cargoes, and the power required in pumping. Gravity or weight determines whether a product will sink or float in water or will separate from water. In other respects gravity is not of much direct significance, but the test is so simple and so widely used that it assumes importance as a means of judging many other properties and in controlling plant operations. Gravity requirements should usually be avoided in specifications.

Vapor Pressure (Reid). This test (D323)[1] is used for volatile non-viscous products such as motor gasoline and, by using a special sampling procedure, for natural gasoline of 26 lb or more vapor pressure. A modified equipment and procedure[6] is used for liquefied petroleum gases (L.P.G.). These tests are conducted at 100°F. The ASTM vapor pressure is reported as pounds per square inch absolute pressure, whereas the L.P.G. vapor pressure is gauge pressure. The true vapor pressure is higher than the Reid vapor pressure by about 5 to 9 per cent (page 136), but this relationship varies widely.

[5] ASTM-IP Petroleum Measurement Tables, 1952.

[6] California Natural Gasoline Association, Los Angeles, Calif., Tentative Standard Methods of Test for Liquefied Petroleum Gases, *Bull. T.S.* 441, 1945.

Vapor pressure is an indication of the pressure that a material will develop within a closed container and is particularly significant for materials whose boiling points are so low that they cannot be distilled at atmospheric pressure without serious loss.   The test is important with respect to safety in transport, vapor lock in gasoline feed systems, types of storage tanks employed (Fig. 8-7), and the starting characteristics of motor fuels.

ASTM Distillations.   These tests[1] for gasoline, naphtha, and kerosene (D86); natural gasoline (D216); and gas oil (D158) involve much the same procedure.   A somewhat similar test known as the "Engler distillation" has been used in the past, and often the ASTM distillation is referred to as "an Engler."

One hundred cubic centimeters of oil is distilled at a uniform rate of 5 cc per min.   The distillate is condensed in a brass tube surrounded by cracked ice.   The temperature of the vapor when the first drop (F.D.) of condensate drips from the condenser (in not less than 5 or more than 10 min) is recorded as the "initial boiling point" (I.B.P.).   The vapor temperature is also recorded as each successive 10 per cent is collected. When 95 per cent has been distilled, the burner flame may need to be increased, and the maximum temperature is recorded as the "end point" (E.P.).

Virtually no fractionation occurs in this distillation, and the hydrocarbons in the oil do not distill one by one in the order of their boiling points but as successively higher and higher boiling mixtures.   The details of this inadequacy will be discussed under vaporization in Chap. 15. Actually, the initial boiling point, the end point, and the intermediate vapor temperatures have little significance except when compared with corresponding points from other ASTM distillations (but see Fig. 3-3). Materials boiling below the initial boiling point and above the end point are present in the oil, although these points are the extreme ends of the ASTM distillation range.   In routine plant reports the loss is plotted at the end of the distillation curve, but for more scientific work it is usually plotted at the beginning of the curve.   A comparison between ASTM and true boiling point (T.B.P.) distillations is given in Fig. 4-17.

Flash and Fire Points.   The flash point and the fire point are further indications of the range and nature of the boiling-point curve.   They designate, respectively, the temperature at which the vapor above an oil will momentarily flash or explode when in the presence of a flame and the temperature at which the vapors are evolved rapidly enough to burn continuously.   These tests serve to indicate the temperature below which an oil can be handled without danger of fire.   Certain high-boiling oils, such as lubricants, cannot be distilled at atmospheric pressure without thermal decomposition, and in such a case the flash point helps to indicate the relative amount of low-boiling oil present in the material.

The common flash-point instruments are the *open cup*[1] (D92) and *Pensky-Martens*[1] (D93) closed tester for heavy oils and the *Tag*[1] (D56) closed tester for light oils. The oil is heated at the rate of 10°F per minute in the heavy oil testers and at 1.8°F in the Tag tester. A test flame is introduced into the vapor at 30-sec intervals. The flash point by the Martens tester is about 10° lower[7] than by the open tester; but if the flash point is above 510°F (Martens), a larger difference exists between flash points by the two instruments. The closed instrument is the more exact of the two, but the open cup is used extensively because of its simplicity.

Color. The color of an oil serves as an indication of the thoroughness of the refining process. True, oils of different boiling range and from different crude oils may have different colors; but, other things being comparable, the color indicates the degree of refining that the material has undergone. Distilled products that are discolored are an indication of (1) thermal decomposition, (2) the entrainment of dark-colored tarry material, or (3) materials that are inherently dark in color. Discoloration by decomposition is due to the use of too high temperatures, and discoloration by entrainment is usually due to "throughputs" above the maximum capacity of the equipment. Color is important where staining of fabrics, etc., may occur.

The *Saybolt chromometer*[1] (D156) is used to determine the color of gasoline and burning oils, and the *Union colorimeter*[1] (D155) for lubricating oils, cylinder oils, and petrolatum. Both these instruments have empirical color scales that bear no direct relation to the Lovibond color analysis. For lubricating-oil colors, the Tag Robinson color instrument is also finding favor. The Saybolt chromometer color scale ranges from 30 for fine gasoline to 15 for mineral-seal burning oil. Normally, one or two color disks are used, but a half disk is available for colors from +25 to +30. In commercial usage, colors are often described by names, and the relationship of the names to the common color numbers is indicated in Table 3-2.

The "bloom" or "cast" of lubricating oils observed in reflected light can be measured by the Bloom Index.[8] It measures how much the blue or the yellow predominates in reflected Lovibond colors.

Viscosity. The viscosity of an oil is a measure of its resistance to internal flow and is an indication of its oiliness in the lubrication of surfaces. In the centimeter-gram-second (cgs) system the unit of viscosity is the poise or centipoise (0.01 poise). Viscosity may be defined as the force in dynes required to move a plane of 1 sq cm area, at

[7] Nelson, W. L., Flash-point by Different [older] Instruments, *Oil Gas J.*, July 26, 1947, p. 254.

[8] Kinsel and Phillips, *Pet. Refiner*, May, 1950, p. 93.

TABLE 3-2. COMPARISON OF COLOR SCALES

Saybolt chromometer numbers	Institute of Petroleum numbers[a]	Color names	ASTM and NPA[b] numbers	Union Pet. Co. letters	Tag Robinson numbers	Lovibond color analysis (12-in. cell except 1-in. for amber)			
						Red 200 series	Yellow 510 series	Amber 500 series[c]	Blue 1180 series
30	...	....							
25	...	Water white	...	...	....	......		0.32	
24	1	Water white							
21	1½	Water white	...	...	....	......		2.0	
19	2	Superfine white							
17	2½	Prime white							
16	...	Prime white	...	...	....		1.02	4.0	
15	3	Prime white							
14	3½	Standard white	...	...	....		1.1	4.0	
12	4	Standard white	...	...	....		1.1	5.0	
11	5	Standard white							
10	6	Standard white							
9	7	Standard white							
8	...	Standard white	...	...	....		1.1	6.0	
6	...	Standard white	...	...	....		1.0	7.0	
3	...	Standard white	...	...	....		1.2	9.0	
1	...	Standard white							
−2	...	....	...	...	....		1.1	14.0	
−4	...	....	...	...	....		1.1	15.0	
−11	...	Lilly white	1	G	20¾		0.12	2.4	(1.4–1.9)
−16	...	....	...	...	....		1.1	27.0	
−24	...	Cream white	1½	H	17½		0.6	8.0	(5–7)
−28	...	....	...	...	....		25.5	27.0	
−32	...	Extra pale	2	I	12¼		2.5	26.0	(20–23)
....	...	Extra lemon pale	2½	J	10		4.6	27.0	
....	...	Lemon pale	3	K	9½		6.9	32.0	(50–63)
....	...	Extra orange pale	3½	L	9		9.4	45.0	
....	...	Orange pale	4	M	8½	14.0	50.0	(110–125)	0.55
....	...	Pale	4½	N	5½	21.0	56.0	....	0.55
....	...	Light red	5	O	3¼	35.0	93.0	(220–250)	
....	...	Dark red	6	P	2	60.0	60.0	(300–340)	0.55
....	...	Claret red	7	Q	1¼	60.0	106.0	....	1.8
....	...	....	8	R	....	166.0	64.0		
....	...	Extra light[d]	A	A	....	10.2	29.0		
....	...	Light[d]	D	D	....	21.0	31.0		
....	...	Medium[d]	E	E	....	89.0	56.0		

[a] Approximate relationship to Saybolt color.
[b] National Petroleum Association.
[c] Used alone without other color disks.
[d] For filtered cylinder stocks.

a distance of 1 cm from another plane of 1 sq cm area, through a distance of 1 cm in 1 sec.

The *relative viscosity* is the ratio of the viscosity of the liquid to that of water at 68°F. The viscosity of water at 68°F is 1.002 centipoises, and hence the relative viscosity and the viscosity in centipoises are numerically equal. Two other common terms are *kinematic viscosity*, which is the viscosity in centipoises divided by the specific gravity at the same temperature, and *fluidity*, which is the reciprocal of viscosity. The units of kinematic viscosity are stokes and centistokes. The English unit "reyn" (1 lb-sec per sq in.) is equal to 69×10^5 centipoises.

The common viscosimeters do not read directly in centipoises. All employ arbitrary scales of viscosity. The *Saybolt Universal viscosity*[1] (D88) is the time, measured in seconds, required for the efflux of 60 cc of oil from a container tube at a constant temperature through a calibrated orifice in the bottom of the tube. The procedure involves straining the oil to remove particles that might lodge in the orifice, bringing the oil to a constant temperature by means of a constant-temperature bath, and accurately measuring the time for efflux. The *Saybolt Furol viscosity*[1] (D88) is determined exactly as is the Universal viscosity except that a larger orifice is used. The viscosity of lubricants is usually reported as Saybolt Universal seconds at 100, 130, or 210°F, and of fuel oils as Saybolt Furol seconds at 122 or 210°F.

Kinematic viscosity may be determined directly by means of Ubbelohde, FitzSimmons modification, or modified Ostwald viscosimeter pipettes[1] (D445). A series of these pipettes which cover the entire useful range of viscosity may be suspended in a single constant-temperature bath. Great accuracy is possible with these instruments, and a somewhat smaller sample is satisfactory, but each instrument must be calibrated. The pipette method must be used for gasoline, naphthas, or kerosene, because turbulent rather than streamline flow occurs in the large orifices of the Saybolt equipment. The viscosity of kerosene is sometimes determined in the Saybolt thermoviscosimeter,[9] and *thermoviscosity* (at 60°F) is related to the kinematic and Saybolt Universal viscosity (at 60°F) approximately as follows:[10]

$$\text{Thermo.} = 15 + 148.5 \text{ kinematic} \tag{3-2}$$
$$\text{Thermo.} = 46 \text{ SSU} - 1,183 \tag{3-3}$$

If t is the Saybolt Universal viscosity and z and s are the viscosity in centipoises and the specific gravity, respectively, all three factors taken at the same temperature, the relation among these variables, according to the Bureau of Standards, is

$$\text{Kinematic viscosity} = \frac{z}{s} = 0.219t - \frac{149.7}{t} \tag{3-4}$$

The ASTM recommends a series of conversion factors[1] (D446) by which centistokes can be converted into Saybolt Universal viscosity.

[9] *New and Revised Tag Manual* . . . , The Refinery Supply Co., Tulsa, Okla.
[10] Nelson, W. L., *Oil Gas J.*, Nov. 24, 1952, p. 138.

Figure 3-1[11] may be used to convert the viscosity by any one of the viscosimeters to the viscosity by any of the other common instruments. Somewhat more exact comparisons are available in tabulated form.[12] Although Fig. 3-1 and the tabulations are useful for approximating the viscosity for design work or estimates, they should not be used for exact specifications. If the viscosity of a shipment of oil is specified in particular units, the viscosity should be determined in these units by using the proper instrument.

In using Fig. 3-1, the viscosities by various instruments must be determined at the same temperature. If the viscosities are available at different temperatures, then one or the other of the viscosities must be corrected for temperature as explained in Example 5-13.

Example 3-1. Use of Viscosity Conversion Chart (Fig. 3-1). The Saybolt viscosity is 1,000 sec at 210°F. What is the Furol viscosity at 210°F?

Trace the 1,000 time line to the intersection with the Saybolt Universal line. Follow the horizontal line (kinematic viscosity of approximately 215.0) to the Saybolt Furol line. Read down from the intersection. The Saybolt Furol time at 210°F is approximately 103 sec.

The Engler time corresponding to the foregoing is 1,500 sec. The Engler degrees (or number) corresponding to the foregoing is 30.

The lower and left scales are used for Saybolt Universal viscosities up to 8,000. For higher viscosities the upper and right scales are used.

Cloud and Pour Points. The cloud and pour points are useful in estimating the relative amount of wax in an oil. However, all oils will solidify if cooled to a low enough temperature, and hence these tests do not indicate the actual amount of wax or solid material in the oil. They do indicate that most of the wax, melting above the pour point, has been removed.

In the *cloud test*[1] (D97) the oil is cooled, from at least 25°F above the cloud point, in a specified test jar. The cooling bath is held between 15 and 30°F below the cloud point of the oil. At intervals the test jar is removed from the brine bath without disturbance to the oil, and the temperature at which a distinct cloudiness or haziness appears in the bottom of the jar is recorded as the cloud point. The cloud point of dark-colored oils may be estimated by the temperature at which the viscosity increases rapidly.[13] The *pour test*[1] (D97) is conducted in much the same manner. However, the oil is first heated to 115°F, to be sure that all wax has dissolved, and cooled to 90°F before the test. As in the cloud test, the bath is held 15 to 30°F below the estimated pour point.

[11] The Texas Company, "Lubrication," May, 1921.

[12] Dunstan, Nash, Brooks, and Tizard, "The Science of Petroleum," 4 vols., Oxford University Press, New York, 1938; also Nelson, W. L., Refiner's Notebooks 108 and 132, *Oil Gas J.*, Aug. 31, 1946, and Feb. 15, 1947.

[13] Young, Y. C., *Oil Gas J.*, May 31 and June 7, 1951.

At intervals of 5°F, the test jar is removed from the bath and tilted to ascertain if the oil will flow or move.   If it shows no movement when the jar is held horizontal for 5 sec, it is said to be solid.   The pour point is taken as the temperature 5°F above the solid point.

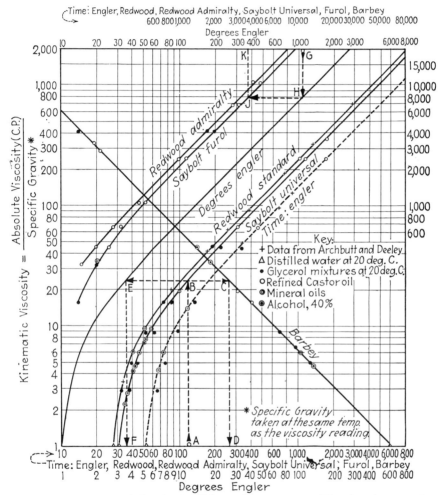

Fig. 3-1. Comparison of viscosity by different instruments.   (The viscosites must be determined at the same temperature.)   (*The Texas Co.*)

Years ago the industry had a specified *cold test* which indicated the capacity of the oil to flow after vigorous stirring at a low temperature. This test proved to be inadequate and should not be confused with the cloud or pour tests of today.

Knock Characteristics. The confusion that has long characterized methods of knock testing has not abated.[14] *Normal heptane* and *2,2,4-trimethylpentane* (so-called "isooctane") were adopted as standards in 1930 along with a standard CFR (Cooperative Fuel Research) engine. The unit of knock intensity, known as *octane number* is defined as the percentage by volume of isooctane that must be mixed with normal heptane in order to match the knock intensity of the fuel undergoing testing.

The Ethyl Series 30 and 30B engines were used during 1929–1930, but in 1930 the CFR engine was developed and the research method of test (1931) was recommended. Various test methods were employed in a continual attempt to duplicate road performance in the laboratory— 1933, ASTM or motor method; 1936–1937, Ethyl Corp. L-3 method; 1939, modernized research method; 1940–1946, aviation methods 1-C (lean) and 3-C (rich); and in 1948 the present methods of test known as F-1 or Research (D908),[1] F-2 or Motor (D357),[1] F-3 or Aviation (D614),[1] and F-4 or Supercharge (D909)[1] were adopted.[15] The Research method is conducted at an engine speed of 600 rpm and the Motor method at 900 rpm. Different octane numbers are obtained by each of the tests and the difference in octane number between the Research and Motor methods is called the *"spread"* or *"sensitivity."* Spread is related to road performance because the Research method more properly represents the performance during city driving when the speed is generally low and acceleration is frequent, whereas the Motor method indicates good high-speed performance on the highway.[16] Likewise, the F-3 or 1-C Aviation methods check best with the performance during cruising, whereas the F-4 or 3-C mixture methods are related to the great power required during fighting maneuvers. In the range of 80 to 100 octane number, the F-3 Aviation method rates a fuel at about 1 octane number higher than the F-2 or Motor method.[17] The approximate relationship between octane numbers by the Motor and Research methods is indicated in Table 3-3.

---

[14] At least eight distinct methods have been used since 1928 and none of them properly represent road performance. Agencies promoting cracked gasoline, leaded gasoline, and catalytic gasoline have vied in sponsoring methods of testing. The latest (1956) modification, the empirical Wiese scale for octane numbers above 100, is a compromise between the desire of engine manufacturers to use the Performance Numbers of aircraft engines for automobiles and the refiners' desire to have a scale that properly reflects the cost of producing high-octane fuels.

[15] Nelson, W. L., History of Octane Number Tests, *Oil Gas J.*, Dec. 22, 1949, p. 286.

[16] Nelson, W. L., *Oil Gas J.*, May 12, 1949, p. 116.

[17] Nelson, W. L., *Oil Gas J.*, July 13, 1950, p. 98. Range is 0.5 to 1.6 units, decreasing again for octane numbers above 100.

TABLE 3-3. AVERAGE RELATIONSHIP BETWEEN MOTOR AND RESEARCH OCTANE NUMBERS (SENSITIVITY OR SPREAD)

Motor method[a]	Research method											
	Straight run		Reformed (cat.)		Reformed (thermal)		Thermal cracked		Cat. cracked		Polymer (cat.)	
	Clear	3 cc TEL	Clear	3 cc TEL	Clear	3 cc TEL	Clear	3 cc TEL	Clear	3 cc TEL	Clear	3 cc TEL
30	30.5[b]	30.0[b]										
35	36.0	35.0[b]										
40	41.5	40.5										
42	43.5	42.5										
44	46.0	44.5										
46	48.0	46.5	46.0[b]	......	47.5[b]							
48	50.5	48.5	49.0	......	50.0							
50	52.5	50.5	51.5	......	52.5							
52	55.0	52.5	54.0	......	55.0							
54	57.0	54.5	56.0	.... .	57.5							
56	59.5	56.5	58.5	......	60.5							
58	61.5	58.5	61.0	......	63.0	......	62.0[b]					
60	64.0	60.5	63.5	......	65.5	......	65.0[b]					
62	66.0	62.5	65.5	......	68.0	.. ...	68.0					
64	68.5	64.5	68.0	......	70.5	64.0[b]	70.0					
66	70.5	67.0	70.5	66.0[b]	73.5	66.0	74.0					
68	73.0	69.0	73.0	69.0[b]	76.0	69.0	78.0					
70	75.0	71.0	75.5	71.5	78.5	72.5	82.0	73.5[b]	78.5[b]			
72	77.0	73.0	78.0	74.0	81.0	75.5	85.0	76.5	81.0			
74	79.0	75.0	80.0	76.5	83.5	78.5	87.0	79.5	83.5	81.0[b]		
76	81.5[b]	77.0	82.5	79.5	86.5	82.0	89.5	82.5	86.5	84.0	91.0[b]	
78	83.5[b]	79.0	85.0	82.0	89.0	84.5	92.0[b]	85.0	89.0	86.5	92.0	
80	......	81.0	87.5	85.0	91.5[b]	87.5	......	88.0	91.5	89.0	93.0	93.0[b]
82	......	83.0	90.0	87.5	......	90.5	......	91.0	94.0	91.5	96.0	95.0
84	......	85.0	92.5	90.0	......	93.5	......	94.0[b]	96.5[b]	95.0	99.0[b]	97.0
86	......	87.0	95.0	93.0	......	97.0	......	......	......	97.0	......	98.0[b]
88	......	89.0	97.5	95.5	......	100.0[b]	......	......	......	100.0[b]		
90	......	91.0	100.0	98.0								

[a] Used as "clear" Motor method with the "clear" Research octane numbers, and as "leaded" with the "leaded" columns.

[b] Extrapolated. Such extreme octane numbers are seldom encountered.

Detonation performance of fuels at levels above 100 Research octane number will probably be designated by the so-called Wiese scale. Performance Number, originally developed to show the percentage increase in aircraft engine power for additions of TEL to isooctane, is generally related to engine output. The relationship between Research octane number, Performance Number, tetraethyllead additions, and the Wiese scale is shown in Table 3-4.

Sulfur Tests. The sulfur[1] (D90) content of gasoline and burning oils is an important specification. About 10 g of oil is burned in a small lamp, and the products of combustion are drawn through a sodium carbonate absorption solution. The sulfur is determined by titrating the unused sodium carbonate solution. Sulfur in residual fuel oil and crude oil is determined by the ordinary oxygen-bomb method[1] (D129).

TABLE 3-4

Octane number		Performance number	cc TEL plus isooctane[c]
Research[a]	Wiese scale[b]		
81.4	. . . . .	60	
88.0	. . . . .	70	
93.0	. . . . .	80	
96.9	. . . . .	90	
100.0	100.0	100	0
102.6[d]	103.3	110	0.29
104.7[d]	106.7	120	0 68
106.4[d]	110.0	130	1.27
108.0[d]	113.3	140	2.15
109.4[d]	116.7	150	3.50
110.5[d]	120.0	160	5.80

[a] R.o.n. = 128 − 2800 ÷ P.N.
[b] O.n. = 100 + (P.N. − 100) ÷ 3. Purely a compromise scale.
[c] Approximate.
[d] No longer used. See Wiese scale.

The presence of corrosive materials such as free sulfur and corrosive sulfur compounds is always objectionable. The test[1] (D130) consists in noting the effect of the heated oil on a strip of polished copper. More than a slight discoloration of the copper after heating for 3 hr indicates that the oil is corrosive.

Tests for Bituminous and Semisolid Materials. The most common tests for asphaltic substances are the ductility, penetration, ring-and-ball softening point[18] (E28), and specific-gravity tests. The ductility[18] (D113) of an asphalt is a measure of its capacity to elongate or stretch and is an indication of the ability of the material to flow and thereby mend a rupture in the surface of the material. A briquette of the asphalt

[18] ASTM Standards on Bituminous Materials for Highway Construction, Waterproofing, and Roofing, ASTM, Philadelphia, Pa., yearly.

is pulled apart at a uniform rate, and the elongation, measured in centimeters, that occurs before rupture takes place is called the "ductility." The test is usually conducted at 77°F, and the briquette is pulled apart at a uniform rate of 5 cm per min. Penetration[18] (D5) allows a needle or cone to penetrate the material without mechanical friction and is arranged to read the depth of the penetration in hundredths of a centimeter. A standard needle is used for asphalt materials[1] (D5), and the common test conditions are temperature, 77°F (25°C); time, 5 sec; and load, 100 g; but temperatures of 32 and 115°F are also used.

For greases and petrolatum[1] (D217) the needle is replaced with a standard cone. The procedure is the same as for asphalt materials except that the temperatures of 32 and 115°F are seldom used.

Road oils are examined for flash point, viscosity (Furol) at 77, 122, 140, or 180°F, and by a distillation test[18] (D402). The residue is tested for penetration, ductility, and solubility in carbon tetrachloride[18] (D4). The distillation test sometimes ruins the ductility of the asphalt, and hence the value of the test is being questioned.

Gum and Gasoline. The determination of gum in gasoline has been a troublesome test. The copper dish method of determining gum has been replaced by a method[1] (D381) that utilizes a measured and heated stream of air to assist in the vaporization. This test indicates the amount of gum at the time of test and the amount of deposition that may take place in service if the gasoline is used immediately. In addition, a test for *gum stability*[1] (D525) which involves heating the gasoline at 212°F in a bomb at a pressure of 100 psi, all in an atmosphere of oxygen, is useful in estimating the amount of gum that will be formed during storage. In this test the gum stability is indicated by the rate at which the pressure decreases or the rate at which oxygen is consumed.

REFINERY PRODUCTS

Specifications are the result of a compromise between desirable performance characteristics in the product and the ability of the refiner to make such products from the crude oil at hand. Thus the whole operation of refining must be governed by the performance of the product when in use. Nevertheless, wide ranges in physical properties can be tolerated or may be advisable for some products. As one example, gasoline may have an end point between 300 and 437°F and may vary in gravity from 50 to 70 API, depending upon the sales region, the source, or its use.

In general, finished refinery products may be grouped as

1. *Volatile products*—liquefied gases and natural gasoline.
2. *Light oils*—gasolines, rocket and jet fuels, solvents, tractor fuel, and kerosene.
3. *Distillates*—range oil, furnace distillates, diesel fuel, and gas oil.

4. *Lubricating oils*—motor, engine, machine, cylinder, spindle, gear, etc., oils.
5. *Greases and waxes*—paraffin wax, microcrystalline wax, petrolatum, salve bases, and greases.
6. *Residues*—fuel oil, coke, asphalt, carbon black, etc.
7. *Specialties*—medicinal products, hydrocarbons, chemicals, insecticides, etc.

The evaluation of crude oils for the yields of products is discussed in Chap. 4 (also see Appendix B).

Volatile Products. Liquefied petroleum gases are graded primarily with respect to vapor pressure[6] and the temperature at which 90 per cent is evaporated. In unauthorized usage B-95-10 refers to a gas of Grade B (see Table 3-5) that has a vapor pressure of 95 psig and a 90 per cent

TABLE 3-5. STANDARD GRADES OF LIQUEFIED PETROLEUM GASES

CNGA[a] grade	Maximum vapor pressure, psig at 100°F	Range of allowable specific gravity, 60°F/60°F	Approximate composition
A	80	0.585–0.555	Predominantly butanes
B	100	0.560–0.545	Butane-propane mixtures, mainly butanes
C	125	0.550–0.535	Butane-propane mixtures, about equal
D	150	0.540–0.525	Butane-propane mixtures, rich in propane
E	175	0.530–0.510	Butane-propane mixtures, mainly propane
F	200	0.520–0.504	Predominantly propane

[a] California Natural Gasoline Association.

evaporation temperature of 10°F. Had the number been B-95-M10 it would have meant that the 90 per cent temperature is minus 10°F. Grades B, E, and F are used widely. The National Board of Fire Underwriters presents standards for the safe handling of liquefied petroleum gases in its *Pamphlet* 58.[19]

The specifications (June, 1951) of the NGAA (Natural Gasoline Association of America) for commercial propane and commercial butane require (1) a minimum of 95 per cent of propane and/or propylene (or butanes and/or butylenes), (2) no hydrogen sulfide, (3) a negative copperstrip corrosion test (3 hr at 122°F), (4) no water by the cobalt bromide test, and (5) a maximum of 15 grains per 100 cu ft of total sulfur. The vapor pressure of propane must be below 215 psi at 100°F and of butane below 70 psi.

Natural gasolines are graded by the Natural Gasoline Association of America as follows:

[19] NBFU, Standards for Liquefied Petroleum Gases, *NBFU Pamphlet* 58, National Board of Fire Underwriters, New York, August, 1940.

Reid vapor pressure.................... 10–34 lb
Percentage evaporated at 140°F.......... 25–85
Percentage evaporated at 275°F.......... Not less than 90
End point............................ Not higher than 375°F
Corrosion............................ Noncorrosive
Doctor test.......................... Negative, "sweet"
Color................................ Not less than plus 25

In addition, natural gasoline is divided into 24 possible grades on a basis of vapor pressure and percentage evaporated at 140°F. These grades are shown in Fig. 3-2. Grade 26–70 is the standard grade for accountancy and pricing purposes even though the average gasoline now has a vapor pressure of about 18.

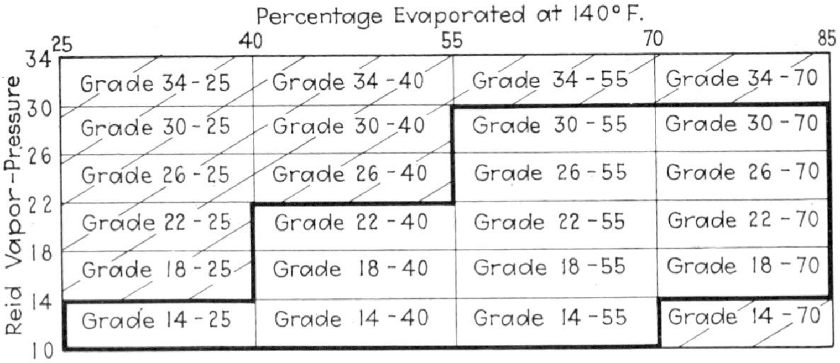

Percentage Evaporated at 140°F.

FIG. 3-2. Grades of natural gasoline with the common grades shown within the block.

Gasoline. In an industry of many by-products, gasoline is the major product. The general properties of gasolines are indicated in Table 3-6. United States government agencies specified at least 12 gasolines during World War II.[20] *White Unleaded Undyed* gasoline is used for stationary engines, cleaning, and as stove gasoline. *Motor Fuel 72* was used within the continental limits of the United States for nearly all vehicles—type A at climates of 50°F and up, type B at 25 to 70°F, and type C up to 45°F. *Red All Purpose* gasoline was used for all military vehicles—Grade A at 0°F and up in temperature and Grade C for arctic climes up to 10°F. *Aviation Grades* 80, 87, 91/96, and 98/130 were used for training purposes and Grades 130 and 140 for combat cruising and fighting.

The ASTM specifications are perhaps the most comprehensive. In addition to the three types of gasolines specified in Table 3-6, types A and

[20] White No. 2-116; Fuel 72, No. 2-114A; All Purpose, No. 2-103B; Grade 80, AN-F24; Grade 87, AN-F25; Grade 91/96, AN-F26; Grade 98/130, AN-F27; Grade 130, AN-F28; and Grade 140, AN-F29, Superintendent of Documents, Washington, D.C.

TABLE 3-6. ABBREVIATED GASOLINE SPECIFICATIONS AND PROPERTIES

Name or grade	Max % evaporated at temps below, °F — 10%	50%	90%	E.P.	Gum, mg per 100 ml	Reid vapor pressure	Octane number — Motor (or lean rating)a	Research (or rich rating)a	TEL fluid, max ml per gal	Sulfur max, %
ASTM, aviation D910-53T:[1]										
1. Grade 80-87	158	221	212–257	338	6b	7	80	87	0.5	0.05
2. Grade 91-96	158	221	212–257	338	6b	7	91	96	2.0	0.05
3. Grade 100-130	158	221	212–257	338	6b	7	100	1.28c	3.0	0.05
4. Grade 108-135	158	221	212–257	338	6b	7	0.22c	1.68c	3.0	0.05
5. Grade 115-145	158	221	212–257	338	6b	7	0.47c	2.8c	4.6	0.05
ASTM, automotive D439-55T:[1]										
6. Type A, normal	140–158	284	392		5	9.5–15				
7. Type B, volatile	140–158	257	356		5	9.5–15		82 or 89		
8. Type C, nonvolatile	167	284	392		5	9.5–15		82 or 89		
Avg fuels, aviation:d										
9. 1940, Grade 91-98	150	201	236			6.6				
10. 1940, Grade 100-130	152	205	243			6.1				0.015
11. 1947, March, Grade 80-87	150	197	242	314		6.4	80.4		None	0.018
12. 1947, March, Grade 91-98	148	198	241	306		6.5	93.3	98.6e	2.8	0.016
13. 1947, March, Grade 100-130	152	207	246	322		6.3	105.9e	130.9e	3.36	0.012
14. 1956, Grade 80-87	147	194	232	342i		6.5	82.0e	88.0e	0.41	0.014
15. 1956, Grade 91-96	147	193	232	340i	0.9	6.5	93.8e	98.8e	3.72	0.016
16. 1956, Grade 100-130	147	207	246	354i	1.2	6.6	107.0e	131.0e	3.71	0.016
17. 1956, Grade 108-135	146	214	249	361i	1.1	6.7	112.0e	136.0e	2.92	0.015
18. 1956, Grade 115-145		211	246	357i	0.9	6.6	120.0e	146.0e	4.48	0.014
Avg. fuels, automotive:d										
19. 1928 regular	146	267	379	426			56			
20. 1934 regular	135	242	354	403		9.5	69			
21. 1939 regular	127	225	352	396		10.6	73			
22. 1946 regular	125	229	338	395		9.8	75.9	80.5		
23. 1946 premium	123	218	326	387		10.0	80.9	85.8		0.081
24. 1946 competitive f	144	236	341	395		7.5	54			0.057
25. 1954 regular, summer f	133	230	342	407	2.1	8.3	80.3	85.5	2.24	0.092
26. 1954 regular, winter	120	219	334	403	2.0	10.8	80.8	86.2	1.86	0.088
27. 1954 premium g	118–130	210–221	330–367	401–406	2.3–2.6	8.3–10.8	84.0–84.5	92.9–93.6	2.27–2.48	0.076–0.085
28. 1954 premium, max g	140–147	256–260	369–384	437–442	6.0–8.1	10.7–13.5	88.8–89h	95.9–97.8h	3.03–3.05	0.247–0.304
29. 1955-56 prem um, winter	116	209	332	403	2.2	11.0	86	95.6	2.34	0.060
30. 1956-57 premium, winter	115	209	330	402	2.3	11.0	86.8	96.7	2.38	0.051

a The "lean" and "rich" rating methods apply to aviation fuels.
b Potential gum (D873); other figures are ASTM preformed gum.
c Isooctane plus the ml of TEL shown.
d Various yearly U.S. Bur. Mines Repts. Invest. Earliest figures: Ziegenhain, W. T., Yearly Review, *Oil Gas J.*, June 8, 1939.
e Performance Numbers.
f Estimated from data inadequate for Bur. Mines commitment.
g Range of average winter and average summer.
h Minimums were: Motor 79–79.5 and Research 87.2–87.8.
i Sum 10 + 50% evaporated.

B are further divided according to volatility to care for seasonal changes, as indicated in the following tabulation:

	10 per cent point	Vapor pressure
Cold or winter (W)..............	140	13.5
Medium (F)....................	149	11.5
Warm or summer (S)...........	158	9.5

All parts of the United States have been classified as W, F, or S areas, as used above, with regard to climatic conditions during each month of the year.

The most significant performance characteristics of motor fuels may be summarized as follows (somewhat in order of importance):

1. Freedom from water, gum, and corrosive sulfur.
2. Vapor lock.
3. Warm-up and acceleration.
4. Antiknock quality.
5. Crankcase dilution.

Color, gravity, initial boiling point, end point, and noncorrosive sulfur are of little importance. Water, sediment, or corrosive sulfur quickly lead to difficulties in the feed system. *Gum* that has already been formed in the gasoline, known as "preformed gum" (ASTM, D381),[1] can be tolerated in only small amounts:

Gum, mg per 100 ml	*Performance*[21]
6–10	Satisfactory
15–25	Only a few hours and up to 1,000 miles

Potential or *ultimate gum* that may in time be formed in a gasoline is of little significance except to indicate the difficulties that may be encountered if by accident or error the gasoline is not marketed for many months. A high manifold temperature increases intake-valve and chamber deposits,[22] and a rich mixture generally causes larger engine deposits.[22] Engine deposits increase greatly as the gum content is increased from zero up to 7 or 10 mg, but higher gum content causes scarcely more trouble than gum contents of 10 mg. The *induction period* in hours (D525)[1] is approximately equal to the months that the gasoline can be stored under conditions of commerce. The rate of gum formation in storage has been related to the time required to produce 10 mg of gum

[21] Nelson, W. L., Allowable Gum in Gasoline, *Oil Gas J.*, Jan. 11, 1946, p. 85.

[22] Marley, Martin, and Gruse, Moderate Gum Content Gasoline Not Harmful, *Oil Gas J.*, Nov. 10, 1932, p. 12.

in a laboratory accelerated oxidation test,[23] and hence it is possible to foretell the length of time that a gasoline can be stored.

The amount of *sulfur* (noncorrosive) that can be allowed is probably in excess of the 0.25 per cent permitted during World War II.   This quantity led to no serious trouble, and gasolines containing in excess of 0.4 have been marketed in some parts of the United States.   High sulfur causes corrosion in the muffler and tail pipe of the exhaust system during cold weather because of the condensation of moisture and formation of sulfurous and sulfuric acid.   Mono- and disulfides and mercaptan sulfur compounds are extremely harmful to the susceptibility of gasolines to tetraethyllead (see Table 3-7).

TABLE 3-7. APPROXIMATE EFFECT OF SULFUR ON LEAD SUSCEPTIBILITY[a]
(Each compound used alone)

Percentage of sulfur by weight	Percentage of TEL used in overcoming the effect of sulfur (L)					
	Poly-sulfides	Mer-captans	Disulfides	Sulfides and carbon dilsulfide	Free sulfur	Thio-phenes
0.01	36	33	31	23	20	Under 6
0.015	44	40	37	28	24	10
0.02	50	45	42	33	28	13
0.03	57	52	48	40	33	18
0.04	62	57	53	45	37	23
0.05	67	60	57	48	40	27
0.06	70	63	60	52	43	31
0.08	75	68	65	57	47	38
0.10	. . .	71	68	61	51	43
0.15	. . .	76	73	67	57	53
0.20	. . .	. . .	77	72	61	60
0.30	. . .	. . .	. . .	77	66	69

[a] Mapstone, G. E., *Pet. Refiner*, February, 1952, p. 132.

The percentage of TEL used in overcoming the effect of sulfur compounds (Table 3-7) may be defined as L.

$$L = \frac{a_o - a}{a_o} \times 100$$

in which a_o, is the actual concentration (ml/gal) of TEL in the fuel, and a is the concentration needed if the fuel were free of sulfur.   Thus, if the

[23] Walters et al., Practical Test for Estimating Storage Stability of Gasolines, *Ind. Eng. Chem. Anal. Ed.*, **19**, 987 (1947); also, Gum Formation in Cracked Gasolines, *Ind. Eng. Chem.*, **32**, 83 (1940).

value of L is 60, it means that 60 per cent of, say, 2 ml of TEL is used to overcome sulfur, and only 0.8 ml would be required if the sulfur were absent. If several types of sulfur compounds are present, the equivalent of these is stated in terms of disulfides (Example 3-2).

Example 3-2. Effect of Sulfur on TEL Required. In the first column of the tabulation is shown the amounts of sulfur in Foster West Texas gasoline. The second column shows the equivalent of each of the compounds if it were disulfides, i.e., 0.045 per cent mercaptans indicates in Table 3-7 a value of L of about 58.5, and if 58.5 is located in the disulfide column, the equivalent amount of disulfide is about 0.055. The other equivalents were obtained in a similar manner from Table 3-7.

	Wt %	Disulfide equivalent %
Mercaptans.................	0.045	0.055
Disulfides.................	0.021	0.021
Elemental sulfur...........	0.006	0.002*
Sulfides..................	0.015	0.007*
Thiophene.................	0.008	0.000*
Total..................	.....	0.085

* By extrapolation of Table 3-7.

A disulfide content of 0.085 indicates (Table 3-7) a loss in lead efficiency of 66 per cent. A similar value of L is obtained if mercaptan or sulfide equivalents are used.

If the actual gasoline required 3 cc of TEL, it would require only 0.34 times 3 or 1.02 cc if it were completely desulfurized.

The color of gasoline indicates little about its quality, although it is an indication of the thoroughness of the refining operation and of the tendency to produce gum. The highly desirable antiknock compounds are partly removed by treating, and hence the specification of color has become less and less important. Most refiners resort to the use of oil-soluble dyes to mask the color of the natural product. Dyes ranging in color from yellow to dark purple are available.[24] These dyes also serve (1) to identify a gasoline and thus promote confidence in its advertised quality, (2) to preserve the antiknock properties that would be partly lost during treatments used to improve color, and (3) to reduce the cost of refining.

Tetraethyllead is the most important additive used in gasoline. It greatly increases the octane number. Antioxidants are used to inhibit gum formation by oxidation and polymerization in storage, and they prevent potential gum-forming substances from depositing in engine fuel lines, carburetor jets, and on intake valves. Military specifications for

[24] Egloff et al., Dye Saves Dollars in Treating Gasoline, *Oil Gas J.*, Mar. 5, 1931, p. 133. Also, Thompson and Johnson, *Ind. Eng. Chem.*, **48**, 1869 (1956).

all-purpose gasoline require a minimum of 5 lb per 1,000 bbl of the
following oxidation inhibitors, separately or in combination:

N, N' disecondary butylparaphenylenediamine
N, n or isobutyl-p-aminophenol
Di-N, N sec-butyl-p-phenylenediamine

Minute amounts of metal impurities, especially copper, catalyze the oxidation of gasoline components, and 1–3 lb per 1,000 bbl of metal deactivators such as N, N' disalicyledene, 2 diaminopropane, are used. Rust
or corrosion inhibitors are usually surface-active agents that coat ferrous
metals and prevent water-metal contact in pipelines, storage tanks, or in
vehicle fuel systems. Ammonium sulfonates and organic phosphorus
compounds are examples of rust inhibitors. Various alcohols are used
as anti-icing additives to prevent freezing of water in gasoline tanks,
strainer bowls, or carburetors. Most recently preignition preventers
have been developed which tend to prevent spark-plug fouling and preignition. Upper-cylinder lubricants (light lubricating oils) added to
gasoline help in the lubrication of valve stems and the upper walls of the
cylinder. C. M. Larson[25] has estimated the annual consumption of these
additives during 1955 (Table 3-8).

TABLE 3-8. ESTIMATED 1955 CONSUMPTION OF GASOLINE ADDITIVES[a]

Additive type	Approximate dosage	Millions of pounds	Millions of dollars
Tetraethyllead	0–3 ml/gal	400–450	250
Antioxidants	2–16 lb/1,000 bbl	6.0	7
Metal deactivators	1–3 lb/1,000 bbl	1.5	2
Corrosion inhibitors	10–50 ppm	5	1
Preignition preventers	0.01–0.02%	8	3
Anti-icing	½–1%	190	10
Upper-cylinder lubes	a few 1/10%	140	5
Dyes and decolorizers	trace	1	1
Totals		776	279

[a] Larson, C. M., Additives for Fuels and Lubricants, *Pet. Engr.*, March, 1955, p.
C-44.

Among the latest additives (1957) are methyl cyclopentadienyl manganese tricarbonyl of the Ethyl Corporation, and an organic boron compound of the Standard Oil Company of Ohio. The boron compound in
small amounts (0.008—0.03 per cent) not only reduces combustion-zone
deposits and surface ignition but also increases the effectiveness of tetraethyllead. Antiknock effects are greatest with leaded straight-run or

[25] Additives for Fuels and Lubricants, *Pet. Engr.*, March, 1955, p. C-44.

alkylate fuels, causing an increase of 2 to 4 units in octane number, whereas with highly aromatic fuels (catalytic reformates) the octane number may decrease slightly. The new Ethyl Corporation additive is more effective than tetraethyllead but its cost will probably be so great that it may be used only for aviation fuels.

The boiling range [26] governs the ease of starting, rate of acceleration, loss by crankcase dilution, and tendency toward vapor lock somewhat as indicated in Fig. 3-3. Holaday and Happel[27] utilize the percentage dis-

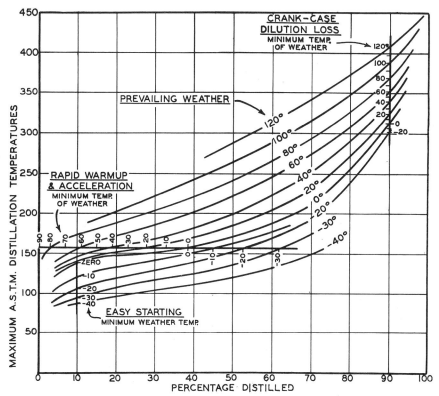

FIG. 3-3. Performance of gasoline in average automotive equipment. About nine out of ten vehicles behave as indicated. (*Oil Gas J.*)

tilled at 158°F and the 90 per cent distillation temperature in an ASTM distillation to judge the time required to warm the engine. Most generally, warm-up is used as the miles of operation required to allow full power development without excessive use of the choke, and a 2- to 4-mile warm-up is generally thought to be satisfactory. This is similar to the

[26] Nelson, W. L., Gasoline Performance, *Oil Gas J.*, Sept. 29, 1945, p. 139.

[27] A Refiner's Viewpoint on Motor Fuel Quality, *Pet Engr.*, Ref. Annual, 1943, p. 251.

older usage of the 35 and 65 per cent ASTM temperatures[28] to judge rate of acceleration and smoothness of performance after the engine is started. If the fuel provides adequate warm-up and acceleration characteristics, it is always sufficiently low-boiling at the 10 per cent point to allow easy starting (Fig. 3-3). Crankcase dilution loss is related[17] primarily to the temperature at 90 per cent distilled, but it is also affected by lower-boiling-range material. The crankcase dilution loss for the gasolines suggested in Fig. 3-3 is below 5 per cent. Agreement on tendency to vapor lock is not good,[27,29] but the general situation is

Climate, °F	Allowable maximum Reid vapor pressure	Climate, °F	Allowable maximum Reid vapor pressure
60	12.7	100	7.0
70	11.0	110	6.0
80	9.4	120	5.3
90	8.0		

Vapor pressure also governs storage and handling losses,[30] particularly at high altitudes. The relative tank-filling losses for an 8.5 R.v.p. (Reid vapor pressure) gasoline at 80°F at different altitudes is somewhat as follows:

Altitude	Relative loss
Sea level	1.0
5,000 ft	1.5
10,000 ft	2.3
15,000 ft	5.5
20,000 ft	111.0

With the advent of high-compression motors, the tendency of a fuel to *spark-knock* or *detonate* violently has attracted much attention. Knocking is thought to be due to autoignition of part of the charge in front of the flame. Mild knocking has little effect on the performance of the engine, but severe knock may result in loss of power and damage to pistons or bearings. Certain substances such as lead tetraethyl,[31] iron pentacarbonyl,[32] etc.,[32] tend to prevent knocking. All hydrocarbons have different antiknock properties, and certain of these, such as benzol[33] and

[28] Brown, G. G., The Volatility of Motor Fuels, *Eng. Research Bull.* 14, University of Michigan, 1930, p. 7.

[29] Good Gasoline, *Natl. Bur. Standards Letter Circ.* 551, Apr. 19, 1939.

[30] Nelson, W. L., Evaporation Losses at High Altitudes, *Oil Gas J.*, Dec. 9, 1944, p. 83.

[31] Midgley, Thomas, Jr., Tetraethyl Lead Poison Hazard, *Ind. Eng. Chem.*, **17**, 827 (1925).

[32] Gaylor, P. J., Patent Trends in Petroleum Refining-gasolines, *Natl. Pet. News*, Aug. 7, 1946, p. R-584.

[33] Campbell, Lovell, and Boyd, Standard Fuel for Anti-knock Quality, *Oil Gas J.*, Jan. 23, 1930, p. 42.

those in cracked gasoline, are useful in suppressing knocking. Octane number is greatly affected by altitude.[34,35] The octane number may be about three units lower for each 1,000 ft of elevation at elevations near sea level (growing to 7.5 per 1,000 ft at 12,000-ft elevation). Thus, if an octane number of 67.5 is necessary at sea level, 50 is satisfactory at 6,000-ft elevation, and at 12,000-ft elevation even 20 is satisfactory.

Knocking occurs[27,36] in average cars somewhat as indicated in Table 3-9 for a polyform gasoline that was rich in olefin and aromatic hydrocarbons.

TABLE 3-9. OCTANE NUMBER REQUIRED TO PREVENT KNOCKING

Motor method octane number	Approximate percentage of cars that knock		
	Approx. 15 mph	Approx. 40 mph	Approx. 60 mph
60	. . .	80	50
65	80	54	28
70	68	30	8
75	50	10	
80	25		
85	5		

TABLE 3-10. APPROXIMATE OCTANE NUMBERS REQUIRED TO SATISFY 10, 50, AND 90 PER CENT OF NINE 1953 MAKES OF CARS OPERATING ON FULL-BOILING-RANGE GASOLINES

Car make	No. cars tested	Research octane number to satisfy		
		10 % of cars	50 % of cars	90 % of cars
1	28	88	93	96
2	24	86	91.5	95
3	27	87.5	91.5	95
4	24	87.5	92	94.5
5	28	84	88.5	94.5
6	22	85	89.5	93
7	30	83	86	93
8	27	84	87	91.5
9	25	78	85.5	90

[34] MacCoull, Hollister, and Crone, Effect of Altitude on Anti-knock . . . , *Ref. Nat. Gaso. Mfr.*, November, 1937, p. 534.

[35] Effect of Altitude on Knock Rating in CFR Engines, *J. Research Natl. Bur. Standards*, **28**, 713 (1942).

[36] Offutt, Ostergard, Fogle, and Beuther, Naphtha Reforming with Outside Gas, 26th Ann. Meeting of API, Chicago, Nov. 12, 1946.

TABLE 3-11. APPROXIMATE LEAD SUSCEPTIBILITY OF GASOLINES
AND HYDROCARBONS[a]

Type of gasoline	Octane number	Increase in Motor o.n. with					Number of tests
		1 cc	2 cc	3 cc	4 cc	6 cc	
n-Heptane[b]................	0.0	10.1	29.1	43.0	....	....	1
Catalytically desulfurized straight run[d]............	54.5	14.9	21.3	25.2	27.9	31.8	20
Catalytically desulfurized natural[d]................	61.6	13.6	19.6	23.1	25.5	28.9	6
Straight run, low sulfur, low octane..................	43.4	10.7	16.9	21.1	24.0	28.2	12
Straight run, low sulfur, regular octane..............	55.9	9.7	14.6	17.7	19.8	22.9	26
Straight run, low sulfur, high octane..................	64.0	9.4	13.9	16.6	18.5	21.1	28
Straight run, low sulfur.....	71.6	8.0	11.8	13.8	15.3	17.4	12
Natural gasoline...........	65.7	8.4	12.4	14.8	16.8	18.8	38
Straight run, high sulfur....	55.9	7.5	11.3	13.7	15.3	17.7	23
Catalytically desulfurized cracked[d]................	69.9	8.3	10.4	11.7	12.6	13.7	6
Isooctane mixes[c]...........	83.0	8.1	11.6	14.1	16.2	18.4	8[c]
Cracked, low octane........	57.5	8.1	12.2	14.7	16.5	18.9	4
Cracked, regular octane....	64.5	6.5	9.5	11.3	12.6	14.4	38
Cracked, high octane.......	71.6	4.0	5.8	6.9	7.6	8.6	16
Aromatic gasolines.........	72.6	6.2	9.0	10.6	11.6	13.2	13
Methylcyclohexane[b]........	73.0	2.5	9.6	12.2	....	....	1
Houdry catalytic..........	75.8	5.9	8.5	9.9	10.9	12.4	30
Catalytically cracked.......	78.4	5.0	6.6	7.5	....	9.5	38
Polymer, catalytic.........	82.5	2.0	2.9	3.4	....	4.3	9
Diisobutylene[b].............	84.3	2.2	2.7	3.2	....	....	1
Isooctane[b].................	100.0	3.8	6.9	8.9	....	....	1
Toluene[b]..................	105.3	1.8	3.2	3.2	....	....	1

[a] Nelson, W. L., Lead Response, *Oil Gas J.*, Oct. 6, p. 106; Oct. 13, p. 137, 1945.
[b] Buerstetta and Warren, *Oil Gas J.*, Nov. 21, 1955, p. 142. Numbers over 100 based on: R.o.n. = 128 − 2,800 ÷ P. N.
[c] Taken from *Oil Gas J.*, Nov. 27, 1941, p. 70.
[d] Desulfurized at high temperature with bauxite or clay.

The octane number required by cars of even the same make ranges by at least 7 to 12 Research octane units (see Table 3-10).[37] Although additional power can be developed by the use of high-octane fuels in suitable engines, the extra power or mileage obtained by the use of high-octane-

[37] CRC Octane Number Requirement Survey, 1953.

number fuels in current vehicles is not impressive[38] or conclusive. Under some conditions of operation a 10 per cent increase in mileage[39] appears to be possible by increasing the octane number from 68 to 83, but tests on some vehicles indicated no improvement or even a decrease in mileage. High-octane fuels do provide smoother, more satisfactory performance.

TABLE 3-12. APPROXIMATE LEAD SUSCEPTIBILITIES OF VARIOUS TYPES OF GASOLINES AS A FUNCTION OF CLEAR OCTANE NUMBER

Clear octane number, Motor, or Research, as applicable[a]	Increase in octane number with 3 cc TEL											
	Straight run[b]		Reformed (catalytic)		Reformed (thermal)		Thermal cracked		Catalytic cracked		Polymer	
	Motor	Res.	Motor	Res.	Motor	Res.	Motor	Res.	Motor	Res.	Motor	Res.
30	26.0	26.0										
35	25.0	25.0										
40	23.5	23.0	.....	....	23.5	23.5						
45	22.0	21.5	25.0	26.5	21.5	21.0						
50	21.0	20.0	23.0	24.5	19.5	20.0						
55	20.0	18.5	20.0	22.0	17.0	18.0	16.0	17.0				
60	19.0	17.0	18.0	20.0	15.0	16.5	14.0	15.5				
65	17.5	15.5	16.5	18.0	13.0	15.5	11.5	13.5				
70	16.5	14.5	14.5	16.5	11.0	14.0	8.5	10.5	10.0·			
75	15.5c	12.5	11.5	14.5	8.5	11.5	5.5	7.5	8.5	....	6.5c	
80	.....	11.0	9.5	12.0	6.5c	10.0	....	....	6.0	10.0	4.0	
85	.....	....	7.0	10.0	....	8.5	....	....	4.0	8.0	2.5c	8.5c
90	.....	....	5.0	8.0	....	7.0c	....	....	....	6.5	....	6.5
95	.....	....	....	6.0	....	....	....	....	....	4.0	....	4.5

[a] Use Motor method with Motor octane columns and Research with Research columns.

[b] Gasolines that contain 0.1–0.3 % sulfur are less susceptible (about 4 units); Nelson, W. L., Oil Gas J., Oct. 13, 1945, p. 145. Catalytically desulfurized gasolines are more susceptible (about 3 units); Nelson, W. L., Oil Gas J., Oct. 27, 1945, p. 127.

[c] Extrapolated. These are extremes, seldom encountered.

The susceptibility of fuels to tetraethyllead is not uniform. The octane number is increased greatly if (1) the clear or unleaded octane number is low, (2) the sulfur content (particularly mercaptans, monosulfides, and disulfides) is low, and (3) the percentage of olefin hydrocarbons (cracked gasolines) is low. Although variations are great, the general situation is indicated in Table 3-11,[40] which is an average of about 327 tests. Table 3-12 can be used to estimate the effect of tetraethyllead on the octane

[38] Nelson, W. L., Power versus Octane Number, Oil Gas J., Nov. 16, 1946, p. 317.

[39] Van Hartlesveldt and Field, Knocking Octanes, Pet. Refiner, June, 1940, p. 93.

[40] Nelson, W. L., Lead Response, Oil Gas J., Oct. 6, p. 106; Oct. 13, p. 137, 1945.

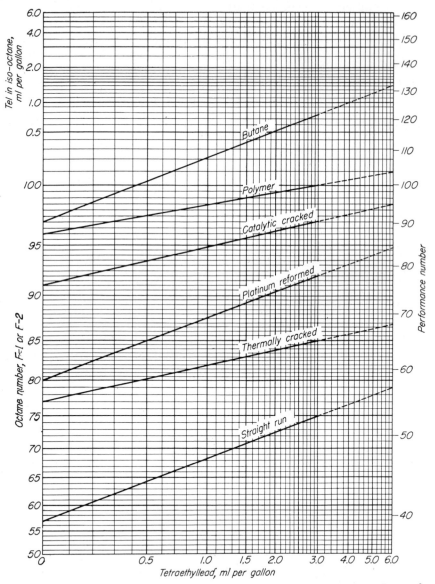

FIG. 3-4. Ethyl Corporation lead susceptibility chart. Lines illustrate Research (F-1) octane numbers of typical gasolines.

number of various types of gasoline. A substantially straight line results when the octane numbers of leaded gasolines are plotted on charts such as Fig. 3-4.[41] The Performance Number shown on the right-hand scale of Fig. 3-4 represents the approximate relative amount of power that can be developed.

In summary, our motor fuels consist of butanes and natural gasoline for front-end volatility, cracked or polymer gasolines and antiknock agents for allaying knocking, inhibitors for the delaying of gum formation, and straight-run gasoline. Thermally cracked gasolines are desirable in motor fuels because of their good low engine-speed performance. The low-boiling olefin hydrocarbons cause such performance. At high speeds the aromatic hydrocarbons found in catalytically cracked gasolines provide superior performance. Thus a mixture of the two kinds of fuels is advisable, particularly so that the L-head engines which knock at high speeds and the valve-in-head engines which knock at low speeds are both satisfied.

Naphthas or Solvents. The enormous number of uses for specialty materials intermediate or embracing parts of the boiling range of gasoline and kerosene makes for confusion and overlapping of specifications. Tables 3-13 and 3-14 show the average properties and uses for 20 representative naphthas[42] grouped generally with respect to boiling range. Straight-run petroleum naphthas contain only small amounts of aromatic hydrocarbons and hence are not good solvents for some materials, notably nitrocellulose lacquers, dry paint, or certain resins. High-solvency naphthas dissolve such materials, and special solvency tests[43] such as aniline point, kauri butanol number, and dilution ratios of nitrocellulose in ethyl or butyl acetate are employed. The low-gravity naphthas of Tables 3-13 and 3-14, shown in boldface type, are high-solvency naphthas produced by special processing methods that increase the percentage of aromatic hydrocarbons. A 48.4 API naphtha similar to No. 16 of Table 3-13, but containing 15 per cent of aromatic hydrocarbons, is used to deweed crops of carrots, parsnips, dill, or caraway.

Among the special requirements of solvents may be white color; low unsaturated and aromatic content for stability; high aromatic content for solution of lacquers or synthetic resins; or low boiling for rapid volatilization. In general, however, naphthas should be free from acidity, noncorrosive by the copper-strip test, free from gums or suspended matter, sweet smelling so that a petroleum odor is not imparted to the

---

[41] Ethyl Corp. Research Laboratory Chart, Apr. 15, 1949.

[42] Nelson, W. L., Classification of Solvents and Naphthas, *Oil Gas J.*, Apr. 15, 1943, p. 134.

[43] Nelson, W. L., Dilution Ratio Tests, *Oil Gas J.*, June 30, 1945, p. 117.

[44] Blade, O. C., Annual Surveys, *U.S. Bur. Mines Rept. Invest.* 5132, April, 1955.

Table 3-13. Approximate Properties of 20

Property	Key number of solvent							
	1	2	3	4	5	6	7	8
API gravity	75.1	75.5	74.6	**53**–70.5	71.5	**40**	64	62
I.B.P., °F	95	145	125	160	105	179	195	205
10 per cent	115	....	136	....	....	...	....	....
50 per cent	135	150	162	175	180	191	200	210
90 per cent	156	....	188	195	220	245	210	220
E.P., °F	186	160	206	210	260	275	215	240
Flash (Tag C.C.), °F	−73	....	−40	....	....	...	....	....
Kauri butanol No	....	30.5	34.5	33.5–**49**	34	**77**	35.5	37.5

[a] Solvents high in aromatic hydrocarbons (high solvency) are shown boldface.

Table 3-14. Uses of 20 Representative

Use of solvent	Boiling range, °F	Key number of solvent with					
		1 95–186	2 145–160	3 125–206	4 160–210	5 105–260	6 179–275
1. Perfume extraction	160–260	...	...	...	x	x	
2. Castor oil or fat extraction	125–300	...	...	x	x	x	...
3. **Toluene** substitute, **lacquer** formulas, fast-setting varnishes	179–275	...	...	...	...	...	x
4. Seed extraction	160–300	...	...	...	x	x	...
5. Rubber cements, tire manufacture	95–370	x	x	x	x	x	...
6. Lacquers, art leather, rotogravure ink, adhesive tape	95–370	x	x	x	x	x	...
7. Rosin extraction, shade cloth, rubber dip goods	205–300	...	...	...	...	...	...
8. Brake linings, leather degreasing, bone degreasing	125–400	...	...	x	x	x	...
9. **Printer's ink**, cellulose **lacquer diluent**	160–370	...	...	...	x	...	...
10. Paints and varnishes, thinners	105–455	...	...	...	...	x	...
11. Textile printing and proofing	160–410	...	...	...	x	...	...
12. **Paints** and coatings (aircraft), **paint removers** and **solvents**	179–410	...	...	...	...	...	x
13. Paint shop rinsing and cleaning (aircraft)	240–340	...	...	...	...	...	...
14. Floor coverings, wax, polish, wash for printing plates or rolls	200–410	...	...	...	...	...	...
15. Dry cleaning, metal and machinery cleaning	200–400	...	...	...	...	...	...
16. **Zylol** substitute (in many instances)	275–370	...	...	...	...	...	...
17. Flat finishes, rustproof compounds	300–455	...	...	...	...	...	...
18. **Synthetic resin** thinner	357–410	...	...	...	...	...	...
19. Wood preservatives	312–650	...	...	...	...	...	...

[a] Solvents high in aromatic hydrocarbons (high solvency) are shown boldface.

Key number of solvent

9	10	11	12	13	14	15	16	17	18	19	20
59.5	37–58	46	58	40	35	35–50	50	48	30–50	45	40
200	200	225	220	240	275	303	312	325	357	350	320
210	215	...	230	...	280	317	322	333	367	375	375
217	232	242	250	285	300	328	337	350	380	400	485
232	253	...	270	...	330	352	368	370	397	430	
247	286	280	300	340	360	376	380	400	410	455	650
25	25	...	45	...	80	99	...	115	136	142	145
38.5	39–69	54	38	72	73	35–63	33	35	31–65	32	

NAPHTHAS AND SOLVENTS[a] (see Table 3-13)

boiling ranges, °F

| 7 | 8 | 9 | 10 | 11 | 12 | 13 | 14 | 15 | 16 | 17 | 18 | 19 | 20 |
195–215	205–240	200–247	200–285	225–280	220–300	240–340	275–360	300–370	312–380	325–400	357–410	350–455	320–650
x	...	x	x	...	x	...							
...	...	x	x	...	x								
x	...	x	x	x	x	...	...	x					
x	...	x	x	...	x	...	...	x					
...	x	x	x	...	x								
x	...	x	x	x	x	...	...	x	...	x			
...	...	...	...	x	...	...	...	x					
...	...	x	x	...	x	...	x	x	...	x	x	x	
x	...	x	x	...	x	...	...	x	...	x	x		
...	...	...	x	...	...	x	x	...	...	...	x		
...	...	...	...	...	...	...	x						
...	...	x	...	...	x	...	...	x	...	x	x		
...	...	x	x	...	x	...	...	x	x	x			
...	...	...	...	...	...	...	x	x					
...	...	...	...	...	...	...	...	x	x	x	x	x	
...	...	...	...	...	...	...	...	...	...	...	x		
...	...	...	...	...	...	...	...	x	...	...	...	...	x

manufactured products, and well fractionated to eliminate as much of the fire hazard as possible.

There is an increasing tendency to offer extremely narrow-boiling-range naphthas (under 30°F) which are superior for some services but which can often be replaced by cheaper naphthas of wider or conventional boiling range. Nearly pure hydrocarbons ranging from propane through hexane are also being offered.

The mineral-oil solvents should not be considered as substitutes for other solvents that are now used, because mineral solvents possess properties that are unique and useful, and for many purposes they can be selected because of their own merits.

Jet Fuels. The production of military jet fuels reached 95,000 bpd in 1953 and the expected demand in 1957 is about 250,000 bpd (2.9 per cent of crude oil). Although a kerosene-like material (JP-1 Grade) was first used and a similar high-boiling fuel (JP-5) is still supplied in limited quantities, the main current fuels (JP-3 and JP-4) are wide-boiling-range materials which extend through gasoline and kerosene. Table 3-15 indicates the kinds of fuels supplied and Table 3-16 shows[44] in detail the 1954 properties and the specifications of jet fuels. Production has been almost totally straight-run material, but there are indications that small amounts of cracked materials and heavy alkylates or reformates can be incorporated. In the event of war, such materials will have to be tolerated. The Smoke Volatility Index of Table 3-16 is the IP smoke point plus 0.42 times the per cent distilled at 400°F. Its superiority as a means of judging deposition tendencies over plain smoke point has not been completely established. The low freezing point of minus 76°F is a difficulty in meeting specifications, and if certain naphthenic or aromatic crude oils are processed, the gravity requirement becomes limiting.

Throughout the world, specification DERD-2482, which is an Eastern Hemisphere kerosene, is used almost exclusively (1956), but some airlines require a freeze point of −50°F rather than −40°F.

Burning Oils. These oils, represented by kerosene, long-time burning oil, lighthouse kerosene, and 300°F mineral-seal oil, are used, as their names imply, in household, marine, passenger-coach, and railroad illuminating lamps. Kerosene is the main product in the United States but ASTM No. 1 Distillate has such similar properties that it is increasingly being sold as kerosene. Likewise, Eastern Hemisphere kerosene is sold as jet fuel. The 300°F mineral-seal oil is a high-grade oil having a Cleveland open-cup flash point of not less than 250°F. Signal oil for railroad lamps is compounded from 300°F mineral-seal oil and lard or sperm oil. Long-time burning oil is the finest grade, and in the burning test 650 cc of oil must not be consumed in less than 120 hr.

The value of kerosene is directly dependent upon its behavior in the burning or lamp test. An unsatisfactory burning test is terminated by smoking, by a white cloud on the chimney, or by a "toadstool" formation on the wick. Smoking is due primarily to aromatic hydrocarbons; a white cloud is probably produced by disulfides (over 0.01 per cent); and toadstools are thought to be related to both aromatics and disulfides.

TABLE 3-15. CHARACTERISTICS OF JET FUELS, 1952–1956[a]

Fuel	No. of samples	API gravity	Dist. temp., °F			Reid vapor pressure	Sulfur, wt %	Aromatics, vol. %	Gum existent steamjet
			10% evap.	50% evap.	90% evap.				
Avg. Grade JP-1:									
1952	3	42.3	338	368	421	...	0.057	14.3	
Avg. Grade JP-3:									
1952	6	52.5	166	316	433	6.0	0.081	14.7	
1954	4	56.5	160	265	421	5.7	0.089	10.3	1.5
1956	3	55.6	157	272	430	5.6	0.063	9.3	1.1
Avg. Grade JP-4:									
1952	24	50.5	222	332	430	2.6	0.075	11.9	
1954	23	51.5	216	319	425	2.6	0.080	11.3	0.6
1956	31	52.4	217	317	409	2.6	0.054	10.5	0.8
Avg. Grade JP-5:									
1953	1	37.3	397	432	491	0.5	0.46	8.3	2.0
1955	3	39.8	392	428	485	...	0.167	12.0	0.9
1956[b]	1	37.7	389	418	468	...	0.26	10.0	1.0
1956[b]	1	39.3	386	422	472	0	0.18	12.8	0.5

[a] Blade, O. C., National Annual Survey of Aviation Fuels, 1956, *U.S. Bur. Mines Inform. Circ. 7782*, March, 1957.
[b] Both of two samples are shown.

Although the Institute of Petroleum (British) smoke test[45] is not usually specified in the United States, it is used widely throughout the world. The smoke point is the height in millimeters of the flame that can be produced in a standard lamp without causing smoking. Mid Continent kerosene exhibits a smoke point of 21 to 24, and the smoke point of these materials is raised to more than 30 by acid treating.[46] A smoke point of 17 is satisfactory for most world trade.

[45] IP 57/55, Standard Methods for Testing Petroleum and Its Products, 26 Portland Place, London, W.C.1, England.
[46] Nelson, W. L., Smoke Point and Ring Number of Kerosenes, *Oil Gas J.*, June 14, 1954, p. 151.

TABLE 3-16. SPECIFICATIONS AND 1954 PROPERTIES OF JET FUELS[a]

| | Grade JP-3 | | Grade JP-4 | | Grade JP-5 | | DERD[d] 2482 specification |
	Average	Specification[b]	Average	Specification[b]	Range[c]	Specification[b]	
Gravity	56.5	45–63	51.5	45–57	37.8–41	35–50	
Distillation temp							
10% evap., °F	160	....	216	250 max	384–395	410 max	
50% evap., °F	265	....	319	370 max	418–424		
90% evap., °F	421	400 max	425	470 max	470–480	550 max	
400°F point, % evap	84	....	82.5	....	27.5–16		
End point, °F		600 max		550 max			572 max
Reid vapor pressure, psia	5.7	5–7	2.6	2–3			
Freezing point, °F	<−76	−76 max	<−76	−76 max	<−40 to −59	−40 max	−40 max
Viscosity, kinematic at −40°F	2.15	....	3.26	....	12.1–13.36	20 max	6 max[e]
Aniline point, °F	130.5	....	133.8	....	129–146		
Aniline gravity constant	7,373	....	6,891	5,240 min	4,876–5,986		
Bromine No., wt % Br	1.06	30 max	1.59	30 max	3.7–0.8	5–30	
Sulfur							
Total, wt %	0.089	0.4 max	0.080	0.4 max	0.33–0.075	0.5 max	0.2 max
Mercaptan	0.001	0.005 max	0.0016	0.005 max	0.001	0.005 max	
Aromatics, vol. %	10.3	25 max	11.3	25 max	20.3–15.13	25 max	20 max
Olefin content	0.6	....	1.3	5 max	0.9–0.87		
Smoke point	29.4	....	28.7	....	21		
Smoke Volatility Index	64.7	....	63.4	54 min	33–27.7		
Gum							
Existent		10 max		7 max		10 max	6 max
Air-jet, 400°F mg/100 ml	1.6	....	1.3	....			
Steam-jet, 450°F, mg/100 ml	1.5	....	0.6	....	1.0		

TABLE 3-16. SPECIFICATIONS AND 1954 PROPERTIES OF JET FUELS[a] (*Continued*)

	Grade JP-3		Grade JP-4		Grade JP-5		DERD[d] 2482 specification
	Average	Specification[b]	Average	Specification[b]	Range[c]	Specification[b]	
Accelerated							
Air-jet, 400°F mg/100 ml	1.8	20 max	....		....	20 max	
Steam-jet, 450°F, mg/100 ml	1.9	....	2.5	14 max	1.0		
Heat of combustion, net Btu/lb	18,715	18,400 min	18,678	18,400 min	18,391–18,569	18,300 min	18,300 min
Hydrogen-carbon ratio	0.168	....	0.1635	....	0.157–0.151		

[a] Blade, O. C., Annual Surveys, *U.S. Bur. Mines Rept. Invest.* 5132, April, 1955.
[b] JP-3 and JP-4, MIL-F-5624, 1956; JP-5, MIL-F-7914 (AER), Mar. 11, 1952.
[c] Only 2 fuels. One fuel is shown at left and the other at right.
[d] British Ministry of Supply. Kerosene used world wide in civil jet operations (1956).
[e] At 0°F.

The Saybolt thermoviscosity is also used to indicate the behavior of the oil in a lamp by means of the so-called Ring Number which is:

$$\text{Ring No.} = \frac{\text{thermoviscosity}}{5} - 10 \ (46 \text{ minus API})$$

The viscosity usually ranges between 325 and 450. However, an oil may have a proper viscosity and yet fail to burn satisfactorily. Kerosenes may have a gravity of 39 to 48 API and a flash point (Tag) of 120 to 180°F. The initial boiling point is usually under 370°F, and the end point about 500°F, although the government at one time allowed an end point of 620°F. Although gravity is not important, many refiners strive to produce a 41.5 to 43 API kerosene, and hence most of the kerosene sold in the United States has this gravity. A small amount of light material (naphtha) is necessary in order to produce a high-quality burning oil. For this reason a little heavy gasoline must always be present in the kerosene, and hence the boiling ranges of kerosene and gasoline (or naphtha) overlap to some extent. If the gasoline (or naphtha) and kerosene are too well fractionated, the flash point and initial boiling point of the kerosene will be so high that it will not burn properly.

The color instability of some kerosenes has at times been a mysterious difficulty. Several inhibitors and tests for color instability have been developed.[47] The properties of a few kerosenes and related products are given in Table 3-17. Range oil has no close specifications and is usually considered as an off-brand kerosene that is too high in sulfur, has a bad odor, etc.

Tractor fuel oil is discussed by A. T. Colwell,[48] but the motor fuel tax limitations, the need for cheapness, and the wide variety of engines make clear-cut specifications impossible. In general, the properties of fuels that have been marketed are somewhat as follows:

Flash point, min	Low to 115°F
10 per cent temperature, min	176–422°F
95 per cent temperature, min	437–555°F
End point temperature, max	480–600°F
Sulfur, per cent, max	0.1–0.5

Distillate Fuels. Among these are stove gasoline (torches or lamps), tractor fuels, domestic fuel oils (stove or furnace), industrial distilled fuels, spray oils, insecticides, smudge oil, straw oil, absorption oil, and gas oil. Table 3-18 presents the properties of these not closely specified oils. In northern New Jersey the average quality of No. 2 heating oil has been

---

[47] Hillman, McHatton, and Moerbeek, *Proc. World Petroleum Cong.*, **2,** 704, 708, 713, and 721 (1933); and Rather and Beard, *Ref. Nat. Gaso. Mfr.*, **15,** 217 (1936).

[48] Fuel Requirements for Farm Tractors, *Pet. Refiner*, January, 1945, p. 124.

TABLE 3-17. PROPERTIES OF KEROSENE, TRACTOR FUEL, AND RELATED PRODUCTS

Name of product	Gravity, API	Flash, °F min	Dist. temp, °F			Sulfur %, max	Smoke point, min	Corrosion, copper strip	Color, Saybolt, min	Burning test, time	Others
			I.B.P., min	10% recovered, max	E.P., max						
Kerosene:											
Special arctic export	46–49	110–120	300–325		465–490	0.05–0.1			+30	24 hr	10 wick char
Signal or long-time burning oil	44–48	110–125	300–335		480–600	0.04–0.1	29–34		+25 to +30	120 min (and 14 day)	
Domestic, 41–43, w.w.	41–44	105–130	350–370		480–572	0.05–0.1	25–30		+16 to +30	24 hr	20 wick char
Domestic, 44–46, w.w.	44–46	110–130	350–370		470–572	0.03–0.1	26–32		+30	24 hr (and 21 day)	
Federal, VV-K-211a	36–39	115			572	0.13			+16	24 hr	
300°F mineral-seal		250–260	480–540		600–700				+16 to +25	20 hr	
Range oil	43	145			515				+25	72 hr	
Tractor fuel, ASTM D1215:											
Light grade				347	465–518 [a]	1.0		Pass			35 min o.n.
Regular grade				347–401	465–518 [a]	1.0		Pass			35 min o.n.
Distillate, ASTM D396:											
1955 Grade No. 1	35.2–48.5	114–185	317–396	350–420	487–586	0.018–0.5 [b]		Pass			−10 to −60 pour point
1956 Grade No. 2	34.8–44.9	120–185	312–382	360–428	474–620	0.01–0.96 [b]		Pass			Zero to −65 pour point
Rocket fuel, RP-1	42–45	110	365–410		525	0.05	28	Pass			Freezing point −40°F Aromatics, 5% max

[a] Temperatures at 95% recovered.
[b] Special services require 0.5 max.

as follows:

Year	API	Diesel Index	Per cent distilled at 440°F
1938–1941	36.4	52.8	20.1
1942	35.9	52.0	15.9
1944	32.6	43.5	10.5
1945	32.9	44.5	13.0

Thermally and catalytically cracked distillates have not been entirely satisfactory for the types of domestic burners now available, because of carbonization. The kinds of domestic burners and the fuels required are:

Type of burner	ASTM grade of fuel required	Per cent of sales (1947)
Vaporizing type....................	.....	10.8
Natural draft....................	1	
Pot type, forced draft.............	1 or 2	
Vertical rotary, forced draft.........	1 or 2	11.0
Vertical rotary, atomizing...........	1 or 2	
Atomizing-gun type:		
Low pressure....................	3 or 2	6.2
High pressure....................	2 or 3	71.7

The *flash point* of domestic fuels is limited because of safety, and an upper limit is imposed to ensure easy ignition in vaporizing-type burners. Carbon residue on a 10 per cent ASTM residue indicates something of the tendency to produce coke in vaporizing-type burners, but the 90 per cent *distillation temperature* is probably equally significant, and a good correlation is obtained only upon consideration of the *carbon-hydrogen ratio*,[49] Diesel Index, or aniline point. *Viscosity* naturally falls within proper limits, but in general each atomizing-type burner exhibits a maximum capacity at some intermediate viscosity.[50] *Sulfur* is normally of little significance; but, for chicken brooder heaters, heat-treating, and glass or ceramics ware furnaces, it may be specified. *Color and odor* are not vital, but purchasers note them. The increasing use of cracked distillates or cycle stocks in distillate fuels has helped the pour point but has introduced difficulties with stability. Various additives are employed to

[49] Cauley and Delgass, Carbon Hydrogen Ratio of Catalytically Cracked Distillate Fuel Oils, *Oil Gas J.*, July 27, 1946, p. 166.
[50] Glendenning and Sullivan, Characteristics of Fuel Oil, *Natl. Pet. News*, Aug. 21, 1936, p. 41.

Table 3-18. Distillates and Related Fuels

Grade or name	API	Flash point, °F	Pour point, °F	Distillation, °F				Sulfur %	Viscosity at 100°F max	Others
				I.B.P.	Max 10%	90%	Max E.P.			
1. Lighter fluid[a]	64–70	.....	.....	130	155	280	350			
2. Stove gasoline	64–70	.....	.....	112	162	293	335			
3. ASTM No. 1, specification	35+	100+	0	.....	420	.....	625	.....	1.4–2.2[b]	Carbon res. 0.15[c]
1956 range	34.8–44.9	120–185	−65 to zero	312–382	360–428	440–554	474–620	0.01–0.96	1.38–2.43[d]	
4. ASTM No. 2, specification	26+	100+	20	.....	440	675	.....		40	Carbon res. 0.35[c]
1955 range	25.8–44.7	126–230	−60 to +20	300–460	368–491	451–630	487–708	0.03–0.99	1.6–4.3[d]	B.S.W. below 0.01
1956 range	24.1–47.2	128–230	−45 to 25	312–457	370–498	457–650	491–714	0.05–1.4	1.5–4.48[d]	
5. ASTM No. 4, specification	.....	130+	20	.....	.....	.....	.....		125	B.S.W. below 0.5
1955 range	12.8–35.9	154–240	−45 to 70	351–504	447–544	630–748	686–842	0.1–3.27	5.8–25[d]	
1956 range	8.7–36.3	152–230	−30 to 25	375–528	438–620	635–730	655–840	0.23–2.2	35	
6. Gas oil (gas enrichment)	33	195	.....	302	460	.....	700+	.....	35	
7. Gas oil (industrial fuel)	30	210	35	440	475	.....	800+	.....	70	
8. Absorption oil	45	.....	.....	344	386	.....	505	.....	.....	Demulsibility 9 min
9. Absorption oil	37	.....	.....	482	518	.....	630		39	Mol. wt 217

[a] Copper dish gum 2 max and Reid vapor pressure 7 max.
[b] Centistokes at 77°F.
[c] On the 10% residue of an ASTM distillation.
[d] Kinematic at 100°F.

55

TABLE 3-19. PROPERTIES AND SPECIFICATIONS OF DIESEL FUELS

Description of fuel	Flash point, °F min	API gravity	Pour point, °F, max	Distillation range, °F				Viscosity at 100°F	Carbon residue, % max[a]	Cetane number	Sulfur, % max	Aniline point, °F
				I.B.P.	10%	90%	E.P.					
1940, high quality	170	37	0		440	645		35		57[b]		
1940, medium quality	170	33	0		470	700		38		48[b]		
1944, all-purpose, Army	140		−10			650	700	1.6–4.28[c]	0.15	50[d]	1.0	
1944, arctic grade, Army	110		−50			600	650	1.5–4.28[c]	0.15	45[d]	1.0	
1947, misc. samples	190–200	32–41	0 to −35	400–416	453–476	500–680	560–724	34–39	0.03–0.1	44–51	0–0.7	
ASTM Grade 1-D:												
1950, avg	159	40		369	417	532	575	33.8	0.053	52	0.2	153
1952, avg Eastern U.S.		40.3		366	409	523	566	33.1	0.064	51.6	0.142	151
1954, avg Eastern U.S.		41.3		358	401	518	563	32.7	0.061	52.1	0.128	150.8
1956, avg Eastern U.S.	122[e]	40.5	−60[e]	364	408	524	567	33.0	0.076	51.3	0.142	150.2
1955, ASTM, D975	100		20				625	1.4 min[c]	0.15	40	0.5	
ASTM Grade 2-D:												
1950, avg zero pour	171	36.5		380	441	593	652	35.8	0.081	50.1	0.326	153
1950, avg higher pour	185	34.8		396	471	621	677	38.8	0.091	50.3	0.457	157
1956, avg Eastern U.S.	138[e]	36.8	15	369	431	587	645	35.0	0.106	50.3	0.273	150.0
1956, avg Central U.S.	143[e]	35.9	15	375	438	590	645	35.6	0.100	49.5	0.285	149.0
1956, avg Western U.S.	154[e]	33.5	25	387	455	606	668	37.0	0.112	45.7	0.523	143.0
1955, ASTM, D975	125		20			675		32–45	0.35	40	1.0	
Marine (typical)	150	32.0	0					30–40	0.35	35–40	1.0	
ASTM Grade 4-D:												
1950, avg	199	25.3		417	510	695	759	76.8	1.07[f]	39.5	0.79	146
1955, avg Eastern U.S.	160[e]	27.3	10	398	500	728	773	81.1	1.48[f]	36.0	0.577	163
1956, avg Eastern U.S.	156[e]	22.5	−20[e]	451	511	720	780	46.5	0.50[f]	47.2	0.39	151.0
1955, ASTM, D975	130		20					45–125		30	2.0	

[a] On a 10% ASTM distillation residue.
[b] Diesel Index.
[c] Centistokes.
[d] War shortages forced reduction to 40 during 1944.
[e] Minimum, not average.
[f] On entire material.

alleviate the clogging of screens, the formation of sediment or gum-like materials, deterioration in color, and corrosiveness.[25]

Most middle-boiling-range material (400–900°F) is cracked into gasoline, but in meeting the specifications of such materials as kerosene, No. 1 Distillate, diesel fuel, and jet fuel, it is necessary to use mainly straight-run material.

Diesel Fuels. The major performance characteristics of diesel fuels, somewhat in the order of importance, are

1. Cleanliness—carbon residue, B.S.W., sulfur, etc.
2. Ignition quality—cetane number or Diesel Index.
3. Fluidity and atomization—viscosity, pour point, etc.
4. Volatility—flash point, distillation, and carbon residue.

Even the small amount of dirt carried in dusty air can pollute diesel fuel, because the plunger of the injection pump is lapped to a tolerance of 0.00001 in. Excessively large amounts of *sulfur* are thought to contribute to engine wear, and sulfur obviously can cause muffler and exhaust-pipe corrosion. Good ignition quality, as measured by cetane number or Diesel Index, assists in easy starting, starting at low temperatures, low engine pressures, and smooth operation; whereas a fuel with poor ignition quality promotes misfiring, varnish on pistons, engine dirt or deposits, and rough operation. Fuel economy is slightly better for medium- or low-cetane-number fuels, but engine load is much more important. High-viscosity, high-boiling-range fuels cause engine deposits, smoke, and odor; but too low a viscosity may lead to a slightly lower efficiency because of poor lubrication of the injectors, leakage, or the low heating value of such a fuel.

The approximate relationship among ignition quality properties is indicated in Table 3-20. The most important of these is Diesel Index, which is defined as the API gravity times the aniline point (in degrees Fahrenheit) divided by 100. Ignition accelerators, such as alkyl nitrates (especially amyl nitrate) or nitrites, aldehydes, ketones, esters, ethers, and peroxides, have been investigated.[51] A major difficulty has been the incompatibility often encountered when two fuels are mixed. They tend to produce sediment during storage. Anti-screen-clogging additives and inhibitors of gum formation now permit refiners to blend straight-run and catalytic cycle stocks[25] into diesel fuels.

Ease of starting, according to Shoemaker and Gadebusch,[52] depends mainly upon ignition quality but also upon viscosity and pour point.

[51] Bogan and Wilson, Ignition Accelerators for Compression-ignition Engine Fuels, *Pet. Refiner*, July, 1944.

[52] Effect of Fuel Properties on Diesel Engine Performance, *Oil Gas J.*, Jan. 12, 1946, p. 74.

Fuels more viscous than 550 sec Saybolt Universal at the starting temperature cannot be handled by some fuel-ignition pumps. Plugging of screens or cloth filters tends to occur at the cloud or haze point, which is usually about 10°F above the pour point. Finally, the cetane number

TABLE 3-20. COMPARISON OF IGNITION QUALITY AND
OTHER PROPERTIES (APPROXIMATE)

Cetane number	Diesel Index	Blending octane number (Motor method)	Characterization Factor	Boiling-point gravity number[a]
30	26	51	11.05	201
35	34	43	11.25	196
40	42	35	11.45	191
45	49	27	11.6	187
50	56	19	11.8	183
55	64	11	12.0	180
60	72	2	12.2	178

[a] $G = B + (68 - 0.703B) \log T$, in which G = API gravity, T = °C, and B = the constant.

TABLE 3-21. PROPERTIES OF DIESEL FUELS FOR EASY STARTING

Air temperature, °F	Maximum viscosity Saybolt Universal at 100°F	Maximum pour point, °F	Cetane number, min
−20	42	−30	90
−10	46	−20	83
0	50	−10	76
10	57	0	69
20	65	10	63
30	70	20	56
40	98	30	49
50	. . .	40	43
60	160	50	36

must be high enough to permit ignition when the air that is compressed is cold. The properties required are somewhat as shown in Table 3-21. Obviously viscosity gives little trouble.

Lubricating Oils—General. There are so many uses for mineral oils that a formidable array of names, based on uses, has arisen. Several grades of viscosity are useful for each general type of oil, but a relatively few types of oils will satisfy most of the needs of industry. Table 3-22

TABLE 3-22. RANGE OF PHYSICAL PROPERTIES OF LUBRICATING OILS

Name of oil	Used for	API	Viscosity at 100°F	130°F	210°F	Viscosity Index	Flash (open cup)	Pour point	Carbon residue	Compounding oil, per cent	Special property
Motor, light	Automotive engine	24-30		90-185	40-55	70-100	360-400	-10 to 15	0.03-0.5		Detergency and Viscosity Index
Motor, medium	Automotive engine	22-28	400-650	185-293	62-90	50-100	400-450	0 to 25	0.1-0.9		Detergency and Viscosity Index
Motor, heavy	Automotive engine	20-27			80-155	40-100	440-510	0 to 25	0.2-1.8		Detergency and Viscosity Index
Aircraft engine, light	Airplanes	24-26			60-85	90-100	400-425	-10 to 0	0.8-1.0		Settle from salt solution, 60 min
Aircraft engine, heavy	Airplanes	23-25		120-185	100-145	90-100	475-500	0 to 30	1.5-2.0		Settle from salt solution, 60 min
Diesel engine, lightest	Diesels	23-25				40-70	330-350	-10 to 10	0.2-0.5		
Diesel engine, heaviest	Diesels	22-25			75-90	40-70	390-410	0 to 20	0.3-0.8		
Transmission oil, lightest	Automobiles	21-23	800-1,500				300-420	-10 to 10			Precipitation number, 0.1 max
Transmission oil, heaviest	Automobiles	20-22			200		500+	0 to 30			Precipitation number, 0.1 max
Engine and machine, spindle	Textiles, etc.	25-27	100-125				320-350	0 to 30			Viscosity
Engine and machine, heaviest	Heavy machinery	21-26	700-800				375-400	0 to 30			Viscosity
Cold test, light	Refrigeration, etc.	27-32	140-170				310-350	-20 max			Low pour point
Cold test, heavy	Refrigeration, etc.	25-28	300-325				340-400	-10 max			Low pour point
Cylinder oils, unfiltered:											
Light mineral	Engine or compressor cylinders	25-28			135-165		490-540	20 to 60	2.0-3.0	None	Neutralization number, 0.15 max
Heavy mineral		20-26			175-220		520-600	30 to 60	3.0-4.0	None	Neutralization number, 0.15 max
Light compounded		25-28			95-110		450-510	10 to 40	1.0-2.0	9-10	Neutralization number, 1.0 max
Heavy compounded		20-26			175-220		520-600	30 to 60	3.0-4.0	5-7	Neutralization number, 1.0 max
Marine engine, mineral	Marine engines	23-28			65-75		350-410	35 max		None	Neutralization number, 0.1 max
Marine engine, compound	Marine engines	23-28			65-80		350-410	35 max		15-20	Neutralization number, 3.0 max
Turbine oil, light	Steam turbines, dynamos, high speed, etc.	29-31	120-175				310-360	0 to 35	0.02-0.1		Steam emulsion number, demulsibility, and Sligh oxidation number also specified
Turbine oil, medium		27-30	175-340				320-410	0 to 35	0.05-0.3		
Turbine oil, heaviest		26-28	475-525				350-450	35 max	0.1-0.4		
Transformer oil	Electrical transformers	28-30	55-65				275-325	-50 to -30			Dielectric strength, 1-in. disk, 0.1-in. gap, 25,000 volts
Black oil, summer	Rough slow-speed bearings, crushers, etc.	20-25	400-500					0 to 30			Insoluble per cent, 0.1
Black oil, winter		20-27	200-300					-20 to 0			Insoluble per cent, 0.1
White oil	Food manufacturing, textiles, paper, etc.	29-32	55-140				260-380				Colorless

shows the properties of some of the major types of oils, and the approximate amounts sold during 1950 are shown in Table 3-23.

In general, oils may be grouped as follows:

1. *Engine and Machine Oils.* High viscosity Index oils are required for aircraft engines and automotive engines operating in temperature and arctic climates and for machinery or instruments that are subject to wide variations in temperature. Viscosity and Viscosity Index (see Fig. 4-2) are important considerations.

TABLE 3-23

Type of oil	Thousand bbl	Percentage
Motor oil:		
Straight............................	7,000	18.0
Premium............................	4,800	12.3
Heavy duty (2-104 B)...............	7,650	19.6
MIL −2104.........................	2,550	6.5
Total............................	22,000	56.4
Industrial:		
Straight............................	9,700	24.8
Rust and oxidation inhibited..........	2,250	5.8
Premium............................	2,250	5.8
Heavy duty.........................	150	0.4
Railroad diesel.....................	450	1.2
Total............................	14,800	38.0
Gear oil and grease.................	2,200	5.6
Total domestic...................	39,000	100.0
Total export.....................	14,200	

Medium Viscosity Index oils are suitable for almost all industrial machinery including stationary spark-ignition engines and automobiles in temperate or warm climates.

Low Viscosity Index oils are suitable for most industrial lubrication and for diesel engines. Except for poor starting characteristics, these oils are thought to be best for general automotive service (except arctic) because of their natural detergent properties. Others feel that a chemical detergent should be added to the higher-viscosity-index oils to gain detergency properties.

Obviously the entire range of viscosity of 60 sec at 100°F to 250 viscosity at 210°F must be available to provide service for the lightest spindles (of zero clearance) and the heaviest machinery operating at high temperatures. In general, the useful life of an oil is halved by each 15°F increase in operating temperature (above 140°F). In connection with gravity-feed systems, etc., it is useful to recognize that the viscosity is about halved by each 20°F increase in temperature.

2. *Compounded Oils.* The addition of fatty oils such as lard, tallow, rapeseed, castor, and sperm causes the oil to spread over and more thoroughly wet a metal surface, and they tend to permit the formation of emulsions with water that will stick to the metal surface. Thus compounding is practiced for steam engine, air compressor, quenching, cutting, marine engine, and tempering oils. Fatty oils also mildly increase the film strength. Tests for emulsibility, neutralization number, and percentage of fatty oil are useful.

3. *Turbine Oils.* High-speed machinery, such as steam turbines and dynamos, may cause emulsions with water; and hence the ASTM steam emulsion number (D157) and demulsibility test of the Federal government (Method 320.13) are useful. Extreme stability, attained mainly by long filtration through fuller's earth, is necessary because these oils may be used for several years.

4. *Cold Test Oils.* Pour point, viscosity, and sometimes Viscosity Index are important for oils used for refrigeration equipment, hydraulic mechanisms, machine guns, instruments, or any machinery in arctic climates.

5. *Transformer Oils.* These and insulating oils must withstand large electrical voltages, and hence the dielectric strength (usually 1-in. disks, 0.1-in. gap, 25,000 volts minimum) is important. The steam emulsion number is usually specified in order to assure stability during several years of service.

6. *Color Oils.* Such services as food, paper or textile manufacture, and medicinal uses require a white or very light-colored oil. Lubricant quality is destroyed to a large extent by decolorization. The cheap black oils might also be included here, because color is of no significance.

7. *Corrosive Oils.* Several services depend in part on the corrosiveness of an oil at least in certain temperature ranges. Such oils as extreme-pressure lubricants for hypoid or heavy-duty gears, and cutting oils require the addition of sulfur, chlorine, or compounds of these. Suitable corrosion tests and special performance tests are required for each service.

Since nearly all industrial services can be met by the above seven general types of oils, it is doubtful if an attempt should be made to classify the many specialties used as putty, leather, quenching, penetrating, preservative, wire rope, chain, harness, floor, furniture polish, shoe polish, wax mixtures, denaturing, wool, shock absorber, hydraulic, brake band, etc., oils.

The SAE viscosity classification of oils shown in Table 3-24 is most widely used. The 10W and 20W grades are for winter service. Perhaps

TABLE 3-24. SAE CLASSIFICATION SYSTEM FOR CRANKCASE OILS

SAE viscosity number	Saybolt Universal, sec		Redwood		Engler		Centistokes	
	0°F	210°F	0°F	210°F	0°F	210°F	0°F	210°F
5W	Below 4,000	......	Below 3,500	....	Below 115	....	Below 869	
10W	6,000–12,000	40 min	5,250–10,500	....	172–344	....	1,303–2,606	
20W	12,000–48,000	45 min	10,500–42,000	....	344–1,376	....	2,606–10,423	
20	....	45–58	....	40.9–51.6	....	1.46–1.8	....	5.73–9.62
30	....	58–70	....	51.6–61.9	....	1.8–2.12	....	9.62–12.94
40	....	70–85	....	61.9–75.2	....	2.12–2.52	....	12.94–16.77
50	....	85–110	....	75.2–97.5	....	2.52–3.19	....	16.77–22.68

a better (but more complicated) classification system is that of the Bureau of Ships.[53] It consists of a series of numbers of four digits each, and a detailed tabulation of the properties of the oils that have thus far been assigned numbers. The tabulation[53] of properties is too extensive for publication here. The first digit designates the general kind of oil, and the last three digits are used to show the numerical value of the viscosity. The kinds or types of oils adopted by the Navy are

Class		Viscosity measured at
1xxx	Forced feed, high Viscosity Index (95–100)............	210°F
2xxx	Forced feed, low Viscosity Index....................	130°F
3xxx	Forced feed, medium Viscosity Index (65–75).........	210°F
4xxx	Compounded marine engine........................	210°F
5xxx	Mineral cylinder.................................	210°F
6xxx	Compounded steam cylinder (tallow)................	210°F
7xxx	Compounded steam cylinder (lard or tallow)..........	210°F
8xxx	Compounded air cylinder..........................	130°F
9xxx	Diesel engine (heavy duty)........................	130°F

As examples, 1042 is SAE 10W oil, and 3050 (or 9170) is SAE 20 oil.

Motor Oils. Spark-ignition and diesel-engine oils differ primarily because the diesel oils must exhibit "detergency" properties to keep carbon from accumulating in the engine after a few hours of operation. Naphthene-base oils (low Viscosity Index) are somewhat satisfactory as diesel oils, but most heavy-duty oils are made by introducing a detergency additive to an oil manufactured from paraffin or mixed-base crude oils.

Much importance has been attached to Viscosity Index[54] because it measures the suitability of an oil to lubricate properly at the elevated

[53] N.B.S. 431, Lubricating Oil, Bureau of Ships, Navy Department, Washington, D.C., 1942.
[54] See Figs. 4-1 and 4-2 for viscosity-temperature relationships.

temperatures of the engine and at the same time not to be too viscous for operation during starting.

Easy starting is said to occur if the viscosity does not exceed 40,000 sec Saybolt Universal at the starting temperature,[55] and, of course, the pour point must be adequately low. Thus viscosity, Viscosity Index, and pour point together govern ease of starting. The lowest temperatures at which easy starting (quick-cranking) can occur are somewhat as follows:

Kind of oil	Lowest easy starting temperature, °F		
	40 Viscosity Index	60 Viscosity Index	100 Viscosity Index
40 viscosity at 210°F..........	−23	−25	−34
SAE 10W...................	−18 to −27	−19 to −29	−20 to −30
SAE 20W...................	0 to −18	0 to −19	0 to −20
SAE 20 (thinnest)............	−2	−6	−12
SAE 30 (thinnest)............	13	9	0

Obviously 10W and 20W oils of any base are satisfactory for normal winter service. Zero Viscosity Index oils are not shown in the tabulation, because such oils are not marketed. So called "multigrade" oils are being marketed which meet the requirements of several or all SAE grades.

Viscosity in itself appears to be of little direct significance, and such might be expected because the piston rings scarcely push against the cylinder wall. The oil must be fluid enough during starting to flow through the lubrication system, but it may be quite thin (even diluted with kerosene) at the engine temperature without causing excessive wear. Thinner and thinner oils are being employed. Although thin oils may contribute to oil consumption, less gasoline is used and the over-all cost of operation may be less[56] or scarcely different. The factors that affect oil consumption are (1) low-boiling or low-flash oils, (2) low-viscosity oils that allow blow-by, (3) excessively high engine temperatures, (4) high engine speed or load, (5) leaks at gaskets or rotating seals, (6) carburetor out of adjustment so that crankcase dilution occurs, and (7) a worn engine.[57] Of these, a worn engine, a poor carburetor adjustment, or a high speed accounts for most cases of excessive oil consumption.

Flash or *fire point* indicates little of engine performance, but it indicates the source of the oil and whether it is a blend of low- and high-boiling

[55] Otto, Miller, Blackwood, and Davis, Improved Motor Oils, *Ref. Nat. Gaso. Mfr.*, November, 1934, p. 411.

[56] Nelson, W. L., Significance of Viscosity . . . , *Oil Gas J.*, Nov. 23, 1939, p. 46.

[57] Nelson, W. L., Consumption of Engine Oil, *Oil Gas J.*, Feb. 17, 1944, p. 73.

oils. *Sulfur* has little direct effect, but Merrill, Moore, and Bray[58] find inconclusive evidence that high-sulfur oils cause engine corrosion—that the wear may have been caused by the different types of hydrocarbons in the oils rather than by sulfur.

Carbon residue is not directly related to carbon formation in the engine. The extremely high-carbon-residue Pennsylvania oils produce only a little more carbon in the engine than do the low-carbon-residue naphthene-base oils, but the paraffin-base carbon is much harder and is attached more firmly to the cylinder parts.[59]

Short-time *engine tests* such as the Lauson, Underwood, and Chevrolet 36-hr tests[60] and the Work Factor test of the Bureau of Ships[53] are necessary in making real evaluations of oils. However, even such elaborate test methods sometimes produce confusing results and they indicate clearly that the results are a function of the way the engine is operated as well as of the properties of the fuels or lubricants being tested.

Additives are now widely used to alter the properties of lubricating oils. Pour-point depressants act differently on each oil, but on the average cause reductions in pour point[61] about as follows:

Per cent	Average lowering, °F	Range of lowering, °F
0.1	11	1–21
0.3	22	5–39
0.5	30	17–44
1.0	38	24–53

Wax-naphthalene or wax-phenol condensation products and their polymers are said to be effective as pour-point reducers.[25] Viscosity Index may be improved by the addition of butene polymers or polymers of methacrylic acid esters. Detergency additives are usually complex calcium or barium sulfonates or phenates. Such additives tend to keep carbonaceous sludgelike materials from settling out of the oil and will even clean such materials from a dirty engine. When a detergency additive is used, the crankcase oil almost immediately appears dark and dirty because the sludge is carried in suspension. When such an oil is

[58] Service Characteristics of Motor Oil, as Related to Chemical Composition, *Oil Gas J.*, June 13, 1935, p. 59.

[59] Livingston and Gruse, Carbon Deposits from Lubricating Oils, *Ind. Eng. Chem.*, **21**, 904 (1929).

[60] Georgi, C. W., Subcommittee Report, *SAE Journal*, February, 1943, p. 52.

[61] Nelson, W. L., Reducing Pour-point with Depressants, *Oil Gas J.*, Dec. 30, 1944, p. 269.

first used in a dirty engine, it loosens so much material that the oil should be changed at least two extra times at 300- and 500-mile intervals to remove the debris.

Detergency oils are necessary for diesel engines, although straight naphthene-base oils are reasonably good, and such oils are advisable for heavy-duty spark-ignition engines. The engine temperatures in spark-ignition and diesel engines are somewhat as follows:

Location	Spark-ignition	Diesel
Piston head, °F	500–650	650–750
Top ring, °F	....	475–500
Lower ring belt, °F	200–325	350
Cylinder wall, °F	300–350	350
Crankcase oil, °F	160–250	170–250

These high temperatures tend to cause rapid oxidation of the oil on the piston head and top ring, with the formation of solid asphaltic material from paraffin-base oils but only sludge[62] in the naphthene- or detergency-type oils. Thus, when paraffinic oils are employed, varnishlike deposits tend to "cook down" on the lower walls of spark-ignition pistons, and coke deposits are formed around the top ring of diesel-engine pistons. Detergency oils do not assist greatly in removing the varnishlike deposits of spark-ignition engines, but they do suppress to a large extent the coking of diesel engines by keeping the carbonaceous material in suspension.

TABLE 3-25. ESTIMATED ANNUAL CONSUMPTION OF ADDITIVES FOR (MAINLY) AUTOMOTIVE LUBRICANTS, 1955[a]

Kind	Dosage, per cent	Millions of pounds	Millions of dollars
Detergents	2–10	280–300	57
Antioxidants—corrosion inhibitors	0.4–2	70–75	15
Viscosity Index improvers	0.5–10	60–65[b]	15
Pour point depressants	0.1–1	5	2
Extreme pressure agents	5–10	60[c]	14
Defoamants	0.0002–0.07		
Antirust agents	0.1–1		
Odor control	0.001–0.005	....	6
Oiliness imparters	0.1		

[a] Larson, C. M., Additives for Fuels and Lubricants, *Pet. Engr.*, March, 1955, p. C-44.

[b] Used also as pour depressant.

[c] 60% automotive and 40% industrial usage.

[62] Faust, J., Asphaltization Tests for Lubricating Oil, *Oil Gas J.*, Jan. 20, 1944, p. 29.

Antioxidant additives to alleviate oxidation, sludging, or corrosion are extensively used. An enormous number of agents have been recommended or used; and a few are calcium petroleum sulfonates, sulfurized terpenes or olefins, metal salts of phenol sulfides, phosphorus pentoxide-treated terpenes, and zinc methylcyclohexylthiophosphate. Antifoaming agents such as silicone compounds when used in minute amounts effectively reduce the tendency to foam.

Lubricants. This term is applied primarily to greases, semisolid compositions, and gear oils, even though some of the materials are as much like liquid oils as like solids. Most generally, greases may be grouped into three classes.[63]

1. *Admixtures of mineral oil and solid lubricant.* Some of the common solid lubricants are graphite, mica, talc, sulfur, and asbestos fiber. These greases are invaluable in the lubrication of ill-fitting machine parts functioning under heavy or intermittent loads. Examples of this type are tractor-roller lubricants, lubricants for concrete mixers, ditch-digging equipment, and railroad-car unloading devices.

2. *Blends of residuum, waxes, uncombined fats, rosin oils, and pitches.* This group is particularly suited to the lubrication of rock bits, steel cables, water pumps, dredges and chains, and gears operating under water or under exposed weather conditions.

3. *Soap-thickened mineral oils.* Common thickeners are sodium, calcium, aluminum, lithium, and lead soaps. The soaps of these metals are prepared by saponification of a fatty glyceride of either animal or vegetable origin. This group is widely useful because a large variety of different-consistency greases can be produced by selecting various metallic soaps, fatty glycerides, and mineral oils.

There are also three general bases[64] used for manufacturing the extreme-pressure lubricants now used almost exclusively for differential, transmission, and general gear lubrication.

1. Blends of saponifiable oil containing chemically combined sulfur with a suitable lubricating oil—or mineral oils to which flowers of sulfur has been added.

2. Blends of a sulfur chloride-treated saponifiable oil base and a lubricating oil of suitable viscosity—or chlorine combined directly with chosen mineral-oil fractions.

3. Lubricants containing lead soaps of fatty or naphthenic acids and sulfur. These may contain sulfur that has been added or only the sulfur that is naturally present in the mineral oil. However, the most common

[63] Simpson and Welch, Manufacture of Grease, *Ref. Nat. Gaso. Mfr.*, March, 1931, p. 77.

[64] Ebaugh, I. A., Service Tests Must Determine Value of Extreme Pressure Lubricants, Part 2, *Natl. Pet. News*, Jan. 15, 1936, p. 26.

practice in manufacturing gear "lubes" is to add a specific sulfur compound such as dibenzyl disulfide, which is noncorrosive at room temperature but corrosive (to copper) at about 300°F.

The general theory regarding sulfur and chloride lubricants is that iron sulfide or iron chloride should be formed on the surfaces of the bearing or shaft and that the films of these materials are responsible in part for good lubrication. Thus the extreme-pressure lubricants are somewhat corrosive and probably should not be used on bearings that contain copper. Others believe[65] that the high temperature generated at the gear-tooth surface causes the rough or high points on the surface to be destroyed by corrosion so that the surface is smoothed. In addition to customary tests, gear oils for automotive transmissions are subjected to full-scale "shock" tests. In these an automobile is operated at a high speed; the clutch and transmission are disengaged; and then, while the vehicle is still traveling rapidly, the clutch is engaged. Gear lubricants, transmission oils, and many rear-axle or steering-knuckle applications[66] are furnished in the following grades (with or without extreme-pressure additives), which are generally similar to the SAE grades:

Grade	Use	Saybolt Univ. viscosity
75	Extreme low temperature	15,000 max at 0°F
80	Winter service	15,000–100,000 at 0°F
90	....	75–120 at 210 °F
140	....	120–200 at 210 °F
250	Highest temperature service	200 min at 210°F

Most greases are soap-thickened mineral oils. The National Lubricating Grease Institute Classification (1955) based on worked consistency is:

NLGI number	Consistency (D217)*	Description and use at room temperature
0	355–385	Semifluid
1	310–340	Very soft, grease gun
2	265–295	Soft, grease gun
3	220–250	Grease cup
4	175–205	Grease cup
5	130–160	Grease cup and block
6	85–115	Block type

* ASTM, *Report of Committee* D-2.

[65] Nelson, W. L., Corrosion Tests of Gear Lubes, *Oil Gas J.*, Apr. 7, 1945, p. 97.
[66] Thompson, J. W., Varied E. P. Lube Specifications . . . , *Natl. Pet. News*, Sept. 30, 1936, p. 36.

TABLE 3-26. CHARACTERISTICS OF GREASES[a]

Soap base	Calcium (general)	Calcium resinate (cold-set)	Sodium (general)	Sodium, brick type	Aluminum	Lithium	Mixed sodium calcium
Texture	Buttery	Buttery	Fibrous or smooth	Hard or brittle	Buttery, rubbery, or stringy but never fibrous	Buttery or stringy	Buttery to fibrous
Dropping point, °F (approx.)	220–225	275	300–450	300–450	200	400	315
Condition after having heated to melting point	Separates	Foams at 200°F. Separates upon prolonged heating	No change if worked	No change	Changes texture upon cooling but does not separate even above melting point	No change if worked	No change if worked
Maximum temperature, °F (continuous service)	175	200	300–400	300–450	150 or perhaps 200	300	300
Softening upon working	Fair to poor	Fair to poor	Varies—excellent to poor	Varies—fair to poor	Fair to poor	Varies—excellent to poor	Varies—excellent to poor
Effect of water	Resistant	Resistant	Susceptible	Susceptible	Resistant	Resistant	Susceptible
Primary use	General-purpose lubricant for plain bearings and line shafting. Pressure gun and water pumps	Rough heavy bearings at slow speeds, also skids, track curves, and wagon wheels. Oil field and agricultural machinery	Ball and roller bearings up to medium speeds and light to heavy loads, also wheel bearings and chassis	Locomotive driving journals and similar services	Applications requiring adhesiveness or resistance to centrifugal force	Aircraft or services down to −100°F	All types ball and roller bearings and special applications at both high and low temperatures
Notes	Some moisture left in grease. Certain greases stabilized with chemicals instead of water can be used at higher temperatures	Cheapness is major factor	Normally does not channel. Highest temperature service except strontium greases	Difficulty is susceptibility to water. Smooth greases used for antifriction bearings. Long-fiber greases for chassis lubrication	Does not oxidize or crust readily. Good slow flow properties. Relatively expensive	Offers possibilities for general purposes	Special types are resistant to oxidation or crusting and can be used for electric motors or seldom lubricated equipment

[a] Taken mainly from Greases Part II, "Lubrication," The Texas Co., August, 1945.

An enormous number of combinations of oils and soaps is possible. Oil content ranges from 42 (waterproof grease) to 93 per cent, oil viscosity ranges from 90 at 100°F (waterproof greases) to 220 at 210°F, and numerous metals and fats are employed. Thin oils are used in greases for high-speed bearings.

Although soaps of barium, cerium, chromium, cobalt, iron, lead, magnesium, mercury, nickel, manganese, silver, strontium, tin, and zinc[67] have been proposed for grease manufacture, the main greases and their characteristics are as shown in Table 3-26.[68] Such metallic soaps as calcium, aluminum, barium, and strontium produce greases resistant to water; such soaps as those of barium, strontium, and lead are useful for extremely heavy duty services; and the sodium and calcium (particularly resinate) greases are relatively cheap. The National Lubricating Grease Institute has been active in developing test methods, particularly the Norman-Hoffman oxidation test,[69] and performance characteristics in antifriction bearings at elevated temperatures.[69]

Waxes. Paraffin and microcrystalline (petrolatum) waxes are used for so many widely different services that not many specifications other than melting point have been adopted. Microcrystalline waxes may contain natural or additive substances that partly inhibit crystalline growth. This generally tends to increase the flexibility or plasticity[70] of the wax, and in fact paraffin wax can be added to some microcrystalline waxes without destroying the flexibility. A common additive material to produce plasticity is Vistanex or polybutenes. Paraffin waxes range in melting point from about 105 to 155°F, and the most common grades range in melting point from 118 to 132°F. Petrolatum waxes from long-residuum stocks may have a melting point as low as 106°F. Regular petrolatum produces microcrystalline waxes melting up to about 180°F, whereas the highest melting point microcrystalline waxes (195°F) are produced from "tank bottoms." Some of the petrolatum or microcrystalline waxes on the market are shown in Table 3-27. Color ranges from black to white in almost all grades; and, of course, odor and sometimes taste are important properties.

Waxes are applied in two general ways, as a molten liquid or in the form of a dispersion or emulsion in water stabilized with dispersing agents. John C. Dean[71] discusses the many uses of waxes. Among these uses are

[67] Boner, C. J., Metallic Soaps for Thickening Mineral Oils, *Ind. Eng. Chem.*, **29**, 58 (1937).

[68] Taken mainly from Greases Part II, "Lubrication," The Texas Co., August, 1945.

[69] *Tech. Bull.* 5 and 6, NLGI 164 Chandler St., Buffalo, N.Y.

[70] Nelson and Stewart, Effect of Oil on Plastic Properties . . . , *Ind. Eng. Chem.* **41**, 2231 (1949).

[71] Petroleum Waxes, *Pet. Refiner*, May, 1946, p. 87; and Processing Materials from Petroleum, *Chem. Eng. News*, **23**, 1164 (1945).

TABLE 3-27. MICROCRYSTALLINE AND PETROLATUM WAXES

Wax	Melting point, °F (D127)	Con- sistency (D217)	Needle penetration (D5)	Flash point, °F	Gravity,[a] API
Petrolatum........	106–118	200–240	.....	360–370	
Petrolatum........	112–124	160–200	.....	410–430	
Petrolatum........	127–137	170–200	.....	360–370	
Microcrystalline...	155+	....	25–35	460+	36
Microcrystalline...	166+	....	15–25	460+	36
Microcrystalline...	170–175	....	10–20	460–500	37
Microcrystalline...	185–190	....	5–15	470–500	
Microcrystalline...	190–197	....	2–10	480–500	21–22

[a] Varies widely. Gravity is a function of the properties of the parent crude oil.

adhesives; ammunition; bandages; burns; belting; candles; carbon paper; cheese wrappers; coatings for drums or cans; cobbler's wax; concrete mixtures; dental cavities; electrical condensers, cables, coils, transformers, batteries, etc.; electrotyping; emulsions; food sealing; floor polishes; fuel briquettes; foil coatings; illuminants; ink; insulations; glossing agent in laundries; lipstick; lubricants; embalming preparations; matches; impregnating cloth and paper; milk and liquid containers; modeling waxes; moistureproofing paper coatings, candy wraps, laminated paper, bags, etc.; paperboard for boxes, cartons, can substitutes, drinking cups, frozen-food packages, milk cartons, etc.; pastes; pencils; pipelines for acid; plasticizers; polishes for shoes, leather, or furniture; pyrotechnics; plastic molding; ropes; roofing; rubber blooming; rust preventatives; salves or ointments; ski wax; stencils; stonework; surgery cavities or deformities; textiles for bath curtains, canvas, tarps, felt hats, lubricated threads, shoelaces, yarn finishes, waterproofing, etc.; toilet creams, pastes, etc.; washers; wire coatings; and wood fillers.

Residues. The residual petroleum products usually do not command a high market price. Often they are merely by-products of the regular refining operation. Some of the residual products are residual fuel oil, fuel oil for diesel power engines, road oil, spray oil, coke, and paving, roofing, or paint asphalts.

Typical residual fuel oils and dusting oils exhibit the properties shown in Table 3-28. Oils 1 and 4 are the 1955 standard (ASTM D396),[1] the older oils (2 and 3 of 1933) are still representative,[72] and the average coal-spray oils were taken from Technical Report 6 of Bituminous Coal Research, Inc.[73]

[72] Nelson, W. L., Bunker Fuel Oil Specifications (1918–1946), *Oil Gas J.*, July 27, 1946, p. 196.

[73] Nelson, W. L., Coal-spray Oils, *Oil Gas J.*, Aug. 21, 1941, p. 56.

TABLE 3-28. FUEL AND DUSTING OILS

Oil	Flash point, °F, min	Water and sediment, max %	Pour point, °F, max	Maximum viscosity, sec
1. ASTM No. 5.........	130	1	....	40 Furol at 122°F
1955 range[a].........	130–306	0–0.8	−20 to +60	11–40 Furol at 122°F
1956 range..........	136–300	0–0.8	−30 to +50	11–40 Furol at 122°F
2. Low viscosity, 1933...	150	1	....	100 Universal at 100°F
3. Bunker B, 1933......	150	1	....	100 Furol at 122°F
4. ASTM No. 6.........	150	2	....	300 Furol at 122°F
1955 range[a].........	150–430	0–1.8	5 to 80	51–295 Furol at 122°F
1956 range..........	140–420	0–1.6	0 to +60	28–292 Furol at 122°F
5. Light dusting oil......	305–350	....	0 to −50	111–223 Universal at 100°F
6. Heavy dusting oil.....	300–365	....	−5 to −20	246–599 Universal at 100°F

[a] U.S. Bur. Mines Inform. Circ. 7730, October, 1955.

All the oils should be free from rust, grit, acid, or fibrous material that might clog or injure burner tips, and free from chemical agents (neutralizers for corrosion) that will flux with the fireclay walls of furnace settings.

The very small amounts of vanadium and sodium found in some oils may lead to extreme corrosion when such fuels are burned in boilers or are used as gas turbine fuels. This difficulty can be almost totally eliminated by the use of magnesium, calcium, zinc, etc., additives. The following requirements (1953) of the General Electric Co.[74] for residual gas turbine fuels illustrate how the additives are applied.

1. The amount of sodium should be under 10 ppm (preferably under 5 ppm). It can be reduced by customary desalting operations, washings, centrifuging, etc.
2. The weight ratio of sodium to vanadium should be under 0.3. This may necessitate more reduction of sodium, but if the vanadium is under 5 ppm, the Na/Va ratio requirement may be ignored.
3. The weight ratio of magnesium (additive) to vanadium should be adjusted to higher than 3.0. If the vanadium content is lower than 2 ppm, magnesium is not needed.
4. Calcium should be under 10 ppm.
5. After the above adjustments, the total ash should not exceed 2,000 ppm.

Similar additive formulas are being developed for distillate or jet fuels.

Gravity is of little significance except that low-API-gravity fuels have slightly higher heating values. At gravities below 10 API, water and

[74] Buchland, B. O., Ind. Eng. Chem., **46**, 2163 (1954).

sediment do not settle out of the oil and such oils cannot be displaced from tanks by water. The heating value of residual fuel ranges from about 6,260,000 to 6,450,000 Btu per bbl. Its main competitor is bituminous coal (13,100 Btu per lb). The parity price O (dollars per bbl) of Bunker C fuel oil may be computed from the cost of delivered coal C (\$ per ton) by the following formula[75] in which E_o and E_c are the thermal efficiencies at which oil and coal can be fired, H_o and H_c are the heating values of oil (Btu per bbl) and coal (Btu per ton), and x is the ratio of operating costs for the year under consideration to the cost during 1951.

$$O = \frac{(E_o/E_c)C}{H_c/H_o} + \frac{0.165x}{H_c/H_o} \qquad (3\text{-}5a)$$

or for average values of the constants:

$$O = \frac{C}{4} + 0.04x \qquad (3\text{-}5b)$$

Oil can be fired more cheaply than coal (about 16.5 cents per ton during 1951). Sulfur in fuels (oil, coal, or gas) requires higher cold-end temperatures in the air preheaters or economizers of boilers[76] in order to prevent corrosion and fouling of the tubes. A 6 per cent sulfur fuel requires a temperature about 60°F higher than a 2 per cent fuel.

A high pour or solid point is important in gravity-feed systems because

TABLE 3-29. FUEL-OIL TEMPERATURE FOR BURNERS

Furol viscosity at 122°F	Firing temperature, °F	
	Mechanical atomization	Steam atomization
30.....................	130–182	97–130
35.....................	136–191	103–136
40 Fuel 5 max..........	143–199	108–143
45 Fuel 6 min..........	148–205	113–148
60.....................	161–216	123–161
80.....................	171–226	132–171
100....................	179–233	139–179
120....................	184–239	145–184
160....................	193–248	154–193
200....................	200–254	160–200
240....................	204–259	164–204
300 Fuel 6 max.........	210–265	170–210

[75] Nelson, W. L., *Oil Gas J.*, Dec. 22, 1952, p. 353.
[76] Nelson, W. L., *Oil Gas J.*, Sept. 13, 1954, p. 138.

it may cause plugging of screens and filters. Viscosity is the single most important property[77] because of difficulties in the handling and atomizing of viscous oils (Table 3-29). Cracked fuel oils are desirable[78] as fuels because they usually have a lower pour point, lower viscosity, and a slightly higher heating value than the residues from which they are produced. However, certain cracked oils deposit carbonaceous material on steam heating coils;[79] and hence cutter stocks having a high solvent power such as low-aniline-point extracts or cracked gas oils, rather than straight-run gas oils, should be employed for reducing the viscosity of heavy cracked fuel oils. The Naval Boiler and Turbine Laboratory heater test[80] may be used to determine the stability of fuel blends.

Petroleum coke is used commercially as a refinery and commercial fuel (often powdered); in the manufacture of carbon electrodes, brushes, plates, etc.; in the manufacture of abrasives and artificial graphite; in the manufacture of calcium carbide; as a metallurgical fuel; in paints and pigments; in gas manufacture; and in the ceramics industries. The high heating value and freedom from clinker-forming substances and the small quantity of ash make it a desirable industrial fuel. The hardness and strength of coke increase as the volatile matter is reduced, but it is seldom strong enough to be used for foundry cupolas. Until 1954, petroleum coke was made by the delayed coking or chamber processes, but in the future most coke will be made by a continuous process.[81] Such coke consists of small pellets which can be handled by fluidizing techniques or air-activated pneumatic transport systems, and accordingly it is called "fluid" coke. Table 3-30 indicates the properties of some cokes.[82]

The major uses[83] of petroleum asphaltic materials are indicated in Table 3-31. The properties of typical asphalts are shown in Table 3-32,[84] and a few properties of other asphalts are shown in Table 3-33.

Consistency[85] (viscosity, penetration, and softening point) determines the temperature required for use or application and the final hardness and

[77] Nelson, W. L., *Oil Gas J.*, Aug. 24, 1946, p. 92; Sept. 14, 1946, p. 95; Jan. 18, 1947, p. 89; and Feb. 15, 1947, p. 109.

[78] Morrell and Egloff, The Congealing Temperature . . . of Cracked Residue, *Ref. Nat. Gaso. Mfr.*, April, 1923, p. 17.

[79] Batchelder, A. H., The Stability of Residual Fuels, *Oil Gas J.*, Nov. 12, 1936, p. 159.

[80] Smith, F. L., Blending Residual Fuel Oil, *Pet. Refiner*, April, 1945, p. 95.

[81] Barr and Jahnig, Fluid Coking and Fluid Coke, *Chem. Eng. Prog.*, April, 1955, p. 167.

[82] Nelson, W. L., *Oil Gas J.*, Nov. 28, 1955, p. 117.

[83] Shearon and Hoiberg, *Ind. Eng. Chem.*, **45**, 2122 (1953).

[84] Petroleum Asphalt, "Lubrication," The Texas Co., June, 1946.

[85] Roediger, J. C., Asphalts and Their Evaluation for Commercial Uses, ASME Meeting, Tulsa, 1946.

TABLE 3-30. ANALYSES AND PROPERTIES OF PETROLEUM COKES

	Early pet. cokes, 1930–1935		Oven cokes	Delayed process cokes	Continuous or fluid cokes
	Cracking still	Coking still			
Moisture, wt %	0.15–3.3	0.3–1.8	0.3–2	Nil–0.5	
Volatile combustible matter, wt %	8–18	2–13	0.6–7.4	8–18	3.7–5.3
Ash, wt	0–1.6	0.5–1.2	0.2–1.8	0.5–1.6	0.1–2.8
Sulfur, wt %	0.2 –4.2	0.5–1.2	0.8–1.5	0.5–4.2	1.4–7.0
Bulk density, lb per cu ft	56–69				55–65
True or real density, g per ml				1.28–1.42	1.5–1.6
Btu per lb as rec'd	15,300–16,400	14,500–15,500	14,400–14,700		14,000
Hydrogen, wt %					1.6–2.1
Carbon, wt %					88.3–92.5

TABLE 3-31. PETROLEUM ASPHALTS (1951[a] and 1955[b])

Uses	Short tons 1951	Per cent 1951	Short tons 1955[b]
Paving:			
Asphalt cements	4,574,112	35.6	
Cutbacks and road oils	4,124,564	32.0	
Emulsions	216,247	1.7	
Total		69.3	12,300,000
Roofing, waterproofing, and mastics:			
Roofing and waterproofing	2,208,409	17.2	
Flux for roofing	882,283	6.9	
Mastic and mastic cake	16,508	0.1	
Total		24.2	3,400,000
Briquetting	210,323	1.6	200,000
Specialties:			
Blending with rubber	21,414	0.2	
Pipe and metal coatings	26,273	0.2	
Molding compounds	38,868	0.3	
Paints, enamels, etc	69,607	0.5	
Misc. uses	475,469	3.7	
Total		4.9	400,000
Grand total	12,864,077	100.0	16,300,000

[a] Shearon and Hoiberg, *Ind. Eng. Chem.*, **45**, 2122 (1953).
[b] Estimated.

TABLE 3-32. TESTS ON TYPICAL ASPHALTS[a]

Use	Paving		Roofing			Floor-ing satu-rant	Water-proofing	Mineral rubber
	Pene-tration mac-adam	As-phaltic con-crete	Shingle satu-rant	Shingle coating	Built-up roof mop-ping			
Softening point, B&R, °F	112	129	146	226	190	157	151	302
Ductility at 77°F cm	60+	100+	100	2.0	2.0	12	22	0
Penetration at 32°F	40	25	13	12	14	8	10	2
Penetration at 77°F	135	64	33	18	30	20	27	4
Penetration at 115°F	Soft	249	108	31	65	67	92	8
Evaporation (50 g, 5 hr, 325°F), per cent	0.01	0.06	0.03	0.01	0.01	0.0	0.0	0.02
Flash, Cleveland open cup, °F	550	540	560	570	560	645	600	635
Solubility in CCl₄, per cent	99.8	99.8	99.8	99.7	99.8	99.8	99.8	99.8

[a] Petroleum Asphalt, "Lubrication," The Texas Co., June, 1946.

TABLE 3-33. OTHER ASPHALT MATERIALS

Materials	Penetra-tion at 77°F	Ductility at 77°F	Melting point, B & R
Paving binders:			
Mastic foot pavements and floors	10–15	.....	180–220
Asphalt blocks	10–25	20+	
Sheet asphalt pavement	25–40	40+	105–140
Grout filler	40–70	50+	113–140
Grout filler (blown type)	30–50	3+	150–230
Asphalt concrete (aggregate sand, etc.)	30–70	45+	113–150
Asphalt macadam	70–150	90+	104–113
Roofing asphalts:			
Saturant for felt or paper	75–140	100+	110–120
Heavy saturant for felt and rugs	28–32	40+	140–150
Roof coatings (blown)	10–50	1+	160–260
Sealing:			
Pipe sealing (sewers, etc.)	40–60	1+	200–225
Pipe coatings	10–15[a]	1+	200–215
Waterproofing	25–50	15+	140–170

[a] Consistency.

pliability of the finished product. Temperature susceptibility measures the change in penetration (D5)[1] with temperature and also the ability of the asphalt to withstand loading and shocks. Ductility (D113)[1] measures the elongation or stretch, suitability for paving purposes, and ability to resist vibration. Shock tests are also used for vibrational services, and pliability tests are necessary for compositions used for wire coating or for laminated paper. Stain tests are often important. Solubility (D165)[1] in carbon tetrachloride indicates inert material, asphaltenes, and difficulties caused by overheating during manufacture or application.

TABLE 3-34. TESTS ON TYPICAL LIQUID ASPHALT MATERIALS[a]

	Rapid curing RC-3 (D597)	Medium curing MC-3 (D598)	Slow curing SC-3	Slow setting emulsion SS-1 (D631)
Flash, °F (Tag open cup)............	90	170	230	
Viscosity Saybolt Furol:				
At 77°F.......................	.....	.....	.....	70
At 140°F......................	350	350	350	
Distillation (ASTM D402) per cent distillate off:				(D244)
At 437°F......................	28	2		
At 500°F......................	60	30	.....	42
At 600°F......................	83	75		
At 680°F......................	100	100		
Residue from distillation:				
Per cent asphalt.................	74	76	90	58
Penetration at 77°F.............	100	200	Soft	150
Ductility at 77°F...............	100+	100+	.....	100+
Solubility in CCl₄, per cent........	99.7	99.7	99.7	98.5
Asphalt, of 100 penetration, per cent..	.....	.....	74	

[a] Petroleum Asphalt, "Lubrication," The Texas Co., June, 1946.

The ASTM[18] has published at least 30 specifications for the numerous types of petroleum asphalts and road oils. The most fluid road oils of the RC, MC, or SC grades are designated as No. 0 and the heaviest as No. 5. The rapid curing (RC) grades contain a cutback of kerosene or distillate-like material, whereas the slowest curing (SC) grades may consist of asphalt and the heavy distillates that are naturally associated with asphalt in crude oil.

CHEMICALS AND SPECIALTIES

According to "Synthetic Organic Chemicals, U.S. Production and Sales," which is published yearly by the U.S. Tariff Commission, the

TABLE 3-35. CRUDE PRODUCTS FROM PETROLEUM AND NATURAL GAS
Thousand pounds per year

	1955	1953	1950
Aromatics:			
Distillates and solvents.........	642,649	404,545	
Benzene.....................	722,650	462,105	72,927
Cresylic acid, crude.............	24,470	16,080	16,080
Naphthenic acids...............	16,687	23,123	24,684
Toluene......................	1,038,290	836,473	329,122
Xylenes, mixed................	699,455	749,010	449,587
Other.......................	30,404	14,355	532,571
Total aromatics..............	3,174,605	2,505,691	1,424,961
Aliphatics:			
Methane......................	131,527		
Ethane......................	445,214	144,623 ⎱	1,821,893
Ethylene.....................	3,048,225	2,135,740 ⎰	
Propane.....................	2,007,140	1,366,175	998,842
Propylene and C₃ mixtures.......	1,331,475	1,222,622	694,047
1,3-Butadiene.................	1,411,285	1,152,197	610,056
n-Butane.....................	753,461	418,144	641,072
Butylenes....................	1,171,596	906,732	
Isobutane....................	444,532	155,589	
Isobutylene..................	124,562		
Other C₄s....................	663,748	534,507	
C₅ hydrocarbons...............	250,752	122,048	
Diisobutylene.................	....	23,157	20,044
Dodecene....................	371,948	176,926	
Nonene......................	146,204	60,986	
Derivatives..................	8,128	2,681	
Other aliphatics..............	694,560	219,242	336,625
Total aliphatics..............	13,004,357	8,641,369	5,510,100
Grand total....................	16,178,962	11,147,060	6,935,061

number of oil companies that participate in the manufacture of chemicals has risen from a few in 1935 to 48 by 1944, and to 63 in 1955. At least 187 chemical, petroleum, etc., companies used petroleum or natural gas as the raw stock for chemical manufacture during 1955, and the petrochemical production amounted to about 25 per cent[86] of all chemical manufacture. J. C. Reidel[86] estimates that basic petrochemicals appear finally in the form of 7,000 end-use chemicals. The 1955 production, according to the U.S. Tariff Commission, is indicated in Table 3-35, and the production[87] of major chemicals produced largely from petroleum is shown in Table 3-36. Some important chemicals are produced mainly from petroleum:

[86] Petrochemicals . . . Today and Tomorrow, *Oil Gas J.*, Sept. 6, 1954. p, 83.
[87] Katzen, R., *Pet. Refiner*, December, 1954, p. 128.

Per cent   *Per cent*

Acetic acid....................	96	Isopropanol....................	100
Acetic anhydride..............	96	Methanol.....................	85
Acetone......................	95	Nylon........................	60
Acetylene....................	30	Phenol.......................	50
Acrylic plastics................	100	Phenolic plastics..............	50
Ammonia.....................	90	Polyethylene..................	100
Benzene......................	36	Polyester plastics..............	70
Butanols.....................	53	Propylene.....................	100
Butadiene....................	100	Polystyrene...................	50
Epoxi plastics.................	95	Styrene.......................	50
Ethanol......................	83	Synthetic rubber...............	75
Ethylene.....................	99+	Toluene.......................	77
Ethylene glycol...............	80	Urea and melamine plastics......	70
Ethylene oxide................	90	Vinyl plastics.................	80
Formaldehyde.................	90*	Xylenes.......................	89
Glycerol......................	40		

* Estimated.

TABLE 3-36. PRODUCTION AND CAPACITY FOR MAJOR CHEMICALS OBTAINED
FROM PETROCHEMICAL AND NONPETROLEUM SOURCES[a]
Million pounds

	Production 1955	Capacity 1955
Hydrocarbon intermediates:		
Ethylene..................	3,000	3,200
Propylene................	1,500	1,600
Butylenes................	2,200	2,000
Butadiene................	1,200	1,200
Acetylene................	750	850
Benzene..................	2,400	2,600
Toluene..................	1,300	1,350
Xylenes..................	1,100	1,100
Styrene..................	1,000	1,000
Polyethylene..............	350	400
Synthetic rubber...........	1,800	4,200
Phenol....................	575	585
Ammonia..................	6,000	6,800
Aliphatic chemicals:		
Formaldehyde.............	550	600
Acetaldehyde.............	800	860
Methanol................	1,500	1,570
Ethanol..................	1,800	2,250
Isopropanol..............	1,200	1,200
Butanols.................	400	450
Ethylene oxide............	800	970
Ethylene glycol...........	750	850
Acrylonitrile..............	180	200
Acetic acid...............	550	650
Acetic anhydride..........	800	900
Acetone..................	600	700

[a] Katzen, R., *Pet. Refiner*, December, 1954, p. 128

CHAPTER 4

EVALUATION OF OIL STOCKS

Although it is theoretically possible to produce any type of refined product from any crude oil, it is not usually economically feasible to do so. Occasionally the demand for a particular product or the elimination of a low-value one becomes so insistent that major conversions of a chemical nature have been adopted. Among these are thermal or catalytic cracking for increasing the yield of gasoline from crude oil, catalytic cracking for reducing the yield of residual fuel oil, polymerization for recovering olefinic waste gases, solvent extraction processes by which unsuitable hydrocarbons are eliminated from lubricating oils, diesel fuels, etc., and most recently catalytic reforming for producing motor fuels of superior detonation characteristics. It is the purpose of this chapter to aid in the selection of the best combination of products that is possible from each crude oil, never forgetting that each oil must be processed to supply its own particular marketing environment.

The routine or control tests mentioned in Chap. 3 are not entirely satisfactory for plant design or plant operation, and hence special distillations, vaporizations, and equipment have been developed by which the yields of the various products contained in a charge stock can be evaluated. Admittedly many evaluation methods are approximate. They must be so because so many combinations of yields are possible and the market demand varies so rapidly that more precise methods would lead to endless testing. Nevertheless, the somewhat gross methods outlined here must always be used with caution, and they should be augmented at the first opportunity with more complete tests.

Large refiners usually obtain more complete data than suggested here, by means of pilot- or semiplant-scale equipment in which the essential physical and chemical processes of the operation are duplicated in laboratory equipment. Smaller operators sometimes find that commercial-scale experiments are cheaper. Although pilot plants can usually provide more complete and accurate operating information than commercial operations, pilot plant operation is in some ways more difficult than commercial operation, and thus carelessness may result in misleading data.

The refiner desires information of the following types:

1. Base and general properties of the crude oil.
2. Presence of impurities such as sulfur, salt, and emulsions which cause general difficulties in processing.
3. Operating or design data. Primarily this necessitates curves of temperature and gravity vs. per cent distilled.
   a. Fractionating or true-boiling-point distillation curve.
   b. Equilibrium or flash-vaporization curve.
   c. API or specific-gravity curve of each fraction distilled.
4. Curves of the properties of the fractions vs. per cent distilled (mid per cent curves) or the average properties of a series of fractions vs. percentage yield (yield curves), by which realizations of yields can be prepared. Among common property curves are
   a. Viscosity of lubricating-oil fractions.
   b. Octane number of gasoline fractions.
   c. Aniline point of solvent, kerosene, or diesel fractions.
   d. Penetration of asphaltic residues.
   e. Viscosity of distillation residues.
   Large samples (from 2 liters up to pilot sizes) of the feedstock are required in order to obtain large enough fractions for the above tests.
5. Finished products. Having established the general properties and yields by means of distillations and property curves and exploring the economy of the various breakups of the crude oil, most refiners feel that large samples of the most promising products should be produced. Batch- or semiplant-scale stills are employed; and such details as chemical treatment, sulfur content, susceptibility to tetraethyllead, pour point, etc., may be investigated.

BASE OF CRUDE OIL

The classification of crude oils as Paraffin, Intermediate, or Naphthene "base" is admittedly inadequate, but long usage has led to concepts that are valuable to experienced technical men. When used or defined with respect to various properties, indexes, etc., as in Table 4-1, the term "base" is justified. The U.S. Bureau of Mines[1] designates eight bases of crude oil according to key fraction No. 1, which boils at 482 to 527°F at atmospheric pressure, and key fraction No. 2 which boils at 527 to 572°F at 40-mm pressure (approximately 733 to 779°F at 760 mm) in the standardized Hempel distillation[2] of the Bureau of Mines. The first word of the name of the base (such as "paraffin" in "paraffin intermediate base") applies to the gasoline or low-boiling fractions, and the second word applies to the lubricant or high-boiling parts of the crude oil. Key fraction No. 1 should have a gravity higher than 40 API for paraffin base crude oils and a gravity below 33 API for naphthene base oils. Likewise, key No. 2 classifies an oil as paraffin base if the gravity is

[1] Lane and Garton, "Base" of a Crude Oil, U.S. Bur. Mines Rept. Invest., 3279, September, 1935.

[2] Smith et al., U.S. Bur. Mines Bull. 490, 1950.

above 30 API, or as naphthene base if its gravity is below 20 API. In addition, the presence of wax in key fraction No. 2 is noted by means of the cloud point. If the cloud point is below 5°F it indicates little wax, and the name of the base is augmented by the statement "wax-free." Characterization Factor is not specified by the Bureau of Mines, but approximate values are shown in Table 4-1. Finally, other significant names for paraffin-base crude oil are "Pennsylvania" and "green or light Mid Continent" crude oil; for intermediate-base, the terms "Mid Continent" and "mixed-base"; and for naphthene-base, the terms "Coastal," "Gulf Coast," "California," or "asphalt-base." These names are often misleading, because the base of an oil is not necessarily related to the region of origin, or the presence of asphalt or of paraffin wax. In addition to the three common designations of base, a few oils[3] contain significant amounts of aromatic hydrocarbons, and these are called aromatic or benzenoid base. Such crude oils are rare in the United States but are found in some regions, notably Burma and Borneo[3] (see also Fig. 2-2). A major danger in a "base" classification is our tendency to imbue a crude oil with all the attributes of its base. Consideration of Table 4-1 indicates clearly that wide ranges of properties are probable in any base of crude oil.

Although most of the indexes, factors, etc., used in classifying crude oils and their products were originally based on the properties of pure hydrocarbons, none of them are truly successful in indicating chemical composition. They fail to distinguish between a mixture and a compound of the same physical properties. Even aniline point, which has a long-established reputation as a means of indicating the presence of aromatic hydrocarbons, is of little value in judging chemical composition unless the proportions between the other series of hydrocarbons are also known.

Characterization Factor. The most widely used index is the Characterization Factor of Watson, Nelson, and Murphy.[4] It was originally defined as

$$K = \frac{\sqrt[3]{T_B}}{S} \tag{4-1}$$

in which T_B is the average molal boiling point (°F absolute) and S is the specific gravity at 60°F. It has since been related to viscosity, aniline point, molecular weight, critical temperature, percentage of hydrocarbon, etc., so that almost any laboratory data can be used to estimate the factor (see Table 4-1 and Fig. 5-9). Typical Characterization Factors are indicated in Table 4-2.

[3] Nelson, W. L., Aromatic Base Crude Oils, *Oil Gas J.*, Oct. 28, 1944, p. 101; also Dec. 2, 1944, p. 91.

[4] Characterization of Petroleum Fractions, *Ind. Eng. Chem.*, **27**, 1460 (1935).

TABLE 4-1. CHARACTER OR BASE OF CRUDE OILS AND THEIR PRODUCTS IN TERMS OF CHARACTERIZATION FACTOR AND OTHER SIGNIFICANT PROPERTIES[a]

UOP Characterization Factor[a]	API gravity Gaso. Mid bp 235°F	API gravity Kero. Mid bp 504°F	API gravity Gas oil Mid bp 755°F	Corr. Index Key No.1 Mid bp 493°F	Corr. Index Key No.2 Mid bp 715°F	Viscosity gravity constant[b] Mid bp 800°F	Aniline pt Solvents Mid bp 300°F	Aniline pt Diesel fuels Mid bp 550°F	Diesel Index[b] Mid bp 550°F	Cetane No.[b]	Kerosene Smoke point Mid bp 437°F	Kerosene Ring No.[b] Mid bp 437°F	Kauri butanol number[b] Mid bp 300°F	Visc. Index Raw lubes	Visc. Index Dewaxed +20°F	Thermal cracking Feed API Mid bp 680°F	Thermal cracking Octane No.[c]	C/H ratio[b] Mid bp 200°F	C/H Mid bp 500°F	C/H Mid bp 900°F
Paraffin base:																				
12.9	74.5	53.5	39.4		10.0															
12.8	73.3	52.0	38.3		13.0															
12.7	71.8	50.1	36.8		16.0									151						
12.6	70.1	49.2	35.5		19.0									144	118					
12.5	68.4	47.6	34.2	9.5	22.0	0.798								136	109			5.42	5.54	6.12
12.45	67.7	46.9	33.5	11.0	23.6	0.802		187	84.0	72.0				131	105			5.49	5.59	6.20
12.4	67.0	46.2	32.8	12.5	25.2	0.806	153	185					28.0	127	101			5.55	5.65	6.28
12.35	66.2	45.4	32.2	14.0	26.9	0.810	152	183	80.0	66.0				122	97			5.60	5.72	6.35
12.3	65.2	44.7	31.5	15.5	28.6	0.815	150	181	76.0	63.0	42.5		29.0	118	93			5.66	5.79	6.42
12.25	64.5	44.1	30.9	17.0	30.3	0.819	148	179	74.0	61.5	38.5			113	88			5.72	5.85	6.50
12.2	63.7	43.4	30.2	18.5	32.0	0.824	146	177	72.0	60.0	35.5		30.5	108	83			5.78	5.91	6.58
12.15	62.9	42.7	29.5	20.1	33.7	0.828	144	175	70.0	59.0	32.5	81		103	79			5.84	5.98	6.66
Intermediate base:																				
12.1	62.1	41.9	28.8	21.7	35.4	0.833	142	173	68.0	58.0	30.0	75	32.5	98	76			5.90	6.05	6.74
12.05	61.2	41.2	28.2	23.3	37.1	0.837	140	171	66.0	56.5	27.6	66		93	70		66.2	5.96	6.11	6.82
12.0	60.3	40.4	27.5	25.0	38.8	0.842	137	169	64.0	55.0	25.7	57	34.0	89	65	31.1	66.7	6.03	6.18	6.90
11.95	59.5	39.7	26.9	26.6	40.5	0.847	135	167	62.0	54.0	24.0	47		83	61	30.4	67.2	6.11	6.24	6.97
11.9	58.8	39.0	26.3	28.2	42.2	0.852	132	164	60.0	52.5	22.6	37	36.5	78	58	29.7	67.8	6.19	6.30	7.05

TABLE 4-1 Continued

UOP Characterization Factor[a]	API gravity of fractions			Correlation Index		Viscosity gravity constant[b]	Aniline point, °F[b]		Diesel fuels		Kerosene		Kauri butanol number[b]	Viscosity Index		Thermal cracking		Carbon-hydrogen ratio[b]		
	Gaso.	Kero.	Gas oil	Key No. 1	Key No. 2		Solvents	Diesel fuels	Diesel Index[b]	Cetane No.[b]	Smoke point	Ring No.[b]		Raw lubes	Dewaxed +20°F	Feed API	Octane No.[c]	Mid bp 200°F	Mid bp 500°F	Mid bp 900°F
	Mid bp 235°F	Mid bp 504°F	Mid bp 755°F	Mid bp 493°F	Mid bp 715°F	Mid bp 800°F	Mid bp 300°F	Mid bp 550°F	Mid bp 550°F		Mid bp 437°F	Mid bp 437°F	Mid bp 300°F			Mid bp 680°F				
11.85	58.0	38.3	25.7	29.8	43.9	0.857	129	162	58.0	51.0	21.4	27	....	73	53	29.1	68.3	6.24	6.37	7.14
11.8	57.2	37.6	25.0	31.7	45.7	0.862	126	160	56.0	50.0	20.4	17	38.5	68	49	28.4	68.9	6.29	6.44	7.23
11.75	56.3	36.9	24.4	33.3	47.4	0.867	123	158	54.0	48.5	19.5	7	....	61	41	27.8	69.4	6.35	6.51	7.31
11.7	55.4	36.2	23.7	35.0	49.2	0.872	120	156	52.0	47.0	18.8	−3	41.0	55	39	27.1	69.9	6.41	6.59	7.40
11.65	54.7	35.5	23.0	36.7	51.1	0.877	117	153	50.0	46.0	18.1	−14	....	49	34	26.4	70.4	6.48	6.66	7.48
11.6	54.0	34.8	22.3	38.5	53.1	0.882	113	150	48.0	44.5	17.5	−24	43.5	44	29	25.7	70.9	6.55	6.74	7.57
11.55	53.1	34.0	21.7	40.2	55.0	0.887	110	147	46.0	43.0	17.0	−34	....	37	24	25.0	71.4	6.62	6.81	7.66
11.5	52.3	33.2	21.0	42.0	56.9	0.892	106	143	44.0	42.0	16.5	−45	46.5	31	20	24.3	72.0	6.70	6.88	7.75
Naphthene base:																				
11.45	51.4	32.5	20.4	43.7	58.7	0.897	102	140	42.0	40.5	16.0	....	....	24	15	23.7	72.5	6.78	6.96	7.84
11.4	50.6	31.9	19.7	45.5	60.8	0.902	97	136	40.0	39.0	15.6	....	50.0	18	10	23.0	73.0	6.85	7.05	7.93
11.35	49.9	31.2	19.0	47.3	62.8	0.907	92	132	38.0	38.0	15.1	....	....	11	4	22.3	73.5	6.92	7.13	8.03
11.3	49.2	30.6	18.3	49.2	64.8	0.913	87	128	36.0	36.5	14.7	....	54.0	4	−2	21.6	74.0	7.00	7.21	8.14
11.25	48.4	30.0	17.7	50.1	66.8	0.918	81	124	34.0	35.0	14.4	....	....	−7	−10	21.0	74.5	7.09	7.30	8.24
11.2	47.6	29.3	17.0	53.0	68.8	0.924	76	120	32.0	34.0	14.1	....	59.0	−18	−18	20.3	75.1	7.19	7.40	8.34
11.15	46.8	28.6	16.4	55.0	71.0	0.929	70	116	30.0	32.5	12.2[d]	....	....	....	....	....	75.6	7.28	7.50	8.46
11.1	46.0	27.9	15.7	57.0	73.2	0.935	63	112	28.0	31.0	12.0[d]	....	66.0	−60	−60	....	....	7.37	7.61	8.59
11.05	45.2	27.2	15.1	59.0	75.5	0.941	56	106	26.0	30.0	11.8[d]	....	....	....	....	....	....	7.47	7.71	8.71
11.0	44.5	26.4	14.4	61.0	77.8	0.947	48	100	24.0	28.5	11.6[d]	....	....	....	....	....	....	7.58	7.82	8.83
10.9	42.8	24.9	13.0	65.2	79.0	0.959	....	89	20.0	26.0	....	....	....	....	....	....	....	....	....	....
10.8	41.1	23.4	11.7	69.5	80.5	0.972	....	....	16.0	23.0	....	....	....	....	....	....	....	....	....	....
10.7	39.4	22.0	10.4	73.7	83.0	0.985	....	....	12.0	20.0	....	....	....	....	....	....	....	....	....	....
10.6	37.8	20.5	9.2	....	....	0.998	....	....	....	....	....	....	....	....	....	....	....	....	....	....
10.5	36.2	19.0	7.9	....	....	1.012	....	....	....	....	....	....	....	....	....	....	....	....	....	....

[a] The various factors or properties should be determined in terms of the Characterization Factor because they are not altogether consistent with one another.
[b] Approximate.
[c] ASTM Motor method F-2, des. D357; approximate.
[d] Based on Far East stocks.

83

TABLE 4-2. CHARACTERIZATION FACTORS OF A FEW HYDROCARBONS, PETROLEUMS, AND TYPICAL STOCKS

Characterization Factor	Hydrocarbons	Typical crude oils	Miscellaneous products
14.7	Propane		
14.2	Propylene		
13.85	Isobutane		
13.5–13.6	Butane	....	94.5 API absorption gaso.
13.0–13.2	Butene-1 and isopentane	....	4 Venezuelan paraffin waxes
12.8	Hexane and tetradecene-7	....	Paraffin wax[a]; M. C. 82.2 API natural gaso.
12.7	2 methylheptane and tetradecane	....	Calif. 81.9 API nat. gaso.
12.6	Pentene-1, hexene-1, and cetene		
12.55	2,2,4 trimethylpentane	Cotton Valley (La.) lubes	Debutanized E. Tex. nat. gaso.
12.5	Hexene-2, and 1,3 butadiene	....	San Joaquin (Vene.) wax distillate
12.1–12.5	2,2,3,3-tetramethyl butane	Pennsylvania Rodessa (La.)	Panhandle (Tex.) lubes
12.2–12.44	2,11-dimethyl dodecadiene	Big Lake (Tex.)	6 Venezuelan wax distillates
12.0–12.2	....	Lance Creek (Wyo.)	Paraffin base gasolines
11.9–12.2	....	Mid Continent Okla. City (Okla.)	Middle East light products Cracked gaso. from paraffinic feeds East Texas gas oil and lubes
11.9	Hexylcyclohexane	....	Light cycloversion gaso. from M.C. feeds
11.8–12.1	....	Fullerton (W. Tex.)	Middle East gas oil and lubes
11.85	....	Illinois; Midway (Ark.)	Cracked gaso. from intermediate feeds
11.7–12	....	W. Tex.; Jusepin (Vene.)	East Tex. and La. white products Tia Juana (Vene.) white products
11.75	....	Cowden (W. Tex.)	Cracked gas oil from paraffinic feeds
11.7	Butylcyclohexane	Santa Fe Spgs. (Calif.)	Cat. cycle stocks from paraffinic feeds
11.6	Octyl or diamyl benzene	Slaughter (W. Tex.); Hobbs (N. Mex.)	Cracked gaso. from naphthene feeds
11.5–11.8	....	Colombian	Tia Juana (Vene.) gas oil and lubes
11.5	....	Hendrick and Yates (W. Tex.) Elk Basin, heavy (Wyo.)	Naphthenic gaso.; cat. (cracked) gaso. Cat. cycle stocks from M. C. feeds
11.45	Ethylcyclohexane and 9-hexyl 11 methylheptadiene	Kettleman Hills (Calif.)	Cracked gaso. from highly naphthenic feeds
11.4	Methylcyclohexane	Smackover (Ark.)	High conversion cat. cycle stocks from paraffinic feeds
11.3–11.6	....	Lagunillas (Vene.)	Typical cat. cycle stocks
11.3	Cyclobutane and 2,6,10,14 tetramethyl hexadiene	Gulf Coast light distillates	Light-oil coil thermal feeds Cat. cycle stocks from 11.7 C.F. feeds Gaso. from cat. reforming

TABLE 4-2. CHARACTERIZATION FACTORS OF A FEW HYDROCARBONS,
PETROLEUMS, AND TYPICAL STOCKS (*Continued*)

Characterization Factor	Hydrocarbons	Typical crude oils	Miscellaneous products
11.2	Cyclopentane	Kern River (Calif.)	Thermal gas oil from naphthene feeds
11.1	1,2,3,4 tetraethyl benzene	Greta or Placedo (Tex.) Signal Hill (Calif.)	Naphthenic gas oil and lubes 8.8 API viscosity breaking residuum
11.0	Cycloheptanes and dicyclohexyl	Lowest C.F. crude oils	Lowest C.F. naphthenic products Cat. cycle stocks (high conversion) from 11.7 C.F. feeds Thermal heavy coil feeds Gas oil in fluid coking of 11.9 C.F. feeds
		Thermal Products	
10.9	2-phenyl-4-methylhexene-2-	. . . .	Cat. cycle stocks from naphthenic feeds
10.8	Butylbenzene	Residuum by severe viscosity breaking	
10.6	Propylbenzene or 1,2,3,5 tetramethylbenzene	25 API light (pure) recycle 6.5 API residuum	Lowest C.F. cat. cycle stocks
10.5	2-phenylhexadiene-1,3	17.5 API flash distillate from M.C. residuum	Thermal recycle stocks
10.4	Ethylbenzene or *m*-xylene	8.8 API vapor phase residuum	
10.3	Phenylcyclohexane	8.5 API flash distillate[b]	Extracts from cracked diesel fuels
10.1	Toluene	5.5 API flash distillate[b]	Extracts from cracked diesel fuels
10.0	Benzene or 2-isopropyl naphthalene	Lowest C.F. cycle stocks	
9.8–9.9	Diphenylmethane	Lowest C.F. pitches (−4 API) Residuum from cat. cycle stocks	Gas cracking residues

[a] 12.88 (range 12.1–13.65) calculated from factors of raw and dewaxed lube stocks.
[b] From residuum when feeding gas oil or distilled stocks.

Viscosity Index. This index is a series of numbers ranging from 0 to 100 which indicate the rate of change of viscosity with temperature.[5] A Viscosity Index of 100 indicates an oil that does not tend to become viscous at low temperatures or become thin at elevated temperatures. Typically paraffin-base lubricating oils exhibit a Viscosity Index of nearly 100, whereas naphthene-base oils on the market show about 40 Viscosity Index, and some naphthenic oils have a Viscosity Index of zero or lower. Paraffin wax has a V.I. of about 200, and hence its removal reduces the

[5] Dean and Davis, Viscosity Variations of Oils with Temperature, *Chem. Met. Eng.*, **36**, 618 (1929); Applying Viscosity Index to the Solution of Lubricating Oil Problems, *Oil Gas J.*, Mar. 31, 1932, p. 92.

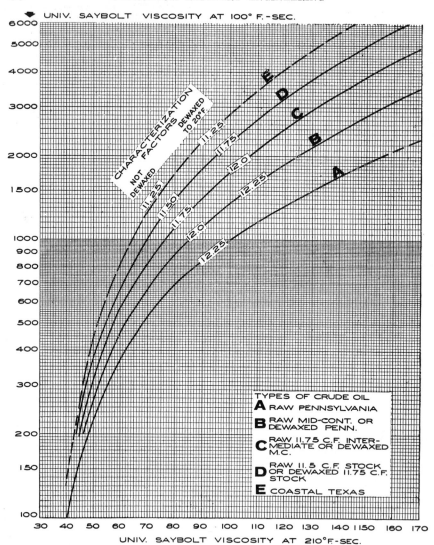

FIG. 4-1. Relation of Saybolt Universal viscosity at 100°F to viscosity at 210°F.

V.I. of raw lube stocks (see Table 4-1). By solvent extraction processes, lubricating oils of Viscosity Index higher than 100 can be produced. Figures 4-1 and 4-2 indicate the relationship between Viscosity Index and Saybolt Universal viscosity at 100 and 210°F. The Viscosity Index tabulations of the ASTM (D567)[6] must be employed (rather than Fig. 4-2) for accuracy.

[6] Petroleum Products and Lubricants, ASTM, 1916 Race St., Philadelphia 3, Pa., yearly.

Example 4-1. Viscosity Index (Fig. 4-2). An oil has a viscosity of 1,600 sec at 100°F and 80 at 210°F. Reading from 1,600 on the left, to the slanting line marked 80 at the right, the Viscosity Index on the bottom scale will be seen to be about 3.

Viscosity Gravity Constant. This constant[7] involves gravity as well as viscosity,

$$VGC = \frac{10G - 1.0752 \log (V - 38)}{10 - \log (V - 38)}$$

(4-2)

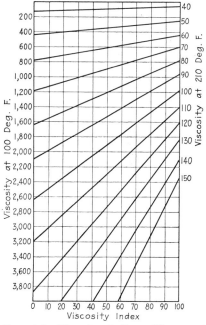

FIG. 4-2. Viscosity Index. (*Dean and Davis, Chem. Met. Eng.*)

where G is specific gravity at 60°F and V is viscosity at 100°F. It is used mainly for lubricating oils, and the general relationship of VGC to Characterization Factor is indicated in Table 4-1.

Correlation Index. The Correlation Index,[8] like the Characterization Factor, relates boiling point and gravity:

$$C.I. = 48,640/°K + 473.7g - 456.8 \quad (4-3)$$

in which K is absolute boiling point degrees Kelvin (°C + 273), and g is the specific gravity $^{60}\!/_{60}$. It is especially useful in appraising the 3,000 or more Hempel assays[9] which have been conducted by the U.S. Bureau of Mines (over 200 foreign oils were tested).

Numerous other constants are more limited in usefulness (see Table 4-1) as (1) aniline point (D611),[6] (2) Parachor,[10] which involves surface tension and gravity, (3) carbon-hydrogen ratio,[11] (4) characterization gravity,[12] which is used in judging stocks for thermal cracking, (5) Diesel

[7] Kurtz, S. S., Jr., et al., Relationship between Carbon-type Composition, Viscosity-Gravity . . . , *Anal. Chem.*, **28**, 1928 (1956).

[8] Smith, H. M., *U.S. Bur. Mines Tech. Paper*, 610, 1940.

[9] Hughes and Blade, *U.S. Bur. Mines Inform. Circ.* 7470, June, 1948.

[10] Heinze and Marder, *Brennstoff-Chem.*, **16**, 286 (1935).

[11] Cauley and Delgass, C-H ratio of Catalytically Cracked Distillate Fuel Oils, *Oil Gas J.*, July 27, 1946, p. 166.

[12] Mithoff, MacPherson, and Sipos, *Oil Gas .*ʳ Nov. 6, 1941, p. 81.

Index (Table 3-20),

$$D.I. = \frac{\text{aniline point (°F)} \times \text{gravity (API)}}{100} \qquad (4\text{-}4)$$

and (6) boiling-point gravity constant,[13] which in terms of B, a constant, G, the API gravity, and T, the boiling point (°C), is designated as:

$$G = B + (68 - 0.703B) \log T$$

TYPICAL CRUDE OILS

Crude petroleums vary widely in composition from almost gaslike materials of 65 API gravity to semisolid asphaltic material having an API gravity of 10 (see Table 4-3 for average gravities). The percentage of

TABLE 4-3. GRAVITY DISTRIBUTION OF THE CRUDE OILS PRODUCED IN VARIOUS AREAS—CUMULATIVE PERCENTAGES (1951)

Below these API gravities	U.S.[a]	U.S. east of Calif.[a]	Imports U.S.[a]	California	West Texas[b]	Vene- zuela[b]	Saudi Arabia[c]
10	.....	....	....	1.0[b]	.....	.....	1.0	
15	1.0	....	6.0	9.5[b]	8.76[a]	.....	9.1	
20	4.0	1.3	17.0	20.4[b]	24.7[a]	.....	41.3	
25	11.3	4.5	24.0	45.3[b]	47.4[a]	.....	47.7	
30	23.4	15.6	27.7	63.5[b]	64.7[a]	10.5	65.8	1.5
35	52.0[d]	....	....	83.6[b]	......	38.0[d]	85.7	32.5
40	83.0[d]	....	....	97.0[b]	......	65.0[d]	97.1	99.8
45	96.0[d]	....	....	......	......	81.0[d]		
Avg API	34.7	36.3	29.6	.....	26.2[a]	.....	25.3	35.8

[a] Rept. of Committee on Bunker C Fuel Oil of the Natl. Pet. Council, Dec. 9, 1952.
[b] Nelson, Thery, and Sahagun, "Venezuelan and Other World Crude Oils," Ministerio de Minas e Hidrocarburos, Caracas, Venezuela, 1952.
[c] Aramco Report.
[d] Estimated.

sulfur ranges from 0.03 in high gravity oils from Venezuela, Bolivia, and Argentina to as high as 7.31 in 14.4 API Qaiyarah oil from Iraq. When compared on a gravity basis as when being marketed, the amounts of sulfur in various crude oils compared with the amount in United States and Venezuelan oils (basis is 1.0) are as shown in Table 4-4.[14]

[13] Jackson, E. A., Oil Gas J., Mar. 21, 1935, p. 16.
[14] Nelson, Thery, and Cordero, Relationship between Sulfur Content of Crude Oils and the Sulfur Content of Conventional Refinery Products, Proc. Fourth World Pet. Congr., sec. V/A, Rome, June, 1955.

Analyses of a few typical or unique crude oils (of the thousands known) are tabulated in Appendix B.

TABLE 4-4. AVERAGE GRAVITIES AND SULFUR CONTENTS OF CRUDE OILS[a]

Crude oil	Ratio of % sulfur to % sulfur in U.S. oils[b]	Average gravity	Average % sulfur
Typical Gulf Coast (U.S.).............	0.15	22.0[c]	0.19
Far East (India, Pakistan, Burma)[d]....	....	.....	Under 0.2
East Texas field....................	0.67	38.0	0.26
U.S.S.R. & Eastern Europe[d]..........	....	.....	Under 0.4
California........................	0.75	26.2	1.05
Average U.S......................	1.00	34.7	0.75
Venezuela........................	1.00	25.3	1.36
Western Europe[d]...................	....	.....	Under 1.0
Mississippi.......................	1.50	26.0[c]	1.60[c]
West Texas.......................	1.75	36.0[c]	1.38
Eastern Texas (low gravity)..........	2.00		
Middle East (Iran, Saudi Arabi, Kuwait, Iraq, Bahrein, Egypt).............	3.00	35.0	1.60

[a] Nelson, Thery, and Cordero, Relationship between Sulfur Content of Crude Oils and the Sulfur Content of Conventional Refinery Products, *Proc. Fourth World Pet. Congr.*, sec. V/A, Rome, June, 1955.

[b] Comparing oils of the same gravity.

[c] Estimated.

[d] Tait, T., "25 Years of Progress in Petroleum Technology," ACS Meeting, New York, p. 151, September, 1951.

So-called "sour" crude oils contain hydrogen sulfide,[15] but many technologists carelessly refer to "high sulfur" oils as "sour" oils. Crude oils are classified as "sour" if they contain as much as 0.05 cu ft of dissolved hydrogen sulfide per 100 gal[16] because such oils are dangerously toxic. Even 0.5 cu ft per 100 gal can be present before severe corrosion tends to occur. Oils from West Texas and New Mexico are "sour," and many fields of Kansas, Wyoming, Arkansas, and the Middle East produce "sour" oils. The high-sulfur oils of California, Venezuela, and Mexico do not contain hydrogen sulfide and they should never be classified as "sour."

With the exception of highly naphthenic oils and the very few oils that are highly paraffinic, the distillation curves of crude oils are reasonably

[15] Nelson, W. L., *Oil Gas J.* (definition) July 28, 1952, p. 375, and Aug. 4, 1952, p. 103; (determination of) Oct. 27, 1952, p. 145; (penalty for) Jan. 26, 1953, p. 403; (fields) May 4, 1953, p. 145.

[16] Esso Standard Oil Co., "Safety Instructions . . . ," Sec. J.

consistent with one another. Figure 4-3 represents the average of over 350 distillation curves,[17] and if the curve of a particular oil deviates from the average curves of Fig. 4-3, it may be considered to be abnormal (or one should examine the laboratory data for their accuracy). Paraffinic

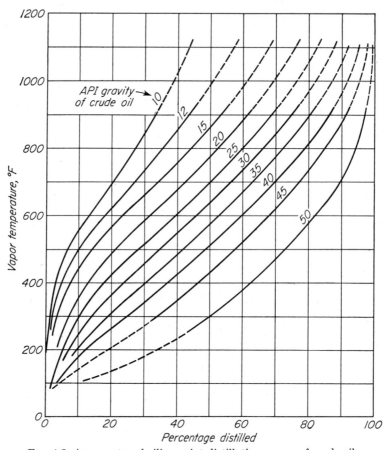

FIG. 4-3. Average true-boiling-point distillation curves of crude oils.

crude oils are usually deficient in low-boiling materials, and highly naphthenic oils usually have much flatter distillation curves, often being deficient in both low- and high-boiling fractions. Examples of distillation and property curves of three different bases of crude oils are shown in Figs. 4-4, 4-5, and 4-6. The percentage distilled at 1100°F is approximately equal to 100 minus 3 times the percentage of carbon residue.

[17] Private files and see Nelson, Thery, Medina, et al., "Venezuelan Crude Oils" (1951) and Nelson, Thery, and Sahagun, "Venezuelan and Other World Crude Oils" (1952), Ministerio de Minas e Hidrocarburos, Caracas, Venezuela.

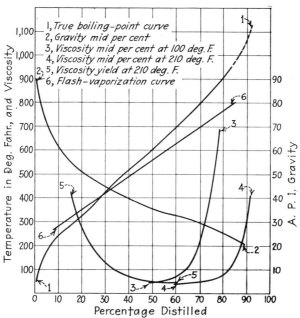

Fig. 4-4. True-boiling-point evaluation curves of a 37.3 API intermediate-paraffin-base crude oil.

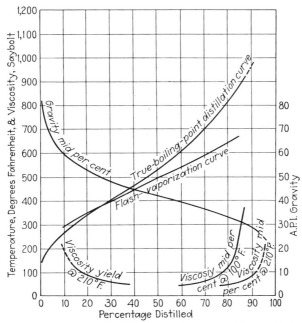

Fig. 4-5. True-boiling-point evaluation curves of a 42.2 API paraffin-base crude oil.

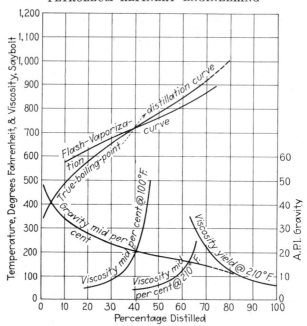

FIG. 4-6. True-boiling-point evaluation curves of a 20.2 API asphaltic-naphthene-base crude oil.

The change of viscosity with temperature for more than 80 crude oils has been reported.[18]   For most Oklahoma crude oils and for most Middle East crude oils, the viscosity curves are a consistent function of API gravity, but no such consistency is evident among the oils from other regions.

The amount of gaseous hydrocarbons dissolved in crude oil is almost totally a function of the degree of weathering that the oil has undergone or the pressure at which it is collected (see Table 4-5).   The percentage involved when the dissolved gases are lost cannot be stated with accuracy but it is about:

$$\text{Liquid vol. \% loss} = \frac{\text{Reid v.p.} - 1}{6}$$

If the gases have a molecular weight of 40, the gas amounts to about 16.1 cu ft for each 1 per cent loss of liquid.

Salt carried into the plant in the brine associated with crude oil is a major cause of the plugging of exchangers and the coking of pipestill tubes.   The Universal Oil Products Company Method A-22-40 for determining salt may be used.[19]   Theoretically, the amount of salt that

[18] Nelson, W. L., *Oil Gas J.*, Jan. 5, 1946, p. 70; Jan. 12, 1946, p. 87; and Nov. 15, 1954, p. 269.

[19] Laboratory Test Methods, 310 S. Michigan Ave., Chicago, Ill.

TABLE 4-5. FRACTIONAL HYDROCARBON ANALYSES (WT %) AND VAPOR PRESSURES OF A FEW CRUDE OILS

	Mid Continent		Jusepin (Vene.)	Kirkuk (Iraq)	Ras Tanura		Qatif (Saudi Arabia)	Qatif unstabilized	Pegasus (Tex.)	Healdton (Okla.) weathered
	3,000 psig[a]	12 psig[a]	250 psi 100°F	50 psi[a]	Refinery	Off-shore shipments				
API of crude oil	......	......	......	......	36.6	36.2	27.2	35.5	52.3	32.1
Reid vapor pressure, psia	......	......	......	......	6.7	3.5	2.3	11.5	8.0	
Hydrogen sulfide, ppm	......	......			243		......	641		
Methane	7.0	0.003	6.25	0.07	trace	......	0.03	trace	0.0	0.0
Ethane	2.4	0.03	3.64	0.17	0.05	......	0.04	0.06	0.05	0.02
Propane	3.0	0.26	6.29	0.22	0.34	0.05	0.06	0.62	0.66	0.21
i-Butane	2.8	0.90	3.16	0.21	0.15	0.12	0.19	0.27	0.44	0.14
n-Butane			4.07	0.49	0.89	0.84	0.33	1.27	1.96	0.78
Pentane plus	84.8	98.80	76.59	98.84	98.54	99.19	99.35	97.71	96.89	98.85
i-Pentane	......	......	......	......	0.76	0.75	0.49	0.62	1.62	0.62
n-Pentane	......	......	......	......	1.45	1.25	0.99	1.52	3.02	1.08
Hexane plus	......	......	......	......	96.33	97.19	97.87	95.57	92.25	97.15

[a] Pressure at which oil was collected.

can be deposited from 10,000 bbl of crude oil is approximately as follows:

Lb salt per 1,000 bbl	Possible deposit, cu ft per day
1,000	29.0
100	3.0
20	0.6

Refiners endeavor to reduce the salt content of their crude to one-tenth of that originally present. Even 20 lb of salt per 1,000 bbl requires frequent shutdowns to "wash out" exchangers and pipestills.

Little has been published on the amount of salt contained in crude oils, and little consistency is evident because the brine which contains the salt tends to settle from the crude oil during handling. Thus, the salt content of oil at the field is higher than the salt content at the pipeline or at the refinery. Neither crude oil gravity nor bottom sediment and water content appear to be related to salt content except when studying a particular field or region. Oils from various regions contain approximately the amounts of salt shown in Table 4-6.

TABLE 4-6

Region	Lb salt per 1,000 bbl		No. of samples
	Average[a]	Range	
Pennsylvania...................	1	....	6
Wyoming......................	5	1–13	8
Middle East....................	8	1–1,085	9
Venezuela......................	11	0–63	124
East Texas.....................	28	9–44	5
Gulf Coast.....................	35	2–70	11
Pipelines (U.S.)................	65	22–200	12
Oklahoma and Kansas...........	78	7–305	15
Canada........................	200	10–8,250	14
West Texas....................	261[b]	4–2,580	173

[a] Very high samples omitted from average.
[b] Most samples taken at field.

The nitrogen compounds in petroleum are not of major importance, but they do tend to cause a reduction in the activity of the catalysts used in catalytic cracking and they may assist in the formation of so-called "gum" in distillate or diesel fuel oils. California oils contain[20] the largest amount of nitrogen and, from scant data, the Mississippi oils appear to contain the least nitrogen. Other crude oils from West Texas, Wyoming, Middle East, Venezuela, etc., contain an intermediate amount of nitrogen.

[20] Nelson, W. L., Oil Gas J., Mar. 14, 1955, p. 139.

The highest-boiling fractions of a crude oil contain most of the nitrogen, and this has led some investigators to feel that there is a relationship between nitrogen and such properties as percentage of sulfur, gravity, asphaltenes, or Conradson carbon residue.

LABORATORY EQUIPMENT

In the operation of a replica plant, only one set of yields, properties, and conditions can be obtained during a single "run" or test; and hence many of these expensive runs must be made in order to judge the economy of the proposed operation. Most designers therefore rely upon a more general type of analysis which involves a true-boiling-point distillation and a series of curves of the significant properties of the fractions collected during the distillation.

True-boiling-point Apparatus. This equipment is used to obtain a so-called "true-boiling-point distillation curve" (see Figs. 4-3 and 4-9). Any equipment that accomplishes a good degree of fractionation is termed "true-boiling-point" equipment.

Technical men trained for handling 2-component mixtures are often disturbed by the fact that the number of plates or the amounts of reflux used in much T.B.P. equipment are not large or even specified. In actuality, when dealing with gross mixtures which may contain several components boiling within less than 2 degrees of each other (or even a fraction of a degree), the use of 60 plates rather than 5 or the use of infinite reflux rather than a ratio of 5 to 1 causes no significant change in the shape and position of the distillation curve or in the properties of the products. The best known types of equipment are those of the Peters type[21] for crude oil, gasoline, or heavier oils, and the Podbielniak[22] fractional distillation equipment used mainly for gaseous or low-boiling hydrocarbon mixtures, but numerous designs of equipment have been developed.[12,23,24]

An apparatus of the Peters type built during 1934 is shown in Fig. 4-7. The fractionating column differs from most laboratory columns because it is completely insulated from the surroundings. The outer jacket A, through which heated air flows, is kept at substantially the same tempera-

---

[21] Peters and Baker, *Ind. Eng. Chem.*, **18**, 69 (1926).

[22] Apparatus and Methods for Precise Fractional Distillation Analysis, *Ind. Eng. Chem.*, *Anal. Ed.*, **3**, 177 (1931); also for heavier oils, *Ind. Eng. Chem.*, *Anal. Ed.*, **5**, 119 (1933).

[23] Beiswenger and Child, True Boiling Crude Analysis, *Ind. Eng. Chem. Anal. Ed.*, **2**, 284 (1930).

[24] Taylor and Patten, Analyses of Texas Crude Oils, Railroad Commission of Texas, Oct. 25, 1940.

ture as the temperature of the vapor within the column, so that no heat passes into or out of the fractionating column. The disturbing influence of changing room conditions is particularly important in the operation of laboratory equipment, because the heat losses, even though the equipment has been carefully insulated, are often larger than the useful heat input.

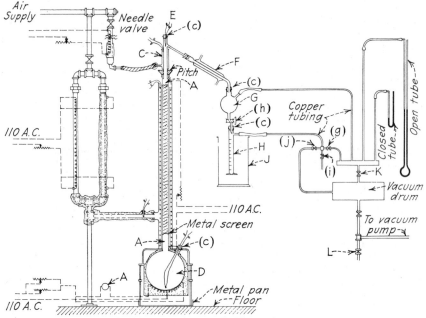

FIG. 4-7. Diagram of a true-boiling-point apparatus.

The true-boiling-point still consists of a flask D (Figs. 4-7, 4-8) ranging in capacity from 1,000 to 5,000 cc. The larger still is advisable for the evaluation of heavy stocks, because fractions of 100 cc are required for the determination of gravity, viscosity, flash point, etc. However, obtaining very low pressures is difficult in the larger still unless a large vacuum pump is available. A vacuum pump having a displacement of 2 to 3 cu ft of air per minute is large enough for the 1,000-cc still, but the larger still requires a pump having a displacement of at least 6 cu ft per minute. Heat is supplied throughout the entire apparatus by electrical resistance coils. At the top of the column the vapor is cooled by the reflux air jacket C so that most of it condenses and is returned to the column as reflux. The purified vapor passes the thermocouple E in the column head and is condensed in the water- or air-cooled condenser F.

The temporary receiver G is for operation at reduced pressure. During

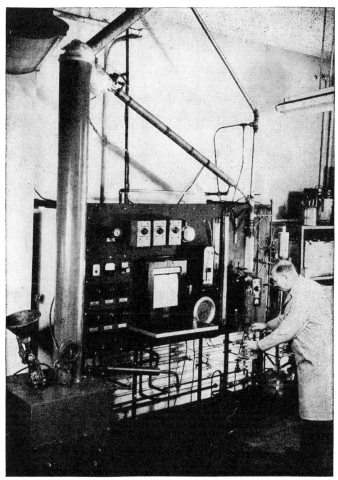

FIG. 4-8. True-boiling-point still. *Left:* encased still with jacketed column; *center:* control board with condenser across top; *right:* sample collection. (*Socony-Mobil Oil Company.*)

vacuum distillation the product normally drips through the receiver G into the graduate H. When the graduate is full, the stopcock h and the cock g are closed, and the graduate is removed by venting to the atmosphere through cock i. After an empty graduate is in position, the cock j is slowly opened so that the vacuum on the main system is not violently disturbed. An auxiliary vacuum pump may also be used to evacuate the graduate. After the graduate has been evacuated, cock j is closed and the cocks g and h may be opened again. Throughout the entire operation of changing the graduate, the pressure-regulation valve K need not be touched. Fine regulation of the pressure is obtained by means of the valve K, but for large adjustments of the pressure, i.e., at pressures above 50 mm, the valve L located near the pump may be used. A small amount of noncondensable vapor is always present during distillation, and this vapor passes through valve K causing the throttling action

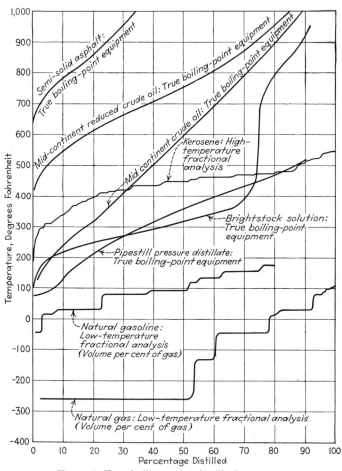

Fig. 4-9. True-boiling-point distillation curves.

that is necessary for regulation of the pressure. Manometers are used to measure the pressure in the equipment and in the graduate while it is being evacuated. When the equipment is operated at atmospheric pressure, the first product may be volatile, and, if so, the graduate should be immersed in the removable ice bath J. Many materials have been used for sealing the corks c, etc., but LePage's glue, although it must be frequently applied, appears to be most satisfactory. Ground-glass joints are excellent up to temperatures of about 450°F.

The distillation may be conducted in two ways, viz., at a constant or at a variable rate of distillation. The more common method of operation is to collect the distillate at a constant rate. The curve obtained by this manner of operation is smooth, with the exception of slight irregularities, and is more convenient for design purposes than one that shows flat steps for each component. The method does not accomplish such good fractionation as the second method of operation in which the rate of distillation is governed by the amount of material that boils at each temperature. The curves in Fig. 4-9 by the Podbielniak equipment were obtained by the second method of operation. At present, our knowledge of the theoretical behavior of complex mixtures and of the individual components that constitute complex oils is so meager that the more exact curve, obtained by the variable rate of distillation, is almost useless except in the preparation of pure compounds.

When the column is operated by the constant-rate method, the rate of heating should be such that distillate is collected at the rate of 1 per cent in 2 min for atmospheric distillations and 1 per cent in 3 to 5 min for vacuum distillations. The temperature of the air that enters the bottom of the column jacket should be about 5°F below the flask temperature, and the temperature of the air leaving the jacket should be about 5°F higher than the vapor temperature in the column head. If the air loses heat too rapidly in the jacket, more air may be used; and if this fails to sustain the temperature, the resistance wires, strung within the jacket, may be heated. The quantity of cooling material or reflux that is used should always be the maximum amount that the capacity of the column will permit. At all times the packing in the column should be wet with liquid. However, if too much reflux is used, the column will "flood" or "prime," and reflux will accumulate in it to such an extent that vapor cannot pass upward without carrying the liquid with it.

Fractional Analysis. Equipments for obtaining true-boiling-point analyses of somewhat simple mixtures are shown in Figs. 4-10[25] and 4-11.[22] Exceedingly low temperatures are maintained in the gas-analysis equipment (Fig. 4-10) by means of liquid ethylene, ethane, air, nitrogen, etc., in the dewar flask at the base of the column. In theory, pure hydrocarbons are separated one by one, but in practice great difficulty is encountered in deciding when a compound has been completely separated, particularly in splitting iso and normal compounds. Gas samples of 2,000 cc are advisable, although samples of only 100 cc have been successfully analyzed by the use of a microfractionating tube. Liquid samples (Fig. 4-11) of 50 cc are desirable. The high-temperature equipment may be obtained with flasks having capacities from 250 to 2,000 cc.

[25] NGAA Publication 1146, . . . Analysis of Saturated Hydrocarbon Gases by Low Temperature Fractional Distillation, NGAA, Tulsa, Okla., 1946.

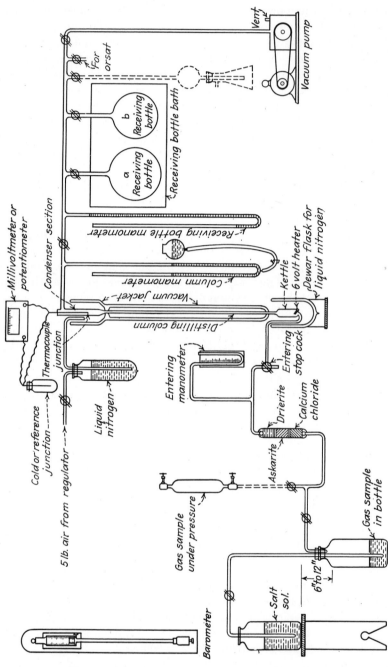

Fig. 4-10. Apparatus for low-temperature fractional analysis of saturated hydrocarbon gases. (*Natural Gasoline Association of America.*)

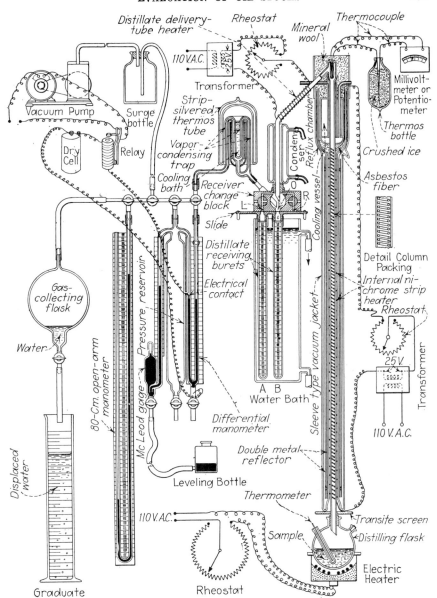

FIG. 4-11. Podbielniak high-temperature precision fractional-distillation apparatus.

In analyzing gases (Fig. 4-10) the sample is introduced into the chilled distilling bulb, and all gas except the air, hydrogen, and methane is condensed. These permanent gases are collected in an evacuated receiver, and the pressure in the receiver is recorded. The condensed hydrocarbons are then allowed to warm, and the components are fractionated and collected one by one in evacuated receivers. Heat may be required to vaporize the highest boiling part of the liquid. When a plateau occurs in the distillation curve or, in other words, material is collected at a constant temperature, the reflux is decreased by allowing the component to escape from the column more rapidly. As the temperature tends to rise, the reflux is increased by using a slower rate of distillation until finally little or no more material collects. At the same time the pressure in the equipment tends to drop, indicating that the component has been removed. The pressure in the equipment is held at 760 mm in removing methane through isobutane, but pressures of 300 and 200 mm are maintained in separating butane and the pentanes. Components may be collected in different evacuated receivers, but more often the gases are collected as a mixture. The volume of each component is measured in mole or volume percentage by noting the change in pressure in the gas receiver. The temperature and volume of the receiver remain constant, and hence the pressure is a direct measure of the moles of gas in the receiver.

High-boiling Materials. Even though a pressure of 0.5 mm of mercury is maintained in a true-boiling-point column, the highest-boiling oils, such as bright stock and asphalt, cannot be completely vaporized. The highest vapor temperature that can be obtained in the true-boiling-point apparatus is approximately 1000°F (when corrected from vacuum to atmospheric pressure by Fig. 5-27); and, since lubricating oils boil to even higher temperatures, recourse must be had to an equilibrium or "flash" type of vaporization. The laboratory operations required to vaporize heavy lubricating oils are

1. Remove gasoline from crude oil in a batch still so that gasoline will not enter the vacuum still next described.
2. Distill the gasoline-free residue in a continuous vacuum flash equipment, leaving a residue of asphalt and collecting all the useful lubricating oils as distillates.
3. Distill the lubricating-oil distillate in a true-boiling-point equipment so that individual fractions of oil are available for tests.

Such a procedure has the advantage of eliminating asphaltic materials that cannot easily be removed from the lubricating oils by laboratory treating operations.

As an example, we may wish to evaluate the lubricants in a Mid Continent reduced or topped crude oil of 26 API gravity. By a steam-atmospheric distillation in a small shell still a 23 API reduced crude-oil and a

32 API gas-oil distillate may be produced. The 23 API reduced crude oil is then distilled in the vacuum-flash vaporizer (Figs. 4-13, 4-14), leaving as a residue a 9 API tar and obtaining as a distillate a 25 API heart-cut lubricating-oil stock which is suitable for evaluation in the true-boiling-point column. The percentage "breakup" would be approximately as follows:

Material	Per cent	API
Gas oil...............................	20	32
Lube stock (heart-cut).................	73	25
Tar...................................	7	9
Reduced crude (charge stock)..........	100	26

Such an operation is also indicated in Fig. 4-27.

As an alternate to the above procedure, residuums or asphaltic charge stocks can be distilled up to vapor temperatures of about 1100°F (corrected to atmospheric pressure) by the use of very low pressure. The equipment of Mithoff et al.[12] (Fig. 4-12) is suited for such distillations.

Continuous Vacuum-flash Vaporizer. The vaporizer shown in Fig. 4-13 is a continuous-flow equipment in which the heating is done by a coil embedded in an aluminum casting (electrical heating elements) and the vaporizer is kept hot by condensing mercury vapor. Other vaporizers may employ a gas-fired furnace for the heating coil, and molten lead[26] or salts may be used for heating.

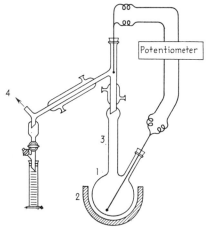

FIG. 4-12. Compact equipment for high-temperature, high-vacuum distillation: (1) flask, (2) electric heater, (3) short packed column, and (4) main vacuum connection. (*Oil Gas J.*)

The purpose of the flash vaporizer is to prepare a lubricating stock for evaluation purposes, and hence the residue of tar should be as small as possible and should contain no lubricants that can be removed from the asphalt in a commercial vacuum plant. For this reason the apparatus is always operated at the maximum allowable temperature of about 700°F and at as low a pressure as possible. With an almost leak-free apparatus

[26] Scheumann and Stewart, Laboratory Apparatus for Evaluating Crude, *Oil Gas J.*, May 16, 1935, p. 74.

and with a vacuum pump having a capacity of approximately 9 cu ft per minute the apparatus can be operated at a pressure of 7 mm.   Superheated steam may also be used to assist the vacuum in causing vaporization, but this necessitates the use of a water-cooled jet (contact) condenser for the steam.   The capacity of the equipment ranges between 1 and 4 gal per hr depending upon the character of the charging stock.   The aim is to vaporize as large a percentage of oil as possible, even though the

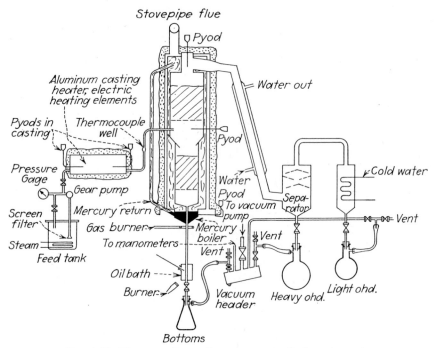

FIG. 4-13. Diagram of a continuous vacuum-flash equipment.

fractionation is imperfect, and hence no more reflux is used than the small amount that is required to prevent entrainment of tar into the distillate.

Equilibrium-flash Vaporizer.   When a mixture is heated without allowing the vapor to separate from the remaining liquid, the vapor assists in causing the high-boiling parts of the mixture to vaporize.   Thus continuous-flash vaporization is used in almost all plant operations.   Figure 4-14 indicates one such apparatus.[27]   Small-capacity equipments are desirable, but they cannot be easily controlled.

In determining a flash-vaporization curve, a series of runs at different

[27] Leslie and Good, The Vaporization of Petroleum, *Ind. Eng. Chem.*, **19**, 453 (1927).

temperatures are conducted, and each run constitutes one point (of temperature and percentage vaporized) on the flash curve.

Mid Per Cent Curves. The physical properties of an oil are found to vary gradually throughout the range of compounds that constitute the oil. Distillation is a means of arranging these chemical compounds in the order of their boiling points. The properties such as color, specific gravity, and viscosity are found to be different for each drop or fraction of the material distilled. The rate at which these properties change from drop

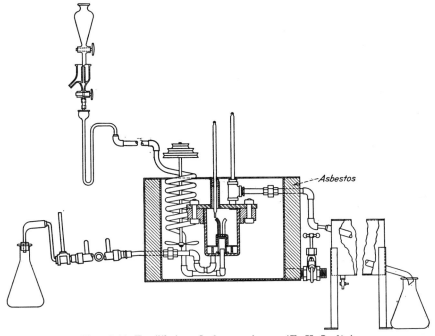

Fig. 4-14. Equilibrium-flash vaporizer. (*E. H. Leslie.*)

to drop may be plotted as mid per cent curves, such as curves 2, 3, and 4 in Fig. 4-4.

The refinery engineer is most often interested in determining the properties of a commercial width of fraction. In reality, the gravity or viscosity of a fraction is an average of the properties of the many drops that constitute the fraction. If each drop is equally different from the last drop and from the succeeding one, then the drop that distills at exactly half of the fraction has the same property as the average of all the drops. This would be the condition for a mid per cent curve that is a straight line. Mid per cent curves are never exactly straight lines (Fig. 4-15), but they are substantially straight through any short range of percentage. For a short range of percentage the average property is equal to the property at the mid-point of the fraction. The arithmetical average of the properties of these small fractions is the property of the total or large fraction, or even the entire sample. The mechanism of using the foregoing principles can be best illustrated by an example:

Example 4-2. **Use of Gravity Mid Per Cent Curve.** Compute the specific gravity of a 41.4 API (0.8183 sp gr) mixed-base crude oil from the specific-gravity mid per cent curve. Figure 4-15 is the gravity mid per cent curve as determined in the laboratory.

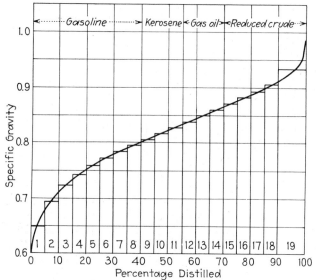

FIG. 4-15. Gravity mid per cent curve (see Example 4-2).

Assume that the curve is broken up into 19 fractions as indicated in Fig. 4-15. The gravities of the 19 materials are indicated by the 19 short horizontal lines. The curve is substantially straight through fractions 5 to 18, inclusive, and the horizontal lines pass through the centers of these fractions. The horizontal lines (average gravities) for the other fractions (1 to 4 and 19) do not pass through the mid-point but are so arranged that the triangular areas above and below the curve are equal. The gravities of the 19 fractions are tabulated in Table 4-7.

The gravity of the crude oil is equal to five times that of each of the fractions 1 to 18 inclusive plus ten times the gravity of fraction 19, all divided by 100. The computed gravity is 0.8171, and the actual gravity of the crude oil was 0.8183. This is a reasonable check and is sufficiently accurate for most engineering design work.

This crude oil contains 40 per cent gasoline, 15 per cent kerosene, 15 per cent gas oil, and 30 per cent reduced crude oil. The gravity of the gasoline equals five times the gravity of fractions 1 to 8 inclusive divided by 40 and numerically is 0.7399 (59.8 API). In a similar manner the gravity of the kerosene is equal to five times the gravity of fractions 9, 10, and 11 divided by 15 and is 0.8172 (41.6 API). Likewise the gravities of the gas oil and reduced crude oil are respectively 0.8496 (35 API) and 0.9037 (25.1 API).

In this example the actual fractions that were produced in the laboratory were used. In the usual case only the curve is available, and it is arbitrarily broken up into suitable fractions.

TABLE 4-7. TABULATION OF THE FRACTIONS OF FIG. 4-15

Fraction No.	Range of percentage	Sp gr	Fraction No.	Range of percentage	Sp gr
1	0–5	0.6506	11	50–55	0.8280
2	5–10	0.6936	12	55–60	0.8388
3	10–15	0.7227	13	60–65	0.8498
4	15–20	0.7420	14	65–70	0.8602
5	20–25	0.7583	15	70–75	0.8713
6	25–30	0.7720	16	75–80	0.8827
7	30–35	0.7844	17	80–85	0.8939
8	35–40	0.7958	18	85–90	0.9065
9	40–45	0.8067	19	90–100	0.9340
10	45–50	0.8170			

By inspecting the specific gravities computed in Example 4-2, it will be noted that the gravities of the kerosene and gas oil are the same as the gravities at the mid boiling points of these fractions, namely 47.5 per cent and 62.5 per cent. Such might have been expected because the curve is nearly a straight line throughout these materials. Following this reasoning we may state that, if the property curve is nearly a straight line between the limits of the fraction, the average property of the fraction is equal to the value of the property at the mid per cent point of the fraction, and the laborious method of integral-averaging by graphical methods, as in Example 4-2, need not be used except throughout sharply curving sections of the curve.

Integral-averaging by adding together the properties of a series of short fractions and dividing by the number of fractions cannot be used on properties that are not additive. Specific gravity (not API gravity) is an example of an additive property, e.g., 10 volumes of an oil of specific gravity 0.8 when mixed with an equal volume of 0.9 specific gravity oil yields a mixture that has a specific gravity 0.85. Among the properties that are not additive are

1. Viscosity (Fig. 4-44).
2. API gravity.
3. Color.
4. Flash point.

Boiling points taken from a true-boiling-point distillation are additive, and vapor pressures when based on molal percentages are additive (Raoult's law). Common additive properties are specific gravity, aniline point, per cent sulfur, hydrogen-carbon ratio, etc. However, since any property can be plotted in a mid per cent manner, i.e., at the mid-points of narrow fractions, it behooves the designer or user of such curves not to obtain average properties of wide-range fractions from them unless the property is known to be an additive one.

Although viscosity is not an additive property, it is a fortunate coincidence that the viscosity of a wide fraction from a crude oil is almost exactly the same as the viscosity at the mid-point of the fraction. Apparently the curvature exhibited by viscosity mid per cent curves is just right to compensate for the lowering of viscosity by blending, so that the mid-point can be used.

Mid per cent curves are sometimes described by the following descriptive names: (1) differential curves, (2) stream curves, or (3) instantaneous curves. These curves are drawn by plotting the property of each narrow-boiling fraction at the mid percentage point of the fraction. If the fractions are so large that the final curve exhibits sharp curvature, the properties should be plotted not at the mid-point but as horizontal lines throughout the percentage limits of the fractions as indicated in Fig. 4-15. As an example, note fraction No. 19 of Fig. 4-15 which is plotted not at 95 per cent but at about 96 per cent or in such a way that the two triangle areas above and below the curve are of the same area.

Yield Curves. If a property is not additive, the properties of various ranges or fractions of material can be determined experimentally by blending fractions together and plotting the property value so obtained as a function of the yield or amount of blended material. Curves 5 (viscosity yield) and 6 (flash vaporization) of Fig. 4-4 are examples of yield curves. The viscosity yield curve is a plot of the viscosity of the bottom or residue product vs. the percentage of residue, and the flash yield curve is a plot of temperature vs. percentage distilled. Since the viscosity yield curve (Fig. 4-4) describes residue products that terminate at 100 per cent distilled it is called a "residue yield curve"; and similarly, since the flash yield curve (Fig. 4-4) describes products that start at zero per cent distilled, it is classed as a "distillate yield curve." Obviously, a yield curve can be used to describe blends that start (or end) at any desired percentage distilled, such as the viscosity yield curve of Fig. 4-29, which describes oils that terminate at 91.8 per cent on the crude oil, but such "intermediate yield curves" must be carefully labeled to designate the terminal of the blends.

Data for yield curves can be obtained by making a large number of runs each for a different percentage of residue (or distillate or intermediate) product, but this is so expensive that the common method is to blend suitable fractions together to represent various yields of product. In order to have enough oil for several blends, aliquot portions of the fractions are used rather than the whole fraction.

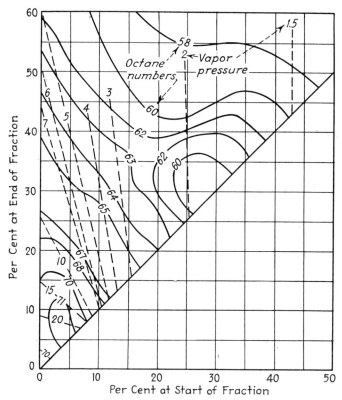

Fig. 4-16. Octane numbers (F-2) and vapor pressures of the gasolines in one Mid Continent "rough cut" naphtha. (*Oil Gas J.*)

Example 4-3. Construction of (Residue) Viscosity Yield Curve. This method applies in general to all residue yield curves.

Consider 19 fractions of oil obtained by a fractionating type of distillation. The properties such as gravity and viscosity of the fractions have already been recorded so that the fractions can be used in the following blends. Fractions 1 to 18 inclusive consist of 100 cc each, and the last or bottom fraction (not distilled) amounts to 200 cc. The fractions can be blended in aliquot parts to make several bottom products as follows:

Per cent residue or bottom	Blend of fractions	Total quantity of blend, cc
10	No. 19, 75 cc (residue from the distillation)	75
20	No. 19, 40 cc; No. 18 and 17, 20 cc each	80
30	No. 19, 30 cc; No. 18, 17, 16, and 15, 15 cc each	90
45	No. 19, 20 cc; No. 18 to 12 incl., 10 cc each	90
60	No. 19, 14 cc; No. 18 to 9 incl., 7 cc each	84

The viscosity of each blend is determined, and the four blends, along with fraction 19, constitute five points on the viscosity yield curve; also refer to Table 4-10.

Contour Charts. If enough data are available, the most suitable method of showing yield data (both mid per cent and yield) is by means of a contour chart. The bottom scale of such a chart shows the percentage distilled at the start or beginning of the fraction, and the vertical scale shows the percentage at the end of the fraction. Figure 4-16 shows such a chart[28] for the octane number and vapor pressure of the gasolines contained in a "rough-cut" naphtha. The lines across the chart are lines of constant octane number. Thus points along the 45-deg line are mid per cent points (of differentially small fractions), and points along the vertical axis are distillate yield curve points. Turner and Canant[29] first utilized contour charts, and now several such analyses appear in the literature.[12,28,30] Any kind of data may be plotted in this manner.

Example 4-4. Use of Contour Chart (Fig. 4-16). The droplet of material that starts and ends at 26 per cent has an octane number of 60, and its vapor pressure is just under 2.0. Likewise a fraction extending from 23.5 to 35 per cent (a yield of 11.5 per cent) also has an octane number of 60 but a vapor pressure of about 2.1.

Note that there are two lines of 60 octane number. On the other line, yields are as follows:

Range, per cent	Yield, per cent	Vapor pressure
42–42	One drop	1.5
40–45	5	1.6
30–45	15	1.8
15–47	32	2.7
8–60	52	3.3

Finally, the yields of gasolines starting at zero per cent (or utilizing all the light constituents) are

Octane number	Yield, per cent	Range, per cent	Vapor pressure
70	15	0–15	15
67	26	0–26	10
64	46	0–46	6.6
62	58	0–58	5

[28] Nelson, W. L., Evaluating Aviation-gasoline Content of Crude Oil, *Oil Gas J.*, May 13, 1943, p. 52.
[29] Correlating and Showing Crude Assay Data, *Oil Gas J.*, Mar. 25, 1937, p. 86.
[30] Nelson, W. L., Evaluation Curves, *Oil Gas J.*, Jan. 13, 1945, p. 91.

Distillation Curves. In addition to T.B.P. or good fractionation distillations, there are at least three other major types of distillation curves or ways of relating vapor temperature and percentage vaporized: (a) equilibrium or flash vaporization, (b) ASTM or nonfractionating distillations, and (c) Hempel or semifractionating distillations.

Flash Vaporization. The feed material is heated as it flows continuously through a heating coil. As vapor is formed it travels along in the

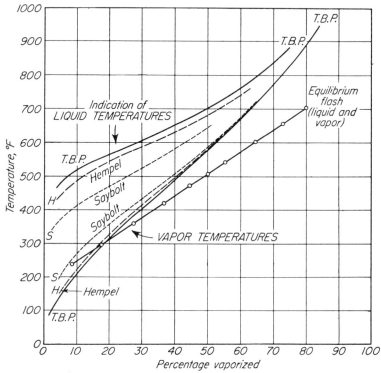

FIG. 4-17. Typical liquid- and vapor-temperature distillation curves of a 35 API crude oil.

tube with the remaining liquid until separation is permitted in a vapor separator or vaporizer. By conducting the operation at a series of outlet temperatures, a curve of percentage vaporized vs. temperature may be plotted.

Nonfractionating. ASTM designation D-86 applied to gasoline, naphtha, kerosene, etc.,[6] is the best known nonfractionating distillation and it is frequently called simply an "ASTM" and sometimes an "Engler" because a similar Engler distillation was once widely used. Likewise, the older Saybolt distillation for crude oil has now been standardized[6]

as ASTM D-158.   It involves distilling 200 ml of oil at a rate of 8 to
10 ml per min.   In distilling the highest boiling materials[6] a vacuum is
employed, as in ASTM D-116 or various modifications such as the equipment[12] of Fig. 4-12.

In these distillations there is no deliberate attempt to fractionate, and
accordingly the vapor temperature does not represent the true or actual
boiling point of the material situated at that percentage in the crude oil.

Semifractionating.   In these distillations a mild degree of fractionation
is attained by the use of a section of packed column between the flask

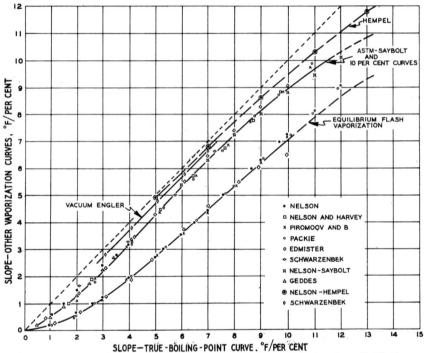

Fig. 4-18. Relationships between the slopes (degrees/per cent) of various distillation or
vaporization curves.   (*Oil Gas J.*)

and the condenser.   The best known method is the Hempel distillation
of the U.S. Bureau of Mines,[2] and ASTM D-285 for crude petroleum[6]
is a similar method.   The crude oil curves obtained by these methods
are nearly the same as from T.B.P. distillations because of the tiny differences in boiling point between successive hydrocarbons in the mixture.

Figure 4-17 is a comparison of distillation curves by these various
methods.   Although the curves cannot be computed with accuracy from

DISTILLATION 50 PER CENT POINT MINUS FLASH
50 PER CENT POINT

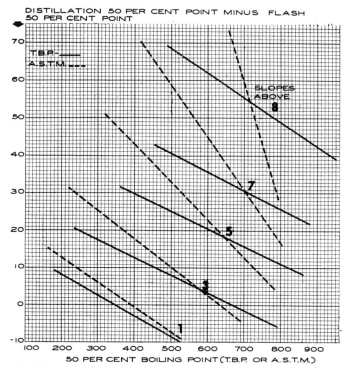

FIG. 4-19. Relationship between distillation temperatures at 50 per cent vaporized and the flash (E.F.V.) temperature at 50 per cent. (*Oil Gas J.*)

one another, they can be approximated from the relationship of Figs. 4-18 to 4-21 and Table 4-8.[31]

Example 4-5. Estimate of Flash Vaporization Curve. The T.B.P. curve of Fig. 4-17 has a slope (degrees/per cent) between the 10 and 70 per cent points of

$$\frac{775 - 210}{60} = 9.4 \text{ deg/per cent}$$

According to Fig. 4-18, the slope of the flash vaporization curve will be 6.5 deg/per cent, and the 50 per cent temperature of the flash curve (Fig. 4-19) will be about 64°F below the 50 per cent temperature of the T.B.P. curve:

$$576 - 64 = 512°F$$

A straight line flash curve can be drawn through 512°F with a slope of 6.5. Thus, at zero per cent the temperature is 512 minus 325 or 187°F and at 100 per cent, 837°F.

Figure 4-18 may be used to relate the slopes of any of the distillation curves, and Table 4-8 or Fig. 4-19 relates the 50 per cent temperatures.

[31] Nelson, W. L., *Oil Gas J.* (Hempel), Sept. 1, 1952, p. 117; (Saybolt), Dec. 29, 1952, p. 101; and Mar. 16, 1953, p. 149.

These may be used to estimate the central portion of the various distillation curves or those central ranges of percentage which are substantially straight lines. Figures 4-20 (Hempel) and 4-21 (Saybolt) indicate another method of correlating distillation curves.

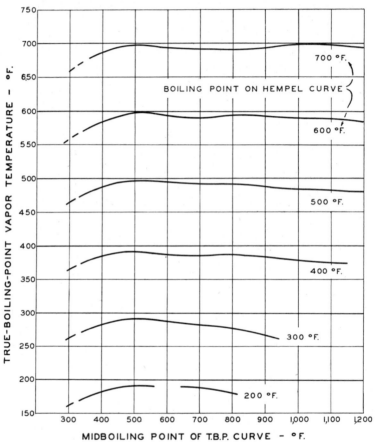

FIG. 4-20. Correlation of Hempel and true-boiling-point distillation curves (based mainly on crude oils). (*Oil Gas J.*)

Note that Fig. 4-18 can be used to relate the slopes of any pair of distillation curves. Thus, an ASTM distillation curve with a slope of 6.32 (reading from left scale) will have the following slopes when distilled by other methods (reading on vertical line):

T.B.P.............. 7.0 (bottom scale)
Flash.............. 4.5 (left scale)
Vac. Engler......... 6.65 (left scale)
Hempel............. 6.8 (left scale)

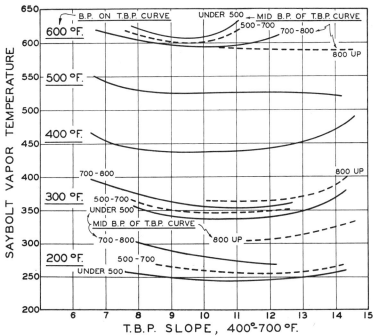

Fig. 4-21. A correlation of true-boiling-point and Saybolt distillation curves (based mainly on crude oils). (*Oil Gas J.*)

Table 4-8. Relation of 50 Per Cent Boiling Points (°F). T.B.P. versus Other Distillation Curves

T.B.P. 50% boiling point, °F	T.B.P. 50% boiling point minus ASTM[a] 50% boiling point						T.B.P. 50% minus Hempel 50% (all slopes)[b]
	T.B.P. slope of 1	T.B.P. slope of 3	T.B.P. slope of 5	T.B.P. slope of 7	T.B.P. slope of 9	T.B.P. slope of 11	
100	−5	−17[c]					
200	−2	− 6	−12	−39[c]			
300	−1	− 3	− 6	−24[c]	−40[c]		
400	+1	+ 2	− 2	−16	−30	−42[c]	−11
500	+2	+ 4	+ 2	− 7	−18	−30	− 6
600	+4[c]	+ 9	+ 6	− 1	−10	−21	− 1
700	....	+14[c]	+15	+10	+ 1	−10	2
800	....	.....	+21[c]	+20	+16	+10	7
900	....	.....	.....	+37[c]	+44	+50[c]	12

[a] Includes ASTM, Saybolt, and so-called 10 per cent distillations.

[b] Slope is also a factor but not to a significant degree.

[c] Doubtful, but useful in interpolations.

Finally, somewhat more detail is useful in correlating the ASTM and T.B.P. curves of narrow-boiling-range products such as gasoline and kerosene. From scant data,[32] the 80, 90 and 99 per cent points of the two curves are related somewhat as follows:

T.B.P., °F	Add these number of degrees to obtain ASTM, °F	
	at 80%	at 90 and 95%
250	. . .	10
350	. . .	11
450	1*	14
500	1*	16
600	2*	

* From vacuum Engler distillations.

No entirely adequate method of correlating the low-boiling ends of such curves has been developed, although approximate results can be obtained by a method suggested by Hansburg.[32] A complete study of this relationship has been published by Geddes[33] and still another by Edmister[34] but none of these attempts is entirely successful.

The various curves may be corrected for pressure or vacuum by means of vapor pressures (Figs. 5-25, 5-26, 5-27) applied at the 50 per cent point or at the crossing point of the curves with the T.B.P. curve. However, the flash vaporization curve tends to become horizontal at the critical point or range (Fig. 15-13) and accordingly, Edmister[35] suggests an approximate correction based on Fig. 4-22. The method is termed approximate because the "focal point" pressures of the phase diagrams of petroleum mixtures are not known with accuracy. The estimation of focal points and phase diagrams is discussed on pages 456 to 460.

Curvature of Flash-vaporization Curves. The foregoing correlation method (Figs. 4-18 and 4-19) results in a straight-line flash curve. If the distillation curve of the material is substantially a straight line, then the flash curve is also nearly straight. If curvature exists, then the flash curve also exhibits a curvature but to a lesser degree. The approximate deviation from the 10–70 per cent slope that any particular section of the distillation curve may exhibit is directly proportional to the deviation

[32] Hansburg, M., Master's thesis, University of Tulsa, 1939, or Nelson and Hansburg, Oil Gas J., Aug. 3, 1939, p. 45; and Schwarzenbek et al., Third World Pet. Congr., The Hague, sec. IV, p. 166, 1951.

[33] Geddes, R. L., Ind. Eng. Chem., **33**, 795 (1941).

[34] Edmister and Pollock, Chem. Eng. Prog., **44**, 905 (1948).

[35] Pet. Eng., August, 1947, p. 49.

of the actual flash curve from the straight-line flash curve. Thus

$$\frac{\text{Slope of dist. curve, } 10\text{--}70\%}{\text{Slope of flash curve, } 10\text{--}70\%} = \frac{\text{slope of dist. curve through short range}}{\text{slope of flash curve through short range}} \quad (4\text{-}5)$$

A somewhat similar method has been described by J. W. Packie.[36]

In applying curvature corrections by the use of Eq. (4-5), difficulty is encountered in selecting a 50 per cent point. The proper 50 per cent

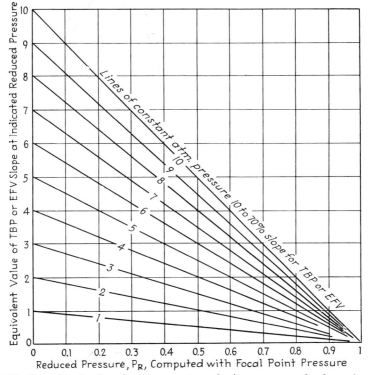

FIG. 4-22. Correction for the effect of superatmospheric pressure on the slope of equilibrium-flash-vaporization (E.F.V.) curves. (*Edmister, Pet. Eng.*)

temperature is intermediate between the temperature on the distillation curve and the temperature on a straight line connecting the 10 and 70 per cent points, and usually about halfway between.

The flash curves of extreme materials such as bright stock solution (Fig. 4-23) or rich absorption oils cannot be determined by these methods, nor have any methods been suggested.

[36] Distillation Equipment in the Oil Refining Industry, p. 60, *Trans. A.I.Ch.E.*, **37**, 51 (1941).

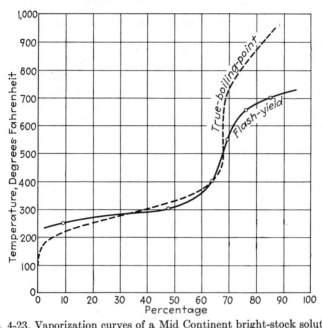

FIG. 4-23. Vaporization curves of a Mid Continent bright-stock solution.

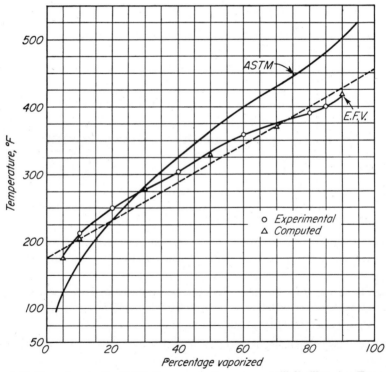

FIG. 4-24. Curvature in the distillation curves of a pressure-still distillate (see Examples 4-6 and 15-2).

118

Example 4-6. Curvature of Flash-vaporization Curve. The experimental flash-vaporization curve and the ASTM distillation of a pressure distillate are shown in Fig. 4-24. The computed straight-line curve is shown dotted, the triangular points are computed points, and the circular points are experimental ones.

Slope of ASTM, 10–70 per cent $\dfrac{430 - 170}{60} = 4.34$

Slope of flash, 10–70 per cent (Fig. 4-18) $= 2.8$

The 50 per cent point on a straight line connecting 430 and 170 on the ASTM curve is:

$$(170 + 4.34 \times 40) \text{ or } (430 - 4.34 \times 20) = 343°F$$

whereas it is about 365 on the ASTM curve. A compromise temperature halfway between, i.e., 354°F, is selected

50 % on the flash curve (Fig. 4-19) 354 − 37 = 317°F
100 % on the flash curve 317 + 50 × 2.8 = 456°F
0 % on the flash curve 317 − 50 × 2.8 = 176°F

Computing curvature,

$$\text{Ratio of 10–70 slopes} = \frac{2.8}{4.34} = 0.645$$

Starting at the 10 per cent point and computing the 5 per cent point as an illustration,

10 % on flash curve: 317 − 40 × 2.8 = 205°F
Slope of ASTM curve between 5 and 10 %: $\dfrac{170 - 125}{5} = 9.0$
Slope of flash curve between 5 and 10 %: 9 × 0.645 = 5.8
Temperature at 5 % on flash curve: 205 − 5.8 × 5 = 176°F

Other points are computed in Table 4-9.

TABLE 4-9

Range, %	Slope of ASTM curve	Computed slope of flash curve	Temperature increment	Points on flash curve
5–10	9.00	5.80	29	176 and 205
10–30	5.64	3.64	73	205 and 278
30–50	3.95	2.55	51	278 and 329
50–70	3.30	2.13	43	329 and 372
70–90	3.60	2.32	46	372 and 418

In this instance the predicted curve is slightly high, owing mainly to inaccuracy in determining the 50 per cent temperature. In other instances the predicted curve will be low.

ASTM End Point of Distillates. End point is an important specification or way of describing gasolines, naphthas, or middle distillates. The approximate relationship between the end point of a fraction and its T.B.P. (and other) cut point[37] is indicated in Fig. 4-25. The triangle

[37] Nelson, W. L., *Oil Gas J.*, Oct. 18, 1954, p. 127.

points represent the average relationships for hundreds of 300, 400, 450, and 500°F cut-point products[17] from T.B.P. distillations, and the meanings of the other curves are:

A—ASTM end point vs. T.B.P. cut temperature for gasoline fractions starting at T.B.P. temperatures of 200°F or lower.

B—ASTM end point vs. T.B.P. cut temperature for solvent or naphtha fractions at T.B.P. temperatures of about 300°F.

C—ASTM end point vs. T.B.P. cut temperature for naphtha or kerosene fractions starting at T.B.P. temperatures of 400 to 450°F.

D—ASTM end point vs. T.B.P. cut temperature for gas-oil fractions starting at T.B.P. temperatures of about 500°F.

E, F—ASTM end point vs. T.B.P. cut temperatures for 300-ml standard column distillations and for a 5-ft packed column.[38]

G—ASTM 90 per cent temperature vs. temperature at 90 per cent of T.B.P. cut for all types of products.

H—ASTM end point vs. Hempel cut temperature of the standard[2] 45°F Hempel fractions.

I—ASTM initial boiling point vs. Hempel[2] starting temperatures of 45°F Hempel fractions.

It must be noted that the relationships are only approximate because each type of laboratory equipment exhibits a different relationship between cut point and ASTM end point.

The end point of a blend is much higher than one would expect from the end points of the two components that are blended[39] and occasionally is even higher than the end point of either component. In adding butanes (0-15 per cent), 1 per cent butanes cause a decrease in the end point of about 0.25°F, and pentanes cause 0.28°F for each per cent added.

Example 4-7.   ASTM End Point and T.B.P. Cut Point.   It is desired to determine the cut point on a true-boiling-point analysis curve that will give a product having an ASTM end point of 437°F.   At an end point of 437 (curve A, Fig. 4-25) the true-boiling-point cut point is 21°F higher than the ASTM end point.   The cut point is 437 plus 21, or 458°F.   The following tabulation indicates approximate end points as well as cut points for other distillates:

Material	Initial boiling point, °F	End point, °F	Correction	True boiling cut point, °F	Curve
Gasoline.........	Less than 200	437	21	458	A
Gasoline.........	Less than 200	390	18	408	A
Naphtha.........	300	460	21	481	B
Kerosene........	450	530	26	556	C
Distillate........	500	590	16	606	D

[38] Data of Good and Connell and of Garton et al., used in the *Oil Gas J.*, Dec. 30, 1944, p. 277.

[39] Stanley and Pingrey, *Ind. Eng. Chem.*, **46**, 2182 (1954).

True-boiling-point Analysis of Crude Oil. The property curves that have been discussed heretofore are of general usefulness. In the following pages the necessary laboratory procedure, the construction of the curves, and the evaluations of several stocks will be discussed.

The evaluation of a *paraffin-base crude oil* is particularly simple because the oil contains no asphalt. Only a true-boiling-point distillation, con-

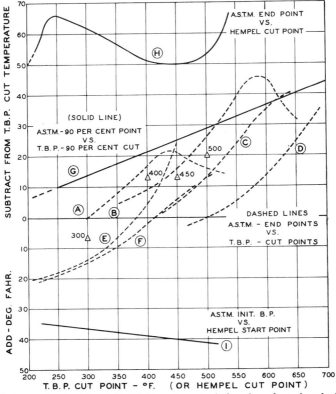

Fig. 4-25. Approximate ASTM distillation characteristics of products in relation to the cut temperatures of crude-oil distillations. (*Oil Gas J.*)

ducted at first at atmospheric pressure and later at a low pressure, is necessary. Of course, the fractions from the distillation must be examined by routine tests. Table 4-10 is a log sheet of the data obtained in the analysis of a typical paraffin-base crude oil, and Fig. 4-26 is a graphical presentation of these data. The vapor-temperature or true-boiling-point curve was plotted directly from the data. The gravity curve was drawn by plotting the specific gravity of each fraction as a horizontal line throughout the limits of the fraction and then drawing the curve by balancing the triangular areas against one another. The highest gravity, extending through 90 to 100 per cent, is the gravity of the residue. The viscosity mid per cent curves were drawn by plotting the viscosity of each of the fractions at the mid per cent points of the fractions. The highest viscosity on the 210°F curve is the viscosity of the final residue. The viscosity yield curve was plotted directly from the blend data given in Table 4-10 with the final bottom from the distillation as the 10 per cent bottom product.

Example 4-8. **Evaluation of Paraffin-base Crude Oil.** The following sets of yields of raw stocks can be computed from the property curves of Fig. 4-26:

Raw stocks	Per cent	Sp gr	API	Notes
Breakup 1:				
(1) 409 E.P. gasoline...............	38.3	0.753	56.4	430°F cut point
(2) 42 API kerosene.................	23.4	0.815	42	Mid-point 50 per cent
(3) 85 viscosity at 100 wax distillate*..	26.0	0.859	33.2	Mid-point 74.7
(4) 150 viscosity at 210 cyl. stock......	12.3	0.892	27.1	Viscosity yield curve
Breakup 2:				
(1) 391 E.P. gasoline...............	36.0	0.751	56.9	410°F cut point
(2) 450 E.P. naphtha...............	5.8	0.795	46.3	458°F cut point
(3) Gas oil (by difference)............	42.2	0.837	37.4	Mid-point 62.9 per cent
(4) 120 viscosity at 210 cyl. stock......	16.0	0.89	27.5	Viscosity yield curve

* Will not be a pressable stock unless some of the heavy material is removed.

In obtaining breakup 1 the percentage of 409°F end-point gasoline was obtained by referring to Fig. 4-25, which indicates that the true-boiling-point cut point is 21°F higher than the ASTM end point. The 42 API kerosene was evaluated by noting that the mid per cent point of 0.815 (or 42 API) gravity occurs at 50 per cent on the distillation curve. Since the kerosene starts at 38.3 per cent, the end point must be at 61.7 and the total yield is 23.4 per cent. The cylinder stock of 12.3 per cent was obtained directly from the viscosity yield curve. Twenty-six per cent of material remains, and this material is the wax distillate. The gravities of the gasoline and cylinder stock were obtained by integral-averaging, but the other gravities were obtained by noting the gravity at the mid per cent points of the cut or at 50 per cent and at 74.7 per cent respectively. The mid per cent viscosity at 74.7 per cent is 85 sec at 100°F.

Abbreviated T.B.P. analyses of more than 150 crude oils are tabulated in Appendix B. Distillation curves may be plotted from the percentages given in the tabulation for temperatures of 80, 300, 400, 450, 550, 700, and 900°F. Gravity mid per cent curves can also be plotted by using the Characterization Factors with the instantaneous temperatures just enumerated.

Evaluation of Dark-colored Stocks for Lubricants. The evaluation of stocks that contain asphalt demands a more elaborate laboratory procedure. Such a stock must be subjected to preliminary distillations. The stock is first reduced by a steam distillation at atmospheric pressure to approximately 26 API (Fig. 4-27). The removal of gasoline and kerosene is necessary because these materials cannot be condensed in the subsequent vacuum-flash distillation that is necessary for the removal of tar.

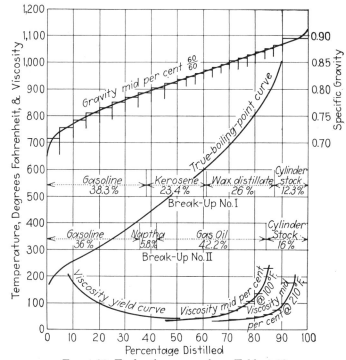

FIG. 4-26. Evaluation curves from Table 4-10.

The reduced crude is then flashed under vacuum, distilling a clear lubricating oil stock and leaving solid tar. The lubricating oil stock can then be evaluated in the true-boiling apparatus. A true-boiling-point analysis of the crude oil is also necessary if the light stocks are to be evaluated.

The curves for such a laboratory procedure are given in Figs. 4-28 and 4-29. The viscosity yield curve is plotted separately (Fig. 4-29) because it was obtained for the heart-cut lubricating oil stock which does not contain the 8.2 per cent of tar. This viscosity yield curve (Fig. 4-29) is not generally useful because the plant must operate making exactly 8.2 per cent of tar bottoms or the yields will be inaccurate.

Dependability of Evaluation. As an indication of the dependability of

TABLE 4-10. TRUE-BOILING-POINT ANALYSIS

Sample_____   Job No._____

From_____   Sample No._____

Quantity of Charge—3,000 cc at 60°F, API–43

Time	Vapor temperature at 760 mm, °F	Cumulative per cent	Fraction No.	Per cent in fraction	Sp gr 60/60	Viscosity 100	Viscosity 210	Notes
1. 9:06 A.M.	170	1	...	.....	.....	...	.....	Atmos.
2. 9:15	210	3.33						
3. 9:22	227	5	1	5	0.706			
4. 9:30	238	6.67						
5. 9:38	248	8.33						
6. 9:46	256	10	2	5	0.728			
7. 9:53	262	11.67						
8. 10:00	270	13.33						
9. 10:07	279	15	3	5	0.739			
10. 10:13	288	16.67						
11. 10:19	297	18.33						
12. 10:26	306	20	4	5	0.751			
13. 10:33	315	21.67						
14. 10:39	327	23.33						
15. 10:45	338	25	5	5	0.763			
16. 10:51	348	26.67						
17. 10:57	359	28.33						
18. 11:03	370	30	6	5	0.775			
19. 11:09	380	31.67						
20. 11:15	393	33.33						
21. 11:21	405	35	7	5	0.784			
22. 11:28	416	36.67						
23. 11:36	430	38.33						
24. 11:43	444	40	8	5	0.793	...	.....	Rate slow
25. 11:51	455	41.67	...	.....	.....	...	.....	Rate slow
26. 12:01 P.M.	465	43.33						
27. 12:10	485	45	9	5	0.801			
28. 12:17	496	46.67						
29. 12:24	510	48.83						
30. 12:30	523	50	10	5	0.809	35		
31. 2:01	536	51.67						
32. 2:11	550	53.33	11	3.33	0.815	...	.....	10 mm pressure
33. 2:19	562	55						
34. 2–26	575	56.67	12	3.33	0.820			
35. 2:32	590	58.33						
36. 2:38	604	60	13	3.33	0.825	42		
37. 2:44	619	61.67						
38. 2:50	633	63.33	14	3.33	0.829			
39. 2:56	649	65						
40. 3:02	664	66.67	15	3.33	0.835	50	33	
41. 3:08	682	68.33						
42. 3:14	698	70	16	3.33	0.840	59		
43. 3:21	714	71.67						
44. 3:28	732	73.33	17	3.33	0.846	72	36.5	
45. 3:37	750	75						
46. 3:44	768	76.67	18	3.33	0.851	87		
47. 3:51	784	78.33						
48. 3:57	812	80	19	3.33	0.857	107	42	
49. 4:03	836	81.67						
50. 4:07	870	83.33	20	3.33	0.865	132	46	1 mm pressure
51. 4:12	903	85	...	.....	.....	...	.....	Fast rate
52. 4:20	925	86.67	21	3.33	0.875	230	54	
53. 4:29	970	88.33						
54. 4:39	1025	90	22	3.33	0.884	...	70	Rate slow

Blend Data

55.			23	10	0.895	...	178	Residue
56. (36 cc, No. 23; 12 cc, each No. 22, 21, and 20)...................			24	20	.....	...	100	Blend
57. (21 cc, No. 23; 7 cc, each No. 22– 17, incl.)....................			25	30	.....	...	62	Blend
58. (15 cc, No. 23; 5 cc, each No. 22– 11, incl.)....................			26	50	.....	...	42	Blend

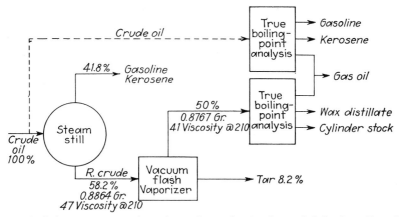

Fig. 4-27. Laboratory processing scheme for evaluating heavy-lubricating-oil stocks.

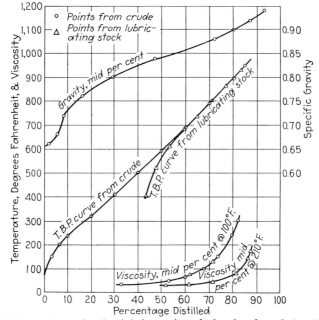

Fig. 4-28. Curves for evaluating lubricants in a dark-colored stock (see Fig. 4-27).

such laboratory data, consider some yields obtained from the crude oil shown in Figs. 4-28 and 4-29. Actual yields were 39.5 per cent of 69 viscosity at 100°F wax distillate, 0.8654 gravity; and 10.5 per cent of 146 viscosity at 210°F cylinder stock, 0.923 gravity. Computed from the curves, these yields are 40.2 per cent and 10.7 per cent respectively. Numerous other data are available, and with few exceptions the yields by these evaluation methods are as dependable as the foregoing.

The preceding method of evaluation is conducted with a minimum of decomposition, and hence the yields are the maximum that may be expected. If the designer expects to get such yields in a commercial plant, the plant must be properly designed and operated. Many poorly designed or carelessly operated plants fail to give the maximum yields, but other plants produce even larger yields than indicated by the evaluation.*

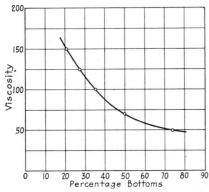

FIG. 4-29. Viscosity yield curve for heart-cut lube stocks which terminate at 91.8 per cent of the charge stock shown in Fig. 4-28.

Treating and Dewaxing. These operations are always troublesome. Most refinery laboratories have conducted hundreds of laboratory treats, but usually the results do not check plant operations. The treating of light distillates, such as pressure-still distillate and kerosene, is most successful, but even in these the color seldom checks with the color of the plant product and the losses in the laboratory are large. However, by conducting a large number of treats over a period of years, it is possible to say whether or not a stock can be successfully treated in the plant, even though the laboratory and plant results do not check.

Light oils, such as gasoline and pressure distillate, are usually treated in the laboratory by placing the sample in a bottle or jug and agitating it with sulfuric acid for 10 to 20 min. The sludge is allowed to settle for several hours and is separated by decantation or by means of a separatory funnel. The settling time is sometimes shortened by centrifuging the "acid" oil for 2 or 3 min at a speed of 1,500 rpm. The oil is then neutralized with caustic soda and washed with water. Treated pressure distillate must be distilled with steam or in a vacuum. The temperature is not allowed to exceed about 225°F during the distillation. If many treats are conducted, special glass or iron stills may be built. These are usually of the batch type. An equipment for redistillation is discussed by Dailey, Meier, and Shaffer,[40] and a comparison of laboratory and plant results is given. A continuous-treating apparatus for light distillates is described by Zublin.[41]

---

* The author has seen a modern vacuum plant produce 18 per cent of 200 viscosity at 210°F bright stock, whereas only 10 per cent was previously manufactured by residual methods. This yield was 0.5 per cent more than indicated by the analysis.

[40] Correlate Plant and Laboratory Procedures for Distilling Acid Treated Cracked Naphtha, *Oil Gas J.*, May 3, 1934, p. 11.

[41] Continuous Treating of Oils in the Laboratory, *Oil Gas J.*, November, 1932.

The laboratory treatment of lubricating oil stocks cannot be so easily systematized. However, Weir, Houghton, and Majewski[42] have developed a standard method of treating lubricating oil stocks. The oil is measured directly into a 100-cc centrifuge tube, and acid is added from a small graduated pipette. The tube is stoppered and shaken either by hand or in a mechanical shaking device. The shaker can be placed in a heated cabinet if the treating is to be conducted at a high temperature. The time for shaking ranges from 10 min for diluted samples to 40 or 60 min for viscous oils. Next the sludge and "pepper" sludge are removed by centrifuging the tube for about 1 hr at 1,500 rpm. The sour oil is then neutralized with ammonia gas, caustic soda, or contact clay.

Most laboratories finish their lubricating oils by contact treatment with fuller's earth. Contacting is usually conducted on oils that have been treated with acid or "acid-stage" oils. About 10 per cent by weight, or less, of 200-mesh fuller's earth is mixed with the oil and heated to 450°F for about 10 min. For neutral oils a temperature of 300°F may be used. The mixture is agitated with steam or by a shaking device, and better color is obtained if the surface of the oil is protected from the air by a blanket of steam or inert gas. The clay is then filtered from the oil, while hot, by means of a Büchner funnel connected to a vacuum system.

Lubricating oil stocks are frequently diluted to allow more intimate mixing, to facilitate settling of the sludge, and to hasten filtration of the contacted oil. The material, usually naphtha, that is used as a diluent must be removed by distillation. Steam or a vacuum may be used, and the temperature should be kept as low as possible.

The dewaxing of oil in the laboratory is also a troublesome operation. A common method is to dilute the oil (about 3 to 1) and chill it in packed ice and salt to about 30°F, below the desired pour point. About 1 oz of filter aid per 100 cc of oil is added, and the mixture is filtered through a Büchner funnel provided with an ice-packed jacket and a cover. A vacuum is applied to the filter. A convenient method of chilling the oil is to use an ice-cream freezer. Filter leaves are also widely used. These are constructed of very fine mesh monel-metal screen and connected to a receiver and vacuum pump. Laboratory methods of dewaxing are troublesome because filtration occurs so slowly, because a low temperature is hard to maintain, and because a low pour point is difficult to obtain.

Davis and Campbell[43] have developed a systematic method of studying wax distillate in the laboratory to determine its pressing characteristics. The examination consists of a vacuum distillation at 40 mm pressure, a

[42] Control of Color of Petroleum Oils by Acid Treating, *Ref. Nat. Gaso. Mfr.*, December, 1930, p. 89.

[43] Laboratory Control of the Quality of Paraffin Distillate, *Oil Gas J.*, May 25, 1933, p. 49.

determination of the viscosity at 100°F, and an examination of the crystal formation with a microscope. Their data indicate that material boiling up to about 650°F at 40 mm pressure can be successfully incorporated in a wax stock. This corresponds to a temperature of about 885°F at 760 mm pressure.

Corrosivity. Sulfur compounds and salt or brine are the major sources of corrosion in refineries although high-temperature oxidation and the low-temperature rusting of iron are also significant. Total sulfur is of some significance, but severe corrosion has been encountered[44] with crude oils that contain only 0.11 to 0.2 per cent sulfur. Almost universally, oils that are classified as "sour" (containing dissolved hydrogen sulfide)[16] prove to be corrosive. In the lowest sulfur (0.1 to 0.2 per cent) "sour" oils, however, the corrosion is only moderately severe. Likewise, some relatively high-sulfur oils (0.38 to 0.85 per cent) are only mildly corrosive.[44] Nevertheless, United States crude oils that contain over 0.5 per cent sulfur usually cause troublesome corrosion. Several laboratory test methods have been devised[44,45] for judging the corrosive nature of a crude oil. One method[44] exposes a steel specimen to the crude oil at a high temperature to measure the corrosion, and others[44,45] measure the evolution of hydrogen sulfide and hydrochloric acid[45] at high temperatures.

EVALUATION OF PRODUCTS

The laboratory products of greatest interest are the same ones as those examined in Chap. 3, and that chapter should be read along with the discussion that follows because the specifications and performance characteristics will not be repeated here. Means of approximating the properties of products will be discussed, and although these methods are not precise, they permit the designer to judge the effectiveness of a proposed operation or simple design before large laboratory expenses are incurred.

In addition, very many basic properties can be determined from the Characterization Factors and boiling points of the products (see Fig. 5-9 and Table 4-1).

Sulfur in Products. The average amount of sulfur in straight-run products is related to the amount of sulfur in the parent crude oil as indicated[46] in Figs. 4-30 to 4-34 for crude oils of the United States, California,

[44] Cataldi, Askevold, and Harnesberger, *Oil Gas J.*, July 20, 1953, p. 100.
[45] Davis, Jones, and Neilson, *Oil Gas J.*, May 26, 1938. Also Samuelson, G. J., *Pet. Engr.*, December, 1954, p. C-31.
[46] Nelson, Thery, and Cordero, *Proc. Fourth World Pet. Congr.*, sec. V, Rome, June, 1955.

West Texas, Venezuela and the Middle East.[47] Conventional oils from Kansas, Oklahoma, Texas, Illinois, Colorado, Kentucky, Ohio, and Pennsylvania are shown in Fig. 4-30 whereas the high-sulfur United

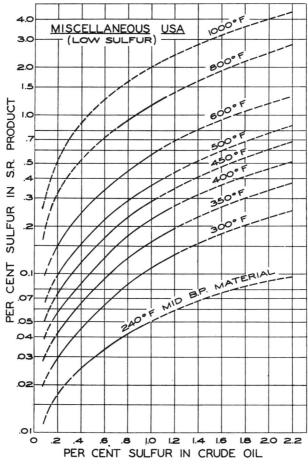

FIG. 4-30. Percentage of sulfur in straight-run U.S. products shown as a function of the percentage of sulfur in low-sulfur U.S. crude oils (excluding oils from West Texas, Mississippi, California, Michigan, and Wyoming). (*Proc. Fourth World Pet. Congr., Rome.*)

States oils are shown in Figs. 4-31 and 4-32. Variations in the original data are large, but the sulfur content usually agrees with the average values found from the figures.

Likewise, the average sulfur content[46] of cracked products can be estimated from Figs. 4-35 to 4-38. Scant information shows that the

[47] Over 1,800 sets of data were correlated, using over 120 references.

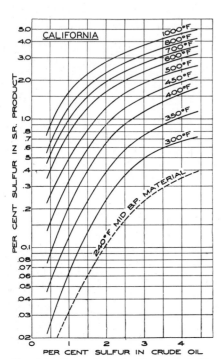

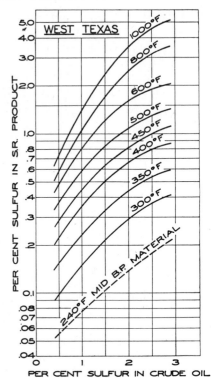

Fig. 4-31. Percentage of sulfur in straight-run California products as a function of the percentage of sulfur in the parent crude oil. (*Proc. Fourth World Pet. Congr., Rome.*)

Fig. 4-32. Percentage of sulfur in straight-run West Texas products as a function of the percentage of sulfur in the parent crude oil. (*Proc. Fourth World Pet. Congr., Rome.*)

ratio of sulfur per cent in cracked residual fuel oil to the percentage of sulfur in the charge stock is approximately as follows:[46]

Miscellaneous (Mid Continent, Illinois, etc.)......... 0.7
West Texas and Panhandle Texas.................. 1.25–1.5
Middle East..................................... 1.33*
Venezuela....................................... 1.5
Wyoming.. 1.8

* Probably should be 1.6 or higher because most data were for exceedingly mild cracking conditions.

The data underlying Figs. 4-35 to 4-38 were adequate except the data on Mexican cracked gasoline (Fig. 4-35) which applies mainly to Panuco and Poza Rica crude oils. Much of the original work on the sulfur content of cracked products was conducted by Fowle and Bent,[48] and their work underlies much of the data shown in Figs. 4-36 and 4-38.

[48] Where Does the Sulfur Go? *Pet. Refiner,* November, 1947, p. 87.

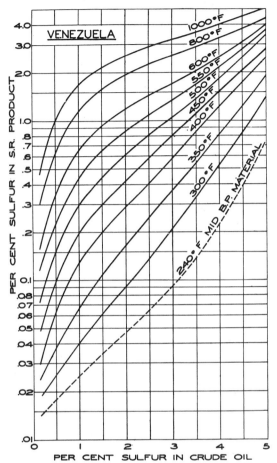

Fig. 4-33. Percentage of sulfur in straight-run Venezuelan products as a function of the percentage of sulfur in the parent crude oil. (*Proc. Fourth World Pet. Congr., Rome.*)

The amount of sulfur in petroleum cokes can be judged from Table 4-11.

Flash Point. The approximate relationship between flash point and 0 to 10 per cent boiling range (°F) is:[49]

$$\text{For distilled fractions} = 0.64T - 100 \qquad (4\text{-}6a)$$

$$\text{For crude oils} = 0.57T - 110 \qquad (4\text{-}6b)$$

More precise but much more complicated relationships have been devised.[50,51] Width of boiling range has also some effect on the flash

[49] Nelson, W. L., *Oil Gas J.*, Mar. 2, 1944, p. 72, and Nov. 17, 1945, p. 284.

[50] Van Winkle, M., *Pet. Refiner*, November, 1954, p. 171.

[51] Butler et al., The Prediction of the Flash Point of Middle Distillates, Cincinnati ACS Meeting, Apr. 4–7, 1955.

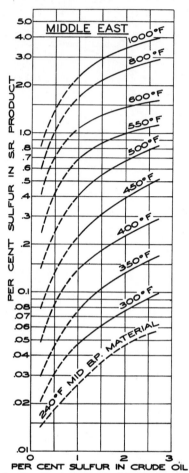

FIG. 4-34. Percentage of sulfur in straight-run Middle East products as a function of the percentage of sulfur in the parent crude oil. (*Proc. Fourth World Pet. Congr., Rome.*)

point (see Fig. 4-49). The flash point of blends is not a linear function of the flash points of the two agents but is related[52] as indicated in Fig. 4-39. The line in Fig. 4-39 for materials whose flash points are 300°F apart is the experimental result of Haidar Ali Ahmed,[53] and the other lines check well with experimental data as well as the work of Daigle and Stripling[54] on lubricating oils. At the flash or inflammability temperature the vapor pressure of the material is about as follows:

[52] Nelson, W. L., *Oil Gas J.*, June 14, 1951, p. 108.
[53] Correlation of the Flash Point . . . , Master's thesis, University of Tulsa, 1949.
[54] Evaluating Coastal Type Crudes . . . , *Pet. Processing*, March, 1949, p. 286.

Very volatile materials........................ 20 mm
Gasolines..................................... 14 mm
Kerosenes, distillates, and residual fuels........ 5 mm
Lubricating oils.............................. 1 mm

Altitude has the effect of mildly reducing the flash point[55] and conversely, pressure increases the flash point.[56]

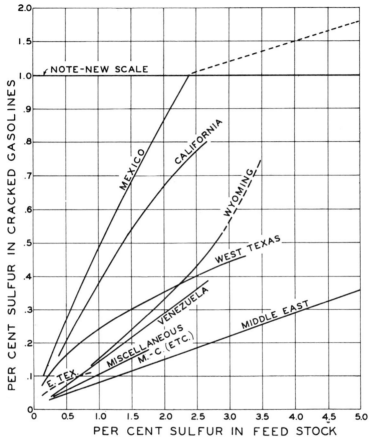

FIG. 4-35. Percentage of sulfur in thermally cracked gasolines vs. percentage of sulfur in various feedstocks. (*Proc. Fourth World Pet. Congr., Rome.*)

Vapor Pressure. No short-cut method of predicting vapor pressures has been devised except in connection with gasoline. The Reid vapor pressure of gasolines in the range of 8–14 R.V.P.ᐧ is about the same as (or a little higher than) the percentage of butanes in the gasoline. Thus, an 8-pound gasoline contains about 6.6 per cent butanes,

[55] Nelson, W. L., *Oil Gas J.*, Dec. 13, 1951, p. 108.
[56] Ormandy and Craven, *J. Inst. Pet. Technol.*, **8**, 145 (1922).

TABLE 4-11. SULFUR CONTENT OF A FEW PETROLEUM COKES

Feed material	API	S%	Coke, S%	S% in Coke / S% in Feed
Elk Basin, Wyo.—pitch............	2.5	3.5	6.5	1.83
Hawkins, Tex.—pitch.............	4.5	4.5	7.0	1.55
Kuwait—pitch..................	6.0	5.37	10.8	2.01
Various—pitches................	6.0[a]	4.0	5–6+	1.2–1.5+
Athabasca (Canada) tar sand oil....	7.3	5.3	5.65	1.06
West Texas—asphalt.............	.....	3.5	3.06	0.875
West Texas—cracked fuel.........	.....	2.94	3.06	1.04
Boscan (Vene.)—crude............	10.0	5.0	5.0	1.0
Boscan (Vene.)—asphalt..........	.....	5.1	5.0	0.98
Boscan (Vene.)—cracked fuel......	.....	6.45	5.0	0.775
East Texas—reduced crude........	10.5	1.26	2.57	2.04
East Texas—asphalt.............	.....	1.8	1.35–1.86	0.75–1.03
South Louisiana mixture..........	13.2	0.9	1.4	1.55
Texas Panhandle—vacuum bottoms.	18.9	0.6	0.6	1.00

[a] Approximate.

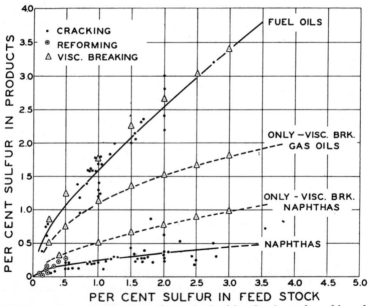

FIG. 4-36. Percentage of sulfur in products obtained by the thermal cracking of West Texas feedstocks. (*Proc. Fourth World Pet. Congr., Rome.*)

and 12 to 14 pound gasolines about 14 per cent butanes. A study[57] of over 2,500 gasolines has resulted in a remarkably accurate chart correlation between the ASTM 5 and 20 per cent evaporation temperatures and the Reid vapor pressure.

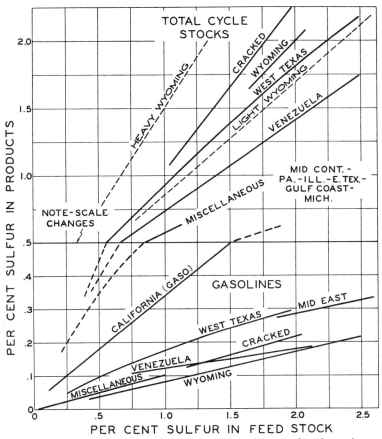

Fig. 4-37. Percentage of sulfur in catalytic cracked gasolines and cycle stocks vs. percentage of sulfur in various feedstocks. (*Proc. Fourth World Pet. Congr., Rome.*)

The vapor pressure of mixtures can be computed accurately by summing the product of the mole fraction times the true vapor pressure, for each component in the blend. However, true rather than Reid vapor pressures must be employed, and the accuracy of correlation between the two kinds of vapor pressures is not good (see Table 4-12).[58] For crude oils, the relationship is even more[58] erratic, the true vapor pressure

[57] Trimble and Richardson, *Ref. Nat. Gaso. Mfr.*, December, 1935, p. 562.
[58] Nelson, W. L., *Oil Gas J.*, June 21, 1954, p. 179.

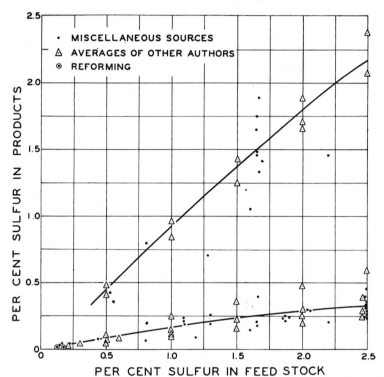

FIG. 4-38. Percentage of sulfur in gasolines and cycle stocks obtained by the catalytic cracking of West Texas feedstocks. (*Proc. Fourth World Pet. Congr., Rome.*)

being 1 to 9.75 times larger than the Reid vapor pressures. This situation arises because evaporation of the highest-vapor-pressure materials tends to occur during the Reid test, leaving a residue in the bomb of lower vapor pressure than the sample. Average ratios of the vapor pressures are about as follows:

	Ratio of true to Reid v.p.	
	Average	Range
Crude oils—low v.p.................	4.52	(1.67 to 10.0)
Crude oils—4–12 v.p................	1.72	(1.0 to 3.2)
Hydrocarbons, bottle gas, etc..........	1.40	(1.17 to 1.6)
Natural gasoline....................	1.085	(1.03 to 1.14)
Gasolines.........................	1.07	(1.03 to 1.45)

Gravity. API (or specific) gravity is usually reported as part of a crude oil or product analysis, and hence no short-cut methods of estima-

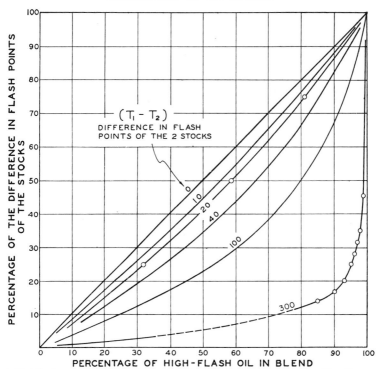

FIG. 4-39. Flash point of blends in terms of the flash points of the two blending stocks. (*Oil Gas J.*)

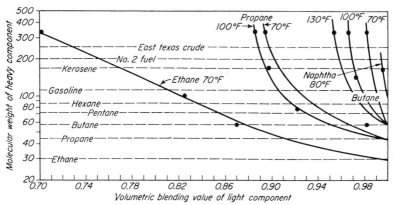

FIG. 4-40. Volumetric blending values of hydrocarbons. (*Pet. Processing.*)

TABLE 4-12. APPROXIMATE RELATIONSHIP BETWEEN THE TRUE AND
REID VAPOR PRESSURES OF MISCELLANEOUS VOLATILE PRODUCTS

Product	Vapor pressure		Ratio $\frac{True}{Reid}$
	Reid	True	
Bottle gas.................	52.0	83.1	1.60
Bottle gas.................	51.0	59.7	1.17
Natural gasoline...........	24.0	26.2	1.09
Natural gasoline...........	22.5	24.2	1.075
Natural gasoline...........	22.0	23.8	1.08
Natural gasoline...........	20.4	22.2	1.088
Natural gasoline...........	20.0	21.8	1.09
Natural gasoline...........	19.7	20.3	1.030
Natural gasoline...........	18.8	19.7	1.048
Natural gasoline...........	18.4	20.1	1.092
Natural gasoline...........	18.3	20.1	1.098
Natural gasoline...........	18.3	20.0	1.093
Natural gasoline...........	18.0	19.5	1.08
Light gasoline.............	18.0	20.0	1.11[a]
Natural gasoline...........	17.8	20.3	1.14
Natural gasoline...........	16.0	17.5	1.09
Light gasoline.............	16.0	17.8	1.11[a]
Light gasoline.............	14.0	15.4	1.10[a]
Natural gasoline...........	14.0	15.3	1.09
Light gasoline.............	12.0	12.9	1.07[a]
Natural gasoline...........	12.0	12.9	1.07
Gasoline...................	10.0	10.4	1.04[a]
Straight-run gasoline.......	8.3	9.7	1.17
Gasoline...................	8.0	8.3	1.04[a]
Gasoline...................	6.0	6.3	1.05[a]
Refinery gasoline..........	5.9	7.2	1.16
Gasoline...................	5.0	5.2	1.04[a]
Aviation gasoline..........	4.2	6.1	1.45[b]
Gasoline...................	4.0	4.2	1.05[a]
Gasoline...................	3.0	3.1	1.03[a]
Gasoline...................	2.0	2.1	1.05[a]

[a] API—"Evaporation Loss of Petroleum from Storage Tanks."
[b] Not representative of aviation gasolines.

tion are needed. However, if only the Characterization Factor or general type of material is known, the specific (or API) gravity can be computed from Eq. (4-1).

In mixing oils heavier than the lowest-boiling naphthas, no significant change in the total arithmetic volume of the two components occurs, and the specific gravity of the mixtures is exactly what would be expected from the proportions used in the mixtures. However, the API gravity of mixtures does not behave as an additive function because API gravity is not a linear function of specific gravity [see Eq. (3-1)]. When adding very light liquid hydrocarbons such as butane to heavier oils, a shrinkage[59,60] in volume occurs as indicated in Fig. 4-40. Light liquids are

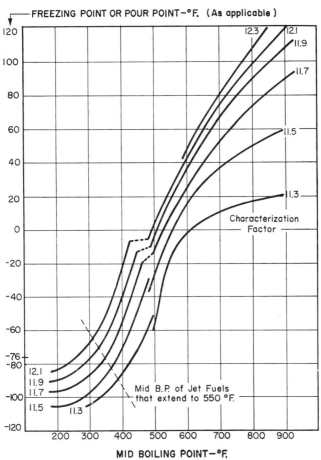

FIG. 4-41. Indication of the effect of boiling range on the pour point or the freezing point. (*Oil Gas J.*)

often transported in pipelines along with crude oil,[60] and the decrease in volume is significant.

Pour and Freezing Points. Congealing temperatures cannot be estimated with accuracy because none of the common methods of classifying materials such as Characterization Factor, Correlation Index, aniline

[59] Reeves, E. J., *Pet. Processing*, April, 1954, p. 478; and *Pet. Refiner*, June, 1954, p. 137.

[60] Childress and Grove, *Oil Gas J.*, Nov. 21, 1955, p. 178.

point, etc., disclose whether or not the material consists of the symmetrical types (ring or straight chain)[61] of hydrocarbons that cause high freezing points. Nevertheless, Fig. 4-41 is an approximation which is usually accurate within the following limits:

Average deviation,
plus or minus

Jet fuels......................	20°F
Diesel or distillate fuels...........	10°F
Lube oils (800°F mid bp)..........	25°F

Pour points are usually lower than freezing points,[62] but exceptions have been encountered. In the jet fuel range, based mainly on the work of Frank Tsai,[63] 2 samples out of 107 deviated by more than 60°F (one high and one low), and 10 samples deviated by more than 40°F. In the diesel fuel range, the accuracy is better with only 15 in more than 300 samples[62] deviating by more than 15°F. Likewise, in the lube-oil range, about 13 of 165 samples deviated by more than 40°F.

The pour point of blends is normally higher than would be expected from the amounts and pour points of the materials that are mixed. However, trace amounts of asphaltenes or natural inhibitive agents found in cracked residues or highly naphthenic crude oil residues sometimes cause the pour point of such mixtures to act in the reverse manner.[63a] Note that pour points are lower than the pour points of either of the base stocks in several of the following blends:

Percentage of thermal-cracked residuum[a]	Pour point, °F	Viscosity, Universal, at 100°F
0	−40	38
15	−74	45
25	−80	49
50	−65	76
60	−40	126
80	4	
100	60	3,500

[a] The other blending stock was thermal cracked distillate.

Normal stocks behave as indicated by Fig. 4-42, suggested by Reid and Allen.[64] In their method a so-called "Blending Index" is employed (see Example 4-9).

[61] Nelson, W. L., *Oil Gas J.*, May 11, 1953, p. 141.
[62] Nelson, W. L., *Oil Gas J.*, Jan. 31, 1955, p. 269.
[63] Freezing Point Correlation of Jet Fuels, Master's thesis, University of Tulsa, 1953.
[63a] Nelson, W. L., *Oil Gas J.*, Nov. 24, 1949, p. 146.
[64] Estimating Pour Points of Petroleum Distillate Blends, *Pet. Refiner*, May, 1951, p. 93.

Example 4-9.   Find the Pour Point of a Blend of the Stocks Shown in Table 4-13.
The indices of the three stocks are read from Fig. 4-42.   After determining the volumetric average index and boiling point (see Table 4-13) of the blend, namely, 6.8 and 530°F, the pour point is found on Fig. 4-42 to be about plus 2°F.

TABLE 4-13. ILLUSTRATION[a] OF EXAMPLE 4-9

Stock	% in blend	Pour point	ASTM 50% temp, °F
A	25	+30	610
B	40	0	550
C	35	−60	450

The index of the blend is found as follows:

Stock	Per cent	Index	Fractional index
A	25	17	4.25
B	40	5.6	2.24
C	35	0.87	0 31
		Index of blend	6.80

The 50% temperature of the blend is:

Stock	Per cent	50% temp, °F	Fractional 50% temp, °F
A	25	610	152
B	40	550	220
C	35	450	158
	50% blend temperature		530

[a] Reid and Allen, Estimating Pour Points . . . , *Pet. Refiner*, May, 1951, p. 93.

Viscosity.   The general range of viscosity of petroleum products is indicated in Fig. 4-43, and the properties of the oils of Fig. 4-43 are shown in Table 4-14.   The figure must be used with caution because the slope of the lines is a function of the Viscosity Index of the oil, and thus several lines can occur for oils that have the same viscosity at some reference temperature such as 100°F or 210°F.

Viscosity is not an additive property.   When mixing one volume of 500-viscosity oil with one volume of 100-viscosity (at the same temperature) oil, the resultant blend does not have a viscosity of 300, but about 200 (imagine a line connecting 500 on the left scale of Fig. 4-44 with 100 on the right scale and read at 50 per cent).   The commonly accepted method of predicting viscosities is that of the ASTM[65] and the use of the method is almost self-evident in Fig. 4-44 which shows a line of the viscosities of mixtures of a 200,000-viscosity pitch and a 34-viscosity cutter or dilution stock.   The viscosities of the two blending stocks

[65] Petroleum Products and Lubricants, D341, ASTM, 1916 Race St., Philadelphia, Pa.   Four large charts, low and high range, for Universal and for Kinematic viscosity may be purchased.   The 0–100°F part of the temperature scale is used as 0–100 per cent of blending agent.

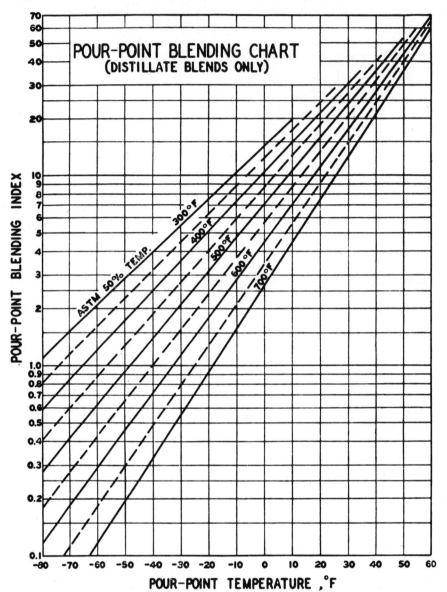

FIG. 4-42. Pour-point blending chart for distillate materials.   (*Pet. Refiner.*)

TABLE 4-14. OILS USED IN PREPARING FIG. 4-43

No.	Kind or type of oil	Saybolt viscosity		API
1	Natural gasoline			76.5
2	Gasoline			57.0
3	Water			10.0
4	Kerosene			42.0
5	Distillate	37 at 100°F		35.0
6	Average light crude oil[a]	33 at 100°F		48.0
7	Average crude oil[a]	40 at 100°F		40.0
8	Average crude oil[a]	50 at 100°F		35.6
9	Average heavy crude oil[a]	60 at 100°F		32.6
10	Salt Creek, Wyo., crude oil[b]	40 at 100°F		36.4
11	ASTM Fuel 3 (max viscosity)	45 at 100°F		26.0
12	ASTM Fuel 5 (min viscosity)	50 at 100°F		15.0
13	SAE 10W lube	10,000 at 0°F	200 at 100°F	31.0
14	SAE 20W lube	40,000 at 0°F	320 at 100°F	29.0
15	Thin SAE 10 lube (100 V.I.)	90 at 130°F	160 at 100°F	30.0
16	Thin SAE 10 lube (0. V.I.)	90 at 130°F	180 at 100°F	27.0
17	Thin SAE 30 lube (100 V.I.)	255 at 130°F	70 at 210°F	26.0
18	Thin SAE 30 lube (0 V.I.)	255 at 130°F	58 at 210°F	21.0
19	ASTM Fuel 5 (max viscosity) or Fuel 6 (min viscosity)	40 at 122°F[c]	800 at 100°F	11.0
20	Average SAE 50 lube (100 V.I.)	90 at 210°F	986 at 100°F	25.0
21	Average SAE 50 lube (0. V.I.)	90 at 210°F	2,115 at 100°F	19.0
22	Thick SAE 70 lube (100 V.I.)	150 at 210°F		23.0
23	Thick SAE 70 lube (0 V.I.)	150 at 210°F		
24	ASTM Fuel 6:			
	Bunker C (max)	300 at 122°F[c]		8.0
	M.C. residuum	300 at 210°F		19.8
25	Asphalt	50 penetration		

[a] Mid Continent, Illinois, California, and most other crude oils.

[b] Example of several Wyoming and Texas crude oils which have maximum change in viscosity.

[c] Furol viscosity—all others are Universal.

must be at the same temperature. However, the ASTM method is accurate only when blending oils that have similar Viscosity Indexes. M. Rahmes,[66] after having blended 30 widely varying sets of components in several proportions, and after having examined 12 prediction methods, concluded that the Wright method[67] was the most dependable.

The Wright method, as illustrated in Fig. 4-45, utilizes the standard ASTM viscosity chart[65] but in a way different from the method recom-

[66] Rahmes and Nelson, *Anal. Chem.*, **20,** 912 (1948); also Master's thesis, University of Tulsa, 1947.

[67] Prediction of Oil Viscosity . . . , Pet. Division, ACS Meeting, Atlantic City, Apr. 8–12, 1946, p. 71.

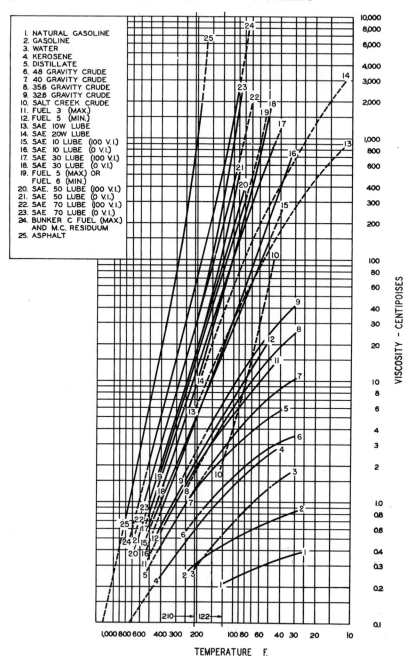

1. NATURAL GASOLINE
2. GASOLINE
3. WATER
4. KEROSENE
5. DISTILLATE
6. 48 GRAVITY CRUDE
7. 40 GRAVITY CRUDE
8. 35.6 GRAVITY CRUDE
9. 32.6 GRAVITY CRUDE
10. SALT CREEK CRUDE
11. FUEL 3 (MAX.)
12. FUEL 5 (MIN.)
13. SAE 10W LUBE
14. SAE 20W LUBE
15. SAE 10 LUBE (100 V.I.)
16. SAE 10 LUBE (0 V.I.)
17. SAE 30 LUBE (100 V.I.)
18. SAE 30 LUBE (0 V.I.)
19. FUEL 5 (MAX.) OR
    FUEL 6 (MIN.)
20. SAE. 50 LUBE (100 V.I.)
21. SAE 50 LUBE (0 V.I.)
22. SAE 70 LUBE (100 V.I.)
23. SAE 70 LUBE (0 V.I.)
24. BUNKER C FUEL (MAX.)
    AND M.C. RESIDUUM
25. ASPHALT

VISCOSITY – CENTIPOISES

TEMPERATURE F.

Fig. 4-43. Approximate relation between viscosity and temperature for the typical products of Table 4-14.   (*Oil Gas J.*)

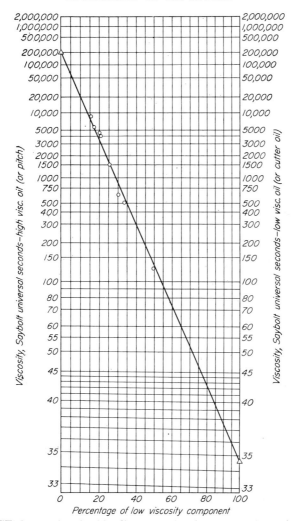

Fig. 4-44. ASTM-type viscosity-blending chart showing one set of experimental blends.

mended by the ASTM. The viscosity curves of the two oils are plotted on the standard chart by experimental data on the oils at two temperatures or by noting the general Viscosity Index properties of the oils. Distances along the horizontal line of the same viscosity as that of the desired blend are measured and used in the following manner to obtain the percentage of each oil that should be used in the blend. Refer to Fig. 4-45.

$$\text{Per cent of oil } B = 100 \, \frac{MO}{MN}$$

Also, the viscosity-temperature line of the blend will lie between the lines for the two blending stocks in such a way that

$$\frac{MO}{MN} = \frac{PR}{PQ} = \text{etc.}$$

Example 4-10. Blending Lubricating Oils. A high-viscosity oil (B) of 100 sec at 210°F. Saybolt Universal viscosity is to be blended with a 200 sec at 100°F oil (A) to produce a blend having a viscosity of 400 sec at 100°F. The curves for oils A and B can be drawn by knowledge of their Viscosity Indexes (Fig. 4-2). The percentage of Oil B to use in the blends is found by measuring distances along the 400-viscosity line

$$100 \, \frac{MO}{MN} = \frac{100 \times 0.64}{1.54} = 41.5 \text{ per cent}$$

The limited usefulness of the ASTM method is clearly evident from this example. Note that when the oils of this example are blended by the use of Fig. 4-44 (ASTM method), the amounts of low-viscosity component required, rather than being 58.5 per cent, are

Blending at 100°F   50%
Blending at 210°F   55%

The viscosity of an oil at various temperatures can be determined by plotting a line on ASTM viscosity paper.[65] Experimental determinations at two temperatures serve to define the straight line, or if the Viscosity Index is known, the viscosity at one temperature suffices. Figure 4-45 shows two such viscosity-temperature lines.

Viscosity Index is not an additive property, and the Index of mixtures can be estimated by plotting the temperature lines of the two components as in Fig. 4-45 and drawing the line for the blend. In Example 4-10, the Viscosity Index of Oil A is 73.3, Oil B is 113, and the 41.5 per cent blend has an Index of 97 rather than the 89.8 that is obtained by assuming that Viscosity Index is an additive property.

Gasolines or Naphthas. The approximate ASTM end points of T.B.P. cuts or fractions of gasolines can be estimated from Fig. 4-25, percentage of sulfur can be estimated from Figs. 4-30 to 4-38, and vapor pressures may be computed using Table 4-12.

The octane number (Motor method) of straight-run gasolines is related to Characterization Factor[68] somewhat as indicated in Table 4-15, but note particularly the wide variation in octane number. Boiling range and particularly the cut point also affect the octane number (see Tables 4-16 and 4-17). Each gasoline differs in its behavior, but the general

[68] Nelson, Thery, and Sahagun, "Venezuelan and Other World Crude Oils," Ministerio de Minas e Hidrocarburos, Caracas, Venezuela, 1952.

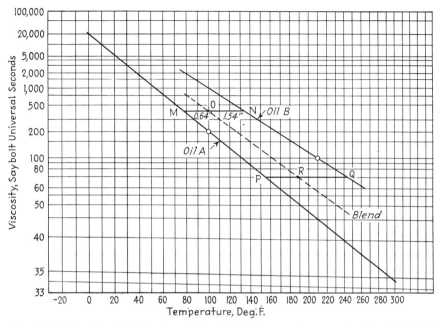

FIG. 4-45. Viscosity of oil blends and the effect of temperature on viscosity (Wright[67] method).

relationship[69,70] is indicated in Table 4-16 for gasolines from the same parent crude oil. The same relationship applies when cuts or fractions of gasolines[70] are considered as in Table 4-17, or in the following tabulation:[71]

Motor octane number for 360–400°F cuts of gasoline	Change in octane number per 100°F change in the 90% point
40	12.0
45	11.3
50	10.6
55	10.0
60	8.0
65	4.7

The average relationship between the Research and Motor method octane numbers is indicated in Table 3-3, and the lead susceptibilities of various types of gasolines are shown in Tables 3-11 and 3-12.

[69] Moxey, J. G., *Pet. Processing*, February, 1947, p. 92.
[70] Holaday and Heath, *SAE Quart. Trans.*, July, 1951, p. 429.
[71] Nelson, W. L., *Oil Gas J.*, Nov. 8, 1951, p. 332.

TABLE 4-15. APPROXIMATE RELATIONSHIP BETWEEN CHARACTERIZATION FACTOR
AND THE MOTOR METHOD[a] OCTANE NUMBER OF 400°F CUT POINT
STRAIGHT-RUN GASOLINES

Characterization Factor of gasoline	Octane number (M.M. clear)	Range of octane numbers
11.4	67	65–68
11.5	66	63–68
11.6	64.5	54–67
11.7	62.5	60–65
11.8	60	57–67
11.9	55	47–57
12.0	49	42–52
12.1	41.5	33–48
12.2	35.5	Low–43
12.3	31	Low–41

[a] Slightly lower than Research method numbers (see Table 3-3).

TABLE 4-16. MOTOR METHOD OCTANE NUMBERS AS A FUNCTION OF
MID BOILING POINT
Representative mid per cent curves

Mid bp, °F	Octane number, Motor method		
	Straight run	Thermally cracked	Catalytically cracked
75	81		
100	77	82	82
150	69	78	80
200	60	74	78.5
250	52	70.5	77
300	44	66.5	76
350	35	63	76
400	. . .	. . ..	75

When two materials are mixed, the high-octane material usually
behaves as if it had a higher octane number than obtained by laboratory
tests of the material. The higher octane number is referred to as the
"blending octane number." Blending octane numbers are apparently a
function of the difference in olefinic content of the two stocks,[72] but since
the olefinic content is not ordinarily available, a possibly less accurate
method[73] is illustrated herein.

[72] Schoen and Mrstik, *Ind. Eng. Chem.*, **47**, 1740 (1955).
[73] Nelson, W. L., *Oil Gas J.*, Sept. 19, 1955, p. 135.

TABLE 4-17. EFFECT OF 90 PER CENT POINT ON RESEARCH OCTANE NUMBER

ASTM 90% point, °F	Octane number, Research method				
	Straight run	Thermally cracked	Thermally reformed	Catalytically reformed	Catalytically cracked
240	77				
280	71	83	83	87	90
320	64	81	82	88	90
360	57	77	79	89	90
400	49	73	77	90	90
440	. . .	70	. . .	. . .	89

The blending octane number of the high-octane component or blending agent is defined as CN_a (clear or leaded) in which C is a factor (Fig. 4-46) for each particular pair of components, and N_a is the octane number (Motor or Research) of the high-octane blending agent. The blending octane number is then used in a regular additive-type equation

$$N = \frac{P_a(CN_a) + P_b(N_b)}{100} \tag{4-7}$$

in which N is the octane number of the blend, P_a and P_b are the respective volumetric percentages of the agent and base stock, and N_a and N_b are the respective octane numbers of the blending agent and the base stock. Variations in the value of C are large because of the inherent differences in gasolines, and in addition the factors are larger or smaller under the following conditions:

1. Slightly larger for Research octane numbers and slightly lower for Motor method numbers.
2. Larger when blending clear or lead-free components and smaller when the components are highly leaded (2 to 3 cc TEL).

Isomate gasoline when blended with catalytic reformate has a blending factor of about 1.09 (Research method).

Example 4-11. Two Component Blends. Forty per cent of thermally cracked gasoline of 77 octane number (Research) is to be blended with 60 per cent of 57 octane straight-run gasoline.

According to Fig. 4-46, the blending factor for thermally cracked gasoline at a concentration of 40 per cent is 1.033.

$$0.4 \times 1.033 \times 77 = 31.8$$
$$0.6 \times 57 = \underline{34.2}$$

Research octane blend 66.0

The octane number of the blend might be slightly lower (65.8) because the Research method of test was used.

In making up two plant blends from several components, two general rules are followed which tend to result in higher octane numbers or the use of smaller amounts of tetraethyllead:

1. Most of the lead should be used in the blend that contains the low-octane gasoline so that the good lead susceptibility of such materials can be fully utilized.
2. Part of the highest-blending-value stock such as (mainly) polymer should be used in each blend because of the high-blending value of such stocks when used in small amounts.

Difficulty is encountered in the use of the method for three or more components because it is necessary to estimate the blending factors of pairs of components not shown in Fig. 4-46. This can be best illustrated by an example.

Example 4-12. Octane Number of Entire Plant Gasoline. The gasolines available in one refinery are indicated in Table 4-18. The computation of the octane number of the entire plant gasoline is shown in Table 4-19. The factors for straight-run gasoline and the butanes is 1.0. Considering the thermal gasoline (15 per cent)

TABLE 4-18. PROPERTIES OF TYPICAL REFINERY BLENDING STOCKS[a]

	Per cent of total gasoline	Clear octane number		3cc TEL octane number	
		Motor	Research	Motor	Research
Butane..................	8.0	95	97	105	105
Straight-run...............	30.0	55	57	75	75
Thermal cracked...........	15.0	69	77	80	87
Catalytic cracked..........	38.0	80	91	85	97
Poly (catalytic)............	9.0	82	96	85.5	100

[a] *Oil Gas J.*, Sept. 19, 1955, p. 135.

TABLE 4-19. COMPUTATION OF CLEAR OCTANE NUMBER (RESEARCH) OF ENTIRE PLANT GASOLINE[a]

	Volumetric per cent	Clear (Res.) octane number	Blending factor	Partial octane number
Butanes..........	8	97	1.0	7.76
Straight-run.......	30	57	1.0	17.10
Thermal..........	15	77	1.06	12.25
Catalytic..........	38	91	1.055 (1.05 and 1.066)	36.40
Poly..............	9	96	1.055	9.12
Plant gasoline...	...	...	....	82.63

[a] *Oil Gas J.*, Sept. 19, 1955, p. 135.

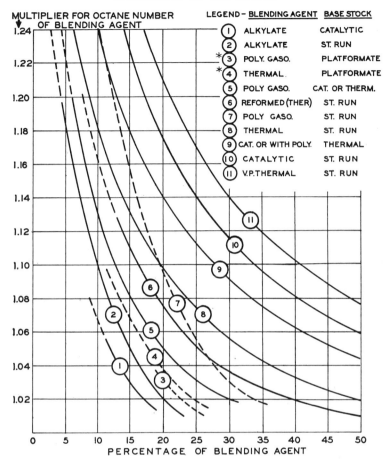

FIG. 4-46. Approximation for obtaining the blending octane numbers of high-octane components.

with respect to the butanes and straight-run (53 per cent total), the factor for thermal gasoline at 15/53 or 28.3 per cent is about 1.06. Likewise, considering 47 per cent of catalytic and poly gasoline together in the entire plant gasoline (100 per cent), a factor of 1.055 is selected (between curves 9 and 10 of Fig. 4-46).

By the use of a lead-susceptibility chart (Fig. 3-4) it is possible to assemble the gasoline stocks in various proportions to produce Regular and Premium Grades of gasoline.[73] Some blending proportions result in lead consumptions that are less than half the amounts required by other blending proportions.[73]

Platinum-catalyst-reformed gasoline exhibits a strange behavior. If the Research method of test is used, it behaves as a base stock as shown in curves 3 and 4 of Fig. 4-46, but if the Motor method is used, the

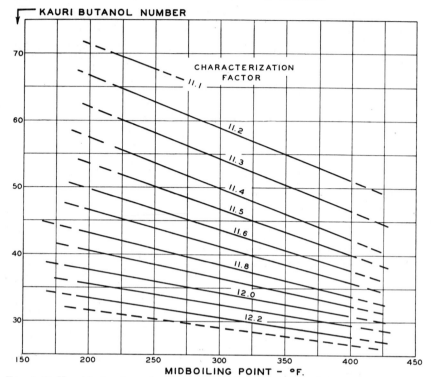

Fig. 4-47. Kauri butanol number (approximate) as a function of the mid boiling point and Characterization Factor. (*Oil Gas J.*)

behavior of the reformate is nearly the opposite, i.e., it becomes the blending agent.

Solvents. Perhaps the single most important property of a solvent is its ability to dissolve various resins, gum-like materials, oils, nitrocellulose lacquers, etc., and accordingly there are numerous solvency tests[74] of which the aniline point and kauri butanol number are the best known. The kauri butanol number[75] consists of ascertaining the volume of sample that will cause a standard solution of kauri gum in butyl alcohol to become so opaque that 10-point type is illegible when viewed through the solution. Similar tests[74] employ nitrocellulose and butyl or ethyl acetate solvents.

Although more than 200 sets of data were used in establishing the relationships[76] shown in Figs. 4-47 and 4-48 between kauri butanol number or aniline point (Fig. 4-48), Characterization Factor, and mid

[74] Nelson, W. L., *Oil Gas J.*, June 30, 1945, p. 117.
[75] Baldeschwieler et al., *Ind. Eng. Chem., Anal. Ed.*, **7**, 373 (1937).
[76] Nelson, W. L., *Oil Gas J.*, May 24, 1954, p. 271.

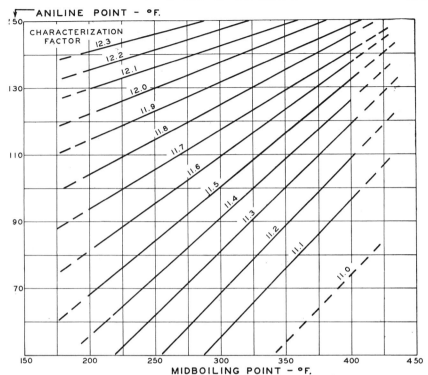

Fig. 4-48. Aniline point (approximate) of petroleum naphthas as related to the mid boiling point and type of oil. (*Oil Gas J.*)

boiling point, the relationships are not entirely satisfactory. The following equations suggested by Harvey and Mills[77] may be more accurate:
For K.B.N. below 50:

$$K.B.N. = 99.6 - 0.806G - 0.177A + 0.0755(340 - B) \quad (4\text{-}8a)$$

For K.B.N. above 50:

$$K.B.N. = 117.7 - 1.06G - 0.249A + 0.10(340 - B) \quad (4\text{-}8b)$$

In these, G refers to API gravity, A to aniline point (°F), and B to mid boiling point (°F).

The kauri butanol numbers of straight-run solvents seldom exceed 50, and a number above 40 is considered as good. However, even a number of 50 is not usually high enough to command a special price, and accordingly one must look to highly aromatic solvents for kauri butanol numbers approaching 100. Superior straight-run solvents (K.B.N. of 40) are nevertheless useful because when treated by solvent extraction they

[77] *Anal. Chem.*, **20**, 207 (1948).

yield larger amounts of the aromatic extracts that are suitable for high-solvency naphthas.

Jet Fuels. None of the current specifications of jet or turbine fuels are troublesome except the freezing point of minus 76°F. Inasmuch as the freezing points of hydrocarbons or mixtures thereof vary greatly depending on the symmetry of the molecules, a simple method of predicting the freezing point of jet or other distillate fuels may never be available. As an illustration, the ranges of freezing points of some of the hydrocarbons[78] found in jet fuels are shown in Table 4-20. Undoubtedly when more hydrocarbons are investigated, the range of freezing point will be even larger.

TABLE 4-20

Carbon atoms	Average, °F		Range of freezing point
	Boiling point	Freezing point	
5	90	−135	2 to −271
7	190	−115	−12 to −217
9	296	− 65	+68 to −198
11	384	− 61	−14 to −109
13	463	− 18	21 to − 58
15	528	+ 15	50 to − 19

Freezing points may be estimated from Fig. 4-41 within an average accuracy of plus or minus 20°F, although variations as great as 60°F were encountered in 2 of the 107 samples examined.[63] Although low Characterization Factor jet fuels have low freezing points, they are so viscous at low temperatures that they are not satisfactory as fuels. This is cared for, however, by the following gravity limitations of jet fuels:

Grade JP-1	35 API (minimum)
JP-2	45–63 API
JP-3	40–58 API
JP-4	35–40 API
JP-5	40–58 API

Thus, the jet fuel yield from a crude oil can be estimated by checking the freezing point on Fig. 4-41, checking the API gravity against current specifications, and starting the fuel at 130 to 150°F so that its vapor pressure is adequate. Sulfur is normally well below the 0.5 per cent specification limit, and the percentage of aromatics, bromine number, and smoke point are satisfactory unless cracked material is incorporated in the jet fuel. Somewhat more accurate predictions of freezing point may

[78] Nelson, W. L., *Oil Gas J.*, May 11, 1953, p. 141.

be made if jet fuels boiling to 500, 550, 600, and 650°F are prepared by a Hempel distillation,[79] but if such complete information is obtained there is little need of short-cut evaluation methods.

Smoke Volatility Index[80] is thought to be significant but it has not been completely investigated.[81] The relationship between smoke point and Characterization Factor appears to be much the same (slightly lower smoke points) as that shown for kerosene in Table 4-21, but the variations are larger. Scant information on the weight of carbon deposits in one type of reactor indicates the following:[81]

IP smoke point, mm	Approx. deposit, grams
10	8.0+
15	4.5
20	2.1
30	0.5
40	0.2

Kerosene and Illuminating Oils. The general characteristics of such oils may be estimated from Table 4-1, the ASTM boiling range by means of Fig. 4-25, and the percentage of sulfur from Figs. 4-30 to 4-34. Flash point is of major importance, and hence Fig. 4-49 is offered as an approximation and as an indication of the general effect of boiling range on flash point.[82] Here it is noted that the flash point of kerosenes taken after a 362°F end point gasoline ranges from about 146°F for a 10 per cent cut to even 180°F for a 30 per cent gas-oil cut. The kerosenes of Fig. 4-49 are more completely stripped than most commercial kerosenes or distillates, and the yields are therefore slightly high. Furthermore, it is advisable purposely to leave some low-boiling material in kerosene so that the wick of the lamp can be easily lighted.

Smoke point is an important property, and it may be estimated[83] from such properties as Characterization Factor, gravity, or even viscosity by means of Tables 4-21 and 4-22 or from hydrocarbon structure.[84] Viscosity assumes importance mainly because it is used in determining the so-called "Ring Number":

$$\text{Ring No.} = \frac{\text{thermoviscosity}}{5} - 10(46 - \text{API gravity}) \qquad (4\text{-}9)$$

[79] F. Tsai, Master's thesis, University of Tulsa, 1953, or Nelson, W. L., *Oil Gas J.*, Feb. 22, 1954, p. 197. Four sets of jet fuels from each of 17 crude oils were prepared and examined.

[80] S.V.I. = smoke point plus 0.42 times volume per cent boiling under 400°F.

[81] Kuhbach et al., *SAE Journal*, August, 1955, p. 64.

[82] Nelson, W. L., *Oil Gas J.*, Sept. 8, 1945, p. 119.

[83] Nelson, W. L., *Oil Gas J.*, June 14, 1954, p. 151.

[84] Russell, A. H., *Ind. Eng. Chem.*, **45**, 602 (1953).

Catalytically desulfurized distillates or kerosene from West Texas raw stocks[85] have smoke points that are a direct function of per cent hydrogen (smoke point = 25.5H − 317), and severe treatment results in a smoke point of 48.

TABLE 4-21. APPROXIMATE SMOKE POINTS AS A FUNCTION OF OTHER COMMON TESTS OR PROPERTIES FOR KEROSENE STOCKS HAVING A MID BOILING POINT OF 437°F[a]

Char. Factor	API gravity	Ring Number	Smoke point	
			IPT	Factor[b]
11.2	32.8	....	14.1	17
11.25	33.5	....	14.4	18
11.3	34.2	....	14.7	18
11.35	35.0	....	15.1	19
11.4	35.7	....	15.6	20
11.45	36.4	....	16.0	20
11.5	37.2	−45	16.5	21
11.55	37.9	−34	17.0	22
11.6	38.7	−24	17.5	23
11.65	39.4	−14	18.1	24
11.7	40.2	− 3	18.8	25
11.75	41.0	7	19.5	26
11.8	41.8	17	20.4	28
11.85	42.5	27	21.4	30
11.9	43.3	37	22.6	33
11.95	44.1	47	24.0	36
12.0	44.8	57	25.7	39
12.05	45.6	66	27.6	43
12.1	46.4	75	30.0	48
12.15	47.2	81	32.5	54
12.2	47.9	....	35.5	61
12.25	48.7	....	38.5	68
12.3	49.0	....	42.5	81

[a] Nelson, W. L., *Oil Gas J.*, June 14, 1954, p. 151.
[b] Smoke points by the Factor lamp are nearly the same as by the Indiana lamp.

Distillate and Diesel Fuels. Boiling range (Fig. 4-25), percentage of sulfur (Figs. 4-30 to 4-34), and flash point (Eq. 4-6a) may be estimated by conventional methods. Although distillates and diesel fuels (as well as cracking stocks) have much the same boiling range (400 up to even 700°F), aromatic and naphthenic hydrocarbons are tolerated in most distillate duels but are a detriment in diesel fuels. However, the paraffinic hydrocarbons of high Diesel Index (or cetane number) also have

[85] Zimmerschied et al., Improving Distillates by Hydrofining, *Pet. Refiner*, May, 1955, p. 153.

TABLE 4-22. RELATIONSHIP BETWEEN SAYBOLT THERMOVISCOSITY,
SAYBOLT UNIVERSAL VISCOSITY, AND KINEMATIC VISCOSITY,
ALL AT 60°F[a]

Saybolt thermoviscosity	Kinematic viscosity	Saybolt Universal viscosity
100	0.57	
150	0.91	
200	1.25	
250	1.58	
300	1.93	32.3
350	2.26	33.5
400	2.59	34.7
450	2.92	35.7
500	3.27	36.8
550	3.60	37.8
600	3.93	38.8
650	4.27	39.9
700	4.60	41.0

[a] Nelson, W. L., *Oil Gas J.*, June 14, 1954, p. 151.

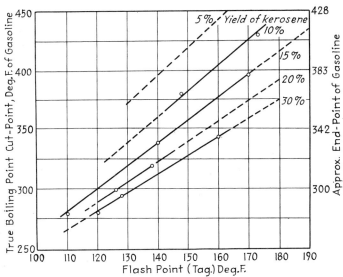

FIG. 4-49. Relation of Tag flash point of kerosenes to T.B.P. cut point of gasolines and the yield of kerosene. (*Oil Gas J.*)

high pour points, and accordingly, pour point usually becomes the factor that limits yield. Pour point may be judged from Fig. 4-41, but the relationships of Figs. 4-50 and 4-51 for commercial diesel fuels are more dependable.[86] Width of boiling range about a fixed mid boiling point has little effect on the pour point and no appreciable effect[86] on the Diesel Index, but lower-boiling fuels have lower pour points (Fig. 4-50) and higher Diesel Indexes (Fig. 4-51).

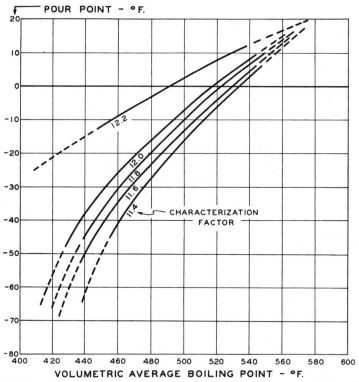

FIG. 4-50. Approximate relationship between mid boiling point, pour point, and Characterization Factor of commercial diesel fuels.   (*Oil Gas J.*)

Somewhat the same information is summarized in Tables 4-23 and 4-24 for world-competitive crude oils and for comparison with thermal and catalytic distillates.[87] Cracked stocks are mixed with straight-run stocks in as large proportions as possible without causing an unsatisfactory Diesel Index. The pour points of cracked distillates will be even lower than those of Tables 4-23 and 4-24 if they have been severely cracked. Additional information on the properties of catalytic cycle stocks is given in Tables 21-7 and 21-8.

[86] Nelson, W. L., *Oil Gas J.*, June 28, p. 132, and July 12, p. 118, 1954.
[87] Nelson, W. L., *Oil Gas J.*, Jan. 18, 1954, p. 117.

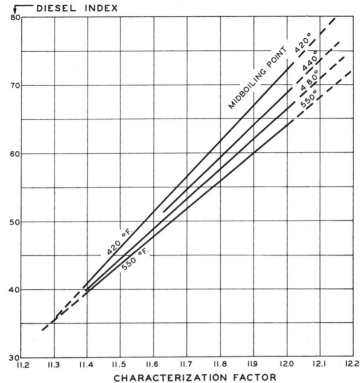

Fig. 4-51. Effect of volumetric average boiling point on the Diesel Index of diesel or distillate fuels. (*Oil Gas J.*)

TABLE 4-23. POUR POINTS, °F, OF DISTILLATE (OR DIESEL) FUEL OILS OF 550 MID BOILING POINT (400–700°F)[a]

Characterization Factor of feed stock or crude oil	Straight-run fuels							Catalytically cracked cycle stock	Thermally cracked distillates
	Misc. U.S.	Coastal	California	West Texas	Miss.	Vene.	Middle East		
11.0	....	−80							
11.2	−57	−60	−35	...	...	−50			
11.4	−10	−40	0	...	...	−30	...	−9	
11.6	3	....	17	2	31	−1	...	5	−16
11.8	10	....	....	7	42	7	10	11	4
12.0	16	....	....	11	...	....	18	15	17
12.2	24	....	....	...	...	....	25	21	

[a] *Oil Gas J.*, Jan. 18, 1954, p. 117.

TABLE 4-24. APPROXIMATE EFFECT OF BOILING RANGE ON THE POUR POINT OF DISTILLATE OR DIESEL FUELS[a]

Mid boiling point (°F)	Degrees above or below pour point at 550° F mid-point[b]	Straight-run				Catalytically cracked			Thermally cracked
		Vene-zuelan	Missis-sippi (heavy oils)	Misc. U.S.		11.4 C.F. of feed	11.8 C.F. of feed	12.2 C.F. of feed	
				11.6 C.F.	12.0 C.F.				
450	....	....	...	−60	−45	....	....	...	−30
500	−25	−26	...	−23	−6	−34	−14	−4	−10
550	0	−1	36	3	16	−9	11	21	4
600	21	20	57	18	36	12	32	42	16
650	40	39	76	35	52	31	51	61	
700	55	54	91	54	70	46	66	76	
750	67	....	103	....	85	58	78	88	

[a] *Oil Gas J.*, Jan. 18, 1954, p. 117.
[b] This approximate relationship appeared independently from studies of both straight-run and catalytically cracked stocks, but the pour point of thermally cracked stocks appears to be less affected by boiling range.

Methods of judging the burning quality of distillate fuel oils have not been standardized, but the performance[88] of one type of pot burner indicates the following general effect of the Characterization Factor (Worrall[88] did not state this relationship):

C.F.	Side deposits, g/2.5 gal	C.F.	Side deposits, g/2.5 gal
11.1	100	11.8	10
11.3	60	11.9	7
11.5	36	12.0	4
11.6	25	12.1	2
11.7	16		

The relationship is based on all types of stocks (straight-run and catalytic-cycle), and Worrall[88] described a 11.7 Characterization Factor oil as poor and one of 11.85 as good. Catalytically desulfurized West Texas distillate (No. 1) produces[85] side deposits of only 6 to 9 grams, which is superior to most Mid Continent kerosenes or acid-treated West Texas distillates.

In making blends, Diesel Index is an additive property, and the pour point may be estimated by the use of Fig. 4-42. Cracking stocks and the yields from them are discussed in connection with Fig. 19-1 and Table 19-7

[88] Worrall, G. I., *Ind. Eng. Chem.*, **46**: 2180 (1954).

(thermal cracking and coking) and Figs. 21-3 to 21-6 (catalytic cracking and reforming).

Lubricating Oils and Waxes. When produced by the conventional pressing and centrifuge methods, the cut point between wax distillate and cylinder stock should preferably[43] be 835°F but pressible distillate can usually be produced up to cut points of 870 to 875°F if the viscosity of the most viscous material does not exceed 600 sec.[89]

Pour point cannot be predicted with accuracy nor can the reduction in pour point that may be expected with commercial depressants be predicted except within the following wide ranges:

Per cent depressant	Average lowering, °F	Range of lowering, °F
0.1	11	1–18
0.2	18	3–34
0.4	25	8–42
0.7	34	20–47
1.0	38	24–53
2.0	43	28–

A method of evaluation of lubricating-oil stocks involving precipitation of asphaltenes with petroleum ether, a fuller's earth petroleum ether fractionation to isolate resins, dewaxing with methyl ethyl ketone and benzene to separate wax, and an adsorption fractionation to provide cuts for determining the Viscosity Index–yield relationship has been developed by N. W. Furby.[90] The results of such a study have been successfully correlated with plant performance.

A highly satisfactory propane deasphalting bomb for laboratory evaluations is described by Ditman and Mertens.[91]

Although the Viscosity Index of raw lubricating-oil stocks may be estimated from Table 4-1, various amounts of wax are associated with the oil. Wax has a Viscosity Index of about 200 (125 to 288) and a Characterization Factor of about 12.88 (12 to 13.65),[92] values derived from a study by F. Tull[93] of the lube stocks (700 to 900°F) contained in 13 Venezuelan crude oils. Removal of wax greatly reduces[92] the Viscosity Index

---

[89] Beiswenger and Child, True Boiling Crude Analysis, Pet. Division, ACS, Atlanta Meeting (not for publication).

[90] *Anal. Chem.*, **22**, 876 (1950); also Gester, G. C., "Progress in Petroleum Technology," p. 177, ACS Meeting, New York, September, 1951.

[91] *Pet. Processing*, November, 1952, p. 1628.

[92] Nelson, W. L., *Oil Gas J.*, Mar. 29, 1954, p. 131.

[93] "A Study of High Viscosity Index Oils," master's thesis, University of Tulsa, 1953.

and the Characterization Factor of the raw lube stock as indicated in Fig. 4-52. In Fig. 4-52, zero per cent wax means the removal of enough wax to reduce the pour point to zero °F. The dashed line is data of J. B. Maxwell,[94] and the circle points are data taken from the literature.

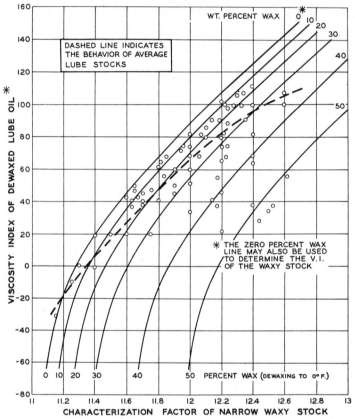

FIG. 4-52. Approximate Viscosity Indexes of dewaxed lube oils (700–900°F boiling range) as a function of the wax content of the raw (waxy) lube stock and its Characterization Factor. (*Oil Gas J.*)

Maxwell's line is probably a good average because the results published in the literature often pertain to oils of unusually high wax content.

Boiling point and melting point are not directly related except for the normal paraffin hydrocarbons. However, viscosity appears to be reasonably consistent[95] for all petroleum waxes. The approximate rela-

---

[94] "Data Book of Hydrocarbons," Esso Research and Engineering Co., D. Van Nostrand Company, Inc., Princeton, N.J., 1950.

[95] Tiedje, J. L., A Laboratory Study of Wax Processing Methods, *Proc. Fourth World Pet. Congr.*, sec. VI, Rome, 1955.

tionship between these properties is shown in Table 4-25 (see also Table 12-1).

TABLE 4-25

Mid boiling point, °F	Viscosity,[a] SSU at 210°F	n-Paraffins		Misc. waxes[a]	
		Melting point, °F	Refract. Index at 80°C	Melting point, °F	Refract. Index at 80°C
700	...	112	1.422		
750	...	124	1.425		
800	37	135	1.427		
850	40	147	1.430	139	1.433
900	43	157	1.432		
920	43	...	.....	143	1.436
950	47	166	1.435	145	1.439
980	50	...	.....	145	1.442
1000	53	175	1.437	143	1.444
1025	58	...	.....	143	1.446
1050	63				
1075	66	...	.....	146	1.449
1100	74	...	.....	148	1.451
1130+	80	...	.....	151	1.453

[a] Tiedje, J. L., A Laboratory Study of Wax Processing Methods, *Proc. Fourth World Pet. Congr.*, sec. VI, Rome, 1955.

The amount of wax contained in crude oils varies widely.[96] N. W. Furby[97] finds that the dry wax (called D.W., wt %) of residua is related to distillable wax (called H.W., wt %) by the Holde method, about as follows

$$D.W. = 2 + 1.35 \ H.W. \qquad (4\text{-}10)$$

Likewise, the asphalt (A., wt %) in a residue may be estimated[97] from the Conradson carbon (C., wt %), within plus or minus 10 per cent, from

$$A. = 5 + 3.1C. \qquad (4\text{-}11)$$

The yield of finished lubricating oil is then estimated by subtracting the amounts of wax and asphalt.

The amount of wax contained in a raw distilled lube stock (700 to 900°F) may be estimated with fair accuracy from the Characterization Factors of the materials that boil at 550 and at 750°F (or 800) in the

[96] Nelson, W. L., *Oil Gas J.*, Feb. 7, p. 127, and Feb. 14, p. 129, 1955.   Tabulations of dozens of crude oils.

[97] A Survey of Petroleum Residua as Sources of Lubricating Oil, Div. Pet. Chem., ACS Meeting, Kansas City, Mo., Mar. 29, 1954.

crude oil.   The presence of wax in a lube stock is associated with a rise in Characterization Factor throughout the 550°F and 800°F boiling range.

Rise in C.F.	Weight % wax in 700–900°F cut	Rise in C.F.	Weight % wax in 700–900°F cut
0.05	10.5	0.60	47.7
0.10	18.2	0.70	51.6
0.20	28.0	0.80	55.2
0.30	34.4	0.90	58.5
0.40	39.4	1.00	61.5
0.50	43.7		

The relationship cannot be used when the Characterization Factor at 750°F is lower than 11.6 because such materials are not solids or waxes. Finally, the pour point and Characterization Factor of 700 to 900°F lube stocks seem to be related to weight per cent wax, somewhat as shown in Table 4-26.

TABLE 4-26

Pour point, °F	Percentage[a] of wax in stocks				
	11.6 C.F.	11.8 C.F.	12.0 C.F.	12.2 C.F.	12.4 C.F.
20	3.0	3.5	4.0	4.5	5.0
40	5.0	5.5	6.0	8.0	10.0
60	7.5	8.5	10.0	12.0	16.0
80	10.0	12.0	14.5	18.0	24.0
100	13.5	18.0	23.0	30.0	40.0
120	17.0	23.0	30.0	40.0	54.0

[a] Above percentage in zero pour point material.

Most United States oils contain very little wax, even those from Pennsylvania or other paraffinic crude oils, but certain intermediate or intermediate paraffin-base oils of Venezuela and Burma contain even 20 per cent of paraffin wax[96] as well as additional wax in residual lube stocks.

There is no entirely satisfactory way of predicting whether a crude oil will contain low-cold-test lubricating oil (0 to 10 pour point, V.I. above 40), such as those in Tia Juana 102 Venezuelan oil or Raccoon Bend, Thompsons, or Sugarland Texas (Gulf Coast) crude oils.   If the fraction in a crude oil that boils at 550°F has a very low Characterization Factor (under 11.15) and at the same time the 750°F fraction has a Factor of 11.4 to 11.5, the chance of encountering a low-cold-test lube stock is good, but there are exceptions.   Numerous crude oil analyses are tabulated in Appendix B.

The cast or bloom of paraffin base lubricants is yellow, that of mixed base is greenish-yellow, and of naphthene base, blue.

Asphalts. The amount of asphalt (100 penetration) contained in crude oils is related to the boiling range[98] somewhat as indicated in Table 4-27. Apparently the bulk of very hard material in high-boiling crude oils permits the incorporation of additional low-boiling material in the asphalt. In addition, the high-boiling crude oils normally are naphthenic

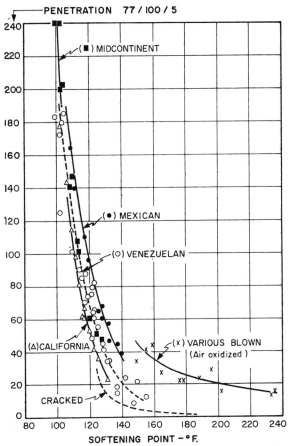

Fig. 4-53. Relationship between softening point and penetration of vacuum-refined asphalts.

or asphalt base. It has also been suggested by Stanfield and Hubbard[99] that the approximate percentage of 100 penetration asphalt is equal to 4.9 times the percentage of carbon residue of the crude oil. Note also that the approximate percentage distilled at 1100°F is equal to 100 minus

[98] Nelson, W. L., *Oil Gas J.*, Feb. 1, 1951, p. 76.

[99] Asphalts from Rocky Mountain Crude Oils, *U.S. Bur. Mines Tech. Paper* **717** (1949).

TABLE 4-27. APPROXIMATE AMOUNT OF VACUUM ASPHALTIC MATERIAL[a] AS A
FUNCTION OF BOILING RANGE

Primary relationship		Secondary relationships[b]	
Per cent 100 penetration asphalt	Asphalt fraction starts to boil at	API gravity of crude oil	Characterization Factor of 750°F bp material
59	850°F	13	11.22
48	890	17	11.32
40	910	20	11.40
30	940	24	11.56
24	950	27	11.63
17	965	30	11.78
10	975	36	11.90
5	980	41	

[a] Hard material but not necessarily suitable for use as asphalt.

[b] Approximate, and the two functions are related to the "primary relationship" not to each other.

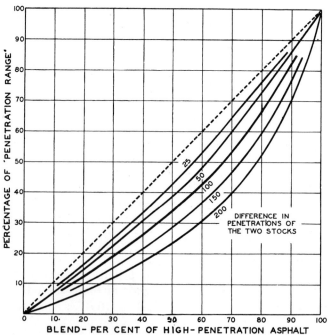

FIG. 4-54. Estimating the approximate penetration of blends of similar asphalts. (*Oil Gas J.*)

3 times the carbon residue. The quality of the asphalt is usually good if its Characterization Factor is below 11.8, and especially good or excellent if the Factor is as low as 11.4.

The relationship[100] between the two major properties of asphalts, namely, "ring and ball softening point" and "penetration" at 77°F, is indicated in Fig. 4-53. Natural asphalts (Trinidad, Bermudez, and Albanian) usually have very high softening points and very low penetrations. Various indexes[100,101] have been devised for classifying asphalts.

When blending two asphalts from the same crude oil, or asphalts of similar type (vacuum with vacuum, blown with blown, etc.), the resulting blend has a lower penetration than would be expected[102] (see Fig. 4-54). Dissimilar asphalts produce blends that bear no clear relationship to the properties of the two components of the blend.

[100] Nelson, W. L., *Oil Gas J.*, Apr. 26, 1951, p. 201, and Jan. 17, 1955, p. 117.
[101] Nelson, W. L., *Oil Gas J.*, Apr. 19, 1951, p. 243.
[102] Nelson, W. L., *Oil Gas J.*, Sept. 21, 1950, p. 369.

CHAPTER 5

PHYSICAL PROPERTIES OF PETROLEUM OIL

Chapters 2, 3, and 4 indicated that petroleum and petroleum products are complex materials. At present the chemical and physical laws that govern the behavior of mixtures of hydrocarbons are not adequate for most calculations, and hence the engineer must base many of his computations on the average physical properties of hydrocarbons.

Specific Heat. The specific heat of a material is defined as the quantity of heat required to raise the temperature of a unit weight of material through a temperature difference of one degree. Universally the oil industry uses the English system in which the specific heat is defined as the number of British thermal units (Btu) required to raise the temperature of 1 lb of oil 1°F and is expressed as Btu per pound per degree Fahrenheit.

The specific heat of petroleum fractions is a nearly linear function of temperature. It is also dependent on the specific gravity.

Figure 5-1 is a chart of the specific heats of Mid Continent petroleum oils.[1,2] The curves for 70 and 10 API material are not so exact as the other curves because not many oils of these gravities were studied. The critical line indicated in Fig. 5-1 is not exact because the critical temperature is governed more by the boiling range than by the gravity, but it is included in the figure as a warning that liquids cannot exist above the critical point.

Example 5-1. Heat Required to Raise the Temperature of Oil. How much heat is required to raise the temperature of 1,000 lb of a 40 API mixed-base oil from 100 to 600°F?

Specific heat at 100 = 0.48
Specific heat at 600 = 0.775
                        ―――
                        1.255

Average specific heat from 100 to 600 = $\dfrac{1.255}{2}$ = 0.627

Also note the specific heat at 350 = 0.627
1,000(600 − 100)0.627 = 313,500 Btu

[1] Specific Heats of Oils, *Ind. Eng. Chem.*, **18**, 795 (1926).
[2] Heat Content of Petroleum Oil Fractions at Elevated Temperatures, *Ind. Eng. Chem.*, **24**, 210 (1932).

168

Specific heats of gases by Holcomb and Brown[3] are shown in Fig. 5-2, which is said to be accurate to ±0.02 Btu per lb per °F. Dotted lines are used above 700°F as a warning that thermal decomposition occurs at such temperatures.

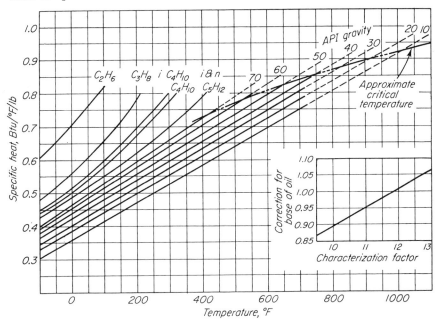

FIG. 5-1. Specific heats of Mid Continent liquid oils with a correction factor for other bases of oils.

The Characterization Factor[4] found to be so useful in cataloguing crude oils (Table 4-1) is of even greater value in accounting for the degree of paraffinicity of individual fractions.

$$K = \frac{\sqrt[3]{T_B}}{s}$$

where K = U.O.P. Characterization Factor
T_B = average boiling point, °R = (°F + 460)
s = specific gravity at 60°F

The factor has been useful in correlating many properties, among which are hydrogen content, aniline point, thermal expansion, and Viscosity Index, as well as the relationships employed in this chapter.

Total Heat Content and the Effect of Pressure. The heat content or enthalpy of petroleum liquids and gases can be obtained most conven-

[3] Thermodynamic Properties of Light Hydrocarbons, *Ind. Eng. Chem.*, **34**, 590 (1942).

[4] Egloff et al., The Modern Cracking Process, *Oil Gas J.*, July 2, 1936, p. 34.

iently from Fig. 5-3, which was compiled by the Shell Development Company[5] and is based on data by Watson et al.[6,7]   Note that the basic temperature is 0°F and that the main lines of the chart are based on a K (Characterization) Factor of 12 rather than 11.8, which is used elsewhere

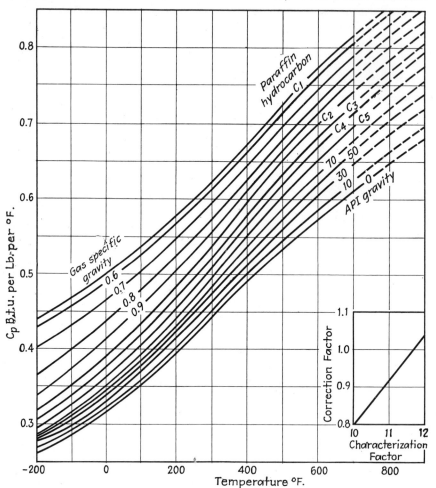

FIG. 5-2. Specific heats of Mid Continent oil vapors with a correction factor for other bases of oils.   (*Holcomb and Brown, Ind. Eng. Chem.*)

in this book.   The upper left corner contains a supplemental chart that permits correction for the effect of pressure.   The heat input between any two conditions is obtained by subtraction.

[5] A folded supplement to, *Pet. Refiner*, **24**(4), April, 1945.

[6] Watson and Nelson, *Ind. Eng. Chem.*, **25**, 880 (1933).

[7] Watson and Smith, *Ind. Eng. Chem.*, **29**, 1408 (1937).

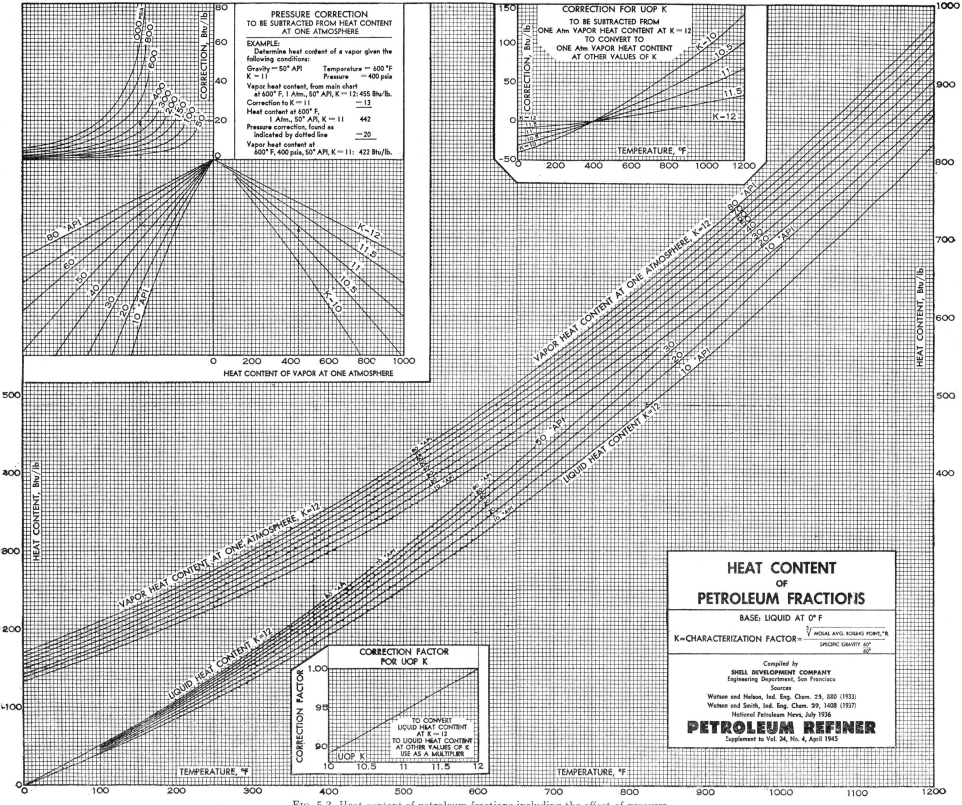

FIG. 5-3. Heat content of petroleum fractions including the effect of pressure.

Total heats at atmospheric pressure can be computed by determining the heat required to heat a pound of liquid to its atmospheric boiling point, vaporizing the liquid at that boiling point, and heating the vapor to the final high temperature using the specific heats of vapors, but such a method cannot be used (except as an approximation) for sub- or super-atmospheric pressure. Total heats at high pressure may easily be computed from Fig. 5-3, and it may also be used to compute the specific heats of vapors at superatmospheric pressure (see Example 5-2). The specific heat of liquids is scarcely altered by pressure.

Example 5-2. Total Heat at Elevated Pressure. A very low-boiling 56 API Coastal gasoline at 60°F is to be heated, vaporized, and superheated to 500°F at an absolute pressure of 200 psi. Its Characterization Factor is 11.4.

According to Fig. 5-3, the heat content at 60°F of a pound of gasoline with a Characterization Factor of 12 is about 28 Btu. Correction for a C.F. of 11.4 results in a liquid heat content of

$$28 \times 0.968 = 27 \text{ Btu/lb}$$

The heat content of a pound of 12 C.F. vapor at 500°F is about 397 Btu. The C.F. correction is almost negligible (perhaps −4 Btu) making a heat content of about 393 Btu per lb.

The pressure correction (upper left corner of Fig. 5-3) is only about 8 Btu per lb, making the total heat

$$393 - 8 = 385 \text{ Btu/lb}$$

The heat input is the difference between the heat of the vapor and the heat of the liquid, or

$$385 - 27 = 358 \text{ Btu/lb}$$

The specific heat of the vapor at 200 psia may be estimated as follows. Such a gasoline has a volumetric mid boiling point of about 190°F (see Fig. 5-9), and at a pressure of 200 psia the mid boiling point becomes (Fig. 5-27) about 400°F. The heat content of vapors at 400°F and 200 psia (Fig. 5-3) is (the C.F. correction is zero):

$$338 - 0 - 12 = 326 \text{ Btu/lb}$$

Heat content at 500°F and 200 psia = 385 Btu/lb
Heat content at 400°F and 200 psia = 326 Btu/lb
Change in heat content   59

$$\text{Specific heat of vapors at 200 psia (between 400 and 500°F)} = \frac{59}{(500 - 400)} = 0.59$$

A similar computation, but leaving out the pressure correction, indicates a specific heat at atmospheric pressure of only 0.55, and this checks reasonably well with Fig. 5-2 which shows about 0.553.

Molal Average Boiling Point. Ordinarily the distillation data obtained from the laboratory are on a liquid-volume-percentage basis, meaning that vapor temperature is plotted against percentage of liquid distilled. The molal average boiling point of the material is sometimes more satisfactory for purposes of correlation than the volumetric percentage. The relationship between these two bases of percentage (as well as other bases) is

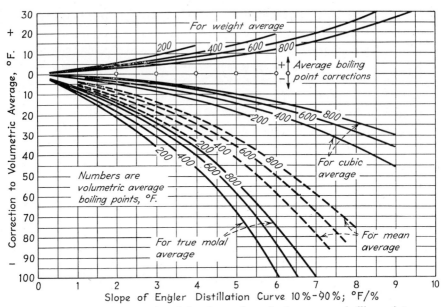

Fɪɢ. 5-4. Relationship between molal, volumetric, and other average boiling points as a function of ASTM slope. (*Ind. Eng. Chem.*)

shown in Fig. 5-4 from Watson and Nelson[6] as a function of the slope of the ASTM distillation curve. However, the use of this figure is usually not necessary because the slopes encountered in commercial products are somewhat fixed. Thus commercial products usually exhibit slopes and corrections (between volumetric and molal percentages) as shown in Table 5-1. Throughout this book, the approximate corrections shown in this table have been used (as auxiliary scales) on such charts (Figs. 5-5, 5-9, and 5-12) as require the molal average boiling point.

TABLE 5-1. APPROXIMATE SLOPES, BOILING RANGES, AND CORRECTIONS (°F) TO CONVERT VOLUMETRIC TO MOLAL AVERAGE BOILING POINT

Material (general)	ASTM slope, deg/per cent	ASTM mid boiling points, °F	Correction,[a] °F
Solvents.....................	1	150–400	8–11
Aviation gasoline and kerosene.....	2	150–450	17–23
Gasoline and diesel fuel............	3	200–700	25–36
Gas oil and lubes................	4	250–900	35–52
Gas oil and reduced crude.........	5	300–800	53–72
Cracking stock and crude oils......	6	350–700	78–102
Crude oils......................	7	400–700	104–128

[a] To be subtracted from the volumetric average boiling point.

Latent Heat. The heat of vaporization, commonly referred to as the latent heat, is usually defined in terms of Btu required to vaporize 1 lb of a liquid at its atmospheric boiling point. If vaporization takes place at another pressure (or temperature), the latent heat should be specified as such. The latent heat varies with the temperature (or pressure) at which vaporization occurs and with the type of hydrocarbon.

Latent heats[8] at atmospheric pressure for petroleum fractions are given in Fig. 5-5 as a function of boiling point and molecular weight or API

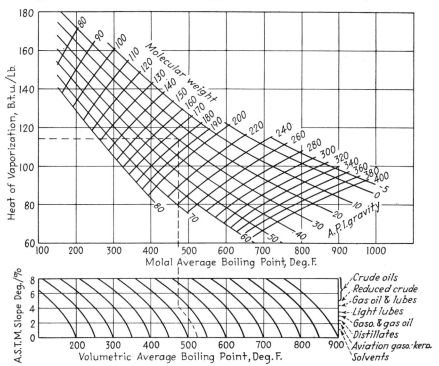

FIG. 5-5. Atmospheric latent heat of vaporization as a function of molecular weight (preferred) or API gravity. (*Courtesy of Hougen and Watson*, "*Chem. Process Principles*," *vol. 1, John Wiley & Sons, Inc., New York.*)

gravity. The dotted lines of Fig. 5-5 show that a 30 API gas oil (or material of slope 4.5) that has an average boiling point of 525°F will have a latent heat of 114 at atmospheric pressure. It also shows that such a material has a molecular weight of 179 and a molal average boiling point of about 473°F.

At other pressures (and temperatures) than atmospheric pressure, the data on latent heat are not extensive, and hence a general method such as

[8] Hougen and Watson, "Chemical Process Principles," John Wiley & Sons, Inc., New York, 1947.

that outlined by Watson[9] must be employed.   The latent heat at any temperature is described in terms of the latent heat at the normal boiling point, as follows:

$$L = \gamma L_B \frac{T}{T_B} \qquad (5\text{-}1)$$

where L = heat of vaporization at absolute temperature T
$\quad L_B$ = heat of vaporization at absolute normal boiling point T_B
$\quad \gamma$ = a factor obtained from Fig. 5-6.
The reduced temperature term used in Fig. 5-6 is explained on page 182.

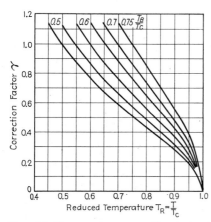

FIG. 5-6. Temperature correction to heat of vaporization.

Latent heat decreases with temperature until it has a value of zero at the critical temperature (Figs. 5-7 and 5-8).   Furthermore, the critical temperatures of high API materials are lower than for low API materials, and hence their latent-heat curves, when plotted as functions of gravity and temperature, cross one another at some point, as can be seen in Figs. 5-7 and 5-8.

Example 5-3.   Latent Heat.   A mixed-base, narrow-boiling-range fraction has a gravity of 35 API.   The latent heat of this fraction at atmospheric pressure and also at 500°F is desired.

A mixed-base stock will have a Characterization Factor of about 11.9.   The following properties were read from Fig. 5-9:

Atmospheric boiling point........... 580°F (1040°R)
Molecular weight................... 250
Critical temperature............... 900°F (1360°R)

From these data, the latent heat at atmospheric pressure is found to be about 92 by reference to Fig. 5-5.

In order to estimate the latent heat at 500°F, additional factors must be set down:

$$\frac{T_B}{T_C} = \frac{1040}{1360} = 0.765$$

$$T_R = \frac{T}{T_C} = \frac{500 + 460}{1360} = 0.706$$

$$\gamma \text{ from Fig. 5-6} = \text{about } 1.16$$

The latent heat at 500°F from Eq. (5-1) is

$$L = 1.16 \times 92 \times {}^{960}\!/_{1040} = 98$$

[9] The Prediction of Critical Temperatures and Heats of Vaporization, *Ind. Eng. Chem.*, **23**, 360 (1931).

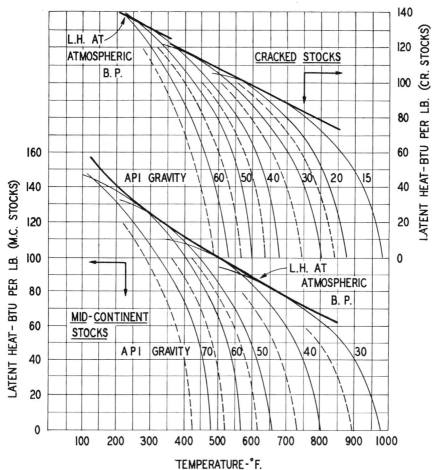

FIG. 5-7. Latent heats (Mid Continent and cracked stocks) as a function of temperature (or pressure). (*Oil Gas J.*)

Note that the latent heat read from Fig. 5-7 is also about 98 Btu per lb, and at atmospheric pressure (580°F) about 92.

Finally, the total heat chart (Fig. 5-3) may also be used to obtain latent heats. The heat contents of 35 API material at 500°F are

$$\text{Heat of vapor} = 378 - 1 = 377 \text{ Btu/lb}$$
$$\text{Heat of liquid} = 282 \times 0.995 = 280 \text{ Btu/lb}$$
$$\text{Latent heat} = \overline{97}$$

However, Fig. 5-3 should not be used in this way except when the vaporization takes place at temperatures somewhat close to the atmospheric boiling point.

The estimation of latent heats by Eq. (5-1) and Fig. 5-6 or even by Fig. 5-3 is laborious, and therefore Figs. 5-7 and 5-8 are suggested[10] for

[10] Nelson, W. L., *Oil Gas J.*, May 26, 1945, p. 163.

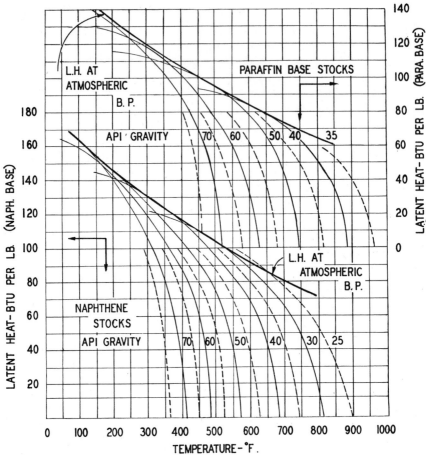

Fig. 5-8. Latent heats (paraffinic or naphthenic stocks) as a function of temperature (or pressure). (*Oil Gas J.*)

all but the most detailed work. All three methods of obtaining latent heat are based on the same basic information and should therefore check with one another. The Characterization Factors used in preparing Figs. 5-7 and 5-8 are

Paraffin base..............................12.1
Mid Continent or intermediate base..........11.8
Naphthene base............................11.4
Cracked (thermal)—60 API.................11.8
Cracked (thermal)—50 API.................11.5
Cracked (thermal)—40 API.................11.2
Cracked (thermal)—30 API.................11.0
Cracked (thermal)—20 API.................10.5
Cracked (thermal)—15 API.................10.5

The heavy line at the top of each figure shows the latent heat at atmospheric pressure (or normal boiling point), such as the latent heats obtained from Fig. 5-5. The curving lines show latent heat at other pressures than atmospheric pressure, or stated another way, at various boiling points.

The average boiling point of mixtures is defined with difficulty. An arithmetic average, from the distillation curve, does not completely describe the vaporization properties because vapor pressure is not directly proportional to temperature. A logical average boiling point is the 100 per cent point of the flash-vaporization curve because the material cannot be completely vaporized at any lower temperature. For batch distillation the arithmetic average temperature should be used for computing the latent heat, but for continuous distillation, as in a pipestill, the 100 per cent point on the flash-vaporization curve is most frequently used. The temperature at the 100 per cent point on the flash-vaporization curve is approximately the same as the temperature at the 70 per cent point of the material on the true-boiling-point curve. For some other purposes, such as estimating the molecular weight, gravity, or viscosity, the 50 per cent boiling point should be used.

Critical Point and Other Properties. Figures 5-9,[8] 5-10,[8] 5-11, and 5-12[4] indicate the relationship among boiling point or range, gravity, molecular weight, Characterization Factor, viscosity, critical temperature, and critical pressure.

Example 5-4. Use of Figs. 5-9 and 5-10. A distillate material of 31.5 API has a volumetric average boiling point of 533°F. According to Fig. 5-9 (see dotted line), such a material will have a molal average boiling point of about 500°F and a Characterization Factor of 11.35. Other properties are

> Molecular weight..................... 195 (Fig. 5-9)
> Critical temperature.................. 845°F (Fig. 5-9)
> Viscosity at 122°F, centistokes.......... 2.1 (Fig. 5-10)

Note that, if any two properties are known, all the other properties can be estimated.

When a pure compound is heated at atmospheric pressure, it eventually reaches its boiling point and is completely vaporized at a constant temperature unless the pressure is increased. If the pressure is increased, the compound is completely condensed and cannot be vaporized again unless the temperature is also increased. This mechanism, alternately increasing the pressure and temperature, functions until at some high temperature and pressure it is found that the material cannot be condensed regardless of the amount of pressure applied. This point is called the "critical point," and the temperature and pressure at the critical point are called the "critical temperature" and "critical pressure," respectively. The liquid phase and vapor phase merge at the critical point

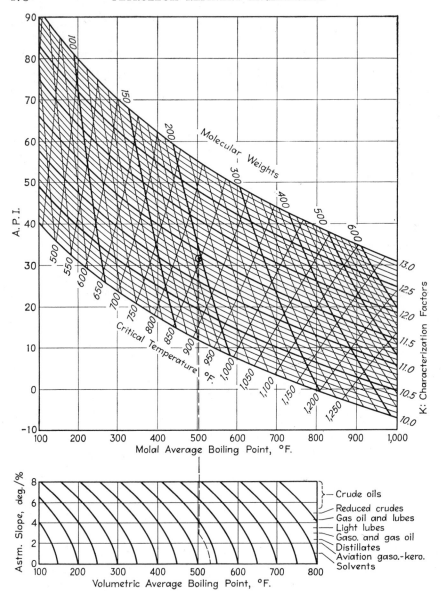

FIG. 5-9. Molecular weights, pseudo critical temperatures, Characterization Factors, and gravities of petroleum fractions. (*Courtesy of Hougen and Watson*, "*Chem. Process Principles*," *vol. 1, John Wiley & Sons, Inc., New York.*)

so that one phase cannot be distinguished from the other. No volume change occurs when a liquid is vaporized at the critical point, and no heat is required for vaporization, but the coefficient of expansion has become large (Fig. 5-14).

The critical temperatures and pressures of some pure compounds are given in Tables 5-2 and 5-3. In addition, Figs. 5-9 and 5-12 may be used

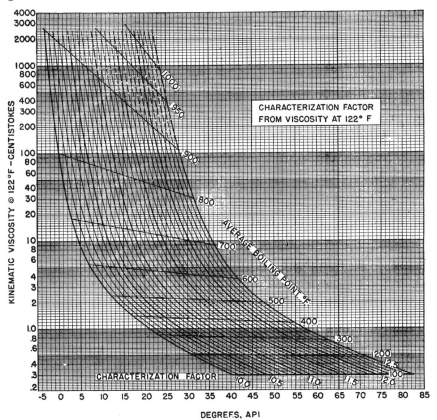

FIG. 5-10. Relation of viscosity at 122°F to Characterization Factor.

to estimate the pseudo critical temperatures and pressures of higher boiling hydrocarbons or wide boiling range fractions.

Insufficient information concerning the behavior of mixtures requires that the pseudo critical temperature and pseudo critical pressure be used for most oil mixtures. The pseudo critical point as developed by W. B. Kay[11] may be defined as the molal average critical temperature and pressure of the several materials that constitute a mixture. It may be used as the critical point of a mixture in computing reduced temperatures, pres-

[11] Density of Hydrocarbon Gases and Vapors, *Ind. Eng. Chem.*, **28**, 1014 (1936).

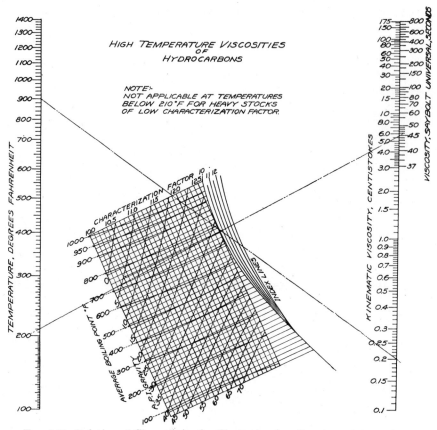

FIG. 5-11. Relation of Characterization Factor to viscosity at any temperature.

sures, etc. However, in computing the pressure-volume-temperature relations of mixtures by use of the pseudo critical point, it must be borne in mind that the values are not accurate in the region of the critical point—and that it cannot be applied to mixtures of gas and liquid (refer to Fig. 15-6).

Example 5-5. Pseudo Critical Point. Critical values for ethane and propane are

	Ethane	Propane
Critical temperature, °R......	549	665
Critical pressure..............	715	616

For a 90 mole per cent propane mixture of these gases:

Pseudo critical temperature......... $(0.1 \times 549) + (0.9 \times 665) = 653.4°R$
Pseudo critical pressure.............. $(0.1 \times 715) + (0.9 \times 616) = 625.9$

These values may be used to compute volumes, pressures, etc., of such a mixture.

Example 5-6. Critical Pressure. A gas oil (or material of slope 4.3) has a volumetric average boiling point of 520°F and a pseudo critical temperature of 830°F. According to Fig. 5-12, its molal boiling point is 465°F and it will have a pseudo critical pressure of about 340 psia.

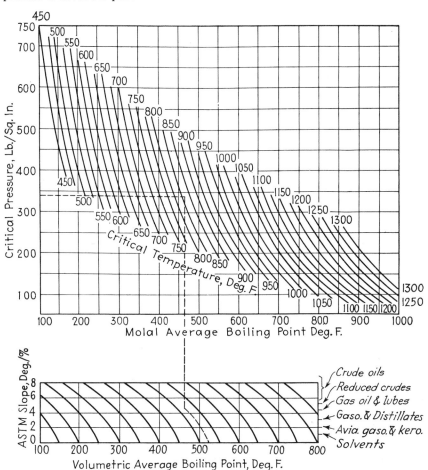

FIG. 5-12. Pseudo critical pressures of hydrocarbons and petroleum fractions. (*Oil Gas J.*)

Example 5-7. Viscosity (Fig. 5-11). A 5.5 API material has a Characterization Factor of 10.32. What is its viscosity at 210°F and at 900°F?

Located on Fig. 5-11 by a dot is the 5.5 API, 10.32 C.F. material. Incidentally, it has an average boiling point of about 750°F. The value indicated by the point is transferred across the chart in the center of the figure to the index line for 10.32 C.F. This point can be connected to any temperature on the left scale and the corresponding viscosity may be read from the scale on the right:

Viscosity at 210°F   5.68 centistokes
or 44.9 Saybolt Universal
Viscosity at 900°F   0.2 centistokes

In the correlation of many properties, reduced properties are useful. Reduced properties are defined as the ratio of the actual value of the property to its critical value. Thus for volume, temperature, or pressure

$$V_R = \text{reduced volume} = \frac{\text{volume at specified condition}}{\text{volume at critical point}} = \frac{V}{V_c}$$

$$T_R = \text{reduced temperature} = \frac{\text{absolute temperature}}{\text{absolute critical temperature}} = \frac{T}{T_c}$$

$$P_R = \text{reduced temperature} = \frac{\text{absolute pressure}}{\text{absolute critical pressure}} = \frac{P}{P_c}$$

Specific Volume. The volume occupied by 1 lb of vapor is called the specific volume. According to the laws governing the behavior of perfect gases, the volume varies inversely as the pressure (Boyle's law) and directly as the absolute temperature (Gay-Lussac's or Charles' law) or

$$\frac{PV}{T} = \frac{P'V'}{T'} = R \text{ (the gas-law constant)} \qquad (5\text{-}2)$$

where P and P' = psia (14.7 + gauge pressure)
V and V' = volume, cu ft
T and T' = absolute temperature or (°F + 460)
R = 10.7 when considering 1 lb-mole of gas
At standard conditions of 32°F and a pressure of 1 atm or 760 mm, the volume of 1 lb-mole of a perfect gas is 359 cu ft. At 60°F and 760 mm the volume is 379.4 cu ft (379 is commonly used).

The volume of 1 lb-mole of a perfect gas, viz., 359 cu ft, is the factor that relates the volume of a gas to its weight. The foregoing laws are sufficiently exact for engineering calculations involving such gases as air, nitrogen, oxygen, flue gas, and natural gas, unless the pressure exceeds about 200 psi. For high pressures and for the vapors handled in the refinery the laws are not exact but they are used extensively.

Example 5-8. Volume of Flue Gas. A flue gas consisting of N_2, O_2, CO_2, and water vapor has a molecular weight of 30. What is the volume of 100 lb of this gas at 200°F and a barometric pressure of 740 mm?

$$\text{Volume at 200°F} = \frac{100}{30} \times 379 \times \frac{760}{740} \times \frac{(460 + 200)}{(460 + 60)} = 1,648 \text{ cu ft}$$

What is the volume of 100 lb at 1000°F and 10 psig?

$$\text{Volume at 1000°F} = \frac{100}{30} \times 379 \times \frac{14.7}{24.7} \frac{(460 + 1,000)}{(460 + 60)} = 2,110 \text{ cu ft}$$

also $$\text{Volume} = \frac{100}{30} \times \frac{10.7 \times 1,460}{24.7} = 2,110$$

Pressure-Volume-Temperature Relations of Vapors. Petroleum vapors do not obey the perfect gas laws. In general, low-molecular-weight vapors such as natural gasoline and gasoline vapors may be handled as perfect gases up to gauge pressures of about 35 psi without introducing great errors. For heavier vapors the laws are not exact, but they are widely used because no other convenient laws are available. Figure 5-13 was prepared[8] for all gases, and the present state of knowledge concerning the compressibility of gases does not warrant closer discrimination.

The theorem of corresponding states affords a method of correlating the scattered data. This theorem postulates that all similar substances have corresponding volumes at corresponding temperatures and pressures, if the reference point of correspondence is the critical point.

Tables 5-2 and 5-3 give critical data by which reduced conditions can be computed. Many of the data were taken from "Physical Constants of the Principal Hydrocarbons" by the technical staff of The Texas Company.

Perfect gases behave as follows:

$$PV = nRT \text{ (ideal)}$$

where R = gas constant = 10.7 for the following units: 1 mole of gas, volume, cu ft; pressure, psia; and temperature, °F abs

n = number of moles of gas

Other gases deviate from the foregoing by the factor Z:

$$PV = ZnRT$$

Values of Z may be obtained from Fig. 5-13.

Example 5-9. Pressure-Volume-Temperature Relations of Gases That Are Not Ideal. *a.* One pound-mole of C_3H_8 (44 lb) is held in a container having a capacity of 31.2 cu ft. The temperature is 280°F. What is the pressure? (See Table 5-2.)

$$T_c = 665°\text{F abs}$$
$$P_c = 616 \text{ psi}$$
$$V_c = 3.12 \text{ cu ft}$$
$$T_R = \frac{460 + 280}{665} = 1.113$$

A trial-and-error solution is necessary because the compressibility factor Z is a function of the unknown pressure. Assume $Z = 0.9$.

$$P \times 31.2 = 0.9 \times 1.0 \times 10.7 \times (460 + 280)$$
$$P = 228 \text{ psia}$$

This indicates a reduced pressure of $228 \div 616 = 0.37$, and according to Fig. 5-13, the value of Z should be about 0.915 rather than 0.9. Thus, the pressure is 232 rather than 228 psia.

By the perfect gas laws, the computed pressure would be:

$$P = \frac{1 \times 10.7 \times 740}{31.2} = 254 \text{ psia}$$

TABLE 5-2. PROPERTIES OF PARAFFIN HYDROCARBONS[a]

Property	Methane	Ethane	Propane	Isobutane	Butane	Isopentane
Molecular weight	16.03	30.05	44.06	58.08	58.08	72.09
Carbon-hydrogen ratio	2.98	3.97	4.46	4.76	4.76	4.96
Liquid gravity:						
Specific 60/60	0.300	0.374	0.509	0.563	0.584	0.625
Density, lb per gal at 60°F	2.5	3.12	4.24	4.70	4.86	5.20
API at 60°F	340	247	147	120	111	94.9
Vapor gravity:						
Relative to air	0.559	1.037	1.521	2.004	2.004	2.494
Cu ft at 60°F, per gal liquid	59.1	39.2	36.5	30.6	31.8	27.3
Boiling point, °F	−259	−128	−44	10.9	31.1	82.2
Critical temperature, °R	344	549	665	733	765	829
Critical pressure, psia	673	715	616	543	550	483
Critical volume, cu ft per lb-mole	1.59	2.29	3.12	3.99	4.14	4.93
Critical viscosity, micropoises	159	210	228	239	239	240
Specific heat:						
Vapor	$0.543^{15.5}$	$0.410^{16.5}$	0.473^{15}	0.462^{15}	0.459^{15}	0.471^{100}
Liquid at 60°F	....	0.78	0.6	0.56	0.55	0.53
Ratio at 60°F	1.31	1.18	1.15	1.11	1.10	
Coefficient of expansion	0.00368^{0-100}	0.0038	$0.00324^{10-37.7}$	$0.00230^{10-37.7}$	$0.00203^{10-37.7}$	0.00155^{5-10}
Inflammability limits:						
Low	5.3	3.2	2.4	1.8	1.9	1.3
High	14.0	12.5	9.5	8.4	8.5	
Heat of combustion:						
Gross, Btu per lb	23,920	22,350	21,690	21,290	21,340	21,060
Net, Btu per lb	21,540	20,450	19,960	19,650	19,700	19,470
Gross, Btu per cu ft[b]	1,011	1,770	2,520	3,261	3,266	4,004
Latent heat, Btu per lb	225	210	183	158	165	146
Vapor pressure, at 100°F, psia	100+	221^0	189	73.5	52	20.3
Octane number, Motor method	100+	100+	97	97	90	90.3
ρ_1/ω_1, expansion constant for liquids[c]	3.679	4.416	4.803	....	5.002	

184

TABLE 5-2. PROPERTIES OF PARAFFIN HYDROCARBONS[a] (*Continued*)

Property	Pentane	Hexane	Heptane	Octane	2,2,4 Trimethyl pentane	Cetane
Molecular weight	72.09	86.11	100.13	114.14	114.14	226.43
Carbon-hydrogen ratio	4.96	5.11	5.21	5.30	5.30	5.62
Liquid gravity:						
Specific 60/60	0.631	0.664	0.688	0.707	0.696	0.799
Density, lb per gal at 60°F	5.26	5.53	5.73	5.89	5.80	6.65
API at 60°F	92.7	81.6	74.2	68.6	71.8	50.1
Vapor gravity:						
Relative to air	2.491	2.975	3.459	3.943	3.943	7.817
Cu ft at 60°F per gal liquid	27.5	25.5	20.8	19.6	19.2	10.87
Boiling point, °F	96.9	155.7	209.2	258	210	536
Critical temperature, °R	846	914	976	1,022	975	1,300
Critical pressure, psia	484	440	405	370	397	222
Critical volume, cu ft per lb-mole	4.97	5.88	6.85	7.86	......	16.5
Critical viscosity, micropoises	238	248	254	259	......	......
Specific heat:						
Vapor	0.409^{86}	0.339	0.335	0.330	......	......
Liquid at 60°F	0.541^{7}	0.531^{22}	$0.533^{6.2}$	0.517	0.492	0.495^{0-50}
Ratio at 60°F	1.120	1.11	1.11	1.10	......	......
Coefficient of expansion	0.00154^{0-30}	0.00135^{0-30}	0.00122	0.00116^{0-30}	......	0.0008
Inflammability limits:						
Low	1.45	1.2	1.0	0.9		
High	7.8	6.9	6.0			
Heat of combustion:						
Gross, Btu per lb	21,120	20,970	20,860	20,780	20,560	20,360
Net, Btu per lb	19,540	19,420	19,340	19,270	19,060	18,920
Gross, Btu per cu ft[b]	4,016	4,762	5,508	6,254	6,190	
Latent heat, Btu per lb	154	145	137	130	117	76
Vapor pressure at 100°F, psia	15.5	5.0	1.63	0.54	1.0	
Octane number, Motor method	61.9	26	0	-17	100	
ρ_l/ω_l, expansion constant for liquids[c]	5.128	5.216	5.290	5.34	5.48	

[a] The numbers above some of the data are temperatures in degrees centigrade at which the data are applicable.

[b] Measured at 60°F and atmospheric pressure, which is hypothetical for the liquid hydrocarbons.

[c] See Fig. 5-15.

TABLE 5-3. PROPERTIES OF VARIOUS HYDROCARBONS[a]

Property	Acetylene	Ethene	Propene	Isobutene	Butene-1	Butene-2 (mix of cis and trans)
Molecular weight	26	28	42	56.1	56.1	56.1
Carbon-hydrogen ratio	11.91	5.96	5.96	5.96	5.96	5.96
Liquid gravity:						
Specific 60/60	0.416	0.351	0.522	0.600	0.601	0.63
Density, lb per gal at 60°F	3.47	2.82	4.35	5.00	5.01	5.25
API at 60°F	209	273	140	104	104	93.1
Vapor gravity:						
Relative to air	0.906	0.968	1.453	2.011	1.937	2.004
Cu ft at 60°F per gal liquid	50.5	39.6	39.5	32.6	33.8	35.5
Boiling point, °F	−119	−155	−54	19.6	20.7	33.8
Critical temperature, °R	522	510	657	762	751	771
Critical pressure, psia	911	748	660	580	620	619
Critical volume, cu ft per lb-mole	1.81	2.04	2.88	3.84		
Critical viscosity, micropoises	237	215	233	250		
Specific heat:						
Vapor	0.407	0.365[18]	0.371[15.5]	0.362[15.5]	0.371	0.366
Liquid at 60°F			0.57	0.55	0.53	
Ratio at 60°F	1.27	1.24	1.16	1.13	1.11	
Coefficient of expansion	0.0037	0.00689[-17.8-10]	0.0017	0.00187[-17.8-10]	0.00191[-17.3-10]	0.001818[-17.8-10]
Inflammability limits:						
Low	2.5	2.7	2.0		1.7	
High	80.0	28.6	11.1		9.0	
Heat of combustion:						
Gross, Btu per lb	21,580	21,650	21,060	20,740	20,860	20,480
Net, Btu per lb	20,850	20,300	19,700	19,380	19,500	19,120
Gross, Btu per cu ft[b]	1,489	1,601	2,335	3,066	3,084	
Latent heat, Btu per lb	296	208	189	169	168	173
Vapor pressure at 100°F, psia	105	397[0]	226	63.4	62.6	47.7
Octane number, Motor method		81	85	87	80	83

TABLE 5-3. PROPERTIES OF VARIOUS HYDROCARBONS[a] (Continued)

Property	1,3 Butadiene	Pentene-1	Cyclohexane	Benzene	Toluene	Alpha methyl naphthalene	Cetene
Molecular weight	54.09	70.1	84.1	78	92.1	142.19	224.42
Carbon-hydrogen ratio	7.77	5.96	5.96	11.91	10.43	13.11	5.96
Liquid gravity:							
Specific 60/60	0.627	0.647	0.778	0.844	0.872	1.028	0.788
Density, lb per gal at 60°F	5.22	5.40	6.48	7.03	7.27	8.56	6.56
API, at 60°F	94	87	50.3	28.6	30.8	6.2	48.1
Vapor gravity:							
Relative to air	1.877	2.421	2.905	2.696	3.181	4.909	7.748
Cu ft at 60°F per gal liquid	36.4	29.1	29.4	36.8	29.9	22.85	11.09
Boiling point, °F	23.6	86.2	177.4	176.2	231.1	469.4	525.2
Critical temperature, °R	785	845	998	1,010	1,068		
Critical pressure, psia	617	594	585	703	611		
Critical volume, cu ft per lb-mole			4.93	4.1	5.05		
Critical viscosity, micropoises			284	312	306		
Specific heat:							
Vapor	0.332						
Liquid at 60°F	0.551		$0.440^{25.9}$	0.414^{27}	0.398^{30}		0.4723
Ratio at 60°F	1.12						
Coefficient of expansion	0.0018		0.00120^{0-30}	0.00121^{0-30}	0.00106^{0-30}		
Inflammability limits:							
Low	2.0	1.6	1.3	1.4	1.3		
High	11.5		8.3	6.7	6.7		
Heat of combustion:							
Gross, Btu per lb	20,230	20,720	20,290	18,225	18,470		20,316
Net, Btu per lb	19,180	19,360	18,930	17,490	17,640		18,957
Gross, Btu per cu ft[b]	2,968	3,829	4,500	3,750	4,480		
Latent heat, Btu per lb	177	148	155	170	155.5		
Vapor pressure at 100°F, psia	64.7	19	3.3	3.4	1.0		
Octane number, Motor method			78.6	113.6	104.2		

[a] The numbers above some of the data are temperatures in degrees centigrade at which the data are applicable.
[b] Measured at 60°F and atmospheric pressure, which is hypothetical for liquid hydrocarbons.

187

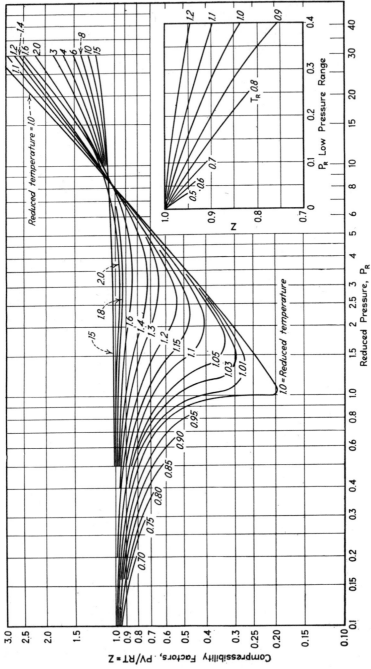

FIG. 5-13. Compressibility (Z) factors of gases and vapors. (*Courtesy Hougen and Watson*, "*Chem. Process Principles*," *vol. 1, John Wiley & Sons, Inc., New York.*)

b. One thousand cubic feet of methane is to be compressed from 60°F and atmospheric pressure to 500 psig and a temperature of 50°F. What volume will it occupy at these conditions?

$$\text{Moles CH}_4 = \frac{1,000}{379} = 2.64$$

At final conditions,

$$T_R = \frac{460 + 50}{344} = 1.48$$

$$P_R = \frac{500 + 14.7}{673} = 0.765$$

From Fig. 5-13,

$$Z = 0.94$$
$$PV = ZnRT$$
$$V = \frac{0.94 \times 2.64 \times 10.7 \times 510}{514.7} = 26.35$$

Coefficient of Expansion. Government bulletins and other agencies[12] present volume-correction tables for (1) four-carbon-atom hydrocarbon mixtures, (2) straight-run products (10 to 95 API), (3) volatile products (95 to 150 API), (4) asphalt and fluxes (0 to 15 API), (5) mixtures of gasoline and benzol (0 to 50 per cent), and (6) cracked gasoline. The mean coefficients of expansion for different gravity materials up to about 400°F are approximately as follows:

Gravity range	*Mean coefficient of expansion*
0– 14.9	0.00035
15– 34.9	0.00040
35– 50.9	0.00050
51– 63.9	0.00060
64– 78.9	0.00070
79– 88.9	0.00080
89– 93.9	0.00085
94–100	0.00090

The coefficient of expansion may be defined as the fraction of unit volume that a unit of material will expand if it is heated through one degree.

Example 5-10. Coefficient of Expansion and Fig. 5-14. One barrel of a 19 API oil is to be heated from 60 to 400°F. What volume will it occupy?

Coefficient of expansion = 0.0004 approximately
Increase in volume = 1(400 − 60)0.0004 = 0.136 bbl
Total volume = 1.136 bbl

Using Fig. 5-14,

$$\text{Sp gr at 60°F (19 API)} = 0.9042$$

[12] ASTM-IP Petroleum Measurement Tables, p. 101, 1952; and Carney, B. R., The Density of the Liquefied Petroleum Gas Hydrocarbons, 21st Annual Convention of the NGAA.

Follow 0.94 line to 400°F

$$Sp\ gr\ at\ 400°F = 0.83$$

$$Volume\ at\ 400°F = 1 \times \frac{0.94}{0.83} = 1.13\ bbl$$

The volume by Fig. 5-14 is probably the more accurate.

Density and Specific Gravity. The approximate density of petroleum products at elevated temperatures[13] can be obtained from Fig. 5-14 (see Example 5-10). The figure relates the specific gravity at 60°F with the

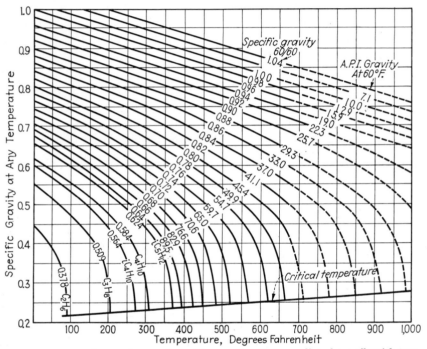

FIG. 5-14. Approximate change of specific gravity of intermediate-base oils with temperature. (*Oil Gas J.*)

specific gravity at other temperatures. The number accompanying each line indicates the gravity of the material at 60°F.

Density is defined as weight per unit of volume. In the petroleum industry, density is usually expressed as pounds per gallon. Since 1 gal of water at 60°F weighs 8.328 lb, the density is

$$Density,\ lb\ per\ gal = sp\ gr \times 8.328$$

The relation[14] among API gravity, specific gravity, and density is given

[13] Nelson, W. L., Determining Densities . . . at High Temperatures, *Oil Gas J.*, Jan. 27, 1938, p. 184.
[14] ASTM-IP Petroleum Measurement Tables, 1952.

in tables in Appendix A. The density of gases can be computed by the mole volume relationship of Eq. 5-2.

Example 5-11. Density and Specific Gravity. What is the density of a 29.3 API material at 60 and at 600°F?

At 60°F

$$Sp \ gr = 0.88; \ density \ 7.328$$

Refer to Fig. 5-14, and follow 0.88 line to 600°F.

$$Sp \ gr \ at \ 600°F = 0.678$$
$$Density \ at \ 600°F = 0.678 \times 8.328 = 5.65 \ lb \ per \ gal$$

What is the density at 60°F, in pounds per cubic feet, of pure methane, and of a flue gas having a molecular weight of 30?

$$Molecular \ weight \ of \ CH_4 = 16$$
$$Density \ of \ CH_4 = {}^{16}\!/_{379} = 0.0422 \ lb \ per \ cu \ ft$$
$$Density \ of \ flue \ gas = {}^{30}\!/_{379} = 0.0792 \ lb \ per \ cu \ ft$$

Since 1 cu ft of water at 60°F weighs 62.37 lb,

$$Sp \ gr \ of \ flue \ gas \ referred \ to \ water \ at \ 60°F = \frac{0.0792}{62.37} = 0.001271$$

Since molecular weight of air = about 28.8,

$$Sp \ gr \ of \ flue \ gas \ at \ 60°F \ referred \ to \ air = \frac{30}{28.8} = 1.04$$

Figures such as 5-14 can only be approximations because hydrocarbons of the same density at 60°F may have different critical temperatures and thus must trace different curves. In addition, pressure greatly affects density at high temperatures. Watson and Gamson[15] provide Fig. 5-15 by which the density of any material at any temperature or pressure can be estimated if one experimental measurement of density is available.

$$\frac{\rho}{\omega} = \frac{\rho_1}{\omega_1} = \frac{\rho_2}{\omega_2} = etc.$$

in which ρ is the density in grams per cubic centimeter and ω is a so-called "expansion factor." Subscript 1 (2, etc.) refers to any defined condition of temperature and pressure. The known density ρ_1 is divided by a value of ω_1 obtained from Fig. 5-15 for the particular conditions of temperature and pressure which apply to ρ_1. When the value of the ratio ρ_1/ω_1 is determined, values of ρ at any other conditions of temperature and pressure can be computed

$$\rho = \frac{\rho_1}{\omega_1} \omega$$

Values of ρ_1/ω_1 for a few hydrocarbons are shown in Table 5-2.

[15] Thermodynamics of the Liquid State, *Ind. Eng. Chem.*, **35**, 398 (1943); and Vapor Pressures and Critical Properties of Organic Compounds, *Natl. Pet. News, Tech. Sect.*, May 3, 1944.

Example 5-12. Liquid Density at Any Pressure or Temperature. A wide-boiling-range distillate material has an average boiling point of 500°F and a gravity of 30 API. According to Figs. 5-9 and 5-12, such a material has critical properties as follows:

$$T_c = 810°F \text{ or } 1270°R$$
$$P_c = 315 \text{ psia}$$

At 60°F and 14.7 psia the density and the reduced conditions are

$$\rho_1 = 0.876$$
$$T_R = \frac{60 + 460}{1270} = 0.41$$
$$P_R = \frac{14.7}{315} = 0.0467$$

According to Fig. 5-15 the value of ω_1 is 0.14.
Other densities can then be computed from

$$\rho = \frac{\rho_1}{\omega_1} \omega = \frac{0.876}{0.14} \omega = 6.25\omega$$

Thus, at such conditions as 650°F and 1,500 psia,

$$T_R = \frac{650 + 460}{1270} = 0.874$$
$$P_R = 1500/315 = 4.75$$
$$\omega = 0.106 \text{ (Fig. 5-15)}$$

and
$$\rho = 6.25 \times 0.106 = 0.662$$

which is quite different from the 0.64 value read from Fig. 5-14.

Change of Viscosity with Temperature and Pressure. The engineer frequently must estimate the viscosity of an oil at other than the customary testing temperatures. This may be done by Fig. 4-43, but greater accuracy is possible by use of ASTM viscosity-temperature charts[16] (see Fig. 4-45). However, in order to use these charts it is necessary to know the viscosity at two temperatures, or to know one viscosity and the Viscosity Index. Kinematic viscosity (or centipoises) can be obtained by the use of Eqs. (3-2), (3-3), and (3-4) on page 25.

Example 5-13. Viscosity at Different Temperatures. Oil A of Fig. 4-45, has a Saybolt Universal viscosity of 200 sec at 100°F and 45 sec at 210°F. A line connecting these points on ASTM viscosity paper (see Fig. 4-45) gives the viscosities at other temperatures.

At	Sec
0°F	20,000
70°F	520
130°F	102
160°F	66
300°F	34.7

[16] Four charts, low and high range, for Universal and for kinematic viscosity are available from the ASTM, 1916 Race St., Philadelphia, Pa.

If the oil has a specific gravity of 0.85 at 100°F the viscosity in centipoises at 100°F, according to Eq. (3-4), will be

$$\frac{Z}{S} = 0.219t - \frac{149.7}{t}$$

$$\frac{Z}{0.85} = 0.219 \times 200 - \frac{149.7}{200}$$

$$Z = 43.05 \times 0.85 = 36.6$$

As a comparison (line 13 of Fig. 4-43), the centipoise viscosity at 100°F is about 32.0.

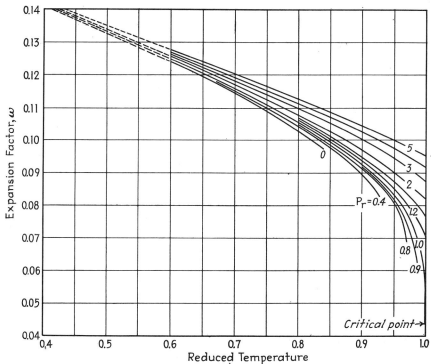

FIG. 5-15. Compressibility of liquids at high pressures and near the critical temperature. (*Courtesy of Hougen and Watson, "Chem. Process Principles," vol. 1, John Wiley & Sons, Inc.*)

It has now become common practice to measure the rate at which viscosity changes with temperature by means of the Viscosity Index. This relation is discussed on page 85 (see also Figs. 4-1, 4-2).

The effect of pressure upon the viscosity of liquids is not great at normal operating pressures, but at a pressure of 1,000 psi and upward its effect is astoundingly great.[17]   As a general indication of the effect of pressure, the

[17] Dow, Fenske, and Morgan, Effect of Pressure on Viscosity of Oils and Chlorinated Diphenyls, *Ind. Eng. Chem.*, **29**, 1078 (1937).

viscosity is increased about 15 per cent at 1,000 lb, three- to eightfold at 10,000 lb, and upon exceeding 55,000 psi most oils begin to solidify.

Viscosity of Hydrocarbons. Although Fig. 5-16, taken from Uyehara and Watson,[18] is based primarily upon light hydrocarbons and organic compounds, it is probably the best method available for estimating the viscosities of heavy refinery vapors. Critical viscosities of such vapors can be estimated[18] from

$$\mu_c = 7.7 \frac{\sqrt{M}\ P_c^{\frac{2}{3}}}{T_c^{\frac{1}{6}}} \tag{5-3}$$

where μ_c is the critical viscosity in micropoises, M is molecular weight, T_c is the critical temperature in °K, and P_c is the critical pressure in atmospheres.

Example 5-14. Viscosity of Vapors. A 60 API gasoline has an average boiling point of 250°F. According to Figs. 5-9 and 5-12, it has the following properties:

Molal average bp............. 215°F
Molecular weight............. 102
Critical temperature.......... 540°F
Critical pressure............. 460 psia

The critical temperature (°C) is

$$(540 + 40) \div 1.8 - 40 = 282°C = 555°K$$

and the critical pressure in atmospheres

$$460 \div 14.7 = 31.25$$

Using Eq. (5-3),

$$\mu_c = 7.7 \frac{\sqrt{102} \times 31.25^{0.667}}{555^{0.167}}$$
$$= \frac{7.7 \times 10.1 \times 9.95}{2.87}$$
$$= 270$$

The viscosity of this gasoline at 50 psia and 450°F can be estimated from Fig. 5-16 as follows:

$$T_R = \frac{450 + 460}{540 + 460} = 0.91$$
$$P_R = {}^{50}\!/_{460} = 0.109$$
$$\mu_R = 0.430 \text{ (Fig. 5-16)}$$

and $\mu = 0.430 \times 270 = 116$
or $= 0.0116$ centipoises

Had the pressure been 1,380 psia, the gasoline would have been a liquid, and the reduced pressure, reduced viscosity, and viscosity would have been

$$P_R = {}^{1380}\!/_{460} = 3.0$$
$$\mu_R = 4.0$$
$$\mu = 4 \times 270 = 1,080$$

or $= 0.108$ centipoises

[18] A Universal Viscosity Correlation, *Natl. Pet. News, Tech. Sect.*, Oct. 4, 1944.

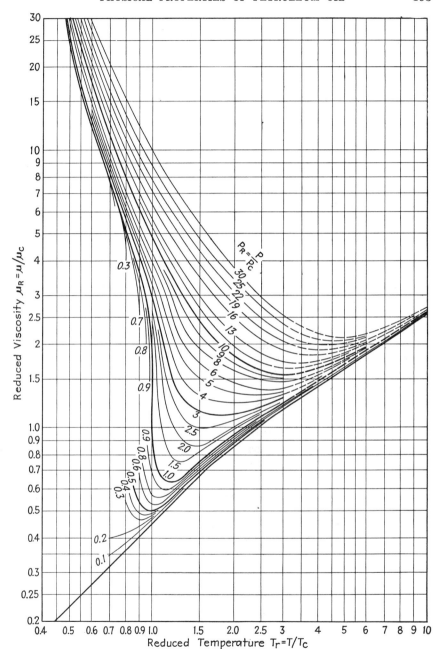

FIG. 5-16. Generalized reduced viscosities of hydrocarbons. (*Courtesy of Hougen and Watson, "Chem. Process Principles," vol. 1, John Wiley & Sons, Inc., New York.*)

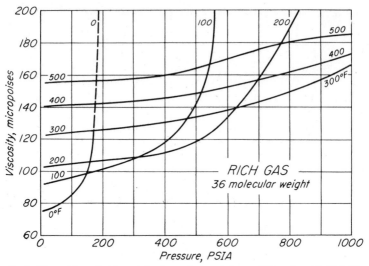

FIG. 5-17. Viscosities of rich gas hydrocarbon mixtures (36 mol. wt.) (*Oil Gas J.*)

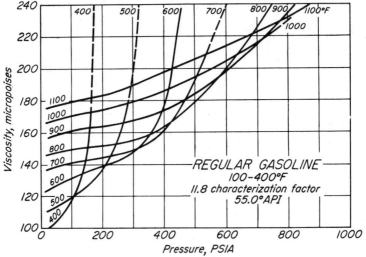

FIG. 5-18. Viscosities of regular-gasoline vapors (100–400°F, 55 API, 11.8 Characterization Factor). (*Oil Gas J.*)

The use of Fig. 5-16 is so cumbersome that viscosity values have been computed[19] for common refinery vapors (see Figs. 5-17 to 5-20 and Table 5-4). At very high pressures the vapors begin to partake of the properties of liquids (see especially the high pressure range of Fig. 5-19).

[19] Nelson, W. L., Viscosity of Vapors, *Oil Gas J.*, Feb. 12, p. 109, and Feb. 26, p. 147, 1948.

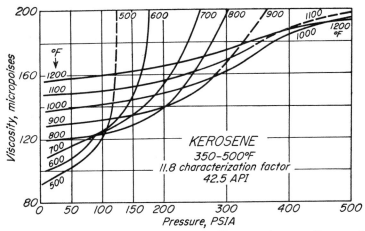

Fig. 5-19. Viscosities of kerosene vapors (350–500°F, 42.5 API, 11.8 Characterization Factor). (*Oil Gas J.*)

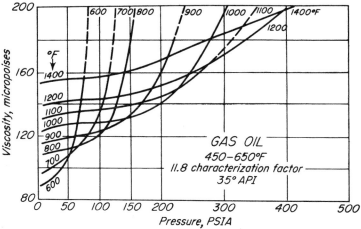

Fig. 5-20. Viscosities of gas oil vapors (450–650°F, 35.0 API, 11.8 Characterization Factor). (*Oil Gas J.*)

The designer usually knows little about the boiling points or molecular weight of lubricating oils, but viscosity data are usually available. Thus, molecular weights can be obtained from viscosity by means[20] of Fig. 5-21.

Heat of Combustion. The heat of combustion of petroleum oils increases with API gravity (or hydrogen content) as indicated in Fig. 5-22.[8] The figure is highly accurate if the percentage of water, ash, and sulfur is accounted for. Tables 14-3 and 14-4 give analyses and heating values

[20] Mills et al., *Ind. Eng. Chem.*, **38**, 442 (1946).

TABLE 5-4. VISCOSITY OF A FEW PETROLEUM VAPORS[a] (see also Figs. 5-17 to 5-20), MICROPOISES[b]

Temp, °F	Pressure, psia									
	14.7	50	100	200	300	400	500	600	700	1000
Lean gas (18 mol. wt)										
0	92	92	93	94	95	97	99	102	105	123
100	110	111	111	112	113	114	116	118	120	134
200	128	129	129	130	132	133	135	137	139	149
300	142	142	143	144	145	147	149	151	153	162
400	158	158	159	160	162	163	165	167	168	174
Light gasoline (100–340°F, 61 API)										
300	94	98	109							
400	106	109	114	140						
500	120	122	125	133	147	180				
600	130	131	131	134	144	164	194	233	280	
700	141	142	142	145	150	159	176	202	238	
800[a]	152	154	156	158	164	170	178	189	202	
900[a]	163	165	167	169	173	178	185	195	213	
1,000[a]	174	176	177	180	182	187	193	202	218	
1,200[a]	196	197	198	200	208	216	224	230	234	244
Naphtha (300–450°F, 46 API)										
400	90	100								
500	99	104	119							
600	109	113	122	161						
700	118	120	125	146	201					
800[a]	129	130	131	139	170	210	258			
900[a]	140	141	143	147	155	172	194	221	257	
1,000[a]	161	162	165	170	177	187	200	215	234	
1,300[a]	180	181	182	186	190	197	206	216	228	

[a] Note that cracking or decomposition will change the composition at temperatures above about 700°F unless the time is very short.
[b] One-millionth of a poise or 1/10,000 centipoise.

of various refinery fuels. The hydrogen content of petroleum fuels may be estimated from Fig. 5-23.

Net heating value may be computed from the gross heating value and the percentage of hydrogen, by subtracting the latent heat of condensation (at calorimeter-bomb temperature) of the water produced during combustion of the hydrogen.

Explosive Limits. The behavior of some materials is indicated in Table 5-5. Pressure has little effect on the lower limit but it tends to

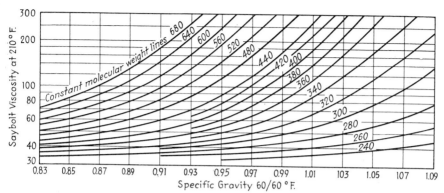

FIG. 5-21. Saybolt Universal viscosity at 210°F, specific gravity, and molecular weight of lubricating oils. (*Mills et al., Ind. Eng. Chem.*)

increase the upper limit as indicated here for one gas mixture.[21]   The explosive limits of mixtures of explosive gases cannot be estimated from the composition of the mixture except by a laborious method.[22]

Pressure, psia	Inflammability limits, vol. %		
	Lower	Upper	Range
1*	4.5	8.0†	3.5
3*	4.15	13.4	9.25
10*	4.3	13.8	9.5
14.7	4.65	14.0	9.35
100	4.9	17.5	12.6
200	4.9	22.6	17.7
350	4.1	37.5	33.4

* Read from a graph.
† Many scattered points.

Heat of Fusion.   The heat of fusion of paraffin wax, as reported by various investigators, ranges from 63 to 78.5 Btu per lb, an average value of about 72.5.   The data of A. Bondi[23] on the heat of solidification and of mixing of wax and oil are shown in Table 5-6.   The paraffin wax completely solidified, but the oils were cooled only through the ranges at which the wax solidified.

[21] Jones and Kennedy, *U.S. Bur. Mines Rept. Invest.*, 3798, February, 1945; also Nelson, W. L., *Oil Gas J.*, Mar. 3, 1949, p. 92.

[22] Handbook and Catalogue No. P-7 of Vapor Recovery Systems Company (Varco); also Nelson, W. L., *Oil Gas J.*, Jan. 13, 1949, p. 66.

[23] Physical Chemistry of Lubricating Oils, VI, Phase Equilibria, *Pet. Refiner*, June, 1947, p. 116.

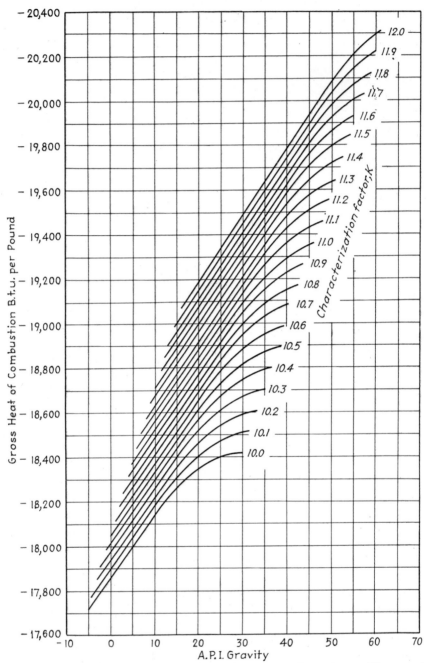

FIG. 5-22. Gross heats of combustion of liquid petroleum hydrocarbons. (*Courtesy of Hougen and Watson, "Chem. Process Principles," vol. 1, John Wiley & Sons, Inc.*)

TABLE 5-5. AUTOIGNITION TEMPERATURES AND EXPLOSIVE LIMITS

Material	Explosive limits, % by volume in air		Autoignition temperature, °F
	Lower	Higher	
Carbon monoxide	12.5	74.2	1204
Hydrogen	4.1	74.2	1076
Acetylene	2.5	80.0	635
Hydrogen sulfide	4.3	45.5	500
Methane	5.3	13.9	999
Ethylene	3.02	34.0	1009
Ethane	3.12	15.0	950
Propylene	2.0	11.1	927
Cyclopropane	2.41	10.3	
Propane	2.37	9.5	871
Natural gas	4.8	13.5	
Butadiene 1-3	2.0	11.5	842
n-Butylene	1.7	9.0	
i-Butane	1.8	8.4	
n-Butane	1.6	8.5	806
Methyl ethyl ketone	1.81	11.5	760
Methyl n-butyl ketone	1.22	8.0	
n-Pentane	1.4	8.0	588
Benzol	1.4	8.0	1076
Cyclohexane	1.31	8.35	
n-Hexane	1.25	6.9	477
Toluene	1.27	7.0	1026
Styrene	1.1	6.1	914
n-Heptane	1.0	6.0	452
o-Xylene	1.0	5.3	924
n-Octane	0.84	3.2	450
n-Nonane	0.74	2.9	
n-Decane	0.67	2.6	Above 500
Petroleum ether	1.4	5.9	475
Stoddard's solvent	1.1	6.0	450–500
Gasoline	1.3	6.0	495
Kerosene	1.16	6.0	490
Lubricating oil, spindle	.....	.....	478
Lubricating oil, cylinder	.....	.....	783

Solubility of Oxygen and of Water in Oils. The approximate solubility of water[24] in hydrocarbons and oils is indicated in Fig. 5-24. Pressure ordinarily has little effect on the solubility, but at higher temperatures the solubility increases except in the range of the critical temperature

[24] Nelson, W. L., *Oil Gas J.*, Apr. 2, 1956, p. 140. Also see Dougherty, R. P., *Oil Gas J.*, Sept. 1, 1952, p. 94.

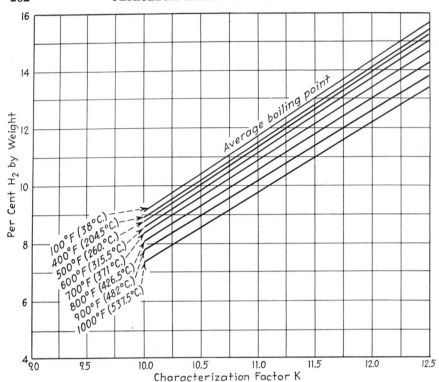

FIG. 5-23. Hydrogen content of hydrocarbons. (*Courtesy of Hougen and Watson, "Chem. Process Principles," vol. 1, John Wiley and Sons, Inc.*)

TABLE 5-6. HEAT OF SOLIDIFICATION OF WAX AND OILS

Material	Range of solidification, °F	Pour point, °F	Heat of solidification of mixture, Btu/lb	Heat of fusion of wax portion, Btu/lb	Heat of mixing, Btu/lb
Paraffin wax...............	124–118	122	75.6		
10 per cent No. 1 in 500 pale oil....	95–61	82	8.1	7.5[a]	0.6[a]
10 per cent No. 1 in 300 white oil....	104–59	90	9.0	7.5[a]	1.5[a]
Pa. bright stock................	59–36	28	2.9		
Pa. 150 neutral................	45–18	23	3.6		
Pa. SAE 30 oil................	46–19	23	3.1		
No. 6 plus 0.5 per cent Paraflow....	46–14	3	3.1		
Waxy 300 pale oil..............	59–36	36	4.3		
No. 8 plus 0.5 per cent Paraflow....	55–32	−17	4.1		

[a] These are based on the entire wax-oil mixture.

where the solubility decreases.   No simple relationship is available for the solubility of oils in water, but at the boiling point of water, the solubility of lubricating oil is about 10^{-5} to 10^{-4} mole per cent oil, depending on the molecular weight of the oil.

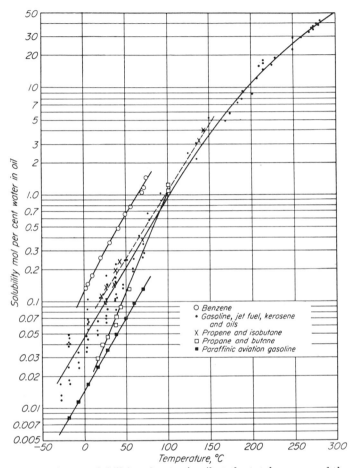

FIG. 5-24. Approximate solubilities of water in oil at the total pressure of the system. (*Oil Gas J.*)

The solubility of oxygen (and perhaps air) in oils is indicated in Table 5-7.[25]

Surface Tension of Hydrocarbons.   Table 5-8 indicates the effect of temperature on the surface tension of hydrocarbons,[26] and the general

[25] Nelson, W. L., *Oil Gas J.*, June 11, 1942, p. 48.
[26] Katz and Saltman, *Ind. Eng. Chem.*, **31**, 91 (1939).

TABLE 5-7. SOLUBILITY OF OXYGEN IN OILS

Partial pressure, mm	Solubility of oxygen, cc per liter				
	Gas oil at 77°F	Transformer oil at 77°F	Paraffin oil at 65°F	Kerosene at 65°F	Pentane at 77°F
100	20.3	20.5	15	20.9	76
400	81	82	60	83.7	304
760	154	156	114	159	576
1,560	380	312	228	318	1,152
3,800	770	780	570	795	2,880
7,600	1,540	.....	...	.....	5,760
53,200	10,780				

TABLE 5-8. SURFACE TENSION OF HYDROCARBONS
Dynes per centimeter

	Surface tension at these temperatures, °F							
	−150	−100	−50	0	100	200	300	400
Methane..............	2.8							
Ethane...............	19.2	14.2	9.7	5.5				
Propane..............	24.6	20.3	16.2	12.4	5.2	0.2		
Isobutane............	27	23	18.9	15.1	8.4	2.8		
Butane...............	....	24.7	20.8	17.2	10.5	4.5	0.1	
Pentane..............	....	....	23.8	20.5	14.0	8.0	3.0	
Hexane...............	....	....	25.8	22.6	16.5	10.9	5.6	1.6
Heptane..............	....	....	27.4	24.4	18.6	13.1	8.0	3.6
Octane...............	....	....	....	25.7	20.2	14.9	9.9	5.3
140 mol. wt..........	....	....	....	27.6	22.5	17.4	12.6	
160 mol. wt..........	....	....	....	28.7	23.7	18.9	14.3	
180 mol. wt..........	....	....	....	29.6	24.8	20.0	15.6	
200 mol. wt..........	....	....	....	30.4	25.8	21.2	16.9	
220 mol. wt..........	....	....	....	31.0	26.6	22.1	17.9	
240 mol. wt..........	....	....	....	31.7	27.3	22.9	18.7	

effect of temperature may be computed from this equation.

$$V_2 = V_1[(T_c - T_2) \div (T_c - T_1)]^{1.2}$$

in which T is the absolute temperature (°R), T_c is the absolute critical temperature, and V is the tension in dynes per centimeter.

Vapor Pressure and Boiling Point Corrections. The vapor pressure or tendency of a liquid to vaporize is involved in condensation, vaporization, fractionation, etc., computations as well as the correction of boiling points from one pressure to another. Figs. 5-25 and 5-26 are the result of an exhaustive study of all available information[27] including Fig. 5-27 also shown here. They (Figs. 5-25 and 5-26) should be used when great accuracy is required and for the correction of the boiling points recorded in vacuum distillations. The Esso Engineering and Research Company has published a series of standard tabulations[28] based on these figures by which recorded distillation temperatures may be converted to their normal (760 mm) boiling points. A more convenient but less accurate method of presenting vapor pressures is shown in Fig. 5-27 and it may be used for most engineering computations.

Charts of the vapor pressures of paraffin, olefin, and naphthene hydrocarbons exhibit a consistent pattern, but the lines for low-boiling aromatic hydrocarbons are quite erratic even showing curvature. Nevertheless, the effect of the kind of hydrocarbon series or Characterization Factor is very small, and need not be considered except when the range of vapor pressure is very great (tenfold or more). Maximum corrections for Characterization Factor are only about plus or minus 10°F when correcting conventional materials from 0.1 mm up to atmospheric pressure. Figs. 5-25 and 5-26 are based on a Characterization Factor of 12.0, and corrections may be computed[27] from:

$$\Delta t = -2.5(K - 12) \times \log_{10}(P_2/P_1) \qquad (5\text{-}4)$$

Here Δt refers to the correction in degrees Fahrenheit, K refers to Characterization Factor, and P_2 and P_1 to the upper and lower limits of vapor pressure (mm).

Example 5-15. Use of Vapor Pressure Charts.

A. What is the vapor pressure of *n*-butane at 77°F (25°C)?

By means of a thread or rule, align on Fig. 5-27 the temperature of 77°F on the right-hand scale with the point for *n*-butane (30+°F) on the center scale and read 1,800 mm or 34.7 psia on the left scale.

B. What is the boiling point of *n*-butane at 1,000 mm?

Align 1,000 mm on the left scale of Fig. 5-27 with the *n*-butane point on the center scale and read 44 or 45°F on the right scale.

C. An oil is boiling at 300°F in a vacuum still at 9 mm pressure. What is the atmospheric boiling point?

On Fig. 5-25 read upward from 300°F to 9 mm. This indicates an atmospheric boiling point of 556°F. Likewise, Fig. 5-27 shows an atmospheric boiling point of about 557°F.

D. If the oil of part *C* has a Characterization Factor of 11.3 rather than 12 (the basis of Figs. 5-25 and 5-26), the atmospheric boiling point is 559.4°F rather than 556°F. This was obtained by using Eq. (5-4):

$$\begin{aligned}\Delta t &= -2.5(11.3 - 12) \times \log_{10} {}^{760}\!\!\!\mathop{/_{\!9}} \\ &= -2.5(-0.7) \times 1.927 \\ &= 3.37°F\end{aligned}$$

Thus, 556 plus 3.37 = 559.4°F

[27] Maxwell and Bonnell, Derivation and Precision of a New Vapor Pressure Correlation . . . , *Ind. Eng. Chem.*, **49**, 1187 (1957).

[28] Vapor Pressure Charts for Petroleum Hydrocarbons, April, 1955.

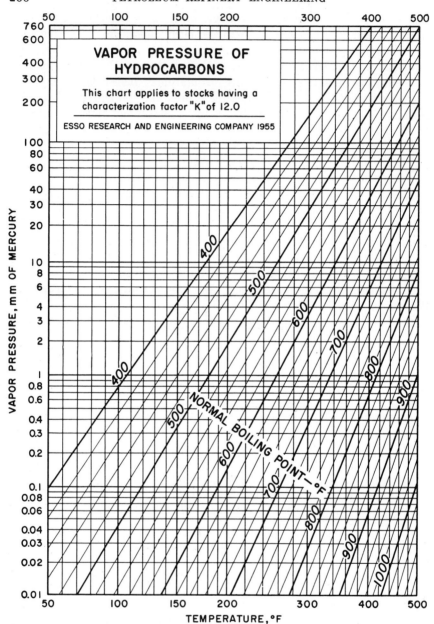

FIG. 5-25. Vapor pressure of hydrocarbon oils (low range). (*Esso Research and Eng. Co.*)

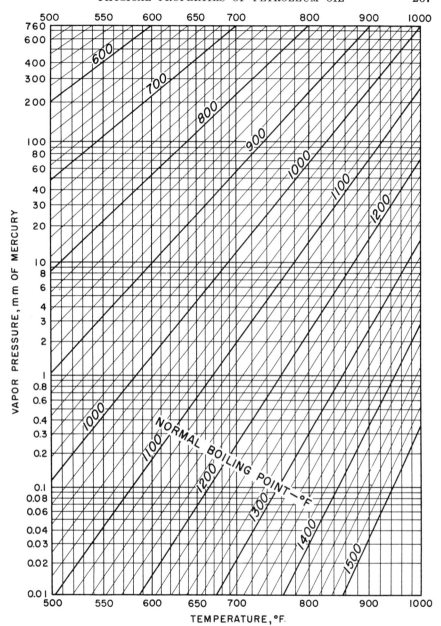

FIG. 5-26. Vapor pressure of hydrocarbon oils (high range).   (*Esso Research and Eng. Co.*)

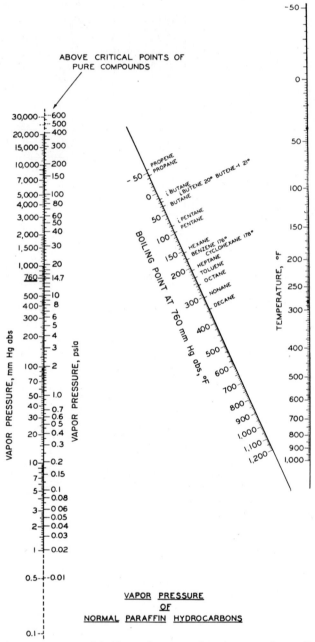

Fig. 5-27. Vapor pressure and boiling-point corrections for normal paraffin hydrocarbons and petroleum fractions.

Width of boiling range as in a petroleum fraction appears to have little effect on the change of boiling point with pressure.[29] Inherently, the true-boiling-point type of distillation curve should correlate most exactly because it consists of the boiling points of nearly pure materials as they distill one by one. The equilibrium flash vaporization curves illustrate the other extreme type of distillation curve, and corrections of this curve from one pressure to another should not be exactly the same as the correction for fractionating distillations. Nevertheless, a large difference does not seem to exist between these two extremes of boiling-point corrections, nor does the slope of the distillation curve seem to alter the vapor-pressure or boiling-point corrections to a great extent.

Piromoov and Beiswenger[30] find that the slopes of flash-vaporization curves are practically independent of pressure, so that the correction of the boiling point or flash-vaporization point is a constant number of degrees throughout the entire curve. They suggest that the correction should be determined by correcting the intersection point between the true-boiling-point curve and the flash-vaporization curve by the vapor-pressure data of the paraffin hydrocarbons. The intersection point is used because the true-boiling-point curve and the flash-vaporization curve intersect at approximately the same percentage point regardless of pressure.

Edmister, Reidel, and Mervin[31] have determined flash-vaporization curves on three oils up to pressures of 200 psia. They find that the higher the pressure the flatter the vaporization curve, and hence the curves at high pressures should not be drawn parallel to the atmospheric-pressure curve. Obviously, the flash curve should be horizontal at the critical pressure, and hence the slope of the flash curve will be flatter and flatter as the pressure is increased. They find that the 50 per cent atmospheric boiling point should be corrected to the new pressure by using the vapor-pressure relationship of the paraffin hydrocarbons (Fig. 5-27). In practical design computations it is common practice to convert to the new pressure by using any convenient point on the atmospheric flash-vaporization curve. Refer also to Figs. 4-22 and 15-13.

Compression or Expansion. When gases or vapors are expanded or compressed under adiabatic conditions, the amount of work done and the amount of heat required are dependent upon the ratio of the specific heat at constant pressure to the specific heat at constant volume. The expansion of a gas can always be expressed by an equation of the form

[29] Nelson and Haltenberger, *Oil Gas J.*, June 11, p. 38, and June 18, p. 40, 1942.

[30] Equilibrium Vaporization of Oils and the Carrying Effects of Light Ends, *API Bull.* 10, no. 2, sec. II, p. 52, 1929.

[31] Equilibrium Flash Vaporization of Three Petroleum Fractions, *Trans. A.I.Ch.E.*, **39**, 457 (1943).

$$P_1 V_1^n = P_2 V_2^n = \text{a constant}$$

At adiabatic conditions the exponent n is referred to as gamma (γ) and is equal to the ratio of the specific heats as mentioned above. Scheibel and Othmer[32] developed Fig. 5-28, which may be used to estimate the ratio of specific heats of petroleum fractions by using the molecular-weight scale on the right. The scales of critical temperature and pressure also shown at the right are provided only for convenience in estimating these constants. The chart (and molecular-weight scale) was developed for the normal paraffin hydrocarbons, and hence the position of the olefin, etc., hydrocarbons on the right scale is empirical and does not correspond to their molecular weights.

Example 5-16. Ratio of Specific Heats (Fig. 5-28). A 100-molecular-weight gasoline is maintained at 500°F and at 60 psia. In determining C_P/C_V from Fig. 5-28, the critical conditions and reduced conditions are

$$P_c = 395 \text{ psia}$$
$$T_c = 970°\text{R}$$
$$P_R = {}^{60}\!/_{395} = 0.152$$
$$T_c = \frac{500 + 460}{970} = 0.99$$

A line is drawn across the reduced condition scales on the left to locate a point on the reference line (8.5). This reference point is connected with 100 on the molecular-weight scale, and C_P/C_V is found to be 1.05.

In solving for the temperature change during adiabatic expansion or contraction, the following relationship is convenient:

$$\frac{T_2}{T_1} = \left(\frac{P_2}{P_1}\right)^{\frac{\gamma - 1}{\gamma}} \tag{5-5}$$

where T represents temperature, P represents pressure, and γ is the ratio C_P/C_V.

The ratio C_P/C_V is small for heavy vapors such as gasoline and kerosene, and it is also lower at high temperatures. Thus little change in temperature occurs when such vapors are expanded or compressed.

Detonation Characteristics. The octane numbers of many hydrocarbons are shown in Table 5-9. Many of the data were taken from the excellent "Physical Constants of the Principle Hydrocarbons," compiled by the Technical and Research Division of The Texas Company (1942). In parentheses are shown blending octane numbers, and in general, the blending octane numbers by the Research method are higher than by the Motor method of test.

The effect of various arrangements or attachments to the molecule

[32] Hydrocarbon Gases . . . Specific Heats and Power Requirements for Compression, *Ind. Eng. Chem.*, **36**, 580 (1944).

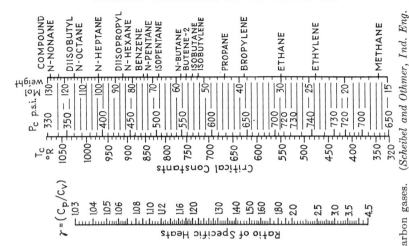

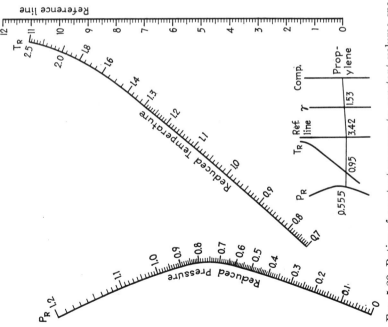

FIG. 5-28. Ratios of constant-pressure to constant-volume specific heats of hydrocarbon gases. (*Scheibel and Othmer, Ind. Eng. Chem.*)

TABLE 5-9. OCTANE NUMBERS[a] OF SOME HYDROCARBONS[b]

	Motor	Research
Paraffin hydrocarbons:		
Ethane................................	+6	+6
Propane...............................	97	+1.9
Butane................................	90.1	93.6
2-Methylpropane.......................	99	>100
Pentane...............................	61.9	61.9 (61.5r)
2-Methylbutane........................	90.3	92.3 (99.5r)
2,2-Dimethylbutane....................	83	— (116r)
Hexane................................	26	24.8 (29r)
2-Methylpentane.......................	73	73.4 (69r)
3-Methylpentane.......................	75	74.5 (85.5r)
2,2-Dimethylbutane....................	93.4	91.8 (97r)
2,3-Dimethylbutane....................	94.3	101.7 (96r)
Heptane (Octane No. standard)..........	0	0 (0)
2-Methylhexane........................	45	— (55r)
3-Methylhexane........................	....	65 (65r)
2,2-Dimethylpentane...................	93	— (80r)
2,3-Dimethylpentane...................	89	88.5 (94r)
2,4-Dimethylpentane...................	82	— (80r)
3,3-Dimethylpentane...................	84	— (98r)
2,2,3-Trimethylbutane..................	+0.7	+1.83 (112.5)
3-Ethylpentane........................	....	62 (68r)
Octane................................	−17	−19 (−19r)
2-Methylheptane.......................	23.8	21.7
3-Methylheptane.......................	35	26.8
4-Methylheptane.......................	39	26.7 (30.5r)
3-Ethylhexane.........................	52.4	33.5
2,2-Dimethylhexane....................	77.4	72.5 (67r)
2,3-Dimethylhexane....................	78.9	71.3 (70.5r)
2,4-Dimethylhexane....................	69.9	65.2 (64.5r)
2,5-Dimethylhexane....................	55.7	55.5 (69r)
3,3-Dimethylhexane....................	83.4	75.5 (72.5r)
3,4-Dimethylhexane....................	81.7	76.3 (80m)
2-Methyl, 3-ethylpentane...............	88.1	87.3 (76r)
3-Methyl, 3-ethylpentane...............	88.7	80.8 (88.5m)
2,2,3-Trimethylpentane.................	99.9	+1.18 (111.5m)
2,2,4-Trimethylpentane (Oct. No. standard).	100.0	100.0 (100.0)
2,3,3-Trimethylpentane.................	99.4	+0.61
2,3,4-Trimethylpentane.................	95.9	+0.22
2,2,3,3-Tetramethylbutane..............	103.0	
Nonane................................	−45	−34 (−34r)
2-Methyloctane........................	−4	
3-Methyloctane........................	12	
Decane................................	....	−53 (−32r)
2-Methylnonane........................	−16	
2,2,6-Trimethylheptane.................	78.7	

TABLE 5-9. OCTANE NUMBERS[a] OF SOME HYDROCARBONS[b] (Continued)

	Motor	Research
Olefin hydrocarbons:		
Propene................................	81	>100 (85.5r)
Butene-1...............................	80	— (111.5r)
Butene-2...............................	83	
2-Methylpropene........................	87	
Pentene-1..............................	....	92 (98.5r)
Pentene-2..............................	80	98 (125r)
Hexene-1...............................	....	80 (85r)
Hexene-2...............................	78	89 (100r)
Heptene-1..............................	....	54 (55r)
Heptene-2..............................	....	70 (71r)
2-Methylhexene-1.......................	75	
2-Methylhexene-2.......................	84	
Octene-1...............................	34.7	28.7 (25r)
Octene-2...............................	56.5	56.3 (74.5r)
Octene-3...............................	68.1	72.5
Octene-4...............................	74.3	73.3
2,4,4-Trimethylpentene-1................	86	>100 (150r)
2,4,4-Trimethylpentene-2................	89	— (133m)
3,4,4-Trimethylpentene-2................	85.6	— (72.5m)
Nonene-1...............................	....	20 (15r)
2-Methyloctene-1.......................	98	— (69.8m)
3-Methyloctene-1.......................	83.5	— (72.2m)
3-Methyloctene-2.......................	94	
2,6,6-Trimethylheptene-2................	73.6	— (70m)
Diisoamylene...........................	75	
Triisoamylene..........................	87	
Hexadiene-1,3..........................	....	84 (79r)
Cyclopentene...........................	....	>100 (140r)
Cyclohexene............................	63	83.9 (137r)
1,3-Cyclopentadiene....................	86.1	+0.29 (217r)
Naphthene hydrocarbons:		
Cyclopentane...........................	85	100 (141r)
Methylcyclopentane.....................	80	91.3 (107r)
Cyclohexane............................	78.6	83 (109.5r)
Ethylcyclopentane......................	....	62 (59r)
1,3-Dimethylcyclopentane...............	....	72 (51r)
Methylcyclohexane......................	73	74.8 (104r)
Propylcyclopentane.....................	28.1	31.2 (16r)
Isopropylcyclopentane..................	76.2	81.1 (83r)
Ethylcyclohexane.......................	40.8	45.6 (43r)
1,2-Dimethylcyclohexane................	78.7	80.9 (85r)
Propylcyclohexane......................	14	17.8 (20r)
Isopropylcyclohexane...................	61.1	62.8 (62r)
1,1,3-Trimethylcyclohexane.............	82.6	81.3 (92m)

TABLE 5-9. OCTANE NUMBERS[a] OF SOME HYDROCARBONS[b] (*Continued*)

	Motor	Research
Aromatic hydrocarbons:		
Benzene.	+2.75	>100 (98.5r)
Toluene.	+0.27	>100 (123.5r)
o-Xylene.	100	>100 (120r)
m-Xylene.	>100	>100 (144.5r)
p-Xylene.	>100	>100 (145.5r)
Ethylbenzene.	97.9	+0.8 (124r)
1,3,5-Trimethylbenzene.	. . . .	>100 (161r)
Propylbenzene.	98.7	+1.52 (127r)
Isopropylbenzene.	99.3	+2.08 (132r)
1-Methyl, 4-isopropylbenzene.	. . . .	>100 (136r)
1,3-Diethylbenzene.	. . . .	>100 (145r)
1,4-Diethylbenzene.	. . . .	>100 (158r)
Butylbenzene.	. . . .	>100 (115r)

[a] Blending octane numbers in parentheses.
[b] A plus sign (+) indicates number of cc of TEL added to isooctane.

has been studied extensively,[33,34] and some of the relationships are evident in Table 5-9. In general, the octane number is lowest for the straight-chain hydrocarbons and highest for the aromatic hydrocarbons, with the olefins and naphthenes in an intermediate position. However, the blending octane number of the olefin hydrocarbons is very high, being almost the equal of the aromatic hydrocarbons. This is offset to some extent by the poor susceptibility of olefin hydrocarbons to tetraethyllead. For the paraffin hydrocarbons the tendency to knock is decreased by

1. Shortening the main chain.
2. Introducing side-chain groups such as methyl groups.
3. Centralizing the molecule by adding methyl groups about the center of the main chain.

The tendency of the olefin hydrocarbons to knock is decreased by

1. The same three factors as for the paraffin hydrocarbons.
2. Moving the double bond toward the center of the chain.

The tendency of the naphthenes to knock is decreased by

1. Decreasing the size of the ring.
2. Decreasing the length of the longest unbranched side chain.
3. Distributing the carbon atoms in the side chains into many short chains rather than one long chain.
4. Centralization of the side chains.

[33] Lovell, Campbell and Boyd, *Ind. Eng. Chem.*, **23**, 26 (1931); olefins, **23**, 555 (1931); and naphthenes, **25**, 1107 (1933).
[34] Kettering, C. F., *Ind. Eng. Chem.*, **36**, 1079 (1944).

CHAPTER 6

INTRODUCTION TO PROCESSING

Because of the wide differences in crude oils (see Chap. 4), we find that processing methods differ. We may safely say that no two plants are employing exactly the same processing scheme. What may be a perfect method of handling one oil may be inadequate for another. The refining of an oil is, of course, an economic problem. (1) What are the value and the accessibility of the raw stock; (2) what are the value of the products and the possibilities of marketing them; (3) what yields of products are to be expected; and (4) what will it cost to process the stock? These factors promote the use of many different processing plans.

Refinery Products.* A listing of the more important products of refining will help to show why so many different processing methods are used.

1. *Natural and refinery gas*—household and industrial fuel.
2. *Gasoline*—fuel for internal-combustion engines.
3. *Naphtha and benzene*—cleaner's solvents, paint thinners, chemical solvents, and stocks for the blending of motor fuels.
4. *Jet fuel*—fuel for jet or gas turbine engines, and for rockets.
5. *Kerosene*—burning oil for household lamps.
6. *Distillates, diesel fuel, and gas oil* (distilled products)—fuels for industrial and household furnaces, enriching agents in gas manufacture, absorbents for hydrocarbon gases, and fuels for diesel engines.
7. *Neutral oils*—light or low-viscosity lubricating-oil stocks for the compounding of motor oils and light machine oils.
8. *Bright stock*—heavy or high-viscosity lubricating-oil stocks for the compounding of motor oils.
9. *Cylinder oils*—unfinished heavy-oil stocks used directly as lubricants for steam-engine cylinders or for the manufacture of bright stock. Usually filtered but not dewaxed.
10. *Paraffin wax*—used for the manufacture of wax paper, insulating material, package sealing, etc.
11. *Petrolatum* (microcrystalline wax)—base material in the compounding of greases, salves, ointments, and package sealing.
12. *Fuel oil* (residual product)—industrial fuel.
13. *Tar and asphalt*—asphalt, road oil, roofing materials, and protective coatings.
14. *Petroleum coke*—solid industrial fuel.

* See Chap. 3 for details.

215

General Processing. The most important method of separating petroleum products is distillation, and hence the products should be compared with one another in the order of their boiling ranges. A mixed-base oil might yield products as indicated in Fig. 6-1. Figure 6-2 likewise indicates the relation among the raw materials, the intermediate refinery

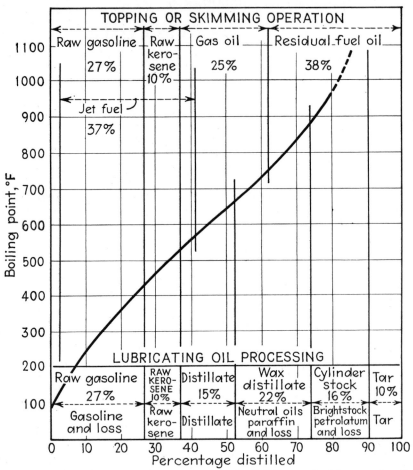

FIG. 6-1. Boiling range of refinery products (31.7 API Texas mixed-base crude oil).

stocks, and the finished market products. The dotted lines indicate products obtained by cracking. The products obtained by distillation are called "raw products," and most of them cannot be sold until they have been further refined.

Raw gasoline and raw naphtha are often treated with chemical agents such as caustic soda, copper chloride, or doctor solution. Much naphtha is now catalytically reformed into high octane gasoline. Kerosene usually requires only a sweetening treatment; but for fine colors, acid treatment or filtration is used. Diesel fuels, distillate fuels, gas oil, and residual fuel oil are usually sold without treatment. Pressure distillate or cracked gasoline, obtained by cracking or thermal decomposition (Fig. 6-2), is sweetened, and an inhibitor of gum formation is added. Natural gasoline, obtained from natural gas, usually requires only a sweetening treatment for the removal of hydrogen sulfide and mercaptan compounds.

Wax distillate, the raw stock for the manufacture of the light lubricating oils or neutral oil-blending stocks, contains crystalline wax. The wax is removed by chilling the distillate and filtering the wax from the oil in filter presses. Two unfinished stocks, *slack wax* and *pressed distillate*, are obtained in the pressing operation. *Neutral oils** are produced from the pressed distillate by distillation and subsequent filtration through fuller's earth. Crude scale is produced from slack wax by "sweating" or, in other words, by slowly warming the chilled slack wax so that the oil and low-melting materials, which together are called *foots oil*, melt and drain from the slack wax. Crude scale is slightly yellow in color, and this coloration may be removed by treatment with acid or caustic or by filtering the melted wax through clay. Cylinder stock is another wax-bearing product, but the wax is such that it cannot be filtered from the oil in wax presses. This so-called "amorphous wax" or *petrolatum stock* may be removed by dissolving the oil in naphtha, filtering the solution to a proper color through fuller's earth, and centrifuging the chilled solution in high-speed centrifuges. The products from this separation are solutions of *bright stock* and *petrolatum*. The naphtha is removed from the solutions by distillation, leaving finished bright stock and petrolatum.

Since 1935, the dewaxing processes described above are being replaced by the use of solvents such as methyl ethyl ketone for dewaxing both wax distillate and cylinder stock. Likewise, lubricating oils (light or heavy) are being treated with furfural, phenol, etc., for the removal of the low Viscosity Index portions. Figure 11-1 shows the relation of solvent refining to the general processing outlined in this chapter.

Cracking. Materials such as *cracking-still gas, pressure distillate, cracked gas oil,* and *pressure-still tar* are products of cracking. By cracking we refer to the decomposition of heavy or high-boiling oils by exposure to extreme temperature. At temperatures exceeding about 680°F materials such as gas oil, fuel oil, and tars are decomposed into (1) gas, (2)

---

* The neutral oils are often referred to as pale or red oils. In the past it was thought that part of the wax distillate had to be cracked to produce a pressable material, and the neutrals from the cracked distillate, being a deep-red color, were called "red oils." The terms have now lost their original significance, and the term "red oil" is usually reserved for any neutral oil that is darker than 3NPA.

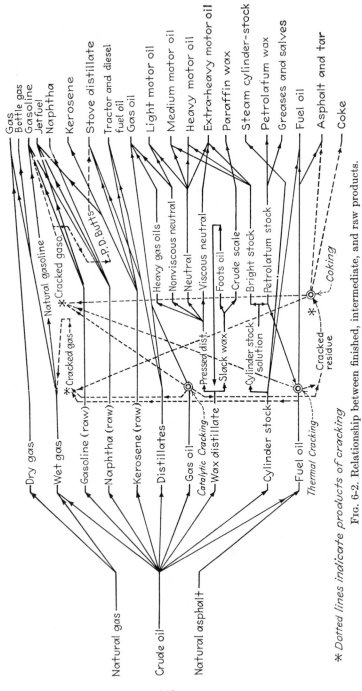

RAW STOCKS — — — INTERMEDIATE PRODUCTS — — — MARKET PRODUCTS

Market products: Gas, Bottle gas, Gasoline, Jet fuel, Naphtha, Kerosene, Stove distillate, Tractor and diesel fuel oil, Gas oil, Light motor oil, Medium motor oil, Heavy motor oil, Extra-heavy motor oil, Paraffin wax, Steam cylinder-stock, Petrolatum wax, Greases and salves, Fuel oil, Asphalt and tar, Coke

Intermediate products: Natural gasoline, Cracked gaso., L.P.D.Butts, Heavy gas oils, Nonviscous neutral, Neutral, Viscous neutral, Foots oil, Crude scale, Bright stock, Petrolatum stock, Coking, *Cracked gas, Pressed dist., Slack wax, Cylinder stock solution, Cracked residue

Raw stocks: Dry gas, Wet gas, Gasoline (raw), Naphtha (raw), Kerosene (raw), Distillates, Gas oil, Wax distillate, Cylinder stock, Fuel oil, Catalytic Cracking, Thermal Cracking

Natural gas, Crude oil, Natural asphalt

*Dotted lines indicate products of cracking

FIG. 6-2. Relationship between finished, intermediate, and raw products.

218

volatile materials (pressure distillate) having the same boiling range as gasoline, and (3) a residue of heavy material (cracked fuel oil) or coke. Pressure distillate receives its name by reason of the high pressures that are usually maintained in the cracking equipment. Cracked gasoline from pressure distillate is valuable as an ingredient of the superior anti-knock motor fuels. Likewise the cracked residue, if cracking is not conducted to the ultimate formation of coke, is called "pressure-still tar."

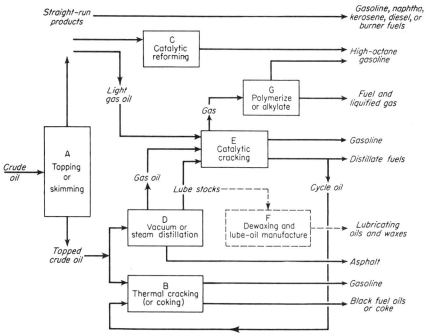

Fig. 6-3. Basic refinery operations of topping, vacuum distillation, thermal cracking, catalytic reforming, and catalytic cracking.

Recycle stock or cracked gas oil, an intermediate between the two foregoing products, is also produced. Recycle stock has about the same boiling range and somewhat the same physical characteristics as gas oil. This material is normally recycled through the cracking system until it is completely converted to gasoline, but a part is sometimes sold as distillate or gas oil.

Catalytic cracking, as well as thermal cracking, has been widely used since 1941. It differs from thermal cracking mainly in the introduction of an adsorbent-type catalyst which holds the asphaltic or tarlike products of cracking on the surface of the catalyst in the form of coke. Only distilled charging stocks are employed. Figure 6-3 indicates the relationship of catalytic cracking to the operations described here.

Summary. In general the refining of petroleum is conducted as outlined in this chapter. However, crude oils vary widely in their properties, and some may not yield all the foregoing products or may contain such small amounts of certain of the products that their manufacture is not profitable.

In general, paraffin-base raw products are the most easily treated, and the others follow in the order mixed-base and naphthene-base. This applies to the light distillates such as gasoline, as well as to the heavy lubricating oils. Many naphthene-base oils contain more *sulfur* than mixed-base oils, and paraffin-base oils may contain scarcely any sulfur. Paraffin- and mixed-base crude oils contain troublesome wax. The fact that a true naphthene-base oil contains *no wax* simplifies the manufacture of lubricants.

These characteristics govern the methods of processing that are used for the different bases of oils and the products that are manufactured. Paraffin-base oils are particularly suited for the manufacture of lubricating oils. However, the gasoline knocks badly in modern automotive engines. Lubricating oils are also produced from mixed-base oils, but acid or solvent treatment is usually necessary, and hence the expense of manufacture is greater. Vacuum distillation, or precipitation of asphalt by liquid propane, is particularly adapted to the processing of mixed- and naphthene-base oils because, most of the asphalt or tarry material may be left behind as a residue, and the cleaned lubricating-oil stocks can be treated more cheaply than asphalt-bearing stocks. Naphthene-base oils produce good asphalt and usually in quantities large enough to justify its manufacture. The gasoline from naphthene crude oils is usually highly antiknock and may often be sold directly as premium-grade motor fuel. Some residual fuel oil and gas oil of mixed- and naphthene-base origin is sold directly, but most of the residue that remains after skimming the gasoline and kerosene is cracked. By cracking, the total yield of gasoline may be increased from about 30 per cent by simple topping to as much as 70 per cent by topping and cracking.

The following general types of processing are fairly well defined:

Skimming or Topping Processing. By simple atmospheric-pressure distillation the crude oil is separated into gasoline, kerosene, fuel oil, or reduced crude oil, and sometimes reformer charge stock, jet fuel, or gas oil. Topping in some form must be practiced on all types of crude oils (Fig. 6-4a).

Cracking Processing. This type usually refers to a combined operation of topping and thermal cracking, and in most refineries the gas oil is catalytically cracked. No lubricating oils are produced in this type of operation. Catalytic cracking (not shown in Fig. 6-4b) results in smaller yields of residual fuel oil. Refer to Fig. 6-5. More detail on gas recovery is indicated in Fig. 7-14.

Lubricating-oil Processing. Topping with the manufacture of lubricants from the residue of the crude oil is implied by this classification. Paraffin-base crude oils are always processed for lubricants. Mixed-base oils are often processed thus (Fig. 6-4c) or by solvent extraction, but naphthene oils are processed for lubricants only under the most favorable conditions. The operations of Fig. 6-4c are now becoming obsolete, but it is included here as a means of introducing the numerous terms used in refinery processing. Refer to Chaps. 10, 11, and 12 for modern details and especially Figs. 11-1 and 12-7.

Complete Processing. Most large refiners practice topping, viscosity breaking (thermal cracking), catalytic cracking, catalytic reforming, and lubricant manufacture simultaneously, and this enormously complicated complete processing cannot be shown on a single diagram. The manu

TABLE 6-1. TYPES OF REFINERY OPERATIONS DURING 1956

	Per cent of crude oil capacity
Topping................	99.6
Catalytic reforming........	10.5
Thermal cracking..........	24.0[a]
Thermal reforming........	4.0
Catalytic cracking........	39.4
Polymerization of gases......	1.6[b]
Alkylation of gases........	2.8[b]
Lube manufacture.........	3.5
Treating..............	50.0

[a] Not including gas or hydrocarbon cracking.
[b] Based on product rather than feed.

TABLE 6-2. ESTIMATE OF CAPACITIES OF VARIOUS UNITED STATES CRACKING FACILITIES DURING 1956

Thermal cracking, % (28% of crude capacity)		Catalytic reforming, % (10.5% of crude capacity)		Catalytic cracking, % (39.7% of crude capacity)	
Reforming..........	14.3	Platforming........	51.9	Fluid.............	70.9
Crude cracked.......	1.2	Hydroforming[a].....	11.5	T.C.C.............	19.2
Coking.............	5.5	Ultraforming......	10.2	Houdry...........	3.7
Viscosity breaking[b]....	10.0	Houdriforming.....	6.2	Houdriflow.........	5.8
		Sovaforming.......	5.1	Cycloversion........	0.4
Cracking:		Catforming........	4.7		
Heavy oil coil[c]......	39.0	Thermofor.........	4.2		
Gas oil coil........	30.0	Others............	6.2		

[a] Both fixed-bed and fluid.
[b] Separate coil.
[c] Essentially viscosity breaking.

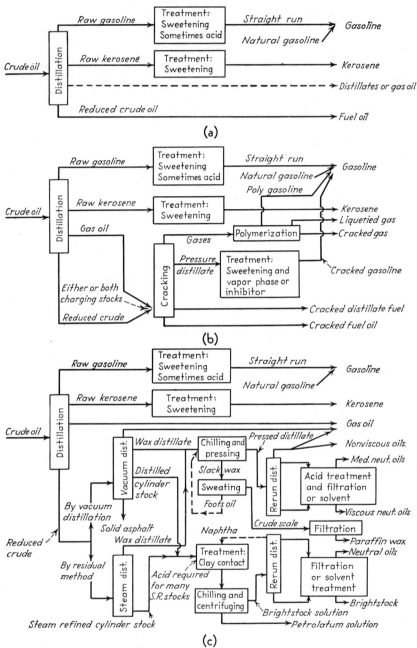

Fig. 6-4. Types of refinery processing. (a) Topping or skimming processing (catalytic reforming now also widely used); (b) cracking processing (vacuum distillation and catalytic cracking now widely used); and (c) lubricating-oil processing (solvent treating and dewaxing now used).

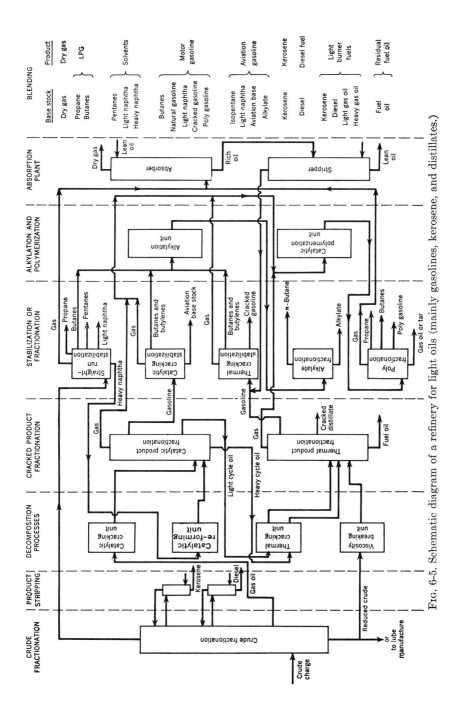

FIG. 6-5. Schematic diagram of a refinery for light oils (mainly gasolines, kerosene, and distillates.)

223

facture of chemicals is not ordinarily included, but the relationship of petrochemicals to the entire processing is evident in Fig. 20-3.

The materials and methods outlined in this chapter constitute the most important ones. Many of the products found on the market are made by blending these stocks together to meet particular industrial requirements. As an example, the various grades of motor oil and machine oil are prepared by compounding different amounts and grades of the neutral oils and bright stock. Very heavy aero oils, etc., consist mainly of bright stock, but sewing-machine oil consists mainly of nonviscous neutral oil. Details of processing operations and processing equipment will be enlarged upon in Chaps. 8 to 12 and 19 to 22.

The extent to which the various operations are conducted can be judged from plant capacities. During 1956, the crude oil capacity

TABLE 6-3. ESTIMATED COMPOSITION OF UNITED STATES GASOLINE POOL

Type	1951	1953	End of 1954
Light straight-run naphtha..........	25.7	24.8	24.5
Heavy straight-run naphtha.........	8.9	7.1	0.7
Catalytic cracked.................	25.6	28.5	34.3
Thermal cracked..................	15.2	13.8	7.1
Catalytic reformate...............	0.4	3.4	14.9
Thermal reformate................	9.3	8.5	6.3
Polymer.........................	1.2	1.2	1.3
Natural gasoline..................	8.7	7.7	6.2
Butanes.........................	5.0	5.0	4.7
Pool R.o.n., clear.................	76	78	81
Pool, R.o.n., +3 ml TEL...........	88.5	90.5	93.5

TABLE 6-4. SHUTDOWN TIME AND INSPECTIONS

Units	Months of operation		Average stream-time efficiency, %	Average man-hours per turnaround, per 1,000 bpd
	Average	Range		
Crude and vacuum.........	9.7	8.2–13.8	96	400
Thermal cracking...........	4.3	3.3– 5.3	92	800
Cat. polymerization and re-forming................	9.4	7.8–14.0	95	1,000
Catalytic cracking..........	11.6	9.4–13.6	94	1,800
Alkylation................	13.3	9.3–16.3	95	3,600
Solvent extraction..........	12.9	10.3–15.6	94	1,500

exceeded 8,300,000 bpd and the average relative amounts processed by cracking, etc., were about as shown in Table 6-1. Thus, an average refinery would have a pumping capacity for all of its various units at least twice as large as its crude oil capacity. Even more, by recycling or rerunning, treating, etc., the total amount of oil handled would be threefold or more compared with the crude oil capacity. The various kinds of cracking and reforming operations can be judged from Table 6-2 and by the United States gasoline pool estimate[1] for early 1955 (Table 6-3).

The length of runs, cycle-time efficiency, and man-hours of labor required for inspecting and repairing various units are indicated[2] in Table 6-4.

[1] Weber, George, *Oil Gas J.*, Aug. 9, 1954, p. 62.
[2] Shannon, R., *Pet. Refiner*, March, 1955, p. 131.

CHAPTER 7

REFINERY AND DISTILLATION PROCESSES

All petroleum distillation processes are fundamentally the same. The process engineer can make no headway in initiating new processes or in truly understanding the flow diagrams of processes until this fact is clearly understood. In the main, all distillation processes require the following essential units of equipment: (1) pipestills or other heaters, (2) fractionating towers, (3) steam-stripping columns, (4) heat exchangers, (5) condensers and coolers, (6) pumps and connecting lines, (7) storage and accumulator tanks, and (8) instrumentation. However, in adapting these units of equipment to the processing of a particular stock, many factors must be considered. Among the most important of these are

1. The boiling range of the stock.
2. The stability of the stock with respect to heat.
3. The specifications of the products to be produced.

Phases of processing other than heavy-oil distillation processes are discussed in many chapters, particularly under treating (Chaps. 10–11), dewaxing (Chap. 12), thermal cracking (Chap. 19), chemical manufacture (Chap. 20), catalytic cracking and reforming (Chap. 21), and natural gasoline (Chap. 22).

Boiling Range of Stock. Some stocks boil at such a high temperature that they cannot be vaporized at atmospheric pressure without decomposing them, and other stocks must be kept under pressure or they will vaporize at room temperature. Raw natural gasoline contains relatively large amounts of gaseous hydrocarbons and is an example of a stock that must be distilled under pressure. Although gaseous hydrocarbons are the overhead product from the column, a liquid reflux of propane and butane must be condensed, and this requires a pressure of 125 to 300 psia. Of course, the top of the column could be kept at a low temperature by refrigeration, but such methods have not proved practical. The temperature in the reflux condensers is governed by the temperature of the cooling water. The pressure that is used is dependent on the vapor pressure of the reflux material at the temperature that exists in the condenser.

226

With high-boiling stocks the opposite difficulty arises. Vigorous decomposition starts to take place at temperatures exceeding about 710°F, and for this reason many stocks such as reduced or topped crude oil, tars, and heavy crude oils cannot be distilled at atmospheric pressure. These stocks have such high boiling ranges that they must be distilled in a vacuum or by the use of large amounts of steam. Some cannot be distilled unless both steam and vacuum are employed.

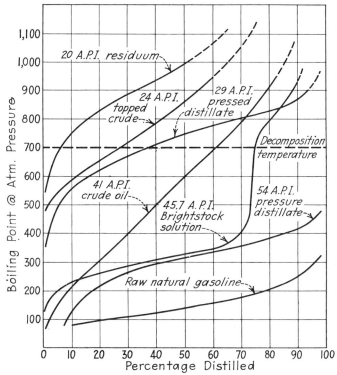

FIG. 7-1. Distillation ranges of typical Mid Continent stocks.

Between these two extremes are stocks such as crude oil, pressure distillate, pressed distillate, bright stock solution, and special naphtha stocks, which can be distilled at atmospheric pressure but which may require the use of some steam. Figure 7-1 indicates the relative boiling ranges of typical Mid Continent stocks. In distilling crude oil for gasoline, kerosene, and a part of the gas oil, a pipestill-outlet temperature of about 740°F may be required. Thus a small amount of steam is normally required to keep the temperature down to 710°F. This results in a vaporizer temperature in the tower of about 660°F. For other stocks, commonly used vaporizer and outlet temperatures are given in Table 7-1.

Sensitive Stocks. Although the boiling range of a stock is an important factor, the sensitiveness of the stock to high temperatures must also be considered. All stocks start to decompose at about 680°F, yielding lower boiling products, but even lower temperatures may cause discoloration. In distilling crude oil a slight discoloration of the products (except kerosene) is not important because most of the products receive chemical treatment before they are sold. Likewise, discoloration is not important in the distillation of a reduced crude oil for the production of a gas-oil cracking stock or for the production of asphalt. However, in distilling treated pressure distillate, pressed distillate, or bright stock solution, a discoloration during distillation cannot be allowed because such products are substantially ready for marketing. If treatment follows these distillations, then the cost of the treatment will be increased by the discoloration.

High temperatures also result in a loss of heavy lubricating-oil stock. The yield of lubricating oils is often decreased by 10 to 15 per cent by the use of too high temperatures. A mild decomposition takes place in which light lubricating oil and gas oil are produced from the heavy stocks.

TABLE 7-1. VAPORIZER TEMPERATURES

Stock	Products	Temperature, °F		Pressure, psi or mm	Steam
		Vapor-izer	Heater outlet		
1. Natural gasoline..	Gas	210	230	120–200	No
2. Pressure distillate.	Gasoline	275	325	Atmospheric	Yes
3. Crude oil.........	Light oils	660	710	Atmospheric	Some
4. Pressed distillate..	Neutral oils	670	710	Atmospheric	Yes
5. Bright stock solution.............	Naphtha and neutral	670	710	Atmospheric	Yes
6. Reduced crude....	Lube oils	690	730	30–80 mm	Yes
7. Fuel oil or tar....	Asphalt residue	730	770	30–80 mm	Yes
8. Fuel oil or tar....	Distilled cracking stock	775	850	Atmospheric	Yes

Treated pressure distillate is particularly sensitive to high temperatures. Redistillation should not be conducted at temperatures exceeding 375°F, and many refiners find that a maximum temperature of 275°F is economical because of the reduction in treating costs.

In the manufacture of asphalt most refiners limit the temperature to 770°F. Nevertheless, the temperature that may be used without ruining the ductility of the product is greatly dependent upon the characteristics of the stock and upon the manner of heating. One refiner has successfully used a temperature of 835°F at the pipestill outlet, but others have found that 770°F was too high. If the stock is held at 835°F for more than a few minutes, extensive cracking will occur, and the operation will become a cracking process. Thus the temperature that can be attained without serious decomposition is dependent to some extent upon the time. Although a lubricating-oil stock can be heated to 710 or even 740°F in a low-absorption-rate pipestill heater, this same temperature, if maintained in a shellstill, will cause serious losses in yield and a discoloration, the removal of which may necessitate a costly chemical treatment.

Arrangement of Towers. In separating a series of products from a charge stock, three main tower arrangements are employed. Heavy-oil stocks, such as crude oil, are usually separated in a single tower, as indicated in Fig. 7-7. In such a system the feed enters somewhat low in the column, the lowest-boiling product issues from the top as a vapor, and the heavier distilled products are withdrawn from the side of the column. The small towerlike equipment shown in the center of Fig. 7-7 is not a fractionating tower. It is a series of three steam strippers set one above another. The system of Fig. 7-7 is unsatisfactory for producing highly pure products such as pure hydrocarbons because the lighter products pass the withdrawal trays of the heavier products as they proceed from the feed plate to the top. For precise separations a series of towers (one tower less than the number of products) as shown in Fig. 7-2a or b is often employed. In Fig. 7-2a the lowest boiling product is vaporized in tower No. 1 by reboiler heat at the bottom of tower No. 1, and successively higher and higher boiling materials are removed in the remaining six towers. The feed is pumped from tower to tower, each tower is cooled by refluxing a part of the overhead product into the top of the tower, and the bottom of each tower is heated by steam or a hot circulating oil by means of reboilers. Successive fractional condensation is practiced in Fig. 7-2b. Here an almost completely vaporized stock is cooled in tower No. 1 to condense the highest-boiling product, and successively lower-boiling products are condensed in the remaining six towers. The novel but little used Brugma[1] arrangement of towers shown in Fig. 7-2c employs only three towers, but the total length of the three towers is about the same as the length of the seven towers in Fig. 7-2a and b. Obviously, many combinations of these tower arrangements are possible, as in Fig. 7-8.

More material can be vaporized (at a given temperature) by a single flash vaporization than by several flashes, and hence the use of a single multidraw tower (Fig. 7-7) is better in this respect than the series arrangements of Fig. 7-2a and b. Refer to Chap. 15 for a mathematical discussion of methods of vaporization.

Steam Stripping. Steam is used to raise the flash point of most of the heavy-oil products withdrawn from the side of multidraw towers and for

[1] *Ref. Nat. Gaso. Mfr.*, September, 1941, p. 86.

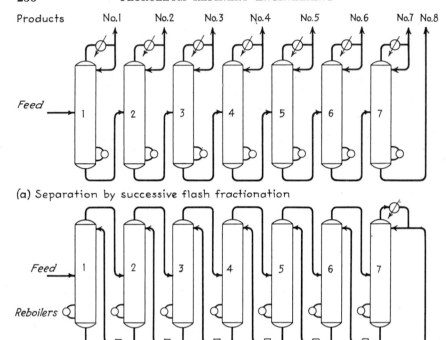

(a) Separation by successive flash fractionation

(b) Separation by successive fractional condensation

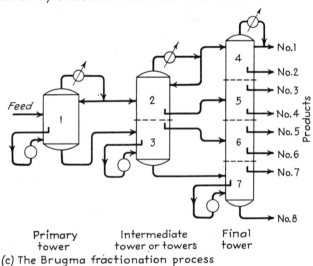

Primary   Intermediate   Final
tower   tower or towers   tower

(c) The Brugma fractionation process

FIG. 7-2. Basic arrangements of fractionating towers. (a) Separation by successive flash fractionation; (b) separation by successive fractional condensation; and (c) the Brugma fractionation process.

the bottoms product of heavy-oil towers. The hot oil is contacted with the steam in a so-called "stripping tower" which may be a packed tower (up to 20 in. diameter) but usually consists of bubble trays or side-to-side pans. The use of four bubble trays (about seven side-to-side pans) is common, but in the extreme ten plates have been used. If as much as 6 to 10 per cent of low-boiling material must be removed by stripping, it is usually more economical to adjust the composition of the product in the fractionating tower than to steam-strip.

The approximate relation between flash point and (0 to 10 per cent) boiling range is given in Eq. (4-6a). With this relationship it is possible to estimate the amount of material that should be removed by stripping in order to obtain a satisfactory flash point. Figures 7-3 and 7-4 indicate the approximate amounts of steam required in stripping naphtha, kerosene, distillate, gas oil, topped crude oil, and similar products.[2] Figure 4-49 indicates the wide range of kerosenes (or similar products) that can be produced by adjustment of the fractionating tower and degree of stripping. The dotted lines (Fig. 7-4) are examples of the effect of infinite plates on gas oil and on topped crude oil. Stocks such as

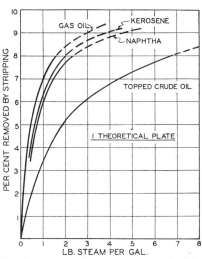

Fig. 7-3. Approximate steam required to strip when using only a bath of liquid, i.e., only one theoretical plate.

topped crude oil (which are wide-boiling or have been disengaged from a wide-boiling material (such as crude oil) require large amounts of stripping steam.

Example 7-1. Amount of Stripping Steam. An unstripped kerosene has an initial boiling point of 200°F, a 5 per cent point of 310°F, and a 10 per cent point of 355°F, which is an average temperature of about 288°F. Its flash point is about 90°F.

According to Eq. (4-6a), a 0 to 10 per cent front boiling range of 344°F will be required to obtain a flash point of 120°F. Six or seven per cent of the material must be removed to produce a 344°F front end; and, according to Figs. 7-3 and 7-4,

No. of plates	Lb steam per gal
1 (Fig. 7-3)	1.0
4 (Fig. 7-4)	0.45
10 (Reference 2)	0.40

[2] Nelson, W. L., *Oil Gas J.*, Mar. 2, 1944, p. 72; July 21, 1945, p. 128; and May 12, 1945, p. 51.

For ordinary conditions the following amounts of steam are used:

Lb per gal

Naphtha.....................	0.2–0.5
Kerosene or diesel fuel...........	0.2–0.6
Gas oil.......................	0.1–0.5
Neutral oils...................	0.4–0.9
Topped crude oil...............	0.4–1.2
Residual cylinder stock..........	1.0 up

Distillation with Extractive Solvents. Hydrocarbons of nearly the same boiling point (1 to 3°C) or constant-boiling mixtures cannot readily be separated by plain fractionation, and hence a combination of fractionation and solvent extraction known as the "Distex process" is employed.[3]

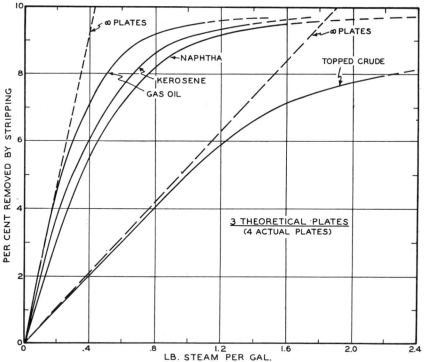

FIG. 7-4. Approximate steam required to strip with three theoretical plates.

It is particularly valuable in separating aromatic hydrocarbons which tend to form constant-boiling mixtures with many other hydrocarbons. Solvents such as aniline, furfural, phenol, nitrobenzene, or chlorex are introduced at the top of the fractionating column and withdrawn at the bottom. The solvent is recovered from the bottoms products by means

[3] Griswold, Andres, Van Berg, and Kasch, *Ind. Eng. Chem.*, **38**, 65 (1946).

of subsequent distillations, as shown in Fig. 7-5.[4]   The solvent must be higher boiling than the highest boiling product, but it should not be so high-boiling that immiscibility (as in solvent extraction) occurs at the temperatures existing in the main fractionating tower.   In association with the solvent, the vapor-pressure characteristics (or activities) of the hydrocarbons are altered so that their boiling points are spread apart.   In general, the paraffinic hydrocarbons distill overhead to a greater degree than their regular boiling points indicate, and the naphthenes and particularly the aromatics tend to associate themselves with the solvent.

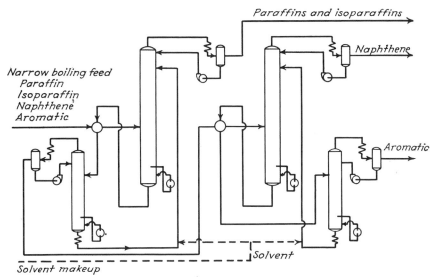

FIG. 7-5. Simplified flow diagram of the Distex or extractive distillation process.

The separation of butylene from butane by extractive distillation in the presence of acetone or acetonitrile is illustrated in the central part of Fig. 20-16.

Azeotropic distillation[5] is a somewhat similar process.   It involves the formation of an azeotropic or constant-boiling mixture with one or part of the components of a mixture.   The azeotropic mixture can then be separated by distillation, but it must subsequently be resolved by solvent extraction or other processes for recovery of the solvent.

Drying.   The drying of hydrocarbon liquids and vapors is important in the use of anhydrous catalysts.   Although the drying of gases can be

[4] Nelson, W. L., *Oil Gas J.*, June 22, 1946, p. 127.

[5] Hartley, F. L., Synthesis of Toluene by Hydroforming and Recovery by Azeotropic Distillation, *Pet. Eng.*, December, 1945, p. 156.

accomplished by compression, cooling, and refrigeration; by contacting with hygroscopic chemicals; or by absorption of moisture into diethylene glycol—the common method for both gases and liquids is adsorption of the moisture by activated alumina, silica gel, or fuller's earth.   In the drying of liquids (Fig. 7-6), the wet liquid is passed through one chamber while another is being dried and a third chamber may be nearly spent or may be in process of draining.   The feed is usually passed upward through the chambers so that slugs of water- or chemical- (caustic) laden liquid may settle before it contacts the adsorbent.   The spent adsorbent

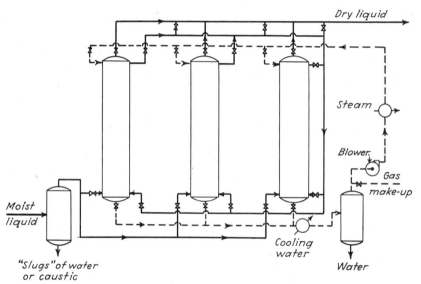

FIG. 7-6. Drying of liquids with solid adsorbents.

is regenerated by draining the liquid, or steaming it from the adsorbent if it is particularly valuable, and passing hot flue gas or superheated steam at 300 to 400°F through the adsorbent.   Water vapor in the hot gas may be removed by cooling the gas in a water cooler.   The rate of liquid flow is 14 to 16 gal per hr for each pound of clay.   The clay is supported at several points to prevent channeling and to allow settling of impurities.   Gasoline and kerosene, etc., can easily be dehydrated to less than 30 ppm; and, if frequent regeneration is practiced, the following low values can be obtained: naphtha, 2–4 ppm; toluene, 10 ppm; and benzene, 4 ppm.

Fractionation is also widely used for drying liquids that are substantially immiscible with water, as propane or the hydrocarbon oils.   The low-boiling product of such a system is a constant-boiling mixture of water and the hydrocarbon (in proportion to their vapor pressures) which upon condensation separates into a hydrocarbon layer and a water layer. The hydrocarbon layer, along with fresh feed, constitutes the feed to the fractionator. The solubility of water in various hydrocarbons is indicated in Fig. 5-24.

The general effect of mesh size on the drying capacity[6] of bauxite is:

Mesh size	Relative capacity, %
10–20; 20–35	100
6–14	94
6–10	90
4–8	80

Likewise the effects of air velocity[6] and relative humidity[6] of air on bauxite drying are:

Air velocity, cu ft/hr/lb	Rel. capacity, %	Rel. humidity (80°F), %	Rel. capacity, %
10	100	97	100
15	97	75	85
20	85	50	68
25	69	10	39

The drying of gases is similar to the drying of liquids. Plants are designed for moisture contents in the clay of 4 to 7 per cent, but new clay will hold 12 to 25 per cent. Hydrogen sulfide in the presence of oxygen causes the deposition of free sulfur, particularly if the clay contains iron compounds. Caustic soda, alkaline materials, and cracked gases cause rapid plugging of the clay or alumina. With regular sweet natural gas hydrocarbons the adsorbent lasts for many years. Two chambers are usually adequate. While one of these is being used, a portion (10 to 15 per cent) of the feed gas is bypassed through a heater (300 to 400°F) and through the spent chamber as a drying agent. The hot moist gas is cooled to condense the moisture from it, and it may be cycled back through the system so that all the outgoing gas is dry.[7] Capell and Amero[8] provide an "onstream" cycle of 12 to 24 hr and employ a gas velocity based on an empty tower of 0.33 to 1.0 ft per sec.

Senatoroff has published[9] a complete discussion of the principles and plant design details of the diethylene glycol dehydration process.

[6] Heinemann and Heinemann, Adsorbents and Catalysts, *Pet. Refiner*, June, 1954, p. 159.

[7] Nelson, W. L., *Oil Gas J.*, Mar. 30, 1946, p. 273.

[8] Dehydrating Liquids and Gases with Granular Adsorbents, *Oil Gas J.*, June 18, 1942, p. 37.

[9] Application of Diethylene Glycol-water Solution for Dehydration of Natural Gas, *Oil Gas J.*, Dec. 15, 1945, p. 98.

FLOW DIAGRAMS AND OPERATING CONDITIONS

The remaining pages of the chapter are devoted to the common processing systems. The systems that are presented are not necessarily the best for all conditions. In fact, in some cases they are presented merely because they are novel or because they illustrate principles that would otherwise be neglected.

The operating conditions are likewise of a general nature, although in most cases they are conditions that have been recorded in plant operation. The evaluation curves that are shown with the processes are discussed in Chap. 4.

A survey of the processing methods used in refineries appears to show that there are as many methods as there are refineries. Nevertheless, upon close inspection these many methods are found to be essentially the same, and the major differences are in the arrangement and shape of the equipments rather than in the manner of operation. In most refineries the processing methods are the result of years of development; and although the processing methods may be modern, the equipment that is used may appear to be obsolete. This is often the result of the use of existing shellstills, towers, chambers, coolers, etc., from antiquated equipment. They appear obsolete; but if they are properly utilized, they may perform as satisfactorily as new equipment.

Topping or Skimming Crude Oil. In many ways the initial breakup of crude oil into raw products is the most simple distillation process. Certainly it is the most widely known operation.

In the topping unit shown in Fig. 7-7, oil is pumped continuously through the heat-exchange system at a pump pressure of 125 to 200 psi, through the tubestill, and into the vaporizer section of the multiple-draw fractionating tower. At this point the temperature must be sufficiently high to cause vaporization of all the products that are collected at points above the vaporizer, and the temperature may be a little higher, so that about 20 per cent of the bottoms stock is also vaporized. The purpose of the additional vaporization is to provide better fractionation on the plates that are situated just above the vaporizer. Without excess vaporization, very little reflux will exist at these plates and no reflux will flow from the plate above the vaporizer into the vaporizer section. Reflux is circulated through the top of the column. The hot reflux material is drawn from the tower, cooled by a heat exchanger and a water cooler, and returned to the tower. It serves to cool and condense the vapors that arise from the vaporizer. The recirculating type of reflux shown in Fig. 7-7 is not the most common method of removing reflux heat, but it is an excellent method for certain conditions. Various means of removing reflux heat are shown in Fig. 16-3. The plates above the vaporizer or feed plate act as rectifying plates, but the plates below the feed are steam-stripping plates. Steam is admitted below or on the bottom tray, and the low-boiling materials in the vaporizer residue are removed so that a high-flash-point bottoms product is produced. The steam ascends the tower, and at the vaporizer it is effective in lowering the vaporizer temperature.

The system as shown in Fig. 7-7 is not limited to the production of four overhead products. As many as eight products have been withdrawn from a single tower. Furthermore, by the use of a large amount of steam, such heavy stocks as wax distillate and even cylinder stock may be vaporized from crude oil. However, the vaporizer temperature must be high

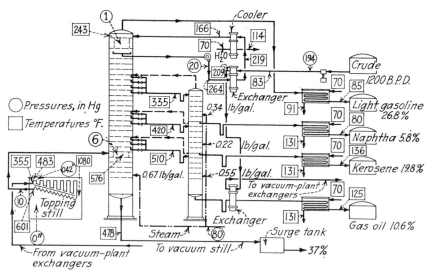

FIG. 7-7. Continuous pipestill topping plant.

(800 to 870°F),[10] and such temperatures result in discoloration and losses by decomposition. The difficulties with dewaxing are also troublesome. Plants operating at atmospheric pressure for the manufacture of distilled cylinder stocks have never been entirely successful, but many refiners distill wax distillate at atmospheric pressure.

In existing refineries, nearly every possible combination of flow or of towers may be found. Figure 7-8 illustrates[11] two of these (also see Fig. 7-7 again), and nearly all refiners employ a crude preflash tower to

[10] One plant operated at 870°F, distilling a 160 viscosity at 210 cylinder stock, but the color was so poor and the loss of heavy stock was so great that the operation was discontinued.

[11] Nelson, W. L., Topping Plant Flow, *Oil Gas J.*, Nov. 25, 1944, p. 103.

stabilize[12] the crude oil or to produce a high-octane or aviation gasoline.[13] The aim in Fig. 7-8 is to show tower arrangements, and hence condensers, coolers, exchangers, etc., are not shown.

Topper crude oil must always be stripped with steam to improve its flash point or to recover the last portions of gas oil. The composition of the topped crude oil is primarily a function of the flash or vaporizer temperature, and hence Fig. 7-9 is a good approximation of topped crude oils

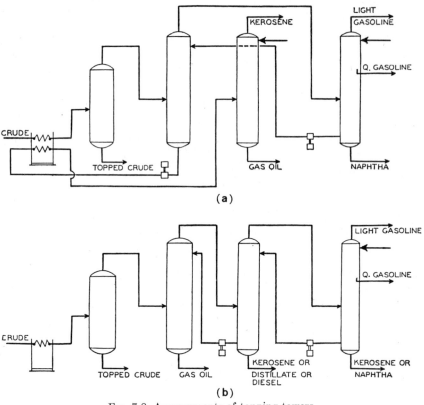

Fig. 7-8. Arrangements of topping towers.

from all normal-boiling-range crude oils.[14] The distillation curves are entirely adequate for computing the amount of stripping steam required.

Heat-exchange and Combination Plants. The number of heat exchangers that may be wisely utilized depends upon the quantities and temperatures of the several products. Heat exchangers are often

[12] Nelson, W. L., Combination Topping Plants, *Oil Gas J.*, Dec. 23, 1944, p. 101.

[13] Nelson, W. L., Straightrun Aviation Gasoline Manufacture, *Oil Gas J.*, Jan. 6, 1945, p. 81.

[14] Nelson, W. L., *Oil Gas J.*, July 21, 1945, p. 128, and July 20, 1946, p. 123.

expected to pay for themselves in 2 years but the general situation is presented in Fig. 23-5. In complete plants, which conduct vacuum and cracking operations as well as the topping of crude oil, the crude oil may be advantageously heated by products from these other units because they are at a relatively high temperature. For example (Fig. 7-10), the crude oil may be pumped through the condenser exchangers of the topping plant, through the condenser exchangers and side-product exchangers of a vacuum plant, through the bottoms exchangers of a cracking plant, and

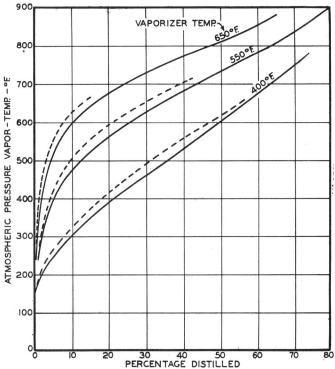

Fig. 7-9. True-boiling-point and ASTM (dotted) distillation curves of topped crude oils produced by flashing at 400, 550, and 650°F. (*Oil Gas J.*)

finally back to the topping tower. In some plants a crude-oil temperature of 600 to 650°F is attained by heat exchange alone. Figure 7-10[15] is an attempt to indicate the main sources of heat in an exchanger system. In isolated topping plants, exchangers are also used on the side-draw products of the topping plant. In general, it is usually economical to bring the crude oil to within 40°F of the temperature of the hottest heat-exchange stock that is available. In deciding which stocks to employ

[15] Nelson, W. L., *Oil Gas J.*, Dec. 23, 1944, p. 101.

for heat exchange the product of the percentage of material based on crude oil times its temperature[16] may be computed; and, if this index is larger than about 5,000, the exchanger is economical. In applying this method the quantity of stocks that condense should be multiplied by about 2; and, if the stock is associated with reflux, it should be multiplied again by 2 (or more).

Although such an extensive use of heat exchange appears to be advantageous, such systems are not without disadvantages. The dependency of several units upon one another is a serious complication. Thus if one unit must be shut down, the other unit or units must be shut down or operated in a crippled condition. Sometimes these plants are constructed with extra heating equipment so that any one of the plants can be operated independently, but the extra heaters cost almost as much as if they had been originally provided instead of exchangers. Exchangers may also

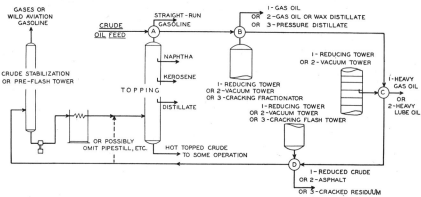

FIG. 7-10. Sources of heat for heat exchange. (*Oil Gas J.*)

be a source of great expense unless they are wisely chosen and the stocks are clean and noncorrosive.

In the extreme, exchangers could be utilized on every tray of a fractionating tower as well as on each of the products and perhaps succeed in attaining a thermal efficiency of 60 to 80 per cent. One such system[17] succeeded in operating without condensers. The real merit of such a system, however, depends upon the cost of installing and maintaining the heat exchangers, and it is doubtful if such a system is economically feasible in view of the low cost of heat in most refineries. Extra trays would also be required in a fractionating tower employing such a large amount of heat exchange because the tower would operate with very little reflux.

[16] Nelson, W. L., *Oil Gas J.*, Nov. 24, 1945, p. 147.

[17] Ziegenhain, W. T., No Condensers Used in Topping Unit, *Oil Gas J.*, Dec. 18, 1930, p. 30.

Even after a complete use of heat exchange some products will go to the water coolers at 250 to 400°F. These stocks along with the hot flue gases from a pipestill or other heater may be used to generate steam in what is known as a "waste-heat boiler." Such an installation[18] is generalized in Fig. 7-11. Feed water that has already been preheated with exhaust steam in an "economizer" is heated further by any suitable hot oil stock that is on the way to storage (or water coolers) and is introduced into a steam drum. Meanwhile, hot water is circulated from the drum through tubes that are heated by flue gases. High-temperature gases from a cracking still, thermal polymerization still, catalyst burn-off still, gas reversion still, etc., are suitable. Waste-heat boilers would appear to be

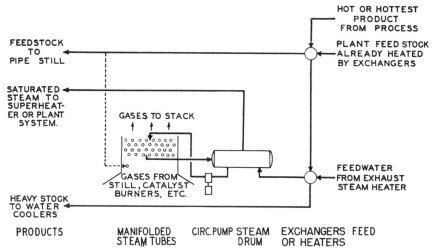

Fig. 7-11. General arrangement of waste-heat boilers. (*Oil Gas J.*)

a source of free steam. Actually they require two or three times as much surface as a regular boiler, and hence they are seldom economically feasible.

Pressure-still Distillate. In thermally cracking stocks from high-sulfur crude oils, the cracked distillate contains large amounts of sulfur and no means of significantly reducing the sulfur content except acid treating has been devised (but catalytic hydrogenation may soon be used). After acid treatment, the distillate is still a bright-yellow-colored material. Although part of the coloring material is high boiling and may be separated by distillation, some of it decomposes if a high temperature is used and causes discoloration of the distillate. Gumlike materials are also produced at high temperatures. These difficulties are apparently caused by the decomposition and hydrolysis of alkyl sulfates which are

[18] Nelson, W. L., *Oil Gas J.*, Oct. 26, 1946, p. 129.

242   PETROLEUM REFINERY ENGINEERING

produced during acid treatment. The exact temperature below which discoloration and the formation of gum occur depends upon the chemical nature of the distillate, the manner in which the chemical treatment was conducted, and the way in which heat is applied. With one particular distillate,[19] the effect of increasing the steam[20] which is used to reduce the temperature, other conditions and operations being the same, was as follows:

Per cent steam in overhead	Color
0	18
5	22
20	25

Refiners usually limit the temperature of redistillation in continuous pipestill and fractionator plants to 325°F by the use of steam, although some plants have been operated at 375°F. The tendency has been to decrease the temperature because the treating operation is much simplified if the temperature is low. Several companies have installed vacuum systems[21] in which the temperature is limited to 275°F. The vacuum redistillation systems are usually of the two-stage type, in which part of the distillate is distilled at atmospheric pressure and the heavier part is vaporized in a second fractionator which operates at a reduced pressure.

TABLE 7-2. ANALYSES OF UNSTABILIZED PRESSURE DISTILLATES[a]

	Volume percentage analyses of pressure distillates collected at pressures of psi			
	14.7	30	40	165
API	52.6	58.2	55.3	61.3
Methane	.....	0.02	0.06	0.47
Ethane	0.33	0.24	0.69	2.22
Propane	3.4	1.63	3.22	5.67
Butanes	8.43	9.39	9.33	10.31
Pentanes	10.93	13.11	12.05	11.26
Hexanes and heavier	76.91	75.61	74.65	70.07

[a] The distillates were not from the same charging stock.

Stabilization. Cracked gasoline, crude oil, wild natural gasoline, and similar stocks contain dissolved gaseous hydrocarbons that tend to escape during storage. Analysis of crude oils were shown in Table 4-5, and

[19] Trusty, A. W., Acid Treatment of Cracked Distillates . . . , *Ref. Nat. Gaso. Mfr.*, August, 1932, p. 455.

[20] The sulfur content of the distillate was lower when more steam was used.

[21] Noll, H. D., *Oil Gas J.*, Mar. 31, 1932, p. 66.

Table 7-2 by Burket[22] indicates the composition of cracked distillates. The equipments used for the removal of gaseous or very low-boiling materials are all fundamentally similar to the natural-gasoline stabilizer[23] shown in Fig. 7-12.   Heat is supplied at the bottom of the tower by means of a steam-heated reboiler; and, if the feed is heated by heat exchange with

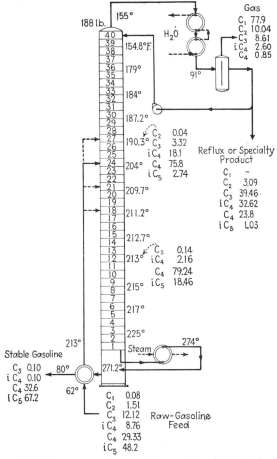

FIG. 7-12. Natural-gasoline stabilizer.   (*Burdick, Oil Gas J.*)

the stabilized gasoline, the feed need not be otherwise heated.   An effective separation of propane requires the use of a large number of fractionating plates (Fig. 7-12 shows more plates than necessary) and a somewhat high reflux ratio.

The fractionation of pressure distillate is conducted in a manner similar

[22] P.D. Stabilization . . . , *Ref. Nat. Gaso. Mfr.*, March, 1931, p. 75.
[23] Burdick, G., *Oil Gas J.*, Apr. 9, 1931, p. 26.

in all respects to the stabilization of raw natural gasoline (Fig. 7-12). However, pressure distillate contains less propane and butane than raw natural gasoline, and hence the feed must be heated to a higher temperature. Pressure distillate is often "deep-stabilized" for the removal of substantially all the four-carbon-atom and lighter hydrocarbons so that the stabilizer overhead will contain all the olefins that are suitable for polymerization. The propane rejected from the polymerization unit may be collected as bottle gas, and the butanes are collected and returned to the plant gasoline for increasing its vapor pressure.

Recent developments of polymerization, dehydrogenation, alkylation, etc., processes, which are now practiced primarily on gaseous hydrocarbons, all require high-pressure fractionators similar to stabilizers. In

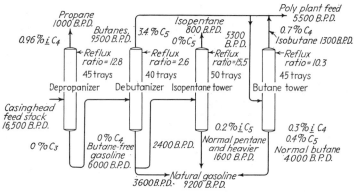

FIG. 7-13. Fractionation system for separating pure hydrocarbons (see Table 7-3). (*Turner and Rubey.*)

most of the conversion processes it is necessary to produce pure hydrocarbons, and hence such elaborate systems as that shown in Fig. 7-13 are widely used.[24] This plant was used primarily for making an isobutane-butane feed for polymerization units, but during World War II all the products became useful. In the separation of pure hydrocarbons the stabilizers or fractionators are referred to as deethanizers, debutanizers, deisobutanizers, etc., depending upon the hydrocarbon that is being removed.

The gas recovery and stabilization operations of a refinery may be centralized[25] into a single system, as indicated in Fig. 7-14. The stabilization of cracked gasoline is not shown because cracked and straight-run gasolines are not usually mixed during processing.

Reboilers. In fractionating two-component feed stocks a part or sometimes all of the heat input is supplied at the bottom of the fractionator.

[24] Turner and Rubey, Light Hydrocarbons . . . , *Ref. Nat. Gaso. Mfr.*, September, 1938, p. 423.

[25] Nelson, W. L., *Oil Gas J.*, Aug. 5, 1944, p. 75.

TABLE 7-3. DATA CONCERNING THE FOUR COLUMNS OF FIG. 7-13

	Col. 1, depropanizer	Col. 2, debutanizer	Col. 3, isopentane	Col. 4, butanes
Capacity, bbl/day..................	10,450	10,160	2,266	2,900
Impurities, in overhead, per cent....... {	$0.96C_4$	$3.5C_5$	$0.0nC_5$	$0.7nC_4$
	......	$0.0C_3$	$0.0C_4$	$0.0C_3$
Impurities, in bottoms, per cent........ {	$0.0C_3$	$0.0C_4$	$0.2iC_5$	$0.3iC_4$
	......	.....	......	$0.4C_5$
Number of trays....................	45	40	50	45
Height, ft.........................	111	103	120	111
Diameter, ft.......................	8.0	10.5	7.0	8.5
Safe working pressure, psi.............	275	100	50	120
Reflux ratio (design figure)...........	12.8	2.6	15.5	10.3

In such systems the part of the column below the feed, viz., the exhausting section, effects some separation. The lower part of most petroleum oil columns does not function as a fractionator but as a simple steam-stripping section. In practicing reboiling on heavy-oil towers, oil is circulated from the bottom of the tower, through a few tubes in the pipestill or other heating equipment, and back into one of the lower plates of the tower, as in Fig. 7-15. Reboilers do increase the efficiency of fractionation, but a satisfactory degree of separation can usually be obtained more cheaply by the use of a stripping section. The use of two coils in a pipestill is difficult because the exact heat input in each coil cannot be accurately determined except by experiments with the pipestill during operation.

Occasionally the temperature attained by heat exchange is not high enough to vaporize the desired amount in a crude preflash tower, and hence hot topped crude oil is cycled from the topping still to increase the preflash vaporizer temperature. This practice is generally not good[26] because the high-boiling topped crude oil suppresses vaporization (see Fig. 15-16).

Reboilers heated by steam are used in stabilizer towers for natural gasoline, pressure distillate, butane-propane mixtures, and some solvents. In these cases the bottoms product must be well fractionated, whereas in most of the processes that have been discussed heretofore the fractionation of the overhead product was most important. Fractionators for the production of special cuts, such as solvents, are frequently operated with reboilers or with fired shells at the bottom of the towers.

Naphthas and Specialty Products. The manufacture of solvents is an exacting operation not only because of the short boiling range but because

[26] Nelson, W. L., *Oil Gas J.*, Aug. 3, 1946, p. 96.

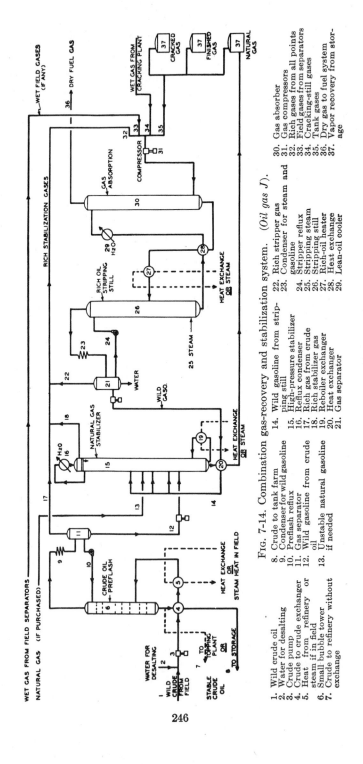

FIG. 7-14. Combination gas-recovery and stabilization system. (*Oil gas J*).

1. Wild crude oil
2. Water for desalting
3. Crude pump
4. Crude to crude exchanger
5. Heat from refinery or steam if in field
6. Small bubble tower
7. Crude to refinery without exchange
8. Crude to tank farm
9. Condenser for wild gasoline
10. Preflash reflux
11. Gas separator
12. Wild gasoline from crude oil
13. Unstable natural gasoline if needed
14. Wild gasoline from stripping still
15. High-pressure stabilizer
16. Reflux condenser
17. Rich gas from crude
18. Rich stabilizer gas
19. Reboiler exchanger
20. Heat exchanger
21. Gas separator
22. Rich stripper gas
23. Condenser for steam and gasoline
24. Stripper reflux
25. Stripping steam
26. Stripping still
27. Rich-oil heater
28. Heat exchange
29. Lean-oil cooler
30. Gas absorber
31. Gas compressors
32. Rich gases from all points
33. Field gases from separators
34. Cracking-still gases
35. Tank gases
36. Dry gas to fuel system
37. Vapor recovery from storage

246

the color must be excellent and stable with respect to light. Only straight-run or highly treated stocks can be used for the manufacture of solvents.

In small refineries in which the shipments of solvents may not exceed a tank car per month, a common method of processing is to withdraw a small quantity of roughly cut material from the main distillation process and rerun this cut in a shellstill and tower, using a large quantity of reflux and conducting the distillation very slowly.

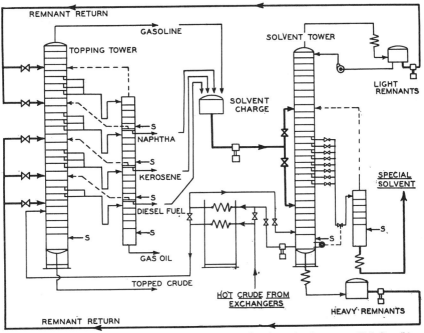

FIG. 7-15. A universal flow diagram for the production of solvents. (*Oil Gas J.*)

A product that is withdrawn from the side of a multiple-draw column can never be well fractionated. It will always contain some low-boiling material because the vapor that passes the draw plate always contains the lighter products of the process. The end point can be regulated to some extent by the use of many plates and large amounts of reflux, but a satisfactory initial boiling point cannot be obtained by these methods. Regulation of the initial boiling point is usually accomplished by the use of a steam stripper. However, these common methods are ordinarily not satisfactory for the manufacture of solvents, and it is usually necessary to withdraw a partly fractionated material from the main tower and redistill this material under controlled conditions. Figure 7-15 indicates some of the principles involved in the manufacture of specialty products.[27] The

[27] Nelson, W. L., *Oil Gas J.*, Mar. 10, 1945, p. 83.

solvent tower is an exhausting system for rejecting parts of the stock that are too low- or too high-boiling.   It may be fed with any suitable charge stock.   Reboiler heat is supplied by circulating some of the bottoms product through a pipestill coil so that bottom temperatures higher than those possible with steam or oil-heated reboilers can be attained.

Pressed Distillate and Bright Stock Solution.   The redistillation of pressed distillate in the manufacture of neutral oils must be conducted under vacuum or with the use of large amounts of steam.   In other respects the equipment and method of operation are similar to those used in topping crude oil.   Discoloration will result in a high treating cost, and hence the pipestill must be built with a large amount of radiant surface and for high oil velocities.   Figure 7-16 shows a typical steam-atmospheric pressure-distillate rerun plant, and Fig. 7-17 the evaluation curves of the stock.

The same equipment may be used to redistill bright stock solution, but, of course, a different quantity of material will be processed.   The unit is operated for several weeks on one of the stocks while the other stock is being accumulated in storage tanks.   One small Pennsylvania refiner stored bright stock solution for about 3 weeks out of a month and processed it during the fourth week in the topping plant.   It was reported that only 1 hr was required to switch from the crude oil charging stock to bright stock solution as the charging stock.

Bright stock solution, like pressed distillate, must be distilled with as little discoloration as possible.   Several two-flash systems have been built.   In the first flash, the naphtha is removed.   The residue is then further heated in a part of the pipestill, and gas oil and a neutral oil are vaporized in the second flash.   The two-flash system holds no important advantages over the single-flash system, but as an illustration the two-flash method of operation is shown in Fig. 7-18.   Evaluation curves are shown in Fig. 7-19.   The steam required in a pipestill rerun system is often less than one-fifth the amount required by shellstill redistillation.   Modern practice is tending toward single- rather than two-flash systems.

Reducing Operations.   Reducing is a term used to describe those distillation operations by which a topped crude oil is further distilled to leave behind a very high-boiling residue or to produce additional distilled products.

Steam reduction involves heating to 550 to 660°F in the presence of large amounts of steam.   In early refinery practice cylinder stock was exposed to steam in shellstills for many hours.   Modern practice simply involves the use of steam in large amounts in a continuous distillation system.   The effect of steam in reducing the boiling point is discussed in connection with Eq. (15-8) and Example 15-2.

Destructive distillation involves heating to 650 to 750°F with or without

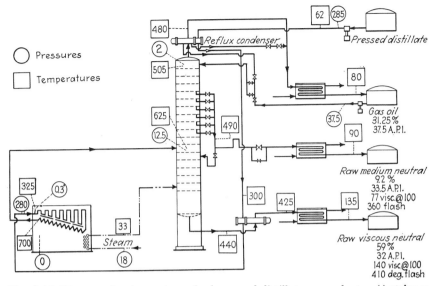

FIG. 7-16. Diagram of a steam-atmospheric pressed-distillate rerun plant. (A stripper is usually employed for the side-draw product.) (*Smith Engineering Co.*)

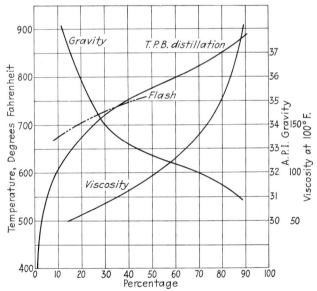

FIG. 7-17. Evaluation curves of a pressed distillate.

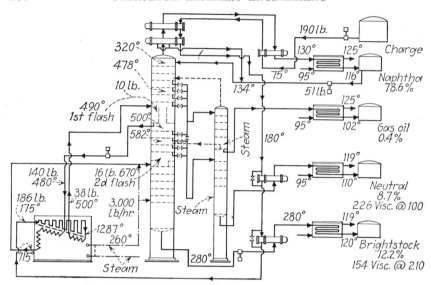

FIG. 7-18. Diagram of a two-flash solution-rerun unit.

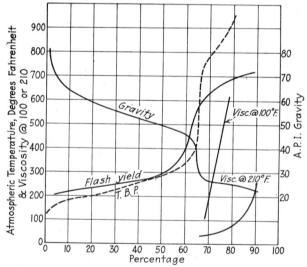

FIG. 7-19. Evaluation curves of a bright-stock solution.

steam, and it should not be employed if cracking, discoloration, or viscosity breaking are detrimental.

Coking is an extreme case of destructive distillation which produces large amounts of thermal or catalytic cracking stock.[28]

[28] Armistead, G., Jr., The Coking of Hydrocarbon Oils, *Oil Gas J.*, Mar. 16, 1946, p. 103.

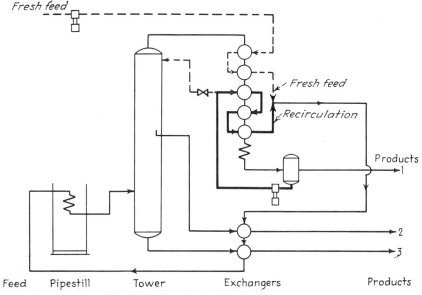

FIG. 7-20. The Carrier distillation process.

Vacuum distillation for the production of lubricants or asphalt will be discussed later in this chapter.

Carrier distillation involves the recycling of the overhead product so that its "carrying"[29] or partial-pressure effect can reduce the vaporization temperature. The process has been developed by the Lummus Company. Figure 7-20[30] shows features of the process, and Fig. 7-21 indicates the reduction in boiling point that may occur. According to Fig. 7-21, the amounts of material vaporized at 700°F are

Operation	Percentage vaporized	
	Based on pipestill charge	Based on feed stock
T.B.P. distillation.....................	25	25
Flash vaporization.....................	45	45
With 50 per cent recirculation..........	70.5	56
With 100 per cent recirculation.........	84.0	68
With 200 per cent recirculation.........	94.0	83.0

[29] Piromoov and Beiswenger, Equilibrium Vaporization of Oils and the Carrying Effect of Light Ends, *API Bull.* 10, no. 2, sec II, p. 52, 1929.

[30] Nelson, W. L., *Oil Gas J.*, June 29, 1946, p. 103.

Although the extra vaporization permitted by the carrier process is attractive, the pumping, heating, fractionating, and condensing of large amounts of recirculated material are expensive, and the plant equipments must be large.

An outstanding application of the Carrier principle is the reduction system used in Thermofor or Houdriflow catalytic cracking.   In these

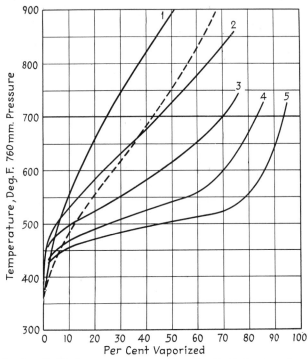

Fig. 7-21. Carrier distillation curves of a crude oil.   Dotted curve shows the vapor temperatures in a T.B.P. distillation of the feedstock; curve 1, liquid temperatures in a T.B.P. distillation; 2, flash-vaporization curve of the feedstock; 3, flash-vaporization curve of feed plus 50 per cent recirculation; 4, flash-vaporization curve of feed plus 100 per cent recirculation; and 5, flash-vaporization curve of feed plus 200 per cent recirculation.

processes (Fig. 21-7) topped crude oil is heated along with cycle stock to 790 to 860°F and released in a vaporizer or tar separator.   The somewhat low-boiling cycle stock, when used in ratios larger than 1 : 1, is so effective in removing gas oil from the topped crude oil that further reduction by means of vacuum distillation is often unnecessary.   The vaporized catalytic feed and cycle stock is then fed directly to the catalytic plant reactor as a vapor.

Vacuum Producing Systems.   The common method in the petroleum industry of maintaining a vacuum is the use of a barometric condenser for condensing process steam followed by two stages of steam-jet ejectors as shown in Fig. 7-22.   If pressures lower than 20 to 25 mm are needed at the vaporizer, a booster ejector and two or three stages of steam-jet ejectors, as indicated in Figs. 7-23 and 7-25, are usually required.   The booster ejector of Fig. 7-23 is simply a large steam jet that is used to compress both the process steam and noncondensable gases into the barometric condenser, whereas the customary smaller steam ejectors are used to remove only noncondensable gases from the barometric condenser.

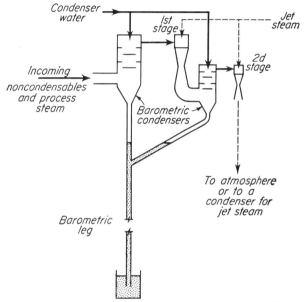

FIG. 7-22. Two stages of ejectors with a barometric condenser.

Vaporization is accomplished by reducing the partial pressure of the oil vapors at the vaporizer, first by the use of vacuum but also by the use of process steam.   At some pressure the sum of the jet steam and process steam is a minimum.   Table 7-4 and Fig. 7-24 illustrate how the total steam consumption is a function of vaporizer temperature, cooling water temperature, and absolute pressure.   They are based on the processing of 1,000 bpd of a conventional Mid Continent topped crude oil for the vaporization of material distilling up to about 950°F.

Barring leaks, the amount of noncondensable gases that must be removed per 1,000 bpd of charge stock ranges from 15 to 50 pounds.[31]   It consists primarily of the (1) tail of lower-boiling material almost necessarily associated with any feedstock (0.2 per cent represents about 25 lb of gas), (2) gases produced by cracking or overheating of the feed-

[31] Nelson, W. L., *Oil Gas J.*, April 5, 1951, p. 100.

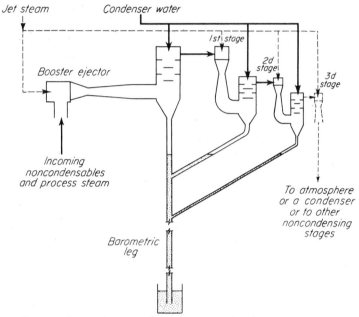

FIG. 7-23. Booster ejector, barometric condenser, and two or more ejector stages for low-vacuum systems.

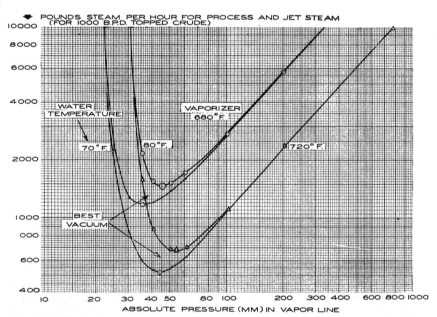

FIG. 7-24. Examples of most economical pressure for vacuum-tower operation (see Table 7-4).   (*Oil Gas J.*)

stock (2 per cent decomposition results in about 10 lb of gaseous tail), and (3) air dissolved in the charge stock and in the water used in generating steam (usually under 2 to 3 lb).[31]   The noncondensable gases are contacted with water in the barometric condenser, and hence the total pressure must be well above (5 to 15 mm) the vapor pressure of the hottest water in the barometric system.   The vapor pressure of water is indicated in Table 7-5.

TABLE 7-4. TOTAL STEAM REQUIRED (APPROX.) IN VACUUM DISTILLATION
for 1,000 barrels per day topped crude

Pressure (mm Hg) produced by the vacuum system[a]	760	200	100	60	50	40	35	30	25
Temp at vaporizer, if no process steam is used, °F.	950	830	780	750	735	725	715	708	700
Process steam,[a] lb, for:									
Vaporizer at 720°F......	10,300	2,490	1,070	460	325	190	122	54	
Vaporizer at 680°F......	24,000	6,220	3,020	1,800	1,340	1,040	885	733	580
Jet steam, lb, for:									
80°F cooling water............	......	150	232	378	492	830	1,600		
70°F cooling water............	......	146	222	312	368	480	600	857	2,010
Total steam required, lb:									
680°F—80°F water......	24,000	6,370	3,252	2,178	1,832	1,870	2,485		
680°F—70°F water......	24,000	6,366	3,342	2,112	1,708	1,520	1,485	1,590	2,590
720°F—80° water.......	10,300	2,640	1,302	838	817	1,020	1,722		
720°F—70°F water......	10,300	2,636	1,292	772	693	670	722	911	2,010

[a] In addition, a pressure drop of about 10 mm to the vaporizer for the lower pressures, and a larger pressure drop at higher pressures.

TABLE 7-5. VAPOR PRESSURES OF WATER

°F	mm	°F	mm
55	11	80	26.1
60	13	85	30.8
65	15.7	90	36
70	18.8	95	49
75	22.2	100	56.7

The total pounds of noncondensables plus water vapor for saturation must be ejected from the system by means of the steam jets, and the approximate amount of steam required to operate the jets is indicated in Table 7-6.   The steam required to operate the booster ejector is included in the values shown in Table 7-6 in the pressure range of 4 to 20 mm.   The wide range evident in Table 7-6 is due primarily to the various cooling water temperatures encountered, and the average values of the table

TABLE 7-6. APPROXIMATE STEAM CONSUMPTION OF CONDENSING STEAM JET
EJECTORS OPERATING WITH 100 PSIG STEAM

Pressure, mm	System	Lb steam per lb of total mixture[a]
200	2-stage	4.3 (2.5–11)
100	2-stage	6.0 (3–17)
70	2-stage	7.0 (4–23)
50	2-stage	8.2 (4.5–27)
40	2-stage	9.0 (5–30)
30	2-stage	10.2 (6–35)
20	3-stage	12.3 (7–40)
10	3-stage	16.8 (10–50)
7	3-stage	20.0 (12–58)
5	3-stage	23.0 (14–64)
4	3-stage	25.5 (16–70)

[a] Noncondensables and water vapor.

are very low ones that can be attained only under the most favorable conditions.

Example 7-2. Water Vapor Associated with Noncondensable Gases. A vacuum system with outgoing cooling water at 82°F is to remove 30 pounds per hour of noncondensables at a pressure of 45 mm.

Some of the water is at 85°F before it becomes fully mixed with the rest of the water (a 5°F difference rather than 3°F is sometimes allowed) and this water exerts a vapor pressure of 30.8 mm (Table 7-5). Accordingly, the partial pressure of the water vapor in the gas phase is 30.8 mm and the rest of the pressure, i.e., 45 − 30.8 or 14.2 mm, represents the oil vapor. The pounds of water vapor associated with the noncondensables (use 60 molecular weight as illustration) is:

$$\frac{30.8}{14.2} \times \frac{18}{60} \times 30 = 19.6 \text{ lb}$$

Thus, the total gases to be handled by the ejectors will be 30 + 19.6 = 49.6 lb.

At a pressure of 32 rather than 45 mm, the total gases rises to 261 lb and at 30.8 mm or lower, an infinite amount of water vapor must be handled, and a booster ejector must be employed to raise the pressure to higher than 30.8 mm.

A booster ejector is necessary if the pressure of the system must be below the vapor pressure of the water that is available. A booster ejector enormously increases the amount of jet steam required because the booster must handle process steam as well as noncondensables.

A large amount of water must be used in the barometric condenser because the highest water temperature (plus 3 to 5°F for inadequate mixing) determines the amount of water vapor that will saturate the noncondensable gases and have to be removed by the jets.

Vacuum Distillation. Vacuum distillation may be employed for the redistillation of pressure distillate, pressed distillate, or bright stock solution. It may be used for distilling topped crude oils for the production of wax distillate and cylinder stock, or it may be used to reduce a residual stock to asphalt or pitch. Vacuum systems are widely used to produce catalytic cracking plant feed stocks of low carbon content.

The advantages of vacuum distillation for producing lubricants from topped crude oils are obvious, because the asphalt in such stocks makes the cost of acid treatment almost prohibitive. In the case of paraffin-base oils the advantages are not so obvious. The advantage with such oils lies in the larger recovery of the valuable heavy stocks, which in the case of residual steam operation are partly decomposed into lower-boiling, less viscous oils.

Although the wax distillate and the cylinder stocks from vacuum units are usually dewaxed without difficulty, some refiners have found that an intermediate heavy wax distillate cut must be produced to the amount of 3 to 6 per cent if the wax distillate and the cylinder stock are to have good dewaxing characteristics. The use of solvent dewaxing processes has eliminated most of these difficulties.

Because of the high boiling points of lubricating-oil stocks the use of vacuum alone is seldom sufficient. Process steam must also be used and sometimes in such quantities as 1 lb of steam for each gal of reduced crude oil that is processed. Of course, the exact amount of steam to be used is dependent upon the boiling range of the stock and the quantity vaporized. Many plants have operated with process steam not exceeding 0.3 lb per gal. The dry process of vacuum distillation, which utilizes no steam, has many theoretical advantages. Most important among these are the much smaller tower and condensing equipment required. Nevertheless, the absolute pressure that is required for the dry processing of most petroleum oils amounts to less than 10 mm, and such a vacuum cannot be produced at a reasonable cost in most large-scale vacuum equipment.

The pressure drop that occurs between the barometric condenser and the vaporizer section of the tower (Fig. 7-25) is of great importance. The purpose of vacuum operation is to produce a low effective pressure at the vaporizer, and hence the vacuum must not be lost by excessive friction loss through the vapor line, condensers, and tower plates. The avoidance of a few millimeters of pressure drop, from the barometric to the vaporizer, is worth many pounds of process steam (see Table 7-4). The saving in the quantity of steam is important, but the reduction in tower diameter and quantity of cooling water are also significant. From Fig. 7-24 it might be assumed that economical pressures range from 30 to 60 mm, but such is not the case. Although it is seldom feasible to operate

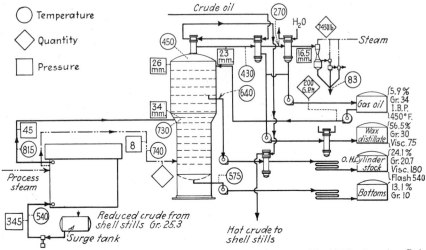

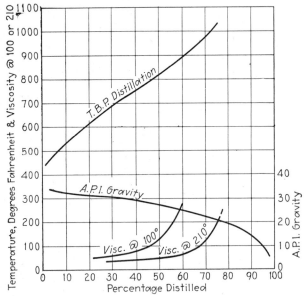

FIG. 7-25. Vacuum distillation plant using a booster ejector. (*Smith Engineering Co.*)

FIG. 7-26. Evaluation curves of the reduced crude oil charged to the plant shown in Fig. 7-25.

below about 25 mm, many systems operate most economically at 100 to 140 mm.

In an effort to obtain a minimum pressure drop, many novel arrangements and designs of vacuum towers and condensing equipment have been developed. The plates are designed for as low a liquid head above the slots of the caps as possible, and sometimes the customary bubble caps are discarded entirely for baffle or splash types of plates. In some installations the vapor line has been eliminated by doing the condensing in the top of the tower. In this arrangement the barometric and jet equipment is situated along the side of the vacuum tower (Fig. 7-27). The processing of a reduced crude oil in a vacuum unit for the production of distilled cylinder stock is illustrated in Figs. 7-25 and 7-26. In this plant a reflux condenser is placed in the top of the tower and the partial condensers for gas oil and wax distillate are outside the tower but not at a great distance. One of the difficulties with the arrangement shown in Fig. 7-25 is the weight of the large condensers. They are so heavy for a large installation that they cannot be supported by the tower. This necessitates independent structural supports and an elaborate expansion joint between the tower and condensers. Vacuum steam strippers are sometimes used on vacuum systems.

Although fractionation is more effective at low temperatures or in a vacuum than at high temperatures (Table 7-7), this behavior is not usually

TABLE 7-7. RELATIVE VOLATILITIES AT HIGH AND AT LOW PRESSURE

	Vapor pressures, mm, at				
	−50°F	+50°F	600°F	700°F	800°F
Propane..........................	630	4,395			
Pentane..........................	12	350			
Lube fraction—bp of 750°F........	.....	....	110	425	1,450
Lube fraction—bp of 850°F........	.....	....	22	115	465
Relative volatility...............	52.5	12.5	5.0	3.7	3.12

an adequate reason for operation at low pressures. It does account in part, however, for the relatively small number of plates used in vacuum towers.

A practical way to increase the efficiency of fractionation or the quality of products is to employ wire-mesh mist extractors below the points at which products are withdrawn. In the production of an asphalt bottom product and at the same time a gas-oil catalytic feedstock that is free from entrained asphalt or metal contaminants that tend to poison the catalyst, wire-mesh has resulted[32] in phenomenal increases in capacity or in large reductions in contaminants.

[32] Symposium (Case Histories) . . . Use of Wire-Mesh Sections . . . , *Oil Gas J.*, Nov. 2, p. 82; Nov. 23, p. 94; and Dec. 28, p. 70, 1953.

The distillation of tarry residues in a vacuum for the production of either catalytic cracking plant feedstock or asphalt differs little in principle from the operations already described except that the vacuum tower can be much simplified (Fig. 7-27) because of the following considerations.

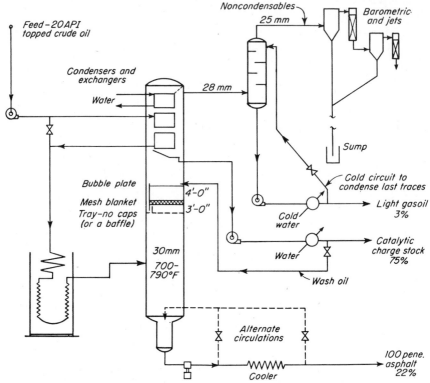

FIG. 7-27. Vacuum distillation for catalytic feedstock or for asphalt.

1. Elaborate fractionation is not necessary. In the case of lubricating-oil distillation, entrainment may discolor the products and increase treating costs, and poorly fractionated wax distillate or cylinder stock may result in trouble with dewaxing. Some asphalt or feed preparation towers employ only one or two bubble plates in addition to a mist separator (Fig. 7-27). More detail on vacuum-tower construction is presented in Chap. 16.

2. Higher vaporizer temperatures can be maintained. Whereas vaporizer temperatures in lube towers are usually limited to a maximum of about 710°F, the vaporizer temperature in asphalt towers sometimes exceeds 780°F. However, vacuum decomposition, which causes violent foaming, begins to occur at about 800°F, and at such a temperature the material in the bottom of the tower must be removed quickly. Means of rapid cooling by recirculation have been employed.

3. Only one product need be taken overhead. This eliminates the extra plates that are required for a side-draw cut or the partial condensers for two overhead cuts

(Fig. 7-27).   If two overhead cuts are taken, the separation is not difficult because both cuts are gas oils and they need not be well fractionated.

4. Tar stocks are usually available at a high temperature.   A small heater is usually required, but in some cases a sufficient amount of vaporization occurs by simply reducing the pressure without the addition of heat.

Air-blown Asphalt.   Most asphalt used for paving is produced by vacuum or steam distillation.   Such asphalt has a relatively high ductility.   Shingle saturants or coatings, roofing saturants, and laminating asphalts require a material of lower penetration and higher softening

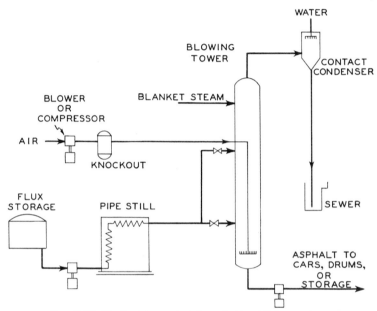

FIG. 7-28. Vertical-tower batch asphalt oxidizing system.

point (see Fig. 4-53), and these are obtained by air blowing.   Even higher ratios of penetration to softening point are obtained by the use of catalysts such as ferric chloride or phosphorus pentoxide.[33]   Batch systems (Fig. 7-28) are most widely employed.   Heavy topped crude oil or vacuum-reduced residue is heated to within 50°F of its flash point and blown with 30 to 50 cu ft per minute of air for each ton of asphalt.[34]   One and one-half to twenty-four hours of blowing, depending on the amount of mechanical agitation and catalysts used, is required to cause hardening.   Fumes can be burned or they can be scrubbed with water to remove obnoxious gases or odors and to recover small amounts of oil.

[33] Shearon and Hoiberg, *Ind. Eng. Chem.*, **45**, 2122 (1953).
[34] Nelson, W. L., *Oil Gas J.*, Aug. 23, 1954, p. 156.

TABLE 7-8. SPACING OF REFINERY UNITS[a]

From one item or unit—to another item or unit	Distance, ft[b]
Cracking unit (low pressure)[c]—cracking unit (setting to setting)....	25–50
Cracking unit (high pressure)[d]—cracking unit (battery to battery)..	75–150
Cracking unit (either)—pipestill unit..........................	Separate block
Cracking unit (either)—any other process unit...................	Separate block
Pipestill unit—pipestill unit (setting to setting).................	25–50
Pipestill unit—any other process unit..........................	100
Shellstill unit—shellstill unit (battery to battery)................	25–50
Steam still battery (shell type)—any other process unit...........	100
Condenser box—shellstill unit.................................	15–20
Receiving house—running-tank fire wall........................	20
Treating unit (agitator)—treating-plant pump house..............	50–100
Boiler and power house—any process unit.......................	100–200
Oil-transfer pump house—any process unit......................	50–100
Foam pump house—any process unit............................	100–200
Main water pump house—any process unit......................	100–200
Warehouse (oil storage)[e]—any process unit.....................	50–100
Treating plant—any process unit..............................	100–200
Gas plants[f]—any process unit.................................	150–200
Gas holders—any process unit.................................	150–200
Main separator (covered)—any process unit.....................	50–100
Main separator (uncovered)—any process unit..................	100–150

[a] "Fire Protection in Refineries," 3d ed., API, 1941.

[b] In case there is a conflict between spacings as shown below, the greater of the two distances applies.

[c] Units operating at 350 psi or less.

[d] Units operating at over 350 psi.

[e] This is meant to cover fireproof structures used for storing low-flash products, and includes sample storage and can-filling buildings.

[f] This is intended to include such plants as gasoline-recovery, debutanization, stabilization, and absorption plants, when they are not an integral part of any process unit.

Spacing of Refinery Units. Units having the same general function are usually kept together in one general area. Within the area, the separate units are spaced apart[35,36] as indicated in Table 7-8. Likewise, the entire block is separated and protected from other similar areas.

[35] "Fire Protection in Refineries," 3d ed., API, 1941.
[36] Attaway, Don, Natural Gasoline Plants, *Pet. Eng.*, January, 1956, p. C-16.

CHAPTER 8

AUXILIARY PROCESSES AND OPERATIONS

Many auxiliary operations were neglected in Chap. 7, and space is available here for discussions of only instrument control, crude oil desalting, waste-water disposal, water cooling, storage tanks and blowdown systems. Refinery practice in the operation of boiler plants, generators, water treating, and pumping does not differ greatly from other standard practice.

Instrument Control. The full usefulness of refinery equipment can be attained only by the use of automatic control instruments, and the use of instruments has contributed much to the productivity of refinery workmen (see Table 23-1). The handling of 10,000 bpd of capacity required 262 men during 1925 and 158 men in 1956. An attempt to discuss the merits of each individual instrument or type of instrument would be unsatisfactory because there are several different types of satisfactory instruments for each purpose and because significant improvements are being made each year.

Figure 8-1 indicates the location of the various control instruments that may be used in a topping plant. Among the most important are (1) top temperature controller; (2) recording pyrometer at vaporizer and at inlet and outlet of pipestill; (3) pressure at inlet and outlet of pipestill, at charge pump, and in tower; (4) rate of flow of crude oil; and (5) level controls at bottom of tower and the side-draw plates. Control instruments are extensively used in natural gasoline plants (Fig. 8-2). Finally, Figs. 12-6 and 12-7 on dewaxing, and Fig. 20-11 on alkylation, show instrumentation.

In the control of a continuously operating system, certain variables must be fixed or the control of others is almost impossible. Of prime importance are (1) the rate of feed, (2) the temperature of feed, and (3) the top temperatures of the towers. With these variables fixed, the control of the others is well within the capability of a competent operator. Even an expert operator is almost helpless if these three variables are not fixed. A plant can be operated with these controls alone, but the operation will be much more efficient if other controls are utilized. The rate of feed may be controlled by manual operation with the help of stroke

263

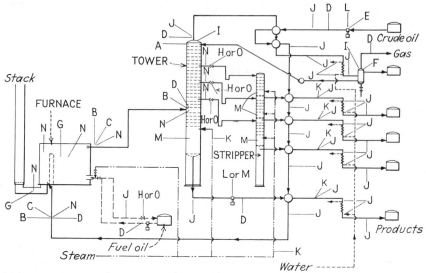

Fig. 8-1. Instruments that may be used in a topping plant. The letters refer to the following instruments: A, temperature-recorder controller; B, recording pyrometer; C, recording pressure gauge; D, indicating pressure gauge; E, rate-of-flow controller; F, pressure regulator; G, draft gauge; H, hand-control valve; I, safety valve; M, liquid-level control.

Optional instruments: J, industrial thermometers or thermocouple wells; K, flow meter; L, stroke regulator and counter; N, indicating thermocouples or connections for them; O, bypass adjustment valves or proportional draw-off devices.

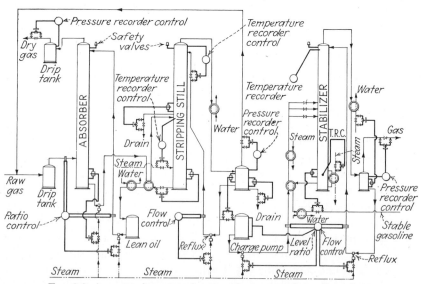

Fig. 8-2. An extensive control system for a natural-gasoline plant.

regulators and stroke counters, but flow regulators or indicators are now widely used. The effect of a variable feed rate can be minimized by the use of proportional draw-off weirs.[1] The temperature of the feed normally gives little trouble, and several types of satisfactory top temperature controllers for towers are available.

The principle of trend analyzing has been one of the notable improvements in instrument design. A trend-analyzing instrument will begin to stop the actuating mechanism before the condition (temperature, pressure, or rate of flow) has been brought back to the desired condition. In this way the tendency to overcontrol, or "hunt," has been corrected. Such instruments apply a large correction if the condition is far from the control point and a small correction (or none at all) if the condition is nearly at the control point.

A central control room has become an integral part of all modern petroleum units. The grouping of recording and controlling instruments facilitates the work of the operator and concentrates responsibility for the operation of the plant. Although the first cost is high, it reduces the number of operators required to man the plant and provides an appreciable saving in operating cost. In dealing with emergency shutdowns, such as those arising from explosions and fires, the facility afforded by centralized control is vital.

On the other hand, control instruments and the lines between the control room and the equipment are costly. For this reason the less important measurements should be taken at the equipment, and indicating instruments should be given preference over recording instruments except where a record of the operating conditions is of definite service. A large number of instruments divides the attention of the operator, and hence careful thought should be given to the selection of truly useful operating data. Figure 8-3 shows the instrument room and boards of a catalytic cracking unit.

Desalting of Crude Oil. The small amount of brine that is associated with crude oil is far more important than its quantity would indicate. In addition to the mechanical accumulation of debris in the processing equipment, the chloride salts (particularly magnesium chloride) liberate hydrochloric acid that causes corrosion during processing. This causes a decrease in heat-transfer rates by fouling and promotes the formation of coke in the pipestill tubes. The removal of the brine often results in increasing the length of the operating cycle tenfold or more. Even a few parts per billion of arsenic will quickly poison platinum catalysts.

Brine is associated with crude oil both as a fine suspension of droplets and as more permanent emulsions. The demarcation line between these two types is not always clear; but the less stable mixtures can be separated

[1] Chillas and Weir, *Ind. Eng. Chem.*, **22**, 206 (1930).

by simple settling methods, and the more permanent mixtures must be handled by chemical or electrical methods of separation. Long standing in storage tanks results in some settling—in one instance the salt content was decreased from 25 to 18.5 g per gal by standing for 4 days. A high temperature is also useful, and the most common settling system consists simply of a horizontal tank operating at 200 to 300°F (an oil viscosity of 2 centipoises) and at sufficient pressure to suppress violent vaporization (50 to 250 psi). The coalescence of particles is hastened also by the use

FIG. 8-3. Instrument boards and control room for a catalytic cracking unit.   (*Minneapolis-Honeywell.*)

of towers packed with sand (or gravel) or excelsior,[2] either before or after[3] the settling vessel.   The time of settling may be cut in half by the use of a packed column of excelsior.[2]   The use of Fiberglas has been thoroughly studied by Burtis and Kirkbride,[4] and reduction of salt content to 5 lb per 1,000 bbl appears possible.   Packings greatly assist settling, but they become plugged with debris and must be replaced.   Water is usually

[2] Hawthorne and Bedell, The Removal of Inorganic Salts from Crude Petroleum, API, 8th Midyear Meeting, Wichita, Kans., May 24, 1938.

[3] Blair, C. M., Jr., Removal of Inorganic Salts from Petroleum, *Oil Gas J.*, Apr. 4, 1940, p. 52.

[4] Desalting of Petroleum with Fiberglas Packing, *Trans. A.I.Ch.E.*, **XLII**, 413 (1946).

mixed with the incoming crude oil to produce a brine containing 2 to 5 lb of salt per bbl. Union of the water with brine droplets is reported to be 75 per cent or more complete,[5] and hence the brine droplets that remain in the crude oil after settling contain little salt. The pressure drop through the water mixers ranges from 12 to 40 psi.

Settling times of 1 hr are common, but 2 hr is sometimes employed. Caustic soda is often added[6] in amounts large enough to produce a pH of 8 to 9 in the brine. The oil is passed upward through a 10- to 25-ft bath

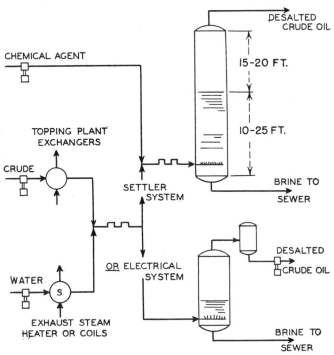

FIG. 8-4. Salt-settling systems. (*Oil Gas J.*)

of brine and then through 15 to 20 ft of oil. Accumulations of debris at the interface should be drained at frequent intervals. The general arrangement is indicated in Fig. 8-4, and it also shows the now widely used electrical process.[7]

In handling more stable mixtures, the aforementioned simple heat- and water-diluent system may be assisted by the use of chemicals or a high-

[5] Egloff, Nelson, Maxutov, and Wirth, III, Crude Oil Desalting, AIME Meeting, Oklahoma City, Oct. 8, 1937.

[6] Nelson, W. L., *Oil Gas J.*, Feb. 17, 1945, p. 121.

[7] St. Hill and Hanson, Extraction of Salts from Refinery Stocks by the Electrical Process, *Ref. Nat. Gaso. Mfr.*, October, 1937.

potential electric field (16,500 to 33,000 volts) across the settling vessel to cause more rapid coalescence of droplets. By these methods the salt content can usually be reduced by 90 per cent or more, and the time of settling may be reduced in some instances to only 20 min. Among the ingredients[8] of treating compounds are the following:

Per cent

Modified fatty acids partly or wholly saponified with ammonia..... 35–48
Oil-soluble sodium petroleum sulfonate........................... 13–31
Water-soluble solvents, dilute alcohol (10–14 per cent), etc......... 10–20
Oil-soluble solvents, kerosene, crude oil, naphthas, cresol, etc....... 4–25
Inorganic sulfates, sodium sulfate, sodium sulfite................. 1–2

Few directions can be given for the selection of treating agents, but in general, for alkaline brines of high pH value the neutral soaps of oleic acid, solid fatty acids, liquid-saturated fatty acids, linoleic acid, etc., should be used; for alkaline brines of lower pH ordinary turkey-red oil, with the sulfonate group esterified and loosely linked, may be successful; and finally, for more acid brines "one should consider the soaps of naphthenic acids, preferably having a low sulfate content, and the more stable fatty acid, alcoholic, or aromatic sulfonates, having a higher sulfate content, provided these are adapted to the pH of the water, and do not contain antagonistic constituents" (ones that cause precipitation).[9] The use of small amounts of very dilute caustic soda (3 per cent of a 0.3 per cent solution) or phenol-saturated spent caustic solution is found to be beneficial in some instances.

Waste-water Disposal. The pollution of streams and harbors by waste water from refineries is a problem that must be met by all refiners.[10,11] Simple gravity-type settlers are widely used. These function according to the basic law of Stokes which for spherical particles is

$$v = \frac{gD^2(\rho_s - \rho_l)}{18\mu} \qquad (8\text{-}1)$$

in which v is the maximum velocity of settling, D is the diameter of the spherical particles, ρ_s and ρ_l are the densities of the solid and liquid, and μ is the viscosity, all in cgs units. Commercial settlers deviate from the theoretical behavior, but Eq. (8-1) constitutes a guide by which com-

[8] Bennett, H., "The Chemical Formulary," vol. 2, p. 179 (Tretolites), D. Van Nostrand Company, Inc., Princeton, N.J., 1935.

[9] Van Dedem, G. W., Chemical Methods for Separating Petroleum Emulsions, *Oil Gas J.*, Aug. 12, 1937, p. 65.

[10] Hart, W. B., Elements of Waste-water Separator Design, API, 8th Midyear Meeting, Wichita, Kans., May 24, 1938.

[11] API, Disposal of Refinery Wastes, sec. I, 5th ed., 1953.

mercial relationships can be correlated. A complete review of settling has been made by A. C. Ingersoll.[12]

Somewhat the same layout of settler as that developed by API studies[11] is shown in Fig. 8-5. The flight scraper serves to move sediment out of the box in a continuous manner. A filter[11] that utilizes cloth as the filter medium may be used after the settler for removing the last traces of iridescent oil film. Settlers are usually constructed of concrete and have a depth of 6 to 8 ft. Other dimensions are not of great significance, provided that the retention time is adequately long and provided that the incoming waste water is evenly distributed across the settler. Many settlers are producing waste water that contains only 5 ppm of oil. A film of oil ranging from 0.000006 to 0.000012 in. thick on the surface of

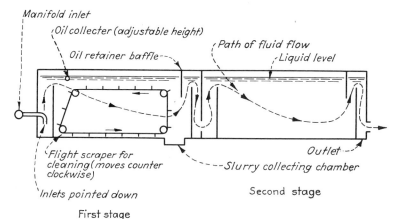

FIG. 8-5. Vertical section of a waste-water separator.

water will produce an iridescent coloration. W. B. Hart[13] has published numerous articles on nearly every feature of refinery waste disposal.

Separators cannot be expected to handle waters more highly acid than a pH of 4.5 or more alkaline than a pH of 10 or to handle true emulsions of oil in water such as so-called "white water." In such an emulsion the oil is dispersed through a continuous water phase and is carried through the separator. Later the emulsion may be destroyed by dilution or other effects that will liberate the oil. Emulsions of water-in-oil which may contain asphalt, clay, dirt, alkaline earth soaps, lead sulfide, or coke as the emulsifying agent are not usually troublesome. Occasionally, however,

[12] Fundamentals and Performance of Gravity Separation, Pet. Refiner, June, 1951, p. 106.

[13] Disposal of Refinery Wastes, a series of 20 articles, Natl. Pet. News, Tech. Sec., Jan. 2, 1946; Feb. 6, 1946; Mar. 6, 1946; Apr. 3, 1946; May 1, 1946; June 5, 1946; July 3, 1946; Aug. 7, 1946; and continued in monthly issues of Pet. Processing throughout September–December, 1946, and January–September, 1947.

one of these emulsions will have a specific gravity that is the same as that of water, and it will not settle.   All these special cases should be met by corrections in the general processing scheme of the refinery rather than in the waste separator.   Burroughs[14] recommends methods of disposing of emulsions from traps, separators, yard tanks, and treating plants, and the disposal of tank bottoms, spent caustic solutions, and obnoxious gases. Water is becoming so valuable that it, too, is being recovered for reuse.[15]

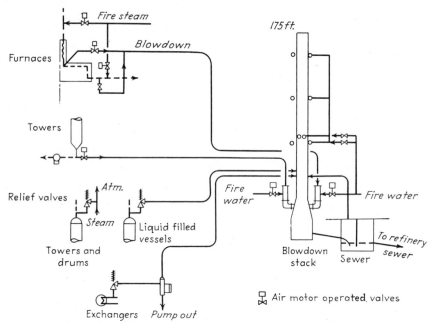

Fig. 8-6. Emergency disposal of hot oil.   (*Pet. Refiner.*)

Emergency Drains and Vents.   This important and complicated topic can only be mentioned.   In case of fire or similar emergency three methods of blowdown are employed: (1) hot oils of low vapor pressure are released into a blowdown stack as in Fig. 8-6.[16] where they are quenched with water, the liquid is released to the sewer, and the vapor is vented to the atmosphere; (2) gases and cold oils of high vapor pressure are released into a drum which is vented to a flare stack where the gases burn at the top of the stack, and the liquid in the drum is pumped to storage tanks; and (3) cold oils of low vapor pressure are pumped directly to storage tanks.   Figure 8-6 is typical of most hot-oil disposal systems.   All air-

[14] Disposal of Refinery Wastes, *Pet. Refiner*, July, 1946, p. 81.

[15] Pursell and Ferguson, *Oil Gas J.*, Aug. 16, 1944, p. 114.

[16] Johnson, J. H., Fundamental Requirements for Safe Arrangement of Drains and Vents, *Pet. Refiner*, June, 1947, p. 91.

motor-operated valves are operated from a central control station located to give maximum safety and accessibility. Several other blowdown diagrams are given by Johnson.[16]

Storage. The types of storage required for volatile and other types of liquids are indicated in Fig. 8-7 as a function of vapor pressure and temperature (also see Fig. 8-8). Thus, spherical shapes may be used to store gasolines and low-vapor-pressure natural gasoline, and if the temperature never exceeds about 80°F, as in some arctic climes, even high-vapor-pressure natural gasoline may be kept in such storage. Of course, if sufficiently refrigerated, any material can be stored at atmospheric pressure in simple insulated tanks connected to a compressor which is used to liquefy and return to the tank the small amount of material that evaporates. Liquefied methane (natural gas) has been transported in this way in specially insulated barges and tankers.[17] A common method of gauging sealed storage tanks involves the difference in pressure in the vapor space and in the bottom of a gas-filled tube which extends nearly to the bottom of the tank. In calibrating[18] or "strapping" horizontal cylindrical tanks, tables of the segments of circles appearing in handbooks are useful, but special consideration must be given to the volumes contained in various types of heads.[19]

Evaporation losses are a function of so many variables such as (1) liquid or surface temperature, (2) variation in atmospheric temperature, (3) true vapor pressure of liquid, (4) volume of vapor space (how full), (5) color or reflectiveness of surface, (6) frequency of filling, (7) construction of tank, (8) degree of saturation attained in gas space, etc., that only the gross approximation indicated in Table 8-1 for a 10 R.v.p. gasoline

TABLE 8-1. INDICATION OF EVAPORATION LOSSES FOR 10-LB R.V.P. GASOLINE
IN SMALL (5,000 BBL) CONE ROOF TANKS
Aluminum paint, half full

Temperature, °F	Standing loss, % per year	Working loss, % per filling
20	1.65	0.09
40	2.5	0.14
60	5.0	0.20
70	6.8	0.25
80	9.6	0.30
90	14.5	0.35
100	25.0	0.41

[17] Nelson, W. L., Natural Gas to Move by Barge, *Oil Gas J.*, Mar. 22, 1954.
[18] Instructions for Measuring, Sampling and Testing Petroleum Shipments, Standard Inspection Laboratory, Standard Oil Development Co., New York.
[19] Nelson, W. L., *Oil Gas J.*, Sept. 23, 1944, p. 203.

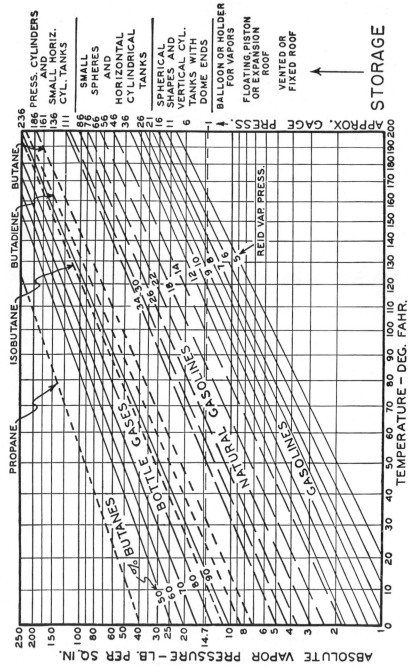

FIG. 8-7. Type of storage tank as a function of vapor pressure of the stored liquid.

272

can be given.[20]   The effectiveness of various colors of paints in reflecting light, based on white as 90 and black as zero, is[21,22] about as follows:

	Reflection of heat	Approx. relative breathing loss
Black...................	0	1.25
No paint................	10	1.25
Aluminum, old...........	59	1.00
Aluminum, new...........	67	0.80
White..................	90	0.75

Losses are also smaller in large tanks[21] being about 80 per cent as large in a 60,000-bbl tank as in a 5,000-bbl tank, and only 50 per cent in a

Fig. 8-8. Spherical storage tanks—2,500 and 1,500 bbl.   (*Photographer E. M. Payne, Houston, Texas, and Chicago Bridge and Iron Company.*)

120,000-bbl tank.   Finally, vapor pressure is vitally effective in changing the losses[23] (see Table 8-2).   All of these data are most general (Tables 8-1, 8-2, etc.) and accordingly, computations[22,24,25] are necessary for each situation.   The losses from floating roof types of tanks (or their use by

[20] Nelson, W. L., *Oil Gas J.*, Feb. 22, 1951, p. 202, and Mar. 1, 1951, p. 78.

[21] Nelson, W. L., *Oil Gas J.*, Nov. 2, 1953, p. 130; also Symposium, Evaporation Loss of Petroleum, *Oil Gas J.*, Nov. 17, 1952, pp. 266–298.

[22] API Evaporation Loss of Petroleum from Storage Tanks, Symposium 32d Ann. Meeting, Chicago, Ill., Nov. 10, 1952; or *Oil Gas J.*, Nov. 17, 1952, pp. 266–298.

[23] Nelson, W. L., *Oil Gas J.*, Apr. 26, 1954, p. 254.

[24] Nelson, W. L., *Oil Gas J.*, June 23, 1952, p. 111.

[25] Prater, N. H., *Pet. Processing*, April, 1954, p. 537.

TABLE 8-2. APPROXIMATE EFFECT OF VAPOR PRESSURE ON EVAPORATION LOSSES

	Vapor pressure, psia		Loss relative to loss of 10 R.v.p. gaso.
	Reid at 100°F	True at 60°F	
Light gasoline.............	12	6.0	125
Gasoline (the basis)........	10	4.8	100
Heavy gasoline............	8	3.6	76
Crude oil................	6	4.7	98
Crude oil................	4	3.2	67
Crude oil................	2	1.6	33
200–300° solvent..........	...	0.9	19
300–400° solvent..........	...	0.6[a]	12
120° flash, kerosene.......	...	1.5 mm[a]	0.6
150° flash, distillate.......	...	0.5 mm[a]	0.2

[a] Based on vapor pressure required to cause the flash point.

manifolding several tanks to one floating roof tank) are much smaller, and the use of a blanket of tiny plastic balloons is said to decrease losses by 40 to 90 per cent.[26]

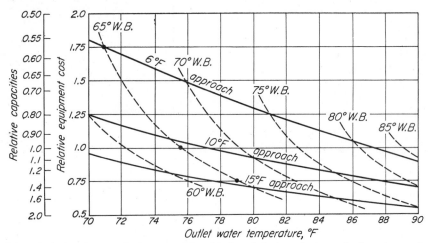

FIG. 8-9. Approximate relative capacities of induced-draft and atmospheric water-cooling towers as a function of operating conditions.

Water Cooling. Water is becoming so scarce that cooling by means of ponds, spray ponds, or cooling towers must be practiced in nearly all refineries. Heat dissipation from ponds is affected by the air temperature and its humidity, by the amount of sunshine, and by the wind velocity,

[26] Ellerbrake and Veatch, *Oil Gas J.*, Nov. 16, 1953, p. 223; and *Oil Gas J.*, Oct. 10, 1955, p. 248.

but it usually ranges from 2 Btu per sq ft per hr per deg difference in air and water temperatures in winter, to about 4 Btu during the summer.[27] More detail is given by Langhaar.[28] If the warm water is sprayed through nozzles at a pressure of 7 to 10 pounds, a much smaller area of pond may be used. Each square foot of surface can handle 150 to 250 pounds of water per hr. The temperature attained in the pond when the hot water is at 110°F is usually within 10 to 20°F of the wet-bulb temperature. Even better control of losses and contamination is possible with atmospheric or induced-draft cooling towers. The approximate relative capacities of induced-draft or atmospheric towers are indicated in Fig. 8-9, and the reciprocals of the same factors may be considered as the relative costs of such towers. Thus, a tower operating at a 6°F approach to a wet-bulb temperature of 65°F (cooling to 71°F) will handle only 57 per cent as much as when it operates for 75.6°F water (an approach of 10.6°F). Note also that the capacity is about 33 per cent more if an outgoing water temperature of 79°F is adequate.

Figure 8-9 can only be an approximation because it neglects the sensible heat introduced by the dry-bulb temperature and by the inlet water temperature. However, it (Fig. 8-9) was based on a water-cooling range of about 20°F, and the effect of a cooling range of 30°F is to increase the capacity by about 17 per cent whereas a cooling range of only 15°F decreases the capacity by about 15 per cent.

The amount of evaporation loss ranges from 0.85 to 1.25 per cent of the circulation over the tower for each 10°F of temperature drop through the tower. Windage loss for induced-draft towers usually ranges from 0.1 to 0.3 per cent of the circulation but may be 0.8 to 1.3 per cent for atmospheric-type towers. The make-up water continually brings salts or solids into the system, and although the windage loss removes salt, an equilibrium in salt concentration is established which eventually requires that water be discarded from the system.

[27] Hicks, T. G., *Pet. Refiner*, April, 1952, p. 164.
[28] Langhaar, J. W., *Chem. Eng.*, August, 1953, p. 194.

CHAPTER 9

REFINERY CORROSION AND METALS

Corrosion cost refiners about \$560,000,000 during 1956 (Table 9-1),[1] and if the cost of corrosion in the production, transportation, and marketing divisions is added to this, the levy exceeds 2 cents per gal of gasoline. Those refiners who escape sulfide and acid corrosion by processing selected oils still must contend with soil corrosion, atmospheric oxidation, naphthenic acids, and high temperature oxidation. Chemical analyses of the oil are useful, but it is also necessary to determine corrosiveness by plant tests and by special laboratory tests (refer to Chap. 2, pp. 17–18, and Chap. 4, pp. 89 and 128). The cost of corrosion due to high sulfur and sourness shown in Table 9-1 is an average, and accordingly, the cost varies with the amount of sulfur and degree of sourness from as low as 2 cents per bbl for a crude oil that contains only 0.5 per cent sulfur (plus 2.7 cents if it is sour) to as high as 28 cents for an unstable type of oil that contains 5 per cent of sulfur (plus 8 cents if it is sour).[2] Extensive tabulations[3] of the high-temperature strengths, applications, and analyses of the alloys and steels used for refinery services have been published.

Sulfide Corrosion. Hydrogen sulfide is often found in natural gas or dissolved in crude oil, and in addition it may be formed by the decomposition of organic sulfur compounds at high temperatures. It rapidly attacks steel parts that are exposed to the gas. Equipment that suffers by this corrosion comprises storage tanks and gas lines, and at temperatures exceeding 400°F, pipestill tubes, evaporators, and fractionators. Liberation of hydrogen sulfide is very rapid at 650 to 700°F, but at temperatures higher than 900°F the rate of liberation appears to decrease. The presence of moisture facilitates the action of hydrogen

[1] Nelson, W. L., Cost of Refining High Sulfur Crudes, *Oil Gas J.*, Aug. 16, 1954, p. 150.

[2] Nelson, W. L., *Oil Gas J.*, Aug. 1, 1955, p. 117.

[3] Nelson, W. L., *Oil Gas J.*, Creep Strengths of Stainless Steels, Mar. 30, 1953, p. 195, and Apr. 27, 1953, p. 291; Applications of Stainless Steel, Aug. 17, 1953, p. 156; Metals for Low Temperatures, Apr. 12, 1954, p. 163; Where to Use Aluminum Alloys, Aug. 30, 1954, p. 103; Application of Metals and Alloys . . . , Sept. 27, 1954, through Apr. 18, 1955; and Alphabetical List of Alloys . . . , Sept. 14, 1953, through Jan. 4, 1954.

Table 9-1. Estimates of Cost of Corrosion to the Refining Industry, 1956[a]
(Cents per barrel)

	All corrosion	High sulfur alone	High sulfur with sourness
1. Maintenance (about 70% of total maintenance)....	7.6	5.3	6.9
2. Lost production (5 days per year)...............	2.0	1.1	1.4
3. Depreciation more rapid.......................	1.6	1.0	1.3
Total stated by F. N. Speller (1927)[a,b]........	12.3		
4. Material and labor for corrosion repair............	0.3		
Total of items 1, 3, and 4 stated[b] in 1953[a]....	10.1		
5. Built-in resistance (13% of plant cost)...........	2.3	2.0	2.6
6. Inspection cost of tools, workmen, and inventory...	0.2	0.4	0.5
Total by API, items 1, 2, 5, and 6 (1954)[c].....	12.1		
7. Neutralizing chemicals (incl. half of desalting cost).	0.6		
8. Cathodic protection of lines.....................	Nil		
9. Unscheduled shutdown time....................	1.6	2.9	3.8
10. Product loss by leaks or contamination...........	0.8		
11. Fires, accidents, and insurance.................	0.3		
12. Over-design of equipment......................	0.5		
13. Waste disposal................................	0.1		
Total of all[c].............................	17.9	12.7	16.5

[a] All costs converted to 1956 by Nelson Refinery Construction Cost Index, *Oil Gas J.*, July 27, 1952, p. 105. The Index is published in the first issue each month of the *Oil and Gas Journal*.

[b] What Does Corrosion Cost You, *Pet. Processing*, November, 1953, p. 1625.

[c] Guthrie, V. B., *Pet. Processing*, May, 1954, p. 708. Estimate of total was 19.4 cents per bbl.

sulfide, and the concentration of oxygen in the gaseous mixture is of great importance.[4]

In handling[5] high-sulfur crude oils, chromium steels are employed (Table 9-2). The cost of expensive equipment is due mainly to labor costs and the intricacy of design, and hence higher chromium contents are justified for vessel linings, bubble caps and trays, centrifugal pumps, pump liners, wear rings, pump rods, connections to vessels, pipestill bends, etc. The relative prices, strengths, and protection afforded by chromium steels show that their use is usually justified (see Table 9-3).

The corrosiveness of sulfur-bearing oils is not directly proportional to the sulfur content. Crude oils that contain 2 per cent sulfur and that

[4] Devine et al., Oxygen Effect on Hydrogen Sulfide Gas Corrosion, *Oil Gas J.*, Apr. 7, 1932, p. 16.

[5] Nelson, W. L., Applications of Stainless Steel, *Oil Gas J.*, Aug. 17, 1953, p. 156.

TABLE 9-2

Max temp, °F	Per cent chromium		
	Vessels or tanks	Pipestill tubes or hangers	Expensive equipment
450– 550	None	1–3	5
450– 800	1	2–9	7–12
700– 950	5–13 linings	7–12	12–16[a]
900–1,000	13–18[a] linings	5[c]–8[c]	12–27[a]
1,000–1,300	18[a]–27[a] linings	18[a]–27[a]	25[a]–27[a]
1,300–1,600	. . . .	18[a]–27[a]	
1,750	. . . .	20.5[b]	

[a] Usually with about half as much nickel.
[b] Inconel.   About 32% Ni and 44% Fe.
[c] Applies only to tubes.   Sulfide corrosion is less active at this temperature.

TABLE 9-3. EXTRA COST VERSUS EXTRA PERFORMANCE (APPROXIMATE) FOR
ALLOY STEELS USED IN REFINERY PIPESTILLS
Applies primarily to chromium and chrome-nickel steels, some with molybdenum

Number of times greater cost	Number of times better performance (than for carbon steel)					
	Strength alone[a]	Oxidation alone[b]	Sulfide corrosion alone[b]	Using twice thickness required by strength of carbon steel		
				Oxidation	Sulfide	Oxid. and sulfide
1.3	1.5	1.1[c]	1.3[c]	1.38	1.62	1.5
1.5	1.5[c]	1.2	1.5	1.5	1.87	1.69
2.0	1.5	1.5	2.0	1.87	2.5	2.19
3.0	1.6	2.7	2.8	3.7	3.8	3.8
4.0	1.8	4.9	3.2	7.05	4.6	5.8
6.0	2.0	9.4	4.4	14.1	6.6	10.3
8.0	2.5	13.7	5.8	22.0	9.3	15.6
10.0	3.2	18.1	7.4	30.6	12.5	22.2
12.0	4.5	22.7	9.5	40.5	16.9	28.6
14.0	6.8	48.0	11.8	High	22.0	55.5
16.0	9.7	74.0	14.3	. . . . .	27.2	High
18.0	13.4	100.0	16.8	. . . . .	32.2	
20.0	17.2	High	19.4	. . . . .	High	
24.0	23.0	. . . . . .	23.0			

[a] At customary temperatures, 900–1200°F.

[b] No credit for strength.

[c] Bold face indicates that the extra cost of alloy steel is not justified by the performance.

cause little trouble by sulfide corrosion have been reported, but others containing less than 0.7 per cent have destroyed distillation equipment in less than 6 months. As a further example, the sulfur content of gasoline marketed in the United States has been limited to less than 0.1 per cent, but at one time fuels were marketed in Germany that contained as much as 1.5 per cent sulfur and no serious engine corrosion has been reported.

Chromium steel is the standard material for withstanding sulfide corrosion. Resistance becomes noticeable at about 1 per cent chromium, but in most instances the use of more than 13 per cent is not justified. The high-chromium (13 per cent up) steels tend to lose ductility, particularly if used at high temperatures, and hence nickel is employed with the chromium to assist in avoiding loss of ductility.

The additional cost of high-temperature or resistant alloy steels as compared with carbon steel must be justified by such factors as (1) oxidation resistance, (2) strength at elevated temperatures, (3) sulfide resistance, (4) great cost of replacing complicated equipment, (5) maintenance labor and warehouse inventory, and (6) avoidance of shutdowns. The approximate relationship between some of these variables is indicated in Table 9-3 for the tubes and tube hangers used in refinery pipestills,[6] and the general relationship is undoubtedly valid for many other applications. It is clearly evident that the extra cost of alloy steels cannot be justified by consideration of strength alone or sulfide resistance alone. The increase in cost is nearly always greater than the increase in strength or the increase in sulfide resistance. Oxidation helps to justify the use of alloy steels, and strength indirectly alters the situation because more metal thickness becomes available for destruction by corrosion if the alloy steel has a high strength. Thus, a 1-in. thick carbon-steel tube, which must be only ½ in. thick for strength, provides only a ½-in. thickness for corrosion whereas a 1-in. thick 2 per cent chromium steel of 50 per cent greater strength provides ¾ in. of material which can be destroyed by corrosion before the tube must be retired from service.

Neutralizing chemicals, particularly lime, are widely used to combat sulfide corrosion. The effect of ammonia is not entirely known,[7] but caustic soda causes troublesome scaling or clogging of tubes and evaporator surfaces.

Processing Sour Crudes. Points of corrosive attack are marked on the flow diagram[8] of Fig. 9-1 by letters, and the letters are used as paragraph headings in the following discussion.

A. Poison Hazard. Hydrogen sulfide is one of the most poisonous gases. Percentages of 0.1 per cent in air are fatal in less than 30 min, and

[6] Nelson, W. L., *Oil Gas J.*, May 25, 1953, p. 267.

[7] Puckett, R. E., Preventing Corrosion, *Oil Gas J.*, Sept. 23, 1937, p. 44.

[8] Nelson, W. L., Hazards and Corrosion with Sour Crudes, *Oil Gas J.*, Dec. 16, 1944, p. 107.

lower percentages are also dangerous.   Warning signs should be posted at dangerous spots such as sewer openings and tank hatches.   It is a heavy gas and therefore tends to collect on the ground at low points.

B. *Fire Hazard.* Fresh sulfide corrosion scale may burst into flame spontaneously upon exposure to air.[9]   Most difficulty is encountered with exchanger-tube bundles and with the scale in naphtha-rundown tanks. Upon shutdown, the lines and vessels should be flushed with water and left full until the equipment is opened.   Tube bundles should be sprayed with water while being withdrawn, and all scaled surfaces should be kept moist.   The scrapings are kept moist until they are buried.

C. *Elimination of Sulfide Gas.* Dangers can be minimized by early elimination of the hydrogen sulfide by burning it under boilers, by stabilization of the incoming crude oil, and by washing straight-run products with caustic soda.   Sulfur is recovered from hydrogen sulfide in many plants.

D. *Desalting.*   This is particularly important because a combination of sulfide and hydrochloric acid corrosion is exceedingly troublesome. Reduction of the salt content to 5 to 10 lb per 1,000 bbl crude oil greatly reduces the sulfide corrosion.   Ganister linings may be used in the settler vessels.   Injection of caustic ahead of settlers to a pH of 8 to 9 helps corrosion and aids settling.

E. *Ammonia and lime* are used in the naphtha-rundown and cracking systems, respectively.   Ammonia, used in amounts (often 0.01 to 0.03 lb per bbl) to give a pH in the condensed water of 7, is introduced into the top tray or vapor line of naphtha towers along with enough steam to wash ammonium chloride out of the condenser system.   Unsuccessful desalting may require the use of Monel metal in the naphtha condenser system.   At temperatures past 700°F, lime in amounts of 0.3 to 1.0 lb per bbl is said to decrease corrosion by 75 to 85 per cent.

F. *Field lines* may be cement-lined if corrosion is severe.

G. *Tank corrosion* is usually not serious except for crude oil (6 to 8 years), and naphtha-rundown tanks (4 to 7 years) if the naphtha is not caustic-washed.   Steam may be injected in the vapor space, or the roof rafters and the bottom may be covered with gunite.

H. *Topping piping.*   Corrosion is not severe except at points where the temperature exceeds 500°F as in transfer lines (use 5 per cent chromium). Occasionally Monel metal is required in naphtha-rundown lines if desalting and ammonia are not successful.

I. *Cracking piping* requirements range from plain steel for feed, pressure distillate vapor, and coke transfer lines; 5 to 9 per cent chromium for flash or coke chamber vapor lines, still transfer lines, recycle, and resid-

---

[9] Anon., Ferro Sulfide Source of Unexplained Tank Fires, *Oil Gas J.*, Feb. 4, 1943, p. 33.

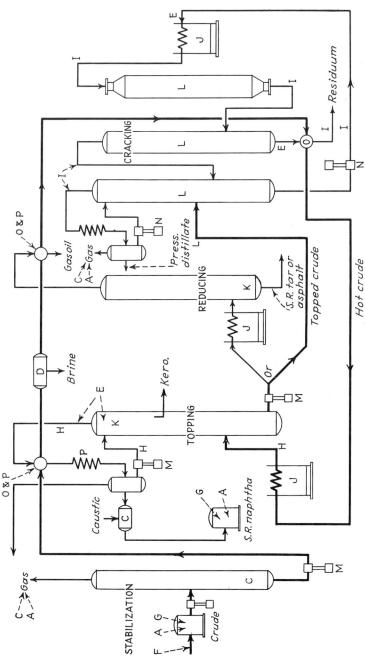

Fig. 9-1. Corrosion of equipment when handling sour crude oils. (*Oil Gas J.*) See pages 279–282 for the meaning of the letters.

uum lines; to 9 to 18 per cent chromium for the line from the reaction chamber to the flash chamber.

J. Still-tubes and transfer-line materials are indicated in Table 9-2.

K. Crude towers suffer little loss except below the feed tray when the feed is at 600 to 700°F (use 12 per cent chromium lining), and on the top tray if ammonia and desalting are unsuccessful (use Monel-metal liner).

L. Cracking towers and chambers are lost in 6 to 12 months unless lined with 12 per cent chromium (also trays and caps), but one refiner finds 5 to 12 per cent liners on inlet nozzles or openings is all that is required. Gunite is used successfully for some soakers, reaction chambers, and flash chambers.

M. Pumps for topping may require no special materials, although 12 per cent chromium and 18–8 chromium-nickel liners, rods, valves, and seats are sometimes used. Centrifugal pumps may require 12 per cent impeller wear rings and shaft sleeves. Naphtha reflux pumps may require Monel metal.

N. Pumps for cracking must utilize 5 per cent chromium blocks, and liners ranging from 12 per cent chromium to 25–12 chromium nickel as well as 12 per cent chromium rods, valves, and seats. Centrifugal pumps may be 12 per cent chromium throughout with Stellited impeller rings and shaft sleeves.

O. Exchanger tubes are usually steel for oil-to-oil or admiralty for oil-to-water, but 5 to 7 per cent chromium tubes are used for cracked residuum.

P. Condensers may require Monel-metal shells or lining, but admiralty metal is usually satisfactory for tubes.

Acid Corrosion. Hydrochloric acid is not present in crude oil, but it may be produced during distillation by the hydrolysis of chloride salts, particularly magnesium chloride, that are present in the brine found in crude oils. Sulfuric acid is probably produced by the oxidation of hydrogen sulfide in the presence of moisture, but only small amounts of sulfuric acid have been detected. These acids constitute the "acid" corrosion that occurs in vapor lines, condensers, coolers, and rundown lines and particularly at points in which water accumulates, such as in valves in horizontal lines.

The corrosive action of dilute hydrochloric acid at the temperatures encountered in distillation equipment cannot be satisfactorily withstood by any common materials. However, the copper-base alloys have been widely used for hydrochloric acid and brine corrosion. Although conditions are not the same in all plants, the use of copper-base alloy tubes for condensers and water-cooled exchangers appears to be increasing. One refiner[10] has been using the following kinds of tubes:

[10] Wilten, H. M., *Mining Met.*, March, 1937, p. 143.

	Percentage of tubes in service			Approx. relative costs
	1930	1933	1936	
Steel..................................	18.0	16.3	12.0	1.0
Stainless steel (18–8).....................	60.3	14.9	5.6	4.8
Admiralty metal or other copper-base alloys.	21.7	68.8	82.4	1.2

Ammonia is unsuitable as a neutralizer if copper-base alloys are used, because if used in excess it may destroy the metal faster than acid corrosion. The other neutralizers appear to produce protective films so that corrosion halts after an initial action. If scale-forming water is used, admiralty-metal tubes must be cleaned frequently, because corrosion occurs mainly beneath breaks or porous spots in the scale. The zinc in the brass is dissolved and is replaced by spongy copper.[11]

Corrosion due to acid and that due to sulfide can never be completely segregated. Thus Table 9-4 on the corrosion of copper-base alloys[12] shows "attack by sulfur" as well as "attack by water," meaning that copper-base alloys were used at points where acid or brine corrosion required their use but that failure occurred mainly by sulfide corrosion.

Oxidation and High-temperature Strength. Iron and steel oxidize or rust in the presence of air or moisture. At high temperatures such as those encountered in boilers and furnaces, oxidation or scaling occurs very rapidly. The chromium and chrome-nickel steels (usually with molybdenum and limited silicon) are excellent resistors to high-temperature oxidation, and at the same time they retain their strength and toughness at elevated temperatures. For these reasons they are admirably suited for boiler and furnace parts that are exposed to high temperatures and to furnace gases.

The common method of measuring the strength of metals at high temperatures is by long-time heating tests. Short-time tests are unsuccessful because in a furnace the metal stretches or creeps as time progresses and will fail under a load that appears to be safe by short-time tests. The effect of time on the strength of cast carbon steel is shown in Fig. 9-2.[13] The creep strength of creep limit may be defined as the load (pounds per square inch) that a material can withstand at a high temperature without exceeding a given rate of stretch. Creep strengths are frequently given

[11] Pew, A. E., Minimizing Corrosion in Condensers, *Oil Gas J.*, Apr. 16, 1931, p. 112.

[12] Mitchell, N. W., A Study of the Corrosion of Copper Alloy Condenser Tubes, *Trans. ASME*, 1946.

[13] Strauss, Jerome, *Trans. Am. Soc. Steel Treating*, **16**, 191 (1929).

TABLE 9-4. CORROSION OF COPPER ALLOY CONDENSER TUBES[a]

Per cent of original tensile strength lost due to corrosion

	Antimonial admiralty, 72 Cu, 1 Sn, 0.05 Sb, 26.95 Zn	Admiralty, 71 Cu, 1 Sn, 28 Zn	Red brass, 85 Cu, 15 Zn	20 per cent cupronickel, 80 Cu, 20 Ni	30 per cent cupronickel, 70 Cu, 30 Ni	Aluminum brass, 76 Cu, 2 Al, 22 Zn	Muntz metal, 60 Cu, 40 Zn	Copper
Attack predominantly by sulfur:								
4 months in vapor line, top of vacuum tower	2	2	63	66		20		
4 months in vapor to oil exchanger	19	17	27	29		100	79	
4 months in gasoline vapor line	7	8	23	27		7		
3 months in vapor stream, top of bubble tower	62	77	88	52		43		
5 months in vapor side, crude still partial condenser	9	6	7	7				
5 months in oil vapor stream leading to condenser	38	31	79	33				
1 month in bubble tower vapors, 386°F	4	4	16					
4 months in stabilizer reboiler vapors, 386°F	5	4	60					
3 months in gasoline vapor line to condenser	8	5	5	8	8	4		
8 months in vapor side, unit condensing gasoline	3	6	10		15	10		
11 months in unit condensing heavy gasoline vapors	9	4	5	19	2	3		
19 months in vapor side, flash tower overhead condenser	4	10	14	15		13		
6 months in condenser shell, water and gasoline condensed	13	3	3	27		6		
6 months submerged in water-gasoline condensate	8	14	23	7				
3 months in caustic side of stream to caustic exchanger	39	8	10	10				
3 months in treated gasoline vapors, 300°F	48		100	13		63		
9 months in experimental condenser, gasoline vapor	16	55	44		11	10		
8 months in reflux condenser	6	12	22					
5 months in vapor line to condenser	15	11	10		23	44	44	
5 months in high stage condenser—bottom center	17	25	39		30			
3 months in high stage condenser—top center	20	22	49					
High-pressure fractionating column, Dubbs unit:								
1.4 per cent sulfur, 121 days at 698°F	16	13	100				53	
1.4 per cent sulfur, 115 days at 680°F	6	7	100			7	12	
1.4 per cent sulfur, 26 days at 599°F	4	2	100	100	100	16	7	
1.4 per cent sulfur, 27 days at 545°F	2	2	100	100	100	10	1	
1.4 per cent sulfur, 27 days at 491°F			100	57	57		1	
Attack predominantly by water:								
38 days, vapor from alum evaporator	47	96	44	44				
15 months, corrosive water	2	0	1	0		3		
15 months, cooling water to condenser	8	5	5	4		4		
4 months, condenser-box water, 125°F	2	1	0					
3 months in cooling water to condenser	5	3	2	3		2		
5 months in condenser-box water	4	12	3	0		53		
12 months, water side, flash tower overhead condenser	33	50	51		39		34	
Special case, benzol, chlorinated hydrocarbon, and steam at 160°F	36	45	48	14				48
Special case, specimens immersed in carbon-black paste 20 days	2	2	2		2			9

[a] Mitchell, N. W., A Study of the Corrosion of Copper Alloy Condenser Tubes, *Trans. ASME*, 1946.

284

as the pounds per square inch that will not cause an elongation of more than 1 per cent in 10,000 hr. A creep of 1 per cent in 100,000 hr has also been used in many tests. Table 9-5 shows pertinent properties of several common tube steels. The economic usefulness of various tube materials was indicated in Table 9-3.

High temperature (above about 1200°F) steel castings are usually classified with respect to their resistance to (1) oxidizing atmospheres, (2) oxidizing atmospheres in the presence of sulfur, and (3) reducing atmospheres. Most refinery or power plant furnaces operate in an oxidizing atmosphere, or sulfidizing if the sulfur content of the fuel is abnormally high. Gases that contain more than 100 grains of sulfur dioxide per

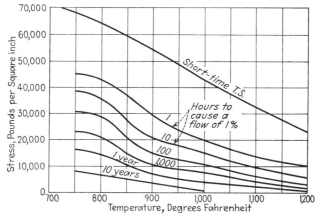

Fig. 9-2. Rate of flow of cast carbon steel at elevated temperatures. (*ASTM*.)

100 cu ft are a source of sulfide corrosion. Natural gas and manufactured gases can be easily desulfurized to below 5 to 10 grains sulfur, but many crude oils and coals produce sulfidizing furnace atmospheres (see Table 14-7). Oxidizing atmospheres are best handled by chromium-nickel steels (18–8 to 25–20), reducing atmosphere by nickel-chrome steels (65–15, 35–15, and 25–20), and sulfidizing atmospheres may be handled with straight-chromium steels because of their cheapness. These relationships are indicated in Table 9-6.

End supports for tubes in pipestills are usually protected from the hot gases by insulation so that plain cast iron or very low alloy irons (1 per cent chromium) may be used. In the hotter regions of convection sections or economizer sections of steam plants, higher alloy irons are useful. At 1500°F gray iron oxidizes about 16 times more rapidly than the Ni-resist iron of Table 9-6.

Low-temperature Services. With the advent of solvent dewaxing processes and ethylene manufacture, the lack of impact or shock resistance of metals became an important consideration. Three general types of

TABLE 9-5. PROPERTIES OF TUBE STEELS

Kind of steel	Approximate composition			Design[a] strength, psi	Relative penetration by scaling	Relative cost[c]
	% Cr	% Si	% Mo			
Killed carbon...............	0	0.2	0	6,500	1.0	1.0
Carbon molybdenum.........	0	0.3	0.5	12,000	1.13	1.35
Silicon molybdenum.........	0	1.5	0.5	9,500	0.73	1.55
1 chromium, silicon, molybdenum...................	1.0	1.25	0.5	12,000	0.84	1.9
1.25 chromium, silicon, molybdenum.................	1.25	0.75	0.5	18,000	0.77	1.87
2 chromium, molybdenum....	2.0	0.5 max	0.5	10,000	0.70	2.1
2 chromium, silicon, molybdenum...................	2.0	1.25	0.5	7,500	0.29	2.2
2.5 chromium, silicon, molybdenum.................	2.5	0.75	0.5	13,000	0.55	2.35
3 chromium, silicon, molybdenum...................	3.0	1.25	0.5	9,000	....	2.5
3 chromium, molybdenum....	3.0	0.5 max	1.0	11,000	0.46	2.6
5 chromium, molybdenum....	5.0	0.2	0.5	9,000	0.48	3.25
5 chromium, silicon, molybdenum...................	5.0	1.5	0.5	9,000	0.06	3.5
5 chromium, silicon, aluminum,[b] molybdenum........	5.0	0.75	0.5	7,600	0.03	3.6
9 chromium molybdenum....	9.0	....	1.5	11,000	0.06	6.0
18-8 chromium nickel........	18.0	(8 Ni)	0	17.500	0.01	11.2

[a] Based on creep strength at 1000°F allowing 1 per cent creep in 10,000 hr.
[b] About 0.7 per cent aluminum.
[c] Based on 1955 prices, but ratios have not changed much since 1940.

materials are suitable: (1) solid-solution alloys such as Monel metal, Inconel, and the austenitic stainless steels, along with low-alloy steels that are low in carbon and contain an alloy element soluble in iron, (2) certain elements such as copper, nickel, and lead, and (3) alloy cast irons. The low-alloy steels, particularly the nickel steels, are cheaper and are widely used down to temperatures of minus 100°F. Figure 9-3 indicates[14] the impact strengths of various materials relative to their impact strengths at higher (often room) temperatures, and Table 9-7 indicates the kinds of materials shown in Fig. 9-3. Note that curves 1, 2, and 3 for chromium and plain carbon steels show almost a complete loss of impact strength at minus 50°F.

[14] Nelson, W. L., Low Temperature Services, *Oil Gas J.*, Aug. 7, 1941, p. 43; and Apr. 12, 1954, p. 163.

TABLE 9-6. MATERIALS FOR HIGH-TEMPERATURE TUBE SUPPORTS

Name	Type of material	Approximate composition, per cent					Scaling temp, °F			Design strength, psi[b]	Notes
		Carbon	Silicon	Chromium	Nickel	Others	Oxidizing[a]	Reducing[a]	Sulfidizing		
Gray iron	Cast iron	3.2	1.5–2.0	......	......	......	600	......	......	......	Insulated end supports
Meehanite	Alloy iron	3.0	1.0–1.4	0.5–1.0	......	......	900	......	......	......	Insulated end supports
Nickel chromium iron	Alloy iron	3.2	1.2–2.7	0.5–0.75	1.4	......	1000	......	......	200	Convection tube sheets
Scale resisting iron	Alloy iron	2.6–3.0	1.25–2.2	......	12–15	......	1300	......	......	300	Convection tube sheets
Ni-resist iron	Alloy iron	3.0	1.6	3.3	14.3	5.3 Cu	1400	......	......	300	Convection tube sheets
Type 410 steel[c]	Steel	0.10	0.35	11.5–14	......	......	1400	1100	......	250[d]	Hottest convection supports
17 Chromium	Steel	......	0.6	17	......	......	1500	1300	1300	350[d]	Hottest convection supports
HC casting[c]	Steel casting	0.4	0.9	26–30	4	0.5 Mo	2100	1700	1700	90[d]	Hottest convection supports
HF 18-8[c]	Steel casting	0.35	1.8	18–23	8–12	0.5 Mo	1600	1300	1600	3000	Radiant supports
HH 24-12[c]	Steel casting	0.35	1.8	24–28	11–14	0.5 Mo	2000	1900	2000	620[d]	Radiant supports
HE 28-10[c]	Steel casting	0.35	1.8	26–30	8–11	0.5 Mo	2100	1900	2000	470[d]	Radiant supports
HK 25-20[c]	Steel casting	0.4	1.8	24–28	18–22	0.5 Mo	2100	2000	2100	560[d]	Radiant supports
HX 65-15[c]	Steel casting	0.55	2.3	15–19	64–68	0.5 Mo	1800	2100	......	2000	Radiant supports
HT 35-15[c]	Steel casting	0.55	2.3	13–17	33–37	0.5 Mo	1900	2000	......	1200[d]	Radiant supports

a With moderate amount of sulfur dioxide.
b Based on creep strength at oxidizing scaling temperature.
c "Types" of the American Iron & Steel Institute; and the HC, HC, HH, etc., designations are those of the Alloy Casting Institute.
d Estimated.

287

TABLE 9-7. MATERIALS SHOWN IN FIG. 9-3

Curve number	Material (steel unless designated)	Per cent C	Per cent others	Notes
1	4–6 chromium...................	0.17	5 Cr	After high-temperature service
2	Carbon (basic bessemer).........	0.04	....	Nearly pure iron
3	Carbon (open-hearth)............	0.15	....	Regular carbon steel
4	Vanadium.....................	0.15	0.46 Va	
5	Manganese vanadium (castings)..	0.32	1.11 Mn average	Normalized and tempered
6	Silicon manganese..............	0.15	0.89 Si, 1.12 Mn	
7	Copper manganese..............	0.19	0.6 Cu, 1.09 Mn	
8	Zirconium.....................	0.16	0.66 Zr	
9	Copper chromium..............	0.15	0.85 Cu, 0.51 Cr	
10	Nickel........................	0.2	2.1 Ni average	Normalized
11	Molybdenum nickel.............	(Average of many kinds[a])		About 300 Brinell
12	Austenitic steels, monel metal, and the elements lead, copper, and nickel........................	....	....	Solutions or pure metals
13	Nickel-rich cast irons...........	....	3–30 Ni, 0.5–5 Cr	

[a] SAE 4130, 4615, 4140, 4815, 4340, and 4640.

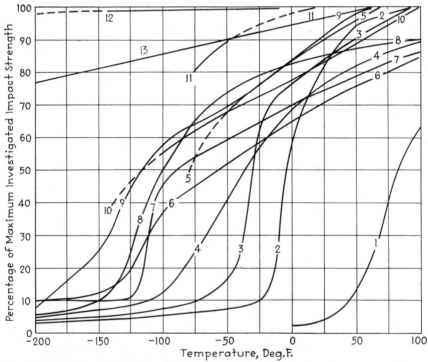

FIG. 9-3. Relative impact strengths of metallic materials at various temperatures. Table 9-7 shows the kinds of materials.

Metals for Refinery Chemicals. The universal materials for handling sulfuric acid are steel and lead. Ordinary mild steel withstands concentrated acid, but chemical lead must be used for dilute acid. Lead is such a ductile material that it presents many structural difficulties. For this reason, lead-lined rather than solid lead equipments, such as pipelines, agitators, and pumps, are gaining in favor. Recently some success has been attained in spraying steel with lead. A number of other materials, including tin, zinc, aluminum, copper, brass, nickel silver, Monel metal, and stainless steel, are also being sprayed. The coating[15] is applied by roughening the surface by a sandblast and spraying the surfacing metal from an oxyacetylene gun. Several coats must be applied. Metallizing is also used to build up worn pump rods, to hard-face cylinder liners, etc.

Certain alloy cast irons such as Duriron (14.5 silicon) and the high-silica irons are useful for lines, valves, pumps, etc., for handling sulfuric acid and acid sludge. In fact, ordinary cast iron is used for many corrosive conditions because of its cheapness. Wilkinson[16] presents an excellent summary of the resistance of alloys to sulfuric acid used in treating, alkylation, reclamation, and concentration processes.

Plain steel and cast iron are the common metals for handling caustic soda or sodium hydroxide, although under certain conditions nickel or Monel metal is superior. Likewise plain steel is the common material for handling anhydrous hydrofluoric acid.

Hydrochloric acid and even brines are so troublesome that scarcely any entirely satisfactory materials are available. Among the best materials are metallic silver or tantalum and glass or ceramics ware. For dilute acid or brines, the standard materials are the copper-base alloys or nickel alloys (see Table 9-4).

Table 9-8 indicates some of the services[3] that have not been discussed in this chapter. Note especially that slight differences in the service may cause an alloy to be unsatisfactory and accordingly Table 9-8 is only an indication of the types of resistant materials that should be explored.

Nonsparking Metals. Certain low-melting metals such as aluminum, copper, tin, and lead are completely nonsparking. Copper-base alloys such as beryllium copper and aluminum bronze are classed as nonsparking, and Monel metal produces such low-temperature sparks that gunpowder, gasoline, or explosive gas mixtures are not easily ignited.

Neutralizing Chemicals. Few materials are satisfactory resistors to "acid" corrosion, and hence neutralizing chemicals such as ammonia, sodium hydroxide, sodium carbonate, and lime are widely used. In gen-

[15] Rice, H. B., Metal Spraying . . . , *Ref. Nat. Gaso. Mfr.*, April, 1933, p. 148.

[16] Mechanical and Metallurgical Control of Sulfuric Acid Corrosion in Petroleum Processes, *Trans. ASME*, 1946.

TABLE 9-8. INDICATION OF ALLOY MATERIALS USED IN PETROLEUM REFINING[a]

Numbers in parentheses indicate materials listed on opposite page

Service or Equipment

Acid sludge—lines and pumps (1, 3, 5)

Acid sludge—pumps (8, 11, 14, 16, 17)

Alkylation—hydrofluoric acid (8, 39)

Antimony chloride & hydrochloric acid (10)

Bolts or bolting—low temperature (20)

Bolts or bolting—submerged condensers (32)

Carbon black paste (13, 23, 24, 33, 34)

Catalytic cracking—elevator bushings (4)

Catalytic cracking—linings or cladding (23, 24, 27)

Coke handling & pulverizing (4, 37)

Condensers—topping (8, 13, 28, 33)

Condensers—vacuum (25, 28, 29)

Copper chloride—solutions (16, 17, 38)

Ethylene-reaction tubes (11, 23)

Fans—blades (24, 25)

Filter cloth (8, 10, 11, 24, 25)

Furfural—condensers or exchangers (28, 29)

Furfural—regenerator tower (3, 8, 10, 26)

Hydrochloric acid—hot (2, 7, 35, 36)

Hydrochloric acid—cold dilute (1, 10, 14, 17, 36)

Hydrochloric acid—very dilute and brines (3, 8, 12, 13, 33)

Hydrofluoric acid—boiling 48% (7, 9)

Hydrofluoric acid—60% at 185°F (7, 9, 13)

Hydrofluoric acid—100% cold (39)

Instrument parts—low coef expansion (19)

Isomerization—dilute HCl or with SbCl₃ (10, 16)

Isomerization—200°F trichloride saturator, HCl reboiler, etc. (8)

Isomerization—194°F. catalyst contactor (10)

Isomerization—pump parts & hot acid (3, 16, 17, 18)

Mercaptans (28)

Monoethylene amines—coolers, exchangers, etc. (7, 28, 29)

Naphthenic acids—550°F (11, 22, 24)

Phosphoric acid—liq blowback in poly plant (8)

Phosphoric acid—low conc, high temp (22, 24)

Phosphoric acid—high conc. high temp (7, 16, 17)

Phosphoric acid—storage, 75–85% at 150°F (8)

Phenol, wet vapor (10, 15, 16, 17)

Propane chillers (28)

Stack—flare tip (11)

Sodium hypochlorite (7, 30)

Sodium hydroxide—10% at 131°F; 67% at 257°F; or 80% at 275°F (7)

Sodium hydroxide—30–50% at 179°F (8, 10, 12, 39)

Sodium hydroxide—conc boiling with H₂S (9, 11)

Solutizer solutions, reboilers, etc. (8, 10, 21)

Sulfur, molten or vapor (8, 28)

Sulfuric acid—25% boiling (5, 6, 7)

Sulfuric acid—75% at 275°F, 96% at 176°F (7, 15, 16, 18)

Sulfuric acid—over 96% cold (7, 39)

Sulfuric acid—over 96% cold, pumps & valves (23, 24)

Sulfuric acid—all conc & temp (1, 7, 16)

Sulfuric acid—fuming (17)

Water—corrosive (13, 29, 30, 33, 34)

Water—salt, centrifugal pumps (3)

Water—salt, bolts (8, 31)

Water—salt, tubing (30)

TABLE 9-8. INDICATION OF ALLOY MATERIALS USED IN PETROLEUM REFINING[a]
(Continued)

Materials

1 High silica irons—Duriron, Tantiron, Corrosiron, etc.	20 Nickel steel, 3½–8 Ni
	21 Nickel steel, SAE 2512
2 Silicon molybdenum irons—Durichlor, etc.	22 Stainless steel, 3% Mo
	23 Stainless steel, Type 304
3 Ni-resist iron	24 Stainless steel, Type 316 or 317
4 Ni-hard iron	25 Stainless steel, Type 405 or 410
5 Chemical lead or linings	26 Stainless steel, Type 502
6 Chemical tile	27 11–13 chromium steel
7 Carbon (Karbate)	28 Aluminum alloys
8 Monel	29 Alclad steel
9 Monel H or S	30 Aluminum bronze
10 Nickel or linings or cladding	31 Everdur brass
11 Inconel	32 Copper silicon manganese alloys
12 Nickel silver	33 Admiralty (or antimonial) brass
13 Cupro nickel	34 Red brass
14 Worthite	35 Silver metal
15 Hastelloy A	36 Tantalum metal
16 Hastelloy B	37 11–14 manganese steel
17 Hastelloy C	38 Haveg
18 Hastelloy D	39 Carbon steel or cast iron
19 Nickel iron, 36–50 Ni	

[a] Inasmuch as only slight differences in the service may cause an alloy to be unsatisfactory, this list is only an indication of the types of materials that should be explored.

eral, these chemicals are introduced into the vapor lines of distillation units. Ammonia is introduced as a gas, and the other materials as dilute solutions, although lime is preferably added as a slurry. Lime is often used in cracking plants by injecting it with the charge to the pipestill, and it serves partly to reduce acid corrosion as well as sulfide corrosion. Brandt[17] explains the use and application of ammonia. Polyaromatic amines having large oxyethylated side chains are widely used as inhibitors to "acid" corrosion, and similar inhibitors are put into the hydrochloric acid used in cleaning refinery equipment.

The solutions are usually injected into the system by direct-acting pumps. A fine dispersion of the chemical in the oil is essential, and hence the solutions are often mixed with a part of the oil by means of mixing columns before they are injected into the system. These columns consist of a pipe containing baffle plates. From 0.15 to 0.3 per cent by volume of caustic soda solution (about 10°Bé) or 0.3 to 1.0 lb of lime per bbl of

[17] Brandt, L. H., Ammonia for Corrosion Control, Ref. Nat. Gaso. Mfr., August, 1937, p. 382.

charging stock is usually sufficient, although the exact amount must be determined by plant experiments. Obviously, an excess of the neutralizer creates alkaline corrosion, which may be more severe than the original acid corrosion, and hence the chemicals are not added in large enough quantities to neutralize the acid or sulfide materials completely. The corrosion can often be reduced to half by adding much less chemical than the amount required for complete neutralization.

Ammonia rapidly attacks admiralty metal, and hence ammonia should not be used in a system having brass condenser tubes or parts. In some instances ammonia has been successfully used with admiralty-metal condensers but under careful supervision so that no large excess was ever present. If the equipment is constructed of iron alone the pH of the rundown water is held between 7 and 7.7, but if copper-base alloys are present the pH is held between 5.8 and 7.2. One refiner reports a decrease in the iron content of the rundown water from 456 to only 45 parts per million when the pH was increased from 4.8 to 6.6. Ammonium chloride gradually accumulates in the lines and condensers, and it must be "flushed out" with water or steam during cleaning periods. Caustic soda also causes deposits, and these deposits are so difficult to remove that the use of caustic has been gradually abandoned. Caustic deposits are particularly troublesome within fractionating towers so that, if acid corrosion occurs within a tower, ammonia has usually been adopted as the neutralizing agent. Caustic soda also causes caustic embrittlement of the steel shells of evaporators, towers, etc., and is said to promote coking in furnace tubes. Two and one-half to twenty pounds of anhydrous ammonia is used for 1,000 bbl of crude oil, depending upon the amount of acid that is produced. Some refiners have reported a decrease of 97 per cent in the extent of acid corrosion by the use of ammonia.

CHAPTER 10

CHEMICAL TREATMENTS

Impurities that are present in crude oils and those produced during refinery distillation and cracking operations must be removed from nearly all commercial products. Improvements in color, stability to light, odor, sulfur content, amount of gumlike or asphaltic substances, corrosiveness, and composition are accomplished by treating. Sulfuric acid was once widely used because it partly removes sulfur, precipitates asphaltic or gumlike materials, improves color and stability, and to some extent improves the odor. Sweetening of "sour" distillates is always necessary, but the long dominant "doctor process" is being supplanted by mercaptan-removal sweetening processes. Acid and adsorbent clays are still used to improve the color of lubricating oils, but the solvent-extraction processes of Chap. 11 are now standard lubricating-oil practice. Desulfurization processes whereby sulfur is eliminated in the form of hydrogen sulfide are becoming significant.

SULFURIC ACID TREATMENT

Paraffin and naphthene hydrocarbons are only slightly attacked by 93 per cent (66° Bé) acid at room temperature. Higher temperatures and concentrations cause attack, particularly upon isomers having several side chains. Benzene is only slightly attacked by 93 per cent acid, but toluene[1] and xylene are more readily attacked. Thus 66° Bé and stronger acid (and also sulfur dioxide) is used to remove the aromatics that cause a smoky flame in kerosenes.

Olefins, diolefins, and acetylenes are attacked by even 75 per cent acid. High temperatures and acid concentrations favor polymerization of olefins, and low temperatures and acid concentrations favor the formation of alkyl acid sulfates, neutral esters, and sec. and tert. alcohols. Higher alcohols, dipolymers, and to some extent acid alkyl sulfates dissolve in cracked distillate; and upon redistillation the acid alkyl sulfates decompose, yielding alcohols, sulfur dioxide, and colored materials. These sul-

[1] Brandt, Lee, and Wadsworth, . . . Toluene Treating, *Ind. Eng. Chem.*, **39**, 1010 (1947).

fates are dissolved by caustic soda, but the neutral esters are not; and at temperatures over about 285°F they decompose, causing discoloration and tar or gumlike materials in the distillate.[2]

Sulfuric acid also removes or dissolves resinous or asphaltic substances that may be present because of poor fractionation, entrainment, or cracking. These materials tend to inhibit the crystallization of wax, and hence acid treatment often raises the pour point. Oxygen compounds, such as naphthenic acids and ketones, and substances such as alcohols and aldehydes that are formed by high-temperature oxidation are dissolved by sulfuric acid, but when diluted with oil their removal is never complete. Nitrogen bases similar to quinoline or pyridine, which are produced in small quantities during distillation, are easily dissolved in dilute acid.

Strong acid (93 per cent or stronger) is necessary to remove mercaptans, but such large quantities are required that "sweetening" is seldom practiced in this manner. Alkyl sulfides, disulfides and sulfates, and most sulfur compounds are removed by 93 per cent or stronger acid, but the acid alkyl sulfates dissolve to some extent in the oil.

The rate of[3] action of sulfuric acid on the various impurities appears to be somewhat as follows: (1) nitrogen compounds such as amines, amides, and amino acids; (2) asphaltic substances; (3) olefins; (4) aromatics; and (5) naphthenic acids.

The loss in octane number of cracked gasoline is not large for normal quantities of acid.[4,5]

Concentration of Acid. Sixty-six Baumé[2] or 93 per cent acid finds most general use. However, for treating light distillates to color only, a more dilute acid may be advantageous.[6] For most other purposes, such as removing combined sulfur, improving the burning qualities of kerosene, and removing tar from lubricating oils, a 93 per cent or stronger acid should be used. For lubricating oil, 98 per cent acid is also widely used.

The weakest suitable acid is employed because sludge losses are higher with strong acid. In treating pressure distillate Potthoff[7] finds that sludge and polymerization losses are almost twice as large when using strong acid. Total losses ranged from 1.6 per cent when using 5 lb acid per bbl, up to 11.3 per cent for 20 lb acid per bbl. Weir, Houghton, and Majewski[8] find somewhat the same for a 289 viscosity at 100°F lubricat-

[2] Brooks and Humphrey, *J. Am. Chem. Soc.*, **40**, 822 (1918).

[3] Pyhala, E., *Petroleum*, **9**, 1506 (1928).

[4] Born and Wilson, *Natl. Pet. News*, Apr. 5, 1933, p. 23.

[5] Wirth, Kanhofer, and Murphy, Control of Color . . . Treating, *Ref. Natl. Gaso. Mfr.*, December, 1930, p. 89.

[6] Kalichevsky and Stagner, "Chemical Refining of Petroleum," p. 51, Chemical Catalog Company, Inc., New York, 1933.

[7] Purification of Pressure Distillate, *Oil Gas J.*, Mar. 5, 1931, p. 141.

[8] Control of Color . . . Treating, *Ref. Nat. Gaso. Mfr.*, December, 1930, p. 89.

ing oil. In the concentration range of 75 to 98 per cent acid, the sludge loss increased 0.002 to 0.0125 per cent for each increase of 1 per cent of acid concentration. Losses ranged up to 4.15 per cent for 31.3 lb acid per bbl when using 98 per cent acid.

Strong acid (93 to 103 per cent) used at low temperatures (25 to 50°F) removes sulfur from gasolines, and aromatic hydrocarbons from burning oils or transformer oils, but the color is generally poorer when using fuming acid. Cooke and Hayford,[9] in treating pressure distillate by the Stratford centrifuge process, found that 80 per cent acid produced a 0.2 per cent sulfur distillate whereas 104 per cent acid reduced the sulfur content to 0.07 per cent.

For improvement of color, an acid of 93 per cent strength is recommended; but if the combined sulfur is low, an acid of only 85 per cent strength may be advantageous. Weak acid is also useful in removing nitrogen bases and for improving the color without removing unsaturated compounds.

A large amount of spent alkylation acid is becoming available to the industry and it has a strength of 90 to 93 per cent because of inactive hydrocarbons and certain oxidation products contained in it. It has been found satisfactory[10] for the treating of naphthas, furnace oils, and lubricating oils (if a subsequent rerunning operation is conducted). Results with wax and other special uses have not been consistent, but ways of utilizing the acid have been devised by most refiners.

Quantity of Acid. Too much acid may result in a poorer color and a loss of aromatic and unsaturated hydrocarbons. If acid is applied to lubricating oils in too large doses, the oil may be discolored by "burning." The remedy is to use the acid in small charges and keep the oil cool. The treatment of spray oils, medicinal oils, and sometimes wax is accomplished by adding fuming acid in 25 or 30 lb per bbl charges and using as much, in some cases, as 200 lb of acid per bbl.

The quantity of acid that is commonly used is about as follows:

Natural gasoline—usually none but occasionally 2 lb per bbl.

Straight-run gasoline—usually none but may require 5 lb per bbl for sulfur removal.

Pressure distillate—usually none but for high-sulfur oils and oils from naphthene-base crude oils even 8 lb per bbl may be required.

Solvents—0 to 5 lb per bbl if high-sulfur stocks must be processed.

Kerosene—1 to 15 lb but as much as 75 lb per bbl for the kerosene from some naphthene-base crude oils. Sulfur dioxide extraction is more feasible for such kerosenes.

Lubricating oils—0 to 60 lb per bbl. Pennsylvanian oils usually require

[9] Distillate Treating, Part II, *Ref. Nat. Gaso. Mfr.*, April, 1934, p. 130.
[10] Bland, W. F., How to Conserve Sulfuric Acid, *Pet. Processing*, August, 1951, p. 865.

no acid treatment; mixed-base oils more; and asphalt-base oils the higher figure. Vacuum-distilled or solvent extracted stocks require much less acid.

Cooke and Hayford[9] find that the desulfurization is directly proportional to the amount of acid that is used.

Temperature of Treatment. Polymerization losses are greater at higher temperatures, so that unless polymerization is desired, as in rare cases when the sludge is to be utilized, lower temperatures are desirable. High temperatures favor the removal of aromatic and unsaturated hydrocarbons and of resinous asphaltic materials. Thus naphthenic kerosenes and solvents are usually refined at a relatively high temperature unless the removal of sulfur is also necessary.

Lower temperatures produce a better color in the product and are favorable for the removal of sulfur compounds. In treating lubricating oils at low temperatures the viscosity of the oil may be so great that settling is slow and the separation imperfect. This results in too long a contact time and a loss in color, and hence lubricating oils are usually treated at relatively high temperatures. The Union Oil Company of California has studied the effect of temperature, acid concentration, and amount of acid on the removal of sulfur from cracked distillates.[11]

The temperatures that are commonly used for various treating operations are as follows:

Straight-run gasoline—70 to 90°F. If large quantities of acid are required, it may be practical to go to lower temperatures.

Cracked gasoline—60 to 90°F. If heavy treats are required, temperatures of 25 to 30°F are recommended, although temperatures of 40 to 50° may be more economical.

Kerosene—90 to 130°F. If the oil is to be redistilled, a higher temperature may be economical. Robinson[12] finds that low temperatures are better.

Lubricating-oil stocks—Customary temperatures[13] (110–180°F) for various stocks are indicated in earlier editions of this book.

Cylinder stock—130 to 170°F[13] and 150 to 180°F if treating is conducted before dewaxing.

The cold-treating methods have many advantages from a treating standpoint, but the refrigeration requirements are enormous.

Contact Time. Two factors are involved in considering the contact time. Prolonged contact of acid sludge and oil results in a poorer color and less stability, but too short a time may prevent complete utilization

---

[11] Table 93, 2d ed. this book; also Kalichevsky and Stagner, "Chemical Refining of Petroleum," p. 51, Chemical Catalog Company, Inc., New York, 1933.

[12] Robinson, C. L., U.S. Pat. 910,584 (Jan. 26, 1909).

[13] Kauffman, H. L., *Ref. Nat. Gaso. Mfr.*, May, 1927, p. 59.

of the acid. Furthermore, the time of contact is intimately associated with the fineness of dispersion of the acid throughout the oil and the time required to separate the sludge.

Straight-run and cracked gasolines are contacted with acid for less than a minute in continuous-treating systems. A short contact time is particularly advantageous for cracked gasolines to minimize polymerization and sulfation of the oil. The time of contact is sometimes held to only a few seconds by mechanical contactors,[14] and the settling time is eliminated almost altogether by centrifugal means. Continuous processes for treating lubricating oils have been investigated,[15,16,17] and a short time of contact (10 min) is found to be advantageous.

In conventional batch agitation, the time of contact is much longer. For light distillates the time of air agitation ranges from 15 to 40 min. Kerosene normally requires 30 or 40 min, and for lubricating oils the time may be 90 min. The time required to settle the sludge in an agitator ranges from a few minutes for gasoline to as long as 15 hr for very viscous stocks.

Inhibitors of Gum. During cracking, unsaturated hydrocarbons are produced that upon exposure to air during storage produce so-called "gum" in the gasoline. Gum may be removed by treatment with sulfuric acid or by vapor-phase treatment with fuller's earth (Gray process), but the use of antioxidants or inhibitors has become standard practice. Inhibitors delay the formation of gum; but if sufficient time elapses, they do not prevent its formation. Exposure to sunlight, elevated storage temperatures, or a high percentage of sulfur contributes[18] to more rapid gum formation. The stability of gasoline[19] is approximately proportional to the induction period in oxidation bomb tests for gum.

Among inhibitor agents are such synthetic materials as dibenzyl-para-aminophenol, monobenzyl-para-aminophenol, para-hydroxyphenyl-morpholine, tributylamine, alpha-naphthol, and catechol; in coal-tar distillates, cresols and xylenols; and in wood-tar distillates, creosote, catechol, ethyl guaiacol, mono ethers of pyrogallol, and the xylenols.[20]

[14] Stratford, C. W., *Natl. Pet. News*, Mar. 12, 1930, p. 32F.

[15] Jones, L. D., Use of Centrifuge in Acid Treating Petroleum Stocks, *Ref. Nat. Gaso. Mfr.*, June, 1934, p. 224.

[16] Walker, R. C., Continuous . . . Centrifugal Separation . . . , *Ref. Nat. Gaso. Mfr.*, June, 1934, p. 228.

[17] Trescott, L. C., Sludge, *Ref. Nat. Gaso. Mfr.*, May, 1934, p. 172.

[18] McNamara, T. L., . . . Gum Stabilities of Gasoline, *Ref. Nat. Gaso. Mfr.*, October, 1934, p. 381.

[19] Yabroff and Walters, Gum Formation in Cracked Gasolines, *Ind. Eng. Chem.*, **32**, 83 (1940).

[20] Rogers and Voorhees, Gum Formation in Gasoline II, *Ind. Eng. Chem.*, **25**, 520 (1933).

The amount of each inhibitor required varies widely, but to some extent this is counteracted by a cost that is inversely proportional to effectiveness. Minute amounts of heavy metals such as copper or vanadium act as catalysts in producing gum, and certain compounds have been developed for counteracting[21] this effect.

SWEETENING TREATMENTS

Mercaptans, hydrogen sulfide, and elementary sulfur are removed (or converted) from light distillates by the so-called "sweetening processes." Mercaptans impart a foul odor, and they seriously decrease the octane number by reducing the susceptibility to tetraethyllead. Elementary sulfur (in the presence of mercaptans) causes corrosion.

There are three major ways of attaining sweetening: (1) processes that oxidize mercaptans to disulfides, (2) processes that remove the mercaptans, and (3) processes that destroy and remove other sulfur compounds along with mercaptans, hydrogen sulfide, and sulfur. The last of these methods is usually considered as a "desulfurization" process. Walker and Kenney[22] present a comprehensive discussion of the various treating processes.

Oxidation Processes. These processes convert mercaptans into less odoriferous disulfides by such processes as the doctor,[23] copper chloride,[24] hypochlorite,[25] and lead sulfide processes.[26] Since disulfides harm the lead susceptibility of gasoline and since the need of reduction of mercaptans to "doctor sweet" (0.0004 per cent) is being questioned,[27] these processes are being gradually abandoned. However, catalysts or inhibitors[28] of the p-phenylenediamine type, which in the presence of air cause mercaptans in some caustic-washed gasolines to be converted during a few days into disulfides (so-called inhibitor sweetening), continue to be used because of the cheapness of such a process. Small amounts of

[21] Downing, Clarkson, and Pedersen, . . . Metal Catalysts in Gaso. Gum Formation, *Oil Gas J.*, July 27, 1939, p. 97.

[22] Removing and Converting Mercaptans, *Pet. Processing*, April, 1956, pp. 58–66.

[23] Lowry, C. D., Jr., The Plumbite Sweetening of Gasoline, Universal Oil Products Co. (Chicago), *Booklet* 242, May, 1940.

[24] Conn, M. W., Perco Copper Sweetening, *Ref. Nat. Gaso. Mfr.*, March, 1941, p. 53; and Schieman, C. T., Jr., Linde Copper Sweetening Process, *Pet. Engr.*, May, 1947, p. 184.

[25] Anon., Treating Natural Gasoline . . . , *Ref. Nat. Gaso. Mfr.*, July, 1933, p. 278.

[26] Happel and Robertson, Lead Sulfide . . . Dry Sweetening Agent, *Oil Gas. J.*, Mar. 31, 1938, p. 125.

[27] Happel and Cauley, Significance of the Doctor Test for Gasoline, *Proc. API*, **21M** (3), 96 (1940).

[28] Moriarity and Johnson, Recent Developments in Petroleum Treating Procedures, presented before Nat. Pet. Assoc., Charleston, W.Va., May 5, 1949; also Jones, M. C. K., Sodafining, *Oil Gas J.*, Apr. 12, 1951, p. 88.

metals (lead, bismuth, thallium, etc.) in the caustic used in inhibitor sweetening hasten the sweetening reaction and help in reducing peroxide or gum formation.

Mercaptan Dissolving Processes. These processes, such as caustic washing,[29] Shell Solutizer,[30] Atlantic Unisol,[31] Pure Oil Mercapsol,[32] and Tannin Solutizer,[33] are still in very common use. All of these except caustic washing employ solubility promoters such as salts of isobutyric acid,[30] alkyl phenols,[30] methanol,[31] cresols,[32] and naphthenic acids,[32] along with caustic soda. Natural promoters are also present in most naphthas,[34] and these will accumulate in the caustic during washing and regeneration. The solutions are regenerated by heating and steam stripping, except in the Tannin Solutizer process in which air blowing is employed.

More recently[34] it has been learned that the use of more concentrated solutions of caustic and solutizer, which causes two phases of treating solution to appear, may result in much more complete mercaptan removal.

The oxidation processes are being abandoned mainly because of the reduction in octane number that occurs. The many processes have been compared by Happel, Cauley, and Kelley,[35] and although the improvement[36] by various processes is dependent upon the particular situation, the general improvement is as indicated in Table 10-1. The catalytic processes give the best octane number, but they are more expensive; and when applied to cracked gasolines the cost mounts rapidly because the catalyst must be regenerated frequently.

The distribution[35] of mercaptan sulfur compounds in gasolines is indicated in Table 10-2. The removal of mercaptans by the solution processes is governed by the following equation,[35] which is applied to each mercaptan present in the gasoline.

$$\frac{RSH \text{ left (per cent)}}{100} = \frac{(1 - S)(E^a - E)V + (E - 1)(S - S^b)K_q}{(1 - S)(E^a - E)V + (E^a - 1)(S - S^b)K_q} \quad (10\text{-}1)$$

[29] Henderson, Ross, and Ridgway, The TEL Susceptibilities of Gasoline . . . Caustic Washing, *Ind. Eng. Chem.*, **31**, 27 (1939).

[30] Yabroff and Border, The Solutizer Process for the Extraction of Mercaptans, *Proc. API*, **20M** (3), 95 (1939).

[31] Field, H. W., The Caustic-methanol Mercaptan Extraction Process, *Oil Gas J.*, Sept. 25, 1941, p. 40.

[32] MacKusick and Alves, Mercapsol Process for Gasoline Treating, *Oil Gas J.*, Apr. 13, 1944, p. 126.

[33] O'Donnell, J. P., Tannin Solutizer Process Practically Automatic . . . , *Oil Gas J.*, July 1, 1944, p. 45.

[34] Duval and Kalichevsky, Dualayer Process, *Oil Gas J.*, Apr. 12, 1954, p. 122.

[35] Critical Analysis of Sweetening Processes and Mercaptan Removal, *Oil Gas J.*, Nov. 12, 1942, p. 136.

[36] Nelson, W. L., *Oil Gas J.*, Mar. 2, 1946, p. 85; also Oct. 3, p. 137, and Dec. 22, p. 75, 1945.

where $S = WK_s$, stripping factor; where W = volume ratio, steam to caustic (steam volume equals condensate volume), K_s = stripping coefficient (Fig. 10-1)

$E = \dfrac{K_q}{V}$, extraction factor; where K_q = extraction coefficient (Fig. 10-2), V = volume ratio, gasoline to caustic, a = number of theoretical extraction stages plus one, b = number of theoretical regeneration stages plus one

The K-2 solution of Figs. 10-1 and 10-2 is $6N$ potassium hydroxide and $3N$ potassium isobutyrate, and the 20 per cent of "organic acids" are natural ones dissolved from Mid Continent cracked and straight-run gasolines. Basic or average susceptibilities of various gasolines to tetraethyllead are shown in Table 3-11, which is based[37] on the behavior of about 327 samples. The color stability of some gasolines is also closely related to sulfur content, to the methods of conducting sweetening, and to certain methods of mechanical separation.[38]

Caustic washing methods, which involve bringing the gasoline in contact with sodium,[39] calcium,[40] or magnesium (brucite) hydroxides for the

TABLE 10-1. OCTANE NUMBER IMPROVEMENT BY DESULFURIZATION[a]

Octane number of stock	Octane number of desulfurized stock with 3 cc TEL		
	Catalytic on only straight-run gasoline[c]	Chemical processes[b]	
		Straight-run and low-sulfur gasolines	Cracked gasolines
40	65.4–73.4	60.4–70.4	
45	68.6–76.6	63.9–73.9	
50	71.5–79.5	65.4–75.4	
55	74.6–82.6	71.1–81.1	
60	77.7–85.7	74.9–84.9	73.0–79.0
65	80.9–88.9	78.8–88.8	75.5–81.5
70	84.3–92.3	82.6	77.3–83.3
75	87.5	86.3	

[a] Nelson, W. L., *Oil Gas J.*, Mar. 2, 1946, p. 85; also Oct. 3, p. 137, and Dec. 22, p. 75, 1945.

[b] Solutizer, Unisol, and Mercapsol.

[c] Bauxite or fuller's earth.

[37] Nelson, W. L., Lead Response, *Oil Gas J.*, Oct. 6, p. 106, and Oct. 13, p. 137, 1945.

[38] Berger, C. W., Practical Aspects of Sun Stability, *Ref. Nat. Gaso. Mfr.*, **15**, 411 (1936).

[39] Ridgway, C. M., Improving Gasoline by Caustic Washing, *Oil Gas J.*, Mar. 31, 1938, p. 83.

[40] Anon., Lime Wash . . . Sulfide Removal, *Ref. Nat. Gaso. Mfr.*, April, 1940, p. 81.

TABLE 10-2. MERCAPTAN DISTRIBUTION IN SOME TYPICAL GASOLINES[a]

	1	2	3	4	5	6	7	8	9	10	11	12	13	14	15	16
	(M.C.)	(M.C.)	(M.C.)	(M.C.)	(M.C.)	(M.C.)	(M.C.)	(Kans.)	(Kans.)	(M.C.)	(M.C.)	(M.C.)	(M.C.)	(M.C.)	(E. Tex.)	(E. Tex.)
				Controlled-coil cracking unit												
	Straight run	Poly-form	Coking unit	Synthetic charge	Crude charge	Crude charge	Houdry	Straight run	Houdry	Straight run	Vapor phase	Houdry	Straight run	Thermal cracked	Thermal cracked	Vapor phase
Boiling range, °F.	100-275	100-400	100-400	100-400	100-400	100-400	100-400	100-300	100-400	100-400	100-400	100-400	100-400	100-400	100-400	100-400
Per cent of total mercaptan content:																
Methyl	3.9	16.5	12.4	6.4	13.1	34.2	16.0	8.5	3.4	21.3	35.6	58.1	3.1	18.6	15.1	13.4
Ethyl	15.7	30.8	21.9	10.9	21.9	21.2	17.0	6.7	6.5	7.1	29.1	11.3	5.3	33.7	15.8	23.4
Propyl	30.6	29.0	24.9	13.4	20.0	21.2	8.0	11.5	5.3	11.0	9.3	7.4	10.0	10.9	19.7	19.8
Butyl	45.2	9.6	23.6	6.2	15.6	14.2	8.0	17.7	3.5	11.3	7.0	3.1	16.0	14.8	14.9	10.4
Amyl	4.6	9.4	15.6	11.1	10.9	11.8	8.0	55.6	5.8	10.5	4.6		12.2	9.5	6.9	6.8
Thiophenols				0.0					61.7				8.2			
Hexyl and heavier		4.7	1.6	43.7	18.5	18.6	43.0		13.8	38.7	14.4	20.1	45.2	12.5	27.5	26.2
Total	100.0	100.0	100.0	100.0	100.0	100.0	100.0	100.0	100.0	100.0	100.0	100.0	100.0	100.0	100.0	100.0
Mercaptan sulfur in sample, per cent by weight	0.009	0.080	0.090	0.006	0.020	0.018	0.0090	0.0099	0.0117	0.0093	0.0314	0.0089	0.0078	0.020	0.035	0.020

[a] Happel, Cauley, and Kelley, Critical Analysis of Sweetening Processes and Mercaptan Removal, Oil Gas J., Nov. 12, 1942, p. 136.

removal of hydrogen sulfide and mercaptans, are feasible for some gasolines because of the improvement in lead susceptibility and the saving in chemicals in subsequent treatments. Caustic solutions ranging from 5 to 15 per cent are employed. Caustic washing is becoming important again as a means of removing dissolved hydrogen sulfide from the products of catalytic desulfurization processes. A recent modification[41] involves regeneration of the caustic along with oxygen in electrolytic cells.

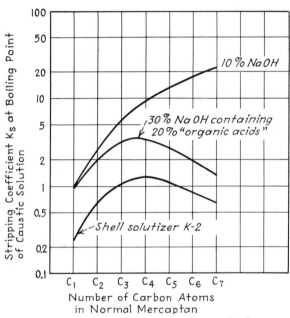

FIG. 10-1. Stripping coefficient vs. number of carbon atoms (in the normal mercaptan) for some treating solutions.

Mercaptans in the alkali are oxidized to disulfides which can be withdrawn as a light liquid layer.

D. L. Yabroff et al.[42] developed the Solutizer process, which permits more complete removal of mercaptans by a caustic solution. An organic agent is used to increase the solubility of mercaptans in the caustic solution. The low-molecular-weight mercaptans are dissolved by caustic alone, but solutizers must be added in order to remove the mercaptans having three or more carbon atoms to the molecule. The *Unisol* or

[41] Duff, Dahl M., Mercaptan Removal Ups Octane, *Oil Gas J.*, July 19, 1954, p. 115; and Mortlock, D. H., *Pet. Refiner*, November, 1954, p. 205.

[42] The Solutizer Process, May, 1939, p. 171; The Regeneration Step . . . , November, 1939, p. 131; and . . . Octane Number and Lead Susceptibility, March, 1940, p. 55; all in *Ref. Nat. Gaso. Mfr.*

caustic methanol process employs methanol at the center of a packed treating column and caustic soda throughout the entire length of the column. Small amounts of methanol are lost with the gasoline, and the methanol must be distilled after it (and the mercaptans) has been stripped from the caustic. The particular cresols and naphthenic acids employed in the *Mercapsol* process can be repeatedly regenerated, and the process operates at a low treating ratio. *Tannin* can be used with the Solutizer

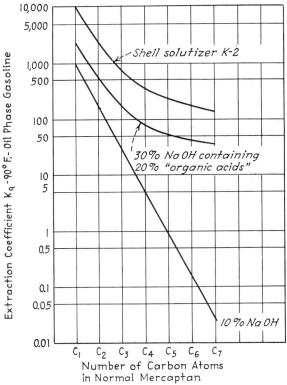

Fig. 10-2. Extraction coefficient vs. number of carbon atoms (in the normal mercaptan) for some treating solutions.

process and perhaps other solution-promoter processes. It is unique because the solutizer solution can be regenerated by air blowing rather than steam stripping. This keeps temperatures low and reduces utility costs.

Although *catalytic desulfurization* differs vitally from what have been termed "sweetening processes," it serves the same purpose and in addition is able to remove more stable sulfur compounds than those involved in plain sweetening. The gum content of cracked gasoline is also reduced by the process. When operated at 1000°F rather than the customary 750°F the process is similar to the Cycloversion catalytic cracking process except that the charge stock is naphtha rather than gas oil.

The *doctor treatment* consists of contacting the oil with a little sulfur and with alkaline sodium plumbite solution.

$$2RSH + Na_2PbO_2 = (RS)_2Pb + 2NaOH$$
$$(RS)_2Pb + S = R_2S_2 + PbS$$

Elementary sulfur in the gasoline is removed by these reactions; but if an excess (about 20 per cent more than required for the reaction) of sulfur remains in the oil, the oil will be corrosive. Gasolines that contain much free sulfur sometimes require the addition of mercaptans or sour distillates before the doctor treatment, because mercaptans are necessary in completing the reactions with sulfur. Stability of color is greatly improved by thorough separation of chemicals during settling and washing.

The concentration of the sodium hydroxide solution should be 12 to 30°Bé (8 to 24 per cent). The solubility of lead oxide in caustic soda increases with the gravity of the solution, being about 1 per cent in a 12°Bé solution and about 3 per cent in a 30°Bé solution. Rhombic or lump sulfur should be used because flowers of sulfur is not sufficiently soluble in oil. Continuous-treating equipments are generally used, but batch treatment with air agitation has the advantage of regenerating the lead sulfide and decreasing the amount of sulfur that is required.

Spent doctor solution is often recovered or used over again by adding more litharge to the solution and carrying the sulfide in suspension. Many refiners oxidize the lead sulfide as a caustic slurry by heating to 150 to 175°F and blowing with air, which converts the sulfide to plumbite.

Lead sulfide itself may be used as a sweetening agent. The over-all reaction is the same as those given for doctor sweetening, but the lead sulfide may act catalytically to cause the two doctor reactions to take place simultaneously as

$$2RSH + S + 2NaOH \rightarrow R_2S_2 + Na_2S + 2H_2O$$

The reaction may be conducted by contacting the sour gasoline, sulfur, and oxygen (air) with a solid bed of lead sulfide catalyst[43] or by recycling the lead sulfide suspended in a strong caustic solution[44] with the introduction of air and current revivification of part of the lead sulfide solution by washing with hot water.

Sodium or calcium *hypochlorite sweetening* has found extensive use in the

[43] Happel and Robertson, Lead Sulfide . . . Dry Sweetening Agent, *Oil Gas J.*, Mar. 31, 1938, p. 125.

[44] Altshuler and Graves, Refinements in Sweetening Technique, *Ref. Nat. Gaso. Mfr.*, June, 1937, p. 272.

treating of natural gasoline and straight-run gasoline, but it is seldom used for cracked products or high-boiling oils.

The *copper sweetening* process involves the oxidation of mercaptans to disulfides and the reduction of cupric chloride to the cuprous state, as

$$4RSH + 4CuCl_2 \rightarrow 2R_2S_2 + 4CuCl + 4HCl$$

The cuprous chloride is then oxidized with air or oxygen:

$$4CuCl + 4HCl + O_2 \rightarrow 4CuCl_2 + 2H_2O$$

In the slurry process both reactions take place simultaneously in the presence of a solution of cupric chloride and fuller's earth. Hydrogen sulfide and lower mercaptans are removed in a preliminary caustic wash.

DESULFURIZATION

Two general methods of reducing the amount of sulfur have been developed, those which involve solvent extraction of the sulfur compounds and those by which most of the sulfur compounds are decomposed by the use of a catalyst into hydrogen sulfide and hydrocarbon remnants of the original sulfur compounds. The solvent extraction processes are not as cheap or effective as the catalytic processes in the removal of sulfur because they remove the entire sulfur-bearing molecule and at the same time certain hydrocarbons, particularly those with aromatic rings. Thus, when the removal of aromatic hydrocarbons as well as sulfur is desirable, the solvent processes may be superior. Sulfuric acid has long been used in dissolving or removing sulfur, and hydrofluoric acid is also an effective solvent, but sulfur dioxide and furfural are mentioned more frequently. When applied to catalytic cycle oil to produce diesel fuel, the effectiveness[45] of the several solvents is about as shown in Table 10-3.

Hydrogen fluoride is effective, but its effectiveness decreases with

TABLE 10-3

Solvent	Solvent vol., %	Raffinate sulfur, %	Sulfur removed, %	Extract, wt, %
Sulfur dioxide (at 68°F)............	100	0.30	73	35
Furfural.......................	100	0.47	56	25
Hydrogen fluoride.................	20	0.34	69	14
Hydrogen fluoride.................	50	0.20	82	16
Hydrogen fluoride.................	100	0.13	85	17

[45] Laszlo, T. S., How to Desulfurize Diesel Fuel, *Pet. Refiner*, January, 1955, p. 115.

increasing molecular weight of the sulfur compound.[46] The solvent processes tend to raise the pour point and moderately improve the Diesel Index, but the catalytic processes of desulfurization do not materially affect either of these properties. Yields by the catalytic processes may exceed 100 per cent especially if outside hydrogen is supplied. The sulfur dioxide and furfural extraction processes are described in Chap. 11.

Catalytic desulfurization of straight-run naphthas[47] with bauxite or fuller's earth was once widely used, and the comparison of octane numbers of Table 10-1 is based on such processes. Vaporized gasoline was passed through the catalyst at about 750°F, and the hydrogen sulfide produced from the decomposition of mercaptans, sulfide, and disulfides was fractionated or washed from the product.

More recently, the use of cobalt and molybdenum catalysts supported on bauxite or fuller's earth has proven to be very effective. When used with hydrogen circulation[48,49] and at a high pressure, catalyst activity can be maintained even when desulfurizing kerosene and straight-run light distillates. Finally, by the addition of hydrogen from outside sources,[50,51,52,53] more vigorous decomposition and hydrogenation can be undertaken, and in the extreme, whole crude oils and residues[54] can be desulfurized. The Shell Hydrodesulfurization process[50] employs a tungsten-nickel-sulfide type of catalyst.

Desulfurization is actually a mild selective hydrogenation, so mild that aromatics are not usually hydrogenated to naphthenes. Sulfur is removed as hydrogen sulfide and the remaining hydrocarbon part of the molecule is hydrogenated. Sulfides and mercaptans are attacked by even plain bauxite, and disulfides and thiophenic compounds are more

[46] Lien and Evering, Hydrogen Fluoride Extraction . . . , *Ind. Eng. Chem.*, **44,** 874 (1952).

[47] Brooner and Conn, Recent Advances in Perco Catalytic Desulfurization, *Oil Gas J.*, Oct. 26, 1946, p. 96; also Martin and Carlson, Catalytic Desulfurization by Use of the Gray Process, *Oil Gas J.*, Mar. 26, 1942, p. 138; and Amero and Wood, Catalytic Desulfurization of Cracked and Straightrun Gasolines, *Oil Gas J.*, May 24, 1947, p. 82.

[48] Berg et al., Catalytic Desulfurization . . . , Cobalt Molybdate Process, *Trans. A.I.Ch.E.*, **43,** 1 (1947).

[49] Hyde and Porter, The Autofining Process . . . , sec. III, *Proc. Fourth World Pet. Congr.*, Rome, 1955.

[50] Hoog, Klinkert, and Schaafsma, Hydrodesulfurization . . . , *Oil Gas J.*, June 8, 1955, p. 92.

[51] Eckhouse, Gerald, and de Rosset, Unifining Upgrades Distillate Fuels, *Oil Gas J.*, Aug. 30, 1954, p. 81.

[52] Patterson and Jones, Hydrofining's Use in Product Improvement, *Oil Gas J.*, Oct. 18, 1954, p. 92.

[53] Odasz and Sheffield (Diesulformer), *Oil Gas J.*, Jan. 23, 1956, p. 64.

[54] McAfee et al., Gulf HDS Process Upgrades Crudes, *Pet. Refiner*, May, 1955, p. 156.

easily attacked than polycyclic sulfur compounds. Mild decomposition results in an evolution of hydrogen which can be recycled for hydrogenation reactions but if higher boiling or refractory stocks are being treated, extra hydrogen must be introduced from outside sources to maintain a higher concentration of hydrogen during the reaction. The decomposition leads to products of slightly lower boiling range than that of the parent material and slightly higher API gravities. The same techniques have been applied to lubricating oil[55] treating.

Although temperatures of 400 to 800°F are mentioned, a temperature of 600°F causes little reaction and if temperatures exceeding 750°F are employed, the deposition of carbon on the catalyst becomes rapid (requiring frequent regeneration) and the losses to light gases or low-boiling materials become larger. In the extreme, the process tends to become similar to catalytic cracking, or with sufficient hydrogen it becomes primarily a process of hydrogenation.[56] Pressure ranges from 300 to 500 psi for the most easily desulfurized low-boiling straight-run feeds to 700 to 1,000 psi when more vigorous hydrogenation is necessary in handling high-boiling or cracked feeds. The amount of hydrogen recycling follows the same reasoning and it ranges from 1,000 to as high as 10,000 standard cu ft per bbl when handling residue feedstocks. Hydrogen disappearance (100 to 1,200 cu ft per bbl) is mainly a function of the amount of sulfur that is eliminated. Low-boiling and easily desulfurized feeds can be handled at space velocities of 8.0, but the more vigorous treatments required for catalytic cycle stocks and residues employ space velocities ranging from 3 down to even 0.5. Zahnstecher and Petrarca[57] conclude that a low space velocity is related to greater desulfurization. At mild operating conditions the catalyst can be used for a year or longer without regeneration; ordinary operations require regeneration at intervals of 4 to 12 months; and when handling residue materials where coke deposition may represent 2 to 6 per cent by weight of the feedstock, regeneration may be required at 6 to 24 hour intervals. The catalyst does not seem to be harmed by repeated regeneration with mixtures of air and steam.

Yields are close to 100 liquid volume per cent even with residue feedstocks, and in some operations the yield exceeds 101 per cent. Efficiency of desulfurization depends upon the charge stock and the severity of treatment, ranging from as low as 50 to 60 per cent for mild operations to 80 to 99 per cent, and 95 to 98 per cent is not uncommon. Processes are discussed on page 332 of this chapter.

[55] Jones, W. A., Hydrofining Improves Low-cost Lube Quality, *Oil Gas J.*, Nov. 1, 1954, p. 81.
[56] McAfee and Horne, Hydrogen Treating, *Pet. Processing*, April, 1956, p. 47.
[57] Achieving Catalytic Desulfurization . . . , *Oil Gas J.*, Dec. 20, 1954, p. 78.

REFINING BY ADSORPTION

Adsorption, although originally utilized by the industry mainly in the decolorization of liquids, is also being applied to the recovery of gases,[58] the removal of moisture from liquids and gases (see Fig. 7-6), the separation of aromatic hydrocarbons[59,60] (by silica gel), and numerous applications in the so-called catalytic processes many of which employ adsorbents for support of the catalyst.   The physical properties of some adsorbents[61] and catalysts are indicated in Tables 10-4 to 10-6.

Various mineral clays, earths, and artificial mineral adsorbents are used to improve the color of oils and remove asphaltic or resinous material.   In general, three methods are followed: (1) percolation through a long column of coarse clay, (2) contact at a high temperature with finely powdered clay, and (3) contact in the vapor phase with loosely packed clay, but a continuous process by which clay moves through a percolation bed and is then continuously burned[62] has recently been applied (see Fig. 10-6).

Percolation is the oldest method and in many ways it is not so satisfactory as contact treatment, but in other ways, particularly its flexibility, it is a desirable method.   The application of vapor-phase treating is limited to the treatment of the lighter distillates, particularly cracked gasoline, because higher boiling oils cannot be easily kept in the vapor state.   The Contact process is now used for neutral oils, gasoline, and diluted cylinder stocks.

The removal of coloring matter from oils by clay appears to be governed by the adsorption isotherm of Freundlich.[63]   This may be stated as

$$\frac{X}{M} = aC^{\frac{1}{n}}$$

or in logarithmic form

$$\log \frac{X}{M} = \log a + \frac{1}{n} \log C$$

[58] Berg and Bradley, Hypersorption—New Fractionation Process, *Pet. Engr.*, May, 1947, p. 115; C. Berg, . . . for Gas Fractionation, sec. III, *Proc. Third World Pet. Congr.*, The Hague, 1951; and Hypersorption Process Produces Four . . . Streams, *Pet. Refiner*, September, 1950, p. 216; also Kehde et al., Ethylene Recovery . . . , *Chem. Eng. Progr.*, **44**, 576 (1948).

[59] Schuman and Brace, Separating Aromatics by the Arosorb Process, *Oil Gas J.*, Apr. 6, 1953, p. 109.

[60] Cyclic Adsorption Refining, *Pet. Refiner*, September, 1954, p. 267.

[61] Heinemann, Felix, and Heinz, Adsorbents and Catalysts, *Pet. Refiner*, June, 1954, p. 159.

[62] Evans et al., Thermofor Continuous Percolation, *Oil Gas J.*, June 8, 1953, p. 116.

[63] Walker, Lewis, McAdams, and Gilliland, "Principles of Chemical Engineering," 3d ed., McGraw-Hill Book Company, Inc., New York, 1937.

TABLE 10-4. DENSITIES, SURFACE, AND PORE PROPERTIES OF ADSORBENTS AND CATALYSTS

Absorbent	Calcination or activation temp, °F	D_B, bulk density, g/cc	D_A, mercury density, g/cc	D_T, helium density, g/cc	Per cent voids[a]	Per cent pores[b]	Surface area, m²/g	Average pore radius, A°
Activated alumina:								
Grade F-1	400	.88	1.58	3.23	44	51	200	72
Grade H-151	400	....	.....	....	...	...	300–350	...
Bauxite:								
Arkansas	450	1.33	2.02	2.54	44	20	27	76
	700	.97	1.68	3.18	43	64	236	33
	900	.95	1.63	3.21	42	49	178	34
	1300	.94	1.61	3.26	42	52	151	43
South American	900	.96	1.51	3.25	36	54	187	38
Silica gel	400	.78	1.32	2.12	41	38	602	10
Synthetic silica-alumina gel:								
Fluid catalyst	400	.82	1.38	2.25	41	39	374	15
Pelleted catalyst A	400	.64	.97	2.37	34	58	372	33
Pelleted catalyst B	400	1.00	1.56	2.37	36	34	280	16
Bead catalyst	400	.79	1.14	2.38	30	52	420	22
Fuller's earth (attapulgite)	400	.56	1.01	2.56	44	60	126	95
	600	.55	.97	2.66	...	...	124	110
	900	.54	.96	2.66	43	64	118	109
	1100	.56	.92	2.69	42	64	119	
Bentonite, acid-activated	700	.68	1.140	2.66	41	57	260	38
	900	.67	1.130	2.66	41	57	236	43
	1300	.67	1.120	2.56	41	56	208	48
Diatomaceous earth	400	.32	.63	2.27	49	44	4	5500
Activated carbon:								
Columbia carbon	....	.42	.75	1.89	44	60	1397	12
Darco carbon	....	.36	.73	2.09	51	66	560	32
Bone char	....	.68	.....	2.8	47	46	110	

[a] Per cent voids = $100\, V_v/V_B$, where $V_v = 1/D_B - 1/D_A$.

[b] Per cent pores = $100\, V_p/(V_t + V_p)$, where $V_p = 1/D_A - 1/D_T$ and $V_t = 1/D_T$.

TABLE 10-5. BULK WEIGHT AND THERMAL DATA OF SOME ADSORBENTS

Adsorbent	Bulk weight, lb/cu ft	Thermal conductivity, Btu/sq ft/hr/ °F/in.	Specific heat, Btu/lb/°F	Heat of wetting of water, cal/g at about 70°F
Silica gel	38–40	1	0.22	29.1
Silica-alumina cracking catalyst	48–52			
Activated alumina Grade F-1	50	1.5	0.25	14.1[a]
Activated bauxite (700 F)	61	...	0.25	19–21
Activated fuller's earth	34	0.4	0.25	23.7
Acid leached bentonite	45	...	0.25	
Bone char	38–42	0.1	0.24	15.9
Activated carbon	25	...	....	9.5

[a] Grade xF-21.

TABLE 10-6. HEAT OF WETTING OF ADSORBENTS
cal/g

Adsorbent	Activated (700°F) bauxite, (Ark.)	Activated (550°F) fuller's earth	Activated carbon	Silica gel	Activated Al₂O₃ (xF-21)
Water	21.8	23.2	9.5	29.1	18.0
Methanol	16.2	20.6	25.7	34.9	
Ethanol	12.8	17.1	27.0	31.7	
n-Propanol	12.6	15.0	26.5	29.2	
n-Butanol	12.3	13.4	27.0	28.5	
i-Butanol	11.0	12.1	23.0	25.5	
tert-Butanol	9.1	6.5	20.2	21.9	
Acetone	10.1	17.9			
Propionaldehyde	36.5	22.1			
Benzene	5.4	4.3			
Nitrobenzene	7.4	9.3			
Aniline	11.9	9.7			
Pyridine	11.0				
n-Heptane	3.0	....	....	....	2.7
Triptane	....	....	....,	....	2.6
Methylcyclohexane	....	....	....	....	4.7
Toluene	4.5	....	....	....	4.1

Note: In the table above, Al_2O_3 denotes activated alumina.

where X = units of impurity removed

M = quantity of adsorbent used

C = concentration of the impurities in the oil or vapor, in equilibrium with the solid adsorbent

a and n = constants that depend upon the characteristics of the adsorbent, oil or vapor, and solvent if one is used

Thus decolorizing data yield straight lines if X/M is plotted against C on logarithmic graph paper. The equation may be used to compare several clays, but this is about the limit of its usefulness, because the value of the constants is usually unknown. L. L. Davis[64] presents a study of five clays (Table 10-7) in the treatment of a lubricating oil. He found the reciprocal of the Tag Robinson color was a satisfactory measure of the impurities or the true color of the oil. For comparing the efficiency of two clays on a particular oil, the foregoing equation may be arranged in a more convenient form by dividing one equation by the other, thus

$$\frac{M}{M'} = \frac{a'}{a}\, C^{\left(\frac{1}{n'}-\frac{1}{n}\right)} \quad \text{or} \quad bC^{\left(\frac{1}{n'}-\frac{1}{n}\right)}$$

In the selection[65] of a clay, examinations of the clays that are available in the vicinity should be made in the laboratory. As an indication of the difference in clays note Table 10-8 by Dunstan.[66] He examined the decolorizing power of the adsorbents using a 0.25 per cent solution of crude asphaltic oil in benzene.

TABLE 10-7. COMPARISON OF CLAYS

Tag Robinson color	Efficiencies as per cent of Riverside earth				
	Riverside, Tex., fuller's earth	Natural, Utah	Treated German clay, dry form	Treated Tex. clay, pulp form	Treated Calif. clay, pulp form
½	100	120	120	170	285
1	100	130	133	235	400
1½	100	140	140	240	465
2	100	150	150	245	500

The more important groups of petroleum adsorbents are (1) fuller's earth, (2) bentonite, (3) various natural and treated clays, (4) bog iron ore, (5) bauxite and alumina, and (6) activated carbon. These are often

[64] *Ref. Nat. Gaso. Mfr.*, March, 1928, p. 90.

[65] Deitz, V. R., "Bibliography of Solid Adsorbents 1900–1942," United States Cane Sugar Refiners and Bone Char Manufacturers, and the U.S. National Bureau of Standards, 1944.

[66] Morrell and Egloff, reference, *Oil Gas J.*, Jan. 28, 1932, p. 22.

TABLE 10-8. COMPARISON OF DECOLORIZING MATERIALS

Material	Cc of colored solution decolorized by 1 g of clay	Approximate bbl per ton
Alumina	60	342
Fuller's earth I	30	171
Bauxite I	30	171
Bauxite II	25	142
Bauxite III	20	114
Ignited peat	15	85
Bone charcoal	14	80
Bog iron ore	12	68
Fuller's earth II	10	57
Ferric oxide	10	57
Ball clay	8	45
Fuller's earth III	8.5	47
Fuller's earth IV	4	23
China clay	2	11.5
Kieselguhr	2	11.5

sold under trade names such as "Palex," "Filtrol," "Floridin," and "Kontak." The chief sources of bleaching clays in the United States are Georgia, Florida, southern Illinois, Texas, Colorado, Utah, Nevada, Arizona, and southern California, although suitable clays are found in many other states.[67] Some are used in the natural state, except for drying and crushing, but others are burned and washed with water, steam, or hydrochloric or sulfuric acid. The treated clays usually have a greater decolorizing power, but the treatment is expensive. Most clays can be reactivated by burning, and some by washing with solvents.

Synthetic adsorbents such as silica,[59] chromia, and alumina gels[68] are expensive, but various other metals can be introduced for improving the catalytic, adsorptive, or regenerative properties of the gels or catalysts. Likewise, various chemicals can be added[68] to the natural adsorbents for enhancing their efficiency.

In general, the hydrocarbons are adsorbed in the following order: unsaturates, aromatics, naphthenes, and paraffins. In each series the high-molecular-weight hydrocarbons are adsorbed more readily, and this doubtless accounts for most of the decolorizing action. Thus the specific gravity, viscosity, and color of the stream of oil from a percolation filter increase as more and more oil flows through the filter, and the first oil

[67] Nutting, P. G., *Ind. Eng. Chem., Anal. Ed.*, **4**, 139 (1932).
[68] Kalichevsky and Kobe, Refining with Adsorbents, *Pet. Refiner*, June, 1953, p. 95.

TABLE 10-9. EFFECT OF PERCOLATION THROUGH FULLER'S EARTH ON THE PROPERTIES OF A LUBRICATING OIL[a]

Material	Gravity, API	Sulfur content, % by wt	Carbon residue, % by wt	Viscosity, SUS at 210°F
Unfiltered stock.....	41.6	0.134	2.25	156
Stream after oil yield of:				
10 bbl..........	48.3	0.02	0.027	87
25 bbl..........	46.2	0.05	0.115	95
75 bbl..........	43.2	0.08	0.546	125
150 bbl..........	42.4	0.13	0.932	135
300 bbl..........	41.9	0.13	1.49	140
500 bbl..........	41.8	0.13	1.61	140
600 bbl..........	41.5	0.13	1.79	140

[a] Kauffman, H. L., Ref. Nat. Gaso. Mfr., April, 1928, p. 74.

will be of a much lower gravity and viscosity[69] than the parent stock (Table 10-9). Resinous and asphaltic substances are actively adsorbed. Little of the sulfur is adsorbed, and hence clay-treating methods are seldom used for desulfurization.[70]

TREATING EQUIPMENT

The mechanical operations involved in treating are primarily those of mixing or contacting and settling or separating. In the most simple arrangement, a *batch system*, which employs a so-called *agitator*, may be used. The system consists of a conical-bottom agitator vessel equipped with a steam coil and having connections for agitation with air or for circulation by means of pumps. Klaerner[71] believes that the explosive temperature of the air-vapor mixture produced in agitators is within 1°F of the Pensky-Martens flash point and that in large commercial agitators it is not affected by rate of blowing. Dangerous voltages (over 300 volts) are generated in petroleum product pipelines, and during air agitation. A single agitator may be used for many operations such as contact with sulfuric acid or alkalies, washing with water, or neutralization with ammonia or clay. A lead lining weighing 8 to 10 lb per sq ft is usually provided. Lead is a ductile material, and hence it should be supported at intervals of about 8 in. by reinforcing bars. The support bars are bolted through the lead to the steel shell, and a strip of lead is burned over each

[69] Kauffman, H. L., Ref. Nat. Gaso. Mfr., April, 1928, p. 74.
[70] Wood, Sheely, and Trusty, Ind. Eng. Chem., 18, 169 (1926).
[71] Formation of Static Electric Charges on Agitating Petroleum Products with Air, Ind. Eng. Chem., 39, 92 (1947).

bar and its bolts, so that no steel is exposed. Hard lead (94 Pb-6Sb) and tellurium lead are gaining in favor because of their greater strength.

Continuous treaters involve many arrangements of mixers and settlers, but in principle they are much alike. The most simple arrangement is a metering and mixing system such as would be employed in adding tetraethyl fluid or inhibitors to gasoline or demulsifying agents to crude oil. Although injection can be controlled by hand, the best methods employ proportioning pumps actuated by the main transfer pump, proportioning orifice flow controllers, or similar automatic proportioning methods.[72] Such systems are illustrated in Fig. 10-3 for introducing an inhibitor into

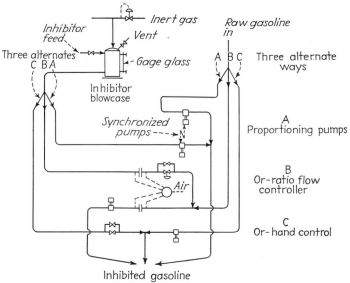

FIG. 10-3. Three methods of adding inhibitor to gasoline.

gasoline. If extremely small amounts of agent are added, as in the case of ethyl fluid or dyes, or if the hand-control method of Fig. 10-3 is used, a more uniform mixture may be attained by recirculating it in and out of the final storage tank.

Eductors are used[73,74] more widely than indicated in the diagrams in this chapter, but an eductor is shown in the copper chloride diagram of Fig. 10-9. In the most simple arrangement, a batch of dye or treating

[72] Lowry, L., Five Methods of Injecting Petroleum Inhibitors, *Pet. Processing,* March, 1955, p. 357.

[73] Fleck, L. R., Mixing Leaded Gasoline, *Pet. Refiner,* July, 1949, p. 139; and Hoyt, H. R., Automatic TEL Blending . . . Products Pipeline, *Oil Gas J.,* Oct. 13, 1952, p. 241.

[74] How to Design In-tank Jet-mixing Systems, a weekly series in *Oil Gas J.,* starting Sept. 6, 1954, p. 125, and extending through Jan. 10, 1955, p. 105.

agent is introduced during a short period by simply allowing the agent to be sucked into the system while an attendant stands by. After the agent is introduced the entire tank of material may be circulated or "turned over" until mixing is complete, or propeller mixers[75] may be used.

A somewhat different system is necessary for contacting a fluid with a solid treating agent, as in passing gasoline and air through a copper chloride solid treating agent or in adding sulfur to gasoline in the doctor sweetening process (see Figs. 10-8 and 10-11). When contacting a liquid reagent with the stock, it is necessary to have some method of recirculation and perhaps of mixing the two fluids, and an additional vessel for settling traces of the treating agent or for washing with water. Such systems are illustrated by the caustic-wash system of Fig. 10-4.

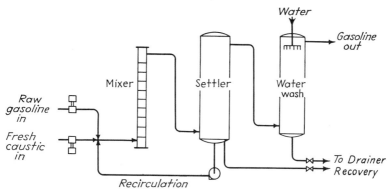

FIG. 10-4. Caustic washing with recirculation of caustic.

Many modifications and elaborations on these systems are possible, such as the use of motor-driven contactors for mixing the stocks, centrifuges for separating the stocks, filters for removing traces of solids, and various sequences of contacting, settling, washing, etc., as illustrated in the pressure-distillate treater of Fig. 10-8.

Contacting Methods. The design of *mixing columns* is normally based on the pressure drop that is available for mixing. A total pressure drop of 30 psi is sufficient to give effective mixing, and many refiners find that mixing is effective at much lower pressure drops. The particular type of mixer is not important, but intimate contacting must be attained. At the same time, many refiners report that too intimate a mixing gives difficulty in the settling and suggest only a pump and several sharp-angle turns for mixing. Among the types of mixers that are used are square-angle bends, orifice-plate columns, baffle-plate columns, perforated buckets, various mechanical mixers operated by motors, jet or nozzle mixers,

---

[75] Rushton, J. H., Design and Operation of Mixers for Large Tank Blending, *Pet. Refiner*, August, 1954, p. 101.

and pumps. Irwin[76] describes a multiple-cone type of mixer and the computation of the pressure drop through the mixer. Bell[77] indicates the utilization and power requirements of propeller-type mixers used for stirring batches of aviation gasoline, distillates, and lubricating oils. Pumps give fair mixing, particularly centrifugal and rotary pumps, but additional mixers and baffle columns for prolonging the time are usually used. An ingenious use of a centrifugal pump for mixing is mentioned by Morrell and Bergman.[78] The impeller of the pump is cut down to about half diameter, and the impeller is reversed in the case.

The *orifice column*[78] is widely used for mixing. With an average orifice discharge coefficient of 0.65, the permanent loss is about 95 per cent of the pressure differential. Using these figures and when expressing velocity as barrels per hour, the following formula results:

$$\text{Bbl per hr} = 17.8D^2 \sqrt{\Delta h} \qquad (10\text{-}2)$$

where D = diameter of orifice hole, in.

Δh = pressure drop across one plate, expressed as head of liquid, ft

The accuracy of this equation is influenced by the arrangement of the orifice hole or holes and by the ratio of the area of orifice holes to the area of the pipe, but great accuracy in the design of a mixing column is not justified. In general, the ratio of pipe area to the total orifice area may range from 3 to 10 and still be satisfactory. Inasmuch as the equation is to be used for only approximate results, Table 10-10 will prove to be a useful simplification. The figures within the block are the pressure drops normally employed. The feet of liquid may be converted to pounds per square inch by the following relation:

$$\text{Psi} = (\text{ft of fluid}) \times (\text{sp gr}) \times 0.433$$

or

$$\text{Psi} = \frac{\text{ft of fluid}}{2.148 + 0.01623\,(\text{API})} \qquad (10\text{-}3)$$

The mixing column may be assembled by welding, by cutting slots at 1 ft intervals and on opposite sides of the pipe. The plates are cut with a recess on one side (as thick as the pipe) so that one side of the plate fits against the inside of the pipe and the other side extends through the slot so that it can be welded. Another way to assemble the column is to use flanged spools with a plate between each spool. The plates may also be strung on rods, spot-welded, and slipped into the column from the end.

[76] *Oil Gas J.*, July 19, 1934, p. 10.

[77] "American Petroleum Refining," 3d ed., pp. 18, 24, D. Van Nostrand Company, Inc., Princeton, N.J., 1945.

[78] Three articles, *Chem. Met. Eng.*, **35**, 210, 291, 350 (1928).

If a longer time of contact is desirable, so-called *contact columns* or time columns may be used. These are attached after the mixing columns as shown in Fig. 10-8. Time columns may consist of large pipe with half-moon baffles or orifice plates having large holes. In arranging mixing equipment, no low points in which the chemical may collect should exist, because the liquid tends to surge in slugs into the settling equipment.

If the chemical is injected by gravity feed or from a pressure feed tank, the rate of feed can be controlled with a valve and no metering device is necessary. If blow cases or eductors are used, the chemical must be measured as it is added. The most common method of metering is by orifice meters. Morrell and Bergman[78] present orifice meter charts. The treater often estimates the material handled by a blow case by noting the time and the pressure during the admission of chemical.

TABLE 10-10. PRESSURE DROP THROUGH ORIFICE MIXERS

Bbl per hr	Pressure drop for each orifice plate, expressed as ft of liquid for the following areas of orifice (total), sq in.						
	0.4	0.6	0.8	1.0	3.0	6.0	10.0
10	1.2	0.54					
20	4.7	2.15	1.11	0.52			
40	18.8	8.6	4.45	2.08	0.35		
60	42.2	19.3	10.0	4.67	0.8		
100	....	53.7	27.7	13.0	2.22	0.57	
150	....	.....	62.5	29.2	5.0	1.29	0.45
200	....	.....	.....	52.0	8.9	2.3	0.79
300	....	.....	.....	.....	20.0	5.2	1.78
500	....	.....	.....	.....	.....	14.2	4.95

Example 10-1. Design of Orifice Mixer. Acid is to be mixed with 8,000 bbl per day of 53 API pressure distillate. A pressure drop of 25 psi is permissible.

$$\text{Bbl per hr} = \frac{8,000}{24} = 334$$

Use about 7 sq in. of orifice holes or openings.
Use a pressure drop, feet of fluid (Table 10-10), of about 5.5 ft.

$$\text{Pressure drop, psi per plate} = \frac{5.5}{2.148 + 0.01623(53)} = 1.83$$

$$\text{Number of plates} = \frac{25}{1.83} = \text{about } 14$$

Use a pipe having about five times the orifice area, or 30 sq in.   Use standard or extra heavy 6-in. pipe with a transverse area of 28.9 sq in.

		Sq in.	Sq in.
Approximate layout of plates:			
Six 1¼-in. holes or	6 × 1.227 = about 7.37		
Twelve ⅞-in. holes	12 × 0.601 = about		7.22
⅟₁₆-in. clearance around one side of plate.........	= 0.42		0.42
Total opening, sq in.	= 7.79	or	7.64

The plate will be 6.07 in. in diameter with a ⅟₁₆-in. recess around half of the circumference.

If the plates are spaced 1 ft apart, the total length of the mixing column will be about 16 ft.

In rare instances the time of contact must be very short, and for such situations mechanical mixers like those employed in the centrifuge treating systems[79] may be employed.   Continuous contacting with acid has also been accomplished[80] by means of a horizontal mixer in which a shaft, equipped with blades, rotates at 900 rpm.

Settlers or Separators.   Although A. C. Ingersoll[81] completely presents the theory of settling, the exact settling time that is required must be determined for each treating operation.   In general, caustic and water mixtures settle more rapidly than acid sludge or "pepper."   Ten or fifteen minutes often suffices for caustic or doctor settlers, but an hour may be required for settling acid sludge.   The settlers are usually about 40 ft high and range in diameter from 2 to 10 ft.   In large-diameter tanks, a gentle circulation takes place and tends to spoil the separation.   The sprays for water-wash tanks are usually of welded pipe in the form of a cross or a six-legged star with ⅛-in. holes drilled on the same side of each pipe in the star.   These sprays, all pointed in the same direction, give a gentle rotating motion to the oil in the tank.   They are placed several feet below the oil outlet.   Horizontal settling tanks are more effective than vertical settlers of the same capacity.   This is due to the lower vertical velocity in the horizontal settler.   The velocity of the fluid in the settler should not exceed about 3 ft per minute.   A higher velocity will require a greater time for settling.   Stokes's law [Eq. (8-1)] governs the rate of settling.

Example 10-2.   Design of Settlers.   A tank for settling caustic from 12,000 bbl of oil per day may be designed as follows:
Caustic or doctor settler:
    Allow 30 min of time, and use a vertical tank 40 ft high.

[79] Trivals, H., *Ref. Nat. Gaso. Mfr.*, May, 1932, p. 312.

[80] Morrison, J. D., Continuous Acid Treating Heavy Lubricating Oil, *Oil Gas J.*, Oct. 14, 1948, p. 87; or *Petroleo Interamericano*, December, 1949, p. 42.

[81] Fundamentals and Performance of Gravity Separation, *Pet. Refiner*, June, 1951, p. 106.

$$\text{Volume of oil per hr} = \frac{12,000}{24} \times \frac{42}{7.5} = 2,800 \text{ cu ft}$$

$$\text{One-half of this} = \frac{2,800}{2} = 1,400 \text{ cu ft to be handled in 30 min}$$

$$\text{Cross-sectional area of settler} = \frac{1,400}{40} = 35 \text{ sq ft}$$

$$\text{Diameter} = \text{about 6 ft 10 in.}$$

If 40-ft tanks are not convenient, then two 20-ft tanks connected in series can be used. Acid sludge settler:
Allow 1 hr and use a 40-ft tank.

$$\text{Cross-sectional area} = 35 \times 2 = 70.0 \text{ sq ft}$$
$$\text{Diameter} = \text{about 9 ft 6 in.}$$

The use of so-called coalescer chambers containing pads of plastic material,[82] finely woven wire-mesh, coalescing membranes, metal wool, etc., is now common practice in handling either liquid or vapor streams from many settling or separating operations, but little appears in the literature about such applications. Cyclone separators for handling liquids[83,84] as well as vapors have been developed.

Mechanical filters packed with sand, gravel and rock, or with rock salt, are also effective in coagulating particles of water or solution. The salt filters used in copper chloride sweetening have the added advantage of drying the stream by the hygroscopic action of the salt. Finally, electrical precipitation[85] can be used in removing traces of treating agents from streams as well as the desalting of crude oil (see Fig. 8-4).

Concentrated sulfuric acid, acid sludge, and caustic solutions do not attack steel rapidly, but dilute acid reacts violently so that water-wash tanks after acid-settling tanks must be lead-lined. The caustic settlers and caustic water-wash tanks are also frequently lined with lead, although lead linings are not really necessary. Self-lubricated cocks, such as the Merco-Nordstrom or MacGregor, should be used on the chemical lines. Steel pipe is used for all connections except the drain lines from acid-water-wash tanks. These lines should be lead-lined or constructed of alloy cast iron. The drains should have air or steam connections into them so that they can be "blown out" in case they become plugged with sludge or scale.

[82] Thornton, D. P., Plastic Solves Scrubbing Problems, *Pet. Processing*, September, 1953, p. 1328.

[83] Fitch and Johnson, Controlling Separation in Liquid-Solid Cyclones, *Chem. Eng.*, June, 1952, p. 172.

[84] News item, "Tiny Cyclones Used as a Battery to Separate Solids from Filtrate," *Chem. Eng.*, December, 1953, p. 218.

[85] Phillips, R. J., Electrical Precipitation . . . in Treating Distillates, *Oil Gas J.*, Dec. 5, 1955, p. 116.

In acid treating, some refiners[86] have found that neutralization and coagulation with clay are more satisfactory than settling and neutralization with caustic. The use of a Hardinge clarifier is reported.[86] The sludge is collected on a bed of sand, and revolving paddles continually scrape the sticky sludge from the top of the filter. The thickness of the bed is finally so decreased that new sand must be added. Still other refiners[87] utilize vessels packed with rock or sand.

Filter Presses. Solids are usually in a finely divided condition, and hence filter presses rather than gravity settlers are often necessary. The

FIG. 10-5. Sweetland filter press for removing fine clay.

only major use of filters is in removing finely divided clay from treated cylinder stock in the clay-contact process and in dewaxing. The Sweetland press, a picture of which is shown in Fig. 10-5, is widely used, and more recently the Oliver precoat continuous rotary filter has been adopted by many refiners. In addition the Kelly pressure filter[88] is used for removing carbon, lime, and other solids from cracking-still residuum, or to remove a large bulk of solid ahead of other filters. Pressure filters are also used to remove clay from pressure distillate.[79]

[86] Willson, C. O., *Oil Gas J.*, Dec. 18, 1930, p. 38.

[87] Vesper, H. G., *Oil Gas J.*, Mar. 30, 1933, p. 44.

[88] Badger and McCabe, "Elements of Chemical Engineering," 2d ed., McGraw-Hill Book Company, Inc., New York, 1936.

The *Sweetland press*[88] consists of a cylindrical horizontal shell having a hinged bottom which can be dropped down for removal of the filter clay. Circular filter leaves are arranged crosswise in the shell, each being suspended by a separate connection at the top to an oil-discharge manifold. The oil-clay slurry is pumped into the shell through a manifold along the bottom. The oil passes through the sides of the leaves by application of a pressure of 40 to 50 psi until a suitable cake thickness is attained. The cake is then washed with naphtha, dried with flue gas or steam, and then removed by opening the bottom of the press, which allows the cake to drop into a conveyor or discharge chute. Difficulties and methods of handling filter clay or cake are discussed by Trescott.[89]

TABLE 10-11. CAPACITY OF SWEETLAND FILTER PRESSES
Oliver United Filters, Inc.

Filter numbers	1	2A	2	3	5	7	10	12
Inside diameter, in	10	16	16	25	25	25	31	37
Inside length, in	20½	19	36½	37	61	82	109	145
2-in. filter leaf spacing:								
Number of leaves	9	9	18	18	30	41	54	72
Filter area, sq ft:								
Smooth rim	8	23	46	111	185	252	523	1,004
Grooved rim	7.5	21	42	105	175	239	500	965
Max cake capacity, cu ft, with								
½-in. cake	0.3	1	2	4.8	8	11	22	42
3-in. filter leaf spacing:								
Number of leaves	7	.....	12	12	20	27	36	48
Filter area, sq ft:								
Smooth rim	6	.....	31	74	123	166	349	670
Grooved rim	5.7	.....	28	70	117	158	333	642
Max cake capacity, cu ft, with								
1-in. cake	0.5	.....	2.5	6.4	10	14	28	56
4-in. filter leaf spacing:								
Number of leaves	5	.....	9	9	15	20	27	36
Filter area, sq ft:								
Smooth rim	4.5	.....	23	55	92	123	262	502
Grooved rim	4	.....	21	53	88	117	250	483
Max cake capacity, cu ft, with								
1½-in. cake	0.6	.....	3	7.2	12	15	33	63
Total weight of filter filled with								
water, lb	550	1,500	2,300	5,500	7,300	9,350	16,500	29,600
Shipping weight, lb:								
Domestic	500	1,300	2,100	4,800	6,200	7,900	13,500	24,000
Export	600	1,400	2,200	5,400	7,600	9,300	16,500	29,000

The *Oliver precoat filter* is a modification of the regular Oliver filter.[88] It consists of a horizontal cylindrical drum, the outside of which is made up of separate segments or compartments. The entire outside of the cylinder is covered with a filtering medium such as fine mesh wire or cloth. Each segment is connected to a discharge line, under vacuum, by a special valve on the end of the drum in such a way that suction is maintained while the drum rotates. A deposit (or precoat) of diatomaceous earth or

[89] *Ref. Nat. Gaso. Mfr.*, February, 1934, p. 54.

similar porous medium is deposited on the drum by rotating the drum for about 30 min in a vat containing a slurry of the precoat filtering medium. The vat is then filled with the oil-clay mixture; and as oil passes through the filter surface, a thin film of clay is deposited on the surface of the precoat. The thin layer of clay is continuously shaved from the surface by means of a knife-edge until the precoat is consumed. The precoat lasts from several hours to as long as several days, depending upon conditions. The coating of clay may be washed with naphtha and dried with air or steam as the drum revolves.

Several derivations of the performance of rotary filters have been presented.[90,91,92]   If the effect of the depth of submergence and the resistance of the filter cloth and connecting lines is neglected, rotary filter performance is described by Holland and Woodham[90] as:

$$F = k_3 \sqrt{(-\Delta P_o)\alpha\Theta_T} \qquad (10\text{-}4)$$

where $k_3 = Dh \sqrt{\dfrac{\pi(1 - X)\rho_s}{r\rho}} k_1$

α = speed of rotation, revolutions per unit of time

D = average diameter of drum or cake

F = volumetric delivery rate of filtrate

h = length of drum

k_1 = constant which depends on physical properties of cake and filtrate (see page 217 of "Unit Operations" by Brown and associates, John Wiley & Sons, Inc., New York, 1950)

ΔP_o = pressure drop across cake exclusive of hydrostatic head of slurry across the cake

ρ and ρ_s = density of filtrate and of solid particles in cake

π = 3.1416 radians

r = ratio of mass of dry cake to mass of filtrate

Θ_T = angle of submergence in radians (the part of the entire drum circle that is submerged)

X = porosity of cake (volume of void space in cake divided by the total volume of the cake)

The equation is especially useful in comparing the effect of operating conditions (see Example 10-3).[90]

Example 10-3. Rotary Filter Performance,   A vacuum rotary filter is able to deliver 50 gal of filtrate per min.   The depth of submergence is one-fifth the diameter

[90] Holland and Woodham, Exact Calculation Methods . . . , *Pet. Refiner*, February, 1956, p. 149.

[91] Reeves, E. J., Wash Solvent Requirements . . . , *Pet. Processing*, August, 1949, p. 885.

[92] Brownell and Gudz, Blower Requirements . . . , *Chem. Eng.*, September, 1949, p. 112.

of the drum and the speed of rotation is 5 rpm. If the resistance of the cloth and lines and the variation in pressure drop due to hydrostatic head are neglected, what is the effect on the delivery of doubling (1) the depth of submergence, (2) the area of submergence, (3) the speed of rotation, or (4) the pressure drop?

The final delivery rate, F_2, is related to the initial delivery rate, F_1, as follows [see Eq. (10-4)]:

$$F_2 = F_1 \sqrt{\frac{\Theta_{T2}}{\Theta_{T1}}}$$

If the depth of submergence is doubled the values of Θ_{T1} and Θ_{T2} are:

$$\cos \frac{\Theta_{T1}}{2} = \left(1 - \frac{2d}{D}\right), \text{ or } \cos^{-1}\left(1 - \frac{2d}{D}\right)$$

$$= (1 - \tfrac{2}{5}) = \tfrac{3}{5}$$

$$\frac{\Theta_{T1}}{2} = 53.133°$$

$$\Theta_{T1} = (106.266°)\frac{3.1416}{180°} = 1.85 \text{ radians}$$

$$\cos \frac{\Theta_{T2}}{2} = \left(1 - \frac{2d}{D}\right) = 1 - \frac{4}{5} = \frac{1}{5}$$

$$\Theta_{T2} = (2 \times 78.467°)\frac{3.1416}{180°} = 2.74 \text{ radians}$$

Therefore, $$F_2 = 50 \sqrt{\frac{2.74}{1.85}} = 60.8 \text{ gpm}$$

Doubling of the area of submergence, speed of rotation, or pressure drop, all have the same effect [see Eq. (10-4)]:

$$F_2 = 50 \sqrt{\frac{2\Theta_{T1}}{\Theta_{T1}}} = 50 \sqrt{\frac{2\alpha_1}{\alpha_1}} = 50 \sqrt{\frac{2\Delta P_o}{\Delta P_o}} = 50 \sqrt{2} = 70.7 \text{ gpm}$$

Clay Burners. Coarse mesh (15 to 90) percolation clay is burned or regenerated. Prior to 1930 most burners were of the rotary type,[93] more recently multiple-hearth[93] furnaces were installed, and at present the Thermofor kiln[94] is attracting attention. The multiple-hearth (Wedge or Nichols Herreshoff) kilns consist of a series of three to eight circular refractory hearths housed in a refractory shell. A large rotating shaft down the center moves rabble arms around each hearth. Clay enters at the top, and air for combustion at the bottom or through openings in the shaft and arms. The rabble arms propel the clay inward on the top hearth and outward on the next, etc. The furnaces are fired near the bottom and on various of the hearths. Temperatures of 1000°F (or even 1200°F) are attained at the second or third hearth from the top, and hence the adsorptive power of the clay is slowly destroyed by sintering. After four or five regenerations the efficiency of the clay is 65 to 75 per

[93] Bell, H. S., "American Petroleum Refining," 3d ed., pp. 405–410, D. Van Nostrand Company, Inc., Princeton, N.J., 1945.

[94] Simpson and Payne, Thermofor Kiln and Clay-regenerating Processes . . . , *Oil Gas J.*, Nov. 17, 1939, p. 147.

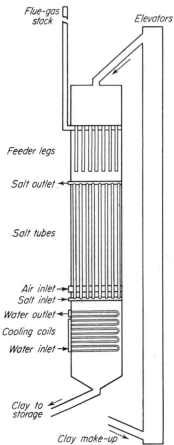

Flue-gas stack

Elevators

Feeder legs

Salt outlet

Salt tubes

Air inlet
Salt inlet
Water outlet
Cooling coils
Water inlet

Clay to storage

Clay make-up

FIG. 10-6. Diagram of Thermofor continuous clay-burning kiln. (*Socony Mobil Oil Co.*)

cent, at fifteen burns 55 to 60, and in a few instances a clay efficiency of 50 per cent can be maintained without rejecting any clay except that which is lost by attrition.

The Thermofor kiln (Fig. 10-6) is probably more efficient and cheaper[95] than other types. It consists of a stationary chamber containing vertical heat-transfer tubes through which molten metal or salt at 850 to 1500°F flows. The heat-transfer medium is pumped through the tubes to control the temperature, and the clay flows downward around the tubes. Short pieces of perforated angle iron with the edges pointing upward are laid between the tubes so that the clay is directed against the hot tubes. Air is admitted at the bottom in amounts large enough to burn the carbonaceous material on the clay, but much of the heating of the clay is accomplished by the heat-transfer medium. If the adsorbent efficiency of the Thermofor clay is kept at the same value as would be expected with multiple-hearth operations, the amount of clay purchased is only one-third to one-eighth as much as for multiple hearths.[95] The Thermofor equipment occupies little ground area. Owing to the exact temperature control that is possible, the used clay can be kept at about 90 per cent of its original decolorizing power. Bauxite is so resistant to heat that it may be reburned even 350 times.

PRACTICE OF TREATING

The foregoing discussion of the chemistry, fundamentals, and equipment of treating was so involved that the manner of conducting these processes could not be discussed. Many arrangements of equipment

[95] Myers and Owen, Economic Survey of Thermofor Installations . . . , *Oil Gas J.*, Aug. 4, 1945, p. 93.

have been successfully used as well as the particular operations or diagrams shown here.

Natural Gasoline. Even though gas desulfurization as by the use of monoethanolamine or other agents (see Table 22-4 and Fig. 20-18) is practiced for the removal and/or recovery of hydrogen sulfide from the gas, it is still necessary to sweeten the liquid products and to dry the propane. With especially sour products, the system indicated by M. H. Rahmes[96] (see Fig. 10-7) is extensively used.[97] If the mercaptan content

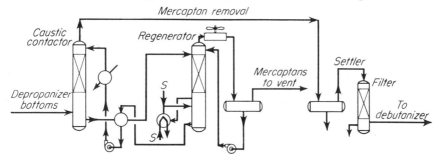

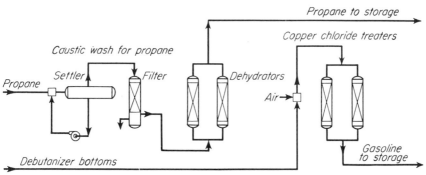

FIG. 10-7. Product treating in a natural-gasoline plant. (*Pet. Refiner.*)

is high, it is usually necessary to pretreat the raw gasoline in a steam regenerative caustic (10 per cent solution) wash plant before the debutanizer (Fig. 10-7) and then sweeten the final gasoline after debutanization. The solid or fixed-bed method of conducting copper chloride sweetening is widely used. Sweetening of the butane is not always

[96] Sour Gas—New Plant Operating MEA, Dehydration, Caustic and Copper Chloride Units, *Pet. Refiner*, August, 1950, p. 118.

[97] Lyon et al. (Elk Basin), *Pet. Engineer*, July, 1949, p. A-41; Bellah et al. (Slaughter), *Pet. Refiner*, June, 1949, p. 154; Hillsman and Kilgren (South Fullerton), *Pet. Refiner*, June, 1950, p. 123; and Glendenning and Sanderson (Cymric) *Pet. Engr.*, May, 1950, p. C-54.

necessary, but a simple caustic wash suffices for either butane or propane (see Fig. 10-4). In very large plants the distillation method of dehydrating propane may be used (see pages 234 and 235).

Gasoline. Straight-run gasolines normally require only a caustic wash or a simple sweetening treatment. In caustic washing (Fig. 10-4) the settler tank can be charged daily (or less often) with fresh caustic and circulated until it is spent. More often the caustic is regenerated by removing mercaptans by steaming until finally the caustic is destroyed by reaction with hydrogen sulfide. Cracked gasolines are always sweetened although simple inhibitor sweetening may be all that is required for catalytic cracked gasolines. If the sulfur content must be further reduced

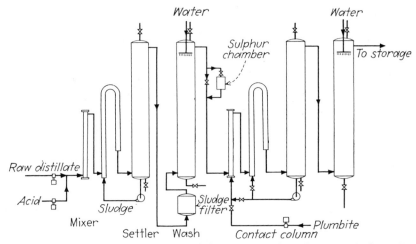

FIG. 10-8. Continuous acid treating and doctor sweetening of raw cracked gasoline.

or if it is feasible to desulfurize in order to improve the susceptibility of the gasoline to tetraethyllead, the gasoline may be treated with sulfuric acid (Fig. 10-8) or by the modern catalytic desulfurization processes. Filtration through coarse fuller's earth is useful in stabilizing certain gasolines that are unstable with respect to light, and a filter ensures removal of the last traces of treating agents.

Doctor sweetening is conducted in equipment similar to that shown in the last part of Fig. 10-8. The sludge filter shown in this diagram is not widely used, and some treaters believe that doctor sweetening is more successful if the sulfur is added after the doctor solution (see also page 304).

Copper sweetening[24] holds some advantages over the caustic washing and doctor processes because of its simplicity. The dry process[98] is suit-

[98] Anon., Perco Solid Copper Sweetening Process, *Ref. Nat. Gaso. Mfr.*, April, 1940, p. 73.

able in most instances for handling natural or straight-run gasoline, but the wet process[99] is shown here (Fig. 10-9) because it can be applied to all stocks including even cracked distillates. Free sulfur and hydrogen sulfide are sometimes removed by a caustic wash, and the outgoing gasoline is sometimes contacted with the spent caustic-wash liquid (sodium sulfide) for the removal of traces of copper, which tend to promote the formation of gum in the finished gasoline. The salt filters of Fig. 10-9 are now standard practice[100] in the removal of traces of moisture. Droplets are coagulated as in a gravel or sand filter but in addition, the rock salt has a hygroscopic action. The last traces of liquid water are eliminated by heating the dry gasoline to 15 to 25°F above the salt-bed temperature. The capacity of the reactor is about 75 per cent of the hourly throughput. Copper slurry has the following composition:[100]

> Attapulgus clay, 200 mesh......... 100 lb
> Cupric chloride crystals............ 14 lb
> Water........................ 1.75 gal

One refiner uses this amount[100] for each 1,000 bbl of capacity. The slurry is prepared in a mix pot or blow case near the reactor. The clay is poured directly from kraft paper bags into a blow case, followed by the cupric chloride and then water. The volume of air required[100] by the process is about 0.5 cu ft per bbl of raw distillate for each 0.01 weight per cent of mercaptan sulfur. The process is suitable for most straight-run and cracked gasolines up to a mercaptan content of 0.04 per cent.

The *Solutizer process*[30,42] (page 302) has the advantage of removing sulfur and hence may result in a product having a higher octane number, an increased susceptibility to the effect of tetraethyllead, and more color stability. The steps in the process (Fig. 10-10a) are caustic washing, solutizer washing to dissolve mercaptans, and stripping of the solutizer solution by means of steam. Contacting is effected by means of a countercurrent tower packed with carbon Raschig rings, and the process is completely continuous. It may be applied for the sweetening of any type of distillate including cracked, reformed, or poly distillates. The ratio of solution to gasoline in commercial plants ranges from 0.1 to 0.2. The equivalent of three theoretical plates is used in the extraction column and ten theoretical plates in the regenerator. Steam consumption ranges from 10 to 30 lb per bbl of gasoline [see Eq. (10-1)].

The *Tannin-Solutizer* process[33] is almost identical with the Solutizer process except that air regeneration as indicated in Fig. 10-10b is employed. The fat solution is heated to 110 to 150°F and blown with

[99] Schulze and Buell, Control of Copper Sweetening . . . , *Oil Gas J.*, Nov. 25, 1937, p. 56.

[100] Anon., *Oil Gas J.*, Dec. 14, 1950, p. 107.

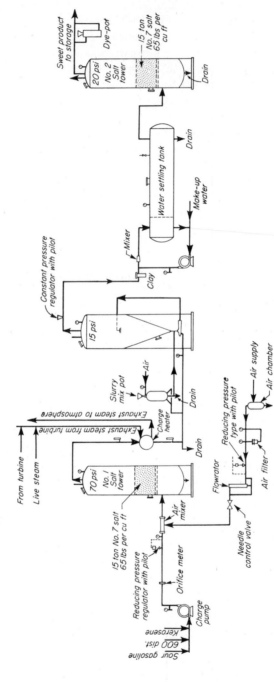

Fig. 10-9. Copper-chloride slurry treater for gasoline and distillates. (*Oil Gas J.*)

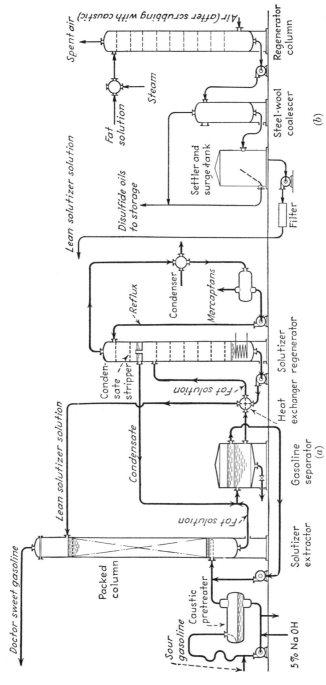

Fig. 10-10. Solutizer and Tannin Solutizer sweetening. (a) Solutizer process with steam generation and (b) Tannin regeneration system. (Shell Development Company.)

329

air (3 cu ft per min for 1,000 bbl per day gasoline) which has been scrubbed with caustic soda. The disulfides produced by the oxidation of the mercaptans in the regenerator are separated by passage through steel wool and by settling. The mercaptan content of the solution must not be reduced to lower than 0.2 per cent because the tannin must be protected from oxidation. The cost of tannin solutizer treatment is less than half the cost of doctor treating, and the main saving is in chemical costs and steam.

The *Mercapsol*[32,35] and *Unisol*[31,35,101] processes are so similar to the Solutizer process that flow diagrams are not shown (see also page 299). These processes are especially useful in handling materials of excessively high mercaptan content but they seldom reduce the mercaptan content to less than 0.0007 to 0.001 per cent. Accordingly, a sweetening after-treatment is required to attain 0.0004 per cent (doctor sweet). Dualayer operations[34] (page 299) may result in doctor sweet products by the solutizer-type processes.

Inhibitor sweetening of catalytically cracked gasoline is successful and economical for mercaptan contents up to 0.02 to 0.03 per cent.[28] About 5 lb of inhibitor is required per thousand bbl. The final mercaptan content is usually below 0.0015 weight per cent.

In the removal of gum from cracked gasolines, sulfuric acid treatment and vapor phase clay treatment were once widely used, but gum inhibitors are now used almost exclusively. Only when acid is useful in several ways, as in desulfurization plus gum removal plus the gaining of stability, is acid-treating useful. Vapor phase and acid processes have been almost totally replaced by catalytic desulfurization.

Gasolines, kerosenes, etc., are sometimes contacted with clay, particularly after acid-treating[79] for removal of the last traces of treating agents, to dry the material, or to neutralize the acid (see Fig. 10-11). The clay is removed in pressure leaf-type filters. About 1 to 5 lb of 200-mesh clay per bbl is required to neutralize the acid.

Kerosene. The quantity of kerosene manufactured in most refineries is relatively small, and hence batch agitators are still used by small refiners.

The batch treatment of kerosene varies greatly depending upon the characteristics of the raw stock. Many kerosenes need only be sweetened; but some require 3 to 6 lb acid per bbl, and kerosenes that are rich in aromatics may require 30 lb per bbl, part of which may be fuming acid. A typical batch acid treatment for kerosene follows:

1. Agitate with acid 30 min. Often the acid is split into a small dose of "water acid," and after this is drained, the main acid is admitted.

---

[101] Lyles, H. R., . . . New Design Unisol stripping tower . . . , *Oil Gas J.*, Mar. 7, 1955, p. 126.

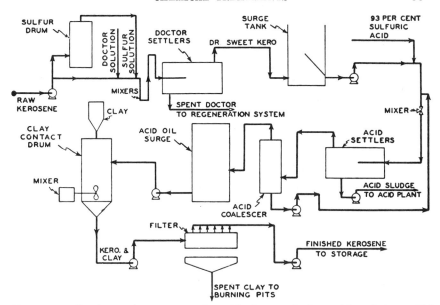

FIG. 10-11. Continuous kerosene treating with doctor solution, acid, and clay. (*Oil Gas J.*)

2. Settle ½ to 1½ hr.
3. Spray with water for two 15-min periods, and drain.
4. Spray with soda and wash with water, 15 to 30 min. Drain.
5. Wash with water 15 min at about 100°F.
6. Settle 45 min to 2 hr.

In the manufacture of prime kerosene from naphthene-base crude oils the following procedure may need to be used:

1. Agitate with water acid (1 lb), 15 min.
2. Settle. Drain.
3. Three treats of 8 lb each of fuming H_2SO_4; settle and drain after each.
4. 3 lb treat with 66°Bé acid. Drain.
5. Three washes with water, agitating during wash, 15 min each.
6. Neutralize with 6 lb of 12°Bé caustic.
7. Settle and drain.
8. Two washes with water, 15 min each.
9. If color is not satisfactory, filter through fuller's earth or agitate with about 0.4 lb of earth.

Methods of improving the color are (1) redistillation with steam as with pressure distillate and (2) filtration through fuller's earth. Continuous methods of sweetening and acid treating kerosene are employed[102] (Fig. 10-11) in most refineries. For the removal of aromatics, the Edeleanu solvent extraction process (Chap. 11) is widely used, but

[102] Sierra, A. V., Better Caustic Utilization, *Oil Gas J.*, June 22, 1953, p. 252.

catalytic desulfurization followed by a caustic wash promises to replace the current methods of treatment.

Caustic Utilization. Sodium hydroxide represents such a large part of the cost of treatment that every effort is made to conserve, reuse, recover, and regenerate it. Such efforts are illustrated in Fig. 10-12 for a plant[102] which conducts Unisol mercaptan extraction of straight-run gasoline; doctor sweetening of kerosene (Fig. 10-11); neutralization of some acid treated No. 2 Distillate (so-called Blend Oil Unit); neutralization of the products of sulfuric acid alkylation; regenerative caustic washing for all cracked gasolines and for butane and propane; prewash

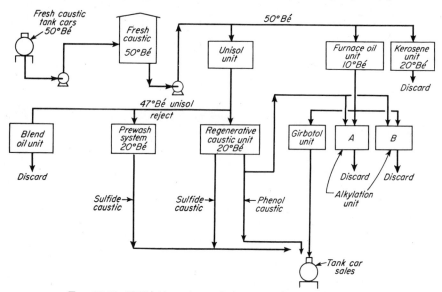

FIG. 10-12. Utilization of caustic by one refiner.   (*Oil Gas J.*)

of all gasoline streams to the Unisol and regenerative caustic units for removal of hydrogen sulfide; caustic washing of furnace oil; and a clean-up treatment at the gas treating unit (Girbotol). Fresh caustic (Fig. 10-12) is used at the Unisol, furnace oil, and kerosene units, but all of the other needs for caustic are met by the reuse of partially spent caustics.

Catalytic Desulfurization. The development of these processes is occurring so rapidly that only a general discussion of the three major modifications discussed on pages 305 to 307 can be mentioned.

1. Fig. 10-13a—no hydrogen recycle or make-up (Perco[47] and Gray[47] processes).
2. Fig. 10-13b—hydrogen recycling but no make-up of hydrogen, illustrated by the Cobalt Molybdate[48] and Autofining[49] processes.
3. Fig. 10-13b—hydrogen recycling with hydrogen from outside sources, as in the Shell Hydrosulfurization[50,103], Unifining,[51] Hydrofining,[52,55,104,105] Diesulforming,[53] and Gulf HDS[54] processes.

The Gulf HDS process employs such high temperatures and low space velocities that it may be more a cracking or hydrogenation[56] process than the others, and thus fractionation recovery equipment should be added to Fig. 10-13b when practicing Gulf HDS.

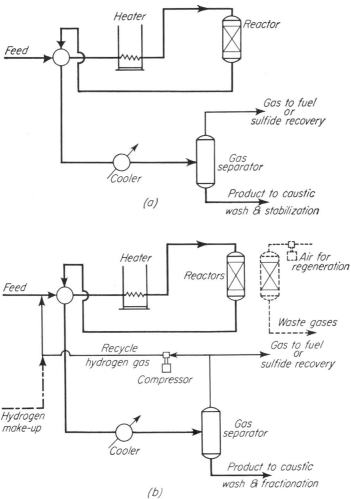

FIG. 10-13. Schematic indication of the practice of catalytic desulfurization (a) without gas recycle and (b) with hydrogen recycle or addition.

[103] Abbott et al., Shell Upgrades Stock by Hydrodesulfurization, *Oil Gas J.*, July 18, 1955, p. 92.

[104] Morbeck, R. C., Hydrofining of Middle Distillates, *Oil Gas J.*, Jan. 3, 1955, p. 94.

[105] Baeder and Siegmund, Hydrofining Is a Natural for Naphthas, *Oil Gas J.*, Feb. 21, 1955, p. 122; also Zimmerschied et al., Improving Distillate Fuels . . . , *Oil Gas J.*, May 23, 1955, p. 113.

Platinum catalyst reforming processes provide a source of cheap by-product hydrogen. The general practice of desulfurization, at this early date, is summarized in Table 10-12, and it is clear that combination processes of desulfurization, hydrogenation, reforming, and even cracking will be the final development rather than simple desulfurization. Likewise, it appears that wide-boiling-range feeds[106] or entire crude oils[54]

TABLE 10-12. SUMMARY OF THE PRACTICE OF DESULFURIZATION

Material treated	API gravity increase[a]	Per cent sulfur reduction[b]	Notes
S.R. naphtha or solvents	Zero	90–99 (94)	R.O.N. of product with 3 cc TEL, less O.N. of feedstock, 20–29 units
Visbroken, cracked, or coker naphthas	1–4	57–99 (85)	R.O.N. increase (as above), 6–13 units
Catalytic naphthas.......	....	60–99 (77)	R.O.N. increase (as above), 4–7 units
Kerosene or No. 1 Distillate	0.3–1.4 (0.8)	60–98 (87)	Smoke point scarcely increased[c]
S.R. distillates and gas oils	0–3.5 (2.2)	46–93 (80)	Cetane increase 0–4 (2.3); pour point remains same
Cycle oils and cracked distillates	0.6–6.0 (3.3)	25–96 (79)	Carbon residue reduction, 0–80%
Crude oils[d].............	9–11	82–85 (83)	Bottoms (670°F plus) reduction, 59–61%
Reduced crude oils[d] (8–11 API)	14–27	68–92 (80)	Bottoms reduction, 53–96 (80)%

[a] A general indication of severity or degree of decomposition or hydrogenation.

[b] Function not only of ease of desulfurization of the feed but also of the severity deemed feasible.

[c] For exceptions see Weber, George, Better Sulfur Removal, *Oil Gas J.*, Mar. 17, 1952, p. 169; Zimmerschied et al., Improving Distillates by Hydrofining, *Pet. Refiner*, May, 1955, p. 153.

[d] Only 2 samples.

will be desulfurized or treated in a single operation, followed by fractionation into suitable fractions. Desulfurization is so relatively expensive that it must rely upon additional product improvements as well as desulfurization, except of course, in upgrading very high sulfur otherwise unsalable oils. In the case of certain gasolines, lead susceptibility and octane number can be the main advantage (Table 10-1). With kerosene and distillate fuels, the advantage may be the reduction in sulfur plus

[106] Weber, George, Better Sulfur Removal (Autofining of 212–662°F fraction), *Oil Gas J.*, Mar. 17, 1952, p. 169.

decrease in carbon residue and improvement in stability; with diesel fuels the reduction of sulfur plus greater stability; and with cycle stocks the possibility of increased yields during subsequent cracking, or the conversion of cycle stocks into suitable heating oils.

Lubricating Oils. There is such a wide variety of heavy-oil stocks and there are so many methods of treatment that only a few general operations can be discussed here. Especially note that solvent treating or extraction is now widely used (Chap. 11). Figure 11-1 indicates the general sequence of operations now conducted in lubricant manufacture. Although solvent treating eliminates most of the dark colored materials, it is usually necessary to conduct some of the older conventional treatments, especially clay percolation or contacting as described next. Pennsylvanian stocks can be finished by clay contacting or percolation alone, most other lube stocks from superior lube crude oils require both acid treatment and clay treatment, whereas many lube stocks must be treated with solvents, with clay, and often by acid treatment. Catalytic desulfurization and hydrogenation are also suggested[55] as a means of preparing superior raw lubricating oil stocks.

The manufacture of low-cold-test lubricating oils[107] is accomplished by vacuum distillation in the presence of a small amount of caustic soda, or soda ash, acid treatment and soda ash neutralization of each of the several lube fractions, and percolation clay treatment. The most viscous oils must be diluted with naphtha, or the lightest lube fraction,[107] before treating. Acid ranges from 10 lb per bbl for the lightest oils to 40 lb for the heaviest (150 to 200 viscosity at 210°F), and the soda ash for neutralization ranges from 1 to 3 lb per bbl.

The acid treatment of lube stocks is usually conducted in batch agitators. Inasmuch as the characteristics of oils vary greatly and the details of treating various oils are so different, the operations can be best illustrated by the operations of several refiners as shown in Table 10-13. Neutralization with soda ash or caustic is accomplished by agitating gently with 3 to 15°Bé caustic until neutral, spraying with hot water or steaming, and settling for 4 to 15 hr. Several washings and settlings are usually necessary. The oil may then be brightened by heating to 120 to 200°F by steam coils in an open pan; heating and blowing with air; or by agitating with dry Sil-O-Cel, etc., and filtering. Fabian[108] reports that steam coils in the roofs of lubricating-oil storage tanks prevent condensation, which in turn prevents haziness due to moisture in the oil.

Neutralization with caustic or soda is a troublesome operation because

---

[107] Jacobi and McMakin, Chemical Treatment of . . . Naphthenic-Base Crude, *Oil Gas J.*, Apr. 1, 1948, p. 169.

[108] Steam Roof Coils Eliminate "Cloud" . . . , *Pet. Refiner*, March, 1947, p. 119.

TABLE 10-13

	Distilled cylinder stock	Residual cylinder stock	225 neutral	Pale oils	Average oils
Refiner....................	I	I	I	II	III
Pounds water acid, 66°Bé, agitate ½ hr.............	4	32	1	4	2–12
Hours of settle and draw.....	6	4	2	4	2–31
Pounds acting acid, 66°Bé, agitate ½–1 hr.............	8	.....	4	10–18[a]	20–60
Hours of settle and draw.....	5	.....	9	12–20	2–8
Water wash.................	.....	.....	(150 gal per 1,000 bbl)		Yes
Neutralized by.............	Clay contact	Clay contact	Clay contact	Caustic	Caustic

[a] 98 per cent acid.

of the frequent formation of emulsions. Often these emulsions are of such stability that only a repeated acid treatment or an application of strong caustic will cause a separation. For this reason, neutralization is being more and more frequently accomplished by the use of ammonia or more frequently by the clay contact process.

The use of centrifuges or horizontal mixers[80] is also being promoted for the treating of lubricating oils.[15,16,109] In general the oil is heated and mixed with acid for about 10 min by a mechanical mixer and/or reaction tank. It is then "soused" with water to prepare the sludge, and discharged through the centrifuges. The sludge accumulates in a hopper and is continuously pumped to fuel oil mixing tanks or to an acid recovery system. The acid is sometimes added in two portions, one portion as outlined above and a second dose at the centrifuge itself. The latter dose of acid aids in producing a fluid sludge. In one plant the sludge was removed from the bowl of the centrifuge by means of hot fuel oil. The properties of lubricating-oil sludge vary so widely[17] that each continuous lubricating-oil treater is a new problem. Cylinder stock has been treated in some of these plants without dilution.

The success of continuous treatment of lubricating oils always depends upon a method for removing the sludge. Cone settlers have been used to some extent.[17] The sludge accumulates continuously in the bottom of the cone, and the oil overflows continuously from the entire periphery of the top of the cone. Thus the oil is skimmed from the top of the settler without causing the currents in the fluid that a connection in the side of the cone would produce.

[109] Sager and Palmquist, Lube Oil Acid Treatment . . . for Italian Refineries, *Pet. Refiner*, June, 1952, p. 139.

Contact Filtration. The most common method of neutralizing with clay is the contact process, but the process also effectively decolorizes the oil. Contacting is usually practiced on oil that is in the "acid stage" or, in other words, oil that has been treated with acid but not neutralized. The process is practiced at 220 to 650°F, but most refiners contact diluted cylinder stocks at 475°F and neutral oils at 220 to 320°F. Occasionally lower temperatures are used, but such an operation should be classed as neutralization. The acid-stage oil is mixed with 200 or 200 to 300 mesh clay, and the mixture is heated in a pipestill to the aforementioned temperatures. The hot oil is then allowed to settle for a short time, and the "fines" (clay dust) are filtered from the oil in Sweetland or similar presses. Sometimes a short percolation filter is used to aid in the removal of the fine clay. R. C. Davidson[110] has made a complete summary of the methods of applying contact treating. The clay is usually not recovered, but Chenault and Miller[111] report the commercial use at 90 to 100°F of a 20 per cent acetone (naphtha) solution for extracting impurities from contact clay. A low contact temperature is employed so that the adsorbed materials will not be too tightly attached to the clay. The reactivated clay has an efficiency of 80 to 85 per cent. Spent clay is mixed with solvent, filtered in a closed rotary-type filter, and washed on the filter with naphtha. The recovery of acetone by distillation from the naphtha and from water constitutes a major part of the process.

Figure 10-14 illustrates the general process of contact filtration, and Fig. 10-15 shows the use of a rotary-type filter. In Fig. 10-14 the naphtha is introduced after contacting, but some refiners add naphtha before the acid treatment.

More viscous oils, such as cylinder stock, are usually acid treated and contacted in solution. The solution contains between 50 and 75 per cent of a high-initial-boiling-point naphtha. The naphtha usually has a boiling range of 160 to 400°F. Dilution is necessary for the subsequent operation of centrifuge dewaxing, and it also simplifies the handling of the stock during the acid treating and contacting operations. In addition, Trescott[17] reports that the amount of dilution vitally affects the losses during acid treatment. In treating a Mid Continent residuum (U.S. 130 at 210) with 30 lb of acid per bbl, the losses were as follows:

Per cent naphtha in solution	Per cent treating loss
None	31
25	23
50	14
75	14

[110] Contact Filtration, *Oil Gas J.*, Mar. 25, 1943, p. 116.
[111] New Lubricating-oil-decolorizing and Clay-reactivating Process, *Ref. Nat. Gaso. Mfr.*, November, 1941, p. 93.

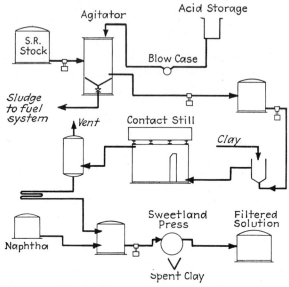

Fig. 10-14. Simple diagram of clay-contact decolorization.

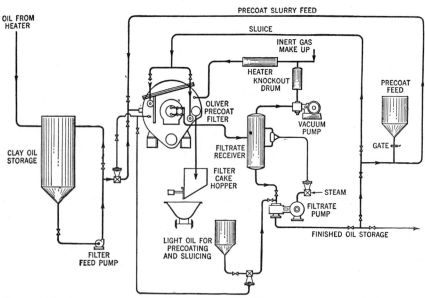

Fig. 10-15. Arrangement of equipment for the Oliver precoat method of contact filtration. (*Oliver United Filters, Inc.*)

The decrease in loss is doubtless due to the fact that less oil is contained in the sludge if the stock is diluted. Neutral oils are usually contacted without diluting them, but they must be heated to a sufficiently high temperature to cause them to be fluid.

The pipestill and vent chamber (Fig. 10-14) of the contact process are increasingly[110,111,112] being replaced by a vacuum rerun distillation so that light lubricating oils leave the contact process as distilled clay-free stocks and only the heaviest stock contains clay. Such operations are particularly suited to the rerunning of solvent-treated oils which are so free from asphaltic material that they need not be acid treated but must be further decolorized. The use of vacuum during the contacting step is helpful.[112]

Two manufacturers of microcrystalline waxes from tank bottoms treated the bottoms with acid, contacted the acid-stage wax with clay by heating to 700°F, and distilled the oil portions of the stock by vacuum. The residue after removal of the clay by filtration is a light-colored wax, but it is not oil-free. Percolation through clay is also used to improve the color of microcrystalline waxes. The solvent dewaxing (or deoiling) processes of Chap. 12 are necessary in producing high-quality oil-free microcrystalline waxes.

Although the contact process yields excellent products, it may be more expensive[113] than percolation, particularly if an efficient clay-burning system is available. However, the cost of installing a complete percolation system is great, and contacting is probably the cheaper method for a new installation. In the contact process, the amount of clay that is required ranges from 5 to 25 per cent of the weight of the oil or 15 to 80 lb per bbl. At least one refiner[114] uses spent contact clay as catalyst for catalytic cracking.

Percolation. Percolation was the original method of decolorizing lubricating oils, and until about 1927 no other method of using clay was widely employed (see also pages 308 to 313). Gurwitsch[115] says,

The advantage of filtration consists in the better utilization and smaller expenditure of the adsorbent to produce a given degree of decolorization . . . the oil comes successively into contact with a great number of very thin layers of the adsorbent, the filtration is equivalent to an extremely fractionated mixing, and so its effect on the reversibly adsorbed substances must be greater than that of mixing, even when carried out in several operations with equal quantities of adsorbent.

[112] Barton, P. D., Modern Lubricating Oil Plant . . . , *Pet. Engr.*, October, 1944, p. 206; also King, E. P., Lubricating Oil Manufacture, *Oil Gas J.*, Mar. 16, 1953, p. 122.

[113] Davis, L. L., *Ref. Nat. Gaso. Mfr.*, March, 1928, p. 90.

[114] Weber, George, Double-duty Catalyst, *Oil Gas J.*, Oct. 19, 1950, p. 78.

[115] "Scientific Principles of Petroleum Technology," 2d ed., D. Van Nostrand Company, Inc., Princeton, N.J., 1924.

Regarding the percolation method, Funsten[116] says,

Thus, percolation permits the manufacture of a wide variety of oils at one time. White oils or petrolatums of varying degrees of refinement can be processed with it equally as well as cylinder oils. . . . Specialties can be made at little, if any, extra cost by selection of proper cuts from the filter stream. Waxes, gasoline, kerosene and furnace oil can be clarified with revivified percolation clay at extremely low cost, since yields are very large in this type of work.

In general, for gravity flow, the longer the packed column the greater the bleaching action, the coarser the earth the less the bleaching, and the higher the temperature the less the bleaching (other conditions being comparable). Activated bauxite generally has a better decolorizing power[117] on a weight basis, and bauxite has good mechanical properties. The efficiency as a function of particle size is somewhat as follows:

Mesh	Per cent efficiency
60–90	100
30–60	87
16–30	72

However, a 30–60 mesh material is most commonly used because it can be more easily handled. Although the temperature should not be so high that the oil drains through the clay with only a short time of contact, nevertheless viscous lubricating-oil stocks must be heated or the rate of percolation may be hopelessly low. Operating conditions[116] for a 1,000-cu ft filter are given in Table 10-14. References must be consulted for details of construction and design,[118,119] and for operating[119,120,121,122] know-how. A continuous clay treating system involving burning, countercurrent percolation, washing with naphtha, and clay drying, has been developed (see Fig. 10-6).[62]

[116] Ref. Nat. Gaso. Mfr., June, 1934, p. 201.

[117] Attapulgas Clay Company, table entitled, Effect of Mesh and Filter Rate on Efficiency of Fuller's Earth and Bauxite, Oil Gas J., Mar. 30, 1946, p. B-99; also Johnson, W. A., Decolorization of Petroleum Waxes by Adsorbent Percolation, Pet. Processing, September, 1947, p. 673.

[118] Bell, H. S., "American Petroleum Refining," 3d ed., pp. 393–405, D. Van Nostrand Company, Inc., Princeton, N.J., 1945.

[119] Weber, George, Flexibility and Efficiency Feature . . . Filter Plant, Oil Gas J., Sept. 8, 1949, p. 67.

[120] Reeves and Turkleson, Cycle Washing of Percolation Filters, Pet. Refiner, March, 1949, p. 135.

[121] Reeves, E. J., Factors Affecting Percolation Yields, Pet. Engr., July, 1953, p. C-23.

[122] Oil Gas J., Nov. 18, 1938, p. 154; or Annual Meeting, API, Chicago, 1938.

TABLE 10-14. OPERATION OF FILTERS

Stock	Saybolt viscosity	Temp of filtration, °F	Rate of filtration, bbl per hr for a 1,000-cu ft filter	Pressure filtration,[a] psi
Light spindles........	Up to 200 at 100°	80–100	5–25	0–25
Heavy spindles.......	200–500 at 100°	100–140	5–15	0–25
Overhead or residual cylinder stock.......	100–160 at 210°	160–200	2–10	15–50
Naphtha solutions of cylinder stock.......	....	100–130	30–50	5–15
Petrolatums..........	100–160 mp[b]	25° above mp[b]	5–20	0–15
Waxes..............	100–160 mp[b]	25° above mp[b]	5–20	0–15

[a] Pressures in the higher range are required where 60–90 mesh earths are used.
[b] Melting point.

The stock may be acid treated before percolation, but it is usually neutralized before it enters the filters. The percolators should be insulated to promote a constant rate of flow. The clay is washed with 56 API, or lighter, naphtha to remove the oil from the clay. The filter is then steamed, and the clay can be removed by allowing it to flow from the bottom of the percolator. An important consideration is the recovery of oil from spent filters by washing with naphtha and steam.[122]

The throughput of percolators cannot be specifically stated because of the differences in stocks, differences in clays, and the degree of decolorization that is practiced. In a general way, 8 to 21 bbl of finished-color motor oils can be filtered per ton of clay. For lighter finished colors, the capacity ranges from 4 to 8 bbl per ton, and for darker finished oils, such as dark-red oils and cylinder stocks, as much as 25 bbl per ton may be filtered. Funsten[116] reports that rates of 40 to 50 bbl per hour can now be obtained. As high as 32 bbl per ton of cylinder stock in the form of a 50 per cent solution of 600° stock has been filtered through new clay. Johnson[117] shows the following decolorizing powers on a few petroleum waxes:

Process of manufacture	Bbl per ton
MEK dewaxing.......................	7–37
Pressing and sweating.................	32–147
Propane-MEK dewaxing...............	105–331
Naphtha centrifuge process.............	1.1–2.4

In general, the refiner uses new clay for light-colored low-viscosity lubricating oils, and the heavy oils with a darker allowable color are decolorized by this same clay after it becomes unfit for decolorizing light oils. Thus the various used clays progress through the plant in a countercurrent manner so that the new earth meets light-colored stocks and the nearly spent earth meets dark-colored stocks.

Grease Manufacture.   In the past, greases were compounded by batch operations involving mixing and saponifying measured quantities of fat, alkali, water, and some oil in an open kettle at about 300°F.   The neutrality was adjusted, and the main oil was added to cut back to the proper consistency.   Now continuous processes[123,124] such as that shown in Fig. 10-16 are being employed.[123]   About 1,300 lb of fat is charged to scale tank 1 and pumped to retort 3.   About 600 lb of lime slurry containing some lubricating oil, catalyst, and the exact amount of water desired in the final grease is mixed in tank 4 by recycling through an orifice mixer.   The slurry is also charged to retort 3 and the whole mixture is saponified for 30 to 45 min by recycling through pump 7 and exchanger 8 while being kept at 300 to 325°F.   Meanwhile retort 9 is being charged and retort 10 is being used as a charging tank for grease blending through the Lancaster mixer 12.   After saponification is completed in retort 3 (30 or 45 min), soap concentrate is pumped continuously from it and mixed continuously with a measured quantity of lubricating oil from tank 13 by means of pump 14.   The mixture is blended in the Lancaster dispenser or mixer 12, which operates at a speed of 3,600 rpm, and passes continuously to packaging through a filter.

Obviously, other operating conditions are employed for other greases; e.g., sodium soap saponification is conducted at 500°F.   In manufacturing aluminum greases,[124] gel tanks are provided for the blended grease.

Adsorption Processes.   At least two of these have attained commercial significance: (1) ethylene or olefin recovery[125,126] from cracked gases, and (2) aromatics recovery by silica gel.[127,128]   The use of fluidized adsorbent charcoal has also been mentioned.[129]   It is to be used as a downward moving bed in which adsorption of the desired olefins occurs in the top of the column, demethanization of the char occurs as the char moves

[123] Houlton, Calkins, and Beerbower, Continuous Process for Lubricating Greases, *Chem. Eng. Prog.*, **43**, 399 (1947).

[124] Houlton, Sutton, and Bevarly, Continuous Process for Aluminum Greases, *Oil Gas J.*, Oct. 19, 1946, p. 127.

[125] Berg and Bradley, Hypersorption—New Fractionating Process, *Pet Engr.*, May, 1947, p. 115; Berg, C., *Pet. Refiner*, September, 1951, p. 241.

[126] Kehde et al., Ethylene Recovery . . . , *Chem. Eng. Progr.*, **44**, 575 (1948); also Berg, C., *Pet. Refiner*, September, 1951, p. 241.

[127] Davis et al., The Arosorb Process . . . New Refining Tool, *Oil Gas J.*, May 19, 1952, p. 112.

[128] Anon., Cyclic Adsorption, *Pet. Processing*, August, 1955, p. 1202.

[129] Anon., Gas Separation Turns to Fluidization, *Chem. Eng.*, March, 1955, p. 120.

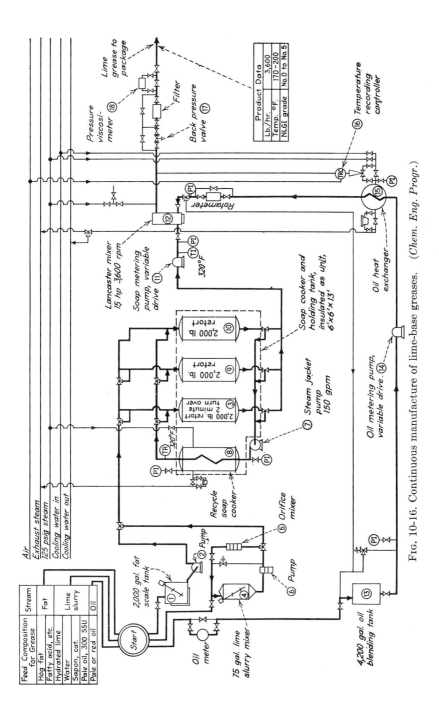

Feed Composition for Grease	Stream
Hog fat	Fat
Fatty acid, etc.	
Hydrated lime	Lime slurry
Water	
Sapon, cat.	
Pale oil, 300 SSU	Oil
Pale or red oil	

Product Data	
Lb./hr.	3,600
Temp. °F.	170–200
NLGI grade	No.0 to No.5

FIG. 10-16. Continuous manufacture of lime-base greases.   (*Chem. Eng. Progr.*)

downward in the next lower section, followed by deethanization and desorption of any remaining propylene, etc., with steam, and then finally by drying and cooling of the char.

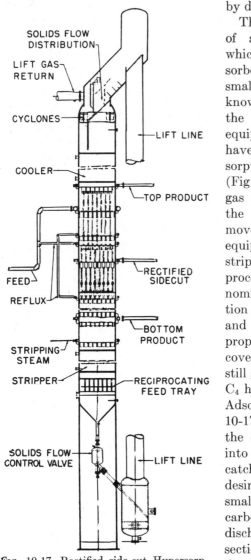

The selective adsorptive action of activated carbon, etc., by which large molecules are adsorbed more completely than small molecules has been well known since World War I, but the batch or semicontinuous equipments employed in the past have not been effective. Hypersorption[125] is a continuous process (Fig. 10-17) whereby not only the gas passes continuously through the process but the adsorbent moves downward through the equipment, and is continuously stripped or regenerated. This process makes adsorption economically feasible for the separation of hydrogen from methane and heavier gases, ethane from propane and heavier gases, recovery of ethylene from cracking-still gases, and recovery of C_3 and C_4 hydrocarbons from lean gases. Adsorbent carbon is cooled (Fig. 10-17) as it moves downward into the equipment.[126] It then flows into an adsorbing section which catches the last traces of the desired hydrocarbon as well as small amounts of lighter hydrocarbons. Waste or lean gas is discharged out of the top of this section. The carbon then passes the feed point and flows into a rectifying section where a stream

FIG. 10-17. Rectified side-cut Hypersorption unit. (*Pet. Refiner.*)

of heavy hydrocarbons liberated in the lower sections displaces any small amounts of light hydrocarbons that may have been adsorbed in the adsorber section. The carbon then passes to a steaming section where a stream of warm hydrocarbon gases from the stripper (even lower)

TABLE 10-15. RECOVERY OF ETHYLENE FROM A REFINERY GAS BY HYPERSORPTION

Composition	Ref. gas, mole %	Hyper. feed, mole %	Overhead product, mole %	Bottoms product, mole %	Hyper. side cut, mole %	Ethylene fractionator overhead, mole %
Hydrogen	2.23	11.91	25.40			
Methane	51.55	35.46	73.92	.....	0.54	1.35
Ethylene	3.92	13.24	0.35	1.79	39.32	97.11
Ethane	22.58	25.18	0.33	3.44	59.84	1.54
Propylene	61.8	4.42	.....	29.35	0.16	
Propane	11.94	8.32	.....	54.30	0.14	
$C_4 +$	1.60	1.47	.....	11.12		

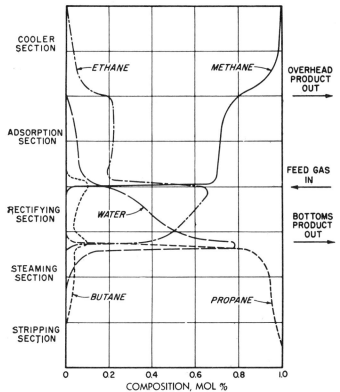

FIG. 10-18. Composition distribution in Hypersorber while separating natural-gas hydrocarbons. (*Pet. Refiner.*)

displaces a side-cut material. Still lower in the column, the carbon is stripped of remaining adsorbed gases by means of a steam stripper producing what is termed the "make-gas." The desorbed carbon is then lifted by a gas stream to the top of the equipment. All products (gases) pass from the equipment through cyclone separators. Meanwhile, a small amount of the carbon drops through a separate high-temperature steam stripper for the removal of small amounts of very heavy hydrocarbons that may accumulate on the carbon. Only 10 to 15 lb of steam is required per 1,000 lb of carbon recirculated.

Figure 10-18 indicates the gas composition[126] throughout the equipment when separating propane and heavier hydrocarbons from natural gas, and Table 10-15 indicates the several products when processing a refinery gas for ethylene.[126] Ethylene is effectively recovered (see side cut of Table 10-15) but it is necessary to fractionate the ethylene from ethane (see last column of Table 10-15) in a separate operation.

The Arosorb process[127] may be used to recover aromatics by silica gel adsorption from the mixture of hydrocarbons produced by catalytic reforming. The equipment consists primarily of fixed-bed silica gel cases and at least three fractionating towers. The feedstock is first dried with activated alumina which also removes trace amounts of nitrogen, sulfur, and oxygen compounds, and reduces the amount of organic polar compounds or polymerizable olefins. The reformate is then passed through one of several gel cases for about 30 min and then is diverted through a second gel case. Saturated hydrocarbons are displaced from the first case by a crude xylene stream (about 65 per cent) called the desorbent or pusher, and after these are removed the xylene stream displaces the adsorbed aromatics. The first material pushed from the case contains only saturated hydrocarbons and desorbent (xylene), but this is followed by a mixture which must be cycled back to the feedstock, and finally, the last of the displaced material consists of aromatics and desorbent (xylene). Thus, desorbent must be recovered for reuse from the saturated and aromatic streams in two fractionating towers. The final separation of benzene and toluene is accomplished in a third or aromatics splitter column.

Finishing of benzene or toluene into ASTM nitration-grade materials consists of sulfuric acid treatment, caustic neutralization, and redistillation. Aromatics derived from straight-run feedstocks require little if any treatment, but if derived from cracked stocks, treats up to 20 to 30 lb of acid per lb of aromatic hydrocarbon may be required.

The Cyclic adsorption process[128] of aromatic recovery employs the same principles as the Arosorb process. However, kerosene or a pentane fraction is used as the desorbent (stripper) when treating reformate, or a light straight-run gasoline when treating kerosene.

CHAPTER 11

SOLVENT TREATING OR EXTRACTION PROCESSES

Prior to 1933 effective methods of recovering solvents had not been developed. The flashing, distilling, and stripping of solvents from the treated oils and the purification of the solvent are still the major parts of a solvent treating system. The general purpose of the solvent processes is to separate a general group of offensive materials or hydrocarbons from the oil and to save the cost of other treatments. As examples, propane deasphalting removes dark-colored resinous materials; liquid sulfur dioxide extracts unsaturated and aromatic hydrocarbons from kerosene; the Solutizer process removes mercaptans from gasoline; furfural, etc., treating produces lubricating oils of high Viscosity Index; and cuprous salt solutions dissolve butadiene from other unsaturated hydrocarbons. The last named may be a chemical as well as a physical process. The material rejected from extraction processes is a salable product, whereas the acid sludge by sulfuric acid treating is a nuisance.

Just as vacuum distillation permits the processing of black crude oils for lubricants, so the solvent processes tend to erase the old crude oil marketing system by which only a few crude oils were considered satisfactory for lubricant manufacture. By solvent methods, the original properties of the oil can be changed so that a uniform grade of oil can be manufactured from a wide variety of crude oils. Of the many[1] processes that have been proposed it now appears that the Furfural,[2] Duo-Sol,[3] Phenol,[4] Edeleanu,[5] and Propane[6] processes have established their usefulness. Table 11-1 indicates the extent of solvent operations. However, if improvement of

[1] *Chlorex*—Bahlke, Brown, and Diwoky, *Oil Gas J.*, Oct. 26, 1933, p. 60; *nitrobenzene*—Meyers, W. A., *Oil Gas J.*, Mar. 19, 1936, p. 81; *crotonaldehyde* and *acrolein* —Poole and Wadsworth, *Ref. Nat. Gaso. Mfr.*, November, 1933, p. 412; *aniline*— Chappell and Ziser, U.S. Pat. 1,741,555, Dec. 31, 1929; *others*—Kalichevsky, V. A., "Modern Lubricating Oils," Reinhold Publishing Corporation, New York, 1938.

[2] Bryant, Manley, and McCarty, *Oil Gas J.*, May 16, 1935, p. 50.

[3] Tuttle, M. H., *Ref. Nat. Gaso. Mfr.*, June, 1935, p. 289.

[4] Stines, D. E., *Oil Gas J.*, Mar. 19, 1936, p. 75.

[5] Cottrell, O. P., *Oil Gas J.*, Nov. 30, 1933, p. 64.

[6] McCluer, Dickinson, and Forrest, *Oil Gas J.*, Oct. 27, 1938, p. 174; and Nov. 18, 1938, p. 209; also Bahlke, Thiele, Adams, and Ginsberg, *Oil Gas J.*, July 22, 1937, p. 44.

TABLE 11-1. LUBRICATING-OIL MANUFACTURE IN THE UNITED STATES
DURING 1955[a]

Processes	Percentage (approx.)	Bpd	Number of plants[b] (approx.)
Finished lubricating oil:	100	175,785[a]	
Conventional treating..........	9.5	16,600	23
Solvent treating...............	90.5	159,185	45[c]
Propane deasphalting.............	......	60,400[d]	17
Solvent extraction processes:	100.0	199,200	
Phenol......................	36.9	....	14
Furfural.....................	27.7	....	13
Duo-Sol.....................	21.3	....	9
Sulfur dioxide.................	5.8	....	3
Others......................	8.3	....	6
Dewaxing processes:	100.0	158,000[e]	
Methyl ethyl ketone (MEK).....	61.5	....	19
Propane.....................	24.7	....	11
Older conventional operations....	13.8[e]	....	41[c]

[a] Only 2.18% of the total crude oil processed.
[b] Probably many more units than plants.
[c] Many of the solvent plants retain some conventional operations.
[d] Also 63,000 bpd in 1954 of propane decarbonizing plants.
[e] If 90% of all finished oil must be dewaxed.

the Viscosity Index is unimportant, as with certain paraffinic crudes, acid treatment and percolation may still be the preferred method of lubricating-oil manufacture.[7] Of the 59 operating refineries of Table 11-1, nearly all retain some conventional processing, especially the clay finishing operations.

Although solvent processes have been applied primarily to lubricating oils, the increasing usefulness of these processes in separating hydrocarbons[8] from one another (Fig. 20-16), particularly in connection with fractionation,[9] should not be overlooked, nor the application of solvent extraction to the purification of gasoline, kerosene, diesel fuel, solvents, butadiene (Fig. 20-16), etc.[10,11] Originally refiners sought to learn how

[7] Foster, A. L., Vacuum Distillation, Chemical Treatment Make Quality Lubricating Oils, *Oil Gas J.*, Sept. 28, 1946, p. 78.

[8] Morrell et al., Purification of Butadiene with Cuprous Salt Solutions, *Trans. A.I.Ch.E.*, **42**, 473 (1946).

[9] Happel et al., Extractive Distillation—Separation of C_4 Hydrocarbons Using Furfural, *Trans. A.I.Ch.E.*, **42**, 189 (1946).

[10] Saegebarth et al., High Octane Number Blending Stocks . . . Solvent Extraction, *Ref. Nat. Gaso. Mfr.*, June, 1937, p. 256.

[11] Jones, J. P. (Extraction of German Brown Coal Tar with SO_2), *Natl. Pet. News*, Mar. 6, 1946, p. R-181.

bad solvent extracts were[12,13] as catalytic cracking charge stocks, but now they have turned to methods of upgrading cracking feedstocks, especially cycle stocks, by propane deasphalting or decarbonizing,[14] sulfur dioxide extraction,[15] and furfural[16] extraction. Solvent extraction with sulfur dioxide,[17] aqueous diethylene glycol,[18] and phenol[19] is being used to produce benzene, toluene, and xylene. Butene is separated from

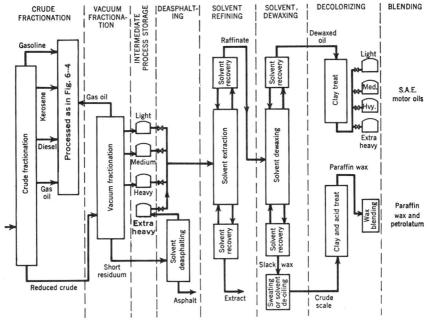

FIG. 11-1. Schematic diagram of a refinery for producing lubricating oils.

butylene with aqueous acetone solution, and butadiene is purified by extraction with aqueous cuprous ammonium acetate (Fig. 20-16) or furfural.

[12] Reynolds, P. M., Factors Affecting Throughout . . . , *Oil Gas J.*, July 19, 1951, p. 115.

[13] Oden and Perry, What Makes a Good Cat Cracker Feed, *Oil Gas J.*, Mar. 22, 1954, p. 164.

[14] Johnson et al., Recovery of Catalytic Stock . . . , *Ind. Eng. Chem.*, **47**, 1578 (1955).

[15] Anon. (Phillips Pet. Co.), SO_2 Extraction of Gas Oils, *Oil Gas J.*, Mar. 22, 1954, p. 137.

[16] Carter, R. C., Furfural Refining Scores . . . , *Oil Gas J.*, Mar. 22, 1954, p. 157.

[17] Ratliff and Strobel, . . . Benzene and Toluene by the Sulfur Dioxide Process, *Oil Gas J.*, May 31, 1954, p. 87.

[18] Thorton, D. P., First Complex Udex "B-T-X" Plant . . . , *Pet. Processing*, March, 1953, p. 384.

[19] Anon., Better-than-nitration-grade Benzene, *Oil Gas J.*, July 13, 1953, p. 105.

General Processing.   The position[20,21] of solvent processing with relation to the entire refining operation may be seen by comparing Fig. 11-1[22]
with Figs. 6-3, 6-4, and 6-5.   Note that rerunning for the separation of
neutral oils, etc., may be eliminated by producing lubricating-oil stocks
of the proper viscosity in the primary vacuum distillation.   To some
extent propane deasphalting is being used as an adjunct to vacuum distillation because of the very low pressure required in a vacuum system
to vaporize high-boiling cylinder stock.   Yields of 85 to 95 per cent are
common in deasphalting; yields of 95 Viscosity Index oil by single solvent extraction processes are 70 to 80 per cent for Mid Continent stocks,
55 to 70 per cent for East Texas stocks, and even higher for Pennsylvania
stocks.   The increase in Viscosity Index of the desired oil for the production of 1 per cent of reject oil is much the same[23] for all commercial
solvents except propane.   The increase in Viscosity Index for a 1 per
cent rejection ranges from about 0.4 for high Viscosity Index charge
stocks to about 1.8 for stocks of zero Viscosity Index.   The Duo-Sol
process may be considered as a combination of propane deasphalting and
solvent extraction, and hence this process may be applied directly to
reduced crude oil.

The extraction operation proper consists of a series of countercurrent
contacts between oil and solvent as in Figs. 11-8 and 11-9; however, vertical packed towers are more widely used than settling tanks.

The physical properties of the solvent govern to a large extent the general type of processing that must be employed.   Thus, low temperatures
and high pressures are advisable in handling such solvents as liquid propane and liquid sulfur dioxide; the partial solubility and the formation of
a constant-boiling mixture in the furfural-water system require an intri-
cate distillation system; and the high boiling points of nitrobenzene, furfural, and cresylic acid necessitate the use of a vacuum in the distillation
of these materials from oil.   Properties of the principal solvents are given
in Table 11-2.

Only a minor part of the total equipment in a solvent treating plant is
devoted to the extraction operation.   Elaborate equipment is required to
distill the solvent (or oil) from the extract and raffinate solutions, to separate the last traces of solvent from the finished oils, and finally to recover

[20] Armistead, G., Jr., Better Technology Equals Better Lube Oils, *Oil Gas J.*, May 4,
1946, p. 115.
[21] Smoley and Fulton, Modern Manufacture of Lubricating Oils, *Pet. Processing*,
August, 1947, p. 594.
[22] Buthod and Nelson, Encyclopedia of Chem. Technology, vol. 10, p. 109, Inter-
science Encyclopedia, Inc., New York, 1953.
[23] Nelson, W. L., Comparison of Solvent Treating Processes, *Oil Gas J.*, Feb. 10,
1945, p. 113.

TABLE 11-2. PROPERTIES OF EXTRACTION SOLVENTS

	Boiling point, °F	Melting point, °F	Specific gravity	Specific heat, Btu/lb	Heat of vaporization, Btu per lb	Solubility in water, per cent at	
						77°F	100°F
Furfural (furfural-dehyde)	323	−34	1.162	0.416	193.5	8.5 (4.0 water in fur.)	9.0
Cresylic acid (Duo-Sol process)	365–400	....	1.045	0.53	180	2.5	3.1
Phenol	361	106	1.072	0.56	206	9(∞ at 151°F)	
Sulfur dioxide	14	−105	1.45	0.32	167	(19 at 32°F) 5	
Chlorex (ββ' dichloroethyl ether)	352	−61	1.222	0.37	115	1.1 (1.7 at 194°F)	
Nitrobenzene	411.5	42.5	1.207	0.34	142	0.2	0.25
Propane	−44	−310	0.51	0.6 / 0.47 vap.	183	Slight	
Benzene	175	42	0.844	0.41	170	0.07	

the solvent from many sources and purify it.   Thus, the design of solvent treating equipment resolves itself to a large extent into the design of equipment for the common operations of fractionation, absorption, stripping, etc., by methods that will be discussed in other chapters.   Several general processing steps are used:

1. *Drying* or *deaeration* of the charge stock.   Water hinders the action of phenol, and air is troublesome with gaseous solvents such as sulfur dioxide.

2. *Extraction with solvent.*   The countercurrent method of contacting is used universally except for such special cases as the single contact sometimes used in propane deasphalting.

3. *Separation of bulk of solvent* from oil.   This is accomplished by heating and fractionating or evaporating.   This is usually a simple operation because the oil and solvent have greatly different boiling points, but the separation of gasoline and sulfur dioxide is an exception.   A vacuum is used for the highest-boiling solvents, but a simple atmospheric flash suffices for propane.

4. *Purification of oil.*   The oil is freed from last traces of the solvent by steam stripping or, if water is troublesome, by vacuum flashing.

5. *Purification of solvent.*   This may involve the removal of water as in the case of furfural, the separation of solvents from one another in case

several solvents are used, or the separation of tars, etc., as in the Duo-Sol process.

A discussion of solvent processes is not complete or of much value without illustrations of the properties of the oils that are produced. Nevertheless, space does not permit such a discussion in this book, and hence the reader must resort to the current literature and the references given here.

The maintenance of a higher temperature at the raffinate outlet than at the extract outlet of an extraction column is useful in propane deasphalting and phenol treating, but the situation with respect to other solvents is not clear. However, in furfural extraction little benefit occurs[24] (the raffinate has a higher Viscosity Index, but the yield is smaller).

Edeleanu Process. This pioneer (1907) solvent process is the only one that has been applied widely to light distillates such as heavy naphtha, kerosene, and diesel fuel.[25] At the boiling point of sulfur dioxide (14°F), aromatic and unsaturated hydrocarbons are completely miscible with liquid sulfur dioxide but the paraffin and naphthene hydrocarbons are not. The process is used as a means of treating light distillates, but it cannot be utilized directly for high-boiling oils because their solubility in sulfur dioxide is too low. Lubricating oils can be treated, however, by using a mixed solvent of benzene and sulfur dioxide. Sulfur dioxide also extracts cyclic sulfur compounds and nitrogen compounds, a behavior that makes the process useful in handling certain high-sulfur kerosenes.

The process has been applied to kerosene to improve the smoke point and for desulfurization.[25] It is applied to selected naphthas for the recovery of high-octane-number blending stocks and for the recovery of lacquer diluents (aromatic hydrocarbons).[11] Diesel fuels of high Diesel Index and ignition quality can be made from selected gas oils.

In treating kerosene the stock is first deaerated by exposure to a vacuum. The kerosene and liquid sulfur dioxide are then cooled by exchangers and coolers to 5 to 20°F and contacted by countercurrent flow through a tower packed with rings. The cold raffinate and the cold extract are each passed through their respective exchanger and multiple-effect evaporator systems for the recovery of gaseous sulfur dioxide. The first stage of the evaporators operates at about 200 psi and at 230 to 270°F, but the last stage is maintained at about 190 mm pressure. The gaseous sulfur dioxide is compressed and condensed to a liquid.

The amount of solvent used depends upon the stock being handled, but in general it is about equal to or a little larger than the charge stock.

---

[24] Reeves and Hardin, Temperature Gradient in Solvent Extraction . . . , *Pet. Refiner*, January, 1950, p. 89.

[25] Dunstan et al., "Science of Petroleum," vol. III, Oxford University Press, New York, 1938.

This results in an extract containing 10 to 20 per cent oil and a raffinate containing 15 to 20 per cent sulfur dioxide. Equilibrium curves for several stocks are given in "Science of Petroleum."[25]

The operation of Fig. 11-2 shows conditions[26] for diesel fuel (5,000 bpd) extraction, but the same plant has been operated on kerosene (5,000 bpd) and naphtha (4,100 bpd). Table 11-3 indicates the yields and properties during operation for diesel fuel. The process has also been applied to catalytic cycle oils[15] and to the recovery of benzene and toluene from catalytic reformates.[17,27]

TABLE 11-3. YIELDS AND PROPERTIES WHEN OPERATING THE PLANT OF
FIG. 11-2 FOR 50 CETANE DIESEL FUEL

Property	Charge	Extract	Raffinate
Volume per cent based on charge............	100.0	25.0	75.0
Cetane number.........................	40.0	......	50.0
Color—Union.........................	3	6	1
Viscosity—SUS 100°F....................	35	35	35
Pour point, °F...........................	−30	......	−15
Sulfur, per cent.........................	0.34	1.25	0.09
Conradson carbon on 10% bottoms..........	0.04	0.22	0.02
Aromatics and unsaturates................	24	78	3
Aniline point, °F........................	139.6	13.9[a]	169.5
Gravity, API...........................	32.8	20.7	38.2
Distillation:			
Initial................................	390	396	394
10 per cent...........................	446	444	446
50 per cent...........................	489	491	493
90 per cent...........................	566	564	567
End point............................	616	628	614

[a] Calculated.

The sulfur dioxide–benzene[5] process derives much of its value from the ease with which the solvent can be recovered and purified. The processing is generally similar to that described for the liquid sulfur dioxide process. Sulfur dioxide–benzene may also be employed for dewaxing.[28]

Furfural Process. The use of furfural for lubricating-oil manufacture has been gaining in comparison with most other solvents. The yield of high Viscosity Index raffinate varies with the stocks being treated but is about 70 per cent for intermediate-base stocks and 95 per cent for par-

[26] Dickey, S. W., Edeleanu Process Plant, *Pet. Refiner*, June, 1948, p. 75.

[27] Wilkinson et al., Aromatics by SO₂ Extraction, *Pet. Engr. Ref. Annual*, 1953, p. C-3.

[28] Anon., *Oil Gas J.*, Dec. 29, 1938, p. 131.

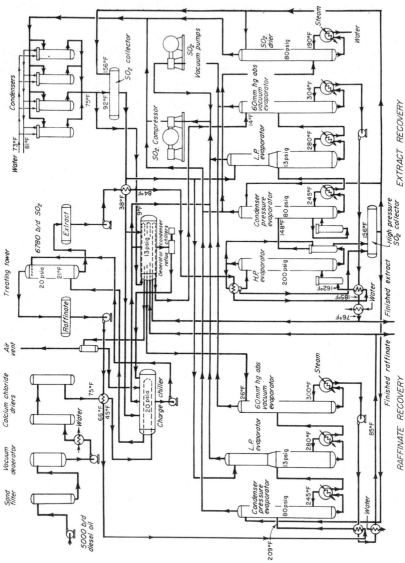

Fig. 11-2. Sulfur dioxide extraction applied to diesel fuel and kerosene. (General Pet. Corp. and Pet. Refiner.)

354

affin-base stocks. Yields from naphthene-base stocks are lower (65 per cent), and the Viscosity Index is necessarily low.[2,25] The general equilibrium relation between furfural and oil is indicated in Fig. 11-10. Temperatures of 150 to 250°F are employed, but most plants are operating at about 200°F. The amount of solvent employed also varies, but two parts of solvent per part of oil have been used in many operations.

In Fig. 11-3 contacting is effected in a countercurrent-flow tower, which may be packed with wood slats. A higher temperature is more usually maintained at the top than at the bottom of the tower, but only a slight enhancement of solvent fractionation is attained thereby.[24] The refined oil mix (raffinate solution) contains so little solvent that it can often be purified by heat exchange and steam stripping, but the extract solution requires a pipestill and atmospheric flashing as well as steam stripping. The furfural-water equilibrium system involves partial insolubility and the formation of a constant-composition constant-boiling-point mixture at 97.9°C. The mixture contains 34 per cent furfural by weight. At room temperature this mixture separates into a furfural-rich solution containing 96 per cent furfural and a water-rich solution containing 8 per cent furfural. Thus, the constant-boiling mixture automatically separates into two solutions at the top of the furfural fractionator of Fig. 11-3—and the furfural-rich solution is freed from water in a separate stripper that receives heat from the hot furfural vapor produced in the extract distillation.

The use of rotating-disk contactors[29] in commercial operations has been highly successful not only because of superior contacting and larger capacities but because very quick change-overs of feedstock are possible.

Furfural extraction has also been used[16,30] for the refining of straight-run gas oil and light and heavy catalytic cycle oils in the plant shown in Fig. 11-4, and it was used extensively during World War II in the separation of butadiene.[31] Solvent treating of cycle oils greatly reduces the percentage of sulfur and metal contaminants, and produces a high yield of treated oil which when catalytically cracked gives yields comparable with those obtained from virgin stocks of the same gravity. The properties of raffinates from various high-sulfur or naphthenic oils are indicated in Table 11-4. The extracts have gravities in the range of 4 to 13 API, slightly higher boiling ranges than the raffinates, and they contain very much more sulfur.

Extraction is accomplished by the use of about an equal volume of fur-

[29] Reman and Van de Vusse, Applying RDC to Lube Extraction, *Pet. Refiner,* September, 1955, p. 129.

[30] Shelley and Rackley, Better Yields from Cat Cracking, *Pet. Processing,* December, 1952, p. 1772.

[31] Seymour, H., Furfural in Refining and Purification, *Petroleum,* May, 1948, p. 104.

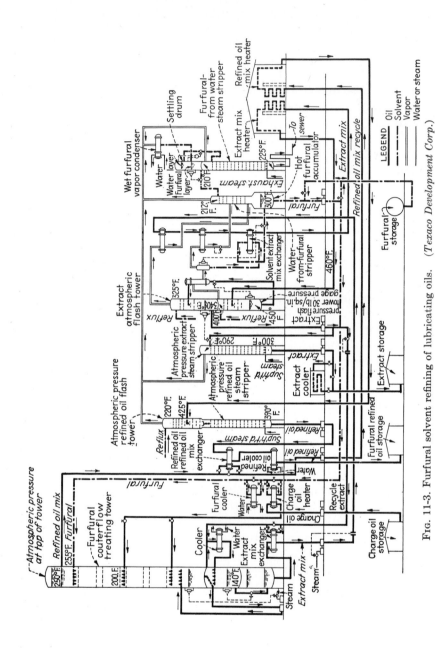

Fig. 11-3. Furfural solvent refining of lubricating oils. (*Texaco Development Corp.*)

Table 11-4. Furfural Refined Cycle Stocks

| | Arabian and Venezuelan mixtures | | | | | | Arabian cycle oil | | Venezuelan cycle oil | | Californian cycle oil | |
| | Light cycle[a] | | Heavy cycle | | Heavy cycle | | | | | | | |
	Charge	Raff.	Charge	Raff.	Charge	Raff.	Charge	Raff.	Charge	Raff.	Charge	Raff.
Yield, vol. %	……	73.9	……	72.4	……	66.0	……	60.0	……	60.5	……	65.5
Cetane number	42.5	61.8	……	……	……	……	49.0	61.0	33.6	53.0	37.7	55.1
Gravity, API	31.4	40.6	27.3	38.1	24.5	37.7	20.2	40.4	24.5	33.6	29.7	38.8
Color, NPA	……	……	……	……	……	……	2½	1½	7	1	……	……
Sulfur, wt %	1.10	0.25	1.48	0.49	1.70	0.45	1.705	0.451	0.58	0.09	0.50	0.06
Distillation, °F												
I.B.P.	484	460	478	482	480	484	454	454	418	452	436	416
10%	505	497	504	506	506	504	488	490	457	477	470	458
50%	528	525	538	536	557	544	521	530	543	561	510	506
90%	567	566	725	671	749	……	586	590	652	666	580	580
E.P.	595	592	……	……	……	……	642	634	716	718	646	638
Pour point, °F	+5	+15	……	……	+10	+50						
Aniline point, °C	59.1	79.6	61.4	80.0	60.7	82.5						

[a] Produced at a 55% "conversion."

357

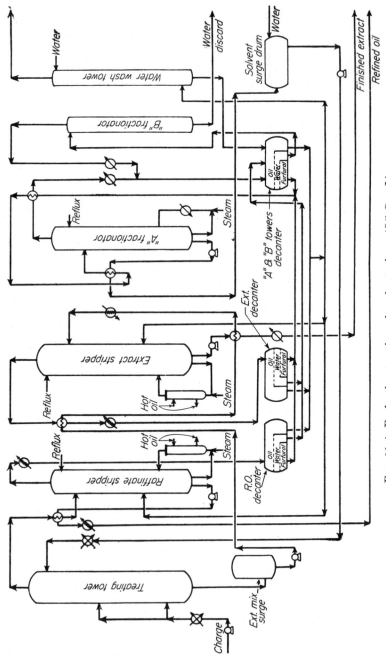

FIG. 11-4. Furfural extraction of cycle stocks. (*Oil Gas J.*)

fural and at a temperature of 90 to 125°F.   A small amount of water is purposely left in the furfural which makes it more selective in improving cetane number and yield, but a slightly larger dosage of solvent is required.   Stripping of the solvent from the two phases is accomplished at atmospheric pressure by the injection of live steam into each stripper, and the bottom temperature is maintained by hot-oil reboilers. Decanters operating at about 100°F serve to separate any oil that may

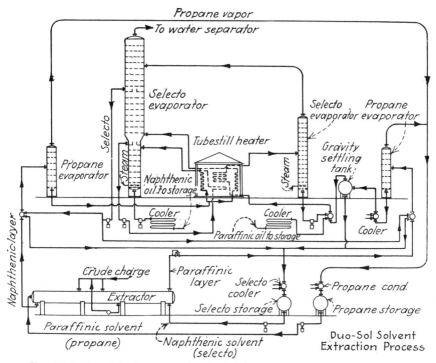

Fig. 11-5. Duo-Sol solvent treating for lubricants.   (*Max B. Miller and Co.*)

distill with the furfural.   The oil-rich phase (Fig. 11-4) contains approximately 5 per cent furfural.   The water-rich and furfural-rich phases are separated into furfural and water somewhat as indicated in the discussion of lubricating-oil treating (Fig. 11-3).

Duo-Sol Process.   This is the only double-solvent process that has been used extensively.   One solvent (propane) dissolves paraffinic hydrocarbons, and the other (cresylic acid or "Selecto") dissolves naphthenic hydrocarbons.   The two solvents are used in a countercurrent system of flow, and the feed is introduced at an intermediate point in the flow system (see Fig. 11-5).   In one end of the extraction system the outgoing cresylic acid solution is stripped of paraffinic material by pure propane, and in the other end the outgoing propane solution is stripped of naphthenic material by pure cresylic acid. Thus, a true countercurrent stripping operation is maintained, although the extraction is conducted as a series of countercurrent batch contacting and settling operations. The extractor is not shown in detail. It consists of nine settlers or compartments. The heavy cresylic acid solution is pumped from one compartment to the next, and the propane solution is also pumped, but in a countercurrent manner. The feed is introduced in compartment 3 nearest the end at which propane is introduced.

From 125 to 400 per cent "Selecto" (based on charge stock) is employed, depending upon the stock, and 150 to 400 per cent propane. In general, the naphthenic stocks require more propane, and the paraffinic stocks require more "Selecto."[25] Contacting is accomplished at about 85°F.

Phenol Extraction.   Interest appears to be returning to this process[32,33] because of the low loss of solvent that occurs and because of certain improvements in the processing. The newest[32] plants employ countercurrent extraction towers, and much of the troublesome constant-boiling water-phenol mixture is eliminated by contacting the phenolic steam strippings with the incoming charge stock. Thus, in Fig. 11-6 extract stripper steam and some other vapors (enough to eliminate currently all water from the system) are sent through an absorber held at 225 to 245°F wherein the incoming charge absorbs phenol from the stripping steam. Total losses of phenol are said to be under 0.04 per cent of the phenol circulated.   The amount of phenol circulated ranges from about 1 part of phenol per 1 part stock, up to a ratio of 2.5 for naphthenic stocks.   An increase of 1 in the Viscosity Index requires the production of about 1 per cent of extract material.   At the extremes, a 2 per cent loss to extract for an increase of 1 in the Viscosity Index of the finished oil occurs when handling high Viscosity Index charge stocks, 1.5 to 1.6 for Arabian stocks, about 1.0 for waxy California or Mid Continent stocks, and only 0.5 per cent for naphthenic stocks.   Steps in the operations (Fig. 11-6):

1. Heated lubricating-oil stock absorbs phenol from steam, etc. (mainly extract and raffinate stripping steam) at about 235°F.
2. Stock is cooled and contacted with phenol in a countercurrent extraction tower. The bottom of the tower is cooled to about 110°F with phenolic water for distillate stocks or 155°F for residual stocks, and the top is kept warm (150°F for distillate and 230°F for residual stocks) by hot phenol.
3. The valuable raffinate (about 20 per cent phenol) is heated to about 550°F and flashed at atmospheric pressure, and it then flows downward into a vacuum fraction-

[32] Kenny and McCluer, Refining Pennsylvania Lube Oils by Phenol Extraction, *Oil Gas J.*, Jan. 16, 1941, p. 48.
[33] Nelson, W. L., *Oil Gas J.*, Feb. 10, p. 113, and Mar. 10, p. 78, 1945.

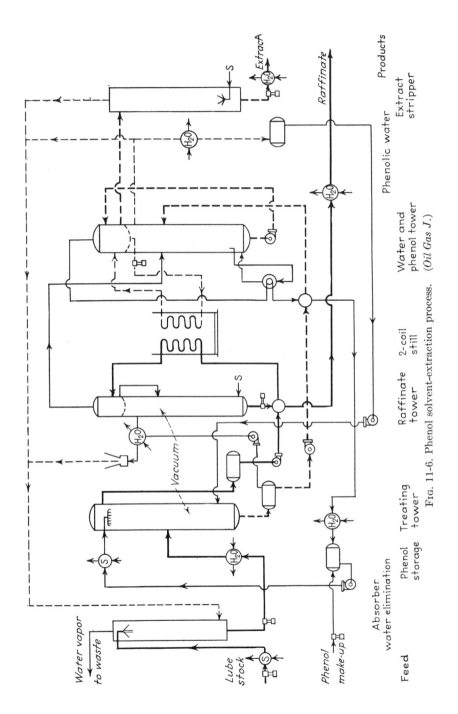

FIG. 11-6. Phenol solvent-extraction process. (*Oil Gas J.*)

361

ation and steam-stripping tower (22 in. mercury vacuum) for the removal of phenol down to about 0.001 per cent.
4. The low Viscosity Index extract when operating on a Pennsylvania stock contains about 85 per cent phenol and 8 per cent water. Phenolic water is removed from it by heating to about 650°F and fractionating in the small tower situated above the phenolic water tower. It passes to storage through a steam stripper which reduces the phenol to about 0.005 per cent.

Phenol has been used extensively in treating low-cold-test naphthenic lube stocks as from Colombia or California,[34] and the process may be modified[34] to employ controlled amounts of water (up to 12 per cent) in the top of the extraction tower, especially if phase separation at 100 to 175°F is necessary.

The Propane Processes. Propane assumes significance as a solvent because it is useful in so many ways. It extracts paraffinic hydrocarbons from oil, or inversely it precipitates asphaltic or resinous materials; it is used as one of the solvents in the Duo-Sol process; it is used for dewaxing; and it greatly facilitates treatment with sulfuric acid. By utilizing a series of these processes, as deasphalting followed by acid treating and by dewaxing, it is possible to avoid a number of the costly solvent-removal operations that would be necessary if several different solvents were employed. The low boiling point of propane facilitates its separation from high-boiling oils, and refrigeration for dewaxing can be obtained by evaporation of the propane. It is exceedingly fluid, and hence the separation of liquids and wax is simplified. Finally, it is a cheap material, and most of the plant losses can be recovered in the regular gas recovery system.

A system combining deasphalting and acid treating in propane solution[6] is shown in Fig. 11-7. This plant was used to process a very heavy mixed-base residuum (18 API) for the manufacture of a 32.5 API green-cast cylinder stock. The advantages in acid saving, yield, etc., are evident in a comparison of regular acid treating and the new procedure (Table 11-5). Recent deasphalting plants[35,36] use a countercurrent vertical baffle-plate tower rather than the mixer and settler of Fig. 11-7. In addition the top of the tower is heated with steam to near the critical temperature of propane so that the last traces of asphalt are precipitated from the oil-propane solution. This improvement is said to reduce the cost of operation greatly and particularly because asphalt content, be it 5 or 60 per cent, no longer[35] greatly alters the cost.

[34] Gester, G. C., Solvent Extraction in the Pet. Industry, "Progress in Petroleum Technology," p. 177, ACS Meeting, New York, September, 1951.
[35] Dickinson and Adams, Lubricant Stocks Improved by Propane Deasphalting, *Oil Gas J.*, Mar. 30, 1946, p. 185.
[36] Anon., Propane Decarbonizing, *Oil Gas J.*, Mar. 22, 1954, p. 134.

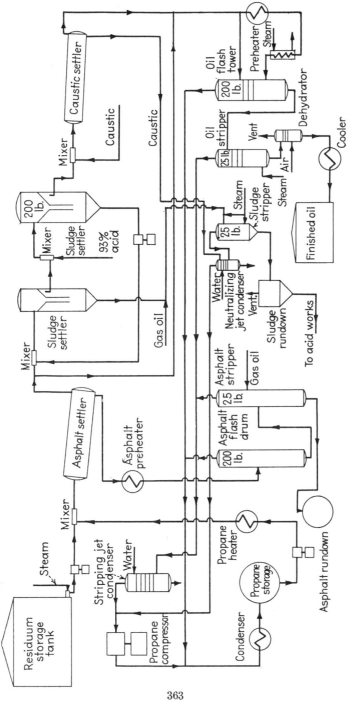

Fig. 11-7. Propane deasphalting and sulfuric acid treating in propane solution. (*Oil Gas J.*)

363

TABLE 11-5. UTILITIES, CHEMICALS, AND BY-PRODUCTS OF PROPANE ACID TREATING
Per 100 gal of unpercolated wax-bearing green-cast stock

	Old procedure	New procedure
Fuel oil, gal...............	20	None
Steam (live), lb..............	2,845	1,040
Steam (exhaust), lb...........	395	365
Electric power, kw-hr.........	12	None
Acid, lb....................	420	40
Caustic, lb.................	1.5	4.2
Acid sludge, gal.............	111	21
Asphalt, gal................	0	20
Slop oil, gal................	1	0
Loss, gal...................	7.5	0

Deasphalting is applied primarily for the separation of small amounts of dark-colored asphaltic materials—and thus may or may not result in an oil product that is a superior lubricating oil, depending upon the characteristics of the raw stock. The amount of propane used amounts to three to ten times as much as the charge stock. The process consists simply in mixing the oil and propane and allowing the asphalt to settle. By a series of settlings at increasing temperatures it is possible to precipitate asphalt followed by lighter and lighter petroleum resins.

More oil is being processed for the recovery of catalytic charge stock (propane decarbonizing) than for lubricant manufacture (propane deasphalting). A temperature of 160 to 190°F is maintained at the top (propane end) of the extraction tower, and a pressure of 400 to 600 psi is maintained. Butane or isobutane is a somewhat superior[36,37] solvent for handling very heavy highly contaminated residua. The main advantage of decarbonizing is the elimination of 96 to 99 per cent of the metallic catalyst deactivators that are always encountered in some degree in residua (Table 11-6). The properties of vacuum and propane treated residua are compared by Johnson et al.[37] They find that solvents are more effective than distillation in the elimination of metallic contaminants and traces of carbon-forming materials. Vacuum distilled gas oils produced almost twice as much carbon deposition during catalytic cracking as gas oils produced by solvent treating.

Recovery of Aromatics. Large amounts of benzene, toluene, and xylenes are contained in catalytic reformates and these may be recovered by (1) adsorption (Arosorb Process), (2) extractive or azeotropic distil-

[37] Recovery of Catalytic Cracking Stock by Solvent Fractionation, *Ind. Eng. Chem.*, **47**, 1578 (1955).

TABLE 11-6. TYPICAL PROPANE DECARBONIZING RESULTS

	Texas	Middle East	Middle East	California
Reduced crude:				
Volume per cent crude.......	11.1	22.2	32.3	20.0
Gravity, API..............	11.3	5.3	10.1	6.3
Conradson carbon, wt %.....	15.0	21.5	16.0	22.2
SUS at 210°F..............	2,193			
SFS at 210°F..............	....	772	162	990
SiO$_2$-free ash, ppm...........	489	350	237	848
Metals, ppm				
Vanadium...............	23.1	84.1	61.6	136.0
Nickel.................	14.2	27.6	19.9	139.0
Iron...................	18.2	13.2	6.7	93.0
Copper.................	....	3.7	0.8	0.04
Decarbonized oil:				
Volume per cent charge......	62.9	35.0	47.0	52.8
Gravity, API..............	19.0	19.3	20.3	18.3
Conradson carbon, wt %.....	4.2	4.3	2.6	5.3
SUS at 210°F..............	294	193	....	251
SiO$_2$-free ash, ppm...........	9.2	8.8	7.6	25.5
Metals, ppm				
Vanadium...............	1.23	1.88	0.73	2.3
Nickel.................	1.10	0.92	0.38	8.1
Iron...................	0.49	0.96	1.70	3.5
Copper.................	....	0.03	0.04	0.03
Asphalt:				
Volume per cent charge......	37.1	65.0	53.0	47.2
Specific gravity............	1.076	1.087	1.059	1.119
B & R soft. point, °F........	188	142	132	246
Per cent of metals rejected to asphalt fraction..........	97.1	99.1	98.6	98.2

lation, and (3) solvent extraction with sulfur dioxide or diethylene glycol (Udex Process). The extractive process[19,38] most widely used today employs phenol. A substantially olefin-free concentrate of benzene (or toluene), obtained by acid treating and fractionation, is distilled in an extractive distillation column in the presence of downflowing phenol. Saturated hydrocarbons are distilled, and the aromatic hydrocarbon remains with the phenol. The aromatic hydrocarbon is easily distilled from phenol, but a solvent cleanup still must be used to eliminate phenol-diolefin reaction products. Each aromatic hydrocarbon must be extracted one at a time. Mixed cresylic acids rather than phenol are used for the recovery of xylenes.

[38] Anon., Extractive Distillation (Shell Development Co.), *Pet. Processing*, August, 1955, p. 1199.

Diethylene glycol solution (8 to 12 per cent water) is used in the Udex[18,39] process.   Materials present in the feed will be absorbed in the following order: alkenylbenzenes, benzenoid aromatics, cyclic dienes, open chain dienes and cyclic olefins, open chain olefins and cycloparaffins, and finally paraffins.[40]   Thus, feeds that are rich in alkenylbenzenes and diolefins must be selectively hydrogenated before or after the extraction operation.   Both benzene and toluene (and the xylenes) can be removed in a single extraction operation, but slightly higher solvent ratios are needed for the high-molecular-weight aromatics.   The equipment consists essentially of extractor and stripper columns for continuous recycling of the solvent.   Depentanized feed enters near the top of the extraction column where it is split into a paraffinic overhead stream which is washed with water to recover traces of diethylene glycol and into an aromatic-rich bottom solution which is sent to a stripper for the recovery of aromatics.   The wash water joins the solvent stream at the top of the extraction tower.   Dissolved aromatics and excess water are distilled in the solvent stripper, and the aromatics require only an acid and clay contact treatment (and fractionation) to produce nitration grade materials.

EXTRACTION THEORY

Although theoretical considerations based on pure components are reasonably successful, the application of such generalizations to complex mixtures is primarily empirical.   Extraction involves two main operations, viz., the obtainment of equilibrium and a separation of the contacted materials.   Separation is somewhat simple in the countercurrent vapor-liquid operations of stripping, absorption, and fractionation; but in extraction both phases are liquids and the difference in liquid densities is relatively small.

The general situation is governed by the distribution law, which states that the ratio of the concentrations of a component distributed between two mutually insoluble phases is a constant.

$$\frac{C_1}{C_2} = K \tag{11-1}$$

where C_1 = concentration of solute in first liquid phase, per cent by weight

C_2 = concentration of solute in second liquid phase, per cent by weight

K = a constant that depends only on temperature

[39] Brien, E. B., First Eastern Aromatics Plant . . . , *Pet. Engr.*, May, 1954, p. C-33.

[40] Bloch and Wackher, Pure Aromatics from Cracked Naphthas, *Pet. Refiner*, February, 1955, p. 145.

If the solute is a mixture, the law holds for each material in the mixture. Modifications of Eq. (11-1) to care for dissociation or association will be found in textbooks on physical chemistry.

Countercurrent liquid-liquid diagrams are shown in Figs. 11-8 and 11-9. The operation is somewhat analogous to countercurrent vapor-liquid systems. Refluxing with extract and raffinate solution, as shown in Fig. 11-9, is not directly practiced in many commercial processes, but the same effect is accomplished by adjustment of temperatures at the top or bottom of the tower in furfural and phenol extraction, and in propane deasphalting. Changes in temperature precipitate reflux agents which are countercurrently washed as they proceed to the other end of the tower. Tower extraction systems have the advantage of utilizing gravity to transfer the materials from one stage to the next. The solvent-rich

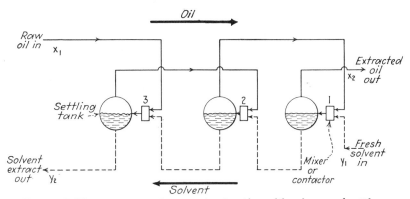

FIG. 11-8. Three-stage countercurrent extraction with mixers and settlers.

solution is called the "extract" solution, and the oil or component-rich solution is the "raffinate" solution. In Fig. 11-9 the raffinate or oil-rich layer is shown as the bottom or heavy solution. In all common petroleum-extraction systems the solvent is heavier than the oil and the solvent-rich extract solution settles to the bottom.

If W represents the pounds of stock to be treated, S the pounds of pure solvent, x the pounds of component to be extracted per pound of stock, and y the pounds of component per pound of solvent (Fig. 11-8),

$$W(x_1 - x_2) = S(y_1 - y_2)$$

and
$$\frac{W}{S} = \frac{y_1 - y_2}{x_1 - x_2} \qquad (11\text{-}2)$$

The subscript 1 refers to the incoming liquids, and 2 to the outgoing liquids.

With materials and conditions for which Eq. (11-1) is valid, the equilibrium relation in terms of x and y may be formulated as follows:

$$K = \frac{C_1}{C_2}$$

$$C_1 = \frac{x}{1 + x} \quad \text{and} \quad C_2 = \frac{y}{1 + y}$$

$$\frac{y}{1 + y} K = \frac{x}{1 + x}$$

$$y = \frac{x}{K + xK - x} \tag{11-3}$$

When plotting y vs. x, Eq. (11-3) is an equilibrium curve and Eq. (11-2) is an operating line. The number of theoretical contacts can be determined by a stepwise method such as that used for absorption and stripping processes (Figs. 22-9 and 22-10). However, the minimum amount

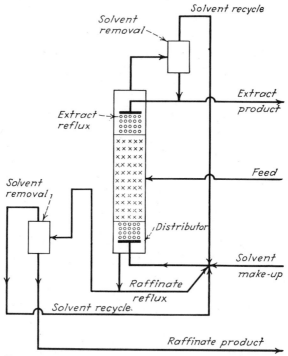

FIG. 11-9. Countercurrent extraction tower using extract and raffinate refluxes.

of solvent that can be used will be governed by the maximum solubility of the solute in the solvent, as well as the material balance of the system which states that the concentration must always be greater in the stock than in the solvent.

Stokes's law for the rate of settling of particles through fluids may be used for the design of settlers, etc.; but inasmuch as the particle size cannot be estimated without empirical tests, the theoretical relationship is of little value. Horizontal settlers are more effective than vertical settlers because the velocity is lower.

Extraction of Oils. In most practical extraction systems the several components are mutually soluble, and hence recourse must be had to triangular coordinate diagrams such as Fig. 11-10 to show the relation between phases. Such a diagram has three percentage scales, each of which reads from 0 per cent on one side of the diagram to 100 per cent at the apex which is directly opposite. Thus, any point on the diagram represents the percentages of each of the three components of the system.

The phase relationship that is most common for petroleum-oil systems is also indicated in Fig. 11-10. When furfural (or other common solvent) is added to a heavy lubricating-oil stock, two liquid phases (or layers) are produced: one which (extract) contains a relatively large amount of furfural with some asphaltic material dissolved in it, and one which is lean in furfural (raffinate) but rich in high Viscosity Index oil. In Fig. 11-10, mixtures of oil and furfural whose compositions fall within the two-phase region bounded by *abc* will separate into two layers whose compositions are shown by the ends of the tie lines labeled 1, 2, 3, and 4; but for all other mixtures the three components are mutually soluble, and no separation occurs. The four tie lines represent experimental data, but additional tie lines can be estimated as necessary.

In all complex mixtures, such as petroleum, it is difficult to define what is meant by pure raffinate (*R*) and pure extract (*E*), and hence the *RE* scale is not read directly in percentages of *R* and *E* but by some significant property such as specific gravity or Viscosity Index. Experimental data are necessary in order to draw the diagrams.

The diagrams are useful in studying single-contact or concurrent multiple-contact operations (Example 11-1) but are not well suited to the study of countercurrent multiple-contact extractions.

Example 11-1. Solvent Extraction Diagram. *a.* Addition or removal of solvent involves travel along a line connecting the pure solvent point *S* and a solvent-free oil situated on the base line. Thus, by adding 49 parts of solvent to 51 parts of feedstock, two layers will separate (see Fig. 11-10) which contain solvent-free oils having specific gravities of 1.047 (extract) and 0.931 (raffinate).

b. Quantities may be computed by material balances involving either the percentage compositions or the properties of the solvent-free oils contained in the mixtures or may be estimated graphically by the distances along a line connecting the three materials under consideration. Thus, the amounts of the two solutions produced in the separation mentioned above would be about equal because point *e* nearly bisects line *def.* Point *e* falls somewhat closer to point *f*, and hence the raffinate solution designated by point *d* is smaller than solution *f*, amounting by careful measurements or computations to 48 per cent of the total. Likewise, the amounts of solvent-free raffinate and extract

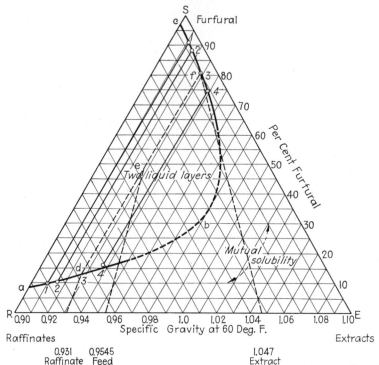

can be estimated by distances along the base line. By inspection it appears that the raffinate will amount to about 80 per cent of the feed, or more exactly

$$100 \times 0.9545 = 0.931R + 1.047(100 - R)$$

$$R = \frac{9.25}{0.116} = 79.7 \text{ per cent}$$

Countercurrent multiple-stage extractions[41] can also be studied by triangular coordinate diagrams (Fig. 11-11), but apparently an empirical correction[42] is necessary when applying the method to oils. In Fig. 11-11, which shows the same oil as Fig. 11-10, F indicates the feed composition in terms of various raffinates and extracts. Adding solvent to the feed traces the line FJS, and the point J represents 56 per cent solvent. If the raffinate solution R_3 is desired, a line connecting R_3 and J shows that the composition of the extract solution must be E_1. Lines connecting the raffinate solution that enters any stage with the extract solution leav-

[41] Perry, J. H. (ed.), "Chemical Engineers' Handbook," 2d ed., p. 1236, McGraw-Hill Book Company, Inc., New York, 1941.

[42] Skogan and Rogers, Stage Estimation in Lubricating Distillate Extraction, *Oil Gas J.*, Aug. 2, 1947, p. 70.

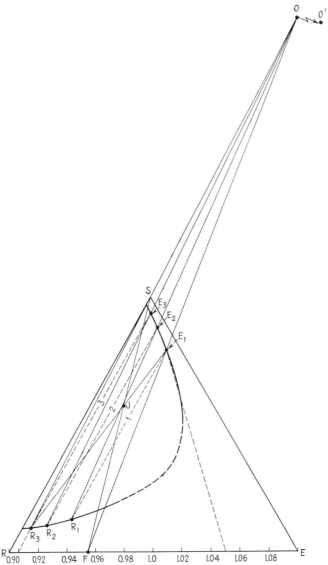

FIG. 11-11. Use of triangular diagram for countercurrent multistage extraction.

ing that stage intersect[43] at a single point O. Thus, lines connecting known points R_3 and S, and connecting F and E_1, intersect at point O. Having located point O, the number of stages required can be estimated as follows: Extract E_3 can be located because it lies on a tie line with R_3. Raffinate R_2 lies on a line OE_3, extract E_2 lies on a tie line with R_2,

[43] Hunter and Nash, *J. Soc. Chem. Ind.* (*London*), **53**, 95T (1934).

raffinate R_1 lies on a line OE_2, and E_1 lies on a tie line with R_1. Three stages or contacts are required to produce the desired raffinate R_3. However, the stages would not have come out to be exactly three if the position of E_1 had not been judged and adjusted. Usually the number of stages is not a whole number, which means that point O has not been located at exactly the right point. This means that a trial-and-error operation must be employed. The method is useful for illustrating the principles of extraction, but Skogan and Rogers[42] find that point O should be at some point indicated generally by O'. The correct point O' (for complex mixtures) can be located only by conducting laboratory countercurrent extractions.

"Science of Petroleum," Vol. III,[44] presents fundamental theory and summarizes experimental data for a number of systems such as those which utilize chlorex, sulfur dioxide, nitrobenzene, cresol, phenol, furfural, benzol–sulfur dioxide blends, and propane. Triangular coordinate diagrams are also useful in studying solvent dewaxing.[44]

Little information is available on the size of tower or number of stages required. In various laboratory towers the height equivalent of a theoretical stage (HETS) ranges[45] from about 1 to 5 ft and in a few instances even more. In large-diameter sieve plate columns, Hunter and Nash[46] found HETS's exceeding 23 ft. Bryant, Manley, and McCarty[2] with respect to furfural extraction utilize a packed section consisting of 20 ft of Raschig rings, with redistribution means at each 4 ft of packed-tower space. Charge rates should average about 35 gal of charge oil per hour per square foot of over-all tower cross-sectional area, although rates as high as 70 gal have been used without excessive entrainment of solvent into the refined oil. Ebner and Mertens[47] report a furfural tower which contains eight nests of Raschig rings each 5 ft in depth, with redistribution plates above each nest. Finally, Elgin[48] reports that 3-ft-diameter towers 30 ft long are used in refining kerosene with liquid sulfur dioxide. In a laboratory study of furfural extraction[48] a 12-ft tower was found to be equivalent to 3 to 6 theoretical contacts, and the tower could handle 400 to 1,700 gal of oil per hr per sq ft of cross-sectional area. In contacting 250 bbl per hr of oil with 40 bbl caustic soda,[48] a 4-ft-diameter 60-ft long tower, with packing arranged in 4-ft sections with 2-ft disengaging space between, was used.

In the solutizer or gasoline-treating processes, bubble plates have been

[44] Dunstan, Nash, Brooks, and Tizard, Oxford University Press, New York, 1938.
[45] Nelson, W. L., *Oil Gas J.*, Oct. 11, 1947, p. 201.
[46] *Proc. World Power Conf.*, Chem. Eng. Congress, 1936.
[47] Solvents . . . New Lubricating Oil Plant, *Oil Gas J.*, Apr. 13, 1944, p. 173.
[48] Design and Application of Liquid-liquid Extraction, *Chem. Met. Eng.*, May, 1942, p. 110.

used for contacting.   Fuqua[49] reports that the Kaskade tray has a contacting efficiency about 35 per cent greater than a bubble tray, and is the equivalent of about 4 ft of carbon-ring packing.   At the same time the capacity is more than 60 per cent greater.   Naphtha velocities of 2.5 ft per min and higher are feasible.   Somewhat the same rates of chemical flow are also possible.

[49] Improved Efficiency in Mercaptan Extraction Using Cascade-type Fractionating Trays, *Pet. Processing*, November, 1948.

CHAPTER 12

DEWAXING

by *Dr. Paul Zurcher*, retired

School of Petroleum Sciences, University of Tulsa

The waxy materials present in the high-boiling fractions of mineral oils are now considered to be crystalline throughout but under certain conditions may behave like a colloid. A solution of petrolatum, bright stock, and naphtha, when agitated over long periods at the crystallizing temperature, will form a completely transparent jelly; but the same solution, when chilled more rapidly and with moderate agitation, will precipitate a wax that can be centrifuged but not filtered because the wax plugs the pores of filter cloth. If the oil is dissolved in such solvents as propane or acetone, the petrolatum forms aggregates upon chilling which are easily separated by filtration.

Straight-chain hydrocarbons (waxes) also form solid complexes at room temperature with urea in the form of needles. The needles can easily be removed by filtration leaving an oil almost totally free of wax.

Composition of Paraffin Wax. The waxes extend throughout the entire boiling range of the lubricating-oil stocks. Attempts to separate wax from oil by fractionation have met with no success. Clark and Smith[1] claim that waxes consist of a high percentage of *n*-paraffin hydrocarbons and a smaller percentage of isoparaffins. Ferris and Cowles[2] show that petroleum waxes are mixtures of hydrocarbons of the various homologous series. The members of each series crystallize similarly as either plates, mal crystals, or needles. If but one type is present (plate, mal, or needle), the crystal form remains the same regardless of such factors as amount or kind of solvent. If the types are mixed, and if the solubility relations are such that more than one type can crystallize simultaneously, either the needle or the mal crystal can impress its form on the plates. If, however, sufficient solvent is present to maintain needles and mals in solution until plates are well established, mals and needles can then deposit upon and thus take the form of plates.

[1] *Ind. Eng. Chem.*, **23**, 697 (1931).
[2] *Ind. Eng. Chem.*, **37**, 1054 (1945).

There is evidence that the distillation range of the material and the degree of fractionation of the stock influence the type of wax crystals developed upon chilling. Davis and Campbell[3] have studied the crystalline structure of 13 fractions of wax oil. The fractions were obtained by a true-boiling-point distillation of a Mid Continent wax distillate. The properties of the fractions are given in Table 12-1. The clean-cut crystals appearing in fraction 13 were probably due to decomposition during the distillation of the last fraction.

TABLE 12-1. FRACTIONS OF WAX OIL

Fraction number	Per cent of crude at end of fraction	Universal viscosity at 100	Temperature, °F, at cut point, approx.		Pour point, °F	Per cent wax by weight	Melting point of wax, °F	Crystalline structure
			At 3 mm	At 760 mm				
1	58.2	40	358	680	3	0	...	None
2	60.4	51	377	700	35	7.2	96	Few plates
3	62.6	66	402	727	53	9.1	106	Plates
4	64.8	75	420	752	58	9.3	112	Plates
5	67.0	89	442	773	66	7.4	124	Plates
6	69.2	115	460	789	76	10.8	128	Plates
7	71.4	152	478	813	85	10.1	132	Partly malform
8	73.6	200	499	832	89	9.7	137	Partly malform
9	75.8	258	520	862	95	9.2	142	Malform
10	78.0	330	541	886	98	8.7	145	Malform
11	80.2	400	567	915	102	9.5	145	Malform
12	82.4	480	598	950	105	6.8	145	Malform
13	84.6	470	625	978	108	5.2	149	Plates

The fractions were blended together as follows: 1 to 6 inclusive, 1 to 7, 1 to 8, etc., including all the cuts. The size of the crystals was progressively smaller and smaller as cuts were added, but with the exception of blends 1 to 12 and 1 to 13 the crystalline size and form were satisfactory. The approximate end points, at atmospheric pressure, of the blends were as follows: 780, 798, 819, 830, 851, 872°F; and for the two unsatisfactory blends (1 to 12 and 1 to 13), 893 and 921°F. Thus it appears that wax oils having end points exceeding about 860°F are not satisfactory for conventional pressing and sweating, and many refiners have found it advisable to limit the end point to 835°F. Nevertheless, other .actors, such as the characteristics of the oil, the degree of fractionation, the viscosity, and the amount of cracking, alter the allowable end point for a pressible stock (see page 79).

[3] *Oil Gas J.*, May 25, 1933, p. 49.

More recent studies[4,5] relate crystal structure to such properties as tensile strength,[4] hardness,[4] gloss,[4] and blocking temperature.[5]   Plate crystals have low tensile strengths and needle crystals high, and the strength of plate wax can be increased by the addition of small amounts of microcrystalline wax or even plate wax of much higher melting point.[4]

Naturally occurring impurities such as asphaltic matter, as well as synthetic compounds (Paraflow, etc.), influence the crystal form of the wax.   Some refiners have used additives in order to control the pressibility and sweatability of waxes.   Plate crystals are desirable for the pressing operation, but the needle form is best for sweating.

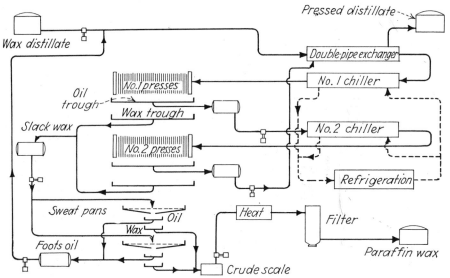

FIG. 12-1. Old conventional operations of pressing (or double pressing) and sweating.

Pressing and Sweating.   Although losing in importance, the old pressing and sweating process for the separation of the wax from wax distillate is still in use.   The wax is crystallized by chilling of the oil and is removed in presses as slack wax.   The latter is melted, chilled into large cakes, and heated slowly.   In this operation, called "sweating," the oil that adheres to the wax drains from the cake (see Fig. 12-1).

The double-pipe chiller has been adopted almost exclusively for chilling wax distillate.   This machine is similar to a double-pipe cooler, except that it is provided with a revolving screw or ribbon-type conveyor in the

[4] Lund, H. A., Meeting Product Quality in Wax Crystallization, *Pet. Processing*, March, 1952, p. 326.

[5] Tiedje, J. L., A Laboratory Study of Wax Processing Methods, *Proc. Fourth World Pet. Congr.*, sec. VI, Rome, 1955.

inner pipe. T. E. Schley[6] describes a spring-loaded scraper. The purpose of a conveyor is to scrape the wax crystals from the walls and move them forward. The common size of chiller has 6-in.-diameter inside pipe and 8-in. outside pipe. It consists of a series of heavily insulated horizontal double pipes, assembled into stacks through which the oil flows in series. The conveyors rotate by a chain drive from one motor. Twenty-four sections of chillers up to 40 ft long can be arranged in four stacks, six sections high, with two chain drives.

Chilling is usually accomplished by exchange with the cold dewaxed oil, followed by direct expansion of ammonia. Ammonia expansion is cheaper and permits lower temperatures than the previously used chilled brine. The rate of cooling depends much on the effectiveness of the scrapers. If they fit poorly, the rate of heat transfer drops to the low value of 2 or 3 Btu per sq ft per deg Fahrenheit per hr. With closely fitting scrapers that remove the wax effectively from the chilled surface, rates of 16 Btu have been obtained (Table 12-2).

TABLE 12-2. TRANSFER RATES IN CHILLERS

Type conveyor	Cooling conditions	Transfer rate, Btu/(°F, diff.) (sq ft) (hr)
Screw..........	Brine circulation	4–5
Screw..........	Direct expansion	7–10
Ribbon........	Direct expansion, nonturbulent flow	8–12
Ribbon........	Direct expansion, turbulent flow, and recirculation	15

Thus a section of chiller having a surface of 55 sq ft will cool 12 to 18 bbl of wax oil per day through the customary range in temperature. The higher capacity is for chilling the oil to 10 to 15°F when some heat exchange is used, and the lower capacity is for cooling to 15°F without exchangers or to 0°F with exchangers.

Conventional oil filter presses consist of as many as 500 canvas-covered plates, generally 48 in. in diameter. Space for a ½-in. cake of slack wax is prov'ded either by recesses in the plates or by spacer rings between plates. Details of plate construction are shown in earlier editions of this book. Chilled oil-wax slurry is pumped through a central hole extending throughout the entire length of the press, and it fills the spaces between the canvas blankets. Pressure forces the oil through the canvas, then through openings in perforated side plates behind the blankets and then outward to the edge of the plates where it leaks to the outside

[6] Develop New Spring-loaded Pipe Scraper for Removing Wax in Lube Oil Plant, *Natl. Pet. News*, June 5, 1946, p. R-416.

of the press.   The wax remains in the space between the blankets, causing an increase in pump pressure until finally a maximum pressure of about 350 psi is attained.   The press is then opened, and the wax cakes are pushed off of each plate dropping into a conveyor under the press. The chunks of slack wax then move to a melting tank and are pumped in liquid form to the sweat pans.   A typical press cycle including charging, emptying, and reassembling the press requires approximately 44 hr. For a normal stock that contains 5 to 8 per cent wax and for single-pressing operation, one or two 48-in. plates are required for each barrel of Pennsylvania oil that is pressed per day and 2 or 3 plates for a Mid Continent oil.   The amount of slack wax that is obtained from the presses is far greater than the 5 to 8 per cent finished wax and may in some cases amount to 30 per cent of the wax distillate.   Oils of two different pour points are made by double pressing, which consists of cooling to 35 to 40°F and filtering for a high-pour-point oil, and then chilling part of the oil to −10 to 0°F for a lower-pour-point oil.   In general, the stock should be chilled to 5 to 10°F below the desired pour point for a single-pressing operation, but for a double-pressing operation the stock need not be chilled to such a low temperature.

The operation of *sweating* consists of cooling the slack wax to a congealed mass and slowly heating it to temperatures of 100 to 140°F. Practice is totally empirical, but a theoretical analysis has been made.[7] The wax is heated in long shallow pans, 10 ft or more wide, 40 or 50 ft long, and sufficiently deep to hold a 5- to 7-in. cake of wax.   A flat perforated metal sheet or a 50-mesh screen lies across the bottom of the pan, and a pipe coil for cooling and heating lies just above the screen.   The pans are arranged, one above another, in stacks of about eight and housed in a building or oven.   The oven has steam coils and water sprays along the walls to aid in maintaining uniform temperature conditions.

In conducting a sweating operation, cold water is turned into the pans up to the screen and circulated through the coils above it, and slack wax is pumped into the pan.   After the wax solidifies into a cake, the water under the screen is withdrawn and the temperature of the wax cake is raised at the rate of 2 to 3°F an hour by increasing the water temperature.   If the wax is in the proper condition, it gathers into well-defined needle crystals, and the oil sweats or drips from the wax cake.   The oil that collects up to about 100°F is called "foots oil," and it may be resweated along with fresh slack wax.   The intermediate wax oil that is collected at higher temperatures may contain 50 per cent of slack wax, and it is often resweated for waxes of intermediate melting point; or it too may be recycled with the fresh charge.   The melting point of the crude scale wax is about the same as the maximum temperature attained

[7] Bowman and Burk, Sweating of Paraffin Wax, *Ind. Eng. Chem.* **41**, 2008 (1949).

in the sweating operation. Very low-melting-point waxes are usually made by resweating the foots oil.

The rate of heating is greatly dependent on the uniformity of temperature within the cake. With circulating water as the main heating medium, the total time for the sweating cycle is about 30 or 40 hr. The exact time depends upon the melting point of the wax that is being produced, the crystalline characteristics, and the uniformity of temperature throughout the cake. For 110 to 112°F melting-point wax, only 24 to 36 hr are required, but for 120°F wax the time is 35 to 45 hr. Automatic temperature control is advantageous.

In a study of wax recovery, L. D. Wyant[8] outlined the basic fundamentals of wax sweating but could not completely explain the range of 23 to 85 per cent efficiency of recovery that was being obtained by Mid Continent refiners. J. P. O'Donnell[9] describes in detail the construction and operation of modern sweaters. Donnell and Burch[10] find that slack waxes containing more than 50 per cent oil yield little crude scale whereas at 20 per cent oil the yield of scale is 52 per cent.

The crude scale has a slightly yellow color, which may be eliminated by treating the molten wax with acid or sometimes dilute caustic solution. Filtration through fuller's earth is all that is normally required.

Pressibility of Wax Stocks. The rate at which distillates can be pressed as well as the yield during sweating depend on such physical properties as viscosity, fractionation, wax content, distillation range, and crystalline structure.

Viscosity. The pressing qualities of wax-bearing oils from the same crude oil depend to some extent on the viscosity. The rate of pressing is inversely proportional to the viscosity. Oils of 55 to 75 sec Saybolt Universal at 100°F can be pressed without dilution with naphtha. The use of naphtha permits single pressing for stocks that might otherwise require double pressing.

The viscosity at the pressing temperature is of more interest than the viscosity at 100°F. Davis and Campbell[3] report viscosities at the pressing temperature of 1,200 to 2,100 sec (Table 12-3). The pressing qualities of a distillate are also dependent on other factors than the viscosity, so that the several factors must be considered collectively.

Fractionation. Degree of fractionation plays an important part in the pressing qualities of an oil.[11] The quantity of material boiling above 800°F, and particularly a "tail" of poorly fractionated material, affects

[8] Separation of Wax from Distillate, *Oil Gas J.*, Oct. **2**, 1924, p. 224.

[9] New Sweater Improves Yields, Lowers Cost, *Oil Gas J.*, July 22, 1943, p. 28.

[10] Experimental Control . . . Sweating, *Ref. Nat. Gaso. Mfr.*, November, 1938, p. 603.

[11] Dunmire, H. J., *Natl. Pet. News*, Apr. 23, 1930, p. 38.

the pressing rate greatly. A poorly fractionated stock may press more slowly than a well-fractionated product that has a much higher end point because of the presence of minute quantities of very high-boiling material. Fractionation also affects the centrifuging properties of cylinder stock. For this reason refiners have sometimes found it necessary to take a "slop" wax cut between the wax distillate and the cylinder stock.

TABLE 12-3. PRESSING TESTS

	Pressing stock number						
	1	2	3	4	5	6	7
Gravity, API	34.2	32	31	31.4	31.7	31.6	
Flash point, °F	90	170	360	280	320	315	
Viscosity of distillate at 100°F	63	70	94	66	68	75	100
Cold test, °F	66	68	74	42	56	80	
Distillation range at 40 mm, °F:							
Initial boiling point	....	256	450	256	312	306	
10 per cent	344	312	476	395	394	416	
20	466	350	493	416	426	445	
30	494	473	509	436	453	469	
40	511	498	525	461	479	491	
50	527	518	541	490	503	513	
60	544	539	557	524	523	533	
70	564	561	573	557	543	554	
80	588	585	593	590	562	580	
90	622	611	615	625	590	616	
End point	648	632	637	643	625	652	
End point, 760 mm approx	862	844	849	859	835	870	
Wax content, per cent	8.75	6.75	7.66	1.58	5.77	4.8	
Melting point of wax, °F	118	123	123	119	124	123	
Per cent raw 200 vis. neutral	50	48	50	51	33	39	
Pressing characteristics:							
Pressing temp	−18	−8	−10	−5	−6	+8 −5	15
Viscosity at 100°F:							
Distillate	63	70	94	66	68	75 75	100
Pressing stock	55	70	58	66	68	75 66	100
Dewaxed oil	57	76	63	68	74	82 69	114
Viscosity at pressing temp. approx	1,400	2,100	1,350	1,380	1,800	1,200 1,400	1,800
Pressing rate, bbl per plate per day	0.43	0.43	0.41	0.4	0.37	0.35 0.3	0.45
Fractionation	....	....	....	....	Poor	Poor	
Crystal formation	Good	Good	Good	Fair	Poorly formed	Very small	

Distillation Range. A common method of determining the boiling range is by the Bureau of Mines vacuum distillation operated at 40 mm pressure. End points at 40 mm pressure of 610 to 640°F (840 to 870°F at atmospheric pressure) are possible without spoiling the pressibility of the stock. In addition, the viscosity of the highest-boiling fraction should not exceed about 580 sec at 100°F.

Wax Content. An abnormally high wax content usually lowers the pressing rate because the presses must be dumped oftener. The average

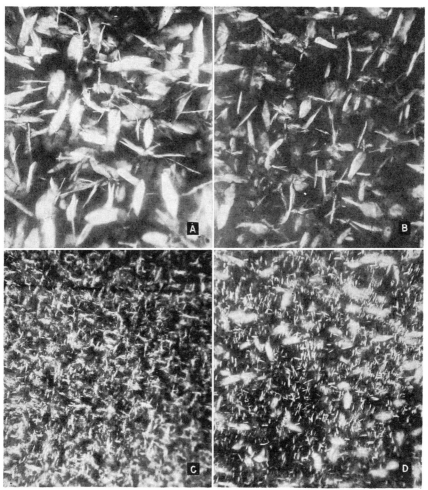

FIG. 12-2. Photomicrographs of wax: (a) very good, (b) typical, (c) high end point, (d) crude oil leaked into distillate in exchanger. Magnification × 350. (*Courtesy L. L. Davis, Continental Oil Company.*)

wax content of distillates is about 6 per cent; but some stocks contain as little as 1 per cent wax, and others contain as much as 25 per cent.

Crystal Structure. This is probably the most important factor, but it is related and dependent on the several other factors that are discussed. A stock[3] having very good pressing properties is shown in Fig. 12-2a; a typical stock in *b*; a stock with too high an end point in *c*; and one indicating that a small amount of crude oil had leaked into the stock during heat exchange, in *d*.

In the control of plant pressing operations, the wax oil should be examined for at least the following characteristics: (1) viscosity, (2) boiling range at 40 mm pressure, and (3) crystal structure.

Centrifuging. Although the centrifuge process (Fig. 12-3) was the exclusive means of dewaxing bright stock for many years, it is rapidly being displaced by solvent processes. Percolated or acid-treated and

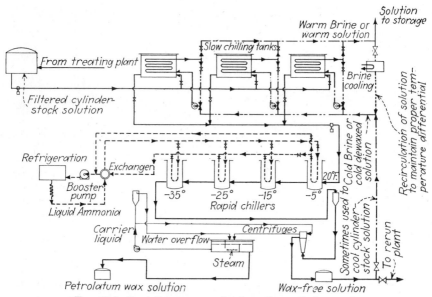

Fig. 12-3. Centrifuge process for dewaxing cylinder stock.

contacted cylinder stock, diluted with 65 to 80 per cent naphtha, is continuously chilled in large insulated vertical tanks provided with cooling coils. Wax-free oil solution is used for initial heat exchange, followed by either brine or direct-expansion ammonia chilling. Doubts have been expressed regarding the established idea that very slow chilling is necessary for successful dewaxing, and at least one refiner has disregarded such precautions with the result that throughputs are greatly increased. Agitation of the oil solution during the precipitation of the petrolatum should be very moderate, since the churning of the solution tends to gelatinize the petrolatum. This tendency is evidenced by an increased pour test for slightly excessive or prolonged agitation, and by complete jelling by very long or very vigorous stirring.

For a pour point of 20 to 30°F the oil is chilled to about −10°F by means of brine solution. In order to obtain a zero pour-test oil, chilling to −40°F is required, and for some stocks even lower temperatures are necessary. The cold oil solution is continuously charged to Sharples supercentrifuges through a constant-head feed device. The centrifugal force separates the wax from the oil. The latter rises in the center of the "bowl" (a 4½-in. rotating tube) and leaves the machine through a discharge opening at the top; while the petrolatum, flowing upward along the wall, emerges from another opening. A stream of hot water (150 to 180°F) is directed at the wax-discharge port in order to prevent accumulation of frozen petrolatum at the outlet.

The capacity of the Sharples machine is from 25 to 55 bbl per day based on cylinder stock, each machine handling from 70 to 240 bbl of solution depending on the pour point desired, the properties of the stock, and the amount of dilution. The centrifuge operates at from 15,000 to 17,000 rpm and requires approximately 1 kw of power. The refrigeration requirement per machine per day is 5 to 10 tons.

Uniform operating conditions in the entire plant are the most essential requisite for successful operation of a centrifuge plant. Most important of all is careful fractionation of the stock in the vacuum distillation to avoid the presence of paraffin wax which clogs the centrifuges. High-boiling dark-colored or asphaltic materials inhibit the growth of crystals, and a light-colored stock of less than 1¾ Tag Robinson will probably give trouble. Some operators have even added colloidal matter to a distilled cylinder stock in order to inhibit the growth of paraffin wax crystals. The chilling surfaces must be kept free from wax, and the equipment should be designed so that masses of wax cannot accumulate on cooling surfaces, tank bottoms, or lines. Deposits not only prevent chilling but cause uneven flow of the charge to the centrifuges. A sufficient amount of naphtha must be used to obtain a nonviscous solution at the centrifuging temperature. A solution containing about 70 to 80 per cent naphtha of gravity 44 to 48 is usually satisfactory for producing zero pour-point oil. For lower pour points, more naphtha may be required. By careful operation it has been possible to lower the viscosity of stocks that can be centrifuged from 110 to 75 sec Saybolt Universal viscosity at 210°F.

Many schemes have been applied to improve centrifuging properties. In processing very waxy stocks and some overhead stocks, it is necessary to recirculate some of the dewaxed oil. Other stocks can be successfully centrifuged by recirculating some of the petrolatum, and in rare cases it has been necessary to add-dark-colored material to the stock. In one plant, evaporation losses are minimized by the use of hexane instead of naphtha and by the use of a completely enclosed circulating system.

NEW DEWAXING METHODS

The use of two dewaxing methods, i.e., pressing and centrifuging, has been a source of great expense to refiners. Almost all new plants employ solvents (Table 11-1). The Weir filter-aid process[12] (patented in 1924) was the first commercial solvent dewaxing process. It involved the filtration of chilled naphtha-oil solution mixed with about 15 per cent of filter aid (fuller's or diatomaceous earth). Modern solvent processes employ special solvents, such as acetone-benzene,[13] trichlorethylene,[14] ethylene dichloride-benzol (Barisol),[15] and particularly propane[16] and methyl ethyl ketone-benzol.[17]

Methyl ethyl ketone (MEK), the most widely used solvent, is used as a mixture with up to 70 per cent toluene to improve the rate of filtration and to raise the temperature required in dewaxing. Two solvents (or three if benzol is also used) are troublesome, and hence the use of larger-molecule ketones is being developed.[18] Methyl n-propyl ketone appears to be superior to toluene-MEK solutions, but several other ketones are also being investigated.

Most recently[18a] urea has been employed in room-temperature dewaxing operations. Straight-chain hydrocarbons react completely with urea forming a large-volume crystal complex which after separation by filtration can be easily decomposed by heating or by the addition of water. Wax is so completely removed that pour points of minus 70°F can be attained from ordinary lubricating oil stocks. In the plant of Deutsche Erdoel A.G., equal volumes of oil, aqueous urea (saturated at 160°F), and methylene chloride (for temperature control) are vigorously agitated. Heat of crystallization boils the methylene chloride which is condensed and returned to the reactor to maintain a temperature of 95 to 115°F. The mixture is filtered and the urea-paraffin complex is decomposed at about 170°F by agitation with live steam yielding aqueous urea and molten wax. Methylene chloride is recovered from both the oil and the wax by distillation, and the urea is concentrated for reuse. The Standard Oil Co. of Indiana installed a 700-bpd plant in 1956 for the production of transformer oils, refrigerator oils, and special oils for arctic services.

[12] Gee, W. P., *Ref. Nat. Gaso. Mfr.*, June, 1933, p. 238.

[13] Gover and Bryant, *Ref. Nat. Gaso. Mfr.*, June, 1933, p. 222.

[14] Pester, C. F., *Oil Gas J.*, May 25, 1933, p. 52.

[15] Albright, J. C., *Ref. Nat. Gaso. Mfr.*, August, 1936, p. 287.

[16] Wilson, Keith, and Haylett, *Ind. Eng. Chem.*, **28**, 1065 (1936).

[17] Porkorny and Stratford, *Oil Gas J.*, Mar. 31, 1938, p. 96.

[18] Tiedje and MacLeod, Higher Ketones as Dewaxing Solvents, *Pet. Refiner*, February, 1955, p. 150.

[18a] Anon., Urea-adduct Process Gains Ground in Lube-oil Dewaxing, *Chem. Eng.*, November, 1956, p. 114.

Rotary-type enclosed continuous filters are used almost exclusively in solvent dewaxing because the solvents are valuable and because they usually form explosive mixtures with air. The principle of operation is the same as that outlined on page 321 with regard to the Oliver precoat filter. However, a precoat is not employed in wax filtering, and the rotating drum is enclosed in a shell so that pressure can be applied (Fig. 12-4). Some plants employ vacuum rather than pressure. The wax cake is sprayed or washed with solvent while it is still on the drum. Closed filtering systems are required because the solvents must be

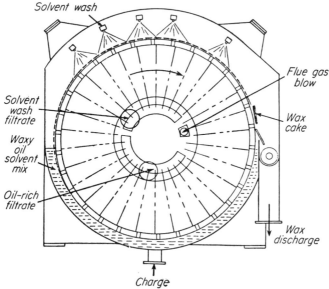

FIG. 12-4. Diagram of a Conkey solvent-dewaxing drum filter. (*Oil Gas J.*)

recovered or the operation will be an economic failure. In fact, the recovery of the solvent has been a great hindrance to the adoption of new dewaxing methods, and no such process can be highly successful unless the solvent can be effectively recovered and is relatively cheap.

The use of a single dewaxing process for both the high- and low-viscosity wax stocks has many advantages. The cuts that must be produced in a vacuum tower are reduced to gas oil, a lubricating-oil stock, and tar; only one type of dewaxing equipment is required; only one rerunning operation is necessary; and the production of several blending stocks is unnecessary. However, many combinations of processing operations are found in commercial plants.

Crystal Structure. The general statement that all types of waxes can be effectively extracted by solvent treatment needs some explanation. In propane dewaxing, light wax distillates produce very fluffy cakes which

crack easily and are difficult to wash.   Wilson, Keith, and Haylett[16] overcome this defect by the addition of 0.3 per cent petrolatum which changes
the structure of the cake so that it can be effectively washed.   The petrolatum, if undesirable, can be separated from the paraffin wax in a subsequent distillation.   Anderson and Talley[19] show that in propane dewaxing

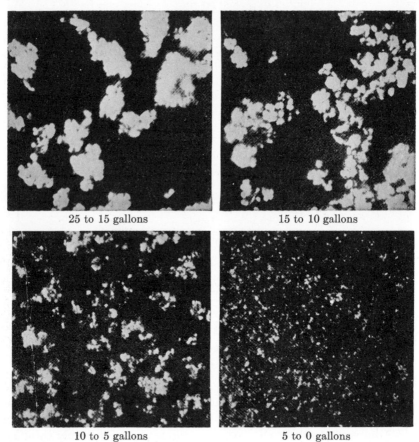

25 to 15 gallons   15 to 10 gallons

10 to 5 gallons   5 to 0 gallons

FIG. 12-5. Effect of wax structure on filtering rate in propane dewaxing (×120).
Rates are gallons per square foot per hour.   (*Shell Oil Co.*)

the most easily filtered wax consists of clusters of small grains cemented
together by naturally occurring aromatic resins.   With this structure
(Fig. 12-5), filtering rates exceeding 5 gal per sq ft per hr can be attained.
The laboratory rates shown in Fig. 12-5 are about five times as large as
plant rates.   Very fine crystals, forming clouds, may reduce the filtering
rate to zero.   Needles, free or interlaced, are undesirable.   The form of
the crystals depends on precipitating conditions, mixing temperature,

[19] Wax Precipitation from Propane Solution, *Ind. Eng. Chem.*, **29**, 432 (1937).

solvent-oil ratio, chilling conditions, and crystallizing agents such as asphaltic compounds. Good filtering rates are obtained by complete solution of the wax oil in the solvent, by avoiding flash-chilling (almost instantaneous by evaporation of propane) during any part of the cooling, and by a judicious amount of agitation. Chilling may be very rapid without affecting the filterability of the wax. Experimental runs were made at an average chilling rate of 14°F per min. The solvent ratio is of little importance as long as it is not below about 1.6 to 1.0.

The cementing material, consisting mainly of aromatic hydrocarbons, is probably present in asphaltic matter and acts somewhat as a filter aid. Asphalt-free stocks have lower filtering rates than asphalt-bearing stocks. Without a dewaxing aid (i.e., asphalt), the wax crystallizes as flat plates or a honeycomb structure,[20] whereas when a small amount of asphalt is present the wax crystallizes into spherelike particles which with further chilling develop a shell of radiating needles. V. N. Jenkins[21] also stresses the importance of the wax crystal structure in MEK solutions. He states that too rapid chilling results in poorly crystallized, bulky wax cakes which crack badly during filtering and wash unevenly.

Propane Self-refrigeration Process. Propane dewaxing is usually combined with deasphalting[16] because an improvement in color can be attained at little extra cost. The propane dewaxing process is unique because part of the solvent is allowed to evaporate and the entire material is chilled by the refrigeration effect of the evaporation. This also eliminates loss of heat through the walls of exchangers, piping, and some vessels. The advantages of the process are

1. Self-refrigeration.
2. Rapid rates of chilling. The entire operation of filling, evaporating, and emptying the chilling vessel requires only about 90 min.
3. Ability to handle all kinds of wax-bearing stocks.
4. High rates of filtration even for viscous oils.
5. A cheap solvent which may be recovered in the regular gas recovery system of the refinery. The make-up solvent requires only a wash with caustic to sweeten it.

According to the Kellogg Company,[22] propane dewaxing is practiced (Fig. 12-6) as follows:

In propane dewaxing of lubricant fractions, such as cylinder stocks, a typical operation blends three volumes of propane under pressure at 180°F with one volume of stock; this solution is cooled to 70°F and sent to chillers where the pressure is reduced to evaporate propane until the temperature of the remaining propane solution has dropped to, say, minus 40°F. Wax crystallizes out of this solution

---

[20] Chamberlin et al., Wax Crystallization from Propane Solution, *Ind. Eng. Chem.*, **41**, 566 (1949).

[21] Refining of High Melting-point Waxes, *Oil Gas J.*, Mar. 25, 1943, p. 98.

[22] M. W. Kellogg Company, *Oil Gas J.*, Mar. 22, 1947, p. 176.

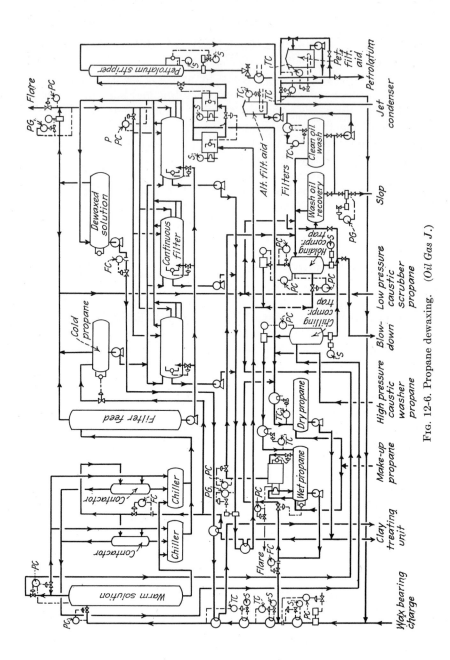

FIG. 12-6. Propane dewaxing.   (Oil Gas J.)

388

which is passed to and held in filter feed tanks. The filters are of the rotating-drum type, in which suction is maintained inside the drum while it dips below the level of the wax-solution slurry in the filter case.

As the drum rotates slowly the cake forming thereon is washed with cold propane in a stream of jets. The surface of the wax cake is cut continuously from the blanket by a knife as the drum rotates, the crude wax being conveyed to the wax tank. Filter pressures range from 3 to 10 psig. If stock is to be deresined the dewaxed solution is diluted with one to five volumes of warm propane, heated to 140° to 180°F, and the resins settled. They are washed with one or two volumes of propane, and the solution is depropanized at an elevated condenser pressure and later at atmospheric pressure. A typical dewaxing-deresining loss is about 14 per cent of the charge.

Product improvement is shown for one Bradford residuum in which carbon residue was decreased from 2.33 to 2.19; color determined by optical density measurements[23] dropped from an O.D. of 3,250 to 2,093; most of this color loss was concentrated in the wax, which showed an O.D. of 11,970. By deresining, the color was reduced to 750, carbon residue to 1.73, and viscosity from 165 SSU at 210°F to 148.

Over-all solvent loss is reported to range from 0.2 to 1 per cent of that used in the process which, at the low cost of the solvent, makes this expense nominal. Control methods are relatively simple and include liquid levels, proportioning equipment, and pressure and temperature controls.

The wax contains from 6 to 8 per cent oil and is converted into a marketable product by sweating, yielding from 50 to 60 per cent scale wax, depending on the melting point. In most recent practice, the slack wax is repulped at the filtering temperature with cold propane and filtered a second time, yielding a wax of the desired low oil content.

Ketone Dewaxing. This process is a development of the benzene-acetone process[13] by the use of various mixed solvents consisting of benzene, toluene, methyl ethyl ketone, methyl n-propyl ketone, methyl n-butyl ketone, or mixtures of these ketones.[17] The advantages of the lower molecular-weight ketones are high filter rates and low solubility of wax, but they have higher vapor pressures and are somewhat soluble in water.

Ketones have very low solvent power for wax but will not hold oils in solution. For this reason benzol and toluol, which are very good solvents for oils, are added in amounts of up to 70 per cent of the total solvent. For each oil a special blend which possesses a low solvent power for wax and a high solvent power for oil must be found. A typical mixture for low-viscosity oils is 55 per cent MEK, 35 per cent benzol, and 10 per cent toluol. The heavier the stock the more benzol and toluol are required. Wax-bearing oils from all sources can be treated.

[23] Weir, Houghton, and Majewski, *Ref. Nat. Gaso. Mfr.*, December, 1930, p. 89. The O.D. color scale is directly proportional to depth of color. For undiluted stocks, NPA color equals $1.08(O.D.)^{0.384}$.

Typical operations[24] employing methyl n-butyl and methyl n-propyl ketones give results as shown in Table 12-4. In one operation wax distillate is diluted with 2.5 parts of solvent and chilled to the desired pour point (or even 10°F higher). Chilling is first rapid, but final chilling is conducted at a rate of 1 to 2°F per minute. The chilled mixture is filtered in a continuous rotary filter under a blanket of flue gas. As the cold filtrate leaves the process it is utilized (in series with cycle wash solvent) in the exchanger system for "controlled" chilling. It is then

TABLE 12-4. OPERATING CONDITIONS AND PRODUCTS OF A MIXED KETONE
DEWAXING PLANT

	Paraffin distillate	Light motor oil	Intermediate motor oil	Heavy motor oil
Viscosity, Saybolt Universal........	150 at 100	250 at 100	77 at 210	205 at 210
Ratio, solvent to oil..............	1.9:1	1.7:1	2.2:1	3.2:1
Filtering:				
Temperature, °F...............	20	12	16	25
Gal dewaxed oil per sq ft per hr...	6.0	6.3	4.2	2.8
Dewaxed oil:				
Yield, per cent.................	89	90	91	92
Viscosity.....................	170 at 100	305 at 100	86 at 210	230 at 210
Pour point, °F[a]...............	20	5	0	25
Ketone, per cent...............	0.001	0.003	0.003	0.002
Wax:				
Yield, per cent.................	11	10	9	8
Oil, per cent..................	7	5	8	12
Ketone, per cent..............	0	0	0.001	0.001

[a] The solid point was 5°F lower than the pour point in each of these operations.

stripped of solvent in a two-stage atmospheric, vacuum, and steam-solvent recovery system. As the filter rotates, the cake is washed with fresh solvent. The slack wax is stripped of solvent and is then acid treated, sweated, and clay contacted.

Methyl ethyl ketone is now used almost to the exclusion of other ketone solvents. Special claims are (1) filtering rate of 6 gal of dewaxed oil per sq ft per hr; (2) pour point as much as 16°F below the chilling temperature; (3) the filter cake contains only 6 to 8 per cent oil; (4) solvent loss averages only 0.1 per cent of oil charged; (5) except for controlled chilling range from 90 to 30°F, shock chilling is applied throughout; and (6) use of atmospheric and vacuum steam in solvent recovery system reduces fuel requirements.

[24] Mueller, A. J., *Oil Gas J.*, Apr. 18, 1940, p. 54.

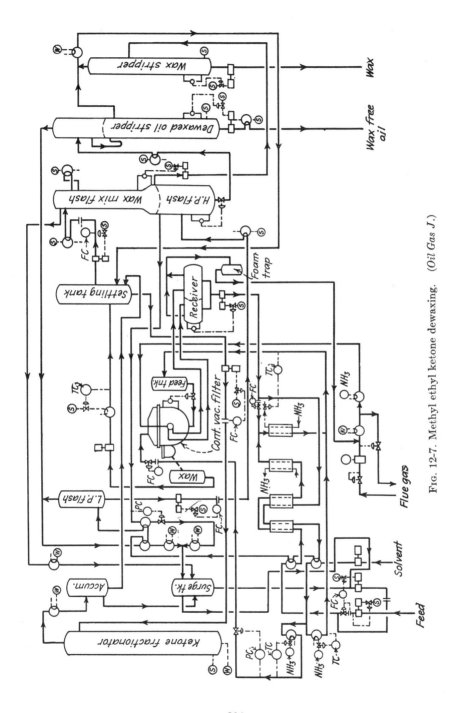

Fig. 12-7. Methyl ethyl ketone dewaxing.   (Oil Gas J.)

391

According to Ebner and Mertens,[25] the essential equipment for an MEK dewaxing plant consists of seven major sections:

1. Direct-expansion ammonia chillers.
2. Double-pipe scraped surface exchangers for both solvent dewaxing and wax recrystallizing process sections.
3. Continuous dewaxing filters.
4. Tubular exchangers to chill wash solvent.
5. Flue gas generation, circulation, and chilling.
6. Products recovery system for
   a. Dewaxed oil.
   b. Slack wax.
   c. Slop wax filtrate.
   d. Product wax.
7. Solvent-water separating and recovery systems.

A diagram of the MEK process[26] is indicated in Fig. 12-7. The wax-bearing oil and the solvent streams are mixed under control of a ratio

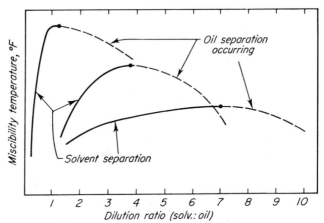

FIG. 12-8. Borderline miscibility curves in dewaxing.

flow controller. The oil-solvent stream flows through exchangers and chillers, from which it emerges at a controlled temperature which is maintained by regulating the pressure on the refrigerant side of the charge mix chiller. The liquid phase of the charge to the filters is adjusted to the proper filtration viscosity by the addition of chilled solvent to the chilled oil-solvent mixture.

Recovery of solvent from the wax cake is accomplished in a manner similar to that from the filtrate, except that any water inadvertently entering the oil or solvent side of the dewaxing system quickly finds its way as ice into the wax cake. To remove this water, the wax cake is

[25] *Heat Engineering* (Foster Wheeler Corporation), March–April, 1944.
[26] Texaco Development Corporation, *Oil Gas J.*, Mar. 22, 1947, p. 174.

heated before evaporation of solvent to a controlled temperature of about 130°F at which the water readily forms a separate layer.

Several stocks are usually dewaxed in a single plant using a single solvent mixture, and accordingly the proper amount of solvent for each stock must be determined. The basic 1937 paper of B. Y. McCarty[27] is still[28] useful. A borderline miscibility curve is prepared for each stock (Fig. 12-8), and the basic MEK content of the solvent is based on the heaviest or residual stock. The critical point of Fig. 12-8 ranges from a solvent ratio as low as 1:1 to as high as 7 or 8:1. In approaching borderline miscibility in plant operations, one of the first indications[28] of oil separation, other misoperation being absent, is failure of the oil to increase in viscosity during the dewaxing.

Wax Finishing. Slack wax from solvent dewaxing processes contains only about 8 per cent oil. Upon sweating, a scale wax containing less than 1 per cent oil is obtained.

Sweating is now being replaced by solvent deoiling. In this operation the slack wax is redissolved in solvent, chilled to the temperature required to make wax of the desired melting point, and filtered on a rotary filter. Jenkins[21] describes the production of high-melting-point paraffinlike waxes from any type of slack wax by MEK deoiling. The molten charge is chilled while being stirred. If it is too stiff, oil may be added. MEK is added before filtering, and the temperature is adjusted to 55 to 70°F' in producing waxes of 130 to 160°F melting point. The wax is then repulped with MEK and filtered again, yielding waxes containing only 0.24 to 0.48 per cent oil. Ebner and Mertens[25] describe a similar deoiling operation conducted at 25 to 50°F. King[28] reports that the oil content of the wax is often only the oil that is contained in the wash solvent. Petrolatum cannot be sweated but it can be deoiled using MEK, or it can be diluted with naphtha and centrifuged.

Decolorization to 30 Saybolt color is accomplished by filtration through bauxite obtaining 5 tons wax per ton of bauxite for dark crude waxes (−2 color), to 60 tons for light-color (20 color) waxes.

Wax has long been molded into cakes (8 to 12 lb) by means of a modified plate and frame press having plates through which cold water flows. This involves much manual labor, and accordingly continuous methods of molding are being developed.[29,30] One method[29] involves automati-

[27] Hall and McCarty, Miscibility Relations in Solvent Dewaxing, *Natl. Pet. News*, July 14, 1937, p. R-15.

[28] King, E. P., Lubricating Oil Manufacture, *Oil Gas J.*, Mar. 16, 1953, p. 122.

[29] Keyes, B., Continuous Molding of Petroleum Waxes, *Oil Gas J.*, Apr. 14, 1952, p. 128.

[30] Thornton, D. P., New Method of Slabbing Wax, *Pet. Processing*, September, 1951, p. 963.

cally measuring molten wax into pans which pass through a cooling chamber on a conveyor belt to a demolding operation. The other method[30] which can be applied to petrolatum as well as paraffin wax, involves a combination crystallization and extruding machine.   The wax ribbon (1½ in. × 12 in.) is brought to just the right temperature for shearing it into slabs.

CHAPTER 13

FLUID MECHANICS

The processing of petroleum consists primarily of three operations—heating, distillation, and fluid transfer—and the handling of fluids is most frequently encountered. The engineer must not rely too completely on hydraulic data, because oils differ from water by exhibiting a wide range of viscosity, by boiling through a wide range of temperature, and by being sensitive to heat.

Mechanism of Fluid Flow. Flow within a tube or pipe occurs by two types of motion, streamline flow and turbulent flow. At low velocities *streamline flow* occurs as a series of cylinders slipping past one another with the material at the center of the pipe traveling rapidly and the cylindrical film at the wall being almost stagnant. The surface of the pipe is relatively rough compared with the thickness of the film, and flow is retarded by entrapment of liquid in irregularities of the surface. In small tubes or at streamline conditions the roughness of the surface vitally affects friction losses, but at diameters of 6 to 12 in. the surface roughness is less important. At higher velocities the drag of the bounding surface causes a rolling or mixing which is known as "turbulent flow," and the effect of surface roughness is not so great as with streamline flow.

Friction Loss. Flow, turbulent or streamline, may be represented by a single mathematical formula, except that a different friction factor is used for each region (streamline or turbulent) of flow. Fanning's equation (originally derived for turbulent flow) for flow in a circular conduit is

$$\Delta P_f = \frac{2fG^2L}{144gD\rho} = \frac{0.323fsu^2L}{d} = \frac{1.488Q^2}{100,000d^5}fsL \qquad (13\text{-}1)$$

where ΔP_f = pressure loss, psi

ρ = density, lb per cu ft; and s = sp gr referred to water at 60°F

u = average velocity, ft per sec (cu ft per sec ÷ cross section of pipe, sq ft)

L = equivalent length of pipe and fittings, ft

g = 32.2 (lb)(ft)/(lb force) (sec)^2

D = diameter of pipe, ft; and d = diameter, in.

Q = discharge, gal per hr

f = friction factor, a function of $\dfrac{DG}{\mu}$ or $\dfrac{7{,}738\,duS}{z}$ (Fig. 13-2)

$G = u\rho$ = mass velocity, lb/(sec)(sq ft)

μ = viscosity, English units, lb/(ft)(sec)

z = viscosity, centipoises

Throughout years of industrial development this equation has been found to be valid for the flow of all kinds of fluids in circular conduits. For sections other than circular, the friction loss is usually computed by using the hydraulic radius m which is defined as the cross-sectional area divided by the wetted perimeter:

$$\Delta P_f = \frac{0.08075 f s u^2 L}{m} \qquad (13\text{-}2a)$$

TABLE 13-1. EQUIVALENT LENGTHS (APPROXIMATE) OF PIPE FITTINGS AND
RESTRICTIONS FOR NOMINAL PIPE SIZES ⅜ IN. (LARGEST EQUIVALENT
LENGTHS) TO 12 IN.
Mainly from Crane Company

Equipment	Diameters of straight pipe	Equipment	Diameters of straight pipe
Gate valve:		Elbows:	
¾ closed................	800–1,100	Standard..............	31–44
½ closed................	190–290	Medium sweep.........	27–39
¼ closed................	39–56	Long sweep............	20–29
Open...................	7–10	45 deg................	15–21
Globe valve, open...........	330–480	Square................	66–94
Angle valve, open...........	165–220	Enlargement, sudden:[a]	
Return bends:		d/D ¼................	31–44
Close...................	73–104	d/D ½................	22–21
Medium radius...........	39–56	d/D ¾................	7–10
Pipestill—square.........	120	Contraction, sudden:[a]	
Pipestill—streamline......	60	d/D ¼................	15–21
Tee, standard:		d/D ½................	12–17
Side outlet..............	66–94	d/D ¾................	7–10
Straight through..........	20–29	Welded 90 deg bends:[a]	
½ reduced..............	31–44	R/D 0.5.............	38–54
¼ reduced..............	27–39	R/D 1.0.............	17–24
Entrance connection........	18–26	R/D 1.5 or 5.0.........	12–17
Couplings or unions.........	neg.	R/D 2.0 ot 4.0.........	10–14
		R/D 3.0.............	9–13

[a] d refers to smaller pipe diameter, D to larger pipe diameter, and R to radius of bend, all in same units. When d is involved, the equivalent length is based on d, not on D.

The equivalent length L is equal to the total length of straight pipe plus the lengths of pipe that are equivalent to the restrictions caused by elbows, valves, bends, etc. Approximate equivalent lengths expressed as diameters of straight pipe are shown, for turbulent flow, in Table 13-1.

Key to Nomographic Gauge Points

Gauge point	Description of fitting
1	Long radius flanged return bend
2	Regular flanged return bend
3	Regular screwed return bend
4	Couplings and unions
5	Long radius flanged 45° ell
6	Long radius flanged 90° ell
7	Regular screwed 45° ell
8	Regular flanged 90° ell
9	Long radius screwed 90° ell
10	Regular screwed 90° ell
10	Square-edged inlet
11	Inward projecting pipe
12	Basket strainer
13	Flanged tee, branched flow
14	Flanged tee, line flow
15	Screwed tee, branched flow
16	Screwed tee, line flow
17	Screwed angle valve
18	Flanged swing check valve
19	Foot valve
20	Flanged gate valve
21	Screwed gate valve

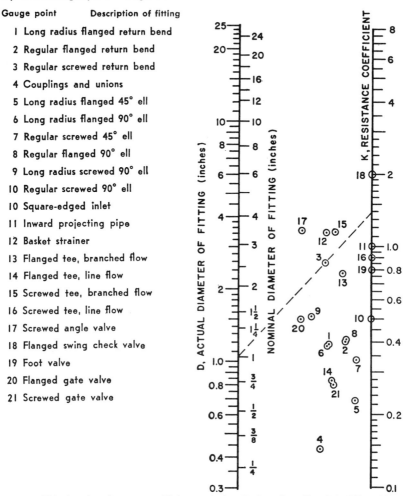

FIG. 13-1. Frictional resistance coefficients of pipe fittings [see Eq. (13-2b)]. (*Chem. Processing.*)

VanDeventer[1] states that for flanged fittings the equivalent lengths should be decreased by factors of 0.75 to 0.96. Equivalent lengths for viscous or streamline flow are so small that they are usually neglected.[2]

[1] *Catalogue* 89 of Walworth Company.
[2] Wilson, McAdams, and Seltzer, *Ind. Eng. Chem.* **14**, 105 (1922).

Fanning's equation is not valid for the flow of gases if the pressure drop is more than 10 per cent of the downstream pressure.

Another means of determining the friction loss through fittings is indicated[3] in Fig. 13-1.

$$h = K \frac{u^2}{64.4} \qquad (13-2b)$$

in which h is the pressure drop in feet of fluid and K is a resistance coefficient (Fig. 13-1) which depends upon the kind of fitting and its diameter.

The relationship between friction factor and the Reynolds number DG/μ for isothermal systems is shown in Fig. 13-2, and Keevil and

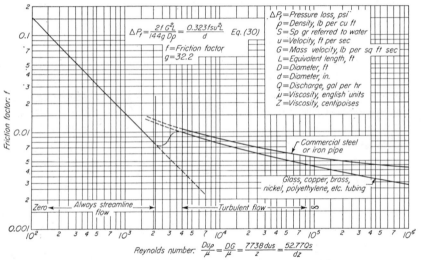

FIG. 13-2. Reynolds friction factor for isothermal conditions.

McAdams[4] have determined the effect of heating or cooling on the friction factor. The relationship has been repeatedly checked using a wide variety of materials, including water, air, natural gas, steam, oils, and solutions, and even the many empirical formulas of flow, yielding friction factors that are in close agreement with those of Fig. 13-2. The value of DG/μ when pumping natural gas in commercial lines is so high[5] that the friction factor (0.0033–0.0045) cannot be read from Fig. 13-2.

Condition of Pipe Surface. The friction factors shown in Fig. 13-2 are for commercially clean new pipe and are smaller than those usually

[3] Coefficients of The Hydraulic Institute, *Pipe Friction Manual*, New York, 1954; and Nomograph by D. S. Davis, *Chem. Processing*, November, 1955, p. 226.

[4] *Chem. Met. Eng.*, **36**, 484 (1929).

[5] Berwald and Johnson, Factors Influencing Flow of Natural Gas . . . , *U.S. Bur. Mines Rept. Invest.* 3153, 1931.

obtained in practice. The smaller the pipe the greater is the effect of the surface in increasing the friction loss. For very large pipe the condition of the surface may be neglected entirely. The friction loss in old or corroded small pipes may be twice as great as for new clean pipe. The factors shown in the following tabulation were published by F. L. Snyder.[6]

Condition or kind of pipe surface	Correction factor for condition of surface
Brass, copper, or lead (smooth)	0.9
Steel, cast iron, or corrosion-resistant metal (new)	1.0
Wood pipe or concrete lined (smooth)	1.2
Riveted steel or *old* cast iron	1.4
Vitrified or *old* steel pipe	1.6
Old riveted steel pipe	2.0
Badly tuberculated pipe	2.5

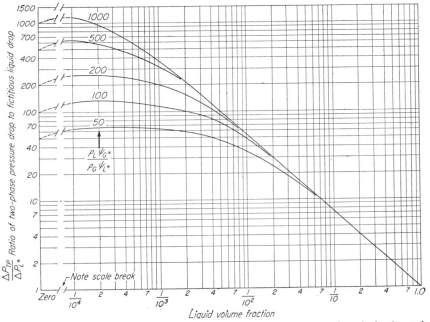

FIG. 13-3. Correlation of turbulent two-phase isothermal pressure drop in horizontal pipe. (*Pet. Refiner.*)

Two-phase Flow. The handling of mixtures of liquids and vapors is encountered in many refinery operations. The pressure drop under such conditions can be computed with fair accuracy (average deviation 19 per cent) from the correlation of Chenoweth and Martin[7] (Fig. 13-3) for tur-

[6] *Heating, Piping, Air Conditioning*, January, 1935.
[7] Turbulent Two-phase Flow, *Pet. Refiner*, October, 1955, p. 151.

bulent flow.   The left scale of Fig. 13-3 designated as $\Delta P_{TP}/\Delta P_{L*}$ is the ratio of the pressure drop for two-phase flow to the pressure drop that would occur if only a liquid were being handled.   However, the "all-liquid" pressure drop is hypothetical because it is based on the total mass flow (liquid and gas) rather than that of the liquid portion, but on a friction factor based on the physical properties of the liquid alone.

TABLE 13-2. DIMENSIONS OF WELDED AND SEAMLESS STEEL PIPE, INCHES

Nominal pipe size	Outside diam.	Nominal wall thicknesses for schedule numbers									
		Sched. 10	Sched. 20	Sched. 30	Sched. 40	Sched. 60	Sched. 80	Sched. 100	Sched. 120	Sched. 140	Sched. 160
⅛........	0.405	.....	.....	.....	0.068	.....	0.095				
¼........	0.540	.....	.....	.....	0.038	.....	0.119				
⅜........	0.675	.....	.....	.....	0.091	.....	0.126				
½........	0.840	.....	.....	.....	0.109	.....	0.147	.....	.....	.....	0.187
¾........	1.050	.....	.....	.....	0.113	.....	0.154	.....	.....	.....	0.218
1.........	1.315	.....	.....	.....	0.133	.....	0.179	.....	.....	.....	0.250
1¼........	1.660	.....	.....	.....	0.140	.....	0.191	.....	.....	.....	0.250
1½........	1.900	.....	.....	.....	0.145	.....	0.200	.....	.....	.....	0.281
2.........	2.375	.....	.....	.....	0.154	.....	0.218	.....	.....	.....	0.343
2½........	2.875	.....	.....	.....	0.203	.....	0.276	.....	.....	.....	0.375
3.........	3.5	.....	.....	.....	0.216	.....	0.300	.....	.....	.....	0.437
3½........	4.0	.....	.....	.....	0.226	.....	0.318				
4.........	4.5	.....	.....	.....	0.237	.....	0.337	.....	0.437	.....	0.531
5.........	5.563	.....	.....	.....	0.258	.....	0.375	.....	0.500	.....	0.625
6.........	6.625	.....	.....	.....	0.280	.....	0.432	.....	0.562	.....	0.718
8.........	8.625	.....	0.250	0.277	0.322	0.406	0.500	0.593	0.718	0.812	0.906
10.........	10.75	.....	0.250	0.307	0.365	0.500	0.593	0.718	0.843	1.000	1.125
12.........	12.75	.....	0.250	0.330	0.406	0.562	0.687	0.843	1.000	1.125	1.312
14 o.d.......	14.0	0.250	0.312	0.375	0.437	0.593	0.750	0.937	1.062	1.250	1.406
16 o.d.......	16.0	0.250	0.312	0.375	0.500	0.656	0.843	1.031	1.218	1.437	1.562
16 o.d.......	18.0	0.250	0.312	0.437	0.562	0.718	0.937	1.156	1.343	1.562	1.750
20 o.d.......	20.0	0.250	0.375	0.500	0.593	0.812	1.031	1.250	1.500	1.750	1.937
24 o.d.......	24.0	0.250	0.375	0.562	0.687	0.937	1.218	1.500	1.750	2.062	2.312
30 o.d.......	30.0	0.312	0.500	0.625							

Thicknesses shown in boldface type in Schedules 30 and 40 are identical with thicknesses for Standard pipe in former lists; those in Schedules 60 and 80 are identical with thicknesses for Extra Strong pipe in former lists.

The decimal thicknesses listed for the respective pipe sizes represent their nominal or average wall dimensions.   For tolerances on wall thicknesses, see appropriate material specification.

The effect of the amount of vapor and the effect of the physical properties of the vapor (and liquid) are introduced by means of the parameter $\rho_L \Psi_{G*}/\rho_G \Psi_{L*}$ in which ρ_L and ρ_G are the densities of the liquid and vapor, and Ψ_{G*} and Ψ_{L*} are friction factor functions described by:

$$\Psi_{L*} = f_{L*}L/D + \Sigma K \qquad \text{and} \qquad \Psi_{G*} = f_{G*}L/D + \Sigma K$$

Here L refers to length (ft), D to diameter (ft), and K to the frictional resistance coefficients of the Hydraulic Institute[3] (see Fig. 13-1).   Asterisks are used on the friction factors f_L and f_G to indicate that they are based on the total mass (liquid and vapor) flow but on the physical properties of the liquid (or of the gas). Moody friction factors are used, and these are four times larger than the factors of Fig. 13-2. Note especially that Fig. 13-3 applies only to isothermal systems, and it therefore does not apply directly to a system, such as a pipestill heater, in which a change of phase occurs.

TABLE 13-3. STANDARD CONDENSER TUBE DATA

O.d. of tube, in.	No. gauge, Bwg	Weight per linear ft, lb	Thickness, in.	I.d., in.	Surface outside, sq ft		Surface inside per linear ft, sq ft	Inside sectional area per tube, sq in.	Velocity for 1 gal per min, ft per sec
					Per lin ft	Per lin in.			
5/8	14	0.520	0.083	0.459	0.16362	0.01364	0.1205	0.165	1.98
	16	0.421	0.065	0.495	0.16362	0.01364	0.1299	0.193	1.633
	18	0.326	0.049	0.527	0.16362	0.01364	0.1382	0.218	1.472
	20	0.238	0.035	0.555	0.16362	0.01364	0.1455	0.242	1.328
3/4	14	0.64	0.083	0.584	0.19635	0.01637	0.1530	0.268	1.20
	16	0.514	0.065	0.620	0.19635	0.01637	0.1627	0.302	1.069
	18	0.396	0.049	0.652	0.19635	0.01637	0.1706	0.334	0.9617
1	12	1.12	0.109	0.782	0.26180	0.02179	0.205	0.479	0.67
	14	0.88	0.083	0.834	0.26180	0.02179	0.2183	0.5463	0.586
	16	0.700	0.065	0.870	0.26180	0.02179	0.2279	0.595	0.540
	18	0.540	0.049	0.902	0.26180	0.02179	0.2360	0.638	0.503
1¼	10	1.73	0.134	0.982	0.32708	0.02725	0.258	0.757	0.424
	12	1.44	0.109	1.032	0.32708	0.02725	0.271	0.838	0.385
	14	1.12	0.083	1.084	0.32708	0.02725	0.284	0.923	0.347
	16	0.890	0.065	1.120	0.32708	0.02725	0.2935	0.985	0.3262
	18	0.680	0.049	1.152	0.32708	0.02725	0.3020	1.045	0.3075
1½	10	2.110	0.134	1.232	0.3925	0.03275	0.3237	1.195	0.2688
	12	1.75	0.109	1.282	0.3925	0.03275	0.3382	1.292	0.2488
	14	1.36	0.083	1.334	0.3925	0.03275	0.3500	1.400	0.2298

Although many flow patterns are possible,[8] including flows described as (1) bubble, (2) plug, (3) stratified, (4) wavy, (5) slug, (6) annular, and (7) spray or dispersed,[9] it is felt[7] that these merge smoothly into one another so that the single relationship of Fig. 13-3 can be used.

Standard Pipe and Tubing. A new standard (ASA B36.10) was adopted in 1939 by the American Standards Association, ASTM, and API, replacing the grades of Standard, Extra Strong, and Double Extra

[8] Alves, G. E., Co-current Liquid Gas Flow . . . , A.I.Ch.E. Meeting, San Francisco, Sept. 14, 1953.

[9] Baker, O. (regions for each type of flow are indicated), *Oil Gas J.*, July 26, 1954, p. 185.

Strong pipe which have long been used. Ten schedules or weights are available (Table 13-2); the boldface numbers indicate the old Standard pipe (Schedules 30 and 40) and the old Extra Strong (Schedules 60 and 80). Double Extra Strong classification has been dropped completely. The schedule numbers are approximately equal to 1,000 times the internal pressure (pounds per square inch gauge) divided by the allowable fiber stress (pounds per square inch). An enormous number of sizes of pipe, tubing, casing, line pipe, etc., as well as Standard pipe are available. Some of the more common tubing sizes are shown in Table 13-3.

Example 13-1. Friction Loss in an Oil Line. One thousand six hundred gallons per hour of a 15 API ($s = 0.966$) fuel oil at a temperature of 200°F is to be pumped through a distance of 1,700 ft in a 3-in. (Schedule 40) well-insulated pipeline. Two open gate valves and six elbows are in the line, and the oil enters a tank through a sharp-edge entry flush with the side of the tank. The Saybolt viscosity of the oil is 300 at 210°F. What is the total friction loss in the line? Assume no change in temperature.

The viscosity of the oil at 200°F (Fig. 4-43) is approximately 80 centipoises. The specific gravity at 200°F (Fig. 5-14) is 0.916. The 1,600 gal is the volume at 60°F.

$$\text{Volume at 200°F} = 1,600 \times \frac{0.966}{0.916} = 1,688 \text{ gal per hr}$$

$$\text{Velocity} = \frac{\dfrac{1,688 \times 231}{3,600}}{\dfrac{(3.07)^2 \times 3.14}{4}} \times \frac{1}{12} = 1.21 \text{ ft per sec}$$

L, the equivalent length (Table 13-1):

Straight pipe............................   1,700 ft

Elbows.................... $\dfrac{6 \times 40 \times 3.07}{12}$ =   61.4

Gates..................... $\dfrac{2 \times 9 \times 3.07}{12}$ =   4.6

Entry.................... $\dfrac{24 \times 3.07}{12}$ =   6.14

$$= \overline{1,772.1 \text{ ft}} = \text{total equivalent length}$$

Using Fanning's equation (13-1),

$$\frac{7,738dus}{Z} = \frac{7,738 \times 3.07 \times 1.21 \times 0.916}{80} = 329$$

The friction factor (Fig. 13-2) is 0.048

$$\Delta P_f = \frac{0.323 \times 0.048 \times 0.916(1.21)^2 \times 1,772.1}{3.07} = 12.0 \text{ psi for clean new pipe}$$

Checking with the engineering unit equation,

$$\Delta P_f = \frac{1.488Q^2}{100,000D^5} fsL$$

$$\Delta P_f = \frac{1.488 \times (1,688)^2 \times 0.048 \times 0.916 \times 1,772.1}{100,000 \times 273} = 12.06 \text{ psi}$$

Example 13-2. Friction Loss in Vapor Line. Four thousand pounds per hour of a 55 API naphtha vapor at a temperature of 300°F passes through a 4-in. (Schedule 40) vapor line that is 130 ft long. The molecular weight is 110, and the pressure is 5 psig. What is the pressure drop?

Volume of vapor

$$\frac{4,000}{110} \times 379 \times \frac{760}{520} \times \frac{14.7}{19.7} = 15,000 \text{ cu ft per hr}$$

If the critical properties of this gasoline are

Critical temperature (Fig. 5-9)......... 575°F
Critical pressure (Fig. 5-12)............ 415 psia
Critical viscosity (Eq. 5-3)............. 276 micropoises

Then Reduced temperature $= \dfrac{300 + 460}{575 + 460} = 0.735$

Reduced pressure $= 20/415 = 0.048$ approx.
Reduced viscosity (Fig. 5-16) $= 0.34$ approx.
Viscosity $= 0.34 \times 276 = 93.5$ micropoises or 0.00935 centipoises

$$\text{Specific gravity} = \frac{4,000}{15,000 \times 62.4} = 0.00427 = s$$

$$u = \frac{15,000}{3,600} \times \frac{144}{12.73} = 47 \text{ ft per sec}$$

$$\frac{7,738dus}{Z} = \frac{7,738 \times 4.03 \times 47 \times 0.00427}{0.00935} = 640,000$$

$$f = 0.0044 \text{ (Fig. 13-2)}$$

$$\Delta P_f = \frac{0.323 \times 0.0044 \times 0.00427 \times (47)^2 \times 130}{4.03} = 0.43 \text{ psi}$$

Other Pressure Losses. Losses due to increasing or decreasing the cross-sectional area of a conduit suddenly are sometimes relatively large. The loss due to a sudden enlargement of the cross section may be expressed approximately as follows:

$$\Delta h_e = \frac{(u_2 - u_1)^2}{2g} \quad \text{or} \quad \Delta P_e = 0.00673s(u_2 - u_1)^2 \quad (13\text{-}3)$$

where Δh_e = pressure drop expressed as ft of fluid
ΔP_e = pressure drop, psi
s = sp gr
u_2 = velocity, ft per sec at smaller section
u_1 = velocity, ft per sec at larger section

The loss due to a sudden contraction in the cross section is approximately

$$\Delta P_c = 0.00673ksu_2^2 \quad (13\text{-}4)$$

where P_c = pressure drop, psi
k = a constant (Fig. 13-4).
u_2 = velocity, ft per sec at the smaller section

Finally, a moving stream of fluid has momentum or kinetic energy **of**

404   PETROLEUM REFINERY ENGINEERING

motion.   The energy at any velocity expressed as head h (feet of fluid) is

$$h = \frac{u^2}{2g} \quad \text{or} \quad P = 0.00673su^2 \quad (13\text{-}5)$$

and the pressure required to impart velocity to a fluid can be obtained by

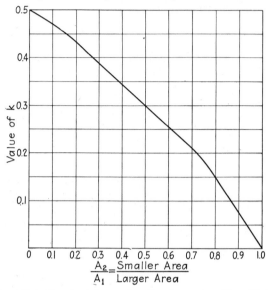

FIG. 13-4. Constant for contraction losses [see Eq. (13-4)].

subtracting the energy of the low-velocity stream from that of the stream at a higher velocity; and, if the specific gravity does not change,

$$\Delta P = 0.00673s(u_1^2 - u_2^2)$$

Example 13-3.   Contraction and Enlargement Losses.   *a.* Sixteen hundred gallons per hour of a 15 API oil at a temperature of 60°F is pumped through a 3-in. pipeline.   A contraction to a 1-in. pipe occurs.   What is the loss in pressure due to the contraction?

$$\Delta P_c = 0.00673ksu_2^2$$

$$u_2 = \frac{\dfrac{1,600}{3,600 \times 7.48}}{0.86/144} = 9.95 \text{ ft per sec (downstream)}$$

$$\text{Ratio of } \frac{A_2}{A_1} = \frac{0.86}{7.39} = 0.116$$

$$k \text{ from Fig. 13-4} = 0.465$$
$$\Delta P_c = 0.00673 \times 0.465 \times 0.966 \times (9.95)^2 = 0.299 \text{ psi}$$

b. The oil then flows back to a 3-in. pipe from the 1-in. pipe.   What is the loss in pressure?

$$u_2 = 9.95 \text{ (upstream)}$$
$$u_1 = 0.116 \times 9.95 = 1.15 \text{ ft per sec (downstream)}$$
$$\Delta P_e = 0.00673(9.95 - 1.15)^2 \times 0.966 = 0.503 \text{ psi}$$

Weirs. In refinery design the two most important weirs are the rectangular or suppressed weir and the V-notch weir. Both are used in the design of the overflow dams in bubble towers. The formula for flow over a rectangular weir is

$$Q = 3L(h)^{3/2} \tag{13-6}$$

where Q = quantity of liquid, gal per min
L = perimeter of weir, in.
h = effective head above weir, in.

Francis (1851), Hamilton Smith (1886), and Bazin (1888) suggest constants between 3.33 and 3.7 for water, but the value of 3 seems to represent more accurately the behavior of petroleum oils. The constant holds only up to heads of 5 or 6 in. and perimeters of 24 in. The formula for the triangular weir having an angle of 90 deg is

$$Q = 2.3L(h)^{5/2} = 1.155L(h)^{3/2} \tag{13-7}$$

Triangular weirs are useful if the capacity of a rectangular weir must be increased without increasing the head or the perimeter.

Bernoulli's Theorem. Bernoulli's theorem is used in the solution of most hydraulics problems. This theorem is a special case of the first law of thermodynamics (conservation of energy) in which changes in the energy content of a fluid system are balanced against one another. Although friction losses are evident as heat, the theorem is concerned only with the pressure and energy changes, and heat is considered lost energy.

$$\left.\begin{array}{l} X_a \text{ (static head)} \\ + \dfrac{u_a^2}{2g} \text{ (velocity head)} \\ + P_a V_a \text{ (pressure head)} \\ + W \text{ (mechanical work)} \end{array}\right\} = \left\{\begin{array}{l} X_b \\ + \dfrac{u_b^2}{2g} \\ + P_b V_b \\ + F \text{ (friction)} \end{array}\right\} \tag{13-8}$$

Each item in Eq. (13-8) must be expressed in the same units, i.e. feet of head or pounds per square inch, etc. The relationship among pressure, feet of head, and specific gravity (or API) is given in Eq. (10-3). The hydraulics of withdrawing side-draw products from fractionating towers is discussed by Nelson.[10]

Example 13-4. Hydraulic Energy Balance. A tank of water at 150°F (specific gravity 0.985, viscosity 0.433 centipoise) is discharging through a standard 2-in. pipe system at the rate of 120 gal per min by its own hydrostatic head. Figure 13-5 indicates the pipe system. What is the height of the water above the discharge point?

In this problem the only energy input to the system is the difference in the static head $(X_a - X_b)$. This energy is dissipated as friction losses in the pipe and fittings, in the entrance to the line from the tank, and as kinetic energy in the fluid as it flows from the end of the pipe.

[10] Tower Hydraulics, *Oil Gas J.*, Sept. 15, 1945, p. 119.

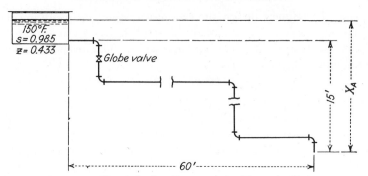

FIG. 13-5. Simple hydraulic system for Example 13-4.

Basis: 1 sec, isothermal at 150°F

$$\text{Velocity} = \frac{120 \times 144}{7.48(1.035)^2 \times 60 \times 3.1416} = 11.5 \text{ ft per sec}$$

$$\text{Velocity head} = \frac{u_b^2}{2g} = \frac{(11.5)^2}{2 \times 32.2} = 2.05 \text{ ft of fluid}$$

Friction losses (see Fig. 13-4):

$$\text{Contraction loss at connection to tank} = \frac{ku_b^2}{2g} = 0.5 \times 2.05 = 1.025 \text{ ft of fluid}$$

Loss in pipe and fittings (see Table 13-1):

$$\text{Equivalent length of pipe} = 60 + 15 + \frac{2.07}{12} \times 350 + \frac{5 \times 2.07 \times 34}{12} = 164.7 \text{ ft}$$

$$\Delta P_f = \frac{0.323 f s u^2 L}{D} \qquad \frac{7{,}738 d u s}{Z} = \frac{7{,}738 \times 2.07 \times 11.5 \times 0.985}{0.433} = 419{,}000$$

Friction factor for new, clean pipe = 0.0046 (see Fig. 13-2):

$$\Delta P_f = \frac{0.323 \times 0.0046 \times 0.985(11.5)^2 164.7}{2.07} = 15.3 \text{ psi}$$

$$= \frac{15.3 \times 144}{62.4 \times 0.985} = 36.1 \text{ ft of fluid}$$

Difference in head required $= X_a - X_b = 2.05 + 1.025 + 36.1 = 39.2$ ft

High-vapor-pressure liquids such as liquefied gases appear to behave strangely because they automatically create their own vapor pressure in the storage tank. Thus, if the temperature is high the pressure is high and vice versa. If two interconnected tanks, as on a butane truck, are at the same level but the heat of the sun warms one of the tanks, that tank will dump itself into the low-temperature tank until the other one is completely full.[11] Vapor will condense in the low-temperature tank, and vaporization will occur in the high-temperature tank.

[11] Nelson, W. L., Hydraulics of Pressure Storage Systems, *Oil Gas J.*, Oct. 4, 1947, p. 94.

REFINERY APPLICATIONS

Little experimental work is available on the pressure drops that occur through vapor lines, condensers, coolers, pipestills, exchangers, etc. Inasmuch as approximate information is better than none at all, a number of cases are presented here which are based primarily on Fanning's equation [Eq. (13-1)] and on logical values of the specific gravity, viscosity,

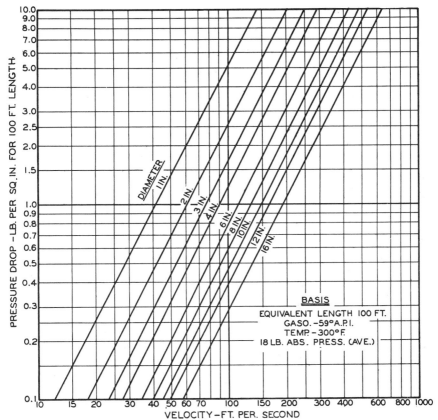

FIG. 13-6. Pressure drop through 100 ft (equivalent length) of vapor line. Based on 59 API gasoline at 300°F and 18 psia. (*Oil Gas J.*)

etc., of the fluid. The pressure drops through exchangers and pipestills are so specialized that they will be discussed in Chaps. 17 and 18.

Vapor Lines. Approximate pressure drops through topping plant gasoline vapor lines are given in Fig. 13-6, and the same data have been published[12] as a function of the number of pounds flowing. They may be

[12] Nelson, W. L., *Oil Gas J.*, Mar. 30, 1944, p. 90; Nov. 4, 1944, p. 73; and Dec. 1, 1945, p. 75.

applied to other vapors by multiplying the pressure drops from Fig. 13-6, by the following factor:[12]

$$\text{Multiplier} = 0.4 \frac{MP}{T} \tag{13-9}$$

The general formula[12] for all kinds of vapors at any temperature or pressure is

$$\Delta P = \frac{58.5 T W^2 L}{10^8 M P d^5} \tag{13-10}$$

where M = molecular weight
  P = pressure, psia
  T = temperature, °F abs
  W = lb per hr; product, reflux and steam
  d = inside diameter, in.
  L = equivalent length, ft

R. G. Lovell[13] suggests a formula which apparently is based on the low velocities of 20 to 30 ft per sec. In practice, velocities of 40 to 75 ft per sec are used for atmospheric pressure and up to 200 ft per sec at 50-mm pressure.

The pressure drop through condenser box headers[14] is small.

Example 13-5. Pressure Drop in Vapor Line. In Example 13-2, 4,000 lb per hr of gasoline vapor (15,000 cu ft) is flowing through 130 ft of 4-in. pipe. The velocity is

$$\text{Velocity} = \frac{15,000}{3,600} \times \frac{144}{(4.03)^2 \times 0.785} = 47 \text{ ft per sec}$$

According to Fig. 13-6 the pressure drop per 100 ft is 0.295 psi

$$\Delta P = 0.295 \times {}^{130}\!/_{100} = 0.383 \text{ psi}$$

It might also be computed from Eq. (13-10)

$$\Delta P = \frac{58.5}{10^8} \times \frac{T W^2}{M P d^5} = \frac{58.5 \times (300 + 460) \times 4,000^2 \times 130}{10^8 \times 110 \times (5 + 14.7) \times 4.03^5} = 0.396 \text{ psi}$$

These values check reasonably well with the 0.43 psi of Example 13-2.

Condensers. Space does not permit theoretical development,[15] but most approximately the pressure drop through a condenser coil in which complete condensation occurs will range from one-third to one-half of the pressure drop through the coil if no condensation took place. Thus, Fig. 13-6 or Eq. (13-10) may be employed, and the value obtained is reduced to half or a third. For Example 13-5, the pressure drop would range from 0.14 to 0.2 psi. Most condenser boxes are built with a header and

[13] Refinery Piping-design of Stock Lines from Tower, *Pet. Engr.*, Midyear, 1941.
[14] Nelson, W. L., Pressure Drop in Condenser Box Headers, *Oil Gas J.*, Apr. 27, 1944, p. 54.
[15] Nelson, W. L., Pressure Drop in Box Condensers, *Oil Gas J.*, May 18, 1944, p. 93.

a number of branches from the main vapor line. The fluid splits itself into the several branches, and the pressure drop for the entire box is the same as through any one of the branches.

Line Sizes. Refinery *steam lines* are relatively small and flow rates are not uniform, and hence lower steam velocities (larger pipe) are used than in power plants. It is poor practice to use velocities in excess of 800 to 1,000 ft per min for each inch of diameter,[16] although for short lines (under 300 ft) values of 1,000 to 1,200 may be used. Velocities in refinery steam lines are shown in Table 13-4.

TABLE 13-4. VELOCITY IN REFINERY STEAM LINES, FT PER MIN[a]

Nominal pipe size	Very long lines	Regular or short lines
1½	1,500	1,800
2	1,900	2,300
2½	2,200	2,700
3	2,800	3,400
4	3,600	4,400

[a] For reciprocating equipment reduce velocity by 35 per cent.

In sizing *water lines* the head loss is usually limited to 2.5 ft of head per 100 ft of pipe,[16] which means velocities of about 1.5 ft per sec in 1-in. pipe, 4 ft per sec in 5-in. tubing, and 5 ft per sec in 14-in. pipe. There is also a tendency to limit the velocity in larger lines (4 in. and up) to 4 or 5 ft per sec.

TABLE 13-5. APPROXIMATE SIZES OF OIL LINES (LIQUID)

Viscosity at pumping temperature		Gal per min				
Saybolt Universal	Centistokes	1½ in.	2 in.	2½ in.	3 in.	4 in.
30	2	10–30	20–50	40–80	60–140	140–260
50	8	.....	15–40	30–60	50–120	100–240
100	20	.....	5–35	20–55	40–100	80–200
300	65	.....	To 25	15–40	35–80	70–180
500	108	.....	.....	10–30	30–70	60–160
1,000	216	.....	.....	.....	To 4	40–120
1,500	324	.....	.....	.....	......	To 80

Table 13-5 indicates common refinery line sizes based on heads of 1 to 4 ft per 100 ft of equivalent line length (0.025 to 0.12 psi per 100 ft). Obviously, this table does not apply to long lines such as crude or prod-

[16] Nelson, W. L., Sizing Steam and Water Lines, *Oil Gas J.*, Nov. 22, 1947.

uct pipelines,[17] not does it apply to pump-suction lines[18] or to main process lines. Customary velocities in pipestill tubes are shown in Table 18-5, and velocities through exchangers are discussed in connection with Figs. 17-11 and 17-12.

Very viscous or low gravity crude oils cannot be economically handled by pressure alone, they must be heated and sometimes diluted.[19] The maximum feasible viscosities for handling viscous oils at room temperature are about:[19]

Line size	SUS at 100°F
4 in.	400
6 in.	1,000
10 in.	2,000
20 in.	5,000

The temperatures required to reduce the viscosity of average crude oils to feasible ranges are indicated in Table 13-6.

TABLE 13-6. TEMPERATURES REQUIRED IN HANDLING AVERAGE CRUDE OILS[a]

API gravity	Conventional pipelines, etc.		Handling at terminals	
	100 SUS[b]	500 SUS[b]	With ease 2,000 SUS[b]	For normal loading rate 3,300 SUS[b]
10	300°F	215°F	168°F	155°F
11	285	200	155	141
12	270	185	140	127
13	255	173	128	115
14	240	160	115	103
15	225	146	104	
16	214	135		
17	202	125		
18	190	112		
19	176			
20	162			

[a] Nelson, W. L., Pumping of Cold Viscous Crude . . . , *Oil Gas J.*, June 6, 1955, p. 143, and Nov. 15, 1954, p. 269.

[b] Viscosity at 100°F reduced to these heading values.

Pump Selection. Space does not permit a discussion of pumps or even a complete discussion of their service characteristics.[20]   *Asphalts or semi-*

[17] Nelson, W. L., Sizing of Refinery Oil Lines, *Oil Gas J.*, Oct. 18, 1947.

[18] Nelson, W. L., *Oil Gas J.*, Aug. 2, 1947, p. 93, and Aug. 30, 1947, p. 103.

[19] Nelson, W. L., Pumping of Cold Viscous Crude . . . , *Oil Gas J.*, June 6, 1955, p. 143; and Nov. 15, 1954, p. 269.

[20] Nelson, W. L., *Oil Gas J.*: (selection) July 26, 1947, p. 287; (suction lift) Aug. 2,

solids are handled with reciprocating steam pumps because they can, up to their limit, develop full pressure and can sometimes dislodge even solid material from the line. In handling large amounts of medium-viscosity oils, centrifugal pumps may be used. Centrifugal pumps are widely used for *boiler feed* because of the smooth flow, ease of automatic regulation, simplicity, and small space required. "Blowing" or "puffing" of burners is avoided by the use of rotary pumps for *circulating fuel oil.* Cargo loading of nonviscous fluids is handled largely by centrifugal pumps because of their inherent high-capacity low-head characteristics, but more viscous materials may be handled with rotaries. *Circulation systems* such as those used in blending of ethyl fluid into gasoline or certain treating plant operations are powered with centrifugal pumps, although asphalt requires rotary or reciprocating circulation pumps. Rotary and very small plunger pumps are used for *chemical feeds.* Spray pond water, cooling-box water, cold-oil charge stocks, and *reflux* are examples of cold general-service operations that are usually handled with centrifugal pumps. Centrifugals are safer than positive-displacement pumps because the discharge line can be closed without bursting valve boxes, blowing gaskets, etc.; they can be repacked while operating (on cold materials); and their capacity or speed can be regulated by the use of steam turbine drives. Multistage centrifugal pumps are widely used for *hot-oil high-pressure* low-capacity services such as charging cracking plant pipestills, because of their relatively low cost, low space requirement, light foundations, and a nonpulsating flow that simplifies the maintenance of instruments, valves, lines, and fittings. Two centrifugals, one for acid and the other for soda, driven by a common prime mover, are now used almost exclusively for *foamite fire smothering.* Centrifugals fill the lines quickly, and they can be built cheaply of cast iron and can easily be flushed with water to remove the chemicals. *Fuller's earth, clay, etc., slurries* are handled by centrifugal pumps by feeding wash oil to the stuffing boxes, but reciprocating pumps or very cheap rotary pumps are employed for the worst combinations of temperature and abrasion so that worn parts can be replaced at little cost. *Volatile fluids* are handled by submerged-type centrifugals, but largest suction lifts are obtained with close-clearance reciprocating pumps. The reciprocating, or plunger pump is standard for *extreme high pressure*, although small rotary pumps can provide 2,500 psi in some services, and multistage centrifugal pumps are occasionally used at 1,000 psi. Centrifugal pumps are widely used on *loading racks*, in *bulk stations*, and in *small blending operations* because the discharge line can be closed while it is being transferred from one container to another. Remote push-button control can be employed. "In-line"

1947, p. 93; (priming) Aug. 9, 1947, p. 111; (services) Aug. 23, 1947, p. 133; (vacuum) Aug. 30, 1947, p. 103; and (viscosity) Oct. 25, 1947.

centrifugal pumps are available which can be set directly in the line avoiding loops, bends, and pipe vibration.

Suction Lift of Pumps. Figure 13-7 serves to illustrate pump suction conditions. The maximum lift that a pump can produce is equal to barometric pressure less the vapor pressure of the liquid. The customary Reid vapor pressure is not usually satisfactory because the small amount of air or gas dissolved in oils often causes the true vapor pressure to be 3 to 60 per cent higher (Table 4-12) than the Reid vapor pressure. In addition, the pump must lift the suction valve against its spring, which seldom

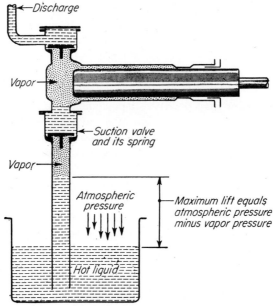

FIG. 13-7. Diagram of a vapor-bound hot-oil plunger-type pump. (*Oil Gas J.*)

requires a pressure in excess of 0.5 psi (weight divided by sectional area) plus the spring tension.[21] In extreme situations the spring may be removed. Finally, friction losses through the suction line and suction ports must be subtracted. These losses plus the loss due to the valve and its spring are about

	Psi
Self-priming pumps	1.7–3.7
Rotary or reciprocating pumps	3.7–4.3
Centrifugal pumps	3.7–7.4

In handling volatile liquids, or liquids that are boiling, the following low piston speeds are recommended:[21]

[21] Nelson, W. L., Vacuum and Close Clearance Pumps, *Oil Gas J.*, Aug. 30, 1947, p. 103.

Stroke, in.	Speed, ft per min
6	25–40
10	32–57
12	35–63
18–24	45–80

The net suction lift possible with a pump amounts to the barometric pressure less the following items: (1) true vapor pressure of liquid at the pumping temperature, (2) pressure caused by weight and spring of suction valve, and (3) entry friction losses.   Should this computation come out to be negative it means that a net positive suction head is necessary, that the pump can produce no lift.   Centrifugal pumps should always be provided with a "flooded suction" (positive head), because there is no convenient way to prime or fill them with liquid and they cannot operate without liquid in the case.

Example 13-6.   Suction Lift.   A rotary pump is handling a 0.8 specific gravity liquid which has a bubble point of 9.3 psia at the pumping temperature.   The maximum possible lift will be

$$14.7 - 9.3 = 5.4 \text{ psia}$$

From this must be subtracted the entry and valve losses shown above.

$$5.4 - \text{about } 4 = 1.4 \text{ psia}$$

This corresponds to a lift in feet of

$$\frac{1.4}{14.7} \times \frac{34}{0.8} = 4.05 \text{ ft}$$

If this liquid is heated to its boiling point, whereat its vapor pressure is 14.7 psia and its specific gravity is 0.62, a suction head (not lift) of about 15 ft is required.

Steam for Pumping.   The amount of steam required by steam-actuated pumps can be approximated from Eq. (13-11).

$$S = (0.058C + 1.0)(P - p) \tag{13-11}$$

where S = steam, lb per hr

C = capacity, gal per min

$(P - p)$ = discharge minus suction pressure, psi

It applies to regular duplex or power duplex pumps, operating on 125-lb saturated steam on common refinery liquids.   If greater accuracy is justified, the following multipliers can be applied:

Kind of pump		Kind of steam	
Reciprocating simplex	0.9	100°F superheat	0.90
Duplex (basis)	**1.0**	40°F superheat	0.96
Power plunger	1.02	100 psi saturated	0.99
In poor repair	1.05	**125 psi saturated**	**1.00**
Pressure over 1,000 psi	1.14	200 psi saturated	1.02
Thick liquids	1.1–1.2	300 psi saturated	1.04
		98 % quality	1.10

CHAPTER 14

COMBUSTION

The amount of heat liberated when a unit quantity of a fuel is burned is called the "heating value" or "heat of combustion." The heat liberation, when 1 lb of a fuel at 60°F is burned and the products of combustion are cooled to 60°F, is called the "net heating value." If the products are cooled to 60°F and in addition the water vapor in the flue gas is condensed, the "gross" or "high heating value" is obtained. In most industrial processes the water vapor contained in the stack or flue gases is not condensed, and hence the most logical basis for judging the thermal efficiency of equipment is the net heating value.

The heat that is evolved when 1 lb of water is condensed at 60°F is 1058.2 Btu or for 1 cu ft of water vapor (measured at 60°F) 50.3 Btu. The net heating value can be computed from the gross heating value by subtracting the quantity of heat that is required to condense the water vapor in the flue gas.

Example 14-1. Calculation of Net Heating Value. *a.* What is the net heating value of methane expressed as Btu per cu ft?

$$CH_4 + 2O_2 = CO_2 + 2H_2O$$

One cubic foot of methane burns and produces 2 cu ft of water vapor. The gross heating value of methane = 1010 (Table 14-4).

Net heating value = $1010 - 2 \times 50.3 = 909.4$ Btu per cu ft

b. Compute the net heating value of fuel oil 5 in Table 14-3

$$H_2 + \tfrac{1}{2}O_2 = H_2O$$

The molecular weight of hydrogen is 2 and of water 18. Two pounds of hydrogen burns, yielding 18 lb of water.

Water produced per lb of fuel = $0.12 \times {}^{18}\!\!/\!_2 = 1.08$ lb

Gross heating value from Table 14-3 is 19,376 Btu per lb

Net heating value = $19,376 - 1.08 \times 1058.2 = 18,234$ Btu per lb

Refinery Fuels. The heating value of petroleum-oil fractions increases with gravity as shown in Fig. 5-22. Table 14-3 indicates the characteristics of the solid and liquid fuels that are used in the refinery. In this

414

TABLE 14-1

API gravity	Kind of fuel	C.F.	Per cent sulfur	Btu per lb[a]	Btu per bbl[a]
5	Highly cracked naphthene base (as Calif.)	10.2	4.8	17,500	6.33 × 10⁶
7	Cracked mixed base (as medium Venezuelan)	10.4	2.7	17,950	6.4 × 10⁶
9	Cracked mixed base (as Ill., M.C., etc.)	10.6	0.85	18,350	6.45 × 10⁶
12	Mildly viscosity broken (as Caribbean)	10.8	2.95	18,200	6.26 × 10⁶
14	Straight-run (as Caribbean)	11.45	2.2	18,900	6.43 × 10⁶

[a] Corrected for sulfur and for minor amounts of oxygen and nitrogen, and 1.5 % of B.S.W.

TABLE 14-2. FACTORS FOR COMPUTING VALUE OF GASEOUS FUELS

Material produced or extracted	Disappearance of gas, cu ft per gal product	Decrease in heating value of gas, Btu per gal product
Propane	36.5	92,000
Propene (propylene)	45.7	107,000
Butane	31.6	103,500
Isobutane	30.8	100,500
Butene (butylene)	35.2	109,000
Isobutene	35.3	108,500
Pentane	27.5	110,500
Isopentane	27.2	108,500
14-lb natural gasoline	26.0	112,000
26-lb natural gasoline	27.5	110,500
Poly gasoline from propene	53.2	119,000
Poly gasoline from butenes	40.0	122,000
Codimer from isobutane	40.6	122,000
Alkylate from B-B cut	38.5	119,000
Cumene from propene and benzene	22.6[a]	52,600[a]

[a] Only the propene comes from refinery gas.

table the heating value, pounds air per pound fuel, and the percentage of carbon dioxide (Orsat analysis) were computed on the "as fired" basis. Typical residual fuel oils[1] have about the properties and gross heating values shown in Table 14-1.

[1] Nelson, W. L., Maximum Variations in Heating Value . . . , *Oil Gas J.*, Sept. 20, 1954, p. 299.

Natural gas and cracked gas are the major refinery fuels. Gas is more easily fired than solid or liquid fuels, but it has the minor disadvantage of producing a long flame and a flame that is often deficient in its ability to radiate heat. Some of the characteristics and combustion constants for gaseous fuels are given in Table 14-4. Note that inert gases in

TABLE 14-3. COMBUSTION CHARACTERISTICS OF LIQUID FUELS

| Fuel | API | H₂O | Ultimate analysis, per cent | | | | Heating value, Btu per lb liquid | | Lb air per lb fuel at zero per cent excess air[a] | Per cent CO₂ at zero per cent excess air[a] |
			C	H₂	S	Undetermined and ash	Gross	Net		
1. Commercial butane	0.581[b]	....	83.0	17.0	....	.....	21,850	20,240	15.42	12.0
2. Stove gasoline	66.0	....	86.0	14.0	....	.....	20,400	19,000	14.76	13.1
3. Furnace distillate	38.0	....	87.0	13.0	....	.....	19,650	18,450	14.47	13.5
4. Topped crude, Calif.	26.2	0.89	85.8	12.09	1.19	0.04	19,053	18,001	14.12	15.6
5. Mid Continent topped crude[c]	27.1	....	86.1	12.0	0.35	0.45	19,376	18,241	14.17	15.7
6. Mid Continent topped crude	25.1	0.33	86.2	12.39	0.39	0.69	19,256	18,076	14.1	15.6
7. Mid Continent residuum	22.0	0.05	87.4	11.1	0.42	1.03	18,778	17,723	14.0	16.0
8. Residual fuel oil, Calif.	16.5	0.05	87.5	10.17	1.14	1.14	18,319	17,351	13.7	16.4
9. Mid Continent residuum	14.3	0.05	87.6	10.27	0.7	1.38	18,454	17,479	13.7	16.4
10. Mexican crude	13.6	1.85	83.7	10.2	4.15	0.10	18,710	17,767	13.4	16.2
11. Cracked fuel oil, Calif.	11.3	0.3	86.5	10.04	1.49	1.67	18,088	17,128	13.5	16.4
12. Mid Continent cracked residuum	9.2	0.4	88.4	9.95	0.68	0.81	18,274	17,324	13.7	16.6
13. Mid Continent cracked residuum	8.6	....	88.9	9.8	0.56	0.74	18,277	17,345	13.7	16.6
14. Mid Continent residuum	8.1	0.25	88.5	9.07	0.67	1.51	18,077	17,212	13.4	16.9
15. Cracked residuum, Calif.	8.0	0.05	88.3	9.5	1.2	0.95	18,084	17,179	13.5	16.7
16. Residual fuel oil, Calif.	7.6	0.10	87.5	9.38	1.37	1.65	17,970	17,075	13.4	16.8
17. Kuwait pitch	5.0	....	83.9	10.4	5.4	0.3	17,500	16,600		
18. Cracked residuum, Ky.	3.3	....	90.6	8.49	0.41	0.50	17,837	17,030	13.4	17.1
19. Bituminous coal, Pa.	....	2.5	77.8	4.8	1.2	13.7	13,997	13,543	10.4	18.6
20. Bituminous coal, Mo.	....	2.6	72.6	4.6	1.8	17.4	13,533	13,098	9.7	18.6
21. Petroleum coke (fluid)	....	2.0	88.6	1.8	6.4	.....	14,000	13,932		
22. Petroleum coke (fluid)	....	3.8	89.1	2.1	6.1	.....	14,000	13,969		
23. Petroleum coke	....	1.2	96.0	2.1	0.41	0.29	15,241	15,040	11.9	18.9
24. Acid sludge	....	(20% weak acid)			....	.....	10,200[a]	9,700[a]		
25. Acid sludge	....	(40% weak acid)			....	.....	7,400[a]	7,000[a]		
26. Acid sludge	....	17.5	63.5	8.1	3.2	7.7	14,341[d]			

[a] On "as fired" basis.
[b] Specific gravity at 60°F.
[c] Also contains 1.1 per cent oxygen and nitrogen.
[d] Dry basis.

amounts of 1 to 10 per cent will reduce the heating values by 11 to about 206 Btu. The flames produced by wet gases, particularly cracked gases, are almost as luminous as oil flames and are good radiators.

Wet gases are particularly valuable because of the liquids that can be extracted or manufactured from them.[2] Such liquids may be worth more than the gases (or heating value of them) from which they are

[2] Nelson, W. L., Value of Refinery Gases, *Oil Gas J.*, Nov. 23, 1946, p. 105.

TABLE 14-4. COMBUSTION CHARACTERISTICS OF GASEOUS FUELS

Material	Molecular weight	Density, lb per cu ft at 60°F	Analysis, volume per cent										Heating value, Btu per cu ft at 60°F		Cu ft air per cu ft fuel at zero per cent excess air	Per cent CO_2 at zero per cent excess air	Heating value, Btu per lb at 60°F, gross
			H_2	CH_4	C_2H_4	C_2H_6	C_3H_6	C_3H_8	C_4H_8	C_4H_{10}	$C_5H_{12}+$	Inert	Gross	Net			
1. Hydrogen	2.0	0.0053	100										325	275	2.38	0	61,400
2. Methane	16.0	0.0422		100									1,010	910	9.57	11.6	23,920
3. Ethane	30.0	0.0792				100							1,770	1,619	16.75	13.1	22,350
4. Ethylene	28.0	0.0746			100								1,614	1,513	14.29	15.0	21,650
5. Propane	44.0	0.1162						100					2,520	2,319	23.90	13.7	21,690
6. Propylene	42.0	0.1110					100						2,336	2,186	21.44	15.0	21,060
7. Butane	58.0	0.153								100			3,265	3,014	31.10	14.0	21,340
8. Depropanizer overhead	21.7	0.0823		4.3		82.7		13.0			0.6		1,865	1,710	17.37	13.0	22,650
9. Cracked gas, dry	31.2	0.0572	9.5	64.5	3.6	16.0	1.9			2.9			1,316	1,200	12.34	11.5	22,930
10. Coking gas, dry[a]	23.8	0.0628	4.9	44.6	7.4	24.3	1.5	6.7		2.5			1,463	1,340	14.00		23,300
11. Reforming, dry[a]	30.2	0.0795	3.8	27.5	3.3	27.6	3.0	14.0		7.2			1,745	1,592	16.90		21,900
12. Cracked gas, dry[a]	28.6	0.0755		40.2		21.2	1.1	22.4		6.6			1,617	1,475	15.2		21,400
13. Natural gas, dry	18.6	0.0491		86.6		8.6		3.9		0.7	0.2		1,160	1,050	10.95	11.89	23,600
14. Cracked gas, wet	30.6	0.0806	6.4	30.6	5.1	19.1	10.6	16.8	5.9	5.5			1,786	1,645	16.72	13.50	22,150
15. Coking gas, wet	23.7	0.0626	9.8	45.9	19.5	3.7	11.3	6.6		3.2			1,425	1,302	13.10		22,800
16. Reforming gas, wet	29.8	0.0787	6.2	29.5	6.7	18.7	14.2	23.7		1.0			1,714	1,565	16.20		21,800
17. Cracked gas, wet	35.0	0.0923		34.6	1.7	21.6	4.7	17.4	3.0	7.5	9.3		2,058	1,892	19.38	12.91	22,250
18. Natural gas, dry	17.9	0.0471		90.7		6.2		2.1		1.0			1,112	1,005	10.58	11.81	23,500
19. Fluid cat., dry	29.4	0.0776	5.5	31.7	7.0	8.7	15.1	24.7		0.4		6.5	1,609	1,470	15.9		20,700
20. Houdry cat., dry	26.0	0.0686	11.8	35.2	6.6	9.3	9.8	19.8		0.4		7.1	1,481	1,353	14.6		21,600
21. T.C.C., dry	25.2	0.0663	19.5	24.6	8.2	9.6	10.0	20.6				7.5	1,384	1,264	13.7		20,900
22. Refinery gas, dry	28.0	0.0740	3.3	36.0	5.4	18.2	7.5	19.7		1.9		8.0	1,540	1,407	15.7		20,800
23. Refinery gas, dry	24.6	0.0650	2.6	33.3	1.9	19.0	6.1			0.7		2.8	1,435	1,310	13.9		22,060
24. Wet thermal gas	30.8	0.0815	4.7	32.7	2.0	21.6	7.4	13.6	5.5	6.4	2.5						
25. Avg. Fluid, butane-free	38.4	0.101	13.3	16.1	7.9	7.1	36.4	17.2					1,804	1,621			21,922
26. Avg. Houdry and T.C.C., butane-free	8.0	0.021	0.5	9.4	6.6	8.0	31.2	19.2					2,214	1,953			21,957
27. Avg. cat. reformer	57.2	0.151	80.8	5.0		4.9		44.3					641	569	5.47	7.02	30,400
28. Avg. Fluid, B-B cut	57.3	0.151							36.2[b]	63.8[b]							21,069
29. Avg. T.C.C., B-B cut									31.1[b]	68.9[b]							21,101

a Poly plant vent gas.
b Includes iso compounds.

417

made.   Table 14-2 shows the cubic feet of gas consumed and the decrease
in gross heating value for each gallon of liquid produced.   The table
may be used in studying the economy of such processes as gasoline
recovery, polymerization, Codimer manufacture, alkylation, or bottle-gas
production.

Example 14-2.   Value of Refinery Gas for Liquid Extraction.   Gas 14 of Table 14-4
is thought to have a value of 30 cents per thousand cubic feet because of its heating
value compared with the market price of fuel oil.   If the gas is processed for poly
gasoline the amount produced will be (see Table 14-2)

$$\left(\frac{10.6}{53.2} + \frac{5.9}{40.0}\right)\frac{1,000}{100} = 3.46 \text{ gal per thousand cu ft}$$

At 11 cents per gal the poly gasoline is worth 38 cents, and the value of a thousand
cubic feet of the gas has become

$$30 + 3.46\left(11 - \frac{120,000}{1,786 \times 1,000} \times 30\right) = 47.2 \text{ cents per thousand cu ft}$$

The 120,000 is the average per gallon heating value of the liquid product, and the 1,786
is the heating value of gas No. 14.   Of course, money must be spent to build and operate the plant out of the extra 17.2 cents per thousand cu ft.

Combustion Reactions.   The fundamental reactions involved in combustion are shown in Table 14-5.   If the ultimate analysis of the fuel is

TABLE 14-5. COMBUSTION REACTIONS

Reaction	Fuel name	Mol. wt	Heating value, Btu per lb	Lb air per lb fuel, no excess
1. $H_2 + \frac{1}{2}O_2 = H_2O$	Hydrogen	2	61,400	34.8
2. $C + O_2 = CO_2$	Carbon	12	14,600	11.6
3. $C + \frac{1}{2}O_2 = CO$	Carbon	12	4,440	5.8
4. $CO + \frac{1}{2}O_2 = CO_2$	Carbon monoxide	28	4,050	2.48
5. $S + O_2 = SO_2$	Sulfur	32	10,160	4.35
6. $CH_4 + 2O_2 = CO_2 + 2H_2O$	Methane	16	23,920	17.28
7. $C_2H_4 + 3O_2 = 2CO_2 + 2H_2O$	Ethylene	28	21,650	14.81
8. $C_2H_6 + 3\frac{1}{2}O_2 = 2CO_2 + 3H_2O$	Ethane	30	22,350	16.13

available, these equations are all that are required to solve many combustion calculations.

An examination of these chemical equations yields information concerning (1) the weights of materials that react and (2) the volumes of
gases that react.   For example, reaction 1 indicates that 1 cu ft of hydrogen reacts with one-half of 1 cu ft of oxygen to produce 1 cu ft of water
vapor.   Likewise reaction 6 shows that one volume of methane requires

two volumes of oxygen for combustion. One volume of carbon dioxide is produced, and two volumes of water vapor. Volumes are directly proportional to moles, and hence the number of moles that react are directly proportional to the number of volumes that react. The molecular weight of methane is 16 and of oxygen 32. With reference to reaction 6, 16 lb of methane reacts with 2×32 lb of oxygen to produce 44 lb of carbon dioxide and 2×18 lb of water. A knowledge of these elemental combustion reactions, along with data on specific heats of the gaseous products, constitutes the basis for almost all combustion calculations. Mekler and Fredersdorff[3] present simple algebraic formulas by which most combustion constants of gaseous fuels can be computed from data such as the specific gravity or molecular weight. In terms of the gas specific gravity g (molecular weight divided by 28.9), the heat of combustion (Btu per cubic foot) and theoretical air required (cubic foot per cubic foot fuel) are

$$\text{Gross heating value} = 215 + 1{,}500g \qquad (14\text{-}1)$$
$$\text{Net heating value} = 155 + 1{,}425g \qquad (14\text{-}2)$$
$$\text{Cu ft air} = 1.15 + 15g \qquad (14\text{-}3)$$

In catalytic cracking plants, the amount of blower air required for regeneration of the catalyst is enormous, and accordingly the combustion of carbon is guided toward the production of carbon monoxide rather than carbon dioxide because only half as much air is required (reaction 4, Table 14-5). Regenerator gases contain useful sensible heat (1000°F), but in addition the monoxide-rich gas may be burned with supplementary fuel to maintain the combustion temperature in otherwise conventional boilers, or it may be oxidized (burned) by contacting it with a bed of platinum catalyst.[4] The catalyst is arranged as a false floor in the boiler so that the gases plus any air needed pass upward through it, and a temperature of 1250 to 1600°F is attained by the combustion. During start-up the boilers are fired with conventional fuels and the catalyst bed is therefore protected with a screen of finned water tubes situated just above the catalyst bed.

Excess Air. The reactions of Table 14-5 do not take place completely to the formation of the products indicated unless an excess of oxygen or air is present. The extent to which the reaction will be completed can be computed by applying the law of mass action, but such computations are of little value in commercial work. In firing a commercial furnace the use of too little excess air is evident at once by carbon monoxide or even smoke in the stack gas. Carbon monoxide is seldom found in the

[3] Refinery Gas Fuels, *Pet. Refiner*, February, 1947, p. 81.

[4] Durham and Leland, Design and Application of CO Boilers, Western Pet. Ref. Assoc., Toledo Meeting, May 24, 1956.

flue gas from oil stills because at least 30 per cent excess air is normally used in order to keep a low furnace temperature, and no carbon monoxide is produced under these conditions if effective burners are used.

The amount of excess air employed ranges from 10 to 75 per cent, the low value for large installations completely automatically controlled and operating on low-heating-value gaseous fuels. Oil requires more excess air, as indicated in Table 14-6. In comparison with coal, oil can be fired at higher thermal efficiencies of 2 to 35 per cent,[5] but in modern large power plants the superiority of oil probably does not exceed 3 per cent.

TABLE 14-6. USUAL AMOUNTS OF EXCESS AIR, PER CENT

	Pipestills		Boilers	
	Minimum	Usual	Large	Small
Gas fuels..........	15–20	35	10–15	15–25
Oil fuels..........	20–25	50	15	25–35

The amount of flue gas can be computed by adding 1 to the pounds of air (per pound of fuel), and for gaseous fuel the cubic feet of flue gas per cubic foot of fuel gas can be approximately obtained by adding 1 to the cubic feet of air (per cubic foot of fuel gas). The molecular weight of flue gas including water vapor (as in stack) is about 30. (See Example 14-6.)

Example 14-3. Weight and Volume of Flue Gas. Fuel 4 of Table 14-3 is to be burned with 40 per cent excess air. According to Table 14-3 the pounds of air required at zero per cent excess air is 14.12, and the amount of flue gas is 1 lb greater, or 15.12 lb. At 40 per cent excess air

$$\text{Lb flue gas} = 14.12 + 0.4 \times 14.12 + 1.0 = 20.8$$

If the stack temperature is 600°F, the volume of flue gas per pound of fuel will be

$$\frac{20.8}{30} \times 379 \times \frac{600 + 460}{60 + 460} = 535 \text{ cu ft}$$

Specific Heats of Combustion Products. Figure 14-1 is a chart of the sensible heat content of the several gases that are found in flue gas. The *sensible heat content* may be defined as the amount of heat required to change the temperature of a quantity of material from one temperature to another by simple heating. No changes of state, such as vaporization or fusion, are involved.

$$\text{Sensible heat content} = W(T_2 - T_1)C_p$$

[5] Nelson, W. L., *Oil Gas J.*, Jan. 12, 1953, p. 131.

where W = lb material (lb-moles in Fig. 14-1)

T_2 = final temperature, °F

T_1 = initial temperature, °F

C_p = average sp ht at constant pressure, Btu per lb through the temperature range of T_2 and T_1

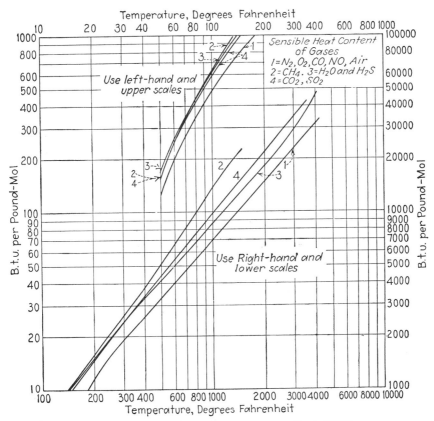

Fig. 14-1. Sensible heat of common gases (basis 32°F).

Figure 14-1 is plotted on a mole basis because the diatomic gases—oxygen, nitrogen, carbon monoxide, air, etc.—can be represented by a single curve. The same applies to other groups of gases. The figure gives the number of Btu required to raise the temperature of 1 lb-mole of gas from 32°F to the desired temperature. The upper and left scales are for temperatures up to about 150°F, and the lower and right scales are for higher temperatures.

Example 14-4. Use of Sensible Heat Chart for Gases (Fig. 14-1). One thousand cubic feet of a flue gas is cooled from 1000 to 100°F. Analysis of gas: CO₂, 10 per cent; H_2O vapor, 12 per cent; O_2, 3.7 per cent; and N_2, 74.3 per cent.   How much heat must be removed?   (Note that 1 lb mole of gas occupies 379 cu ft at 60°F and 14.7 psia.)

$$\text{Moles } CO_2 \quad = \frac{1000 \times 0.10}{379} \qquad\qquad = 0.264$$

$$\text{Moles } H_2O \quad = \frac{1000 \times 0.12}{379} \qquad\qquad = 0.316$$

$$\text{Moles diatomics} = \frac{1000 \times 0.743}{379} + \frac{1000 \times 0.037}{379} = 2.057$$

SENSIBLE HEAT, BTU PER MOLE

Material	At 1000°F	At 100°F
CO_2...............	9850	580
H_2O...............	8650	610
Diatomics...........	7000	478

Heat removed from CO_2	$= 0.264(9,850 - 580) =$	2,445 Btu
Heat removed from H_2O	$= 0.316(8,650 - 610) =$	2,540
Heat removed from diatomics	$= 2.057(7,000 - 478) =$	13,400
	Total heat removed $=$	18,385 Btu

Although heat quantities must sometimes be computed as in Example 14-4, Figs. 14-2 and 14-3 are more convenient and are sufficiently exact for most computations.   These charts are based on the net heating value because the net heating value is a more honest basis for efficiency calculations than the gross heating value.   Although these charts were computed for specific fuels, they can be used for other similar fuels without great inaccuracy.   They should not be used for computations with fuels that are abnormal.   Note that the usefulness of Figs. 14-2 and 14-3 is not limited to computations of stack temperatures.   They may be used for temperatures (or heat contents) at any point in a still.

Example 14-5.   Use of Combustion Charts (Figs. 14-2, 14-3).   A 20 API fuel oil is burned, and the gases are cooled to 300°F.   The heating value of the fuel is 17,900 Btu per lb net; carbon dioxide, 13 per cent.   How much heat is lost to the stack, and how many pounds of flue gas are produced?   Basis: 1 lb of fuel and 60°F (Fig. 14-2).

At 13 per cent CO_2 the percentage of excess air is approximately 23.   Reading close to the 25 per cent excess air curve, the heat lost to the stack at 300°F is about 6.3 per cent.   This amounts to $0.063 \times 17,900$ or 1130 Btu per lb of fuel.   Also, 16 lb of flue gas or 15 lb of air is required to burn 1 lb of the fuel if no excess air is used (Fig. 14-2).   At 23 per cent excess air the pounds of flue gas are

$$15.0 \times 1.23 + 1 = 19.45 \text{ lb per lb of fuel}$$

The lower the stack temperature, the lower the heat loss to the stack (or atmosphere), but the most economical stack temperature for pipestill heaters is about 300°F higher than the temperature of the incoming pipestill feed (see Fig. 23-6).   Even closer approaches are economical in boilers, but at very low stack temperatures severe corrosion and fouling

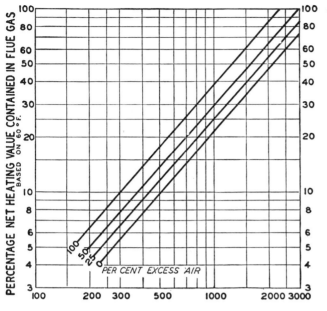

FIG. 14-2. Fuel-oil-combustion chart based on net heat of combustion. (*Oil Gas J.*)

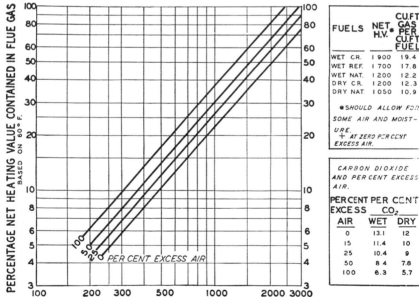

FIG. 14-3. Gas-combustion chart based on net heat of combustion. (*Oil Gas J.*)

occur in the air heaters and economizers of boilers due mainly to the sulfur dioxide (or trioxide) in the flue gases. Table 14-7 indicates the sulfur content of typical fuels and the furnace atmospheres produced by them,[6] as well as minimum metal temperatures (related to dew points) for air heaters or economizers. Significant amounts of sodium sulfate and vanadium in the fuel require even lower "end" temperatures, but

TABLE 14-7. EFFECT OF SULFUR ON STACK TEMPERATURE OF POWER PLANT BOILERS

Per cent sulfur	Type of fuel	Grains SO_2 per 100 cu ft		Minimum metal temp[a] in tubular air heaters or economizers		
					Coal[b]	
		Coal	Oil	Oil[b]	Chain grate	Pulverized
1.0	Lowest of fuel oils	62	49	180[c]	180[c]	160[c]
1.22	East Coast oil	76	60	180[c]	180[c]	160[c]
2.0	....	124	98	180[c]	205	160[c]
2.4	Avg East Coast bunkering fuel	148	118	200	220	160[c]
3.0	....	186	147	222	239	176[c]
4.0	Middle West coal or Middle East fuel oil	248	196	244	259	193[c]
5.0	....	310	235	258	276	206[c]
6.0	Highest sulfur fuel oils	371	287	270	290	217
8.0	Lowest grade Western coal	496				

[a] Really feedwater inlet temp to economizer.
[b] W. H. Rowand, Bull. 3–407 of Babcock & Wilcox Co.
[c] Minimum of 212°F on all economizers.

difficulties with such fuels are being cured by the use of additives. In burning acid sludge or hydrogen sulfide, the minimum metal temperature at the air preheater may be limited to 300 to 400°F,[7] and a coating of milk of lime is sometimes applied to the preheater tubes after their usual washing.

Metal temperatures in the economizer section can be raised by recirculation of hot air or by heating of the inlet air with steam heaters, but both of these remedies result in higher costs or constitute a penalty against high sulfur fuels.

The Burning of Oil Fuels. Although steam-atomizing burners are

[6] Nelson, W. L., *Oil Gas J.*, Dec. 22, 1952, p. 353; Mar. 9, 1953, p. 126; and Sept. 13, 1954, p. 138.

[7] Robinson and Gurney, Steam and Power Economy . . . , ASME Meeting, Sept. 25–28, 1950; or see *Pet. Processing*, June, 1952, p. 806. Also Andrea, K. S., *Oil Gas J.*, Jan. 4, 1954, p. 66.

expensive to operate (see Table 14-8[8]) they are used widely in refineries because they can handle almost any fuel and because steam is universally available. Burners are of two main designs:

1. *Outside-mix* burners by which the oil is released into a high-velocity sheet of steam. Oil and steam issue from the burner through separate openings. Much of the energy in the steam is wasted, and the steam consumption is relatively high.

TABLE 14-8. APPROXIMATE DIRECT OPERATING COST OF BURNING 100 GAL OF FUEL OIL

	Cents
Oil-pressure atomizing	5.0
Low-pressure air-atomizing	7.5
Intermediate-pressure air-atomizing	10–25
Steam-atomizing	20–30
High-pressure air-atomizing	60

2. *Inside-mix* burners are most widely used. In these the steam and oil are mixed in a chamber within the burner, and they issue together from the burner as a single stream. Foam formed in the mixing chamber is directed by the shape and direction of the burner tip so that the flame is of proper shape and size for the furnace box. As foam issues from the tip, it bursts into a fine mist of oil particles.

Residual fuels have better atomizing or foaming properties. Gas oils or distillate fuels do not atomize easily unless they are mixed with residual fuels, but naphthas can be burned satisfactorily if a suitable burner tip is employed. Air-atomizing burners using low-pressure compressed air are sometimes used for asphaltic residues, acid sludge mixtures, or dirty residues. Acid sludge tends to cause corrosion in steam-atomizing burners, and hence high-pressure spray nozzles are sometimes employed. Excessive mineral matter causes deposits of glazed solids on heating surfaces.

Viscous fuels should be heated to such a temperature that the Saybolt Universal viscosity is 130 to 250. Table 3-29 shows preheating temperature vs. Furol viscosity. The higher the temperature the better the performance unless vaporization occurs or unless the water content of the fuel is high. At temperatures past the flash point, operation may be erratic and the flame may splutter. Highly superheated steam may cause excessive coking within the burner tip if the oil temperature is high. About 0.1 sq ft of heating surface (steam coils) is required for each barrel of insulated fuel-oil storage. Heating coils for uninsulated tanks are discussed in connection with Fig. 17-9 and Example 17-7.

Rotary pumps are preferable because of the steady pressure they produce. The pulsation in oil pressure and the "breathing" of burners, caused by reciprocating pumps, can be eliminated by an air surge cham-

[8] Griswold, J., "Fuels, Combustion, and Furnaces," p. 285, McGraw-Hill Book Company, Inc., New York, 1946.

ber at the pump, but air must be added to the chamber with each work shift. Although the fuel may be fed by gravity at a head of only 10 to 15 ft, a pressure of 40 to 60 psig is often employed. To obtain satisfactory atomization of light gas oil a pressure of 125 psig may be required. The amount of atomizing steam for inside burners ranges from 0.2 to 0.5 lb per pound oil (1.6 to 4 lb steam per gallon) and may reach 10 lb per gallon for outside-mix burners. In general the higher the pressure and temperature of the oil, the lower the steam consumption. Moisture in the steam causes spluttering or sparks in the flame and if excessive may put out the flame. Steam may be superheated at the burner by a short length of steam line leading into and out of the furnace.

Robert Reed[9] analyzes oil-burner troubles somewhat as follows:

Spluttery or Sparky Flame. This in general may be caused by (1) wet steam, (2) suspended solids in the oil, (3) improper design of burner tips for the oil and the duty handled, or (4) foreign matter inside the burner or in the tip.

Long Smoky Flame. The cause may be (1) improper design of burner tip, (2) insufficient air for combustion, or (3) insufficient atomizing steam.

Failure of Ignition. This may be caused by (1) too much steam for atomization, (2) fuel pressure low, (3) fuel valve plugged, (4) improper design of tip or too small an included angle on the flame, or (5) wet steam or slugs of water from the steam line.

A dazzling white flame indicates too much excess air. A properly operated oil burner produces a perfectly stable yellow-white flame. A fluttery flame indicates that too much atomizing steam is being used. Puffing in the furnace may be caused by poor tip design, insufficient excess air, or partial stoppage of burner tip.

Mechanical-atomizing burners have not been generally used in the oil industry. However, a mechanical burner or a combination steam- and mechanical-atomizing burner is useful when firing inferior fuels, such as cracked residues that contain suspended carbon or acid sludges from lubricating-oil treating. These inferior fuels are supplied to the burner at 200 to 300°F and at a pressure of 100 to 200 psi. Acid sludge, without any treatment, can be burned in some mechanical burners, but more often the sludge is hydrolized with water and allowed to settle. Sludge may also be mixed with fuel oil and burned. The mixing is facilitated by heating to a temperature not exceeding 155°F. Gentle rolling with compressed air and recirculation by means of a pump (through filter screens) are the methods usually employed. Heating is usually done with steam jets because carbonaceous deposits tend to accumulate on heating surfaces. Sludges or sludge mixtures must be completely mixed at all times, and one refiner has found[10] that a homogenizing mill in the fuel circuit,

[9] *Oil Gas J.*, Mar. 11, 1943, p. 39.

[10] Thornton, D. P., Burn Acid Sludge . . . , *Pet. Processing*, October, 1948, p. 981.

for grinding particles of gritty sludge, is highly useful. The use of sludge as a fuel is not very profitable but other means of disposal are also expensive.

Extremely high-melting-point residues or fuels tend to congeal into particles (black smoke) which cannot be completely burned when the fuel meets large amounts of cold air at the burner. Such behavior can be alleviated by the use of short-flame combustion, substantial amounts of refractory at the mouth of the burner, preheating of the combustion air to the melting point of the fuel, or preheating of the fuel to 500 to 600°F.[11]

In large power installations, oil can be fired more cheaply than coal [see Eqs. (3-5a) and (3-5b)]. This is due to the greater thermal efficiency (2 to 35 per cent)[5] when firing oil, to the lower cost of operation, and to the smaller investment in storage and firing facilities.[12] During 1951, the advantage of firing oil rather than a ton of coal was about 16.5 cents, and this does not include a charge for the large cost of stoker equipment for coal because most large plants are already equipped to fire either coal or oil.

Firing Systems. The liquid fuels that are burned in refineries are often hardly more than waste products. Tars that are almost solid are common. Such fuels must be heated, and they must be circulated continuously past the burner to prevent solidification in the line (Fig. 14-4). The amount of circulation is 1.5 to 2.0 times as much as the oil burned. In large plants the circuit may be so long that a system of parallel flow must be used. The lines should be insulated, and a pair of strainers must be used with residual fuels. Pressure gauges on each side of the strainers will indicate plugging, and one strainer can filter the oil while the other is being cleaned.

Individual circulation systems are often maintained for each pipestill. With such an arrangement the rate of firing may be controlled by regulating the pressure in the fuel line without visiting the burner. The pressure may be conveniently regulated at a central control board. Such a system is not satisfactory unless clean, fluid fuels are available and unless minor adjustments of the firing rate are all that are necessary.

A method[3] of maintaining a constant-pressure fuel gas of uniform calorific value is indicated in Fig. 14-5. Liquid propane or butane may be fed into the system (sometimes actuated by an automatic calorimeter) to maintain the heating value, and natural gas is admitted to carry the main heating load if process gases are insufficient. When sufficient process gas is produced to maintain well over 30 lb pressure in the balance tank, all

[11] Palchik, E. H., How to Use Resid as Furnace Fuel, *Pet. Refiner*, November, 1955, p. 161.

[12] Nelson, W. L., *Oil Gas J.*, July 12, 1951, p. 106; July 19, 1951, p. 114; Sept. 20, 1951, p. 329; Dec. 22, 1952, p. 353; May 25, 1953, p. 265; June 1, 1953, p. 118; June 8, 1953, p. 141; and Sept. 13, 1954, p. 138.

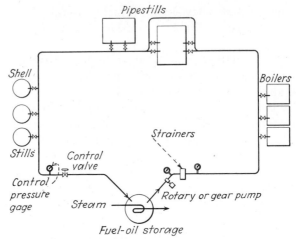

FIG. 14-4. Circulation system for firing fuel oil.

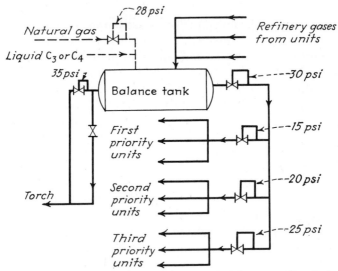

FIG. 14-5. Arrangement of a refinery gaseous-fuel system. (*Pet. Refiner.*)

three priorities of service receive gas. However, as the "make" of process gas decreases and the balance tank pressure falls below 25 lb, oil burners must be lighted on the third-priority units and finally on the second-priority units. The system should be so balanced that the first-priority units always receive gas.

Example 14-6. Analysis of Flue Gas from Fuel Analysis. Fuel 5 in Table 14-3 is burned with 50 per cent excess air. Compute the Orsat analysis of the flue gas and the analysis of the flue gas including water vapor.

Basis: 1 lb of Fuel 5.

$$\text{Moles C} = \frac{0.861}{12} = 0.0717$$

$$\text{Moles H}_2 = \frac{0.12}{2} = 0.0600$$

$$\text{Moles S} = \frac{0.0035}{32} = 0.0001$$

$$\text{Moles N}_2 \text{ and O}_2 = \frac{0.011}{30} = 0.0004 \text{ (assume half and half)}$$

Oxygen required (see Table 14-5):

			Mole
For carbon:	0.0717 × 1 =		0.0717
For hydrogen:	0.06 × 0.5 =		0.0300
For sulfur:	0.0001 × 1 =		0.0001
			0.1018

Less oxygen in fuel: $\dfrac{0.0004}{2} = -0.0002$

Oxygen required (no excess) =	0.1016
Excess oxygen (or air) = 0.1016 × 0.5 =	0.0508
Oxygen required at 50 per cent excess =	0.1524

Composition of air by volume is N_2 79.1 and O_2 20.9 per cent.

	Mole
Nitrogen with this oxygen: $0.1524 \times \dfrac{79.1}{20.9} =$	0.577
Nitrogen in fuel: $\dfrac{0.0004}{2} =$	0.0002
Nitrogen in flue gas =	0.5772

ORSAT ANALYSIS

Material	Number of moles	Per cent by volume
CO_2 (and SO_2).........	0.0717 and 0.0001	10.25
O_2 (excess)............	0.0508	7.26
N_2....................	0.5772	82.49
Total..............	......	100.00

ACTUAL ANALYSIS IN FURNACE

Material	Number of moles	Per cent by volume
CO_2 and (SO_2)..........	0.0718	9.4
O_2.....................	0.0508	6.7
N_2.....................	0.5772	76.0
H_2O*.................	0.0600	7.9
Total..............	......	100.0

* Table 14-5.

Example 14-7. Heat Balance of a Furnace. Fuel 9 (Table 14-3) is fired at 200°F using 0.4 lb (280°F) of steam per pound of fuel. The flue gas has an Orsat analysis of 13.0 per cent CO_2, 4.25 per cent O_2, and 82.75 per cent N_2. The heat gainfully used to heat oil amounts to 1,367,000 Btu. The stack temperature is 800°F. The air is at 80°F and has a relative humidity of 50 per cent. The vapor pressure of water at 80°F is 26.6 mm. The still is operating in a continuous manner.

Basis: 100 lb of oil 9, 60°F temperature datum.

The ultimate constituents in the fuel undergo the following chemical reactions:

$$
\begin{aligned}
C + O_2 &= CO_2 \\
H_2 + \tfrac{1}{2}O_2 &= H_2O \\
S + O_2 &= SO_2 \\
H_2O \text{ (liquid)} &= H_2O \text{ (vapor)}
\end{aligned}
$$

Moles of combustion products:

Carbon.............. $\dfrac{87.6}{12}$ = 7.3

Sulfur.............. $\dfrac{0.7}{32}$ = 0.02 (reported as CO_2 by Orsat)

Hydrogen........... $\dfrac{10.27}{2}$ = 5.14

Water.............. $\dfrac{0.05}{18}$ = 0.003 (neglect)

Undetermined........ $\dfrac{1.38}{30}$ = 0.05 (considered as O_2 and N_2, equal parts)

Material balance of carbon:

Moles of dry flue gas from 100 lb of fuel. Mole per cent = volume per cent (gases). All the carbon is found in the carbon dioxide (13 per cent).

$$
\begin{aligned}
\text{Moles } CO_2 \text{ (and } SO_2) \quad &= \quad 7.32 \\
\text{Moles } N_2 = 7.32 \times \frac{82.75}{13} \quad &= \quad 46.50 \\
\text{Moles } O_2 = 7.32 \times \frac{4.25}{13} \quad &= \quad 2.39 \\
\hline
\text{Total moles of dry flue gas} &= \overline{56.21} \text{ moles}
\end{aligned}
$$

Material balance of oxygen:

Air required:

$$
\begin{aligned}
\text{Moles } N_2 \text{ from air} = 46.5 - \frac{0.05}{2} \quad\quad &= 46.475 \\
\text{Moles } O_2 \text{ used} \quad = 46.475 \times \frac{20.9}{79.1} + .025 &= 12.28 \\
\text{Moles air} \quad = 46.475 \times \frac{1}{0.791} \quad\quad &= 58.7
\end{aligned}
$$

Percentage of excess air:

$$
\begin{aligned}
O_2 \text{ required for C and S} &= 7.32 \text{ moles} \\
O_2 \text{ for hydrogen} = \frac{5.14}{2} &= 2.57 \\
\hline
O_2 \text{ required} &= \overline{9.89} \text{ moles}
\end{aligned}
$$

$$
\text{Percentage of excess } O_2 \text{ or air} = \frac{12.28 - 9.89}{9.89} \times 100 = 24.2 \text{ per cent}
$$

Material balance of water vapor:

Water in	Moles
Atomizing steam $= 100 \times \dfrac{0.4}{18}$	$= 2.22$
From H_2 in fuel (same number moles as H_2)	$= 5.14$
From air $= \dfrac{13.3}{(760 - 13.3)} 58.7$	$= 1.04$
Free moisture in fuel (negligible)	$= 0.00$
Total	$= \overline{8.40}$

The water vapor leaving the system in the flue gas must equal the water coming into the system, or 8.4 moles.

Heat balance:

Heat Entering System		Btu
Net heating value of fuel	$17,479 \times 100 =$	$1,747,900$
Heat in air (note Fig. 14-1)	$58.7(336 - 196) =$	$8,210$
Heat in steam (see Fig. 14-1 or steam tables) $0.4 \times 100(2,200 - 260) \div 18$	$=$	$4,310$
Sensible heat content of fuel oil	$100(200 - 60)0.442 =$	$6,190$
		$\overline{1,766,610}$

All this heat will be recovered from the system if the flue gas is cooled to 60°F.

Heat Leaving System		Btu
Sensible heat content (see Fig. 14-1) at 800°F.		
CO_2	$7.32(7,600 - 245) =$	$53,900$
Water vapor	$8.4(6,800 - 260) =$	$54,900$
Diatomic gases (N_2 and excess O_2)	$48.89(5,500 - 200) =$	$259,000$
		$\overline{367,800}$

Summary of heat balance:

Heat	Btu	Per cent
Into system	1,766,610	100.0
Out of system:		
Useful heat (given)	1,367,000	77.35
Stack loss	367,800	20.85
Unaccounted for and losses	31,810	1.8
	1,766,610	100.0

Approximate stack loss using Fig. 14-2:
Stack loss at 800°F and with 13 per cent CO_2 in the flue gas (25 per cent excess air) = 19.8 per cent (in foregoing, 20.85 per cent)

Stack Draft. The draft[13] that stacks or chimneys will produce is discussed in all boiler and combustion textbooks. A draft of 0.5 to 0.7 in. water is adequate for nearly all refinery stills. The draft at the burner

[13] Nelson, W. L., *Oil Gas J.*, Mar. 15, 1947, p. 101; Mar. 29, 1947, p. 177; Apr. 12, 1947, p. 103; and Apr. 19, 1947, p. 135.

should be 0.1 to 0.2 in. water,[14] and according to Reed[9] the draft at the bridge wall or highest point at which gases are turned down in the still should not be less than 0.02 in. The draft at various elevations in the still can be computed from the following tabulation:[9]

Gas temperature, °F	Draft per ft, in. water
400	0.0057
800	0.0085
1200	0.0100
1800	0.0112
2000	0.0122

If the draft (or pressure) at any point in the still ranges much from atmospheric pressure, air will leak in causing large losses of heat up the stack, or flue gas will leak out (pressure in still) heating the walls and weakening the structure.

Steel stacks are used extensively in the petroleum industry. In these, the loss in gas temperature, particularly during a rainstorm, greatly reduces the stack draft,[15] and hence special tabulations of stack draft and stack capacity corrected for various weather conditions and friction losses due to the velocity of the stack gases have been published.[13] According to the Universal Oil Products Company,[16] the effective temperature in unlined steel stacks and the draft produced by them is indicated by Fig. 14-6 for an atmospheric temperature of 80°F. At lower atmospheric temperatures and during rainstorms, very much greater decreases in temperature are encountered.[13,15] Altitude affects the height and diameter of a stack by the following factors:[16]

Elevation, ft	Height	Diameter
2,000	1.16	1.03
4,000	1.36	1.06
6,000	1.58	1.10
8,000	1.84	1.13

At a mass velocity of about 0.6 lb per sq ft per sec (cold velocity 60°F of 7.5 ft per sec) friction losses are almost negligible but at 0.8 to 1.2 (the common design range) friction loss consumes 20 to 30 per cent of the static draft.[16]

[14] Rickerman, J. H., Heater Designs for the Petroleum Industry, *Trans. ASME*, **67** 531 (1945).

[15] Nelson, W. L., Loss in Temperature of Stack Gases, *Oil Gas J.*, Sept. 30, 1943, p. 56.

[16] Mekler, L. A., *Pet. Engr.*, June, 1956, p. C-26.

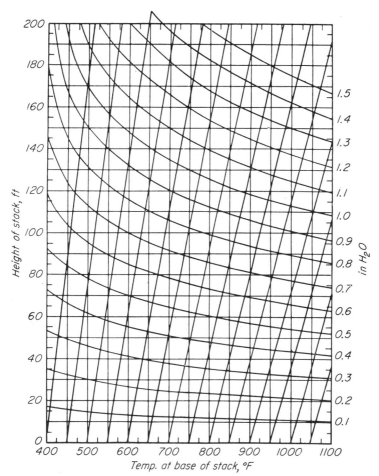

FIG. 14-6. Relationship between temperature at inlet, effective temperature, and draft of unlined steel stacks when the atmospheric temperature is 80°F. (*Universal Oil Products Co.*)

Example 14-8. Effect of Heat Losses on Stack Draft. Figure 14-6 is used as follows:

A 120-ft unlined steel stack receives gases at 800°F. The atmospheric temperature is 80°F. Follow the vertical 800°F line to intersection with the 120-ft line. The effective or average stack temperature can be read by following the slanting straight lines downward to read 680°F on the temperature scale, and the draft is found by following the sloping lines to the right (0.95 in. draft).

CHAPTER 15

VAPORIZATION AND CONDENSATION

The physical laws governing the distribution of a component between the liquid and the vapor above the liquid form the basis of many refinery operations. Among these processing operations are shell- or pipestill vaporization, fractionation, and condensation. In addition, the vapor-pressure laws may be applied to the estimation of fractionating-tower temperatures, partial condenser temperatures, and friction losses in tubular heaters and pipestills, and in computing the quantity of steam that is required for distillation and steam stripping.

Vaporization and Condensation. Vaporization may be defined as the change from the liquid to the vapor state. This change absorbs energy. When heat is applied to a mixture of hydrocarbons (a solution) under constant pressure, part of the energy is absorbed by the change of state and part is expended in raising the temperature of the remaining liquid. This rise in temperature increases the vapor pressure or the tendency of all components of the mixture to leave the liquid and enter the vapor phase. Therefore, the vapor from a liquid contains some of each of the components present in the liquid. However, the vapor is always richer in lower boiling components than the original liquid, unless the mixture is heated to a temperature at which it is completely vaporized, in which case the vapor will have the same composition as the original liquid. The equilibrium diagram shown in Fig. 15-1 illustrates these principles. Below the liquid line the mixture is entirely liquid, above the vapor line a pure vapor phase exists, and between the two lines a mixture of liquid and vapor is present. Raoult's law was assumed to be valid in computing Fig. 15-1.

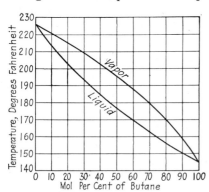

FIG. 15-1. Equilibrium-phase diagram of butane-pentane at 100 psia (Raoult's law).

434

These generalizations are equally valid whether the vapor is removed continuously or remains in contact with the liquid. Nevertheless, the manner of separation of the vapor has a quantitative effect on the composition of the distillate and of the remaining liquid.

Condensation is essentially the inverse of vaporization. It follows, therefore, that the condensate will be richer in higher-boiling and poorer in lower-boiling components than the original vapor and that the remaining vapor will be richer in lower-boiling components than the condensate.

Mechanism of Vaporization. The most common method of vapor formation is *batch vaporization* as conducted in the ASTM distillation or as practiced in early shellstill distillation or in small scale chemical plant operations. The mechanism is differential because, as the temperature is raised a small amount, a corresponding evolution of vapor takes place. As this vapor is removed and the temperature is again raised, another evolution of vapor occurs. In distilling a liquid mixture each component in the liquid exerts a partial vapor pressure or a part of the total vapor pressure, and every component tends to leave the mixture in proportion to its partial vapor pressure at that temperature. The lower boiling components, those with high vapor pressures, compose the most of the first vapors, but some remain in the liquid and are distilled later with other components whose boiling points are much higher. This behavior may be most easily pictured by conceiving that the high-velocity low-boiling molecules bump into slower moving molecules and lose the energy content that would normally cause them to leave the liquid and enter the vapor. Some of the slower moving molecules may receive enough energy by these impacts to leave the liquid, and this occurs because we find that high-boiling components are present in the first vapor even though the temperature is much lower than their boiling points.

Differential or batch vaporization may be mathematically formulated as follows. If L represents the liquid, x the percentage of a component in the liquid, and y the percentage of the component in the vapor, a material balance with respect to the component is

$$xL = (x - dx)(L - dL) + y\,dL$$
$$xL = xL - x\,dL - L\,dx + dx\,dL + y\,dL$$

The second order differential $dx\,dL$ may be neglected:

$$(x - y)\,dL = -L\,dx$$
$$\frac{dL}{L} = \frac{dx}{y - x}$$

The quantity that must be distilled in order to cause a particular change in composition may be determined by integrating between L_0, the initial quantity of liquid, and L_1 the final quantity:

$$\ln \frac{L_0}{L_1} = \int_{x_1}^{x_0} \frac{dx}{y - x}$$

The value of the function $dx/(y - x)$ may be obtained by graphically integrating between the limits x_1 and x_0. The various values of x are plotted against the corresponding values of $1/(y - x)$, and the area under the curve is the integral of the function. The relation between x and y may be obtained by Henry's law or Raoult's law. Data on two-component systems are all that are usually available.

Equilibrium or Flash Vaporization. The mechanism of this type of vaporization differs from differential vaporization in that the vapor is not removed as it is formed but is kept in intimate physical contact with the remaining liquid until the heating is completed. In the refinery such a method is practiced in the pipestill. Any vapor formed in the pipestill tubes is kept in contact with the remaining liquid until the mixture flows from the outlet of the still. Mechanical contacting is effected by the high velocity that results as soon as even a small quantity of vapor is produced. The term "flash" vaporization is unfortunate because it is not necessary to have a reduction in pressure or any very violent phenomenon of flashing.

The equilibrium-flash-vaporization (E.F.V.) curve is drawn just as the batch-vaporization curve, i.e., by plotting temperature against the percentage vaporized. Refer to Fig. 4-17 throughout the following discussion. As vaporization starts, i.e., at zero per cent vaporized, the E.F.V. curve lies above all other vapor-temperature curves. This situation arises because the molecules that normally would be vaporized at a low temperature are unable to separate themselves from the liquid, because they lose much of their energy content to the surrounding high-boiling molecules. However, after having vaporized a considerable percentage of liquid the bombardment of the many high-velocity vapor molecules succeeds in vaporizing enough of the material to cause the E.F.V. curve to cross other vapor-temperature curves. Note, however, that equilibrium flash vaporization is advantageous in all regions (0 to 100 per cent vaporized) with respect to the liquid temperature that must be attained. At all percentages vaporized, the already vaporized high-velocity vapor molecules deliver energy to the remaining liquid molecules causing some of them to be vaporized at temperatures below their normal boiling points. Thus, at 700°F, hydrocarbons boiling up to 890°F can, by flash vaporization, be distilled.

The saving in heat is not the only advantage. Thermal decomposition halts all distillations at liquid temperatures of approximately 700°F and flash vaporization permits the vaporization of materials that boil (when pure) above this temperature. Of course, steam or a low pressure may be used to distill high-boiling oils, but these modifications can be applied to any method of vapor formation.

Commercial Vaporization. In practice, the foregoing methods are often used in combination. *Successive flash* vaporization involves the use of two or more pipestills in series. As an example, crude oil is often heated in an exchanger system and flashed into a fractionating tower, and then the remaining liquid is heated in a pipestill and flashed in a second tower. Two-flash atmospheric and vacuum systems are also important. In such a system the crude oil is heated and flashed at atmospheric conditions and the residue of reduced crude oil (already at a high temperature) is flashed under vacuum to recover gas oil and light lubricating oils. A two-flash system is sometimes used in rerunning bright-stock solution. The naphtha in such a solution is flashed in one operation, and the remaining bright stock is further heated and flashed in the presence of steam. Other examples are the atmospheric-vacuum redistillation of pressure distillate and the production of well-fractionated solvents by the use of several heaters and fractionating towers.

The *continuous shellstill battery* is an operation involving flash vaporization but not flash vaporization alone. In pure flash vaporization the vapor is physically mixed with the remaining liquid, but in a shellstill battery the flash in each still occurs in the presence of an abnormally large quantity of residue liquid. Thus the concentration of slow-moving molecules is high, and these molecules tend to absorb the energy content of the lower boiling molecules. However, some molecules have energy contents bordering between liquid and vapor, and they vaporize. The equilibrium that is established is indeed complicated. In a sense, the laboratory batch distillation, with no fractionation, is equivalent to a shellstill battery having an infinite number of stills.

Distillation Curves. As a summary, a comparison of distillation curves by various vaporization methods is useful. Figure 4-17 shows vaporization temperatures plotted against percentage distilled for (1) flash, (2) ASTM, (3) Hempel, and (4) true-boiling-point distillations of a 35 API crude oil. The same relations hold true for other stocks but to a greater degree for narrow-boiling-range materials.

Although vapor-temperature curves are most widely used, the engineer should be more interested in the liquid temperatures required for a given vaporization than in the vapor temperatures. Hence the same four curves are compared in Fig. 4-17 by plotting liquid temperature against the percentage distilled.

CONDENSATION

In many ways condensation is just the reverse of vaporization, although some of the vaporization mechanisms cannot be mechanically duplicated in condensing equipment. Differential condensation, in which the condensate is removed as soon as it is formed, is not practiced commercially.

Equilibrium Condensation. Equilibrium condensation occurs in most commercial condensers. The condensed liquid is kept in contact with the remaining uncondensed vapor until condensation is complete. The *flash-*

vaporization and the *equilibrium-condensation* curves are identical if intimate physical contacting is maintained during both operations.

In large condensers of the tubular type the condenser usually consists of several separate condensing units and liquid is withdrawn from each. Each of these units is referred to as a *partial condenser*. However, partial condensation does not give an effective separation between products, and hence it is not generally used as a method of fractionation. The partial condensers that are used in a modern vacuum plant for the separation of gas oil and wax distillate may be an exception. This separation need not be exact, and hence partial condensers are satisfactory (Fig. 7-25). In the past, *dephlegmators** or partial-condensation towers, cooled either by air or water, were extensively used.

In certain plant equipment the vapor is suddenly cooled under equilibrium conditions, and such a process may be called *quench condensation*. Jet condensers embody this method, but they are not widely used. However, barometric condensers, in which steam is condensed with water, are common. Of more importance is the condensation of vapor on each plate of a fractionating tower by reflux. In this case, the condensation may take place in the presence of other vapor that does not condense. As an example, kerosene is condensed on a "side-draw" plate of a bubble tower. Gasoline vapor is also present at the plate, but it does not condense. The details of the application of this phase of condensation will be discussed in Chap. 16.

EQUILIBRIUM

In order to use any of the aforementioned operations, the equilibrium relations between liquids and vapors must be ascertained. In other words, the distribution of a component in the two phases after no further interchange takes place must be known. Although Dalton's law of partial pressures, Henry's law of gas solubility, and Raoult's law of vapor-liquid equilibrium are not exact, they are used extensively because complete data are not available.

Figure 15-1 shows the equilibrium relationships between liquid and vapor compositions for butane-pentane mixtures at 100 psia. Upon heating a liquid that contains 70 per cent butane and 30 per cent pentane, no vapor will be formed until the liquid equilibrium line is reached at 163°F. At this point an infinitesimal quantity of vapor will be formed having the composition corresponding to 163°F on the vapor curve, i.e., 88 per cent of butane. If heating is continued, the composition of the liquid

---

* The term "dephlegmator" is usually reserved for partial-condenser towers, but certain cracking processes have retained this name for their fractionating towers. They have changed the process of separation but have retained the older name.

must necessarily change along the liquid curve with the production of increasing quantities of vapor, the composition of which follows the vapor curve. The change in liquid and vapor compositions will continue thus until the total vapor has the composition of the original liquid and the liquid is completely vaporized. Further heating will merely superheat the vapor without changing its composition.

Partial Pressures of Vapor Components. In a mixture of gases, each gas exerts a pressure equal to the pressure that it would exert if it occupied the entire volume by itself, and the total pressure of the mixture is equal to the sum of the partial pressures of the component gases (Dalton's law). The pressure exerted by each component is called the "partial pressure* of the component" and is dependent on the total pressure and the volume or number of molecules of that component in the gas.

In the gas phase if π is the total pressure and y is the volume or mole fraction of an individual component in the mixture, the law of partial pressures may be expressed as

$$p = \text{partial pressure in vapor} = \pi y \qquad \text{or} \qquad \frac{p}{\pi} = y$$

For example, in a vapor mixture composed of 70 per cent butane and 30 per cent pentane at 100 psia pressure, the partial pressures are

$$\text{Partial pressure butane} = 100 \times 0.7 = 70 \text{ psi}$$
$$\text{Partial pressure pentane} = 100 \times 0.3 = 30 \text{ psi}$$

Partial Vapor Pressures of Liquid Components. Just as each component of a vapor exerts a partial pressure, each component of a liquid exerts a partial vapor pressure. This is dependent upon the concentration of the component in the liquid and the vapor pressure of the pure component. The escaping tendency of a component appears to depend upon the percentage of the surface area (mole fraction) covered by the component and the molecular energy (vapor pressure) of the component. If P is the vapor pressure of the pure component at a given temperature and x is the mole fraction of the same component in the liquid,

$$p = \text{partial vapor pressure in liquid} = Px$$

Expressed as a fraction of the total pressure,

$$\frac{p}{\pi} = \frac{P}{\pi} x$$

At equilibrium the partial pressure of a component in the gas is equal to the partial vapor pressure of the component in the liquid. Inasmuch as

* The term "partial pressure" is also used to denote fraction of the total pressure.

p/π is equal to y, the mole fraction of the component in the gas is

$$y = \frac{p}{\pi} = \frac{P}{\pi} x \quad \text{(Raoult's law)} \tag{15-1}$$

Considering two components,

$$\pi y_1 = P_1 x_1$$

and

$$\pi y_2 = P_2 x_2$$

adding

$$\pi(y_1 + y_2) = P_1 x_1 + P_2 x_2$$

but

$$x_2 = 1 - x_1 \quad \text{and} \quad y_1 + y_2 = 1$$

$$x_1 = \frac{\pi - P_2}{P_1 - P_2} \quad \text{and} \quad x_2 = \frac{\pi - P_1}{P_2 - P_1}. \tag{15-2}$$

$$y_1 = \frac{P_1}{\pi} x_1 \quad \text{and} \quad y_2 = \frac{P_2}{\pi} x_2$$

Example 15-1. Raoult's Law. A liquid consists of 42.5 per cent butane by volume and 57.5 per cent pentane by volume at 60°F (see Fig. 15-1). If the liquid is heated to its boiling point of 180°F at 100 psia, what will be the composition of the vapor that is produced? (See Example 5-15, or Fig. 5-25 or 5-27.)

$$\text{Vapor pressure of } C_4H_{10} \text{ at } 180°F = 152 \text{ psi}$$
$$\text{Vapor pressure of } C_5H_{12} \text{ at } 180°F = 56 \text{ psi}$$
$$\text{Sp gr at } 60°F \text{ of } C_4H_{10} = 0.585, \text{ and } C_5H_{12} = 0.631$$

Basis: 100 gal of the mixture. Assume Raoult's law is valid.

$$\text{Moles of } C_4H_{10} = \frac{42.5(8.33 \times 0.585)}{58} = 3.57$$

$$\text{Moles of } C_5H_{12} = \frac{57.5(8.33 \times 0.631)}{72} = 4.20$$

$$\text{Total moles} = 7.77$$

$$x_1 = \text{mole fraction } C_4H_{10} \text{ in liquid} = \frac{3.57}{7.77} = 0.46$$

$$x_2 = \text{mole fraction } C_5H_{12} \text{ in liquid} = \frac{4.20}{7.77} = 0.54 \text{ or } (1 - 0.46)$$

See Eq. (15-1):

$$y_1 = \text{mole fraction of } C_4H_{10} \text{ in vapor} = {}^{152}\!/_{100}\ 0.46 = 0.70$$
$$y_2 = \text{mole fraction of } C_5H_{12} \text{ in vapor} = {}^{56}\!/_{100}\ 0.54 = 0.30$$

Thus a liquid containing 46 per cent butane and 54 per cent pentane (mole per cent) at 180°F and 100 psi is in equilibrium with vapor containing 70 per cent butane and 30 per cent pentane (see Example 15-3 and also Fig. 15-1).

General Vapor-Liquid Relationship. When applied to complex mixtures the general relationship for a system that contains no inert components (those which do not occur in significant amounts in one of the phases) and in which all components form an ideal solution in the liquid phase is

Pressure $= \pi y_1 + \pi y_2 + \pi y_3 +$ etc.

(partial pressures, gaseous phase)

$$= P_1 x_1 + P_2 x_2 + P_3 x_3 + \text{etc.} = \text{vapor pressure} \quad (15\text{-}3)$$

(partial vapor pressures, liquid phase)

The symbols are the same as those used on the preceding pages. In addition to this general relationship the partial pressure of each component is independently equal to its partial vapor pressure in the liquid, as indicated in Eq. (15-1) or Eq. (15-4).

Unfortunately, the ratio of vapor pressure P to the total pressure π used in Eqs. (15-1) and (15-3) is not a constant. It is altered by the total pressure and to some extent by the kind of materials associated with it in the mixture, particularly those far removed in boiling point. For this reason, the ratio y/x must be determined experimentally.

$$K = \frac{y}{x} = \frac{P}{\pi} \text{ approx.} \quad (15\text{-}4)$$

Equation (15-3) expressed in terms of equilibrium ratios or constants (K's or P/π's) becomes

$$1.0 = y_1 + y_2 + y_3 + \text{etc.} = K_1 x_1 + K_2 x_2 + K_3 x_3 + \text{etc.} = 1.0 \quad (15\text{-}5)$$

Finally, an inert gas may be present, designated as y_1 in Eq. (15-6); or an immiscible liquid may be present, designated as material 1 in Eq. (15-7). Of course K's may be used as well as P's in these two equations.

$$\pi = \pi y_1 + \pi(y_2 + y_3 + \text{etc.}) = \pi y_1 + (P_2 x_2' + P_3 x_3' + \text{etc.})$$
$$= \pi y_1 + \text{vapor pressure of solution} \quad (15\text{-}6)$$

In this equation (15-6) the vapor pressure of the liquid is less than the total pressure to the extent of the partial pressure of the inert gas.

$$\pi = \pi y_1 + \pi(y_2 + y_3 + \text{etc.}) = P_1 + (P_2 x_2' + P_3 x_3' + \text{etc.})$$
$$= P_1 + \text{vapor pressure of solution} \quad (15\text{-}7)$$

Likewise the vapor pressure of the hydrocarbon solution in Eq. (15-7) is less than the total pressure by the amount of the vapor pressure of the immiscible component. Prime marks are used on the x's of Eqs. (15-6) and (15-7) to indicate that they add up to 1.0 without regard to the amount of inert gas or of immiscible liquid that is associated with the liquid solution.

Effect of Steam. In many petroleum distillations, steam is admitted to the space in which vaporization occurs. The steam reduces the partial pressure in the vapor by Dalton's law. The boiling point of a material may be reduced in only two ways. The pressure may be reduced, or some inert gas such as steam may be introduced. In both cases, if the boiling point is reduced the same number of degrees, the concentration of oil molecules in a unit volume of vapor is the same. Mathematically, this is the situation represented by Eq. (15-6). The πy_1 term represents the steam, and there is no corresponding liquid term for the right-hand side of the equation. Thus, the effect of steam (or a truly inert gas) is to cause the system to act as if the pressure were lower.

If O denotes the moles of oil vapor, S the moles of steam, p_o the partial pressure of the oil vapor, p_s the partial pressure of the steam, and π the total pressure,

$$\frac{O}{O + S} = \frac{p_o}{\pi}$$

and

$$\frac{S}{O + S} = \frac{p_s}{\pi}$$

Dividing,

$$\frac{S}{O} = \frac{p_s}{p_o} \quad \text{or} \quad S = O\frac{p_s}{p_o}$$

but

$$p_s + p_o = \pi$$

and

$$S = O\frac{\pi - p_o}{p_o} = O\frac{p_s}{p_o} \tag{15-8}$$

The steam need not be bubbled through the oil, although more effective mixing results by so doing. The derivation of Eq. (15-1) shows that if the partial pressure in the gas phase is reduced, the partial vapor pressure in the liquid must decrease. Thus the use of steam causes vaporization to proceed until the partial vapor pressure in the liquid is equal to the partial pressure in the gas phase. Gurwitsch and Moore[1] have reported that steam is more effective in reducing the boiling point than Dalton's law indicates. Nevertheless, the error that is introduced by the use of Dalton's law in design work is probably not important.

The foregoing discussion applies primarily to the gaseous phase. The situation in the liquid phase is different from any situation discussed heretofore, because oil and water are not soluble in each other. In the liquid phase the water exerts its full vapor pressure, but each of the mutually soluble constituents exerts only its partial vapor pressure as shown in Eq. (15-7). If the temperature is high, the vapor pressure of water is so great that no liquid water exists, but at low temperatures or high pressures an insoluble water-oil system must be handled. In most instances, trial-and-error computations are necessary.

Example 15-2. Steam Required for Distillation. A temperature of 370°F is required to vaporize 66.5 per cent of the pressure distillate (Fig. 4-24) by flash vaporization. It is desired to reduce the temperature to 340°F by means of steam. Vaporization takes place at atmospheric pressure.

[1] Gurwitsch, L., and H. Moore, "Scientific Principles of Petroleum Technology," 2d ed., D. Van Nostrand Company, Inc., Princeton, N.J., 1932.

Basis: 100 moles of oil vapor.

In order to reduce the boiling point from 370 to 340°F, the vaporization must be conducted at 490 mm pressure (Fig. 5-27). Enough steam to reduce the partial pressure in the gas phase to 490 mm will be used [see Eq. (15-8)].

$$\frac{S}{100} = \frac{(760 - 490)}{490}$$
$$S = 55 \text{ moles}$$

or
$$= 55 \times 18 = 990 \text{ lb}$$

If the pressure in the tower were 10 psig,

$$\frac{10}{14.7} 760 + 760 = 1{,}277 \text{ mm}$$

$$S = \frac{(1{,}277 - 490)}{490} 100 = 158.5 \text{ moles or } 2{,}860 \text{ lb}$$

Equilibrium Data. The so-called "equilibrium constant" designated as K is not a constant in the ordinary sense because it is a function of the kind of material and the amounts and kinds of other materials that are present, of the temperature, and of the pressure.[2] It is merely the ratio of y to x. However, there are particular situations in which the ratios can be estimated with some accuracy. In general, Raoult's law [Eqs. (15-1) and (15-2)] may be employed for the normal paraffin hydrocarbons if the pressure is below 60 psi.[3] As the pressure approaches the critical pressure of the system, the deviation becomes great. This is indicated in Fig. 15-2 for the high-boiling hydrocarbons or petroleum fractions[4] contained in mixtures of 82.9 API butane-free naphtha (only pentanes, hexanes, and heptanes) and a 40.6 API furnace distillate having an initial boiling point of 181°F but a 10 per cent point of 366°F. The dotted lines indicate the K values of each of the cuts when no other cuts are present. Note that Fig. 15-2 is only for a temperature of 660°F. The point of convergency shown on such a diagram applies only to the particular set of components (or fractions) studied in plotting the diagram. If only two (or a particular range) of the fractions (or hydrocarbons) are involved, they will form their own point of convergency, which is dependent on their particular critical point or critical behavior. The point of convergency is reasonably well defined in the case of complex high-boiling mixtures such as these studied in Fig. 15-2, but for natural-gas–crude-oil mixtures the situation is vitally dependent on the composition because the properties of such gases as methane, ethane, and propane differ greatly

[2] Sage, Hicks, and Lacey, Tentative Equilibrium Constants for Light Hydrocarbons, API Meeting, Wichita, Kans., June, 1938; also *Ref. Nat. Gaso. Mfr.*, July, 1938, p. 350.

[3] Brown and Souders, *Oil Gas J.*, May 26, 1932, p. 41.

[4] White and Brown, Phase Equilibria at High Temperatures, *Ind. Eng. Chem.*, **34**, 1162 (1942).

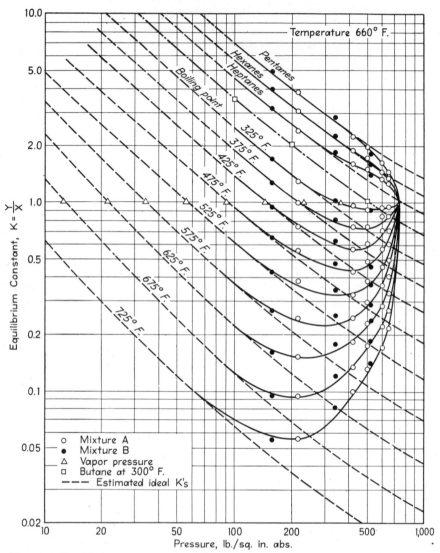

FIG. 15-2. Equilibrium constants (or ratios) at 660°F for the components contained in two complex mixtures plotted as a function of pressure. (*White and Brown, Ind. Eng. Chem.*)

from one another. If the point of convergence (Fig. 15-2) can be determined for a particular mixture, then the pattern of the equilibrium ratio diagram can be approximated with fair accuracy. The convergence pressure is a known point, and the equilibrium ratios at low pressure where Raoult's Law is applicable constitute a series of lines. Accordingly, attention is centering on methods of determining or estimating the con-

TABLE 15-1. EQUILIBRIUM CONSTANTS FOR METHANE

Pressure, psia	At 100°F for less-volatile constituents of these molecular weights[a]					At 160°F for less-volatile constituents of these molecular weights[a]					At 220°F for less-volatile constituents of these molecular weights[a]					At 400°F when associated with a 200-molecular-weight solvent[b]
	60	75	100	200	300	60	75	100	200	300	60	75	100	200	300	200
14.7	....	224	247	259	203	....	247	285	276	226	....	248	293	287	228	292
20.0	....	165	181	190	149	....	181	210	203	166	....	182	216	211	168	220
40.0	....	83[c]	91	96	75	....	91	105	102	83	....	92	108	106	84	110
60.0	....	55[c]	61	64	50	....	61	70	68	56	....	61	72	71	56	75
100.0	....	33[c]	37	39	31	....	36	42	41	34	....	37	43	43	34	46
150.0	....	22[c]	25	26	21	....	25	28	28	23	....	25	29	29	23	30
200.0	....	17[c]	19	20	16	....	18	21	21	17	....	19	22	22	18	23
300.0	11[c]	12	13	13	11	....	13	14	14	12	....	13	15	15	12	15
400.0	8[c]	9	10	10	8	....	10	11	11	9	....	10	11	11	9	11
500.0	6.6	7.2	7.9	8.2	6.8	6.8	7.7	8.7	8.9	7.4	7.1	8.0	8.9	9.1	7.5	9.4
750.0	4.5	5.0	5.5	5.7	4.8	4.6	5.3	5.9	6.2	5.2	4.9	5.5	6.1	6.3	5.3	6.4
1,000.0	3.4	3.9	4.3	4.5	3.9	3.5	4.1	4.5	4.8	4.1	3.7	4.2	4.6	4.9	4.2	5.1
3,000.0	....	1.2	1.7	2.1	1.8	....	....	1.7	2.1	1.9	....	....	1.7	2.1	2.0	

[a] Only for a system whose less-volatile constituent has a viscosity-gravity factor of 0.82. Data from Sage, Hicks, and Lacey, Tentative Equilibrium Constants for Light Hydrocarbons, API Meeting, Wichita, Kans., June, 1938.

[b] At temperatures above 220°F, G. G. Brown, *Pet. Engr.*, April, 1943.

[c] Figures rounded out to whole numbers, here and in many other instances.

445

TABLE 15-2. EQUILIBRIUM CONSTANTS FOR ETHANE

Pressure, psia	At 100°F for less-volatile constituents of these molecular weights[a]			At 160°F for less-volatile constituents of these molecular weights[a]			At 220°F for less-volatile constituents of these molecular weights[a]			For a 200-molecular-weight solvent less volatile constituent at these temperatures[b]			
	100	200	300	100	200	300	100	200	300	280°F	340°F	400°F	460°F
14.7	37.1	38.7	41.2	56.5	55.7	56.9	75.6	77.2	73.7	92.0	103.0	113.0	122.0
20.0	27.3	28.5	30.3	41.5	42.5	41.9	55.6	56.9	54.2	67.6	76.0	83.0	90.0
40.0	13.8	14.4	15.3	20.9	21.4	21.1	27.8	28.6	27.3	34.0	38.2	42.0	46.0
60.0	9.2	9.7	10.3	14.0	14.3	14.2	18.6	19.2	18.4	22.9	26.0	28.8	31.0
100.0	5.6	5.9	6.3	8.5	8.7	8.7	11.2	11.7	11.2	14.0	16.0	17.9	19.3
150.0	3.84	3.99	4.26	5.73	5.90	5.90	7.56	7.88	7.67	9.50	10.9	12.2	13.4
200.0	2.93	3.06	3.28	4.35	4.49	4.52	5.72	6.04	5.90	7.25	8.40	9.40	10.3
300.0	2.05	2.13	2.27	2.96	3.09	3.15	3.89	4.13	4.13	5.05	5.90	6.60	7.2
400.0	1.61	1.66	1.79	2.30	2.41	2.46	2.96	3.22	3.23	3.95	4.60	5.20	5.75
500.0	1.35	1.38	1.50	1.90	2.00	2.07	2.42	2.68	2.71	3.30	3.80	4.30	4.80
750.0	1.04	1.04	1.16	1.35	1.46	1.56	1.70	1.93	2.02	2.36	2.80	3.15	3.50
1,000.0	.....	0.93	1.06	1.09	1.22	1.33	1.35	1.59	1.69	1.91	2.24	2.53	2.77
3,000.0	.....	0.74	0.93	.....	0.83	0.97	.....	0.94	1.06				

[a] The less-volatile constituent has a viscosity-gravity constant of 0.82. Data from Sage, Hicks, and Lacey, Tentative Equilibrium Constants for Light Hydrocarbons, API Meeting, Wichita, Kans., June, 1938.

[b] For temperatures above 220°F, G. G. Brown, *Pet. Engr.*, April, 1943.

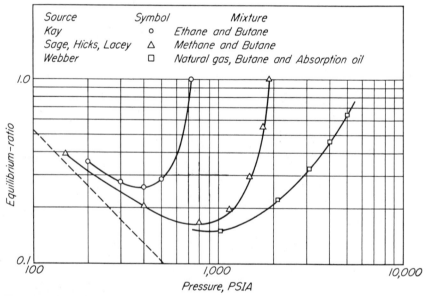

FIG. 15-3. Equilibrium ratios of *n*-butane at 100°F in mixtures with ethane, methane, and with natural gas in absorption oil. (*Pet. Refiner.*)

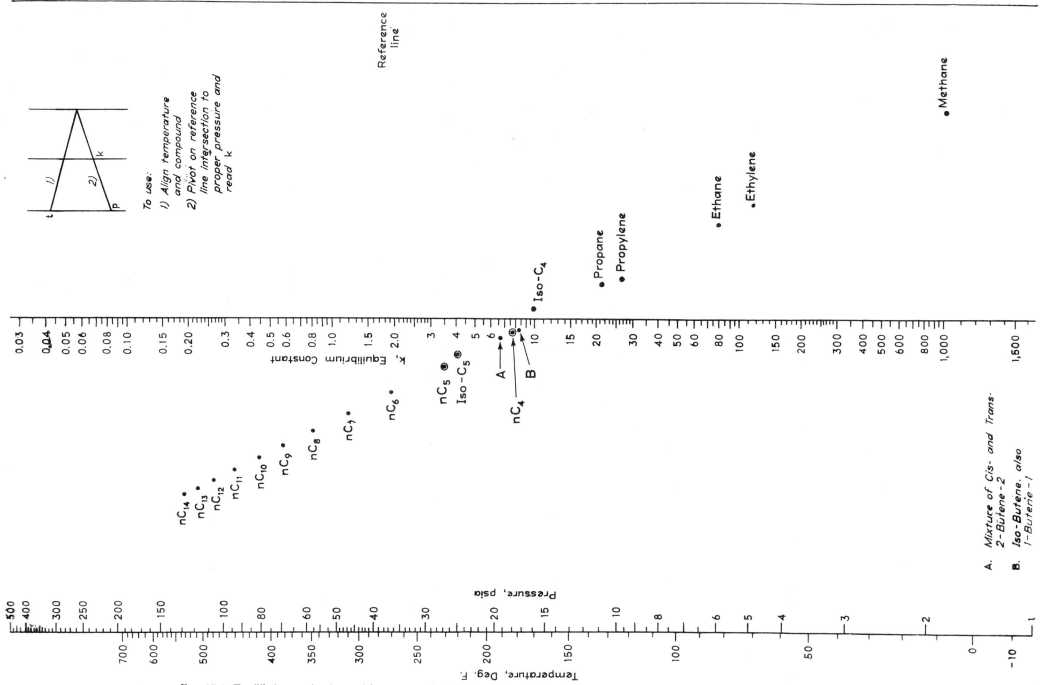

Fig. 15-4. Equilibrium ratios for multicomponent hydrocarbon systems at moderate temperatures. (*Miller and Barley, Ind. Eng. Chem.*)

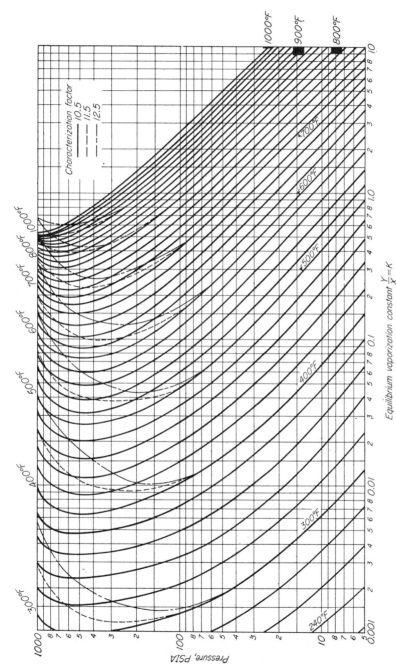

FIG. 15-5. Equilibrium ratios for petroleum fractions that boil at 600°F. (Phillips Pet. Co.)

447

vergence pressure,[5,6] by correlation of the dozens of systems that have been studied experimentally.

The general effect of the kind of mixture on the equilibrium constants of methane and ethane is indicated in Tables 15-1 and 15-2, wherein less volatile constituents ranging from 60 to 300 molecular weight are considered. Examination of Fig. 15-2 also shows clearly that the equilibrium constants of the low-volatility components of a mixture are also affected by the kind of more volatile materials associated with them. Likewise, Fig. 15-3 shows the effect of methane, ethane, and the normal components of natural gas on the equilibrium ratios of normal butane.[6] The dashed line indicates the ratios obtained from Raoult's law.

Inasmuch as experimental values of equilibrium ratios for all systems will not be complete for many years, a folded nomographic[7] chart (Fig. 15-4) is offered as an approximation. Tables 15-1 and 15-2 are more accurate than Fig. 15-4 for methane and ethane, and in general the K values of Fig. 15-4 are not accurate at pressures approaching the convergency pressure of the system, especially if the component is far removed in boiling point from the main boiling range of the mixture. Finally, Fig. 15-5 is an indication[8] of the effect of Characterization Factor on the equilibrium ratios of high-boiling hydrocarbons. Thus, in the lowest temperature ranges, ratios based on the vapor pressures of Figs. 5-25 to 5-27 may be used, but at pressures approaching the convergence pressure, ratios similar to those of Fig. 15-5 are necessary.

For precise equilibrium ratios it is necessary to resort to elaborate sets of curves or tabulations. Ratios for the lighter hydrocarbons are available in the NGAA Equilibrium Data Book,[9] or the Equilibrium Constant and Fugacity Charts of the M. W. Kellogg Co.[10] Information on higher-boiling oils is scant.

Example 15-3. Equilibrium Relations at High Pressures. Example 15-1 will be repeated using the actual equilibrium constants rather than assuming that Raoult's law is valid.

The composition of a butane-pentane mixture that boils at 180°F will not be 46 per cent butane (which was used in Example 15-1) because this composition and Fig. 15-1

---

[5] Lenoir et al., Vapor-Liquid Equilibrium Ratios (2 parts), *Pet. Refiner*, October, p. 121, and December, p. 115, 1953.

[6] Winn, F. W., Equilibrium K's by Nomograph, *Pet. Refiner*, June, 1954, p. 131.

[7] Miller and Barley, Correlation of Vapor-Liquid Equilibria . . . , *Ind. Eng. Chem.*, **36**, 1018 (1944).

[8] Poettmann and Mayland, Equilibrium Constants for . . . Fractions of Varying Characterization Factor, *Pet. Refiner*, July, 1949, p. 101.

[9] Natural Gasoline Association of America, Kennedy Bldg., Tulsa, Okla., 1955. Basic equations of the vapor-liquid ratios have been computed, and punch cards for use with computation machines are available.

[10] *Technical Data Book*, over 320 charts. New York, 1950.

were based on the assumption that Raoult's law was valid. The composition of the mixture that boils at 180°F can be found from the following expression, which is the same as Eq. (15-2) but stated in terms of K's:

$$x_1 = \frac{1 - K_2}{K_1 - K_2}$$

Equilibrium constants can be obtained from Fig. 15-4 by connecting temperature (180°F) on the left with the compound point to locate a reference point at the right. The reference point is then connected with the pressure (100 psig), which is also on the left scale or line, and K's are read on the center scale. Accordingly,

$$K_1 \text{ for butane } = 1.43$$
$$K_2 \text{ for pentane } = 0.56$$
$$x_1 = \frac{1 - 0.56}{1.43 - 0.56} = 0.505, \quad \text{and} \quad x_2 = 0.495$$
$$y_1 = K_1 x_1 = 1.43 \times 0.505 = 0.723$$
$$y_2 = K_2 x_2 = 0.56 \times 0.495 = 0.277$$

Note that neither the liquid nor the vapor composition is the same as in Example 15-1.

Equilibrium Relations for Complex Mixtures. The relationships of Eqs. (15-3) and (15-5) may be applied in the same manner as in Example 15-1 or 15-3 to the solution of problems that involve complex mixtures, except that trial-and-error methods must be used. The percentage vaporized at a given temperature can be computed, and the composition of the residue liquid and vapor can also be determined.

Consider 100 moles of a feedstock called F consisting of F_1, F_2, F_3, etc., moles of the different components designated by the subscripts 1, 2, 3, etc. By equilibrium vaporization of this mixture, by heating to a given temperature at a fixed pressure, V moles of gas is produced which contains V_1, V_2, V_3, etc., moles of the several components. A liquid residue, L moles, is left behind, and it also consists of L_1, L_2, L_3, etc., moles of the several components that constitute the feed.

By a material balance:

Feedstock............$F = F_1 + F_2 + F_3 + \cdots$
Vapor................$V = V_1 + V_2 + V_3 + \cdots$
Residue liquid.........$L = L_1 + L_2 + L_3 + \cdots$

The mole fraction of each component may be expressed as

$$\frac{F_1}{F} \quad \frac{F_2}{F} \quad \frac{V_2}{V} \quad \frac{L_3}{L}, \text{ etc.}$$

Furthermore, for the total material or for any component, material balance equations of this nature may be written

$$F = L + V \qquad F_1 = L_1 + V_1 \qquad \text{and} \qquad F_n = L_n + V_n$$

Henry's law applied to any component is

$$\frac{V_1}{V} = K_1 \frac{L_1}{L} \quad \text{and} \quad \frac{V_n}{V} = K_n \frac{L_n}{L}$$

or
$$V_1 = K_1 L_1 \frac{V}{L} \qquad V_3 = K_3 L_3 \frac{V}{L}, \text{ etc.}$$

Substituting $(F - V)$ for L, for each component,

$$V_1 = K_1(F_1 - V_1) \frac{V}{L}, \text{ etc.}$$

Solving for V_1 and simplifying

$$V_1 = \frac{K_1 F_1}{(L/V) + K_1}, \text{ etc.}$$

Since the sum of volumes or moles is the total moles of vapor,

$$\frac{K_1 F_1}{(L/V) + K_1} + \frac{K_2 F_2}{(L/V) + K_2} + \frac{K_3 F_3}{(L/V) + K_3} \cdots, \text{ etc.} = V \quad (15\text{-}9)$$

A similar statement assuming Raoult's law but stated for the liquid residue is as follows:

$$\frac{F_1 \pi}{\pi + P_1(V/L)} + \frac{F_2 \pi}{\pi + P_2(V/L)} + \frac{F_3 \pi}{\pi + P_3(V/L)} \cdots = L \quad (15\text{-}10)$$

In this equation π refers to the total pressure, and P_1, P_2, etc., to the vapor pressure of each component. The feed F may be totally a liquid, a vapor, or a mixture of liquid and vapor.

In solving these equations it is necessary to assume a value of L (or V); and by substituting this value, a value of L can be computed. If the computed value is not the same as the assumed value, other assumptions must be made until finally the assumption checks the computed value. By solving the equation for several temperatures, an equilibrium-flash-vaporization (E.F.V.) curve may be drawn, but such curves are usually not so accurate as the empirical curves described on pages 112 to 119 unless precise equilibrium ratios for the system are available. The partition between liquid and vapor will occur at or near the component whose vapor pressure is equal to the pressure of the system (or $K = 1.0$).

Graphical methods[11] of conducting the trial-and-error solution are useful if numerous computations must be made, but they are of little assistance in occasional computations.

Example 15-4. Equilibrium Vaporization of Complex Mixtures. A wild gasoline contains 15 per cent CH_4, 10 per cent C_2H_6, 30 per cent C_3H_8, 5 per cent iC_4H_{10}, 10 per cent C_4H_{10}, 15 per cent C_5H_{12}, and 15 per cent C_6H_{14} and heavier materials. Vaporization is conducted at 232 psia and at a temperature of 100°F. What is the composi-

[11] Nelson, W. L., *Oil Gas J.*, June 22, 1937, p. 63; Scheibel, E. G., *Pet. Refiner*, July, 1948, p. 136; Reilly, P. M., *Pet. Refiner*, July, 1951, p. 132; and Wilson, C. L., *Pet. Refiner*, June, 1952, p. 131.

tion of the residue gasoline and of the gas that is vaporized? Basis: 100 moles (or 100 volumes) of gas.

Since Eq. (15-10), which assumes Raoult's law, is the more complicated, this equa' tion will be used. Note, however, that Raoult's law is not valid at these conditions and that more exact results would be obtained by using Eq. (15-9).

Inasmuch as the vapor pressures of C_3H_8 and C_2H_6 are 194 and 750 psi, respectively, and the vaporization pressure is 232, the split will occur between these components, or the amount of vapor will be something larger than 25 per cent. Assume $L = 70$ (see Table 15-3, column 5).

For $L = 70$,

$$\frac{V}{L} = \frac{100 - 70}{70} = 0.429$$

Solving for L_3, as an example [Eq. (15-10)],

$$P_3 = \text{vapor pressure of } C_3H_8 = 194 \text{ psi}$$

$$L_3 = \frac{F_3\pi}{\pi + P_3(V/L)} = \frac{30 \times 232}{232 + 194 \times 0.429} = 22.0$$

The values of L_1, L_2, L_4, etc., are computed in a tabulated form in Table 15-3.

TABLE 15-3

(1)	(2)	(3)	(4)	(5)	(6)	(7)	(8)
Material	Value of F's, moles	Value of P's, psi	F's π	P's $\frac{V}{L}$	(5) $+ \pi$	(4) $\div$ (6) L's, moles	(2) $-$ (7) V's, moles
CH$_4$.........	15	4,100	3,480	1,755.0	1,987.0	1.75	13.25
C$_2$H$_6$........	10	750	2,320	321.0	553.0	4.2	5.8
C$_3$H$_8$........	30	194	6,950	83.1	315.1	22.0	8.0
iC$_4$H$_{10}$......	5	78	1,160	33.4	265.4	4.38	0.62
C$_4$H$_{10}$......	10	56	2,320	24.0	256.0	9.06	0.94
C$_5$H$_{12}$......	15	19	3,480	8.1	240.1	14.5	0.50
C$_6$H$_{14}$+.....	15	4	3,480	1.7	233.7	14.9	0.10
Total......	...	.....	.....	....	....	70.79	29.21

Table 15-3 shows that the assumption of 30 moles vaporized was not exactly correct but the check was close (29.21). About 29 per cent will be vaporized at 100°F.

The mole composition of the equilibrium vapor and liquid may be computed by dividing the moles of each component by the total moles:

Component	Residue liquid	Vapor
CH$_4$...............	2.47	45.37
C$_2$H$_6$..............	5.93	19.85
C$_3$H$_8$..............	31.08	27.39
iC$_4$H$_{10}$.............	6.18	2.12
C$_4$H$_{10}$..............	12.80	3.22
C$_5$H$_{12}$.............	20.49	1.71
C$_6$H$_{14}$+.............	21.05	0.34
Total............	100.0	100.0

Experimental Vaporization Curves. When such complex materials as gasoline and petroleum fractions are dealt with, the application of the aforementioned equilibrium laws is cumbersome. Furthermore, the component analyses of these heavy oils cannot be easily obtained; and even if such analyses are available, accurate vapor-pressure or equilibrium data for the compounds or fractions contained in them are not always available. At present most equilibrium relations are obtained by determining experimental flash-vaporization curves or by computing such curves from the empirical relationships discussed in Chap. 4. Empirical flash curves can be estimated from true-boiling-point or ASTM curves, and with less accuracy from Hempel or Saybolt distillation curves.

Vaporization in the Critical Region. Insufficient information is available for determining the exact behavior of mixtures at temperatures and pressures in the critical region, but the general situation is understood. Lines A and B in Fig. 15-6 indicate the vapor-pressure lines of two hydrocarbons (A and B) that compose a mixture, and line C may be considered to represent another hydrocarbon that exhibits properties that in most respects represent the properties of the mixture—or better, line C represents the molal average vapor pressure of the mixture and the molal average or pseudo critical temperature and pressure of the mixture. Such critical points are indicated as a, b, and c, respectively.

The volume of gaseous mixtures may be computed for any condition that is not close to the envelope in the diagram, from the pressure-volume-temperature relations of the hypothetical material C using the pseudo critical point designated as c (Example 5-5). Lines of constant volume are indicated on the diagram.

The density of the fluid under various conditions is indicated on Fig. 15-6 by the blackness or whiteness of each part of the single-phase area. Thus, highly compressed liquids or vapors are shown as dark areas in the left and upper part of the diagram, and the density graduates smoothly to the low-pressure high-temperature area in the lower right corner, which we refer to as a typical or ideal gas region. Note that it is possible by compressing a liquid, heating it, and reducing the pressure to convert a liquid into a gas without conducting vaporization. The common process of distillation is indicated midway on the diagram as a horizontal line or constant-pressure process in which the liquid is heated, vaporization occurs throughout a range of temperature, and finally the vapor may be superheated. In a similar manner, a constant-temperature expansion (or compression) of a dense fluid is indicated as a vertical line midway on the diagram. In such a process, liquid is produced upon partial expansion, but the liquid vaporizes again upon further reduction of pressure so that nothing but a pure gas phase remains after expansion. This situation has been encountered commercially as *retrograde condensation.*

Extremely high-pressure gas wells deposit a maximum amount of condensate when the pressure is reduced to about 1,000 psi.

It must also be pointed out that the envelope of Fig. 15-6 applies to only one mixture of the two components A and B. Thus, in Fig. 15-7,

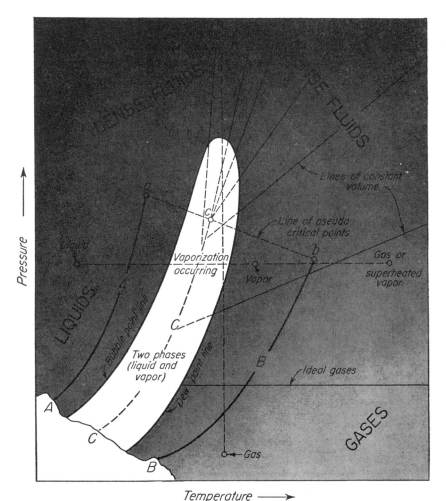

Temperature ⟶

FIG. 15-6. Liquid-vapor phase relationships at extreme temperatures and pressures.

which is the work of W. B. Kay[12] on ethane-n-butane, each combination of ethane and butane has its own envelope, and the whole series of envelopes traces what is called the loci of critical states of this system.

[12] Liquid-vapor Equilibrium . . . Ethane-n-Butane System, *Ind. Eng. Chem.*, **32,** 353 (1940).

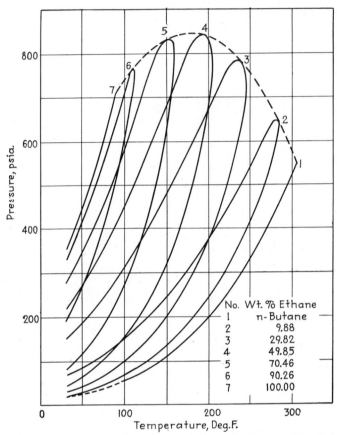

FIG. 15-7. Pressure-temperature phase diagrams at constant composition for mixtures of ethane and *n*-butane.   (*Kay, Ind. Eng. Chem.*)

No.	Wt. % Ethane
1	n-Butane
2	9.88
3	29.82
4	49.85
5	70.46
6	90.26
7	100.00

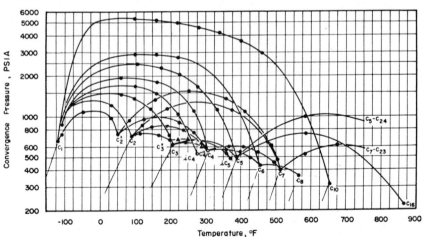

FIG. 15-8. Convergence pressures of binary hydrocarbon systems.   (*Pet. Refiner.*)

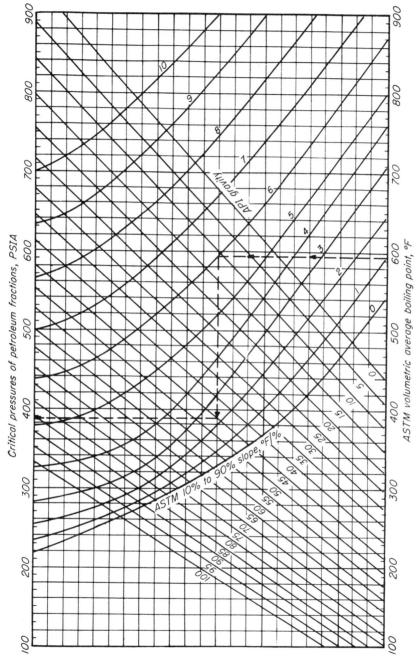

FIG. 15-9. True critical pressures of petroleum fractions. (*Edmister and Pollock, Chem. Eng. Progr.*)

455

Figure 15-8[5] shows the loci of critical states of some of the many systems that have been studied.

Although the pseudo critical temperatures and pressures introduced in Figs. 5-9 and 5-12 are thought to be best for the computation of the compressibility behavior of gases and vapors, they do not represent the true critical point which is necessary in studying phase behavior. The true critical pressure[13] and the true critical temperature[13] can be estimated

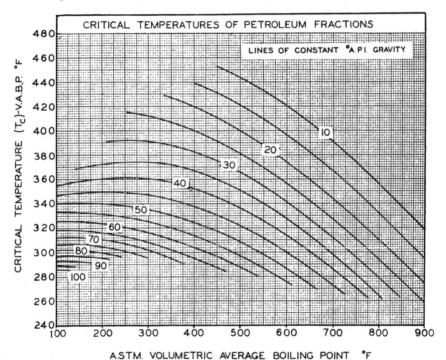

FIG. 15-10. True critical temperatures of petroleum fractions. (*Edmister and Pollock, Chem. Eng. Progr.*)

from Figs. 15-9 and 15-10 as a function of ASTM boiling range and API gravity. Edmister and Pollock[13] have also devised a method of estimating the phase diagram of heavy oil mixtures by location of the focal point (see Fig. 15-13) of such a diagram. In plotting such a diagram, the pressure scale is logarithmic but the temperature scale is a Cox-type[14] scale which is usually proportional to $1/(382 + t)$ where t is degrees Fahrenheit. The focal pressure (Fig. 15-11) and focal temperature (Fig. 15-12 are determined[13] as a function of the true critical pressure and tem-

[13] Edmister and Pollock, Phase Relations of Pet. Fractions, *Chem. Eng. Progr.*, **44**, 905 (1948).

[14] Cox, E. R., *Ind. Eng. Chem.*, **15**, 592 (1923).

perature and the ASTM distillation properties. True-boiling-point, rather than ASTM distillations are often available, and these can be converted one to another by means of the methods introduced in Chap. 4. Although similar phase diagrams, but for vacuum conditions (down to 10 mm), have been determined,[15] they indicate much higher focal temperatures (31 to 67 per cent) than Edmister[13] (the focal pressure is apparently the same). In addition, the true critical points (by Figs. 15-9 and

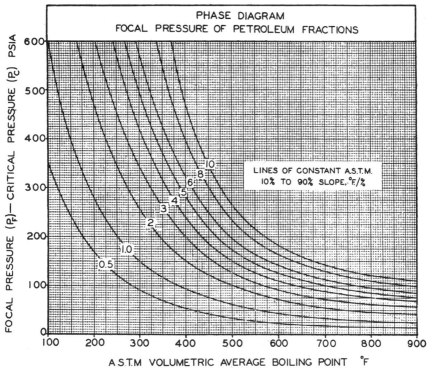

Fig. 15-11. Phase diagram focal pressure of petroleum fractions. (*Edmister and Pollock, Chem. Eng. Progr.*)

15-10) lie much to the left and outside of the phase envelope.[15] Thus, either (1) our methods of estimating the critical and focal points are in error, or (2) the lines of the phase envelope are not straight but tend to be more horizontal at low pressures or steeper at high pressures, or (3) some mechanical difference exists between the behavior of equilibrium equipment operating at a pressure and under vacuum. Little experimental data are available, and the construction of phase diagrams is now

[15] Okamoto and Van Winkle, Equil. Flash Vaporization . . . Reduced Pressures, *Ind. Eng. Chem.*, **45**, 429 (1953).

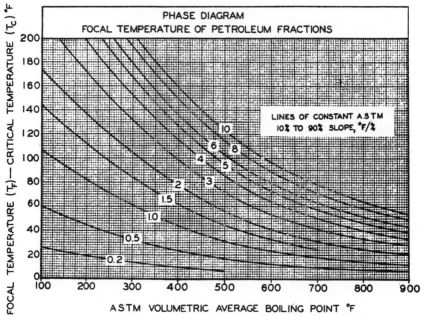

FIG. 15-12. Phase diagram focal temperature of petroleum fractions. (*Edmister and Pollock, Chem. Eng. Progr.*)

only an approximation. Flash temperatures under vacuum can probably be computed most accurately[16] by the methods outlined in Chap. 4.

Example 15-5. Construction of Phase Diagram (Fig. 15-13). A 28 API catalytic
cycle stock has the following distillation curve:

Per cent	T.B.P.	ASTM
5	428	468*
10	447	488
30	494	515
50	549	548
70	590	573
90	672	635

* Corrected for loss.

The phase diagram will be computed as if only the T.B.P. distillation were available
because this is most often the situation. The (10–90) T.B.P. slope is $(672 - 447) \div
80 = 2.82$ deg/per cent. According to Fig. 4-18 the ASTM slope should be about
1.97 (the actual ASTM slope, see above, was 1.84). The average volumetric true
boiling point is 550°F and according to Table 4-8, the ASTM average volumetric

[16] Filak et al., Heavy Fraction Vacuum Flashing, *Pet. Processing*, May, 1955, p. 651.

boiling point will usually be about 5°F lower (actually 2°F higher, for this sample) or 545°F.   In examining Figs. 15-9 to 15-12, it is obvious that the errors found here in converting from T.B.P. to ASTM curves are not significant.

The flash-vaporization curve at atmospheric pressure will lie across the phase diagram on a constant-pressure line at 14.7 psia.   The slope of the straight-line flash-vaporization curve (Fig. 4-18) will be about 1.03, and its 50 per cent temperature

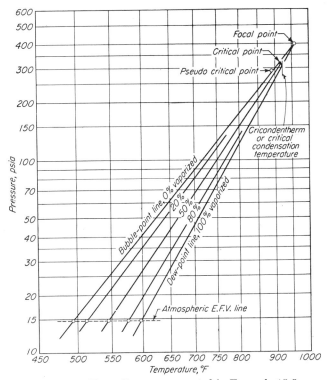

FIG. 15-13. Phase diagram computed in Example 15-5.

(Fig. 4-19) will be about 5 degrees lower or 545°F.   Using the 50 per cent temperature and the slope, the flash-vaporization curve is:

%	°F
0	494
20	514
50	545
80	576
100	596

The critical pressure is read from Fig. 15-9 starting at the bottom at 545°F, reading up to 28 API, then to the left to a slope line of 1.97, and finally at the top we read 315 psia.   Likewise, the critical temperature from Fig. 15-10 is found to be 365°F above the average boiling point, or 910°F.

The focal point determined from Figs. 15-11 and 15-12 is found to be:

Pressure, psia	Temp, °F
315	910
80	48
395	958

It will be noted that the pseudo critical point is different from the actual critical point or the focal point. The pseudo critical temperature (Fig. 5-9) is about 890°F, and the pseudo critical pressure (Fig. 5-12) is about 290 psia. If all of the correlation methods had been perfect, the pseudo critical point would have fallen within the phase envelope.

Separation Obtained in Flash Vaporization. Equilibrium flash vaporization produces the poorest separation between the components of the feed, and in theory some of each component should appear in both the

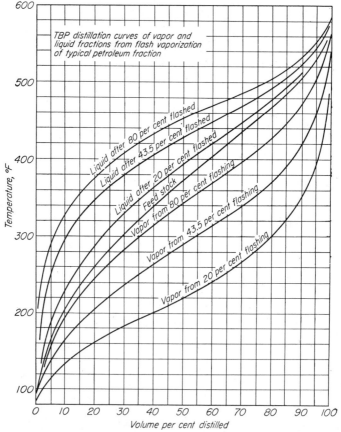

FIG. 15-14. Typical true-boiling-point distillation curves of vapor and liquid products from three equilibrium flash vaporizations of a petroleum fraction. (*Pet. Refiner.*)

vapor and the liquid. Correlation methods (ASTM[17,18] and TBP[18,19]) have not been entirely successful, and probably the best method of obtaining the distillation curves of flash products is to apply Eq. (15-9). This is done by considering the feed as a series of narrow boiling fractions. Percentages are converted to mole fraction, and then equilibrium ratios (or constants) are selected from the best available data (vapor pressures or possibly K values). If the percentage vaporized by equilibrium vaporization is not close to the value obtained from an empirical E.F.V. curve then several computations using Eq. (15-9) should be made in and about the percentage indicated by the empirical E.F.V. curve. The general relationship is indicated[17] in Fig. 15-14.

Successive Flash Vaporization. The effect of light vapors in aiding to vaporize heavier materials has been aptly referred to by Piromoov and Beiswenger[20] as the "carrying effect of light ends." In the case of successive flash vaporization the carrying effect of the lighter materials is forcefully evident. A part of the vapor is removed in the first flash, and hence the carrying effect of this quantity of vapor is no longer available. Owing to the removal of the light vapor, the remaining liquid must be heated for several degrees before additional vaporization occurs. This effect is illustrated in Fig. 15-15 for the same oil as that shown in Fig. 4-14.

Example 15-6. Successive Flash Vaporization.
First flash (0 to 30 per cent) (see Example 4-6).
Second flash (30 to 60 per cent). To avoid confusion, the 70 per cent that remains should be redrawn as 100 per cent. Note the triangular 10 and 70 per cent points.

$$10\text{–}70 \text{ slope of dist.} = \frac{457 - 315}{60} = 2.37$$

10–70 slope of flash curve*   = 1.3 (Fig. 4-18)
50 per cent bp of dist. curve   = 415°F
50 per cent point of flash curve (Fig. 4-19) = 415 − 11 = 404°F*
100 per cent point = 404 + 50 × 1.3   = 469°F

* The use of the remaining part of the curve as an ASTM is not exact.

The third flash (material from 60 to 100 per cent) curve is computed in a similar manner. Note the circle points for the 10 and 70 per cent points.

The disadvantage of successive flashing is apparent. For example, to vaporize 80 per cent requires temperatures of approximately 405, 435, and 455°F respectively by single, double, and triple flash.

[17] Edmister, W. C., Application of Thermodynamics . . . , *Pet. Refiner*, December, 1949, p. 140.
[18] Obryadchikov, S. N., *Ind. Eng. Chem.*, **24**, 1155 (1932); and Katz & Brown, *Ind. Eng. Chem.*, **25**, 1373 (1943).
[19] Vaswani, N. R., *Oil Gas J.*, Oct. 3, p. 149; Oct. 17, p. 141; Oct. 31, p. 132; Dec. 5, p. 143; and Dec. 12, 1955, p. 117. Or see master's thesis, Effect of Pressure on Separation by Flash Vaporization, University of Tulsa, 1955.
[20] Equilibrium Vaporization of Oils and Carrying Effect of Light Ends, *API Bull.* 10, No. 2, sec. II, p. 52, 1929.

Carrying Effect and Reboiling. The Carrier distillation process involves recirculation of the lightest product back through the pipe-still and vaporizer section of the tower, as shown in Fig. 7-20, so that the light ends can exert a greater carrying effect as shown in Fig. 7-21. The recirculated light material lowers the whole distillation curve and particularly the flash-vaporization curve.

Reboiling is the term usually employed to describe the heating of the bottom of a fractionating tower by steam (or hot oil) by means of a shell-and-tube-type exchanger bundle, or by circulating some of the bottoms

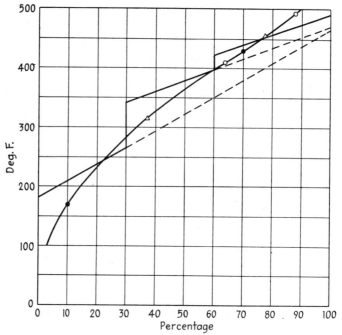

Fig. 15-15. Successive flash vaporization (see Example 15-6).

product through an externally fired heating coil and back to the bottom of the tower. Such recirculation scarcely alters the vaporization conditions at the bottom of the tower, but if the bottom material is cycled back to the vaporizer section of the tower or is used to raise the temperature of some lower boiling material it tends to suppress vaporization of the low-boiling material. Recirculation back through the feed plate decreases the proportion of low-boiling material present at the feed plate. The suppression of vaporization that occurs with one crude oil is indicated in Fig. 15-16.[21]

[21] Nelson, W. L., Reboiling by Circulating a Residue, *Oil Gas J.*, Aug. 3, 1946, p. 96.

Azeotropic Mixtures. Certain hydrocarbons, particularly the aromatic hydrocarbons, have an affinity for some other hydrocarbons and tend to form constant-boiling mixtures with them. Thus, neither of the hydrocarbons in such a mixture behaves according to the general solution laws [Eqs. (15-1), (15-4), (15-10), etc.] outlined here. Some situations can be handled by considering the constant-boiling mixture as one component

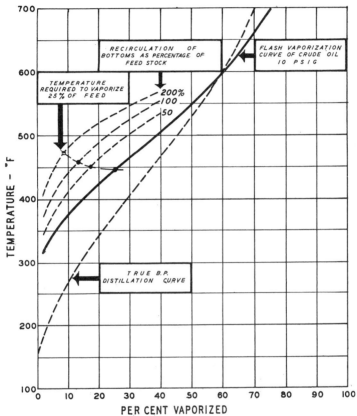

FIG. 15-16. Temperatures required to vaporize 25 per cent of a 42 API crude oil when circulating various amounts of the topped crude oil (75 per cent of the crude oil) through the feed plate of a tower. (*Oil Gas J.*)

and the pure substance that is present in excess as the other component. In such equations as (15-2), (15-3), (15-5), etc., the components would not act according to their vapor pressures but at volatilities that are relative only to one another. Constant-boiling or very close-boiling mixtures can also be separated by the addition of a new substance that will alter the relative volatilities of the components of the mixture. In azeotropic distillation the entraining agent forms a new constant-boiling mixture (of far-removed boiling point) with one of the substances of the original mixture, whereas in Distex distillation[22] the extractive agent alters only the relative volatility of the components. Griswold defines relative volatility in terms of x mole fraction in the liquid and y mole fraction in the vapor as

$$\alpha = \frac{y(1 - x)}{x(1 - y)}$$

and presents volatilities of a few hydrocarbons when in the presence of such agents as aniline, furfural, and phenol. The practice of extractive distillation is indicated in the discussion of Fig. 7-5.

Application of Flash Vaporization. With the possible exception of heat-transfer and fluid-flow computations, no design fundamental is more widely useful than equilibrium vaporization. These many applications will be discussed at appropriate times in succeeding chapters.

1. Pipestill outlet temperature, pages 616 to 618.
2. Tower vaporizer temperatures, pages 111 to 119.
3. Compositions of materials from separators, pages 858 to 860.
4. Amount of vaporization in pipestill tubes or exchangers, pages 614 to 622.
5. Pressure drop in pipestills (caused by vaporization), page 618.
6. Tower top, bottom, and plate temperatures, pages 470 to 471.
7. Heat-transfer rates in condensers, pages 573 to 580.
8. Sizing of transfer lines, condenser shells, etc., page 614.

[22] Griswold et al., *Ind. Eng. Chem.*, **38,** 65 (1946); and **38,** 170 (1946).

CHAPTER 16

FRACTIONATION AND TOWERS

In the practical design of petroleum fractionating towers, the principles outlined for two-component systems are of only general value. These principles operate just as surely in the complex-mixture column as in two-component columns, but means of rigorously applying these principles have not been devised. To complicate their application further, petroleum columns are usually operated as multiple-draw columns; i.e., several products may be withdrawn from the plates intermediate between the top plate and the feed plate. Needless to say, fractionation is not effective at these plates because a part of the vapor that passes them is the overhead or lightest column product, and hence the products that are withdrawn from the intermediate plates must contain some of this low-boiling material. Such products are stripped with steam, in auxiliary stripping columns or stripping sections.

Heat and Material Balances. Inasmuch as satisfactory equilibrium methods of determining the reflux are not available, the reflux is universally computed by means of a heat balance. The vapor-liquid feed enters the tower at a high temperature, and the products are withdrawn at lower temperatures. Hence heat must be removed, and it is referred to as "reflux heat."

The most satisfactory temperature datum is the vaporizer temperature because this temperature can be accurately estimated and is the temperature about which the entire design of tower and pipestill hinges. By using this datum plane, the heat balance consists simply of the sensible heat that is required to (1) cool each product from the vaporizer temperature to its withdrawal temperature and (2) condense the products that are withdrawn as liquids. The reflux that is computed by such a heat balance is about the minimum amount by which the process can function. Upon casual inspection it appears to provide no flow of liquid into the feed plate from higher plates in the column, but since the decrease in temperature of the bottoms product is not caused primarily by reflux, the heat balance mentioned above actually provides a small flow of liquid into the feed plate. At each side-draw plate the internal reflux is depleted by the amount of side-draw product that is withdrawn, as shown in Fig.

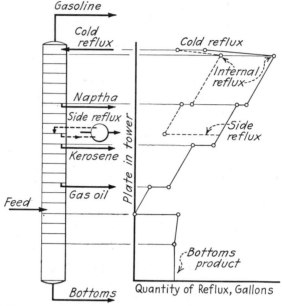

FIG. 16-1. Relative amount of reflux or overflow liquid at each tray of a fractionating tower.

16-1.　The dotted lines refer to the removal of heat at some plate on the side of the column.

Example 16-1. Heat Balance of a Fractionating Tower. A heat balance of the simple tower system shown in Fig. 16-2 will be computed to determine the amount of reflux heat that must be removed to keep the tower in thermal balance. The capacity is 1,200 bbl per day (2,100 gal per hour) of a 12.1 to 12.2 Characterization Factor crude oil. At 576°F the gasoline, naphtha, kerosene, and gas oil are vapors and the reduced crude oil is a liquid. A sufficient quantity of heat must be removed from the vapors

TABLE 16-1. PROPERTIES OF FEED AND PRODUCTS OF EXAMPLE 16-1

	Volume, per cent	API	Lb per gal	Gal per hr	Lb per hr	50 per cent bp	Mol. wt	Latent heat[a]
Gasoline.........	26.8	62.8	6.06	563	3,415	260	110	120
Naphtha.........	5.63	52.8	6.39	118	754	370	155	113
Kerosene.........	19.8	45.6	6.65	416	2,765	460	185	100
Gas oil..........	10.6	39.4	6.89	222	1,530	585	240	90
Reduced crude....	36.97	31.2	7.24	776	5,610			
Loss.............	0.2	....	....	.....	96			
Crude...........	100.00	43.0	6.75	2,100	14,170			

[a] Fig. 5-8 indicates slightly different values.

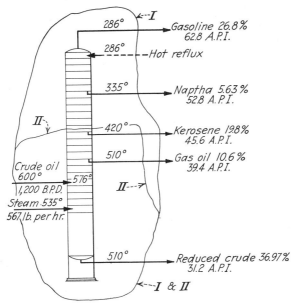

FIG. 16-2. Simple tower system (Examples 16-1, 16-3, and 16-4).

to cool them as vapors to the temperatures at which they are withdrawn from the tower and to condense the naphtha, kerosene, and gas oil at their withdrawal temperatures. Specific heats were taken from Figs. 5-1 and 5-2.

		Btu
Sensible heat:		
Gasoline	3,415(576 − 286)0.56 × 1.06 =	589,000
Naphtha	754(576 − 335)0.55 × 1.06 =	106,000
Kerosene	2,765(576 − 420)0.57 × 1.06 =	261,000
Gas oil	1,530(576 − 510)0.59 × 1.06 =	63,000
Reduced crude	5,610(576 − 510)0.72 × 1.03 =	276,000
		1,295,000
Steam	567(535 − 286)0.5 =	70,600
		1,365,600
Latent heat:		
Naphtha	754 × 113 =	85,100
Kerosene	2,765 × 100 =	276,500
Gas oil	1,530 × 90 =	138,000
Total heat to be removed	=	1,865,200

Kinds of Reflux. Ways of removing reflux heat are indicated in Fig. 16-3. With any of these types, regardless of the amount of liquid reflux, the same quantity of reflux heat is removed, except for slight changes in the top temperature. *Cold reflux* is defined as reflux that is supplied at some temperature below the temperature at the top of the tower. Each pound of this reflux removes a quantity of heat equal to the sum of its latent heat and the sensible heat required to raise its temperature from the storage tank temperature to the temperature at the top of the tower. A constant quantity of reflux is recirculated from the product storage tank into the top of the tower. It is vaporized and condensed and returns in like quantity to the product storage tank.

Hot reflux is reflux that is admitted to the tower at the same temperature as that maintained at the top of the tower. Obviously, the reflux or overflow from plate to plate in the tower is essentially hot reflux because it is always substantially at its boiling point. For convenience, the overflow reflux or reflux in the tower is referred to as *internal reflux*. Both hot and internal reflux are capable of removing only the latent heat, because no difference in temperature is involved.

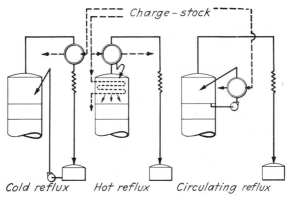

Fig. 16-3. Methods of removing reflux heat.

Circulating reflux differs from the foregoing because it is not vaporized. It is able to remove only the sensible heat quantity that is represented by its change in temperature as it circulates. This reflux is withdrawn from the tower as a liquid at a high temperature and is returned to the tower after having been cooled. This type of reflux may be conveniently used to remove heat at points below the top of the tower (*side reflux*). If used in this manner, it tends to decrease the volume of vapor that the tower must handle. This is illustrated in Fig. 16-1 by the dotted lines. Other means or combinations[1] are occasionally employed, and each manner of withdrawing side-reflux heat requires a different tower diameter.

Reflux ratio is defined as the amount of internal reflux divided by the amount of top product. Since internal or hot reflux can be determined only by computation, plant operators usually obtain the reflux ratio by dividing actual reflux by top product. This is satisfactory, of course, but it should be properly labeled.

[1] Nelson, W. L., Increasing Tower Capacity by Sacrificing Fractionation, *Oil Gas J.*, June 7, 1947, p. 92.

Obviously, hot reflux is subject to fluctuations in the quantity and properties of the feed to the plant or to the quantity of cooling agent used, so that it is not entirely satisfactory. In certain cases, such as in vacuum-tower systems, the major part of the reflux heat may be removed by hot reflux, and cold reflux may be used to remove the rest of the reflux heat. Cold reflux has the advantage of affording an absolute control by means of the reflux pump. Circulating reflux can be controlled in the same manner, but the cost of pumping large quantities of liquid is excessive, and larger heat exchangers are necessary. Regarding the heat that can be saved by heat exchange, the three systems are comparable, although higher transfer rates can usually be obtained in condensers than in liquid-to-liquid exchangers.

The fact that the quantity of internal reflux flowing from the top plate of the tower is always the same, regardless of the type of external reflux used, is confusing. Vapor arises from the plate below the top and is condensed by the reflux on the top plate. If cold reflux is used, it will take about 2 lb of vapor to heat and vaporize 1 lb of cold reflux. Thus about 2 lb of internal reflux flow from the top plate for each pound of cold reflux that is admitted to the top of the tower. Similarly, 1 lb of vapor may deliver enough heat, as it condenses, to heat more than 2 lb of circulating reflux. In this case, the amount of internal reflux is less than the amount of circulating reflux. When hot reflux is used, the amount of reflux is about the same as the amount of internal reflux.

Example 16-2. Quantity of Reflux. A tower fractionating system is such that 2,000,000 Btu per hr of reflux heat must be removed. Example 16-1 illustrates the method of determining the reflux heat. How many pounds and gallons of (1) hot, (2) cold, and (3) circulating reflux are required?

Basis: 1 hr.

The overhead product is assumed to be a 58 API gasoline (6.22 lb per gal). The temperature at the top of the tower is 300°F.

1. *Hot Reflux.* The latent heat of the gasoline is about 123.

$$\text{Lb of hot reflux} \ldots \ldots \frac{2,000,000}{123} = 16,250 \text{ lb per hr}$$

$$\text{Gal hot reflux} \ldots \ldots \frac{16,250}{6.22} = 2,615 \text{ gal per hr}$$

2. *Cold Reflux.* Assume storage tank at 100°F.

$$\text{Lb cold reflux} \ldots \ldots \frac{2,000,000}{123 + (300 - 100)0.575} = 8,400$$

$$\text{Gal cold reflux} \ldots \ldots \frac{8,400}{6.22} = 1,350$$

3. *Circulating Reflux.* Assume the reflux is cooled from 300 to 200°F.

$$\text{Lb circulating reflux} \ldots \ldots \frac{2,000,000}{(300 - 200)0.605} = 33,100$$

$$\text{Gal circulating reflux} \ldots \ldots \frac{33,100}{6.22} = 5,310$$

TOWER TEMPERATURES

The top or side temperatures at which products are withdrawn from a tower that operates at nearly atmospheric pressure can be estimated from Fig. 16-4.[2] Methods of computing such temperatures are given in the next paragraphs, and in most instances it is wise to compute the temperatures because they vary widely, particularly if pressure, vacuum, or

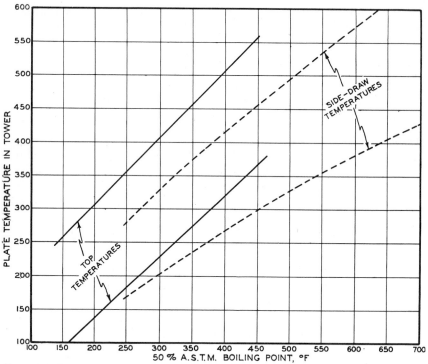

FIG. 16-4. Range of top and side-draw temperatures in a topping (or atmospheric-pressure) tower. (*Oil Gas J.*)

large amounts of steam are employed. With respect to the range of top temperatures shown in Fig. 16-4, the extreme high temperatures shown are for

1. A high tower pressure (15 psig).
2. Minimum amount of steam or gas product.
3. Wide-boiling-range top products.

The highest side temperatures shown are for

1. High tower pressures (15 psig).
2. Minimum amounts of steam or gas.

[2] Nelson, W. L., Tower Temperatures, *Oil Gas J.*, June 30, 1945, p. 129.

3. Narrow-boiling-range products.

4. Small amounts of reflux.

Although the following method of computing[3] tower temperatures is open to many criticisms, it does take into account the several variables mentioned above and yields results that are in close agreement with plant data.[4] In general, computed top temperatures are high by about 3 per cent, but computed side temperatures are about right. Substantially the same methods are presented by J. W. Packie.[5]

Top Temperature. The temperature at the top of the tower must be just high enough to allow complete vaporization of the overhead product. A lower temperature will condense a part of the desired overhead product and incorporate it in the first side-draw product, and a higher temperature will cause the inclusion of high-boiling materials which are not desired in the overhead product. If the top of the tower is at atmospheric pressure and no steam is used, the 100 per cent point of the equilibrium vaporization curve of the overhead product is the top temperature. Such a simple case is seldom encountered, and hence the top temperature at 760 mm must be corrected for the tower pressure and for the partial-pressure effect of steam or gas.

Example 16-3. **Calculation of Top Temperature.** See Fig. 16-2 and Example 16-1. The top temperatures for hot, cold, and circulating reflux will be computed. This system was actually operated with hot reflux and with circulating reflux, and hence a comparison with the actual temperatures is possible. Tower pressure 780 mm at the top.

These computations are based on the assumption that the top temperature is measured in the vapor above the top plate. If the temperature was taken in the liquid on the top tray (or one tray down), the temperature would be the same for all types of reflux. Temperatures taken in the vapor line are very erratic because the vapor that leaves the tower is superheated.

a. Hot Reflux. See the quantities, etc., of Example 16-1.

Moles reflux:

$$
\begin{array}{lll}
\text{Reflux heat} & = 1{,}865{,}200 \text{ Btu (Example 16-1)} \\
\text{L.H. at 286} & = \text{about 120} \\
\text{Lb reflux} & = \dfrac{1{,}865{,}200}{120} & = 15{,}500 \\
\text{Moles reflux} & = \dfrac{1{,}865{,}200}{120 \times 110} & = 141 \\
\text{Moles gasoline} & = \dfrac{3{,}415}{110} & = 31 \\
\text{Moles vapor} & = & \overline{172} \\
\text{Moles steam} & = {}^{567}\!/_{18} & = 31.5 \\
\text{Total moles at top of tower} & = & \overline{203.5}
\end{array}
$$

[3] Nelson, W. L., The Estimation of Tower Temperatures, *Natl. Pet. News*, Dec. 14, 1932, p. 25.

[4] Nelson, W. L., Table 69, p. 468, of the Second Edition of this book.

[5] Distillation Equipment in the Oil Refining Industry, *Trans. A.I.Ch.E.*, **37,** 51 (1941).

According to Dalton's law, the partial pressure in the gas phase is

$$\frac{172}{203.5} \times 780 = 660 \text{ mm}$$

The initial condensation temperature for the gasoline (100 per cent point on equilibrium vaporization curve) is 296°F (Fig. 16-5).

The temperature of 296 corrected to 660 mm is 287°F (Fig. 5-27).

The *actual* top temperature when using hot reflux was 286°F.

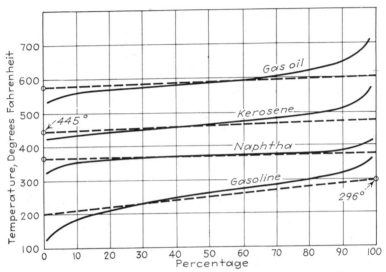

FIG. 16-5. ASTM distillation and flash-vaporization curves of the products used in Examples 16-3 and 16-4.

b. Circulating Reflux. When circulating reflux was used, the top temperature was 244°F. The reflux circulated between 264 and 166°F. The circulating reflux does not vaporize, and hence only the gasoline vapor and the steam need be considered. Although the reflux heat is increased by the lower top temperature of 244°F, it does not affect the computations because no reflux passes overhead.

$$
\begin{array}{ll}
\text{Moles gasoline} \ldots \ldots \ldots \ldots & 31 \\
\text{Moles steam} \ldots \ldots \ldots \ldots \ldots & \underline{31.5} \\
\text{Total moles} \ldots \ldots \ldots \ldots \ldots & 62.5
\end{array}
$$

$$\text{Partial pressure} = \frac{31}{62.5} \times 780 = 387 \text{ mm}$$

Correcting 296 to 387 mm pressure gives 253°F.

The *actual* top temperature was 244°F, but note that the liquid temperature was 264°F.

c. Cold Reflux. With a lower top temperature (approximately 280°F) more reflux heat will be required. The heat balance given in Example 16-1 is correct except that the sensible heat of the gasoline and of the steam will be different.

Corrections to heat balance given in Example 16-1 for a top temperature of 280°F.

$$\begin{array}{lr}
& \text{Btu} \\
\text{Gasoline}\ldots\ldots\ldots\ldots 3,415(286 - 280)0.485 \times 1.06 = & 10,500 \\
\text{Steam}\ldots\ldots\ldots\ldots\ldots\ldots\ldots\ldots 567(286 - 280)0.5 = & 1,700 \\
\text{Correction}\ldots\ldots\ldots\ldots\ldots\ldots\ldots\ldots\ldots\ldots\ldots = & 12,200
\end{array}$$

$$\text{Reflux heat} = 1,865,200 + 12,200 = 1,877,400 \text{ Btu}$$

If the cold reflux is available at 80°F,

$$\text{Lb cold reflux} = \frac{1,877,400}{120 + (280 - 80)0.58} = 7,950$$

$$\text{Moles cold reflux} = \frac{7,950}{110} = 72.3$$

$$\begin{array}{lr}
\text{Moles gasoline}\ldots\ldots\ldots\ldots\ldots & 31 \\
\text{Moles vapor}\ldots\ldots\ldots\ldots\ldots\ldots & 103.3 \\
\text{Moles steam}\ldots\ldots\ldots\ldots\ldots\ldots & 31.5 \\
\text{Total moles}\ldots\ldots\ldots\ldots\ldots\ldots & 134.8
\end{array}$$

$$\text{Partial pressure} = \frac{103.3}{134.8} \times 780 = 600 \text{ mm}$$

The equilibrium temperature of 296° corrected to 600 mm gives 277°F.

Side-draw Temperature. The method of calculating side-draw temperatures is much the same as the calculation of the top temperature except that complications arise because of the presence of the low-boiling materials that pass the draw plate. Furthermore, the equilibrium condensation curve, and particularly the point on this curve that denotes complete condensation, is the basis for computing these temperatures. At the zero per cent point on the flash curve the side-draw product can be completely condensed at 760 mm pressure if no lighter products or steam are present at the plate.

In practice, steam and vapor of lighter products are usually present, and hence the effect of these vapors on the final condensation temperature must be estimated. The lighter vapors extend from materials boiling at almost the same temperature as the side-draw product to materials that are substantially fixed gases. Those vapor materials which are far above their boiling point behave as fixed gases and lower the condensation point by Dalton's law of partial pressures just as steam does, but those vapor materials which are at or near their boiling point are not effective in reducing the partial pressure. Arbitrarily, the vapors of materials that will be condensed at the second or higher draw plate above the plate under consideration may be considered to act as fixed gases. Also, the vapors constituting the material that is withdrawn from the draw plate above the one under consideration are assumed to have no effect at all on the partial pressure. Thus in a tower producing gasoline, kerosene, and gas oil, at the gas oil draw plate the gasoline vapor would be considered as a fixed gas, whereas kerosene vapor would be assumed to have no effect on the condensation point. This arbitrary classification of vapors appears to be accurate unless the quantity of one of the products is very large or very small.

Example 16-4. Calculation of Side Temperatures. This example is a continuation of Examples 16-1 and 16-3. The temperature (420°F) of the kerosene plate will be computed (Envelope II, Fig. 16-2).

The quantity of reflux heat and reflux (or vapor reflux) that is present on the kerosene plate must be determined. This is computed by making a heat balance up to the kerosene plate.

Heat balance to kerosene plate (Example 16-1):

Cool gasoline vapor....................3,415(576 − 420)0.58 × 1.06 =	327,000
Cool naphtha vapor.....................754(576 − 420)0.57 × 1.06 =	71,000
Cool kerosene vapor..................2,765(576 − 420)0.57 × 1.06 =	260,000
Cool gas oil vapor....................1,530(576 − 510)0.58 × 1.06 =	62,000
Cool reduced crude liquid..............5,610(576 − 510)0.72 × 1.03 =	276,000
	996,000
Cool steam..567(535 − 420)0.5 =	44,000
Condense gas oil...1,530 × 90 =	138,000
Condense kerosene...2,765 × 100 =	276,500
Reflux heat at kerosene plate................................. =	1,454,500

$$\text{Moles internal reflux} \ldots\ldots\ldots \frac{1,454,500}{185 \times 100} = 78.6$$

The internal reflux contains the kerosene, and hence the kerosene need not be added as a material whose partial pressure must be reduced.

Moles of materials that act as fixed gases:

Steam...................................	31.5
Gasoline................................	31
Naphtha (no effect one way or other)........	....
	62.5
Total moles of vapor.........78.6 + 62.5 =	141.1

Assume a tower pressure of 950 mm at the kerosene plate.

$$\text{Partial pressure at kerosene plate} = \frac{78.6}{141.1} \times 950 = 530 \text{ mm}$$

The atmospheric complete condensation point is 445°F (Fig. 16-5). Correcting this temperature to 530 mm gives 415°F. The *actual* temperature was 420°F.

The gas-oil plate temperature can be computed in a similar manner except that kerosene is considered as an inert material and the gasoline and naphtha both act as fixed gases.

In applying the foregoing method to the design of a fractionating tower, the lowest draw-plate temperature should be computed first. The temperature on the lowest plate is assumed; and after the heat balance is computed, the assumption can be checked. If it is not correct, then a second assumption must be made. Each draw-plate temperature, progressing upward in the tower, is computed by such a trial-and-error method until all the plate temperatures and the top temperature have been computed.

Bottom and Stripper Temperatures. In those few towers which are heated at the bottom by means of a reboiler, the bottom temperature is the bubble point of the bottoms product, and except for corrections for tower pressure and for process steam, the bottom temperature may be read directly at the zero per cent point of the flash curve of the bottoms product.

With few exceptions, all other bottom temperatures are the result of hot material being stripped by steam and are dependent on such factors as (1) inlet temperature to stripper, or feed-plate temperature of a fractionating tower, (2) cooling by self-evaporation, (3) heat losses through insulation, and (4) cooling or heating by steam. The inlet temperature presents little difficulty because it is either the vaporizer temperature or side-draw inlet temperature. Equations (16-1) and (16-2) summarize[6] the situation:

$$\Delta t = \frac{PL}{100h} + \frac{HA(T - Ta)}{Bh} + \frac{0.65S}{B}(T - Ts) \qquad (16\text{-}1)$$

$$= \text{approx. } 1.2P + 35\frac{D}{B}(T - Ta) + 0.65\frac{S}{B}(T - Ts) \qquad (16\text{-}2)$$

where Δt = feed less bottom temperature, °F
P = per cent removed by stripping
L = latent of oil vaporized, Btu per lb
h = specific heat of oil
H = transfer rate through insulated wall, Btu/(sq ft)(hr)(°F temp diff.)
A = area of walls, sq ft
B = lb oil per hr
S = lb steam per hr
T = temperature of oil, °F
Ta = temperature of air, °F
D = tower diameter, ft
Ts = temperature of incoming steam

Theoretically, the cooling of the bottoms product is not accomplished by reflux [see the three items of Eq. (16-1)], and hence, in making a heat balance, the vaporizer temperature should be used as the temperature of the bottoms product and of any steam introduced at the bottom. However, the inclusion of the actual bottom temperature in the heat balance of a tower is such universal practice that it will be continued in this book. To include it, as is done in Examples 16-1 and 16-4, only results in supplying

[6] Nelson, W. L., Stripper and Bottom Temperatures, *Oil Gas J.*, July 21, 1945, p. 147.

a little extra reflux and indirectly allowing a small amount of excess vaporization to occur.   Bottom temperatures by Eq. (16-1) are generally higher than those found in plant operations.   Apparently, the liquid leaves the vaporizer at a temperature lower than that of the vapor or of the mixture in the vaporizer.

To use Eq. (16-1) or similar methods[5] the amount of stripping or processing steam and the percentage stripped must be known.   The amount of steam can be estimated from Figs. 7-3 and 7-4.

Example 16-5.   Computation of Bottom Temperature.   The tower of Examples 16-1 and 16-4 is 4 ft in diameter, the space below the bottom tray is 10 ft, the air temperature is 76°F, about 8 per cent of the original reduced crude oil is removed by stripping, the latent heat of the strippings is about 83, and 567 lb per hr of steam (at 286°F rather than 535°F) is used.

$$\Delta t = \frac{8 \times 83}{100 \times 0.73} + \frac{0.75(10 \times 4 \times 3.14 + 4^2 \times 0.785)(576 - 76)}{5610 \times 0.73}$$

$$+ \frac{0.65 \times 567}{5610} (576 - 286)$$

$$= 9.1 + 12.7 + 19. = 40.8°F$$

or by Eq. (16-2)

$$\Delta t = 1.2 \times 8 + 35 \frac{4}{5610} (500) + \frac{0.65 \times 567}{5610} (576 - 286)$$

$$= 9.6 + 12.5 + 19. = 41.1°F$$

The computed bottom temperature is $576 - 41 = 535°F$.

TOWER OPERATION

In the operation of multidraw towers there are four main fundamentals:[7]

1. Yield of product is primarily a function of the composition of the feedstock, not the degree of fractionation.
2. Number of plates only mildly alters the boiling range of the products as measured by the I.B.P. and E.P. of an ASTM distillation.
3. The I.B.P. of side-draw products is always low and must be corrected by steam stripping or rerunning.
4. The E.P. of a side-draw product is regulated mainly by opening or closing (changing the yield) its side-draw valve.

To increase the E.P. without altering the I.B.P., open the side-draw valve (or increase the speed of the withdrawal pump) and close the draw valve of the next lower product by a corresponding amount.

To increase the I.B.P. without altering the E.P., close the side-draw valve and open the draw valve of the hext higher product by a similar amount.   The I.B.P. is finally regulated by steam stripping.

For narrow-boiling cuts use more steam for stripping and employ as many plates as possible above and below the fraction.

[7] Nelson, W. L., Regulation of I.B.P. and E.P., *Oil Gas J.*, Aug. 25, 1945, p. 143.

Dirty topping-plant streams[8] may be caused by water carry-over from the salt settlers, excessive charge rate, erratic control of the tower, insufficient reflux to keep the lower trays wet, and too high transfer-line temperatures. Bringing a tower onstream[9] involves maintaining a vaporizer temperature slightly higher than that necessary to distill all overhead products, adjusting the top temperature for the E.P. desired for the top product, and then proceeding down the tower adjusting the withdrawal valve and steam stripping of each side product. To gain maximum capacity[10] from a multidraw tower the top product should be as small as possible, the low side-draw products should be as large as possible, the pressure should be high, and side reflux should be used. Obviously, these conditions are also governed by factors other than a desire for larger tower capacity.

COLUMN DESIGN

Fractionating towers and related equipment are mechanical devices for repeatedly establishing equilibrium between ascending vapor and descending liquid, and repeated separation of the two phases. Violence or time of contact is of little significance, but means of attaining a large interface for contact and effecting a complete separation of the two phases must be incorporated in any successful design. The simplicity of the basic concept is highlighted by the fact that several towers have worked satisfactorily[11] in simple operations such as topping, even though several bubble plates and their caps had been up-ended by an internal explosion. Even such a random arrangement provides some degree of interfacial contact.

Types of Fractionators. Some operations such as the separation of distilled catalytic feedstock from a reduced crude oil can be accomplished by substantially a single flash vaporization (see Fig. 7-27). Entrainment is removed from the vapor by a wire-mesh blanket, means of washing any accumulation of (asphaltic) entrainment from the mesh is provided, and the top of the tower contains only a means of withdrawing the overhead product. Most heavy-oil towers also function in some degree as condensers; note that all overhead product except noncondensable gases is condensed in the top of the tower shown in Fig. 7-27.

Towers filled with packing materials to provide more interfacial area can be used up to diameters of about 20 in. and to even larger diameters

---

[8] Nelson, W. L., Dirty Topping Plant Streams, *Oil Gas J.*, Sept. 1, 1945, p. 87.

[9] Nelson, W. L., Bringing a Tower on Stream, *Oil Gas J.*, Sept. 22, 1945, p. 325.

[10] Nelson, W. L., Conditions for Maximum . . . Capacity, *Oil Gas J.*, Nov. 17, 1945, p. 293.

[11] Nelson, W. L., Tower Works with Upset Trays, *Oil Gas J.*, Mar. 29, 1954, p. 132.

if means are provided for redistribution of the liquid at frequent intervals (it tends to channel to the sides of the tower). Packing materials are usually so expensive and so heavy that packed towers are employed only for very small columns such as the smallest steam strippers. One of the most successful applications of packing involves the use[12] of multilayer expanded metal lath in the form of a corrugated sheet so that the ridges of one sheet and the valleys of the next higher sheet are in contact. Pressure drops are very low, the HETP (height equivalent of a theoretical perfect plate) is half or less than half the tray spacing of conventional bubble towers, and capacities are high.

Many early towers consisted of only baffle plates for directing the liquid back and forth across the tower, and so-called side-to-side pans are still widely used for such services as:

1. Fractionating very high-temperature vapor which tends to deposit coke.
2. Contacting hot vapor and cold oil for the purpose of pure heat exchange, or when the effectiveness of the separation or fractionation is not important, and for steam stripping. The lower parts of most cracking plant fractionators employ this type of plate.[13]
3. For certain vacuum fractionation systems in which only an extremely small pressure drop is permissible.
4. Fractionating materials that contain suspended solid matter, such as lime or coke.

Holes are sometimes drilled in side-to-side baffle trays, and the extreme in such a trend results in perforated trays,[14] sieve plates,[14] Turbogrid trays,[14] and Ripple trays.[14a] In these, both the down-flowing liquid and the rising vapor pass through the same openings.

More elaborate arrangements are the familiar bubble-plate (Fig. 16-6) and such modifications[14] as tunnel trays (vapor slots and vapor troughs extend across the plate) and Uniflux trays, float-valve bubble trays, perforated trays with downcomers for the liquid, and Kaskade-type (Benturi and Flexitray) trays.

Bubble Plates. In the conventional bubble-cap type of tray, the vapor travels up the column by bubbling through a bath of reflux liquid that is contained on each plate (Fig. 16-6). If plate steel is employed, the plates are welded to the shell of the tower, but cast-iron trays must be sealed into the tower shell by means of packing. Cast iron is more resistant to corrosion, or at least is thicker than steel; but the major corrosive action takes place at the liquid-vapor contact line, and hence the superior

[12] Scofield, R. C., Industrial Fractionating Tower Packing, *Chem. Eng. Progr.*, **46**, 405 (1950); also see similar British development, *Chem. Eng.*, August, 1955, p. 234.

[13] Houghland et al., Performance Checked, Baffle Loading Improved, *Oil Gas J.*, July 26, 1954, p. 198.

[14] Symposium Fractionating-Absorption Tray Design, *Oil Gas J.*, Apr. 26, 1954, pp. 152–194.

[14a] Anon., Ripple Trays Boost Capacity, *Oil Gas J.*, Dec. 17, 1956, p. 91.

resistance of the cast-iron plate is of little value. Cast-iron bubble caps are still widely used, but pressed alloy steel caps are gaining in favor especially for vacuum towers. Steel caps can be more closely spaced, thus allowing a larger area for the vapor as it passes through the caps. Many caps are of the removable type; i.e., the vapor uptake and cap proper can be assembled on the plate,[15] but such an arrangement is not entirely satisfactory because the bolt rusts and cast-iron caps are often broken. Hold-down bars may be used as in Fig. 16-6, or a heavy cap may rest by its own weight over the uptake. Removable caps and a manhole above each plate are considered as best practice.

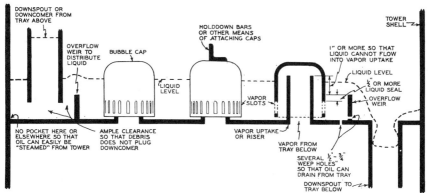

FIG. 16-6. Fundamental features of a bubble-type tray or plate. (*Oil Gas J.*)

The exact shape of the bubble cap is probably of little importance except from the standpoint of cost. Small caps are best for large liquid loads (see Fig. 16-12), and large caps for large vapor loads. However, some designers utilize small caps for small towers and large caps (6 in. or larger) for towers of 10 to 20 ft in diameter. The shape of the slots appears to have little or no effect.[16] The same shape of bubble is produced regardless of the shape of the slot. At low velocities[16] flat disk-shaped bubbles are produced; and at high velocities a channeling appears to occur, and a continuous elongated bubble space extends through the liquid. Exceedingly small caps (1-in. diameter) and tray spacings of only 4 in. have been installed[17] for very low temperature operations in which the area for heat loss must be kept to the minimum.

The bubbles extend out from the slots by not much more than 1 in.,[18]

[15] Nelson, W. L., Tray Details—Bubble Caps, *Oil Gas J.*, Aug. 11, 1945, p. 125; also see Bolles, Wm. L., *Pet. Processing*, March, 1956, p. 82.

[16] Kallam, F. L., Notes on Absorber Design No. 1, *Pet. Engr.*, April, 1934, p. 33.

[17] Anon., Tray Design Saves Space, *Chem. Eng.*, March, 1956, p. 132.

[18] Kirschbaum, E., Distillation and Fractionation Technology, Edwards Bros., Ann Arbor, Mich., 1948.

TABLE 16-2. FEATURES OF BUBBLE CAPS

Outside diameter, in.	Chimney or vapor uptake area, sq ft per cap	Slot area, sq ft per cap	Uptake area over column area	Slot area over column area	Material
2¾.........	0.0085	0.0156	0.048	.....	C.i.
3...........	0.0232	0.0165	0.257	0.183	Steel
3...........	0.0142	0.0167	0.130	.....	Steel
4...........	0.0204	0.0372	0.079	0.144	C.i.
4 hexagonal...	0.034	0.065	0.122	.....	C.i.
4...........	0.0208	0.0396	0.078	0.150	C.i.
4...........	0.031	0.040	0.135	.....	C.i.
4...........	0.029	0.045	0.148	.....	Steel
4½.........	0.0204	0.0348	0.066	0.112	C.i.
5...........	0.031	0.0356	0.100	0.115	C.i.
6...........	0.0745	0.055	0.148	.....	C.i.
6½.........	0.042	0.0496	0.123	0.145	C.i.
3 × 10 rectangular....	0.1001	0.0921	0.175	0.161	C.i.

and the caps are spaced 1 to 3 in. apart. In clean service the clearance between the cap skirt and the plate can be only ½ in., but when material may be deposited on the tray, a clearance of 1½ in. is helpful. The liquid actually moves across the tray as a foam or froth, and hence the concept of a static slot seal is only hypothetical and the actual dynamic seal cannot be computed with accuracy. Nevertheless, some method of comparison must be used, and the following have been suggested:

Pressure of operation	Static seal[19]	Dynamic seal[20]
Vacuum (30–200 mm Hg abs)...........	zero	½–1½ in.
Atmospheric........................	½ in.	1–2 in.
50–100 psig.......................	1 in.	1½–3 in.
200–500 psig......................	1½ in.	2–4 in.

In addition to round or bell-shaped bubble caps, so-called tunnel-type trays and caps have been used since at least 1936. These consist of liquid troughs several feet in length, or even across the entire tray, and vapor uptakes of the same length. A curved elongated cap or tunnel lies over the uptake, causing the vapors to bubble through the trough of liquid. The trays function satisfactorily, although spouting of the liquid

[19] Davies, J. A., Bubble Trays . . . , Part II, *Pet. Refiner*, September, 1950, p. 121.
[20] Geddes, R. L., Local Efficiencies of Bubble Plate Fractionators, *Trans. A.I.Ch.E.*, **42,** 79 (1946).

has been reported. Uniflux trays[21] are a recent tunnel-type development which involves a single S-shape member (set on its side) which, when interlocked with a second such member, constitutes both the liquid trough and the vapor tunnel. It is a highly practical construction because of its simplicity.

The downpipes or downspouts (Table 16-3) for conducting liquid (or froth) down the tower must be large enough to allow disengagement of vapor from the liquid. The froth is about half liquid. A residence time 3 to 5[19] sec (velocity of 0.2 to 0.33 ft per sec) is recommended, which means that the froth travels at about 0.4 to 0.67 ft per sec. Although downcomers are frequently the bottleneck in a tower, some authorities[22,23]

TABLE 16-3. PERFORMANCE OF DOWNSPOUTS

Plate number	Arrangement[a]	Downspout area, sq in.	Downspout periphery, in.	Approximate[b] effective downspout periphery, in.	Allowable vapor velocity, ft per min
1		1.48	4.32	3.0	31.5
2		7.35	6.5	6.5	38.5
3		1.33	6.5	5.0	34.0
4		7.85	13.8	6.5	37.5
5		5.31	13.8	5.5	34.0

[a] Plate area 0.338 sq ft.
[b] Estimated.

suggest and report actual liquid velocities (no froth) of 0.56 to even 1.7 ft per sec. Kallam[16] has studied the performance of several downspout arrangements installed in a single tower. At an oil-to-gas ratio of 30 gal oil per 1,000 cu ft gas, the plates performed as shown in Table 16-3. This indicates that both area and perimeter are involved in the performance of a downspout. A study of the fall distance and the interference of several streams flowing into the same downspout is also discussed. C. G. Kirkbride[24] suggests that vapor disengaging space should be provided between the last row of caps and the overflow weir (Fig. 16-6)—a time of 1 sec for each foot of froth depth on the tray.

[21] Bowles, V. O., Socony Uniflux, *Oil Gas J.*, Apr. 26, 1954, p. 176; and Here's How Uniflux . . . Behaving, *Oil Gas J.*, June 20, 1955, p. 100.
[22] Atkins, G. T., *Chem. Eng. Progr.*, **50**, 116 (1954).
[23] Kelley et al., How to Test Fractionators, *Pet. Refiner*, February, 1955, p. 159.
[24] *Pet. Refiner*, **23**, 32 (1944).

The weir perimeters of Table 16-3 are not equally effective because **part** of the weir length lies too close to the tower wall.   Only plate 2 has a totally effective weir, and even it is somewhat impeded at the ends.   The weir formulas [Eqs. (13-6) and (13-7)] of Chap. 13 or other similar formulas[25] can be used for computing the height or crest of liquid over the weir.   Methods of correction for the constricting effect of the column wall on wedge-type or chord-type weirs have been presented.[25,26]   The overflow weir or dam is usually designed to hold a liquid level (no froth) of 0.5 to 1.5 in. above the top of the slots of the caps[19] but an adjustable (1 to 2 in.) weir has been suggested.[27]   The downcomer should be sealed[19,27] with liquid at its outlet by a (static) depth of 0.5 in. (4-ft diameter towers) to 1.5 in. (12-ft and larger diameters), and although a velocity of 0.7 ft per sec can be tolerated[22] under the downpipe, more space if available should be allowed so that an accumulation of debris does not hamper the flow.   Peavy and Baker[28] found that the height of the overflow weir had little effect on the liquid level in their equipment—the level being lower than the weir owing to surging and splashing of liquid at the last row of caps.   In general, the plate efficiency was greater at deep liquid seals, but the efficiency was lower (for deep seals) at high vapor velocities.   The liquid may tend to short-cut across the plate and cause some of the caps to be ineffective.   This tendency can be corrected to some extent by means of another weir or dam which is used to distribute the liquid as it flows from the downspout into the tray (Fig. 16-6).   For large plates, over 5-ft diameter, special baffles (Fig. 16-7) must be used to direct the flow of the liquid so that all the caps are effective.   Double-pass trays (not shown) are ones in which one tray has two chord-type downspouts and the next tray has a downspout across the diameter of the tower, so that the liquid travels back and forth from the center to the side of the tower.   The parts of the plate that the liquid tends to bypass are shown (Fig. 16-7) as shaded areas.   The passage for the liquid must not be greatly constricted at any point, or the liquid level on part of the plate may become so great that vapor will fail to bubble through some of the caps (see Figs. 16-8 and 16-9).   The caps that are marked on *b* and *c* (Fig. 16-7) may act as dams to the flow of liquid.   In experiments with the type of plate shown as *b*, the liquid level was 1 in. higher on the upstream side when the air velocity was 0.5 ft per sec and the water

[25] White, R. R., Bubble Plate Column Design, *Pet. Processing*, February, 1947, p. 147.

[26] Bolles, W. L., . . . Estimating Tower Diameter and Tray Spacing . . . , *Pet. Refiner*, December, 1946, p. 103.

[27] Bolles, W. L., Optimum Bubble-cap Tray Design, Part II, *Pet. Processing*, March, 1956, p. 82.

[28] Efficiency and Capacity of . . . Column, *Ind. Eng. Chem.*, **29**, 1056 (1937).

rate exceeded 40 gal per min. The removal of the cap at the end of the baffle greatly improved the level gradient. Likewise in plate *d* the caps nearest the center often fail to function because of a high liquid level. In large towers it is sometimes necessary to arrange the plate as a series of cascades, each deck of caps being separated by dams so that the level on each deck will be independent of the level on the deck before it. In this manner, the submergence at each part of the plate can be kept about the same. Plate *c* indicates four such cascade decks.

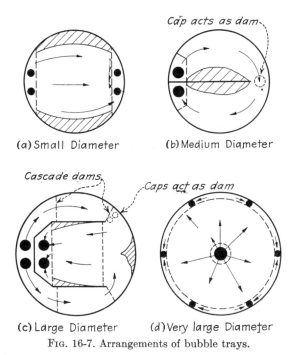

(a) Small Diameter   (b) Medium Diameter

(c) Large Diameter   (d) Very large Diameter

Fig. 16-7. Arrangements of bubble trays.

Liquid flows across the plate as froth and stands in the downcomer to a height (inches), in the case of the Koch Engineering Company Kaskade tray,[14,29] which is double the pressure drop (also stated in inches of liquid) across the plate. Perhaps this is a coincidence, but Souders et al.[30] report the same general relationship. At high rates of liquid flow the froth may not have time to separate as it flows through the downcomer, and hence the computed liquid height (no froth) in the downcomer must be about doubled. Kirkbride[24] also recommends that the height of liquid be multiplied by 2 when computed by his approximate formula [Eq.

[29] Litwin, H., Cascade-type Tray Introduces New Fractionating Principle, *Oil Gas J.*, Mar. 22, 1947, p. 237.

[30] Souders, Huntington, Corneil, and Emert, *Ind. Eng. Chem.*, **30**, 86 (1938).

(16-3)] as stated by Bolles[26]

$$H = 2(h_w + h_{ow}) + h_d + h_{rc}$$

or

$$H = 2\left[h_w + 30\left(\frac{L}{W_1}\right)^{0.67}\right] + 0.6u_d^2 + u_r^2\frac{\rho_v}{\rho_L} \qquad (16\text{-}3)$$

where H = height, in., of liquid backup above tray level, h_w = height of weir above tray, h_{ow} = height of liquid above weir, h_d = head required for

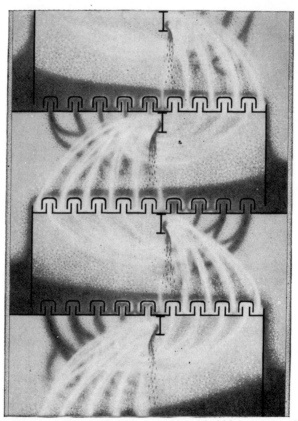

FIG. 16-8. Flow tendencies in the conventional bubble-cap type of tray.

flow through downspout, and h_{rc} = head for friction loss through risers and caps, all expressed in inches fluid. Referring to other symbols, L is liquid flow over weir, cu ft per sec; W_1 is effective[24] weir length, in.; u_d is liquid velocity at restriction of downspouts, ft per sec; u_r is vapor velocity through risers, ft per sec; and ρ_v and ρ_L are density, lb per cu ft of vapor and liquid, respectively. This equation outlines the significant factors, although experimental results fail to indicate the square function of velocity that is indicated by theoretical derivations, particularly at low velocities.

A high velocity of vapor through the bubble-cap slots promotes agitation and is thought to aid in the attainment of equilibrium. However, an excessive slot velocity causes liquid droplets to be thrown to the plate

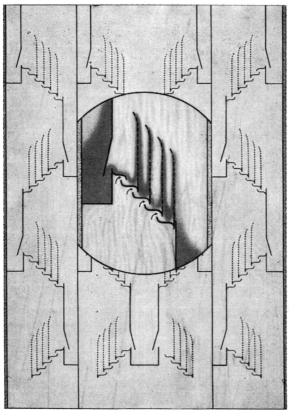

Fig. 16-9. Flow tendencies in the Kaskade contactor (enlargement in center). (*Koch Engineering Co.*)

above unless the plates are far apart, and Kallam[16] finds that mixing may not be effective at high velocities because the gas tends to channel through the liquid. Many petroleum-oil columns are designed for slot velocities of 9 to 14 ft per sec, but in reality the slot velocity is automatically governed to a large extent by the number of caps that can be put on the tray (see Table 16-2).

Weep holes (Fig. 16-6) of a diameter of ⅜ to ⅝ in. are needed to drain the tower in a reasonable length of time prior to steamout. Four sq in. of holes per 100 sq ft plate area has been suggested.[27]

The results of very high rates of liquid flow through trays are indicated in Fig. 16-8 and in Fig. 16-9 which shows a newly developed cascade-type tray.[14,31] The cascade tray (Kaskade, Benturi, and Flexitray designs) apparently exhibits a higher efficiency and greater capacity (about 35 per cent) than conventional trays, but it is more complicated. The single enlarged Kaskade unit indicated in Fig. 16-9 is too small for most commercial operations, and hence several of them are lined up across the tower with each adjacent pair of units dumping into a common downcomer as indicated around the enlargement of Fig. 16-9. The exaggerated crossflow of vapor indicated in the bubble-cap tray of Fig. 16-8 is not troublesome in small towers; but in large towers,[29] particularly if I-beam tray supports extend into the path of vapor crossflow, the operation of the trays may be completely upset.

Davies[32] has derived Eq. (16-4) for the liquid gradient across trays of caps spaced in an equilaterial triangle arrangement.

$$\sqrt{\Delta_{1.1}} \left\{ \Delta_{1.1} \left(\frac{3r}{2} - 1.4 \right) + 3r[d_o + s(\alpha - 1)] \right\} = \frac{r \sqrt{r} \, Q}{2.15 C_d l_1} \quad (16\text{-}4)$$

where $\alpha = l_2/l_1$

C_d = liquid gradient factor (Fig. 16-10)

$\Delta_{1.1}$ = liquid gradient (difference in clear liquid levels between inlet and outlet sides of tray section), for $u \sqrt{\rho_g} = 1.1$, in.

Δ_x = liquid gradient, for any condition, inches liquid

d_o = total flowing clear liquid depth adjacent to overflow weir, in.

l_1 = total free space between caps normal to liquid flow (average of various rows), in.

l_2 = total free space between risers normal to liquid flow (average of various rows), in.

Q = clear liquid flow, gal per min

ρ_g = vapor density, lb per cu ft

r = number of rows of caps perpendicular to liquid flow

s = cap skirt clearance (distance of bottom edge of cap above tray floor), inches

u = superficial tower vapor velocity (using total tower area), ft per sec

In solving the equation, C_d obtained from Fig. 16-10 is inserted in Eq. (16-4) along with other variables to solve for $\Delta_{1.1}$. The value of $u \sqrt{\rho_g}$ is computed, and then by the use of Fig. 16-10, the actual Δ_x can be determined.

Tray Performance. The over-all performance of a bubble tray can be outlined or defined as in Fig. 16-11[27] or 16-12.[33] At minimum vapor

[31] Harrington et al., No Peace for Fractionators, *Oil Gas J.*, Nov. 24, 1945, p. 135.

[32] Davies, J. A., *Ind. Eng. Chem.*, **39**, 774 (1947). See Rodriguez, F., *Chem. Eng.*, November, 1956, p. 230, for a direct nomographic solution.

[33] Munk, P., New Approach to Tray Design, *Pet. Refiner*, July, 1955, p. 104.

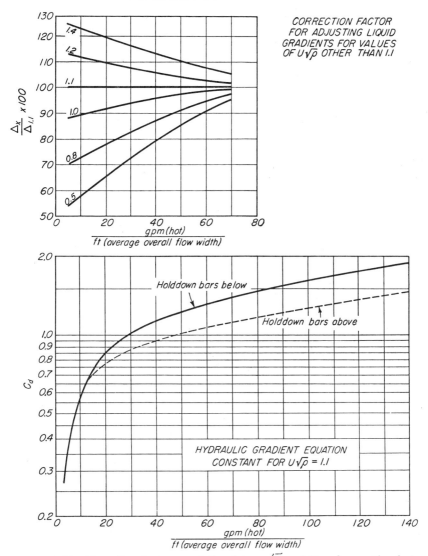

Fig. 16-10. Liquid-gradient-factor correlation (at $u \sqrt{\rho_g} = 1.1$) and correction factor for other values of $u \sqrt{\rho_g}$. (*Ind. Eng. Chem.*)

rates the caps pass vapor only intermittently, and this is called *pulsation*, and between burps liquid tends to overflow through the vapor risers. At the other extreme of vapor velocity, excessive *entrainment* occurs by *spouting* or *jetting* of liquid to the tray above, and in the extreme the cap slots may be so overloaded as to cause excessive pressure drop, spouting, or *coning*. At extremes in liquid flow, liquid or froth backs up in the downpipe (*downspout buildup*) into the tray above and may finally appear at the top of the column by what is called *flooding*. Likewise, at the highest liquid loads, liquid may *dump* or *drain* to the next-lower tray through caps that pass no vapor (Fig. 16-8), but it is common practice to design for such a liquid gradient and vapor velocity that all of the caps are working, and this results in what is called *stability*. A series of charts similar to Fig. 16-12 for various cap arrangements, spacings, etc., are presented by P. Munk.[33] The number of rows of caps

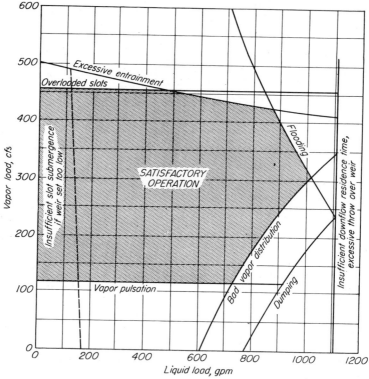

Fig. 16-11. Qualitative effect of liquid and vapor loads on bubble-cap-tray performance. (*Pet. Processing.*)

vitally affects the stability of the tray, and from Fig. 16-12 it appears that the use of several tray levels (cascading) should be practiced more frequently than in the past.

Pressure Drop and Downspout Backup. Pressure drop through the caps can be a little larger than the hydraulic gradient computed by the Davies equation [Eq. (16-4)] for tray stability.[33] At the same time, pressure drop causes liquid to back up into the downcomer. Pressure drops, by the study of T. C. Dauphine[34] for three sizes of caps, based on the

[34] Doctoral dissertation, Massachusetts Institute of Technology, 1939.

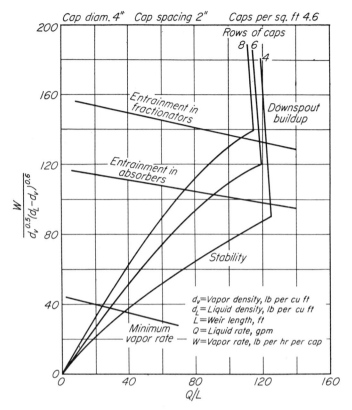

FIG. 16-12. Operating limits of bubble trays (4-in. cap diameter, 2-in. cap spacing, and 4.6 caps per sq ft). (*Pet. Refiner.*)

assumption[33] that the annular area, riser area, slot area, and reversal area are all equal, and equal to one-half of the inside area of the cap, are: For 3-in. caps:

$$H_c = 1.939 \left[\frac{u(d_v)^{0.5}}{(d_L - d_v)^{0.61}} \right]^{0.82} \tag{16-5}$$

For 4-in. caps:

$$H_c = 2.234 \left[\frac{u(d_v)^{0.5}}{(d_L - d_v)^{0.595}} \right]^{0.84} \tag{16-6}$$

For 6-in. caps:

$$H_c = 2.768 \left[\frac{u(d_v)^{0.5}}{(d_L - d_v)^{0.58}} \right]^{0.86} \tag{16-7}$$

where H_c = wet cap pressure drop, inches at flow conditions

u = slot velocity, ft per sec

d_v and d_L = vapor and liquid densities, lb per cu ft

The total buildup in the downcomer in terms of clear liquid heads above the lowest point (the overflow weir) is (1) wet-cap pressure drop, (2) crest above overflow weir, (3) half of hydraulic gradient across plate, (4) height to distribution weir and its crest if such a weir is used, and (5) pressure drops for flow or contraction through the downspout [see (Eq. 16-3)]. For low liquid flows the backed-up height may approach two-thirds[33] of the tray spacing, but at higher rates, lower backups are necessary because of the need of time for the disengaging of vapor from the froth. Munk[33] suggests decreasing the allowable backup by 1 inch for every 10 gpm per ft of weir length above a liquid rate of 65 gpm.

Pressure drop in vacuum towers is vitally important, as well as the pressure drop through any condensing equipment and the vapor line. The drop through pressed-steel caps installed in vacuum towers operating at about 40-mm pressure and with a slot submergence of $\frac{1}{16}$ in. ranges from about 0.7 mm per plate at a superficial velocity of 7 ft per sec to about 1.2 mm at a velocity of 13 ft per sec.

Plate Spacing and Entrainment. The obtainment of equilibrium on a bubble plate is governed by two opposing factors. One of these, the intimacy of vapor-liquid contact, tends to produce equilibrium; but if the contacting or bubbling is too violent, liquid particles will be carried from one plate to the next by the vapor and will tend to destroy the separation that has been obtained. One kind of entrainment is a distinct splashing, spraying, or spouting of liquid particles. The particles are thrown upward by the velocity they attain at the slot of the cap, and they will fall back into the liquid if they expend their energy content before they reach the next plate. The liquid particles are relatively large, and a relatively high velocity is necessary to cause them to be thrown to a height of 18 in. This kind of entrainment can be eliminated almost entirely by placing the trays far apart.

Another kind of entrainment might be referred to as "carrying." Very small particles of liquid do not fall through the vapor as fast as the vapor rises, and they are carried by the vapor stream to the plate above. At a given velocity, all particles smaller than a certain size will be carried by the vapor to the plate above and the larger particles will fall slowly back to the parent plate. At ordinary vapor velocities, the size of the particle that can be carried from plate to plate by the vapor appears to be between 0.1 and 0.2 mm in diameter.

Chillas and Weir[35] report that entrainment is negligible at a velocity of 2 ft per sec but that it amounts to 7 and 20.5 per cent at 4 and 5.5 ft per sec. In commercial columns, having trays spaced at 22 in., the entrainment[36] is approximately as shown in Table 16-4.

[35] *Ind. Eng. Chem.*, **22**, 206 (1930).
[36] Analyses of commercial plates by the author.

TABLE 16-4

Material	Pressure	Linear velocity, lb per sec	Per cent entrainment
Gasoline..........	Atmospheric	1.4	0.25
Gasoline..........	Atmospheric	3.0	0.8
Gas oil...........	20 mm	10.0	1.8
Air-water.........	Atmospheric	0.3	0.04
Air-water.........	Atmospheric	2.2	0.7

Atkins[22] suggests the entrainments of Table 16-5. The a/A designation refers to the ratio of the required cap-covered area to satisfy the widely used Brown and Souders[37] vapor-velocity formula [Eq. (16-8), curve 4], to the actual area provided. Inasmuch as the Brown and Souders formula is conservative and is based on the total cross sectional area, a ratio of $a/A = 1.0$ is thought to be[22] a good basis for design.

TABLE 16-5. ENTRAINMENT AS A FUNCTION OF VAPOR LOADING[a]

	Vapor loading, a/A	Gal per min per sq ft
Dry vacuum, low-pressure drop..................	0.4	0.03
Typical wet-vacuum distillation..................	0.6	0.1
Flash zone of crude tower.......................	0.8	0.3
Basis for design capacity.......................	1.0	1
Refluxed plates, atmospheric tower...............	1.1	2
Refluxed plates, butane splitter..................	1.2	5
Stripping section, butane splitter.................	1.25	10
Ultimate capacity..............................	1.3	25

[a] Atkins, G. T., *Chem. Eng. Progr.*, **50**, 116 (1954).

Spraying or spouting of liquid seldom extends to higher than 18 in. above the tray, and accordingly this type of entrainment is not involved to any extent in the commercial operation of petroleum towers with spacings of 18 in. or more, nor is such entrainment contemplated in any of the figures given heretofore except possibly at the very highest loadings. Thus, the entrainment figures apply to the liquid droplets that are entrained at a theoretical suspending velocity[37] [see Eq. (16-8)]. The effect of tray spacing for this type of entrainment is indicated in Fig. 16-13.

[37] Fractionating Columns—Entrainment and Capacity, *Ref. Nat. Gaso. Mfr.,* January, 1934, p. 32.

In actuality, trays are spaced primarily by mechanical considerations. Manways must be provided, and this requires a spacing of at least 22 in. Although manholes may not be used on every tray, it is nevertheless necessary for a man to crawl across the tray for inspection and repair, and this also requires a 20- to 24-in. spacing. The maximum practical number of trays between manholes has been set at 20 by one designer,[27] but more manholes are usually employed. Means are provided for descending or ascending through trays that are not served by manholes.

Although baffles, louver-like constructions, and wire mesh have long[38,39] been employed in efforts to alleviate entrainment, not until recently has the use of wire-mesh entrainment blankets become widespread.[40,41,42] The allowable[41] velocity u (ft per sec) in gas separators equipped with wire-mesh mist extractors is:

$$u = K[(\rho_L - \rho_g)/\rho_g]^{0.5}$$

in which K ranges from 0.12 to 0.43 and ρ_L and ρ_g are densities (lb per cu ft) of the liquid and the vapor. Under many conditions the amount of entrained liquid that is removed is 90 to 99 per cent. In vacuum tower or jug operations[42] it is possible to attain the vapor capacities of Fig. 16-13 and curve 4, without contaminating the gas-oil product with the metal contaminants that are so harmful to catalytic cracking catalysts, and in many instances it has been possible to produce penetration asphalt as the bottom product while at the same time producing a satisfactory catalytic feedstock. The mesh blankets (4 to 8 in. thick) must be continuously washed with a small amount of liquid to prevent the accumulation of coke or debris. Blankets are being used by some refiners below each draw plate and at the top of the column, but the point of major usefulness is between the feed plate and the lowest side-draw plate.

Many years ago, a device called the Centrifix[38] was found to be effective in removing colored material (Table 16-6) from a lubricating-oil stock that was withdrawn above the vaporizer and in reducing the amount of acid that was required to treat the product. A 9-in. layer of steel wool[38] was able to reduce the color to about one-twentieth of the color when no wool was used. Chillas and Weir[39] have also studied the effect of a special baffle, similar to venetian blinds, on entrainment.

[38] Anon., Prevention of Entrainment . . . , *Ref. Nat. Gaso. Mfr.*, February, 1934, p. 70.

[39] Chillas and Weir, *Ind. Eng. Chem.*, **22**, 206 (1930).

[40] Reynolds, S. C., *Oil Gas J.*, Aug. 10, 1953, p. 117; and Anon., *Pet. Processing*, February, 1954, p. 227.

[41] Campbell, J. M., Knitted-wire-mist Extractors . . . , *Oil Gas J.*, Mar. 5, 1956, p. 115.

[42] Nelson, W. L., Capacity of Vacuum Towers, *Oil Gas J.*, Apr. 9, 1956, p. 131.

Diameter of Bubble Towers. It is evident from the foregoing that no simple method of establishing the diameter of a fractionator is possible. Perhaps the maximum in simplification is the preparation of charts similar to Fig. 16-11 or 16-12 for the situation at hand, or for a number of common situations. Nevertheless, some rapid means of approximation is useful, so the familiar Brown and Souders equation (16-8) will be used. This equation was originally based on entrainment, but some doubt has arisen[27] regarding its relationship to entrainment. The equation was also related to surface tension of the liquid, and this concept has also been discredited.[22] Finally, everyone agrees that the K constants

TABLE 16-6. REMOVAL OF ENTRAINMENT FROM VAPOR

Crude	Per cent of crude	Viscosity at 210°F	Hivis product		
			O.D.[a] color without Centrifix	O.D.[a] color with Centrifix	Color reduced to these per cents of original color
Reagan............	6	140	5,800	1,550	27.0
East Texas.........	6	140	11,900	1,650	13.8
Little Panhandle.....	5	125	13,400	4,000	30.0
Barbers Hill........	8	145	3,600	1,500	42.0

[a] The optical density (O.D.) color scale of the Atlantic Refining Company is directly proportional to the depth of color. See page 389.

used in the original equations were conservative. Accordingly, empirical K values based on general evidence in the literature will be presented here (Fig. 16-13).

The allowable vapor rate is a function of the densities ρ_v and ρ_L (lb per cu ft) at tower conditions and of a constant K which is related to service and to tray spacing (Fig. 16-13).

$$w/a = K \sqrt{\rho_v(\rho_L - \rho_v)} \qquad (16\text{-}8)$$

$$\frac{w}{a} = \frac{K}{3,600} \sqrt{\frac{\rho_L - \rho_v}{\rho_v}}† \qquad (16\text{-}9)$$

The symbol w refers to pounds per hour, and a to the area of the entire tower in square feet. The constant K is dependent primarily on the tray spacing (Fig. 16-13) but also on the type of tray and the kind of service. The various general types of services are:

† The "Chemical Engineer's Handbook," 3d ed., McGraw-Hill Book Company, Inc., New York, 1950, shows the equivalent of Eq. (16-9).

1. Maximum rates with perforated, sieve-type, Turbogrid, and Kaskade trays.[14,43,44,45]
2. Maximum for perfectly designed bubble trays operating at most favorable liquid loads.[22,33] Also, normal performance of Kaskade, Turbogrid, perforated, and similar plate constructions.[14,43−45] Also, liquid-washed side-to-side pans.

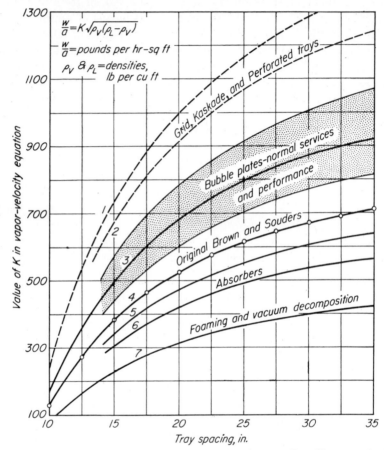

FIG. 16-13. Effect of tray spacing and type of service on allowable vapor load of fractionators [see Eq. (16-8)].

3. Normal performance of bubble plates through normal range of liquid loads[22,33,46] at atmospheric and higher pressures. The lowest values of K apply to high liquid loads and wide cap spacings.

[43] Thronton, D. P., *Pet. Processing*, May, 1952, p. 263; Kellogg, R. G., *Oil Gas J.*, Apr. 18, 1955, p. 128; Duren and Buck, *Oil Gas J.*, Feb. 28, 1955, p. 122; and Mayfield et al., *Ind. Eng. Chem.*, **44**, 2238 (1952).

[44] Fractionator Plate Symposium, *Pet. Engr.*, May, 1954, pp. C-17 to C-31.

[45] Barnes, K. B., *Oil Gas J.*, Sept. 15, 1952, p. 72; Shell Develop. Co., *Chem. Eng. Progr.*, February, 1954, p. 57; and *Pet. Refiner*, November, 1952, p. 105.

[46] Strang, L. C., *J. Inst. Pet. Tech.*, **22**, 166 (1936).

4. Original Brown and Souders[37] values for K dating from 1934 when tower design was not fully understood. Also, vacuum-jug or dry-vacuum service using washed wire-mesh mist extractors.[42] Also, crude flash section of atmospheric topping towers.[22]

5. Stripping stills in absorption plants, and wet-vacuum refinery services.

6. Absorption towers.[33,47]

7. Foaming due to excessively high temperatures (vacuum decomposition) in vacuum service,[42] or very high-viscosity liquids in vacuum service,[22] or high-boiling aromatic fractions used as absorption oils in absorbers.[48] Mist extractors are not of much help for these services.

All of the allowable vapor velocity rates [Fig. 16-13 and Eq. (16-8)] produce about the same degree of fractionation. Note also that the rates are based on the total free cross-sectional area of the tower and that actual velocities in the immediate region of the part of the plate covered with caps is therefore higher. Linear velocity is altered so greatly by various conditions of temperature and pressure that it is not of much use for purposes of comparison. However, for estimating purposes Table 16-7 is helpful.

TABLE 16-7. SUPERFICIAL VELOCITIES IN TOWERS

Operation	Pressure, psia or mm	Tray spacing, in.	Superficial tower velocity, ft per sec
Topping...................	17 lb	22	2.6–3.3
Cracking..................	40 lb	22	1.5–2.2
Pressure dist. rerun.........	20 lb	22	2.8–3.7[a]
Solution rerun..............	25 lb	22	2.8–3.5
Pressed dist. rerun..........	25 lb	22	2.8–3.9[a]
Pressed dist. rerun..........	60 mm	24	6.0–9.0
Vacuum...................	30 mm	30	9.0–12.0
Vaccum...................	90 mm	24	5.0–8.0
Stabilizer.................	160 lb	18	2.2–2.8
Nat. gaso. absorber.........	50 lb	14	1.0–1.3
Nat. gaso. absorber.........	400 lb	18	0.5–0.8

[a] Greatly dependent on quantity of steam.

Example 16-6. Diameter of Topping Tower. See Examples 16-1, 16-3, and 16-4. The quantities and conditions will be taken from these examples. Density of vapor at top of column (the reflux in the column is always hot reflux):

Lb gasoline (Example 16-1)........................	3,415
Lb internal or hot reflux (Example 16-3)............	15,500
Lb steam (Example 16-4)........................	567
Total lb per hr................................	19,482
Total moles (Example 16-3)....................	203.5

[47] Hutchinson, A. J., *Pet. Refiner*, April, 1951, p. 119.
[48] Schutt, H. C., *Pet. Refiner*, July, 1945, p. 93.

At a pressure of 780 mm and a temperature of 287°F, the approximate volume at the top of the tower is

$$\text{Approx. volume} \ldots \ldots \ldots \; 203.5 \times 379 \times \frac{287 + 460}{520} \times \frac{760}{780} = 107,600$$

$$\text{Density} \ldots \ldots \ldots \ldots \ldots \ldots \ldots \ldots \quad \rho_v = \frac{\text{lb}}{\text{cu ft}} = \frac{19,482}{107,600} = 0.181$$

Assume density of liquid ρ_L is 42.7 per cu ft or see Fig. 5-14.

$$w/a = K \sqrt{\rho_v(\rho_L - \rho_v)}$$
$$\rho_v(\rho_L - \rho_v) = 0.181(42.7 - 0.181) = 7.7$$

K at a tray spacing of 22 in. is about 735 (Fig. 16-13).

Mass velocity $w/a = 735 \sqrt{7.7} = 2,040$

Sq ft area $= \dfrac{19,482}{2,040} = 9.55$

Diameter $= \sqrt{\dfrac{9.55}{0.785}} = 3.5$ ft

This corresponds to a linear velocity of $\dfrac{107,600}{9.55 \times 3,600}$ or 3.13 ft per sec

The actual tower (Examples 16-1 and 16-3) was 4 ft 6 in. in diameter (a factor of safety of about 66 per cent), but it may never have worked at full capacity (date 1930).

Example 16-7. Diameter of Vacuum Tower. See Example 17-11. Trays at 30 in. Pressure at top, 30 mm. Top tower temperature, 490°F.

Material	Lb	Moles
Wax distillate and reflux..........	106,000	331.0
Gas oil........................	12,000	49.6
Steam........................	1,400	78.0
Total........................	119,400	459.0

Approx. volume $459 \times 379 \times \dfrac{760}{30} \times \dfrac{490 + 460}{520} = 8,050,000$ cu ft per hr

Density of vapor $\dfrac{119,400}{8,050,000} = 0.0148 = \rho_v$

Assume $\rho_L = 50$ lb per cu ft (it can be computed from Fig. 5-14).

$$\rho_v(\rho_L - \rho_v) = 0.0148(50 - 0.0148) = 0.74$$

The constant K for curve 5 of Fig. 16-13 is about 600. The allowable mass velocity $w/a = 516$.

$$\text{Cross-sectional area of tower} = \frac{119,400}{516} = 231 \text{ sq ft}$$

The diameter is 17.25 ft with no factor of safety. (The actual tower that was used during 1929 for these conditions was 17 ft in diameter.) The linear velocity corresponding to the foregoing is 9.7 ft per sec.

The various perforated or bar-type plates have high capacities (see curve 2, Fig. 16-13) and appear to produce the same efficiencies as bubble or Kaskade plates. Of even greater importance, they are mechanically very simple compared with bubble plates. In several designs, no downcomers whatever are provided. Turbogrid trays fail to function properly if the actual load is under about 40 per cent of the design load.

The centrifuge contactor[49] developed by Podbielniak promises radical improvements in our methods of conducting fractionation and other countercurrent processes. In a bubble tower the separation of liquid and vapor between each plate is effected by means of gravity, whereas in the centrifuge contactor separation is facilitated by means of centrifugal force.

Plate Efficiency. The most useful concept is simply the over-all efficiency represented by the ratio of theoretical plates to actual plates required for a particular separation, but other concepts involving the effectiveness of heat transference on the plate, or the composition of the actual overflow liquid with respect to what its composition would be had a single equilibrium contact been attained, are sometimes useful. In practice, the temperature of the vapor leaving the tray is higher than that of the liquid, particularly at regions where the rate of change of composition is rapid. Actual commercial plates involve not one but a succession of contacts on each plate. It has been repeatedly shown[50,51] that successive-contact plates can produce a greater change in composition than a single equilibrium contact plate, and therefore apparent efficiencies exceeding 100 per cent have been reported,[28] and efficiency computations based on a single contact can theoretically attain even 300 per cent.[51] However, commercial columns seldom exhibit efficiencies[52–54] exceeding 100 per cent. The efficiency of low-pressure hydrocarbon absorbers ranges from about 20 to 45 per cent,[53] high pressure (100 to 500 psia) absorbers[53] 45 to 60 per cent, and petroleum, alcohol, and chemical fractionating columns, 60 to 100 per cent, with many towers operating at efficiencies over 80 per cent.

The most successful methods of correlating plate efficiency involve the molal average viscosity[52,53] μ in centipoises of the feedstock at the average tower temperature as in Eq. (16-10), which checks well[52] with many

[49] Podbielniak Industrial Research and Engineering Laboratories, Chicago.

[50] Brewster, O. C., *Oil Gas J.*, Apr. 3, 1930, p. 41.

[51] Lewis, W. K., Jr., *Ind. Eng. Chem.*, **28**, 399 (1936).

[52] Drickamer and Bradford, Overall Plate Efficiency . . . Function of Viscosity, *Trans. A.I.Ch.E.*, **39**, 319 (1943).

[53] O'Connell, H. E., Plate Efficiency . . . Columns and Absorbers, *Trans. A.I.Ch. E.*, **42**, 741 (1946).

[54] Brown and Lockhart, The Effect of Vapor Load on Plate Efficiency . . . , *Trans. A.I.Ch.E.*, **39**, 63 (1943).

commercial operations.

$$\text{Efficiency} = 0.17 - 0.616 \log_{10} \mu \qquad (16\text{-}10)$$

In applying such an equation to multidraw towers handling a wide range of products, it appears logical to consider each section of tower separately.

In addition, the relative volatilities of the components have an effect,[53] and this effect is introduced in Fig. 16-14. The relative volatility α of the two key components is simply the ratio of the vapor pressure or equilibrium-vaporization constant of the low-boiling component over that of

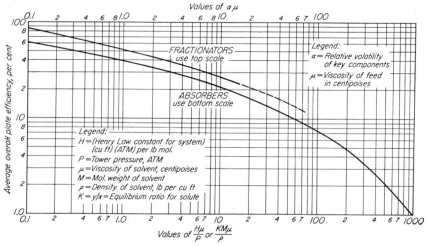

FIG. 16-14. Average over-all plate efficiencies of fractionators and absorbers as functions of relative volatility (or solubility) or viscosity. (*O'Connell, Trans. A.I.Ch.E.*)

the high-boiling component. When dealing with mixtures rather than two pure components, approximations are necessary. Absorbers behave differently from fractionators, and the term $\dfrac{H\mu}{P}$ is used in which H is the Henry's law constant—cu ft atm per lb-mole—and P is the total pressure in atmospheres.

Highest efficiencies are attained at some optimum vapor velocity. According to studies by Brown and Lockhart,[54] the optimum velocity occurs at about the velocities or the capacities found by Eq. (16-8) and curves 3 and 4 of Fig. 16-13.

FUNDAMENTALS OF FRACTIONATION

Although derivations based on two-component systems are not directly applicable to the fractionation of petroleum-oil mixtures, a complete understanding of fractionation cannot be gained without studying them.

Fractionation may be broadly defined as any method by which a liquid or vapor mixture may be separated into individual components by vaporization or condensation. The components may be pure compounds; or if the original material is a complex mixture, the components may be products that are still mixtures but whose distillation range is limited by the fractionation process. In a more detailed way the various means of separation have been given special names. *Distillation* is usually considered to refer to a complete operation in which heating, vaporization, fractionation, condensation, and cooling are practiced. *Dephlegmation* is a particular kind of fractionation in which a vapor mixture is separated into components by partial condensation. In this operation

TABLE 16-8. EQUILIBRIUM DATA FOR PENTANE AND HEXANE

Temperature, °F	Vapor pressure[a]		$760 - P_2$	$P_1 - P_2$	x_1 mole fraction	$P_1 x_1$	y_1 mole fraction
	C_2H_{12}, P_1 mm	C_2H_{14}, P_2 mm					
97	760	238	522	522	1.0	760	1.0
100	800	255	504	545	0.925	740	0.975
105	895	280	480	615	0.78	698	0.92
110	960	325	435	635	0.685	657	0.865
120	1,160	396	364	764	0.477	554	0.73
130	1,350	478	282	872	0.323	436	0.575
135	1,460	530	230	930	0.248	359	0.476
140	1,600	580	180	1,020	0.176	282	0.371
145	1,750	638	122	1,112	0.109	191	0.252
150	1,900	700	60	1,200	0.050	95	0.125
154.4	2,010	740	20	1,270	0.0157	31.4	0.0414
156	2,150	760	0	1,300	0.0	0.0	0.0

[a] Read from a chart which is slightly different from Fig. 5-27.

the vapor is progressively cooled, and successively lower and lower boiling condensates are collected. The condensate is relatively rich in high-boiling components. At one time the term "dephlegmator" was used to designate any sort of fractionating tower, but today the meaning of the term is usually restricted to the use herein given. In a more restricted usage the term *fractionation* is used in referring to a countercurrent operation in which a vapor mixture is repeatedly brought in contact with liquids having nearly the same composition as the respective vapors. The liquids are at their boiling points, and hence part of the vapor is condensed and part of the liquid is vaporized during each contact. By a series of contact treatments the vapor finally becomes rich in low-boiling components and the liquid becomes rich in high-boiling components. The terms *rectification* and *fractionation* are used synonymously. *Stabilization* is a fractionation operation conducted for the purpose of removing high-vapor-pressure components. The plates above the feed point are called "rectifying plates," and all of them together are classified as the *rectifying section* of the column. The plates below the feed are called the *exhausting section*. The plates below the

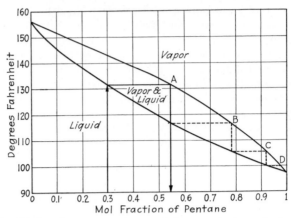

Fig. 16-15. Equilibrium between pentane and hexane at atmospheric pressure (see Table 16-8 and Fig. 16-16).

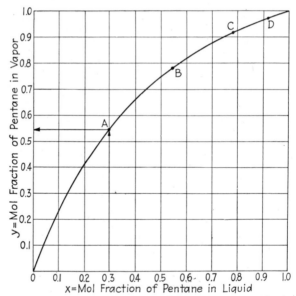

Fig. 16-16. Equilibrium between pentane and hexane at atmospheric pressure (see Table 16-8 and Fig. 16-15).

feed do not function as exhausting plates unless heat is added to the oil at the base of the column. Hence most petroleum-oil columns do not have exhausting sections. The plates below the feed in petroleum columns are usually stripping plates. An exception is the natural-gasoline stabilizer in which the stable gasoline in the base of the column is heated by a steam (or hot oil) reboiler.

Mechanism of Fractionation. In computing the degree of fractionation that is accomplished in a particular equipment, the relation between the composition of the liquid and the vapor at equilibrium must be used. Either experimental equilibrium data must be available, or the engineer must compute such data from known laws. Although Raoult's law is valid for only certain conditions, it is about the only general relationship by which equilibrium data can be computed. Thus, Eqs. (15-1) and (15-2) were used to compute the equilibrium data of Table 16-8.

Two common forms of equilibrium diagrams are shown in Figs. 16-15 and 16-16. As an example, the vapor from a liquid having a composition of 0.3 mole fraction of pentane contains 0.546 mole fraction of pentane. However, only a

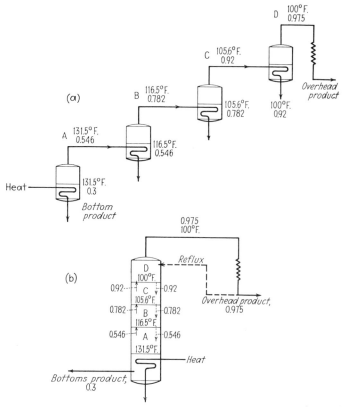

Fig. 16-17. Fundamentals of fractionation (see Figs. 16-15 and 16-16).

very small quantity of this composition of vapor can be produced, because the liquid becomes less rich in pentane as vapor is formed. If the heating is continued, the liquid becomes less and less rich in pentane and finally, after all the liquid is completely vaporized, the composition of the total vapor is the same as that of the original liquid, or 0.3 mole fraction.

As an illustration, the hypothetical case of the fractionation of an infinitely large quantity of liquid by a series of redistillations will be useful. Consider the series of stills shown in Fig. 16-17a, and compare the compositions with the dotted lines on Fig. 16-15. An infinite amount of liquid containing 0.3 mole fraction of pentane is heated a fraction of a degree, and a small amount of a vapor containing

0.546 mole fraction of pentane is evolved. This vapor is condensed by cooling it with a liquid that has the same composition as the vapor; and as the liquid is heated, it evolves a vapor having a composition of $y = 0.782$. By repeating this operation several times, a vapor that is almost pure pentane is produced at still D. The heating coils in the stills are really unnecessary because the vapor within the coils is of the same composition as the liquid on the outside of the coils, and hence the liquid and vapor can be mixed. The same change in composition will result, and the exchange of heat will be much more effective. The bubble tower shown in Fig. 16-17b is essentially the same as the series of stills except that the liquid from each plate is allowed to flow continuously to the still or the plate beneath. The compositions indicated in Fig. 16-17 are not practical ones because only a small quantity of purified vapor can be produced, but exactly the same principle is utilized in actual fractionating towers. In actual towers a finite amount of vapor or product must be produced, and hence the vapor is not so rich in pentane as indicated in Figs. 16-15 to 16-17. Thus more plates are required in actual towers because of the less-rich vapor that is produced at each plate and because several bubble plates may be required to produce an equilibrium. The top plate must be continuously fed with a cooling liquid (reflux), or it would soon become dry. The vapor from the top plate is the final product; and hence the reflux must be rich in pentane, or the vapor will be contaminated. Accordingly, the overhead product (0.975) is used as the reflux medium. The reflux flows down the column, but it changes composition from plate to plate so that all the material that is originally put into the top of the column as reflux is vaporized and returns to the product storage tank.

Theory of Fractionating Columns. The derivation of formulas describing two-component fractionation involves the following assumptions: (1) the molal latent heats of all materials are equal; (2) no reflux for cooling the overhead product from the feed-plate temperature is provided.

The assumption of equal molal latent heats greatly simplifies the calculations. If 1 mole of vapor (any composition) is condensed, the heat that is removed is just sufficient to vaporize a mole of liquid (at its boiling point). Thus the number of moles of vapor that travel up the column is the same at any plate, provided that the feed is introduced as a liquid at its boiling point. Likewise, the reflux or overflow from plate to plate is a constant amount in each section of the tower (see envelope II, Fig. 16-18) because the reflux is equal to the moles of vapor minus the moles of product for the rectifying section and to moles of vapor plus moles of waste for the exhausting section.

Material Balances. A number of envelopes enclosing parts of a fractionating tower are shown in Fig. 16-18. The following symbols are used:

F = moles of liquid feed at its boiling point
P = moles of liquid product at its boiling point
B = moles of liquid residue product
R = moles of reflux, at its boiling point, at any plate above the feed plate (R' below feed)
V = moles of vapor at any plate above the feed plate (V' below feed)
x = mole fraction of lower boiling component in liquid
y = mole fraction of lower boiling component in vapor

Subscripts:

p = product from top
b = residue product
f = feed
n = any plate in rectifying section
$n + 1$ = plate above the nth plate
$n - 1$ = plate below the nth plate
t = top plate
$t - 1$ = plate below the top plate
m = any plate in the exhausting section
s = still

Envelope I encloses the entire tower system and shows the relation between the feed and the products.

$$F = B + P$$

And for the low-boiling component:

$$Fx_f = Bx_b + Px_p$$

Envelopes II and II' show the relation among the vapor, reflux, and moles of overhead product:

$$V = P + R$$
and $$Vy_t = Px_p + Rx_p \qquad (16\text{-}11)$$

Similar equations for the plates *below the feed* are

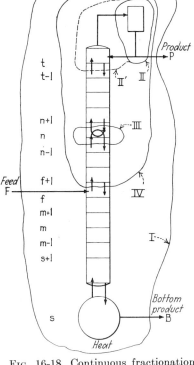

FIG. 16-18. Continuous fractionation system.

$$V' = R' - B \qquad \text{and} \qquad V'y_s = R'x_{s+1} - Bx_b$$

The change in composition from plate to plate is shown by envelope III:

$$Vy_n + Rx_n = Vy_{n-1} + Rx_{n+1}$$
$$R(x_{n+1} - x_n) = V(y_n - y_{n-1})$$
$$\frac{R}{V} = \frac{y_n - y_{n-1}}{x_{n+1} - x_n} \qquad (16\text{-}12)$$

also $$y_{n-1} = \frac{R}{V}(x_n - x_{n+1}) + y_n$$

Minimum Vaporization and Reflux. With *minimum vaporization* or reflux, an infinite number of plates are required for the separation. Although this amount of vaporization cannot be used commercially, it is the limiting condition upon which practical vaporizations are based. The other extreme condition is the use of an *infinite* amount of *vaporization*. For infinite vaporization a minimum number of plates is required to effect a separation. The minimum vaporization may be computed as follows (envelope IV):

$$Vy_f = Rx_{f+1} + Px_p$$

But at minimum vaporization an infinite number of plates are used and the change in composition from plate to plate is very small.   Hence x_{f+1} is equal to x_f.

$$V_{\min}y_f = R_{\min}x_f + Px_p$$

But
$$R_{\min} = V_{\min} - P$$
$$V_{\min}y_f = (V_{\min} - P)x_f + Px_p$$
$$V_{\min} = \frac{P(x_p - x_f)}{y_f - x_f} \tag{16-13}$$

or
$$R_{\min} = \frac{P(x_p - y_f)}{y_f - x_f} \tag{16-14}$$

In practice, more reflux than the minimum is used.   The relative values of x_f and y_f can be found by the equilibrium relation for the compounds that are being separated.   The use of a basis of 1 lb-mole of product P simplifies the computations.

Example 16-8.   Number of Perfect Plates by Mathematical Method.   A mixture of pentane and hexane containing 0.6 mole fraction of pentane is to be fractionated at atmospheric pressure to produce a product containing 0.95 mole fraction of pentane. The feed is at its boiling point.   Use twice the minimum reflux.

How many theoretically perfect plates are required to get the separation?
Basis: 1 mole of product [see Eq. (16-14)].

$$y_f = 0.82 \text{ (Fig. 16-16)}$$
$$R_{\min} = \frac{x_p - y_f}{y_f - x_f} = \frac{0.95 - 0.82}{0.82 - 0.60} = 0.59$$

Actual reflux:

$$R = 2 \times 0.59 = 1.18 \text{ moles}$$
$$V = 1.18 + 1 = 2.18 \text{ moles [see Eq. (16-11)]}$$
$$\frac{R}{V} = \frac{1.18}{2.18} = 0.541$$

Considering the top plate [see Eq. (16-12)]:

$$\frac{R}{V} = \frac{y_t - y_{t-1}}{x_p - x_t}$$

For this plate,

$$y_t = x_p$$

Also x_t in equilibrium with y_t (0.95) is 0.86 (Fig. 16-16).

$$0.541 = \frac{0.95 - y_{t-1}}{0.95 - 0.86} \qquad y_{t-1} = 0.901$$

For the $t - 1$ plate,

$$\frac{R}{V} = \frac{y_{t-1} - y_{t-2}}{x_t - x_{t-1}} \qquad y_{t-1} = 0.901$$
$$x_{t-1} = 0.745 \text{ (Fig. 16-16)}$$
$$0.541 = \frac{0.901 - y_{t-2}}{0.86 - 0.745} \qquad y_{t-2} = 0.839$$

The liquid flowing from this plate has a composition of 0.625.   Obviously only a part of another perfect plate is required to complete the rectifying section, because the feed composition is 0.6.

Graphical Method.   If infinite reflux is used, the composition of the vapor leaving the plate and the liquid arriving at the plate is the same, that is, $y_n = x_{n+1}$,

$y_{n+1} = x_{n+2}$, etc. At each plate the composition of the vapor and that of the liquid are related to each other by the equilibrium relation shown in Fig. 16-16. The equilibrium relation is plotted in Fig. 16-19 and also a 45-deg line whose equation is $x = y$. The 45-deg line is the operating line for the condition of infinite reflux. The operating line relates the composition of the vapor leaving the plate and the composition of the liquid entering the plate. For conditions other than infinite reflux, the liquid composition x does not equal y and the operating line is less steep than a 45-deg line. The equation of the operating line may be formulated as follows: At the top plate when producing 1 mole of product,

$$\frac{R}{V} = \frac{y_{t-1} - y_t}{x_t - x_p}$$

But $y_t = x_p$

$$\frac{R}{V} = \frac{y_{t-1} - x_p}{x_t - x_p}$$

$$y_{t-1} - x_p = \frac{R}{V}(x_t - x_p)$$

$$y_{t-1} = \frac{R}{V}(x_t - x_p) + \frac{V}{V} x_p$$

But
$$V = R + P$$

$$y_{t-1} = \frac{R(x_t - x_p) + (R + P)x_p}{V} = \frac{R}{V} x_t + \frac{P}{V} x_p \qquad (16\text{-}15a)$$

or
$$y_{n-1} = \frac{R}{V} x_n + \frac{P}{V} x_p \qquad (16\text{-}15b)$$

This is an equation of a straight line having a slope of R/V and having an intercept on the y axis of $(P/V)x_p$. Since the operating line extends from (x_p, y_p) to the intercept, the line can also be drawn without using the slope.

Example 16-9. Number of Plates by Graphical Method. Example 16-8 will be repeated using the graphical method.

The y intercept of the operating line is

$$\frac{P}{V} x_p = \frac{1}{2.18} \times 0.95 = 0.435 \quad \text{[see Eq. (16-15a)]}$$

The operating line is drawn through the intercept $y = 0.435$, $x = 0$, and through the point x_p, y_t (0.95) (Fig. 16-19). The number of plates can then be ascertained by drawing horizontal and vertical lines as shown in Fig. 16-19. Each point on the equilibrium curve indicates one theoretical plate. Thus about $3\frac{1}{3}$ perfect plates are required (see Example 16-8) for the rectifying section.

The dotted lines indicate the number of plates required at infinite reflux. The operating line for infinite reflux is the 45-deg line. Only a little more than two plates are required if infinite reflux is used.

Exhausting Section. The number of plates required in the exhausting section in order to separate a particular bottoms product can be formulated in exactly the same manner as for the rectifying section. However, the computation by graphical methods can be simplified by noting that the exhausting operating line passes through the point A (Fig. 16-19) and through point B. Hence the easiest way to handle the exhausting section is to determine and draw the rectifying operating line and then draw the exhausting line. The equation of the exhausting operating line (AB on Fig. 16-19) is

$$y_m = \frac{R'_{m+1}x_{m+1}}{R'_{m+1} - B} - \frac{Bx_b}{R'_{m+1} - B} = \frac{R'_{m+1}x_{m+1}}{V'_m} - \frac{Bx_b}{V'_m} \qquad (16\text{-}16)$$

Example 16-10. Graphical Method for Number of Plates if Feed Is at Center of Column. Examples 16-8 and 16-9 will be continued for a column that is to produce a bottoms product $x_b = 0.05$ as well as a top product $x_p = 0.95$.

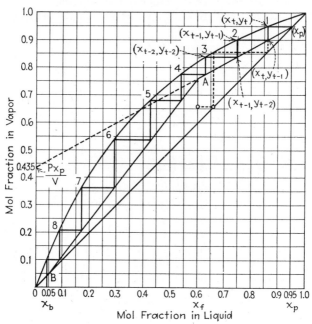

Fig. 16-19. McCabe-Thiele diagram for pentane-hexane (Example 16-9).

The exhausting operating line is drawn as indicated above. The stepwise procedure is continued past the feed composition until the liquid has a composition of 0.05 or less (see Fig. 16-19). About nine perfect plates are required.

If the plate efficiency is 60 per cent,

$$\text{Actual plates} = \frac{8.8}{0.6} = 14.7$$

Ponchon Method. A weakness of the McCabe-Thiele method, as out-lined heretofore, is the fact that the transfer of heat is not directly intro-duced. Heat must be transferred on each plate, reboiler heat must be supplied at the base of the fractionator, and cooling by reflux must be accomplished at the top. The method devised by Ponchon[55] does not ignore these relationships, and although space is not available for an explanation of the Ponchon method, Example 16-11 will indicate its general usefulness.

[55] Ponchon, M., *Tech. mod.*, **13**, 20 (1921).

Example 16-11. Solution by Graphical Ponchon Method. The same problem as that explored in Examples 16-8 to 16-10 will be solved by the Ponchon method.

The total heat contents of liquid and vaporized pentane, and the same for hexane, are plotted at zero and 100 mole fraction of pentane (Fig. 16-20). The enthalpies (Btu per lb) are:

	Boiling point	Vapor	Liquid
Hexane............	155.7°F	325	180
Pentane..........	96.7°F	305	150

The enthalpies of hydrocarbon mixtures are usually straight lines as shown in Fig. 16-20, but for nonideal systems the lines may be curved.

Dashed lines connecting vapor and liquid are the equilibrium compositions of Fig. 16-15 or 16-16. For the condition of minimum reflux, the composition of the vapor leaving the feed plate is in equilibrium with the feed liquid which contains 0.6 mole fraction pentane, i.e., 0.817. This is shown as a dotted line leading to an overhead (x_p or y_p) composition of 0.95, and this indicates that 405 to 305 Btu per lb of product must be withdrawn as (minimum) reflux heat. Twice the minimum is actually employed, and hence heat is present in the reflux in the amount of 505 Btu per lb (point marked $y_{p\Delta}$). A total of 200 Btu per lb of product must be removed at the top of the tower, and the condenser must also handle the product making a total of 355 Btu per lb. A line leading from this point (500 Btu per lb) through the saturated liquid feed composition of 0.6 and on to $x_{b\Delta}$ (located at the bottoms composition) indicates the lack of heat at the reboiler or base of the fractionator. This is negative to the extent of 380 Btu per lb of bottom product and accordingly, 380 plus 178 or 558 Btu per lb must be introduced into the bottom product to heat and reboil the bottom of the column.

The number of plates required, or the heat exchanged on each plate, is obtained by a step-wise operation. The liquid composition (0.86 from Fig. 16-16) in equilibrium with the composition of the top product (0.95) is connected with a dashed line. This point is then connected with the $y_{p\Delta}$ point obtaining the vapor composition y_{T-1} at the $(T - 1)$ plate. Such operations are continued until the feed composition is passed, whereupon the other or $X_{b\Delta}$ turning point is used. Continuing as before, it appears that 8.9 theoretical trays are adequate.

FRACTIONATION OF COMPLEX MIXTURES

Although the process of fractionating complex mixtures can be outlined mathematically for certain simplified situations, the practical application of such computations is not satisfactory because vapor-liquid equilibrium data are inadequate, because human patience is tried to the point of frequent errors by the laboriousness of the computations, and because the assumption of equal molal latent heats should not be made for wide-boiling-range mixtures. The first data that must be had are the compositions of the products that are to be produced, and ordinarily these compositions cannot be wisely selected by the designer because they are fixed by the

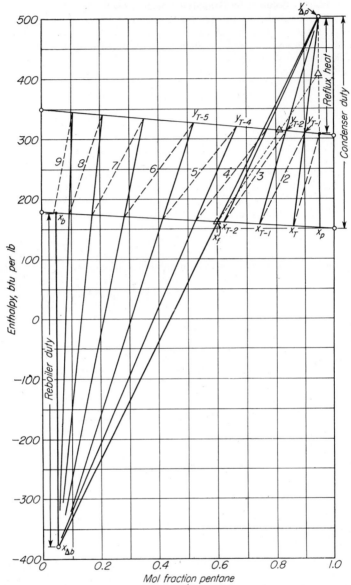

Fig. 16-20. Fractionation by the Ponchon method (see Examples 16-11 and 16-9).

fractionation attained in a system that has yet to be designed. Only when the fractionation is to be so complete that only two of the many components are found in both the overhead and bottoms product, or when the number of components is limited to about three, can the designer adopt reasonable terminal compositions. If at the end of the laborious computations it is found that the *split of each component* between the top and bottoms products is incorrect, a new assumption as to terminal compositions must be made and the entire computation must be repeated almost *ad infinitum*.

Each component in the mixture behaves independently of the others except as the equilibrium constants may be altered by the presence of other components, and for a known reflux ratio an operating equation [Eqs. (16-15a) and (16-16)] can be computed for each component. A plate-by-plate computation can then be undertaken starting at the bottom by assuming a plate temperature and checking by new assumptions until the summation of Kx's [Eq. (15-5)] equals 1.0. The value of x for each component on the next tray can then be computed by use of the operating-line equations [Eqs. (16-15a) and (16-16)]. Similarly, a plate-by-plate computation starting at the top and summing y's/K's is conducted until at some plate the composition found is the same as one found when starting from the bottom. If the assumed terminal compositions are not perfect, a perfect matching of composition at some intermediate plate is never found and new terminal compositions must be assumed.

Example 16-12. Three-component Fractionation. A feedstock contains 50, 30, and 20 mole per cent of pentane (A), hexane (B), and heptane (C). It is desired to produce an overhead product that contains only 0.5 mole per cent hexane and a bottoms product that contains only 1 per cent pentane. The reflux ratio is to be 4 and the pressure 1 atm. The feed is preheated to its bubble point, and it is introduced at a plate which is at the same temperature.

By a pentane material balance based on 100 moles feed, P moles of overhead and B moles of bottoms are produced.

$$50 = P x_{p_A} + B x_{b_A} = (100 - B) x_{p_A} + 0.01B$$

At $x_{p_A} = 0.995$
$$50 = 99.5 - 0.98B \qquad B = 50.25$$
$$P = 100 - 50.25 = 49.75$$

The terminal compositions are

	Feed, moles	Overhead		Bottoms	
		Moles	Fraction	Moles	Fraction
Pentane (A)........	50	49.50	0.995	0.50	0.010
Hexane (B)........	30	0.25	0.005	29.75	0.592
Heptane (C)......	20	0.0	.....	20.0	0.398
	100	49.75	1.000	50.25	1.000

The computations must be started at the bottom because only the bottoms product shows heptane, whereas it was assumed that heptane in the overhead was negligible. The overhead actually contains about 0.000000? mole fraction heptane, and no one could estimate this composition accurately enough on the first trial to arrive finally at a reasonable bottom composition.

$$R = 4 \times 49.75 = 199$$
$$V = V' = 49.75 + 199 = 248.75$$

and for plates below the feed when the feed is at its bubble point

$$R' = 199 + 100 = 299$$

The operating-line equation [Eq. (16-16)] for plates below the feed is

$$y_m = \frac{R'}{V} x_{m+1} - \frac{B}{V} x_b = \frac{299}{248.75} x_{m-1} - \frac{50.25}{248.75} x_b$$

For pentane, the composition of the vapor from a tray (y_A) is related to the liquid on the tray above (x_A) as follows:

$$y_A = 1.202 x_A - 0.00202$$

For hexane

$$y_B = 1.202 x_B - 0.1195$$

For heptane

$$y_C = 1.202 x_C - 0.0805$$

The composition of the vapor leaving the bottom of the column is computed [Eq. (15-5)] from the composition of the bottoms product by assuming a temperature, obtaining values of K's (or vapor pressures), and computing the ΣKx. At the right temperature (169°F) the summation is equal to 1.0.

(1)	(2)	(3)	(4)	(5)	(6)
	x_s	K's at 169°F	Kx's or y_s	y_s	x_{s+1} or x_1
C_5	0.010	3.4	0.034	0.034	0.030
C_6	0.592	1.28	0.759	0.762	0.7315
C_7	0.398	0.51	0.203	0.204	0.2365
			0.996	1.000	

In column (5) the summation of column (4) was made to equal 1.0 by inspection. The x_{s+1} terms in column (6) were computed from the values of y_s in column (5) using the three exhausting operating-line equations as indicated here for heptane:

$$y_C = 1.202 x_C - 0.0805$$
$$0.204 = 1.202 x_C - 0.0805$$
$$x_C = x_{s+1} = x_1 = \frac{0.2845}{1.202} = 0.2365$$

The same procedure is followed up to plate 4, which indicates a liquid composition somewhat the same as the feed composition. Above the feed plate the computations are the same except that rectifying operating-line equations [Eq. (16-15a)] are used to step from plate to plate. The compositions on the plates are shown in Table 16-9. Note that the top product actually contains about 0.00000083 mole fraction heptane; and note also that, had the computations been started at the top of the column, the 0.00000083 would have to be assumed by the designer.

There is no perfect place to introduce the feed. If the feed is introduced on the fourth or fifth plate, much of the hexane contained in it (20 per cent) will be retained on the plates below the feed plate when the fractionator is first operated. This brings the composition closer to x_4 or x_5, in fact close enough to permit the lower trays to produce the bottom composition x_s. All available information indicates that the disturbance caused by introduction of the feed material does not significantly change the number of plates required.

TABLE 16-9. PLATE COMPOSITIONS FOUND IN EXAMPLE 16-12

Temp, °F	169	160	153	143	132	121	109	102	99	98	97
	x_s	x_1	x_2	x_3	x_4	x_5	x_6	x_7	x_8	x_9	x_{10}
C_5	0.010	0.031	0.076	0.170	0.322	0.501	0.713	0.863	0.942	0.976	0.9924918
C_6	0.592	0.732	0.772	0.716	0.582	0.414	0.268	0.134	0.058	0.024	0.0075000
C_7	0.398	0.237	0.152	0.114	0.096	0.085	0.019	0.003	.....	.....	0.0000082
	y_s	y_1	y_2	y_3	y_4	y_5	y_6	y_7	y_8	y_9	y_{10}
C_5	0.034	0.090	0.203	0.386	0.601	0.770	0.889	0.952	0.980	0.993	0.99763917
C_6	0.762	0.808	0.741	0.579	0.377	0.215	0.108	0.048	0.020	0.007	0.00236000
C_7	0.204	0.102	0.056	0.035	0.022	0.015	0.003	.....	.....	.....	0.00000083

Design methods are so unsatisfactory that the designer should never look upon his computations, no matter how complicated they may be, as the exact way that the tower will operate. However, the general relationship among such variables as amount of reflux, number of plates, purity of products, etc., is important and useful.

When applied to wide-boiling-range mixtures such as the customary refinery products (and natural gasoline) the following general facts become apparent.

Amount of *reflux* has little effect on the degree of fractionation or purity of products if normally large reflux ratios (4:1 in topping plants or 8:1 in stabilizers) are employed and if a normal number of plates (5 between cuts in topping plants or 20 in stabilizers) are used.[56,57] These amounts of reflux are almost equivalent in effect to infinite reflux, and hence the composition of the overhead product can be computed by the simple relationship shown in Eq. (16-17). The meaning of the symbols is given on page 518.

$$Y_1 = \frac{100C - wz}{g + \dfrac{hJ}{K_1 K_2 \cdots K_n}} \quad \text{or} \quad y_1 = \frac{100C - wz}{g + \dfrac{h}{K_1 K_2 \cdots K_n}} \quad (16\text{-}17)$$

[56] Nelson, W. L., Effect of Reflux on Fractionation, *Oil Gas J.*, Aug. 18, 1938, p. 58.

[57] Nelson, W. L., Natural Gaso. Stabilizer Fractionation-plant Data, *Oil Gas J.*, Oct. 20, 1938, p. 59.

As illustrations, the computed compositions of overhead products by Eq. (16-17) are compared in the following tabulation with the actual plant[57] product, and Fig. 16-21[58] indicates the distillation curves of products from a topping plant operating with different amounts of reflux.

Component	Percentage of components		
	Actual	Using true reflux	Assuming ∞ reflux
CH₄............	2.58	2.56	2.58
C₂H₆...........	13.35	13.34	13.68
C₃H₈...........	78.20	78.46	79.20
iC₄H₁₀.........	5.27	5.45	4.40
C₄H₁₀..........	0.35	0.19	0.14
iC₅H₁₂.........	0.25*	Trace	Trace

* Analysis in error.

The check on plant operation is not perfect, but the relationship is so complicated if infinite reflux is not assumed that computations are scarcely practical.

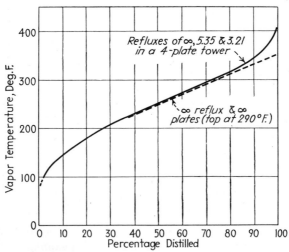

Fig. 16-21. True-boiling-point distillation curves of gasolines produced in a four-plate tower using various reflux ratios. Note the curve for infinite reflux and infinite plates. (*Oil Gas J.*)

The separation of hydrocarbons from one another to produce commercial purities of 95 per cent or more requires many plates. Table 16-10 indicates the approximate reflux ratios required with 20, 30, 50, and ∞ plates.

[58] Nelson, W. L., Effect of Fractionation on Yield, *Oil Gas J.*, Oct. 6, 1938, p. 56.

TABLE 16-10. COMMON REFLUX RATIOS FOR HYDROCARBON COLUMNS

	Relative vola-tility[a]	Reflux ratios when using these numbers of plates			
		20	30	50	∞
Ethane from propane.............	2.5	2.5	1.6	....	1.0
n-Butane from isopentane...........	2.3	2.9	1.8	....	1.2
Propane from isobutane............	2.0	3.8	2.5	2.0	1.6
Isobutane from n-butane...........	1.3	...	...	6.3	4.0
Isopentane from n-pentane.........	1.2	...	...	23.0	6.0

[a] Varies with pressure.

Fractionating towers must operate between two impractical extremes. In one of these the reflux is the minimum that can be used and an infinite number of plates is required, and in the other an infinite amount of reflux is used and a minimum number of plates is required. In practice the engineer must decide whether it pays to purchase a large number of plates or to operate at a higher daily operating cost. The cost of reflux consists of three items: (1) heat to generate the vapor, (2) water or refrigeration to condense the reflux, and (3) cost for extra tower diameter. To compute the entire range of possibilities is a long task, and accordingly, for two-component systems, the tower computations can be considerably shortened[59] by the use of Table 16-11. This shows the average behavior of many systems between the limits of infinite reflux and minimum plates.

TABLE 16-11. PLATES VERSUS VAPOR RATES[a]

N/N_m	V/V_m	N/N_m	V/V_m
1.3	2.15	2.0	1.20
1.4	1.90	2.5	1.07
1.5	1.66	3.0	1.03
1.6	1.50	5.0	1.001
1.7	1.38	7.0	1.000
1.8	1.3	∞	1.000

[a] Donnell and Cooper, Plates vs. Vapor Rates . . . , *Chem. Eng.*, June, 1950, p. 121

Thus, one has only to compute these two extreme conditions and by working with the ratios of actual vapor (V) to minimum vapor (V_m) and the corresponding ratio for number of plates (Table 16-11), the entire economic range of reflux and plates can be explored in a few hours. Each system behaves a little differently, but Table 16-11 enables the establishment

[59] Donnell and Cooper, Plates vs. Vapor Rates . . . , *Chem. Eng.*, June, 1950, p. 121.

of economic balance, and then if more detail is advisable, only a few cases in and about the economic range need be computed.

Example 16-13. Number of Plates versus Reflux. In Example 16-10 a reflux ratio of 2 times the minimum was used, and the number of plates required was about 9. For other amounts of reflux (Table 16-11) it is necessary to compute the minimum reflux and the minimum number of plates.

Minimum reflux or vaporization is easily determined by constructing a line on Fig. 16-19 through $(x_p, y_p) = 0.95$ and the feed composition (0.6) on the equilibrium line. This indicates that x_p/V for minimum reflux has a value of about 0.59 which corresponds to a minimum vaporization or reflux of 1.61 moles per mole overhead product. The minimum number of plates can be stepped off as started on Fig. 16-19 (see dotted lines), and the number of plates is about 5.8. In Example 16-10, the number of plates was found to be 8.8, and this makes a ratio of N/N_m equal to 8.8/5.8 or 1.52. According to Table 16-11, a reflux ratio of about 1.6 (rather than 2.0) would have done the job for most materials. Thus pentane and hexane, as studied here, do not exactly check with the average behavior of Table 16-11. The approximate number of plates required according to Table 16-11 for the same separation as that of Example 16-10, but for several reflux ratios, are:

V/V_m	Actual vaporization	No. of plates
2.15	$2.15 \times 1.61 = 3.46$	$1.3 \times 5.8 = 7.5$
1.9	3.06	8.1
1.66	2.67	8.7
1.3	2.09	10.4
1.07	1.72	14.5
1.001	1.61+	29.0
1.0	1.61	∞

Number of plates has a vital effect on the end point of the product, but at 4 or more plates (topping plant) the difference in end point is only about 10°F if normal reflux ratios are employed. More than 10 plates (topping plants) have little effect on the degree of fractionation.[60]

In gasoline stabilizers the situation is not clear. Ten plates fail to separate propane from the gasoline or recover all isopentane, even at infinite reflux, but the use of more than 40 plates does not appear to be justified for any regular operations.[61]

Experience of the Standard Oil Development Company in its commercial multidraw towers is disclosed by J. W. Packie[5] as shown in Fig. 16-22 for overhead and highest side-stream products. Dotted lines indicate the separation when using maximum amounts of steam. Degree of fractionation is indicated by the gapping or overlapping of the 95 per cent point (ASTM) of the low-boiling product and the 5 per cent point of the

[60] Nelson, W. L., Effect of Varying Number of Plates, *Oil Gas J.*, Sept. 15, 1938, p. 46.

[61] Nelson, W. L., General Application and Summary, *Oil Gas J.*, Dec. 15, 1938, p. 46.

higher-boiling product. Reflux ratio times number of plates is obviously not a generally useful basis for gaging the degree of fractionation; but, for the limited ranges of reflux ratio and of numbers of plates encountered in heavy-oil towers, it is satisfactory.

Since Packie's 1941 work,[5] the behavior of catalytic cracking unit fractionators has been studied in the same manner.[62] Only the dashed steam-stripped lines of Fig. 16-22 could be compared, but it was found that the

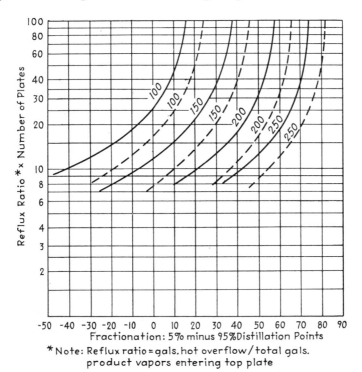

FIG. 16-22. Gap and overlap of top and side-stream products from topping towers. (*Packie, Trans. A.I.Ch.E.*) See discussion for application to cracking-plant fractionators. 1. For overhead and top stream only. 2. Solid curves for no steam. Dotted curves for the maximum stripping steam generally used. 3. Numbers on curves represent degrees Fahrenheit difference in 50 per cent distillation points of the overhead and top side-stream products.

100 and 150°F (difference in ASTM 50 per cent points) lines were the same as shown in Fig. 16-22, whereas the lines for differences of 200 and 250°F were located to the left (Fig. 16-22) by about 8 to 20°F, indicating poorer fractionation in cracking plant fractionators. Houghland[62] found it necessary to work with butane-free products because of the very large amounts of butane and gases associated with the overhead product.

[62] Houghland et al., *Oil Gas J.*, July 26, 1954, p. 198.

With respect to the degree of separation of side-stream products, they[62] nearly substantiate an early Packie[5] chart and were able to extend it downward to lower F factors (product of reflux ratio and number of plates) as shown[62] in Fig. 16-23. The solid lines of Fig. 16-23 for less than 0.1 lb steam per gal of heavy product can also be used according to Packie's data for products which have not been stripped with steam.

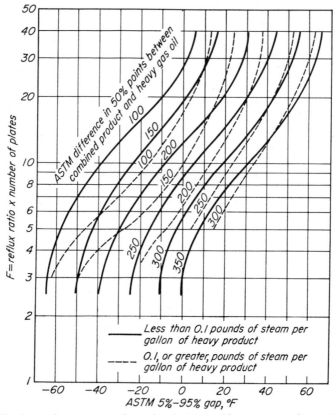

FIG. 16-23. Approximate gap and overlap between side-stream products of topping towers[5] (but see discussion), and between heavy gas-oil and the combined product of cracking-plant fractionators.[62]   (*Oil Gas J.*)

The term "combined product" used in Fig. 16-23 means all of the products lighter (except butane) than the heavy (or heavy gas-oil) product. This is the material that passes through the top tray of the section. However, when applying Fig. 16-23 to topping tower side-stream products, the difference between the plain 50 per cent boiling points of the two side-stream products is used rather than those of the "combined product" and heavy gas oil.

When using reflux ratios of 4 or 5, the gapping or overlapping of solvent or naphtha products is about as shown[63] in Fig. 16-24. The production of only one finished product per tower (or one tower less than the total number of products) is contemplated in using Fig. 16-24.

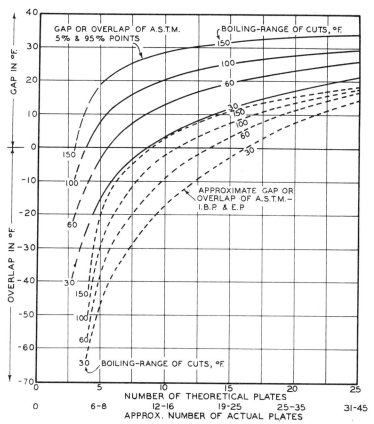

FIG. 16-24. Gap and overlap of products from solvent fractionators when only top and bottom products are produced. (*Oil Gas J.*)

Plate efficiency appears always to exceed 75 per cent and is often close to 100 per cent. It is suggested that an efficiency of 80 per cent is a reasonably safe design value.

The selection of *plate temperatures* is the most unsatisfactory part of the design method suggested below. Intermediate plate temperatures are not of vital significance, but the temperatures at the plates at which products are withdrawn or feeds are admitted must be computed with great care.[61]

[63] Nelson, W. L., Fractionation for Solvents, *Oil Gas J.*, Oct. 20, 1945, p. 161.

Theory of Fractionation. The complicated behavior of complex mixtures requires the use of many symbols and several new concepts (see Fig. 16-25).[64]

R = moles internal (or hot) reflux at top, based on a heat balance and including no reflux for the plates below the first side-draw plate

eR = moles actual reflux as a fraction of R, includes excess reflux that flows from the base of the column to other plates that lie below the first side-draw plate

n = plate number, counting from top

a = total number of plates between two products being separated

D = moles overhead product

b = reflux ratio = eR/D

O = moles overflow liquid or reflux at any point

V = moles vapor at any point

x = mole percentage of fraction being considered, liquids

y = moles percentage of fraction being considered, vapors

P = vapor pressure of fraction

π = total pressure (abs) of system, same units as P

$K = y/x = P/\pi$ = equilibrium constant

m = molecular weight of fraction

m_p = molecular weight of overhead or top product

m_{n+1} = molecular weight of bottoms product ($n + 1$ plate) of tower section studied

d = density of fraction (liquid at 60°F)

d_p = density of overhead product (liquid at 60°F)

d_{n+1} = density of ($n + 1$) material

y_1 = mole percentage of fraction in overhead product

Y_1 = liquid volume percentage of fraction in overhead product

y_{n+1} = mole percentage of fraction in bottoms product of tower section studied

Y_{n+1} = liquid volume percentage of fraction in bottoms product of tower section studied

J = a constant by which the ratio of mole percentages is multiplied to convert the ratio to a basis of liquid volume percentage

$J = m_p d_{n+1}/m_{n+1} d_p$

C = liquid volume percentage of fraction in feedstock

g = percentage of top product based on feedstock

h = percentage of bottoms product based on feedstock

wz = product of percentage and composition of fractions that leave a multi-product tower system in other products than the two that are being studied

Each pair of two products with the plates between them is considered as a separate fractionating tower or section and will be so handled throughout this entire discussion. Reflux in a complex-mixture column decreases from plate to plate by an amount equal to R divided by a, as indicated in Fig. 16-25. Thus, the reflux consists of two parts, a quantity R, which disappears entirely in the column, and

[64] Nelson and Roland, *Ind. Eng. Chem.*, **30**, 730 (1938).

an excess reflux related to e, which flows through the column in undiminished amount and may be considered as reflux for the sections or fractionating columns that are below the one being studied.   The reflux at any or the nth plate is

$$O_n = eR - \frac{R}{a}n = bD\left(1 - \frac{n}{ea}\right) \tag{16-18}$$

Other relationships and a derivation of the final equations that will be presented later may be found in original references,[56-58,60,61,63-66] but they are too long to be presented here.

If the tower products are liquids, mole percentage is converted to a liquid percentage basis by means of the constant J and equilibrium constants.   Thus, for

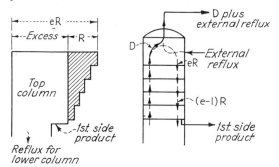

Fig. 16-25. Reflux conditions in the top section of a multiproduct fractionating tower.

relating vapor concentrations at the top and bottom of a tower section, the relation is

$$\frac{y_{n+1}}{y_1}(J) = \frac{Y_{n+1}}{Y_1} \tag{16-19}$$

whereas for relating a vapor at the top to the liquid flowing from the base of the tower section

$$\frac{y_{n+1}}{y_1}\left(\frac{J}{K_{n+1}}\right) = \frac{x_{n+1}}{y_1}(J) = \frac{X_{n+1}}{Y_1} \tag{16-20}$$

Or for an intermediate tower section in which both the top and bottom products are withdrawn as liquids (as in separating kerosene from gas oil in a topping tower), the relation is

$$\frac{y_{n+1}}{y_1}\left(\frac{K_1}{K_{n+1}}J\right) = \frac{x_{n+1}}{x_1}(J) = \frac{X_{n+1}}{X_1} \tag{16-21}$$

The composition of the feed is related to the composition of the products by a material balance.   For a tower section producing a vapor product at the top and a liquid product at the bottom:

$$100C = gY_1 + hX_{n+1} + w_1z_1 + w_2z_2 + \cdot\cdot\cdot \tag{16-22}$$

The sum of the w_1z_1, w_2z_2, etc., terms are combined in Eq. (16-23) as wz.

[65] Nelson, W. L., *Oil Gas J.*, July 21, 1938, p. 41; Aug. 4, 1938, p. 44; Oct. 27, 1938, p. 178; and Nov. 10, 1938, p. 44.

[66] Nelson, W. L., Intermediate Towers, *Oil Gas J.*, Dec. 1, 1938, p. 40.

$$Y_1 = \frac{100C - wz}{(hJ/K_{n+1})(y_{n+1}/y_1) + g}$$ (16-23)

The mole percentage ratio (y_{n+1}/y_1) shown below the line is related to reflux, number of plates, temperature, and pressure (equilibrium constants) as indicated in Eqs. (16-24) to (16-29), which could have been written as a general but very complicated form. Rather than confuse the presentation, it appeared best to let the reader devise additional equations by inspection of those given and not present a confusing general equation.

Intermediate towers, which are defined as those from which both bottom and top products are withdrawn as liquids, are indicated in Fig. 16-26. The study of such towers is complicated by the fact that the reflux (X_R) does not have the same composition as the overhead (liquid) product and in fact is intermediate in composition between Y_1 and X_1. Perhaps the best approach is to use the equations that have already been given, which assume that $X_R = Y_1$, because these equations are more simple than others; but as an illustration of the relationship if X_R is assumed to be equal to X_1, Eq. (16-29) for a three-plate tower is also presented. Note that this is far more complicated than Eq. (16-25), which is also for a three-plate tower. Additional relations for two- and four-plate towers are given in the original references.[66]

All the preceding equations are very complicated, and hence in many instances the use of Eq. (16-17) for infinite reflux may be justified

$$Y_1 = \frac{100C - wz}{g + \dfrac{hJ}{K_1 K_2 \cdots K_n}}$$ (16-17)

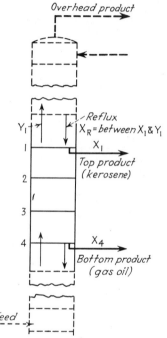

FIG. 16-26. Diagram of an intermediate tower section of four plates. (*Oil Gas J.*)

The use of this equation gives nearly the same results as the more complicated equations if the reflux quantity is as large as that normally used commercially and if a normal number of trays is employed. Another powerful reason for using Eq. (16-17) is the fact that equilibrium constants (K's) are not dependable when applied to complex mixtures and hence great expenditure of energy in using the more rigorous equations may not be justified. The infinite reflux equation should not be used for those intermediate towers which lie just above the feed plate, because such towers operate with very little reflux.

In two-component fractionation studies the term "minimum reflux" is employed as the amount of reflux below which no increase in the number of plates (even to infinity) will cause the separation of the desired product. Although such a situation also exists for complex mixtures, in that a particular boiling range

Two-plate tower:

$$Y_1 = \cfrac{100C - wz}{g + \cfrac{hJ}{K_2R\left(\frac{D}{R} + e - 1\right)}\left[D + \cfrac{R(e-1)}{K_1}\right]}$$

(16-24)

Three-plate tower:

$$Y_1 = \cfrac{100C - wz}{g + \cfrac{2hJ}{K_3R\left(2\frac{D}{R} + 2e - 1\right)^2}\left[D\left(2\frac{D}{R} + 2e - 1\right) + \frac{D}{K}(2e - 2) + \cfrac{R(2e-2)^2}{2K_1K_2}\right]}$$

(16-25)

Four-plate tower:

$$Y_1 = \cfrac{100C - wz}{g + \cfrac{3hJ}{K_4R\left(3\frac{D}{R} + 3e - 1\right)^3}\left[D\left(3\frac{D}{R} + 3e - 1\right)^2 + \frac{D}{K_3}(3e-3)\left(3\frac{D}{R} + 3e - 1\right) + \frac{D}{K_2K_3}(3e-3)^2 + \cfrac{R(3e-3)^3}{3K_1K_2K_3}\right]}$$

(16-26)

Five-plate tower:

$$Y_1 = \cfrac{100C - wz}{g + \cfrac{4hJ}{K_5R\left(4\frac{D}{R} + 4e - 1\right)^4}\left[D\left(4\frac{D}{R} + 4e - 1\right)^3 + \frac{D}{K_4}(4e-4)\left(4\frac{D}{R} + 4e - 1\right)^2 + \frac{D}{K_3K_4}(4e-4)^2\left(4\frac{D}{R} + 4e - 1\right) + \frac{D}{K_2K_3K_4}(4e-4)^3 + \cfrac{R(4e-4)^4}{4K_1K_2K_3K_4}\right]}$$

(16-27)

Six-plate tower:

$$Y_1 = \cfrac{100C - wz}{g + \cfrac{5hJ}{K_6R\left(5\frac{D}{R} + 5e - 1\right)^5}\left[D\left(5\frac{D}{R} + 5e - 1\right)^4 + \frac{D(5e-5)}{K_5}\left(5\frac{D}{R} + 5e - 1\right)^3 + \frac{D(5e-5)^2}{K_4K_5}\left(5\frac{D}{R} + 5e - 1\right)^2 + \frac{D(5e-5)^3}{K_3K_4K_5}\left(5\frac{D}{R} + 5e - 1\right) + \frac{D(5e-5)^4}{K_2K_3K_4K_5}\left(5\frac{D}{R} + 5e - 1\right) + \cfrac{R(5e-5)^5}{5K_1K_2K_3K_4K_5}\right]}$$

(16-28)

Three-plate tower (intermediate products):

$$X_1 = \cfrac{100C - wz}{g + hJ\frac{K_1}{K_3}\left[\cfrac{\frac{D}{R} + e}{\frac{D}{R} + e - 1} - \frac{1}{K_1}\cfrac{e}{\frac{D}{R} + e - 1} + \frac{1}{K_2}\cfrac{e\left(2\frac{D}{R} - \frac{2R}{eD} + 1\right)}{\left(\frac{D}{R} + e - 1\right)\left(2\frac{D}{R} + 2e - 1\right)} + \frac{1}{K_1K_2}\cfrac{(2e-3)}{\left(2\frac{D}{R} + 2e - 2\right)\left(2\frac{D}{R} + 2e - 1\right)}\right]}$$

(16-29)

521

of product cannot be produced unless a certain amount of reflux is employed, the situation of minimum reflux is not clear for practical purposes because the composition of the overhead product cannot be accurately defined. Thus, if the spread in temperature between the 90 and 99 per cent point is fixed, a certain minimum reflux is necessary; whereas if another difference in temperature between the 90 and 99 per cent points is permitted, another minimum reflux will be required. One situation, however, is completely clear; i.e., the *least reflux* that can be employed must always be more than for a value of $e = 1$. This means that in all situations the actual reflux eR must be greater than the reflux R that is demanded by a heat balance. At lower quantities of reflux, no liquid would overflow from the base of the column into lower intermediate columns, and hence any material that once found its way into the column as a vapor would of necessity be found in the two products from the column because no other outlet exists. In many instances the intermediate section of column situated just above the feed plate of a multiple-draw column operates with just slightly more reflux than that required by least reflux.

Application of Fractionation Equations. In applying the fractionation equations a number of factors prove to be confusing. Fractionation computations are based primarily on the moles of the various products undergoing separation and their vapor pressures, and hence a true-boiling-point distillation curve of the feed must be available. The distillation curves obtained by the computation are also true-boiling-point curves. Exact correlations of true-boiling-point vs. ASTM curves are not available, particularly for the low-boiling end of the distillations, but Fig. 4-18 and Table 4-8 are reasonably satisfactory. The segmental correlation method of Edmister and Pollock[67] does not appear to be satisfactory except when applied to very low-boiling materials, but in some instances the method of R. L. Geddes[68] has been useful.

Yields must be estimated as a preliminary step in the computations. These can be determined by the general methods outlined in Chap. 4, but it should be recalled that maximum yields cannot be obtained (perfect fractionation) unless an infinite number of trays and infinite reflux are employed. Thus, the plant yields will be slightly different from those determined in Chap. 4—a slightly lower yield of top product and different yields of intermediate products because of the overlap of the products.

After the yields are determined, the temperatures in the tower must be computed or estimated by the methods outlined in the early parts of this chapter and the general theory outlined in Chap. 15. In heavy-oil towers the temperatures on the plates that lie between the plates from which products are withdrawn can be estimated with relative ease and accuracy, but in gasoline stabilizers and other operations requiring a large number of plates the estimation of accurate plate temperatures is difficult. In general, the plate temperature changes most rapidly at or near the

[67] *Chem. Eng. Progr.*, **44**, 905 (1948).
[68] *Ind. Eng. Chem.*, **33**, 795 (1941).

plates from which products are being withdrawn.   The feed plate does not molest the temperature gradient greatly unless the feed is introduced at the wrong point in the column—and this situation is almost unavoidable in most multiple-draw columns.   In general, the smaller the amount of reflux the greater the change in temperature at or near the withdrawal plates.

The questionable accuracy of the equilibrium constants that are available makes it necessary to look upon the fractionation equations as a method of studying the relation of variables such as amount of reflux and number of plates rather than as a means of designing specific fractionation systems.   This means that for most purposes the somewhat simple equation for infinite reflux [Eq. (16-17)] may be used rather than the more complicated equations.

Example 16-14.   Fractionation of Gasoline and Kerosene.   The crude oil shown in Fig. 16-27 is to be fractionated into gasoline, kerosene, and other products.   The top five plates of the tower, which separate gasoline from kerosene, operate at an equivalent pressure of 1,000 mm including the partial-pressure reduction of steam.   The gasoline is to have an end point of about 380°F, and the kerosene is to have a gravity of 46 API.

By perfect fractionation the yield of gasoline would be about 30.5 per cent and the yield of kerosene about 20 per cent.   However, as a result of the overlap required to produce a kerosene of suitable properties, the yields are assumed to be as follows:

$$\begin{aligned}
\text{Gasoline} &\dots\dots\dots\dots \quad 26.0 \text{ per cent 62 API} \\
\text{Kerosene} &\dots\dots\dots\dots \quad \underline{23.5 \text{ per cent 46 API}} \\
\text{Total} &\dots\dots\dots\dots \quad 49.5 \text{ per cent}
\end{aligned}$$

These yields will be checked in the computations that follow; and should they be found to be incorrect, it will be necessary to make new assumptions and repeat all the computations.

The five actual plates will behave as about four theoretically perfect plates if the plate efficiency is assumed to be 80 per cent.   In order to facilitate the computations, the infinite reflux equation [Eq. (16-17)] will be employed, but at the end of the example, the manner of using Eq. (16-26), which applies to any amount of reflux, will be indicated.

$$Y_1 = \frac{100C - wz}{g + \dfrac{hJ}{K_1 K_2 K_3 K_4}} \tag{16-17}$$

The yield of gasoline is g, or 26, and of kerosene is h, or 23.5.   The value of J must be computed by recourse to Fig. 5-9 and densities

$$J = \frac{m_p d_4}{m_4 d_p} = \frac{115 \times 0.797}{193 \times 0.731} = 0.648$$

If we are interested only in getting the composition of the gasoline and of the front end of the kerosene, the wz term (or terms) can be neglected because essentially none of the hydrocarbons in the gasoline and low kerosene will be lost into heavier products such as gas oil.   By inserting known values, the equation simplifies to

$$Y_1 = \frac{100C - 0}{26 + \dfrac{23.5 \times 0.648}{K_1 K_2 K_3 K_4}} = \frac{100C}{26 + \dfrac{15.2}{K_1 K_2 K_3 K_4}}$$

The remaining variables, i.e., the equilibrium constants (K's) and C, are dependent upon the composition of the feed and the plate temperatures. Values of C are determined by reading from Fig. 16-27 and are smoothed by inspection as shown in column (3) of Table 16-12. The values of K, as shown in columns (5), (6), (7), and (8) of

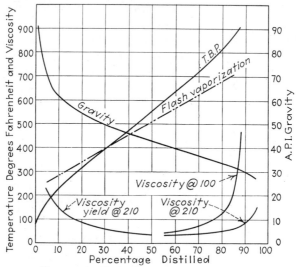

Fig. 16-27. Typical paraffin-base crude oil.

Table 16-12, can be read from Figs. 5-27 or 15-4 and 15-5, but it is first necessary to estimate the plate temperatures. By means of the approximate boiling ranges of the products taken from Fig. 16-27 and the methods outlined in Examples 16-3 and 16-4 of this chapter, the plate temperatures are found to be about as follows:

	Plate number	°F
Gasoline.........	Top plate	310
	2	360
	3	400
Kerosene.........	4	425

In Table 16-12, column (12) should total to 100 per cent if the assumed yields of gasoline and kerosene designated as g and h, respectively, are correct. The total of column (12) was 100.52; and had new values of $g = 26.2$ and $h = 23.3$ been used, the total would have been almost exactly 100. The error so introduced occurs primarily in the first two fractions, and hence the error of 0.52 per cent was corrected in column (13) in the first two numbers, i.e., 27.3 and 35.3.

One other check on the accuracy must be made before the computations can be dismissed as correct. This check consists of determining the tower temperatures from the computed distillation curves shown in columns (13) and (17) of Table 16-12 and on Fig. 16-28. The checks on the assumption of 310 and 425°F were found to be satisfactory. ASTM curves estimated by means of Fig. 4-18 and Table 4-8 are also shown in Fig. 16-28.

TABLE 16-12. TABULATED COMPUTATIONS FOR EXAMPLE 16-14

Columns (5)–(8): Vapor pressures divided by 1,000 at 310°F, 360°F, 400°F, 425°F.

(1) Fraction number	(2) Boiling range °F	(3) C	(4) $100C$	(5) 310°F	(6) 360°F	(7) 400°F	(8) 425°F	(9) $K_1K_2K_3K_4$	(10) $\frac{15.2}{(9)}$	(11) (10)+26	(12) $Y_1=\frac{100C}{(11)}$	(13) Gasoline, percentage	(14) gY_1; 26×(12)	(15) $100C\,(4)-gY_1\,(14)$	(16) X_{n+1} (15)÷23.5	(17) Kerosene, percentage
1	80-200	7.2	720	6.50	11.00	16.0	19.0	21,800	0.0007	26.00	27.70	27.3	720	0	0	
2	200-220	2.1	210	3.00	5.30	8.2	10.5	1,370	0.0111	26.01	8.08	35.3	......	......	0	
3	220-240	2.15	215	2.40	4.20	6.4	8.0	516	0.0294	26.03	8.35	43.6	219.4	0.6	0.02	
4	240-260	2.20	220	1.80	3.20	4.9	6.5	183	0.0830	26.08	8.44	52.1	121	1	0.04	
5	260-270	1.22	122	1.45	2.65	4.1	5.4	85	0.179	26.18	4.66	56.7	120	1	0.04	0.1
6	270-280	1.22	122	1.35	2.40	3.3	4.9	60.4	0.252	26.25	4.65	61.4	119	2	0.09	0.2
7	280-290	1.22	122	0.98	2.10	3.0	4.2	32.0	0.475	26.47	4.61	66.0	116	3	0.13	0.3
8	290-300	1.22	122	0.83	1.85	2.7	3.8	20.7	0.735	26.73	4.57	70.5	113	6	0.26	0.6
9	300-310	1.22	122	0.72	1.60	2.3	3.3	11.8	1.29	27.29	4.48	75.0	107.5	9	0.38	1.0
10	310-320	1.22	122	0.62	1.40	2.1	3.1	7.18	2.12	28.12	4.35	79.4	99.4	14.5	0.62	1.6
11	320-330	1.22	122	0.54	1.24	1.85	2.7	4.35	3.49	29.49	4.14	83.5	90.0	22.6	0.96	2.5
12	330-340	1.22	122	0.47	1.08	1.6	2.4	2.58	5.89	31.89	3.82	87.3	74.1	32.0	1.36	3.9
13	340-350	1.22	122	0.40	0.97	1.4	2.2	1.61	9.44	35.44	3.46	90.8	56.6	47.8	2.03	5.9
14	350-360	1.22	122	0.345	0.83	1.22	1.95	0.905	16.8	42.80	2.85	93.6	42.4	65.4	2.78	8.7
15	360-370	1.22	122	0.295	0.71	1.1	1.70	0.508	30.0	56.0	2.18	95.8	27.3	79.6	3.39	12.1
16	370-380	1.22	122	0.250	0.62	0.96	1.54	0.312	48.7	74.7	1.63	97.4	16.6	94.7	4.03	16.1
17	380-390	1.22	122	0.210	0.54	0.82	1.30	0.168	90.5	116.5	1.05	98.5	9.4	105.4	4.49	20.6
18	390-400	1.22	122	0.162	0.47	0.73	1.13	0.0915	166.0	192.	0.64	99.1	5.7	112.6	4.79	25.4
19	400-410	1.22	122	0.140	0.41	0.64	1.01	0.0490	310.0	336.	0.36	99.5	5.2	116.3	4.85	30.3
20	410-420	1.22	122	0.118	0.36	0.52	0.90	0.0290	524.0	550.	0.22	99.7	0.5	238.8	10.18	40.4
21	420-440	2.44	244	0.086	0.28	0.40	0.74	0.0127	1,200.0	1,226.	0.20	99.9	0.0	242.4	10.32	50.8
22	440-460	2.44	244	0.058	0.21	0.29	0.57	0.00412	3,700.0	3,726.	0.06	......		243.5	10.37	61.1
23	460-480	2.44	244		0.15		0.425	0.00107	14,200.0	14,226.	0.02	100.0		244.0	10.38	71.5
24	480-500	2.44	244							large	0.00	......				

Total = 100.52

Explanation of column headings:
(1) Number assigned for identification.
(3) Percentage of fraction in feedstock.
(5) to (8) Equilibrium constants taken at mean boiling point of fraction except big fractions such as No. 1.
(10) $hJ/K_1K_2K_3K_4$.
(11) Denominator of Eq. (16-17).
(12) Equation (16-17).
(13) Cumulative percentage of fractions.
(14) Starting material balance, Eq. (16-22).
(15) Part of Eq. (16-22).
(16) Equation (16-22).
(17) Cumulative percentage.

The separation found in Fig. 16-28 checks reasonably well with Fig. 16-22 for five plates and a reflux of 6.6 (see below).

Equation for Actual Reflux.   Had Eq. (16-26) been used, it would have been necessary to make a heat balance such as that illustrated in Example 16-1.   According to such a heat balance (using 100 gal as a basis), the actual hot reflux or eR = 6.6 moles.

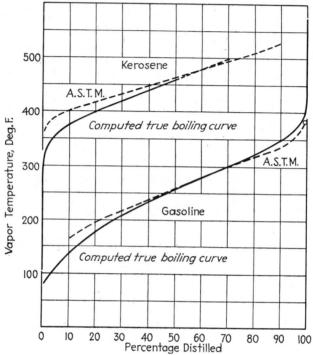

Fig. 16-28. Composition of the products determined in Example 16-14.

The heat-balance reflux R for the top five plates is 191 lb of gasoline.

$$\text{Reflux heat} = 191(425 - 310)0.52 = 11,400 \text{ Btu per hr}$$

$$R = \frac{11,400}{121 \times 113} = 0.833 \text{ mole}$$

$$e = \frac{6.6}{0.833} = 7.93$$

$$D = {}^{191}\!/_{113} = 1.69$$

$$b = \frac{eR}{D} = \frac{6.6}{1.69} = 3.9$$

$$\frac{D}{R} = \frac{1.69}{0.833} = 2.03$$

$$J = 0.648$$

By inserting these values in Eq. (16-26) the following simplified equation results:

$$Y_1 = \frac{100C}{g + h\left(\dfrac{0.1365}{K_4} + \dfrac{0.098}{K_3K_4} + \dfrac{0.0701}{K_2K_3K_4} + \dfrac{0.241}{K_1K_2K_3K_4}\right)}$$

The computations are conducted in the same manner as for infinite reflux. Note, however, that the top temperature will be slightly lower and that the yields will be slightly different.

Plant Practice. Although design computations such as those described on previous pages are useful for outlining fractionation theory, the design of fractionating columns is usually conducted by rule-of-thumb methods. The separation of most refinery products is such as easy separation that four or five equilibrium contacts are usually sufficient. As an approximation, the number of trays (at 22-in. spacing) that are now being used between fractions is indicated in Table 16-13 and in Table 16-10.

TABLE 16-13. TRAYS USED IN COMMERCIAL HEAVY-OIL EQUIPMENT
See Table 16-10 for hydrocarbon fractionators

Operation	Materials separated	Plates between fractions	
		Literature[a]	Recommendation
Steam atmospheric	Light gasoline and naphtha	3–8	4–5
	Naphtha and kerosene	3–6	3–5
	Gasoline and kerosene	6–8	5–6
	Kerosene and gas oil	4–7	4–5
	Gas-oil and lube distillate	4–5	4–5
	Inlet to lowest side product	3–4	2–4
	Stripping bottoms	4–6	4–5
	Side strippers	4–5	3–5
Cracking	Cracked gasoline rerun	10–12	10–12
	Cracked gasoline and naphtha	7–9	6–8
	Cracked gasoline and recycle (or reboiler oil)	10–12	8–11
	Naphtha and recycle (or reboiler oil)	4–5	4–6
Vacuum	Gas-oil and wax distillate[b]	2–4	2–3[c]
	Low- and medium-viscosity oil	4–5	2–3[c]
	Medium-viscosity and cylinder stock	3–5	3–5[c]
	Cylinder stock and inlet	3–4	2–4[c]
	Stripping	3–4	2–4[c]

[a] Bell, H. S., "American Petroleum Refining," 3d ed., D. Van Nostrand Company, Inc., Princeton, N.J., 1945; Mayer, N., *Pet. Refiner*, December, 1946, p. 143.
[b] Also separated by partial condensation.
[c] At wide tray spacing.

Fractionation is more effective at low pressures than at high pressures because of the larger difference in the vapor pressures of the components at a low pressure. This probably accounts for the relatively few plates that are used in many vacuum plants, although the wide tray spacing this is normally used accounts in part for the lesser number of trays.

CHAPTER 17

HEAT TRANSFER AND EXCHANGERS

by *A. Paul Buthod*

Chairman, Department of Chemical and Petroleum Refinery
Engineering, School of Petroleum Sciences, University of Tulsa

Although heat-transfer rates can be computed with reasonable accuracy for clean or new pipe, the effect of dirty or corroded pipe surfaces cannot be satisfactorily estimated. With the greatest possible care, the accuracy with which the rate of heat transfer can be computed is probably not better than ± 5 per cent.

There are three common methods of transferring heat, viz., radiation, conduction through solids, and conduction through fluids. In practice a combination of two or even all of these methods may take place simultaneously. Radiation will be discussed in Chap. 18.

CONDUCTION THROUGH SOLIDS

Conduction is the most simple method of heat transfer. Newton's fundamental law of resistances and driving forces, if applied to conduction, takes the following form:

$$\frac{Q}{A} = \frac{k(T_2 - T_1)}{L} \tag{17-1}$$

where
Q = Btu heat transferred per hr
A = area of surface, sq ft
T_2 and T_1 = temperatures at hot and cold surfaces
k = conductivity as Btu/($°$F diff.)(sq ft)(hr) for 1 ft thickness (Tables 17-1 and 17-2)
L = thickness, ft

In using Newton's law, the factor L/k may be considered to be a resistance (R) to the driving force represented by the temperature difference $(T_2 - T_1)$.

$$\frac{Q}{A} = \frac{\Delta T}{L/k} = \frac{\Delta T}{R} \tag{17-2}$$

TABLE 17-1. THERMAL CONDUCTIVITY OF SOLIDS
Btu/(°F diff.)(sq ft)(hr) for a 1-ft thickness

Material	Conductivity k, at these temperatures, °F:					
	Customary	0	200	400	800	As noted
Aluminum		115		130	140	
Asbestos cement board						0.23 at 212
Asbestos felt						0.12 at 212
Asbestos wool	0.035					
Asphalt	0.10					
Asphalt, road	0.42					
Brass		60			80	
Boiler scale	0.5–1.43					
Brick, fireclay			0.4			0.9 at 2000
Brick, diatomaceous (natural)[a]				0.05		0.08 at 2000
Brick, diatomaceous (molded)				0.12		0.19 at 2000
Brick, magnesite				3.0		2.0 to 2200
Brick, red or common			0.34			0.7 at 1800
Brick, sil-o-cel insulation	0.125 (at 70–1800)					
Calcium carbonate scale						0.5–1.5 at 70
Coke	0.48					
Copper or silver		230	216			
Concrete wall	0.44			0.5		0.7 at 1800
Cork	0.03					
Cracking-coil coke	3.25					
Hi-Temp No. 12[b]			0.051	0.056	0.066	0.077 at 1200
Iron sulfide	4.10					
Jute fibers	0.027					
Kapok	0.023					
Lamp black	0.04					
Magnesium 85 %, insulation				0.037	0.043	
Mineral wool, insulating cement[e]			0.058	0.067	0.083	0.075 at 600
Paraffin wax	0.14					
Rock wool blanket[e]				0.034	0.044	0.054 at 600
Soil, sandy, dry, 24-in. cover[d]	0.24–0.4					
Soil, sandy, moist, 24-in. cover[d]	0.5–0.6					
Soil, sandy, soaked, 24-in. cover[d]	1.1–1.3					
Soil, under river[d]	2.0–2.5					
Soil, sandy, dry, 8-in. cover[d]	0.6–0.7					
Soil, sandy, moist, 8-in. cover[d]	1.2–2.4					
Soil, clay, dry, 24-in. cover[d]	0.2–0.3					
Soil, clay, moist, 24-in. cover[d]	0.4–0.6					
Soil, clay, wet, 24-in. cover[d]	0.6–0.9					
Steel, 0.06 carbon and pure iron		38				
Steel, 0.3 carbon and cast iron		30		18		
Steel, 18–8 chrome nickel		9				
Steel, all kinds						17 at 1800
Superex[e]			0.054	0.057	0.064	0.073 at 1200
Unibestos, Standard[f]				0.038	0.04	0.049 at 600
Unibestos, Super[f]					0.059	0.068 at 1000
Vermiculite			0.044	0.052	0.068	0.084 at 1200
Wood pulp	0.025					

[a] Perpendicular to strata.
[b] Philip Carey.
[c] Commercial Standards CS-117-44 Classes C and E.
[d] Nelson, W. L., *Oil Gas J.*, Sept. 15, 1945, p. 110. Not for 1 ft thickness (see coverings indicated).
[e] Johns-Manville.
[f] Union Asbestos Company.

TABLE 17-2. THERMAL CONDUCTIVITY OF PETROLEUM PRODUCTS AND WATER[a]
(MULTIPLIED BY 100)
100 times Btu/(°F diff.)(hr)(sq ft) for 1 ft thickness

Material	Temperature, °F					Material	Temperature, °F			
	0	200	400	600	800		−100	0	100	200
10 API oil.......	6.83	6.42	6.00	5.58	5.25	Methane (gas).....	1.16	1.57	1.99	2.41[b]
20 API oil.......	7.35	6.91	6.42	6.00	5.58	Ethane (gas).......	0.61	0.94	1.30	1.78
30 API oil.......	7.83	7.35	6.91	6.42	5.91	Ethene (gas).......	0.61	0.87	1.13	1.47
TEMA[c].........	8.16	7.69	7.20	6.72	6.23	Propane (gas)......	....	0.80	1.08[b]	
40 API oil.......	8.33	7.83	7.35	6.83	6.33[b]	Butanes (gas)......	....	0.71	0.95[b]	
50 API oil.......	8.75	8.25	7.75	7.25[b]	6.75[b]	Isopentane (gas)...	....	0.59[b]	0.84	1.13[b]
60 API oil.......	9.25	8.75	8.15	7.65[b]	.....	n-Pentane (gas)...	....	0.61[b]	0.81	1.16[b]
80 API oil.......	10.30	9.69	9.09[b]	8.63[b]	.....	Hexane (gas)......	....	0.53[b]	0.73[b]	1.00[b]
Pentane (liq)....	10.84	10.20	9.52[b]	.....	.....	Water (liq)........	....	33.0[d]	36.3	40.5
100 API oil......	11.14[b]	10.50[b]	9.86[b]	.....	.....	Asphalt...........	(10 from 32°F to melting point)			
Butane (liq)....	11.68	10.98	10.30[b]	.....	.....	Paraffin wax.......	(13.3 from 32°F to melting point)			
Propane (liq)....	13.37	12.59	11.80[b]							

[a] Mainly from Gragoe, C. S., *Nat. Bur. Standards Misc. Pub.* 97, 1929; and Nelson, W. L., *Oil Gas J.*, Oct. 12, 1946, p. 83; but other references also used.

[b] Extrapolated.

[c] Tubular Exchanger Manufacturers Association recommends only these values for petroleum oils, October, 1954.

[d] At 32°F.

Several materials usually compose the vessel or wall through which heat is being conducted, and hence conduction problems involve the conduction of heat through a series of resistances. The quality of heat Q that passes through each material is the same, but the temperature difference across each material will be different for each material. Suppose a wall is composed of three materials having conductivities of k_1, k_2, and k_3, having thicknesses of L_1, L_2, and L_3, and having temperature differences of ΔT_1, ΔT_2, and ΔT_3.

$$\frac{Q}{A_1} = \frac{Q_1}{A_1} = \frac{Q_2}{A_1} = \frac{Q_3}{A_1} = \frac{\Delta T_1}{\dfrac{L_1 A_1}{k_1 A_1}} = \frac{\Delta T_2}{\dfrac{L_2 A_1}{k_2 A_2}} = \frac{\Delta T_3}{\dfrac{L_3 A_1}{k_3 A_3}}$$

also $\quad \Delta T_1 = \dfrac{Q}{A_1} \dfrac{L_1 A_1}{k_1 A_1} \qquad \Delta T_2 = \dfrac{Q}{A_1} \dfrac{L_2 A_1}{k_2 A_2} \qquad \Delta T_3 = \dfrac{Q}{A_1} \dfrac{L_3 A_1}{k_3 A_3}$

The temperature difference across the three materials is the sum of the three individual differences.

$$\frac{Q}{A_1}\left(\frac{L_1 A_1}{k_1 A_1} + \frac{L_2 A_1}{k_2 A_2} + \frac{L_3 A_1}{k_3 A_3}\right) = \Delta T_1 + \Delta T_2 + \Delta T_3 = \Delta T$$

and $\quad \dfrac{Q}{A_1} = \dfrac{\Delta T}{\dfrac{L_1 A_1}{k_1 A_1} + \dfrac{L_2 A_1}{k_2 A_2} + \dfrac{L_3 A_1}{k_3 A_3}} = \dfrac{\Delta T}{R_1 + R_2 + R_3}$ $\qquad$ (17-3)

TABLE 17-3. APPROXIMATE HEAT LOSSES FROM PLANT EQUIPMENT
Btu per hour per square foot

Wall	Conditions	Temperature inside equipmen.			
		200°F	400°F	600°F	800°F
Bare metal (breachings, stacks and pipe)	Still air, 0°F	540	1560	3120	
	Still air, 100°F	210	990	2250	
	10 mph wind, 0°F	1010	2540	4680	
	10 mph wind, 100°F	440	1710	3500	
	40 mph wind, 0°F	1620	4120	7440	
	40 mph wind, 100°F	700	2760	5650	
1½-in. magnesia insulation (vessels, towers, etc.)	Still air, 0°F	54	108	164	220
	Still air, 100°F	28	83	137	192
	10 mph wind, 0°F	59	118	178	230
	10 mph wind, 100°F	30	89	149	210
	40 mph wind, 0°F	61	122	183	246
	40 mph wind, 100°F	31	92	153	215
Magnesia pipe insulation (loss per ft of length) (80°F air temperature)	Standard on 3-in. pipe	50[a]	150[a]	270[a]	440[a]
	Standard on 6-in. pipe	77[a]	232[a]	417[a]	620[a]
	Standard on 12-in. pipe	111[a]	325[a]	590[a]	
	1½-in. on 3-in. pipe	40[a]	115[a]	207[a]	330[a]
	1½-in. on 6-in. pipe	64[a]	186[a]	335[a]	497[a]
	3-in. on 3-in. pipe	24[a]	75[a]	135[a]	200[a]
	3-in. on 6-in. pipe	40[a]	116[a]	207[a]	322[a]

Wall	Conditions	Temperature				
		400°F	600°F	800°F	1000°F	1200°F
3-in. magnesia insulation (vessels, towers, etc.)	20 mph wind, 0°F	62	93	124	155	186
	20 mph wind, 100°F	46	77	108	139	170

Wall	Conditions	Temperature inside equipment					
		1000°F	1200°F	1500°F	1800°F	2100°F	2500°F
Furnace 4½-in. firebrick 4-in. red brick (100°F air and 20 mph wind)	No insulation brick	647	800	1010	1220		
	2½-in. insulation	310	380	500	630		
	4½-in. insulation	230	272	352	448	540	
Furnace 9-in. firebrick 4-in. red brick (100°F air and 20 mph wind)	No. insulation brick	485	570	693	790	833	
	2½-in. insulation	276	328	400	467	527	607
	4½-in. insulation	206	247	306	359	409	470
Furnace 13½-in. firebrick 4-in. red brick (100°F air and 20 mph wind)	No insulation brick	...	...	583	668	715	793
	2½-in. insulation	...	...	369	425	475	541
	4½-in. insulation	...	...	276	314	383	445
	9-in. insulation	...	...	198	230	254	288

[a] Heat loss per foot length rather than per square foot (80°F air).

Thus, we find that resistance to the flow of heat corresponds exactly to resistance to the flow of electricity through a series electrical circuit.

For the special case of heat transfer through a flat wall, the area ratio in each resistance term is unity, i.e., $A_1 = A_2 = A_3$, etc. The temperature differences are directly proportional to the resistances to flow, so that

$$\Delta T : \Delta T_1 : \Delta T_2 : \Delta T_3 : : R : R_1 : R_2 : R_3 \qquad (17\text{-}4)$$

Example 17-1. Heat Loss through a Furnace Wall. A furnace wall consists of 9 in. of firebrick, $4\frac{1}{2}$ in. of sil-o-cel brick, 4 in. of red brick, and $\frac{1}{4}$ in. of transite board. The conductivity coefficients for these materials are given in Table 17-1. The inside wall of the furnace is at 1800°F, and let us assume that the outside of the wall is at 200°F.*

How much heat is lost per hour through a surface of 10 sq ft? (See Fig. 17-1.)

The surface is the same through each of the materials, and hence the area has been left out of all the formulations [see Eq. (17-3)].

$$Q = \frac{\Delta T}{\frac{L_1}{k_1} + \frac{L_2}{k_2} \cdots} = \frac{1800 - 200}{\frac{9}{12 \times 0.82} + \frac{4.5}{12 \times 0.125} + \frac{4}{12 \times 0.52} + \frac{0.25}{12 \times 0.23}}$$

$$= \frac{1600}{0.915 + 3.0 + 0.641 + 0.0905} = \frac{1600}{4.646}$$

$$= 344 \text{ Btu per sq ft}$$

$$= 3440 \text{ Btu through the 10 sq ft}$$

The temperatures within the wall can be computed by Eq. (17-4).

$$\frac{\Delta T}{\Delta T_1} = \frac{R}{R_1}$$

Location	Temperature difference	Temperature, °F
Between firebrick and sil-o-cel.........	$\dfrac{1600}{4.646} = \dfrac{\Delta T_1}{0.915}$ $\Delta T_1 = 315$	1485
Between sil-o-cel and red brick.........	$\Delta T_2 = 1033$	452
Between red brick and transite.........	$\Delta T_3 = 221$	231
At outer wall (as a check).............	$\Delta T_4 = 31$	200

Heat losses from much petroleum equipment are so small compared with other heat quantities that for design work the approximations of Table 17-3 are usually adequate.

Pipe Insulation. In the case of pipe insulation the area through which heat is transferred is not constant. If the thickness of the material is small, compared with the diameter, the arithmetic average of the larger area and the smaller area may be used. The arithmetic mean area may

* Since the outside temperature cannot be easily measured, the air temperature is usually used, but this involves the conductivity of a film of stagnant air at the wall (see Example 17-5).

be used with an error of only 4 per cent for all cylindrical vessels and for pipe sizes down to about 2 in. if standard insulation is used.   If the thickness is great compared with the diameter, the logarithmic mean area must be used in the denominator of the resistance term.

$$\text{Logarithmic area} = \frac{A_2 \text{ (large)} - A_1 \text{ (small)}}{\log_e \dfrac{A_2 \text{ (large)}}{A_1 \text{ (small)}}} \qquad (17\text{-}5)$$

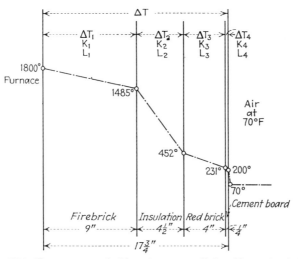

FIG. 17-1. Temperatures inside a furnace wall (see Example 17-1).

CONDUCTION THROUGH FLUID FILMS (CONVECTION)

As indicated in Chap. 13 all fluids are bounded at the retaining walls by a film of stagnant fluid.   Heat must be transferred through these films by conduction.   The films are very thin, their thicknesses cannot be easily measured, and hence the thickness L which is involved in the resistance of the film cannot be determined directly.   In order to avoid this difficulty, the resistances of fluid films have been correlated by expressing the resistance as $1/h$ in which h is the film coefficient of heat transfer.   From commonly accepted heat-transfer coefficients the apparent film thickness varies from about 0.1 for gases to about 0.0001 in. for condensing steam. If the conduction equation is applied to the transfer of heat from a fluid into a solid partition wall and into another fluid, the conduction equation takes the following form:

$$\frac{Q}{A_o} = \frac{\Delta T}{\dfrac{1}{h_o} \times \dfrac{A_o}{A_o} + \dfrac{L_w}{k_w} \times \dfrac{A_o}{A_w} + \dfrac{1}{h_i} \times \dfrac{A_o}{A_i} + R_o \dfrac{A_o}{A_o} + R_i \dfrac{A_o}{A_i}} \qquad (17\text{-}6)$$

In this equation, h_o and h_i represent the outside and inside film coefficients of heat transfer of the two fluids; L_w and k_w the thickness and conductivity of the partition wall; R_o and R_i the resistances due to corrosion, dirt, or roughness of the surfaces; and A_o, A_i, and A_w represent the areas of the wall at the outside, at the inside, and at about the mean of the two (A_w). Two fouling resistances are used throughout this book, but most of the literature fails to indicate whether one or both factors are being reported. Accordingly, a single fouling resistance R_D, which is the sum of R_o and R_i, will be used in this derivation and no correction for outside and inside surfaces will be made except in such necessary cases as fin-tube resistances (see Example 17-8).

The resistance in the denominator may, for convenience, be added and the total equals $1/H_o$ or $1/H_i$, in which H_o is the over-all transfer rate based on outside surface.

$$\frac{1}{H_o} = \frac{A_o}{h_o A_o} + \frac{L_w A_o}{k_w A_w} + \frac{A_o}{h_i A_i} + R_D \tag{17-7}$$

$$H_o = \frac{1}{\dfrac{A_o}{h_o A_o} + \dfrac{L_w A_o}{k_w A_w} + \dfrac{A_o}{h_i A_i} + R_D} \tag{17-8a}$$

or on inside area:

$$H_i = \frac{1}{\dfrac{A_i}{h_i A_i} + \dfrac{L_w A_i}{k_w A_w} + \dfrac{A_i}{h_o A_o} + R_D} \tag{17-8b}$$

Thus, Eq. (17-1), when applied to fluids, becomes:

$$Q = H_o A_o \, \Delta T = H_i A_i \, \Delta T \tag{17-1a}$$

If one film coefficient is small compared with the other coefficients, the resistance $1/h$ which corresponds to it will be proportionally large. In such a case the value of the over-all coefficient will be nearly the same as the small film coefficient corrected to the reference surface. For the same reason the resistance of the metal wall may often be neglected.

Example 17-2. Over-all Coefficient of Heat Transfer. Heat is being transferred from a gas through the walls of a standard 2-in. pipe and into water that is flowing on the inside of the pipe. $h_G = 6$, $h_w = 500$, and k for the pipe wall is 25 [see Eq. (17-8a)].

$$H_o = \frac{1}{\dfrac{A_o}{h_o A_o} + \dfrac{L_w}{k_w} \times \dfrac{A_o}{A_w} + \dfrac{A_o}{h_i A_i}} = \frac{1}{\dfrac{1}{6} + \dfrac{0.154}{12 \times 25} \times \dfrac{2.375}{2.221} + \dfrac{2.375}{500 \times 2.067}}$$

$$H_o = \frac{1}{0.1667 + 0.00055 + 0.0023} = 5.9$$

Thus, the resistance of the metal wall and the water film could be neglected with an error of only 1.66 per cent.

Likewise, the pipe could be made of copper, which is an excellent conductor of heat ($k = 220$), and the over-all coefficient would be scarcely changed:

$$H_o = \frac{1}{0.1667 + 0.000062 + 0.0023} = 5.92$$

Logarithmic Mean-temperature Difference. In exchangers, etc., the temperature difference between the two fluids is not constant because as one fluid is heated the other is cooled. The arrows of Fig. 17-2 indicate the direction of the flow of the fluids with respect to one another for the common arrangements of flow. Almost all commercial equipments are designed for countercurrent flow, but the conditions indicated in d and e

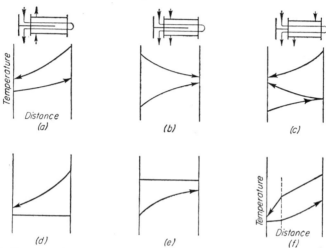

FIG. 17-2. Common arrangements of flow: (a) countercurrent, two-pass shell, 2 tube passes; (b) parallel flow, two-pass shell, two tube passes; (c) mixed flow, single-pass shell, two tube passes; (d) constant-temperature cooling medium; (e) constant-temperature heating medium, and (f) combination condensing and subcooling.

are closely simulated in steam heaters and in coil-in-box coolers. Flow arrangement Fig. 17-2c shows a single shell-side pass but two tube passes. Figure 17-2f indicates condensing of a hydrocarbon mixture followed by cooling of the condensate, all in the same equipment. Such a condition should be considered as two separate zones, each with its own mean temperature difference.

For the simplified case of a constant transfer coefficient and constant specific heats for the two fluids, the logarithmic mean-temperature difference is valid:

$$\begin{aligned}
\theta &= \text{log mean-temp diff.} \\
&= \frac{\text{larger temp diff.} - \text{smaller temp diff.}}{\log_e \dfrac{\text{larger temp diff.}}{\text{smaller temp diff.}}}
\end{aligned} \qquad (17\text{-}9)$$

The logarithm to the base 10 may be converted to base e by multiplying by 2.3.   Experimental[1] tests indicate that the logarithmic mean-temperature difference is not exact for either streamline or turbulent flow of oils, but no means of easily handling the true case are available.

Example 17-3.   The Logarithmic Mean-temperature Difference.   An oil is to be cooled from 200 to 100°F by water that enters at 60 and leaves at 80°F [see Eq. (17-9)]

$$\theta = \frac{(200 - 80) - (100 - 60)}{\log_e \dfrac{120}{40}} = \frac{80}{1.1} = 72.8°F$$

The arithmetic temperature difference would be in error by about 10 per cent.

$$\text{Arithmetic } \Delta T = \frac{120 + 40}{2} = 80°F$$

If the ratio of the temperature differences is less than 2, the arithmetic-average temperature difference may be used with an error of only 4 per cent.

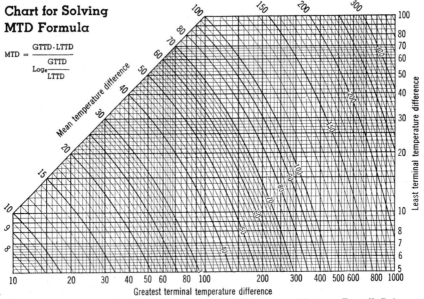

FIG. 17-3. Logarithmic mean temperature difference.   (*Griscom-Russell Co.*)

Multipass Flow.   True countercurrent flow is not attained in most multipass exchangers.   In such exchangers, the fluid is guided back and forth in the shell by means of longitudinal baffles, and in the tubes by means of partitions in the heads.   Efficiencies (or multipliers for the logarithmic mean difference) are shown in Figs. 17-4 and 17-5[2] in terms

[1] Wolke and Freele, master's thesis, School of Petroleum Sciences and Engineering, University of Tulsa, 1947 and 1948.

[2] Standards of Tubular Exchanger Manufacturers Association, 366 Madison Ave., New York, 1949.

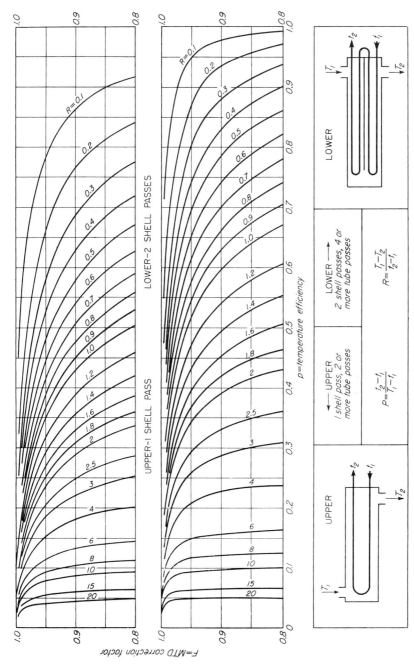

Fig. 17-4. Correction factors for mean temperature difference for single-pass shells with two or more tube passes (above); and double-pass shells with four or more tube passes (below).

537

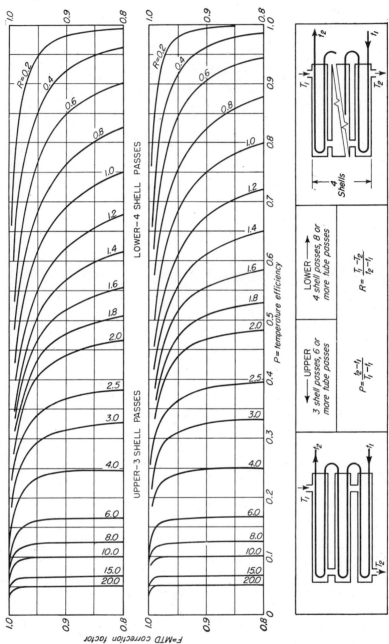

FIG. 17-5. Correction factors for mean temperature difference for 3-pass shells with six or more tube passes (above); and for four-pass shells with eight or more tube passes (below).

of R and P.

$$R = \frac{T_1 - T_2}{t_2 - t_1} \qquad P = \frac{t_2 - t_1}{T_1 - t_1}$$

where T_1 = inlet temperature, shell side
T_2 = outlet temperature, shell side
t_1 = inlet temperature, tube side
t_2 = outlet temperature, tube side

Figures 17-4 and 17-5 extend down to an F factor of only 0.8 because it is not good practice to use lower values. The correction factors are not applicable if a sudden change in phase occurs, so abrupt as to cause a sharp break in the temperature curve of one of the fluids.

EQUIPMENT

The ultimate source of heat in the refinery is the steam boiler and the petroleum shell or pipestill. Indirectly, heat is obtained or saved from the various petroleum products by cooling them with the raw charging stock. If the two materials that exchange heat are liquids, the equipment is referred to as a *heat exchanger*. If the hot material is a vapor and is cooled without much condensation, the equipment is called a *vapor heat exchanger*. If the vapor is condensed, the equipment is called a *condenser exchanger*, and the equipment subsequently used to cool the condensate with water is usually referred to as a *cooler* or *after-cooler*. Equipment for heating the bottom of a fractionator with steam or hot oil is known as a *reboiler*. These cooling and condensing operations may be conducted in so-called *coil-in-box* or *submerged equipments*, although many refiners have discarded the coil-in-box arrangement except for particular services. *Sprayed coils* or *tube units* mounted in cooling towers are replacing coil-in-box equipment because of the higher transfer rates obtained in them.

The large amount of water that is contained in coil-in-box equipment is often an advantage. Thus, if the water supply should fail, the rundown house will not be filled with uncondensed vapors with the attendant danger of a serious fire. In large refineries the water supply is unfailing and tubular equipment can be used with safety. During the last few years the design has been so improved that tubular equipment can be built as cheaply or even more cheaply than coil-in-box arrangements. Owing to higher velocities and the relative ease of cleaning, the heat-transfer rates in tubular equipment are usually more than twice as great as in coil-in-box equipment.

If the cooling water is very hard or dirty or if severe corrosive conditions exist, tubular equipment may not be satisfactory. Tubular equipment must be periodically cleaned or blown with steam, and those refiners who have followed this practice have usually found that the use of tubular equipment is economical.

Equipment with a small pipe inside of a larger pipe is called a *double-pipe exchanger*. Fins, either as a spiral or as longitudinal plates on the inside pipe, are widely used in so-called *fin-tube* or *extended-surface* equipment. Viscous or low-transfer-rate fluids are passed through the fin side so that the extra surface will somewhat make up for the low film rate. Thus, finned *air-cooled condensers and coolers* are becoming important[3] in areas where water is scarce. Forced-circulation or natural-draft towers are used to house the cooling coils. Bundles of tubes rolled into a single tube sheet so that the heating or cooling fluid enters half the tubes and returns through the other half are called *U-tube, hairpin, or bayonet-tube* bundles. They may be inserted in the top or bottom of a tower, in a reboiler shell, or in the wall of a tank of viscous oil.

The foregoing items are standard equipment. In addition, the *jet* type of *condenser* has been finding some application. The *barometric* jet-type condenser is now universally used in vacuum distillation to condense steam and at the same time create part of the vacuum. In this type of condenser, the vapor and the cooling medium are intimately mixed by high-pressure jets, and heat is exchanged by pure mixing or conduction. Theoretically, heat transfer by mixing is 100 per cent perfect and is the cheapest means of transferring heat. For ordinary condensation, jets have not been used extensively, perhaps because of the tendency of water to form emulsions with oil and because the water must be clean.

The use of *partial condensers* for the separation of products that have different boiling ranges is no longer practiced. An exception is the use of partial condensers for the separation of wax distillate and gas oil in a few vacuum plants. Partial condensers can easily be placed near the tower, and the more quickly the large volume of the vapor can be eliminated the less is the pressure drop in the vapor line.

Extremely small (1.5 to 100 sq ft) inexpensive fixed tube-sheet exchangers are used extensively for the cooling of engines, compressors, hydraulic presses, machine tools, etc.

Heat exchangers are built in such a multitude of structural types[4,5,6] that they cannot be discussed here. The primary aim in all these designs

[3] Demarest, K. D., Petroleum Industry Uses of Air Cooling, *Pet. Engr.*, January, 1946, p. 145.

[4] Rubin, F. L., Shell and Tube Heat Exchangers, Buffalo, N.Y., Meeting A.I.Ch.E., Sept. 30, 1947.

[5] Blaylock, P. W., Heat Transfer Equipment, *Trans. A.I.Ch.E.*, **40**, 593 (1944).

[6] Nelson, W. L., Shell and Tube Bundle (Types), *Oil Gas J.*, Feb. 9, 1946, p. 111; and Double Pipe (and Fins), *Oil Gas J.*, Feb. 16, 1946, p. 129.

is to obtain a high transfer rate without exceeding the allowable pressure drop. Sometimes the pressure drop is not important, as in pumping a charging stock through a number of exchangers into a pipestill or in withdrawing hot liquids from a high-pressure process, but often the only pressure that is available is the static head of the fluid above the storage tank. Of course, pumps can be installed, but other factors such as the cost of power and the expense of upkeep, which are involved with all moving equipment, prohibit the use of pumps in many circumstances. In the rest of the chapter it will become apparent that an exchanger for a specific service can be built in a large number of ways and that it behooves the designer to find, or at least approach, the most economical design.

Number of Passes. In order to obtain a high velocity, it is usually necessary to arrange the flow of liquid through the tubes so that the fluid passes through one section of tubes and then returns through another section of tubes. As many as 16 sections or passes have been used. The same effect is produced on the outside of the tubes by means of baffles. In the past, exchangers have been built with as many as six shell-side passes and even more passes within the tubes. Today there is a tendency to utilize only one or two shell passes because of mechanical difficulties with leaks and with the removal of the large tube bundles of highly multipass exchangers. If more passes are used, the conditions of true countercurrent flow may not be attained and the mean temperature difference and total heat transferred may be decreased (Figs. 17-4 and 17-5) even though higher shell and tube velocities are maintained. Bowman, Mueller, and Nagle[7] question the economy of an exchanger design in which the mean-temperature-difference correction factor is under 0.8. As exceptions, multiple tube passes are an advantage if several exchangers are used in series and in the case of vapor condensers.

In an attempt to obtain true countercurrent flow, some refiners require single-pass exchangers for all services, but the cost of several small shells, as against the cost of fewer large shells with several passes, is great. In addition, a single-tube-pass floating-head exchanger requires some type of packed joint or internal expansion joint. From an operating standpoint, the single-pass exchanger has many advantages:

1. Countercurrent flow is attained.
2. Cleaning is facilitated because one unit at a time can be removed from the system and cleaned without markedly interrupting continuous operation or changing the operating conditions.
3. For the same reason the repair of leaky tubes is facilitated.
4. Small tube bundles can be more easily removed and more easily flushed or cleaned.
5. Large multiple-pass units are bulky and cannot be easily installed and removed. In the case of vacuum partial condensers, the weight of the several units of conden-

[7] *Trans. ASME,* **62,** 283 (1940).

ser often amounts to over 50 tons.   This great bulk at a height of 40 ft or more is indeed awkward.

6. If many units (double-pipe or fin-tube) are in service (some refiners have hundreds of units), they may be disconnected and reassembled to meet changes that are constantly occurring in services or operating conditions.

Double-pipe fin-tube equipment[6] meets nearly all these requirements. Even 20 of these units are sometimes used for a single exchanger operation, and they may be assembled in many combinations, such as (1) 5 units in parallel, 4 units in series, and vice versa, (2) 10 units in parallel, 2 units in series, and vice versa, (3) all in parallel or all in series, etc.

Which Material through Tubes.   Fixed rules cannot be given because many of the factors or reasons are at variance with one another.[8]   *Dirty stocks* are passed (1) through the tubes because they can be easily cleaned, particularly if the tube bundle cannot be removed, but (2) through shell if the tubes cannot be cleaned (hairpin bundles) or if large amounts of coke or debris are present which can be accumulated in the shell and removed by dumping the shell.   *High-pressure* fluids, *corrosive stocks*, and *water* are sent through the tubes because the strength of small-diameter (and -thickness) tubes surpasses that of the shell, because corrosion-resistant tubes are relatively cheap, and because corrosion or water scale can easily be removed.   Ordinarily, exchanger shells are built for a pressure of only 125 to 150 psig.   *Large-volume* fluids (vapors) are passed through the shell so that adequate space is available, but *small-volume* fluids are also passed through the shell where cross baffles can be used to increase the transfer rate without producing an excessive pressure drop. Vapors that contain *noncondensable gases* are sent through the tubes so that the accumulation of noncondensables will be swept out.   If the *pressure drop* must be low the material is sent through the shell, and the same applies to *viscous or low-transfer-rate* fluids because maximum transfer rates for a fixed pressure drop can be obtained by the use of cross baffles in the shell.   In fin-tube equipment, *high-pressure, dirty, or corrosive* stocks are sent through the fin tube because it is relatively cheap, can be easily cleaned, and has a higher strength than the outside tube.   Obviously, it is advantageous to keep the *low-transfer-rate fluid* in contact with the fins of a fin-tube equipment.

Baffle Arrangements.   Baffles are widely used to increase the turbulence and film-transfer rate on the outside of the tubes.   With multiple passes on the shell side, the number of possible baffle arrangements becomes so large that they cannot be discussed, but for exchangers having only one or two passes on the shell side the following baffle types have been mentioned, (1) crossflow or half-moon, (2) port and annular space, (3) orifice, and (4) spiral flow.   Of these, the crossflow baffle is

[8] Nelson, W. L., Routing of Fluids, *Oil Gas J.*, Mar. 2, 1946, p. 91.

now used almost exclusively for refinery services. The fluid is caused to flow back and forth across the tubes (Fig. 17-6). Poor heat transfer occurs in the dead space behind the baffles, and corrosion is also most active in these areas.[9] Dead space can be eliminated to a large extent by window-type[9] baffles which consist of baffles that extend entirely across the shell but have several staggered ports for liquid flow. These are said to partially alleviate the disadvantages of crossflow baffles, i.e., high pressure drop, low transfer rates, and high maintenance costs.

The closer the baffles are spaced the greater the turbulence and heat transfer. The pressure drop increases at close spacings but not in proportion to the increased transfer rate. However, spacings of less than 6 in. are seldom used because of the difficulty encountered in cleaning the outside of the tubes. Exchangers in use today have spacings of 2 to

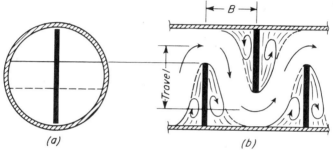

Fig. 17-6. Conventional segmental shell baffling: (a) indicates lognitudinal baffle for a two-pass shell, and (b) shows cross baffles (for either single or two-pass shell).

30 in. Since the clearance between the baffle plate and the shell is only $\frac{3}{32}$ to $\frac{3}{16}$ in. (even $\frac{1}{16}$ to $\frac{3}{32}$ in. if the shell is "bored"), corrosion or dirt tends to "freeze" the bundle into the shell.

Impingement baffles are placed at points that may be eroded by the velocity of the fluid. Usually these baffles are used only at the fluid entrance point, but they may be used at any point where the fluid suddenly changes direction. Tubes in vapor condensers have been entirely severed by erosion in a few months of operation.

Longitudinal baffles are used as indicated in Figs. 17-2 and 17-6, to direct the flow from one end of the exchanger to the other. In another common arrangement (split flow) the longitudinal baffle is open at both ends of the exchanger so that a shell fluid introduced at the center of the shell passes to both ends and then back to the center. This results in both countercurrent and cocurrent flow in various regions, but when used with two or more tube passes, it is considered to be the same as the mixed flow of Fig. 17-2c. Several longitudinal baffles are sometimes used in

[9] Gilmour, C. H., *Chem. Eng. News*, Apr. 23, 1956, p. 2062.

vapor exchangers and condensers, but in liquid-to-liquid exchangers, the use of only one longitudinal baffle (or none) is the common practice. The baffles must be packed at the shell to prevent leakage, but an expandable baffle has also been used. Longitudinal baffles are seldom used in shells of smaller diameter than 12 in. In long small-diameter exchangers the longitudinal baffle provides too much area for by-passing, and efficiency is sacrificed thereby.

The use of spirals or metal strips inside tubes for creating turbulence has not been entirely satisfactory, but they are sometimes used for viscous oils.

If severe corrosion takes place on the shell side or if the fluid contains large amounts of suspended matter, baffles may be a liability rather than an advantage. Removal of the baffles decreases the transfer rate, but a large amount of dirt in the stock may decrease the rate more than the removal of baffles.

Tubes and Tube Spacing. Tubes[4] of $\frac{3}{8}$ to $2\frac{1}{2}$ in. outside diameter are used. In the past, $\frac{1}{2}$- and $\frac{5}{8}$-in.-diameter tubes were extensively used, but they often became plugged and the outside could not be easily cleaned. Hence the use of $\frac{3}{4}$- and 1-in. tubes is now almost standard practice except that diameters over $1\frac{1}{4}$ in. are used for dirty stocks. For tubes above 1 in. in diameter, thicknesses of 10 to 16 Bwg are common, and for smaller sizes the thickness ranges from 12 to 18 Bwg. Owing to the more vigorous cleaning methods that are now employed, the thicker tubes are more in demand. Sixteen-foot tubes are widely used, probably because exchangers of this length are relatively cheap,[10] but other standard[2] lengths of 8, 12, 16, and 20 range in cost only about as 1.3, 1.1, 1.0, and 0.95. The holes through the baffles are about 0.01 to 0.018 in. larger in diameter than the tubes.

Common center-to-center spacings for the various pitch arrangements are:

Tube Size, in.	Pitch arrangements, in.		
	Triangular	Square	Diamond*
$\frac{5}{8}$	$1\frac{3}{16}$	$\frac{7}{8}$	
$\frac{3}{4}$	$1\frac{5}{16}$ and 1	$1\frac{5}{16}$ and 1	1
1	$1\frac{1}{4}$	$1\frac{1}{4}$	$1\frac{1}{4}$

* Rotated square pitch.

The number of tubes can be estimated[4] from

$$N = C \left(\frac{L}{P}\right)^2 \tag{17-10}$$

[10] Sieder, E. N., *Chem. & Met. Eng.*, **46**, 322 (1939).

where C = a constant (0.75 for square pitch and 0.86 for triangular pitch)

P = tube spacing, in.

L = the "outer tube limit," in.

The outer tube limit is about $1\frac{1}{2}$ in. less than the inside diameter of the shell of floating-head exchangers, or $\frac{5}{8}$ in. less than the shell diameter of fixed-head or U-tube constructions.

Exchangers built with closer tube spacing are not accessible for cleaning. Later in the chapter the importance of frequent tube cleaning will be discussed. For severe fouling conditions, a square or diamond-pitch arrangement with wide spacing is suggested, although for regular service the equilateral-triangle arrangement is almost standard. Square-pitch arrangements can be brushed.

Carbon-steel tubes and cast-iron shells are least expensive, but high-sulfur crude oils may justify the use of 5 per cent chromium or even 18–8 chrome nickel tubes[11] particularly in cracking service. Refer to Chap. 9, pages 276 to 284. For the "acid" corrosion produced by salt brine, admiralty metal or occasionally cupronickel tubes are justified. Ammonia is often used as a neutralizer for "acid" corrosion, and it attacks admiralty metal so rapidly that admiralty metal cannot be used for such a situation. The mechanical properties of this alloy are also impaired by temperatures above 500°F, although under favorable conditions it can be used up to tube-wall temperatures of 600°F. Recommendations are as follows:

Material	Highest working tube temp, °F	Max temp difference between adjacent tubes, °F
Admiralty..........	450	145
Steel...............	500	130
Steel...............	800	95

In certain localities brackish cooling water cannot be avoided, and for such a service the tube sheets and if possible the shells should be constructed of the same material as the tubes, in order to avoid localized electrolytic corrosion.

Shells and Heads. Most petroleum oil exchangers are of the floating-head type.[6] As shown in Fig. 17-7,[4] the tubes are free to expand and contract longitudinally by pushing the floating head back and forth within the shell cover. However, the head and tubes are not altogether free from stresses because the tubes that contain the hottest fluid expand more than the others. For this reason a number of floating heads in a single

[11] Nelson, W. L., Shells and Baffles, *Oil Gas J.*, Mar. 9, 1946, p. 93; and Exchanger Tubes, *Oil Gas J.*, Mar. 23, 1946, p. 113.

shell are sometimes employed.   If the temperature difference between the two fluids is great or, in other words, a rapid rate of heat transfer occurs, two floating heads are advisable.   This difficulty is sometimes avoided by the use of several small units of exchanger rather than one large exchanger with several floating heads.   As an example, the hot vapors from a cracking plant evaporator are never cooled with crude oil or water at normal temperatures.   The crude oil must be heated by other means to approximately 300°F before it is sent through the vapor condensers. Such condensers are usually built in several units.   Too cold a medium may produce stresses and cause the tubes to fail.   Tubes lighter than 12 Bwg tend to fail because the joint between them and the tube sheet fails.

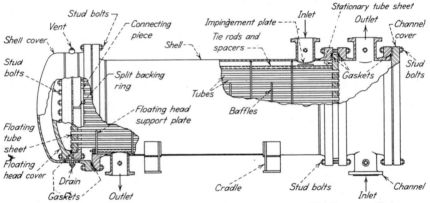

Fig. 17-7. A floating-head type of exchanger.   (*Rubin, The Lummus Co.*)

Cast-iron shells and heads should not be used at temperatures above 400°F and pressures above 150 psi.   Below these maximum conditions, cast iron is to be preferred not alone because of cost but also because cast iron resists corrosion.   At higher temperatures and pressures, cast-, forged-, or welded-steel shells are used.   Forged-steel shells are expensive, but when properly manufactured they can be used safely up to pressures of 1,000 psi and at a temperature of 700°F.   Recently the art of welding has been so improved that shells and particularly heads are now manufactured by machining and welding heavy plate steel.   This method seems to be among the best for very high-temperature high-pressure equipment, and the cost is about equal to that of forged-steel construction.

FILM-TRANSFER RATES

The design of heat-transfer equipment is fundamentally dependent on film heat-transfer rates, but the dirtying or fouling that always occurs in petroleum equipment is such an unknown factor that the highly cumbersome transfer-rate formulas of chemical engineering textbooks and literature lose much of their importance. In addition, the design of an exchanger involves many tedious trial-and-error operations in adopting (1) the most economical size (or approach temperature, Fig. 23-5), (2) the most economical tube length, (3) the most economical velocity, and (4) the number of passes to employ, as well as requiring a consideration of a multitude of mechanical features. Most of these factors are more important than the slightly greater accuracy that accrues by the use of complicated film-transfer-rate formulas, and hence in this chapter every effort has been made to indicate practical and simple methods of estimating film-transfer rates. Buthod and Whiteley[12] have approached this situation by an extensive use of charts.

It must always be remembered that the film-transfer rates given here and elsewhere are far higher than the rates obtained in commercial equipment, that fouling or dirtiness factors must always be used. They are so vital that they are presented ahead of all other heat-transfer data.

Fouling Factors. The great lowering of clean film rates by fouling has often led plant engineers to believe that something must be wrong with the film rates that have been published. As an example, two exchangers operate under such conditions that the over-all rates computed by the film coefficients are 125 and 25. If both exchangers become fouled by the same amount, i.e., a fouling resistance of, say, 0.02, the over-all rates drop to 36 and 17, respectively.

The resistance due to fouling is often so small that the position of the decimal point may become confusing. Hence the use of the term "fouling factor" has become common. The *fouling factor* is obtained by multiplying the fouling resistance by 1,000. Thus, if the fouling resistance is 0.005, the fouling factor is 5.

Although there are many individual conditions of fouling, most of them can be generally classified as follows:

1. *Hard Deposits.* Examples of this type of fouling are water scale, corrosion scales, rust, and hard coke. In general, the thickness and resistance of these deposits increase with time and nearly directly proportional to time. They cannot be effectively removed by blowing with steam or by flushing with hot water, but some of them can be removed by the use of chemicals. The chemical solution may be pumped through the equipment, but sometimes the tube bundle is removed and dipped into a vat that contains the chemical.[13] The usual manner of removing hard deposits is by the use of dry sandblasting,[14] cleaning tools, and brushes.

[12] Heat Transfer, A Manual for Refinery Technologists, *Oil Gas J.*, 17 issues between June 17 and Oct. 21, 1944.

[13] Anon., Cleaning Exchangers, *Pet. Processing*, April, 1951, p. 370.

[14] Fitzpatrick, J. H., Heat-exchanger Maintenance . . . , *Oil Gas J.*, Jan. 28, 1952, p. 372.

The resistance offered by hard, dense deposits is directly related to the conductivity of the material composing the scale.

2. *Porous Deposits.* These deposits often consist of essentially the same materials that compose the hard deposits. In addition, coke or carbon may be deposited from fluids such as topping-still bottoms, asphalt or tar from vacuum plants, or cracking-still bottoms. Scale-forming mud and dirt may be deposited from water or from crude oil. Frequently the scales caused by corrosion are porous but not loose enough to be removed by blowing with steam. These deposits may be more serious than hard scales because the fluid contained in the porous material usually has a lower conductivity than the hard skeleton of the scale, and thus the over-all conductivity is low. Wet sandblasting[14,15] is a successful method of removing many porous deposits, and chemical methods of cleaning are often useful. Sandblasting is less effective with sticky or tarry deposits.

Both the hard and the porous deposits can be removed to some extent by the use of bent-tube sections. These sections consist of a bank of condenser tubes (usually in an open box) which are bowed slightly during manufacture so that, as heating and cooling occur, they bend and cause the scale to loosen. Even to shut down a unit may result in the dislodging of some scales and a definite improvement[16] in the fouling. Thermal shock treatments have been used,[17] and some companies have installed furnaces[17,18] for burning off the deposits.

3. *Loose Deposits.* Examples of this type of deposit are silt, mud, algae, powdered coke, soft carbonaceous material, buttery oxidation products, and even leaves or vegetable fiber. Refinery stocks that have already been processed, as gas oils or naphthas, readily absorb oxygen during storage, and these materials deposit gums[19] or tarry materials particularly during heating from 250 to 450°F. Stripping with steam has been successfully used as a means of removing the dissolved oxygen, but the use of oxidation inhibitors has not been successful.[19] Oxidation products accumulate in recirculated absorption oil to such an extent that it is usually necessary to discard some of the oil.[19] Many of these deposits can be removed with swabs or brushes, and wet sandblasting is useful unless the material is sticky.[15] Some can be effectively removed by blowing with steam or air, or by flushing with hot water. The resistance caused by these deposits is not greatly dependent on the material

[15] Innes and Nanney, High-pressure Wet Sandblasting . . . , *Oil Gas J.*, Sept. 15, 1952, p. 86.

[16] Smith, J. H. (Pipestill transfer line exchangers), *Oil Gas J.*, Aug. 3, 1950, p. 45.

[17] Conners and Weber, Cleaning Heat Exchangers, *Oil Gas J.*, Mar. 3, 1949, p. 61.

[18] Jelinek, F. R., *Oil Gas J.*, Oct. 26, 1953, p. 121.

[19] McCurdy and Butler, Fouling in Heat Exchangers, *Petroleo Interamericano*, April, 1949, p. 53.

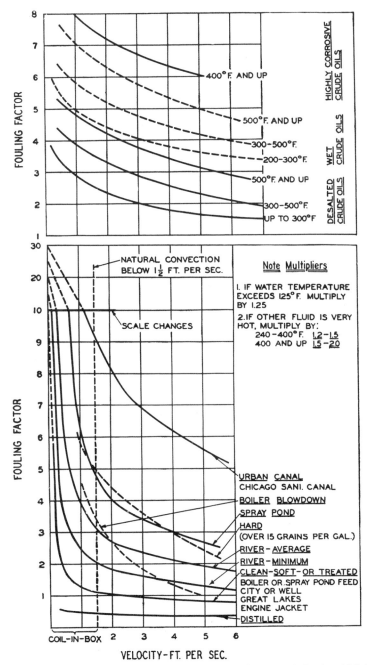

FIG. 17-8. Fouling factors for crude oils (above) and water (below). (*Oil Gas J.*)

composing the deposits but rather upon the liquid that is trapped within them. Thus with respect to heat transfer, loose deposits may be more troublesome than other types. Hard scales and some porous deposits are so tightly fastened to the surface that they are affected little by a high velocity, but many loose deposits can be currently eliminated by maintaining a velocity higher than 4 ft per sec. In handling catalyst laden

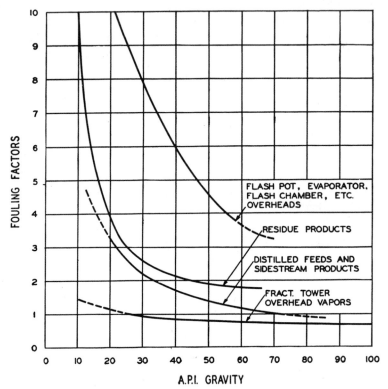

FIG. 17-9. Fouling factors of petroleum and natural-gas products (topping, vacuum, treating, cracking, etc.). (*Oil Gas J.*)

slurry oil, a velocity of 4 ft per sec should always be maintained. The high water velocities used in exchangers usually cannot be justified on the basis of transfer rate, but they are used mainly as a means of keeping the fouling to a minimum.

The effect of blowing with steam, even for a fairly tight scale, was illustrated by Samans.[20] The condenser showed a better rate at 50 days, when blown with steam, than it did at 14 days if no blowing was practiced.

Fouling factors can be computed from the thickness of the scale of dirt if the thermal conductivity of the deposit is known. Not much informa-

[20] ASME Section Meeting, May, 1933.

tion on the conductivity of scale materials has been recorded because of the great variation in types and densities of deposits, but some conductivities are given in Table 17-1.

The first list of commercial fouling factors was published[21] in 1934. Since that date the Tubular Exchanger Manufacturers Association[2] has accumulated much information which is presented here, along with earlier data, in the form of charts and tables (Figs. 17-8, 17-9, and Table 17-4).

TABLE 17-4. MISCELLANEOUS FOULING FACTORS[a]

Steam (free from oil)	0–0.5	Absorption oil	1–5
Steam, exhaust (from engines or pumps)	3–6	Solvent plant feeds (treating or dewaxing)	1–3
Natural gas and air	2–3	Solvents	1–2
Refrigerator vapors (condensing from compressors)	2	Gums, asphalts, and resins	5–10
Coke-oven and manufactured gas	10	Oil-wax cooling	3–20
Diesel-engine exhaust gases	10	Refrigerating liquids, brines, etc.	1
Hydrogen chloride gas	3	Fuel oil	5
Chlorinated hydrocarbon gases	1	Chlorinated hydrocarbons	1–2
Gasoline stabilizer equipments	1	Hydrochloric acid	None
Diethanolamine	2–3	Quenching oils	4–6
Caustic soda	3	Quench (1000°F) exchanger	0.5–2[b]
Hydrogen-rich naphtha streams	1	Catalyst slurry oil	8–17[c]

[a] Based on Standards of Tubular Exchanger Manufacturers Association, 366 Madison Ave., New York, 1954; Nelson, W. L., Fouling of Heat Exchangers, *Ref. Nat. Gaso. Mfr.*, July, 1934, p. 271, and Fouling Factors in Heat Transfer Equipment, *Ref. Nat. Gaso. Mfr.*, August, 1934, p. 292; also Breidenbach and O'Connell, Predicting Commercial . . . Coefficients, *Trans. A.I.Ch.E.*, **42**, 761 (1946).

[b] Thermal poly plant pipestill effluent; Smith, J. H. (Pipestill transfer line exchangers), *Oil Gas J.*, Aug. 3, 1950, p. 45.

[c] Higher factors (20 to 68) are shown by Weiland, McCay, and Barnes, Rates of Fouling . . . , *Oil Gas J.*, Dec. 23, 1948, p. 64; and Clarke, J. S., *Oil Gas J.*, July 23, 1956, p. 76.

Although lines are used on the figures to designate various conditions, the lines are really the average of a range of situations. Thus, the "Residue Products" line of Fig. 17-9 represents an average residual product. If a particular residue contains suspended lime (for neutralizing hydrogen sulfide), or if it is a cracked (rather than a straight-run) material, it will have somewhat higher fouling factors than those shown. This is somewhat, but not entirely, cared for by differences in API gravity. Likewise, distilled stocks or fractionator overheads (Fig. 17-9) normally have low fouling factors; but, if the stock contains corrosive materials, larger

[21] Nelson, W. L., Fouling of Heat Exchangers, *Ref. Nat. Gaso. Mfr.*, July, 1934, p. 271; and Fouling Factors in Heat Transfer Equipment, *Ref. Nat. Gaso. Mfr.*, August, 1934, p. 292.

fouling factors should be used.   Finally, if the equipment is cleaned at periodic and frequent intervals, lower fouling factors than the ones presented here may sometimes be obtained.   However, most of the plant literature on fouling[15,22,23] indicates higher fouling factors than those given here.   There is some indication that spiral-finned tubes do not foul as badly as smooth tubes.[24]   Apparently, eddies develop between fins which help to scour dirt from the surfaces.

The fouling factors of Table 17-4 are miscellaneous ones that are not adequately covered in Figs. 17-8 and 17-9.   The very large fouling factors sometimes obtained with wax stocks, pipestill coke, and corrosive materials will not be discussed because each such situation presents a special case (but see page 377).

The fouling factors given here are for one surface only; i.e., two factors must be obtained, and the sum of the two is the total fouling factor.

Example 17-4.   Selection of Fouling Factors.   *a.*   A desalted crude oil is being heated with straight-run gasoline vapor.   The crude oil is heated to 190°F and flows at 4 ft per sec.

> Crude-oil factor...................... 1.8 (Fig. 17-8)
> Gasoline (60 API) factor.............. 0.8 (Fig. 17-9)

b.   The gasoline condensate of *A* is cooled by river water in a coil-in-box equipment.

> Gasoline (side-stream curve) factor...... 1.2 (Fig. 17-9)
> Water (average river) factor............ 4–6 (Fig. 17-8)

Had the water temperature been allowed to exceed 125°F, the factor would be raised by 25 per cent, or to 5 to 7½.   Had the gasoline temperature been higher (240°F and up), the factor for the water would have been higher by 20 to 100 per cent.

c.   A wax distillate (480 to 280°F) flowing at 3.7 ft per sec is being cooled by wet crude oil (160 to 230°F) which flows at 1.8 ft per sec.   The exchanger will be blown with steam each week.   The crude-oil factor (Fig. 17-8) was taken as 3.6 because it is not so hot as the 200 to 300°F line on that figure.

> Crude oil, wet........................ 3.6 (Fig. 17-8)
> Wax distillate (side-stream curve)....... 2.0 (Fig. 17-9)

Had the exchanger not been blown with steam, the total factor might have been 7 to 10; and, had cold water been used, a wax film might be produced that would increase the total factor to 15–25.

The preferred method of cleaning exchangers is the use of alkaline chemicals such as Oakite for removing oil films, and phosphate-type cleaners such as Calgon for removing water scale.   Inhibited dilute hydrochloric

---

[22] Weiland, McCay, and Barnes, Rates of Fouling . . . , *Oil Gas J.*, Dec. 23, 1948, p. 64; also Clarke, J. S., *Oil Gas J.*, July 23, 1956, p. 76.

[23] Weiland, McCay, and Barnes, Rates of Fouling and Cleaning of Unfired Heat Exchanger Equipment, Annual Meeting ASME, New York, Nov. 28 to Dec. 3, 1948.

[24] Katz et al., *Pet. Refiner*, August, 1954, p. 123.

acid is also used to remove water scale. Polyoxyethylated condensed aromatic amines are said to be good inhibitors. The chemical agents are often used hot and are sometimes allowed to stand for several hours before circulation is started. A settling tank is provided in the circulation system for the accumulation of debris.

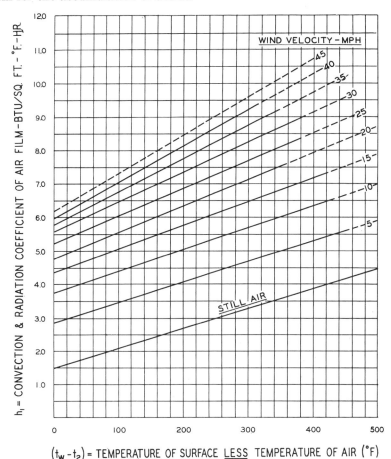

$(t_W - t_2)$ = TEMPERATURE OF SURFACE LESS TEMPERATURE OF AIR (°F)

FIG. 17-10. Combination convection and radiation film coefficients for air in contact with vertical walls or surfaces. (*Oil Gas J.*)

Water at 1,000 to 1,200 psig may be forced between the tubes by means of a fishtail-type nozzle[25] for removing coke and other deposits. Brushing with a stiff wire brush will remove some deposits. Scraper bars may be inserted between the tubes to knock off hard scales,[23] and special tools are available for scraping scale from the fins of fin-tube equipment.

[25] An Effective Method for Cleaning Heat-exchanger Bundles, *Oil Gas J.*, Feb. 3, 1945, p. 65.

Soft lime deposits in straight tubes may be removed by driving rubber-metal composition plugs through the tubes by air or water pressure. Straight tubes are also cleaned mechanically with rotary tube cleaners.[23] After and during such cleaning, the tubes are usually blown with air. There are such an enormous number of situations and so many methods of cleaning that the current literature must be examined. Note especially the survey of chemical cleaning methods by J. C. Reidel.[26]

Gases—Natural Convection and Radiation Combined. Convection is always accompanied by radiation, and hence the most convenient method of computing heat losses from an exposed surface to air is by a coefficient that represents both the convection and radiation transfer of heat. A study of the literature on this subject shows that the coefficient is substantially the same for vertical brick, asbestos, metal, canvas, and wood surfaces. These coefficients must not be confused with the pure convection coefficients found in chemical engineering textbooks. Figure 17-10 indicates the magnitude of these coefficients and the effect of wind velocity.[27] The position of the surface alters the coefficients somewhat as follows:

Vertical......................	1.00	Vertical pipe................	0.95
Horizontal, underside...........	0.70	45-deg slope, upperside........	1.15
Horizontal pipe................	0.80	Horizontal, upperside.........	1.30
45-deg slope, underside.........	0.85		

Example 17-5. Natural-convection Film. In Example 17-1 the temperature of the wall was assumed to be 200°F. This temperature is dependent on the natural-convection air film at the surface. In Example 17-1 the air temperature was 70°F, and hence, by Fig. 17-10, the film coefficient for still air is 2.25. The wall resistance of Example 17-1 was 4.646 and the heat transferred was 3,440 Btu per hr. See Fig. 17-1.

$$\text{Total } R = 4.646 + \frac{1}{2.25} = 5.091$$
$$\text{Heat loss through wall} = \frac{1,800 - 70}{5.091} \times 10 = 3,400 \text{ Btu per hr}$$

Had a 20-mph wind been blowing, the temperature of the wall would have been lower (perhaps 140°F) and the value of h would be about 5.3. A trial-and-error computation is required to obtain the exact wall temperature or exact value of h.

Tube-side Rates. The film coefficient for fluids flowing in forced convection inside tubes has been studied thoroughly by Sieder and Tate,[28] and they found that three regions exist, each of which exhibits different film characteristics. Between Reynolds numbers of 100 to 2,100, viscous

[26] Chemical Cleaning Is Cheaper, Too, *Oil Gas J.*, Dec. 19, 1955, pp. 78–91.

[27] Nelson, W. L., *Oil Gas J.*, Jan. 4, 1947, p. 77; and Rinehart, E., Insulation of Cracking-coil and Tube-still Furnaces, Tulsa Meeting, ASME, Oct. 6, 1930.

[28] *Ind. Eng. Chem.*, **28**, 1429 (1936).

or streamline flow prevails and the following equation can be used:

$$\frac{h_i D_i}{k} = 1.86 \left(\frac{D_i G}{\mu} \frac{C\mu}{k} \frac{D_i}{L} \right)^{0.33} \left(\frac{\mu}{\mu_w} \right)^{0.14} \tag{17-11a}$$

or

$$\frac{h_i D_i}{k} = 1.86 \left(\frac{4}{\pi} \frac{wc}{kL} \right)^{0.33} \left(\frac{\mu}{\mu_w} \right)^{0.14} \tag{17-11b}$$

Between Reynolds numbers of 2,100 and 10,000, a transition type of flow exists for which there is no precise mathematical relationship, but above Reynolds numbers of 10,000, true turbulent flow prevails and the film coefficient is expressed by

$$\frac{h_i D_i}{k} = 0.27 \left(\frac{D_i G}{\mu} \right)^{0.8} \left(\frac{C\mu}{k} \right)^{0.33} \left(\frac{\mu}{\mu_w} \right)^{0.14} \tag{17-12}$$

where h_i = film coefficient, Btu/(hr)(sq ft)(°F) based on inside area
c = specific heat at average fluid temperature
k = thermal conductivity, Btu/(hr)(sq ft)(°F) for 1-ft thickness
μ = absolute viscosity, lb/ft-sec, at average fluid temperature
μ_w = absolute viscosity, lb/ft-sec, at average tube-wall temperature
s = specific gravity at average fluid temperature
G = mass velocity, lb/(hr)(sq ft)
D_i = inside tube diameter, ft
L = heated length of tube, ft
w = lb/hr

These equations are applicable, as far as is known, to such fluids as petroleum oils, organic liquids, aqueous solutions, and gases.

These equations are precise, but for rapid estimation Fig. 17-11 is recommended, especially because of the somewhat indeterminate value of the fouling factors. Properties are read at the average fluid temperature. The film coefficients (Fig. 17-11) are based on inside area and must be multiplied by the proper area ratios to convert them to coefficients based on outside area. Finally, if the temperature drop across the film is very large or if the oil is very viscous, the coefficients should be multiplied by $(\mu/\mu_w)^{0.14}$.

Shell-side Rates. Segmental or half-moon-type baffles are used predominantly in the oil industry because of the ease of manufacture and assembly. Fluid flows alternately across the tube bundle and then along the tubes as it goes through the baffle window. Thus, two distinct types of flow and two mechanisms of heat transfer must be considered. Baffles are spaced from a minimum of 2 in. or one-fifth of the shell diameter to a maximum of 26 in. for ¾-in. tubes or 30 in. for 1-in. tubes. The minimum is fixed by leakage around the baffles and tube holes which, as the baffle spacing is further reduced, overcomes the advantage of high mass velocity.   The maximum length of unsupported tube ranges from 52 in. (¾-in. diameter tubes) to 60 in. (1-in. tubes),[2] and since outer tubes are supported at every other baffle only, the maximum baffle spacings can be only 26 and 30 in.   Window area is usually expressed as the fraction (or percentage) of the total cross-sectional area of exchanger, except that both the window and the total cross-sectional area are corrected for the space occupied by tubes.   Such areas are called "net free areas." Window area ranges from about 10 per cent to 45 per cent but cannot exceed 50 per cent because the center tubes will be left unsupported.

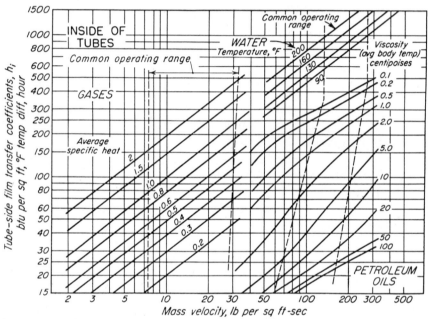

Fig. 17-11. Film-transfer coefficients for fluids inside tubes. Properties are determined at the average fluid temperature, and for very viscous oils a viscosity gradient factor should be applied.

The correlation of transfer-rate studies[29,30,31] with commercial practice has been difficult because not only does the flow range from longitudinal flow along the tubes to crossflow across the bundle, but flow through the bundle varies because of its circular shape.   Commercial tests conducted by Donohue[32] led him to recommend the early equation of Bowman[31]

[29] Tinker, T., Shell Side Heat Transfer . . . , Annual Meeting ASME, Atlantic City, Dec. 1–5, 1947.

[30] Omohundro, Bergelin, and Colburn, *Trans. ASME*, **71**, 27 (1949).

[31] Bowman, R. A., *ASME Misc. Paper* 28, p. 75, 1936.

[32] Donohue, D. A., *Ind. Eng. Chem.*, **41**, 2499 (1949).

for segmental baffle-exchanger transfer rates in unbored shells

$$\frac{h_o D_o}{k} = 0.22 \left(\frac{D_o G_E}{\mu}\right)^{0.6} \left(\frac{C\mu}{k}\right)^{0.33} \left(\frac{\mu}{\mu_w}\right)^{0.14} \tag{17-13}$$

in which new usages are

h_o = film coefficient, Btu/(hr)(sq ft)(°F) based on outside surface

D_o = outside tube diameter, ft

G_E = geometric mean mass velocity, lb/(hr)(sq ft)

= 3,600 $\sqrt{g_x \times g_L}$

g_x = crossflow mass velocity, lb/(sec)(sq ft)

g_L = longitudinal mass velocity, lb/(sec)(sq ft)

With bored shells, the film rates are about 13 per cent higher

The crossflow velocity g_x is determined by assuming that all the flow through the shell passes through an area bounded by baffles on two sides and the sum of all the tube spaces along the center line of the shell

$$g_x = \frac{0.04w}{MB}$$

in which w is the flow rate, lb per hr, M is the net free distance (or sum) of spaces between tubes from wall to wall at the center of the shell circle in inches, and B is the baffle spacing in inches.

The net free distance M may be determined by making a layout of the tube bundle and actually measuring the sum of the spaces between tubes (including space between tube and shell) at the row of tubes nearest the center line. Inasmuch as a layout is not always available except by trial-and-error computations, the following empirical equations may be used as approximations:

O.d. tube, in.	Pitch, in.	Approx. equations
Floating head bundle:		
¾	1⁵⁄₁₆ triangular ⎱	$M = 0.25L + 2.0$
1	1¼ triangular ⎰	
¾	1 square	$M = 0.28L + 2.0$
1	1¼ square	$M = 0.25L + 1.7$
Fixed tube sheet bundle:		
¾	1⁵⁄₁₆ triangular ⎱	$M = 0.25L + 1.0$
1	1¼ triangular ⎰	

In these equations, L is the outer tube limit of the bundle, in inches.

The longitudinal mass velocity g_L is based on the assumption that all of the shell flow passes through the baffle window.

$$g_L = \frac{0.04w}{0.785(d_s^2 - Nd_t^2)C}$$

where d_s = inside diameter of shell, in.
   d_t = outside diameter of tubes, in.
   N = total number of tubes in the bundle
   C = window opening as fraction based on net free areas

The effect of leakage around baffles, through tube holes in the baffle, and around the bundle has been explored by Tinker.[29]

Again, because of the uncertainty introduced by fouling, the approximate shell-side film coefficients of Fig. 17-12 are suggested for most work.

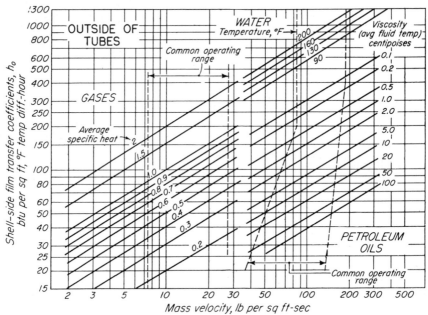

FIG. 17-12. Film-transfer coefficients for fluids outside of tubes. Properties are determined at the average fluid temperature, and for very viscous oils a viscosity gradient factor should be applied.

Only when the film resistance is large or the oil is very viscous need the coefficients be multiplied by the viscosity gradient factor $(\mu/\mu_w)^{0.14}$. Properties are taken at the average fluid temperature.

Reboiler Film-transfer Rates. Heat is transferred by a boiling film in such equipment as reboilers, refrigerator evaporators, and waste-heat boilers. As the rate of heat transfer is increased, vapor tends to blanket the surface and the rate is sharply retarded. This usually occurs at a temperature difference of 120 to 150°F, and the maximum heat density or heat that can be transferred per square foot-hour is about as indicated in Table 17-5.

The two most common reboilers are the kettle and circulation types. The kettle type consists of a large-diameter horizontal shell with a tube bundle situated in the lower half or two-thirds of the shell. Heat is

TABLE 17-5. APPROXIMATE DESIGN RATES FOR REBOILERS

Service	Temperature rise, °F	Boiling film coefficient, Btu/(hr)(sq ft)(°F)	Maximum heat density, Btu/(hr)(sq ft)
Light hydrocarbon reboilers, and chillers using propane or butane	Substantially none	300	12,000
Same.....................	30[a]	250	12,000
Waste-heat boilers, amine reboilers, and chillers using ammonia	Substantially none[a]	500	15,000-20,000

[a] Increase in temperature of the liquid being reboiled. For large temperature rises, handle as a heating zone and a reboiling zone.

applied through the tubes either by steam or hot circulating oil, and the tower bottoms or reboiler feed enter the shell at the bottom. Disengaging space is provided so that substantially dry vapor leaves the top of the kettle or shell. An overflow weir or liquid-level control is used to withdraw the product, and this also serves to keep the bundle submerged.

Liquid is caused to move in recirculation-type reboilers either by forced circulation (a pump) or by thermosyphon action. Boiling may take place either in the shell or more often in the tubes of a standard exchanger set in a vertical position. A mixture of vapor and liquid discharges from the top of the reboiler and back into the bottom of the tower or other disengaging space. In the common vertical single-tube-pass reboiler exchanger, boiling occurs in the tubes, and the difference in weight of the dense liquid in the base of the fractionator and the low-density vapor-liquid mixture in the tubes causes a natural circulation to be established through the reboiler. Surging tends to occur in thermosyphon reboilers when the effluent stream consists of more than about 35 per cent by weight of vapor.

Miscellaneous Film-transfer Rates. Film rates for water flowing in exchangers were given in Figs. 17-11 and 17-12, but lower rates are obtained in coil-in-box equipment because circulation occurs only by convection currents and because countercurrent flow is seldom attained.

Velocity		Film-transfer rate (coil-in-box)
Ft/sec	Lb/sq ft–sec	
0.2	12.5	80
0.5	25	140
1.0	50	220
2.0	100	280

In small equipment operating at small temperature differences, the velocity may not exceed 0.2 ft per sec but in full-scale commercial boxes, a velocity of 2 ft per sec or more is attained when the temperature difference is great.

F. L. Kallam[33] has studied the film-transfer rate on the outside of tubes that are being cooled with water when the water drips or is sprayed on the tubes. He recommends the following equation for the water film coefficient for the outside of tubes:

$$h_o = 190N^{0.05}\left[\frac{W^{0.3}(P-D)^2}{2.42ZVP}\right]^{4.4} \qquad (17\text{-}14)$$

where N = number of tube rows high
G = weight of spray water that strikes cooling surface, lb per hr
L = length of tubes exposed to water, ft
B = width of tube bundle exposed to water, ft
D = outside diameter of tubes, ft
Z = absolute viscosity of spray water at logarithmic mean temperature of water on and off cooling surface, centipoises
P = tube spacing in horizontal plane, ft
V = vertical distance between tubes, ft
W = G/LB

The situation with respect to coil-in-box and sprayed-coil film-transfer rates is so unsatisfactory that perhaps the best way to handle such equipment is to use the over-all rates given at the end of this chapter.

TABLE 17-6. FILM RATES FOR CONDENSING STEAM[a]

Temp difference across film, °F	Horizontal tubes	Vertical tubes
5	3,000–4,000	1,000–1,700
10	2,500–3,300	800–1,400
30	1,800–2,500	600–1,100
50	1,600–2,200	550–1,000

[a] When condensing steam in the presence of even small amounts of oil vapors as in gasoline, etc., condensers, condensation rates are only about 400 rather than the high values shown here.

Customary film rates for condensing steam are indicated in Table 17-6, but when steam condenses in the presence of oil vapor, very low steam rates of 300 to 500 are obtained.

The films formed during the condensation of vapors are complex. Liquid droplets are formed upon the cooling surface; and if the surface

[33] The Open-type Cooler, *Ref. Nat. Gaso. Mfr.*, October, 1940, p. 59.

tension of the condensate is relatively low, the droplets form a continuous liquid film. If the vapor contains a noncondensable gas, the fixed gas is carried to the surface by the condensation and remains there as a gas film. In the case of condensing steam, a film coefficient of 2,800 is dropped to 740 by the presence of 2.89 per cent of air.[34] Likewise, temperature difference across the film is very important. In the case of steam, condensing coefficients of even 10,000 have been obtained[35] at the very low temperature difference of 1°F.

During condensation in the presence of steam, at least three kinds of heat quantities are involved, i.e., sensible heat in cooling vapor, the same for the liquid produced by condensation, and the latent heat of condensation of the vapor and of the steam. Each of these heat quantities should be transferred at appropriate film-transfer rates, and each at its own proper mean-temperature difference. If distinct zones of cooling, hydrocarbon condensing, steam condensing, etc., can be defined, no difficulty arises, but if the several types of cooling are superimposed upon one another (the usual situation) then mixed film-transfer rates must be adopted which account for all of the mechanisms of heat transfer that are occurring. Thus, during the initial condensation of a mixture, the remaining vapor (and steam, if any) accumulates as a gas film at the surface, greatly reducing the condensation coefficients of the pure or narrow-boiling-range materials that are condensing. Shortly thereafter sufficient liquid is being cooled, along with the remaining vapor, that the heat must be conducted through a liquid film as well as through a gas-saturated condensing film. At some stage, steam may begin to condense along with the vapor, and this continues with the remaining traces of vapor constituting a gaseous diluent in the steam condensing film. Finally, condensation is complete, and only liquid is being cooled.

All of this is so complicated that only approximations are possible, such as the way the designs of Examples 17-10 and 17-11 are handled. Accordingly, Table 17-7 indicates combination film rates obtained from commercial over-all rates, and they involve both condensation and liquid cooling, either with or without steam. If the temperature difference is large (i.e., large accumulations of gas in the condensing film), the rate is low, and vice versa. This effect is apparently quite pronounced in vacuum condensers, and accordingly, the condensation rates should be halved for vacuum (30 to 90 mm Hg) services. In parts of condensers in which no vapor remains and the liquid scarcely moves past the tubes, the film rate is very low, probably not exceeding 30 or 50.

Equations for the condensation coefficients of pure materials have been

[34] Badger, W. L., "Heat Transfer and Crystallization, Art. IV," Swenson Evaporator Co., 1928.
[35] Othmer, D., *Ind. Eng. Chem.*, **21**, 576 (1929).

TABLE 17-7. FILM COEFFICIENTS, CONDENSING

| Material | Btu/(°F diff)(sq ft)(hr) | |
	No steam	With steam, but steam not condensing in same temperature range as vapor
Natural gasoline.	210–250	170–210
Gasoline................	180–220	130–170
Kerosene................	150–190	100–120
Gas oil.................	130–180[a]	70–70[a]
Wax distillate............	110–160[a]	50–60[a]

[a] Reduce to half for vacuum service.

developed by many investigators but only the work of D. A. Donohue[36] appears to apply to practical refinery design. His formula for the film condensing coefficient of hydrocarbon vapor mixtures on the outside of horizontal tubes in tubular equipment is:

$$h = C \left(\frac{L}{W}\right)^{0.33}$$

where L = horizontal length of the tube
W = rate of condensation per tube, lb per hr
C = a factor that has the following approximate values:

Light gasoline..........	775	Kerosene.............	680
Pentane...............	775	Decane..............	675
Octane...............	720	Tetradecane.........	640
Gasoline..............	700		

Experimental data on the film coefficients for cooling (not condensing) petroleum vapors are not available, but values for such types of coefficients are given for gases inside tubes[37] in Fig. 17-11 and for gases flowing across staggered tubes[31,32] in Fig. 17-12. Rates for gases flowing across staggered tubes in a pipestill may be obtained from Eq. (18-7.)

Fin-tube Film Rates. The film-transfer rates for either side of the fin tube can be read from Fig. 17-11, but a special heat-transfer equation, Eq. (17-15), must be used and an equivalent fin-side area (Fig. 17-13) must be computed.[38] It might be expected that the fin area could be

[36] Heat Transfer . . . Condensing Hydrocarbon Vapors, *Ind. Eng. Chem.*, **39**, 62 (1947).

[37] Walker, Lewis, McAdams, and Gilliland, "Principles of Chemical Engineering," 3d ed., McGraw-Hill Book Company, Inc., New York, 1937, p. 113.

[38] Nelson, W. L., Fin-tube Exchanger Units, *Oil Gas J.*, June 29, 1946, p. 127.

used directly in the customary heat-transfer formulas [Eq. (17-6) or (17-8a)], but the conduction of heat along the metal fin alters the situation. The equivalent fin-side area may be estimated by determining the fin-side coefficient as if no fins were present (Fig. 17-11), computing the ratio of the actual fin-side area to the inside area (of the tube), and reading a factor (A_f) from Fig. 17-13. This factor is a multiplier by which

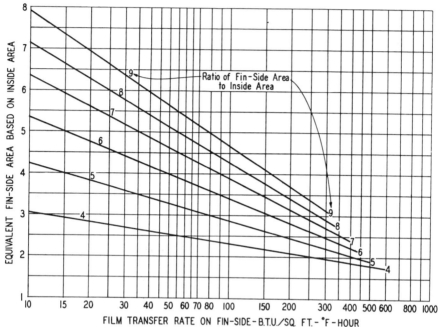

FIG. 17-13. Chart for determining the equivalent fin-side area in fin-tube equipment. (*Oil Gas J.*)

the inside area is converted to equivalent fin-side area. The equivalent area is then used as follows:

$$H_i = \frac{1}{\dfrac{1}{A_f h_f} + \dfrac{R_f}{A_f} + \dfrac{1}{h_i} + R_i} \qquad (17\text{-}15)$$

in which the subscript f refers to the fin-side transfer rate, fouling factor, and area. Example 17-8 indicates how to compute the equivalent area of fin-tube equipment.

Ordinarily the fins extend out from the diameter of the tube, and although such tubes can be installed and removed from double-pipe exchangers (Griscom-Russell and Brown constructions), they are not entirely satisfactory in bundles because replacement tubes cannot be slipped through the holes in the tube sheet. In meeting this difficulty a tube has been devised (Wolverine) which has such short fins that the diameter at the fins is no greater than the (expanded) diameter of the tube at the ends, thus permitting the replacement of tubes in a bundle.

Example 17-6.   Transfer Rate for Exchanger.   Kerosene is to be cooled from 400 to 300°F by means of 35 API crude oil.   The crude oil rises in temperature from 270 to 285°F.   The exchanger has ⅝-in. tubes.   The crude oil has been desalted, and the exchanger will be blown with steam each month.   The conditions are as follows:

Material	Average fluid temp	Viscosity, centipoises (Fig. 4-43)	Velocity		Passes
			Lb/sq ft-sec	Ft/sec	
Shell......... Crude oil	278	1.0	72	1.5	2
Tubes........ Kerosene	350	0.3	140	3.2	4

The film-transfer rates 127 for the crude oil (Fig. 17-12) and 270 for the kerosene (Fig. 17-11) in this instance need not be corrected by $(\mu/\mu_w)^{0.14}$ because the film and wall temperatures are nearly the same.   The fouling factors are about:

Shell (crude) factor (Fig. 17-8)	2.5
Tube (kerosene) factor (Fig. 17-9)	1.6
Total fouling factor	4.1

The inside area of one foot of 16-gauge, ⅝-in. tube is 0.1299 sq ft (Table 13-3) and the outside area, 0.1636 sq ft.   Thus, the over-all transfer rate based on the inside area, but neglecting the wall resistance [Eq. (17-8b)], is:

$$H_i = \cfrac{1}{\cfrac{1}{h_i} + \cfrac{A_i}{h_o A_o} + R_D}$$

$$= \cfrac{1}{\cfrac{1}{270} + \cfrac{0.1299}{127 \times 0.1636} + 0.0041} = \cfrac{1}{0.0037 + 0.00625 + 0.0041}$$

$$= \frac{1}{0.01405} = 71$$

Based on outside area:

$$H_o = \cfrac{1}{\cfrac{0.1636}{270 \times 0.1299} + \cfrac{1}{127} + 0.0041} = 60.5$$

Without periodic cleaning, the inside rate might be:

$$H_i = \frac{1}{0.0037 + 0.00625 + 0.009} = \frac{1}{0.01895} = 52.3$$

At a duty of 550,000 Btu per hr, the surface is:

$$\text{Outside surface [Eq. (17-1a), page 534]} = \frac{550,000}{60.5 \times 63} = 144 \text{ sq ft}$$

A 2-shell, 4-tube pass exchanger tends away from countercurrent flow (Fig. 17-4) but

in this instance to only a small degree because the two outlet temperatures are relatively far apart.

Example 17-7. Transfer Rate in a Steam Heater. A tank of fuel oil, 13 API 60
viscosity at 210°F, is to be heated from 60 to 110°F by means of a steam coil. The
oil has a pour point below 60°F. The oil stands in the tank and circulates only by
natural convection. Exhaust steam is used, and it leaves the coil at atmospheric pressure but not cooled below 212°F.

The situation is complicated because the velocity of the oil must be estimated and
because the operation is not continuous.

Average temperature of oil, approximate: $(60 + 110) \div 2 = 85°F$.

The oil-film resistance constitutes most of the resistance (it can be checked later),
and thus the approximate temperature at the fouling of the metal wall is (the 0.85 is an
estimate):

$$0.85(212 - 85) + 85 = 193°F$$

The viscosity of the fuel oil (curves 18 or 19 of Fig. 4-43) is about 225 centipoises
at 85°F and about 13 at 193°F.

$$(\mu/\mu_w)^{0.14} = (^{225}\!/_{13})^{0.14} = 1.492$$

The velocity at the heating surface (estimated) is probably less than 0.25 ft per sec
(see page 559) and this corresponds to a mass velocity of only about 15.1 [0.97 (from
Fig. 5-14) times 0.25 times 62.4]. According to Fig. 17-12, the film coefficient is only
about 10.5 (extrapolated, and a higher value is probably more correct because the
curves of Fig. 17-12 tend to flatten at high viscosities) and when multiplied by
$(\mu/\mu_w)^{0.14}$, about 15.7.

The oil is relatively clean, or it could not be used as a fuel oil, but the fouling factors
of residual oils are high.

Factor for oily steam (Table 17-4)   4.0
Factor for fuel oil (Fig. 17-9)   7.0
    Total   11.0

For 1½-in. Schedule 40 pipe, the over-all coefficient by Eq. (17-8a) based on outside
area is:

$$H_o = \cfrac{1}{\cfrac{1}{h_o} + \cfrac{A_o}{h_i A_i} + R_o} = \cfrac{1}{\cfrac{1}{15.7} + \cfrac{1.9}{3500 \times 1.61} + 0.011}$$

$$= \frac{1}{0.0637 + 0.00034 + 0.011} = \frac{1}{0.075} = 13.33$$

The surface correction was made by means of diameters rather than areas. The
steam film could have been neglected without introducing error.

If the heater is to heat the oil in one hour and the duty is 200,000 Btu, the surface is:

$$A_o = \frac{200,000}{13.33 \times 125} = 120 \text{ sq ft}$$

The temperature differences at the two ends of the tube or coil were so nearly the same
(152 and 102°F) that the logarithmic MTD was simply estimated as 125.

Example 17-8. Transfer Rate in a Fin-tube Heater. A common type of 24-fin
tube has 50.5 sq ft of external finned surface and an internal surface of 8.4 sq ft. The
actual ratio of surfaces is

$$\frac{50.5}{8.4} = 6.0$$

Crude oil (viscosity of 1.3 at an average fluid temperature of 230°F) flows at 4 ft per sec through the tube, and kerosene (viscosity of 0.3 centipoises at 340°F) flows at 1.0 ft per sec around the fins.

Material	Mass velocity	Film rate	Fouling factor
Crude oil.........	220	225 (Fig. 17-11)	2.5
Kerosene.........	43.3	115 (Fig. 17-11)	1.5

According to Fig. 17-13, the equivalent fin-side area is 3.83 and the transfer rate based on inside surface is [Eq. (17-15)]:

$$H_i = \frac{1}{\dfrac{1}{3.83 \times 115} + \dfrac{0.0015}{3.83} + \dfrac{1}{225} + 0.0025} = 104$$

This same rate based on fin-side surface is only $104 \div 6 = 17.3$, but something is gained by the use of finned surface because the rate in a plain double-pipe exchanger would have been only about 63, and thus about $1\frac{1}{2}$ plain-tube units are required to replace one fin-tube unit.

EXCHANGER DESIGN

High velocities result in high film coefficients, small exchangers, and low equipment cost, but high velocities also mean large pressure drops and increased pumping costs. Accordingly, a properly designed exchanger always represents a compromise in the choice of velocity for both the tube and the shell side. In the ideal case, the velocities will just use up any pressure that is available (or free) in each stream.

Tube-side Pressure Drop. Friction loss inside tubes can be computed from the general formulations given in Chap. 13, but the losses caused by enlargements, contractions, and turns must be included in the calculations. In order to account for nonisothermal flow, Sieder and Tate[28] recommend multiplying the friction loss calculated by isothermal formulations such as Eq. (13-1), p. 395, by the dimensionless ratio $(\mu/\mu_w)^{0.14}$ for turbulent flow or $(\mu/\mu_w)^{0.25}$ for viscous flow (Reynolds numbers under 2,100). In terms of tube passes (n), velocity in the tubes g [lb/(sq ft)(sec)], and specific gravity s, the loss due to inlet, outlet, and pass turns in the header. as psi, is approximately

$$\Delta P_h = 0.00032 \frac{ng^2}{\rho} \tag{17-16}$$

No viscosity gradient correction need be applied to Eq. (17-16).

Shell-side Pressure Drop. The pressure loss produced by the flow of fluids through the shell side of an exchanger is caused primarily by (1) loss by flow through the baffle window and (2) loss by flow across the bundle between baffles.

Pressure loss through the window is similar to losses through orifices. Using a discharge coefficient of 0.7, the pressure drop per baffle is

$$\Delta P_L = 0.00022 \frac{g_L^2}{\rho} \tag{17-17}$$

The pressure drop across the tube bundle cannot be calculated with precision, but the situation has been studied by numerous investigators[30,39,40,41,42] and the following formula is suggested:

$$\Delta P_x = \frac{f N g_x^2}{2318\rho} \quad \text{psi} \tag{17-18}$$

where $\qquad f$ (for viscous flow) $= \dfrac{15}{\dfrac{P - D}{D} \dfrac{DG_x}{\mu}}$

$\qquad\qquad f'$ (for turbulent flow) $= \dfrac{0.75}{\left(\dfrac{P - D}{D}\right)^{0.2} \left(\dfrac{DG_x}{\mu}\right)^{0.2}}$

Transition to turbulent flow occurs at $DG_x/\mu = 42.5D/(P - D)$
and N = total number of rows of tubes crossed
$\qquad g_x$ = crossflow mass velocity, lb/(sec)(sq ft)
$\qquad G_x$ = crossflow mass velocity, lb/(hr)(sq ft)
$\qquad \rho$ = density of fluid, lb/cu ft
$\qquad D$ = tube o.d., ft
$\qquad P$ = tube pitch, ft
Flow is assumed to be from the centroid of one baffle opening to the centroid of the next. This may be counted or computed if a tube layout is available, but often it must be estimated. The total number of rows of tubes across a bundle is approximately L/P for a square-pitch arrangement (or $2L/P$ for triangular pitch) and thus the total number of rows of tubes N traversed by the fluid becomes

N = (total baffle spaces)(total rows across bundle)
$\qquad\qquad\qquad\qquad\qquad\qquad$ (1.0 − window fraction)

The actual pressure drop for crossflow may be as low as 50 per cent of that calculated by Eq. (17-18) because of leakage and poor bundle penetration. Theoretically, the pressure drop across the bundle, ΔP_x, should be multiplied by the viscosity gradient term $(\mu/\mu_w)^{0.14}$.

The total shell-side pressure drop is the sum of ΔP_L and ΔP_x.

[39] Seider and Scott, ASME unpublished papers, no. 83 (1932).
[40] Huge, E. C., Trans. ASME, **59**, 573 (1937).
[41] Pierson, O. L., Trans. ASME, **59**, 563 (1937).
[42] Chilton and Genereaux, Trans. A.I.Ch.E., **29**, 161 (1933).

Miscellaneous Pressure Drops. The pressure drop through a vapor condenser is often the governing factor in design and especially so for condensers for vacuum systems. The Ross Heater and Manufacturing Company suggests the following formula:[43]

$$\Delta p = \frac{Lu^2}{ks}$$

where Δp = pressure drop, psi
L = length of vapor travel, ft
u = average velocity, ft per sec
s = specific volume, cu ft per lb

The constant k probably has a value of 9,000 to 13,000 depending upon the particular design.

The pressure drop through conventional coil-in-box condensers in which complete condensation occurs (but no cooling of liquid) is one-third to one-half of the pressure drop that would occur if no condensation took place. The pressure drop of vapors through straight pipe (vapor lines, pipe coils, etc.) can be estimated from Fig. 13-6 and Eqs. (13-9) and (13-10), Chap. 13.

Design Procedure. Many relationships are involved in the design of an exchanger, and these are so confusing that they must be considered in a logical sequence, especially because numerous preliminary assumptions must be made and then checked as the design is developed. The following list of factors indicates the approximate order in which they will be encountered, and Example 17-9 can be followed along with this discussion.

Heat Balance. Except for radiation losses (usually negligible), the heat delivered by the hot fluid must equal the heat absorbed by the cold fluid. However, the designer must decide how complete an exchange of heat is feasible. This may be judged by means of the most economical approach temperatures of Fig. 23-5. Thermal properties can be obtained from Chap. 5, pages 168 to 176. The heat transferred in Btu per hr is called the "duty" of the exchanger.

Mean-temperature Difference. This may be computed from Eq. (17-9) or Fig. 17-3, and then a correction factor larger than 0.8 for multipass shells is selected from Fig. 17-4 or 17-5, using as few shell passes as possible.

Estimate Surface. Tabulate the physical properties of the fluid and estimate an over-all coefficient. One method is to read individual film coefficients in the common range of velocity, from Figs. 17-11 and 17-12, etc., at the average temperature of each stream (or at temperatures closer to the wall temperature). These may then be combined with fouling

[43] Heat Exchangers, *Bull.* 350, 1931.

resistances to obtain an over-all coefficient [Eq. (17-8a)]. The approximate surface can be computed from the exchanger duty, corrected mean temperature difference, and over-all coefficient by means of Eq. (17-1a), page 534. A final coefficient will be determined in later calculations.

Size of Units. The number of tubes can be computed from the tube size, exchanger length, and estimated surface. They may fit into a single maximum-size bundle, but it may be necessary to use several smaller bundles or shells. A tube layout may be prepared, or Eq. (17-10) may be used in approximating the size of the bundle.

Tube-side Pressure Drop. The number of tube passes per exchanger is selected by trial and error to stay within the allowable pressure drop. In making trials, note that the pressure drop varies approximately as the cube of the number of tube passes.

Tube-side Film Coefficient. After selecting the shell size and number of tube passes, the film coefficient may be calculated using the methods outlined in this chapter [Eqs. (17-11a) and (17-12), Fig. 17-11, etc.].

Shell-side Pressure Drop. The baffle pitch and window fraction may be chosen by trial and error to give the allowable pressure drop [Eqs. (17-17) and (17-18)].

Shell-side Film Coefficient. After the baffle pitch and window fraction have been selected, the crossflow and longitudinal mass velocities, and the mean mass velocity, may be computed; and the shell-side coefficient may then be calculated from Eq. (17-13) or less accurately from Fig. 17-12.

Over-all Coefficient. It is now possible to compute the over-all coefficient with more accuracy. If the coefficient is larger than the one assumed in the surface estimate, a check should be made to see if a smaller exchanger will be adequate, whereas if the coefficient is smaller than the assumed coefficient, it is necessary to repeat all computations for a larger exchanger.

Example 17-9. Complete Exchanger Design. Lean absorption oil at 410°F is to be cooled by means of rich absorption oil available at 90°F. The properties of the materials are:

	Rich oil (tubes)	Lean oil (shell)
Characterization Factor	11.8	11.8
Amount, gpm	695	600
Gravity, API	44	40
Gravity, lb per gal	6.713	6.87
Allowable pressure drop, psi	10.0	16.5

Steel tubes (¾ in. o.d., 14 Bwg, 20 ft long) will be used at a $1\frac{5}{16}$-in. triangular pitch, and the rich oil is sent through the tubes. No vaporization occurs.

No longitudinal baffles are to be used.

The design procedure of page 568 will be followed to determine the size of exchanger, number of tubes, the baffle spacing, and how much to cut out of the baffle (window fraction).

Heat balance.   The pounds circulated are:

$$\text{Lean oil} = 600 \times 60 \times 6.87 \ \ = 247,000 \text{ lb per hr}$$
$$\text{Rich oil} = 695 \times 60 \times 6.713 = 280,000 \text{ lb per hr}$$

For a ratio of fluids of about 1.0 Fig. 23-5 indicates that the lean-oil (smallest quantity) outlet temperature should approach to within about 50°F of the inlet rich-oil

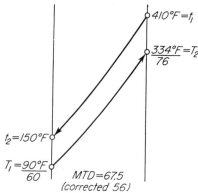

Fig. 17-14. Terminal temperatures in Example 17-9. There are four shell and two tube passes but no longitudinal baffle to produce the pure countercurrent flow indicated here.

temperature if the equipment is to be depreciated in 10 years.   However, fuel is cheap at a gasoline plant, and an approach of 60°F was therefore selected, and the outgoing lean-oil temperature is 150°F.

Heat removed from the lean oil is:

$$247,000(410 - 150)0.585 = 37,600,000 \text{ Btu per hr}$$

This same amount of heat goes into the rich oil so that its outlet temperature must be:

$$90°F + \frac{37,600,000}{280,000 \times 0.55} = 334°F$$

(The specific heat of 0.55 was determined by trial-and-error computations.)

These temperatures are shown in Fig. 17-14.

Mean-temperature difference.   This can be read from Fig. 17-3, but the mean is obviously 67.5°F because the two terminal differences are nearly the same.   However, several shell and tube passes will need to be used, and hence the R and P values needed in correcting for multipass flow (Figs. 17-4 and 17-5) are:

$$R = \frac{T_1 - T_2}{t_2 - t_1} = \frac{90 - 334}{150 - 410} = 0.94$$
$$P = \frac{t_2 - t_1}{T_1 - t_1} = \frac{150 - 410}{90 - 410} = 0.812$$

Examination of Figs. 17-4 and 17-5 shows that one, two, or three shell passes cannot be used, but a correction factor of 0.83 can be read for four shell passes (Fig. 17-5).

Longitudinal baffles could be used to attain true countercurrent flow and thus raise the 0.83 to 1.0, but in this design no longitudinal baffles will be used.

Corrected mean-temperature difference = 67.5 × 0.83 = 56°F

Estimate of surface.

	Rich oil (tubes)	Lean oil (shell)
Average temp, °F...............	212	280
Viscosity (Fig. 4-43), centipoises.....	0.5	0.5
Suitable mass velocity.............	120	150
Film coefficients.................	210 (Fig. 17-11)	235 (Fig. 17-12)
Fouling factors...................	1.5	1.5

The inside diameter of ¾-in. tubes is 0.584 in. (Table 13-3). An approximate over-all rate can be computed from Eq. (17-8a).

$$H_o = \cfrac{1}{\cfrac{0.75}{235 \times 0.584} + \cfrac{1}{210} + 0.003} = 75.5$$

Approximate outside tube surface

$$A_o = \frac{37,600,000}{56 \times 75.5} = 8,900 \text{ sq ft}$$

Size of unit. With four shells, each shell must house 2,225 sq ft, and the tubes per shell will be

$$\frac{2,225}{\cfrac{0.75\pi}{12} \times 20} = 565$$

According to Eq. (17-10) the outer tube limit of the bundle will be about

$$565 = 0.86 \left(\frac{L}{1\,{}^5\!/_{16}}\right)^2 \qquad L = 24 \text{ in.}$$

and this can be housed in about a 25.5-in. i.d. shell. Try a 26.5-in. i.d. shell with 610 tubes.

$$\text{Total surface} = 4 \times 610 \times \frac{0.75}{12} \times 20\pi = 9,600 \text{ sq ft}$$

It is somewhat standard construction practice to use an even number of inches for the outside diameter of shells, but exchangers are also encountered in which the inside diameters are an odd number of inches.

Tube-side pressure drop. Try two tube passes [Eqs. (13-1) and (17-16)].

$$\text{Mass velocity} = \cfrac{280,000}{3,600 \times \cfrac{(0.584)^2 \times 0.785}{144} \times \cfrac{610}{2}} = 138 \text{ lb/(sq ft)(sec)}$$

$$\text{Reynolds No.} = \frac{DG}{\mu} = \frac{0.584 \times 138}{12 \times 0.5 \times 0.000672} = 19,900$$

Friction factor (Fig. 13-2) = 0.0064

For a total of eight passes, the friction loss [Eq. (13-1)] is:

$$\Delta P_f = 8 \times \frac{2 \times 0.0064 \times (138)^2 \times 20}{144 \times 32.2 \times (0.584/12) \times 62.4 \times 0.75} = 3.69 \text{ psi}$$

Inlet and outlet losses [Eq. (17-16)] are:

$$\Delta P = 0.00032 \times 8 \times (138)^2/(62.4 \times 0.75) = 1.04 \text{ psi}$$

Total pressure drop = 3.69 + 1.04 = 4.73 psi

This is below the allowable pressure drop of 10 pounds but it is obvious that four tube passes rather than two passes per shell would certainly [$4.73 \times (\frac{4}{2})^3 = 37.9$ psi] produce too much friction.

Tube-side film coefficient. Using the mass velocity of 138 and a viscosity of 0.5 centipoises indicates (Fig. 17-11) that $h_i = 225$.

Shell-side pressure drop. The baffle spacing and window area must be selected by a trial-and-error computation. Assume a 20-in. baffle spacing and a 20 per cent window fraction.

Net free distance (p. 557) = $0.25L + 2 = 0.25 \times 25 + 2 = 8.25$ in.

The crossflow and longitudinal mass velocities are:

$$g_x = \frac{247,000 \times 0.04}{8.25 \times 20} = 60 \text{ lb/sq ft sec}$$

$$g_L = \frac{247,000 \times 0.04}{0.785(26.5^2 - 610 \times 0.75^2)0.2} = 176$$

At the baffle spacing of 20 in., the number of spaces between baffles and the number of baffles are:

Spaces $\dfrac{20 \times 12}{20}$ = 12 (48 total)

Baffles $12 - 1$ = 11 (44 total)

Reynolds No. (crossflow)

$$\frac{0.75 \times 60}{12 \times 0.5 \times 0.000672} = 11,200$$

Since this is larger than $\dfrac{42.5 \times 0.75}{0.9375 - 0.75}$ or 170, the flow is turbulent and

$$f' = \frac{0.75}{\left(\dfrac{0.9375 - 0.75}{0.75}\right)^{0.2} (11,200)^{0.2}} = \frac{0.75}{0.758 \times 6.45} = 0.153$$

The number of rows crossed and the crossflow pressure drop are:

$$\frac{25}{0.9375} \times 2 \times (4 \times 12) \times (1 - 0.2) = 2,040 \text{ rows}$$

$$\Delta P_x = \frac{0.153 \times 2040 \times (60)^2}{2318 \times 62.4 \times 0.74} = 10.5 \text{ psi}$$

The longitudinal pressure drop is:

$$\Delta P_L = 44 \times 0.00022 \frac{176^2}{62.4 \times 0.74} = 6.48 \text{ psi}$$

Thus, the total pressure drop is 17 psi, which is nearly low enough to meet the requirement of 16.5 psi, and it may possibly be satisfactory because computed pressure drops are usually somewhat high.

Shell-side coefficient. The geometric mass velocity and shell-side film coefficient are:

$$G_E = 3,600 \sqrt{60.2 \times 176} = 370,800 \text{ lb/sq ft-sec, or } 103 \text{ lb/sq ft-sec}$$
$$h_o = 190 \text{ (Fig. 17-12)}$$

Over-all coefficient and size.

$$H_o \text{ [Eq. (17-8a)]} = \cfrac{1}{\cfrac{1}{190} + \cfrac{0.75}{0.584 \times 225} + 0.003} = 71.5$$

The resistance of the metal wall and the viscosity gradient correction are, in this instance, negligible.

$$\text{Surface required} = A_o = \frac{37,600,000}{56 \times 71.5} = 9,400 \text{ sq ft}$$

The design was based on a surface of 9,600 sq ft which means that about 2 per cent extra surface is being supplied. The design is almost in balance, and if a little larger window fraction is provided, or the baffle spacing is increased slightly, the shell-side pressure drop will be satisfactory. A check might be made to see if a smaller exchanger is satisfactory, but in this instance a smaller exchanger probably would not be adequate.

TUBULAR VAPOR COOLERS AND CONDENSERS

Tubular equipment is frequently used to cool superheated vapors and to condense them by exchange with the charging stock. On one side of the exchanger, usually the tube side, the rates of heat transfer found in the preceding discussion are valid. On the other, or shell, side of the exchanger, a new set of conditions arise. Vapor cooling is a straightforward problem, but the condensation of complex vapor mixtures in the presence of steam is indeed complicated.

The film conditions are different in all parts or zones of a condenser and they tend to overlap.

1. Cooling oil vapor, steam, or both.
2. Condensing vapor, cooling vapor, and cooling the condensate.
3. Condensing steam and cooling oil.
4. Cooling oil and water.

As an example, condensation starts soon after cooling of the superheated vapors begins; the cooling of vapor, steam, and condensate occurs throughout the condensation of the vapors; and, finally, the last vapor is not condensed until the steam is condensed. However, for design purposes it is necessary to adopt zones and assign transfer rates to each of them if dependable rates are to be attained.

In the condensation zone, the temperature may be computed with accuracy by means of the equilibrium condensation curve (Examples 4-5 and 4-6) of the oil vapor, corrected for the total pressure within the condenser and for the partial-pressure effect of the steam. In some simple situations the condensation temperature can be estimated without computations.   For example, steam condenses in an atmospheric naphtha condenser between 205 and 185°F unless an abnormally large quantity of steam is used.   In special problems, such as the design of vacuum condensers or condensers handling large quantities of steam, the labor involved in drawing the curves, etc., is justified because more simple methods are not dependable.

The pressure drop in ordinary condensers may be neglected in drawing condensing curves, except for vacuum condensers where pressure drop becomes of great importance.   The following examples will help in clarifying computation methods:

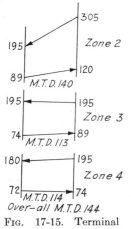

Fig.   17-15.   Terminal temperatures for Example 17-10.

Example 17-10.   Transfer Rate for a Pressure Distillate Condenser. A pressure distillate condenser is to be designed for the following materials:

	Lb per hr
P.D. and reflux (57 API)............	63,000
Cracked gas (wet).................	2,000
Steam.........................	6,000

The materials are available at 305°F, and the vapor is not superheated.   Water is available at 72°, and it will be heated to 120°F.   Pressure at the top of the tower is 10 psi.   This example is primarily an illustration of the organization of computations, and hence specific heats and latent heats have not been corrected to the values shown in this edition.

Duty of Condenser.   Basis: 1 hr.

Assume cooling to 180°F condenses all vapor and steam.
Assume steam condenses at 195°F.   These assumptions can be approximately computed by the methods used in Example 17-11.

Zone 1: Cooling vapor and steam.   No such zone.
Zone 2: Condense vapor between 305 and 195.
Cool steam and vapor to 195.
Cool condensate to 195.

Btu per hr

Cool vapor or condensate......... $63,000(305 - 195) \dfrac{0.60 + 0.46^*}{2}$ = 3,670,000

Cool gas (Fig. 5-2)....................2,000(305 − 195) × 0.52 =   114,000
Cool steam.....................6,000(305 − 195) × 0.5 =   330,000
Condense vapor (Fig. 5-7)....................63,000 × 131 = 8,229,000
                                            ‾‾‾‾‾‾‾‾‾‾
                                            12,343,000

Zone 3: Condense steam at 195.
Latent heat of steam = 981
6,000 × 981 = 5,890,000 Btu per hr
Zone 4: Cool oil, water, and gas.

* Average liquid and vapor specific heat.

$$\begin{array}{rl}
& \text{Btu per hr} \\
63{,}000(195 - 180) \times 0.565 = & 532{,}000 \\
6{,}000(195 - 180) \times 1.0 = & 90{,}000 \\
2{,}000(195 - 180) \times 0.5 = & 15{,}000 \\
\hline
& 637{,}000
\end{array}$$

The percentage of heat that is absorbed in each zone and the rise in water temperature in each zone, for countercurrent flow, are

Zone	Btu	Per cent	Rise in water temperature (total 48°F)
1			
2	12,343,000	65.4	31
3	5,890,000	31.2	15
4	637,000	3.4	2
Total........	18,870,000	100.0	48

The temperatures in the zones are shown in Fig. 17-15.

Computation of Transfer Rate. If ⅝-in. tubes are used and the water flows through them at 1 ft per sec, the water film-transfer rate (Fig. 17-11) will be about 350.

The surface required for each zone can be computed separately and added together, thus:

Zone	Duty	Mean temp diff.	h_o	h_w	R_f*	H†	A	Notes
1. Cooling vapor..........	....	...	...	...	.....	...	.....	No such zone
2. Condensing vapor.......	12,343,000	143	150	350	0.006	64	1,350	Table 17-7
3. Condensing steam.......	5,890,000	113	400	350	0.007	81	643	Table 17-6
4. Cooling liquid..........	637,000	114	45	350	0.009	29	192	Page 561
Total................	18,870,000	...	...	...	.....	...	2,185	

* See Fig. 17-9. A water factor of 5, and different factors for each of the other conditions.

† Should be corrected to a common surface basis such as outside surface.

As a comparison, the over-all transfer rate that corresponds to the four zones is

$$H = \frac{18{,}870{,}000}{2{,}185 \times 144} = 60.0$$

In vacuum condensers the foregoing method (Example 17-10) becomes more involved. Approximations of the steam-condensing temperature, etc., cannot be relied upon. In most modern vacuum plants a large quantity of steam is used to reduce the vaporization temperature of the oil. This steam passes through the partial condensers and is finally condensed in a barometric condenser. Thus the pressure in the barometric condenser and in the partial condenser is dependent upon the vapor pressure exerted by the cooling water. With cold water and several steam jets, the barometric condenser can be operated at 8 mm pressure, and hence the partial condenser operates at pressures of 10 or 12 mm or above, depending upon the processing plan (see Figs. 7-22 to 7-24, etc.). Sometimes these partial condensers are built in several units so that different products, such as gas oil and wax distillate, may be collected from the different units.

If the condensation is conducted in several units or steps, with the condensate removed separately from each partial condenser, each unit may be handled as a separate condenser. For example, if wax distillate and gas oil are separated in a partial condenser, the vapors of wax distillate and gas oil are cooled in the first unit and condensation occurs along the equilibrium condensation curve of these mixed vapors. The wax distillate is withdrawn from this unit, and the remaining gas-oil vapor is condensed according to the equilibrium condensation curve of the gas-oil vapor alone (Figs. 17-16 and 17-17).

The condensing coefficients are lowered greatly by vacuum. The exact values are not known, but it is customary practice to decrease the atmospheric condensation coefficients by half.

Example 17-11. Design of Vacuum Surface Condenser. A large vacuum condenser is to handle the following materials per hour:

> 106,000 lb of wax distillate and reflux, 31 API
> 12,000 lb of gas oil, 33 API
> 1,400 lb of steam

The wax distillate and gas oil are to be separated by partial condensation in four units of condenser. Three of these are for wax distillate, and one for gas oil. The first of the three wax distillate condensers supplies hot reflux to the tower, but cold reflux is also used.

The following pressures are assumed for purposes of calculation. In an actual design the accuracy of the assumed pressures should be checked after the tentative design is completed.

Mm, Hg

Pressure at barometric................	21
Loss in vapor line....................	2
Loss in unit 4.......................	1
Loss in unit 3.......................	1
Loss in unit 2.......................	2
Loss in unit 1.......................	3
Pressure at top of tower............	30
Temperature at top of tower........	490°F

The approximate condensation and true-boiling-point distillation curves of the products are shown in Fig. 17-16, and a diagram of the system is shown in Fig. 17-17. Since this example is aimed at an illustration of principles, the molecular weights, specific heats, and latent heats have not been corrected to the latest values shown in this edition.

Condensation Curves under Vacuum. *Partial Condenser* 1 (*Hot Reflux Condenser*). The conditions are such that equilibrium condensation (page 437) occurs in all four of the condensers. The condensation curve (No. 2) was computed by means of Figs. 4-18 and 4-19.

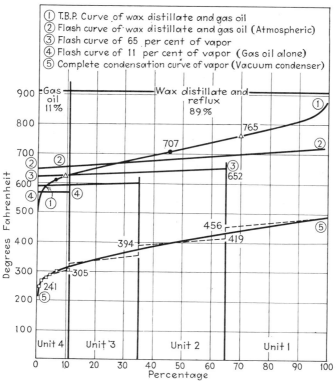

FIG. 17-16. Condensation ranges in vacuum condenser. Refer to Example 17-11 and see Fig. 17-17.

The data given in curves 1 and 2 (Fig. 17-16) apply to condensation at atmospheric pressure, and hence curve 5 for vacuum conditions must be computed.

The total pressure at the inlet to condenser 1 is 30 mm, but at the end it is (30 − 3), or 27 mm. Furthermore, steam is present, and it further reduces the partial pressure of the oil vapor and decreases the temperature of condensation.

$$\text{Moles W.D.} \quad = \frac{106{,}000}{320} = 331.0$$

$$\text{Moles gas oil} \quad = \frac{12{,}000}{242} = 49.6$$

$$\text{Moles vapor} \qquad\qquad = \overline{381.0}$$

$$\text{Moles steam} \quad = \frac{1{,}400}{18} = 78.0$$

$$\text{Total moles} \quad = \overline{459.0}$$

$$\text{Partial pressure} = 30 \times {}^{381}\!/_{459} = 24.9 \text{ mm}$$

The atmospheric initial-condensation temperature (724°F) corrected to 24.9 mm (Fig. 5-27) gives a temperature of 492°F.

Temperature at the Outlet of Unit 1.

About 122 moles of hot reflux are condensed in unit 1 so that at the outlet the partial pressure is

$$27 \times \frac{381 - 122}{459 - 122} = 20.8 \text{ mm}$$

Correcting 696°F to 20.8 mm gives an outlet temperature of 456°F. These temperatures are shown on Figs. 17-16 and 17-17.

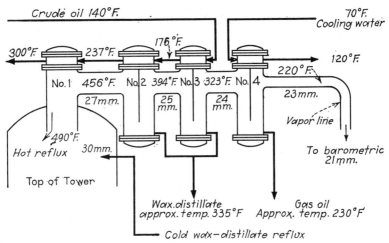

Fig. 17-17. Condenser arrangement for Example 17-11 (also see Fig. 17-16).

Partial Condenser Unit 2. The atmospheric condensation curve for the remaining 65 per cent vapor is computed in a manner similar to the method used for unit 1. This curve is shown as 3 (Fig. 17-16). As the condensate is removed from unit 1, the vapor must be cooled in unit 2 before condensation starts. Note curve 5 (Fig. 17-16) and particularly the two points at 65 per cent. In practice, no sharp break in the temperature is noted because pure countercurrent flow is not attained and perfect equilibrium condensation does not occur.

Furthermore, it would appear in Fig. 17-16 that the hot reflux boils between exactly 753 and 890°F. Actually, the wax distillate and the hot reflux have different boiling ranges but much the same composition because of the very poor separation obtained by partial condensation.

The flash curve (No. 3) should be computed from Figs. 4-18 and 4-19. However, the curve shown (Fig. 17-16) was computed from an older correlation that does not check exactly with Figs. 4-18 and 4-19. The 100 per cent point of curve 3 is 652°F and the zero per cent point is 635°F.

Partial pressure at inlet to unit 2 is the same as for the outlet of unit 1, or 20.8 mm. Correcting 652 to 20.8 mm gives 419°F.

About 130 moles are condensed in unit 2 so that the partial pressure at the outlet of 2 is

$$25 \times {}^{129}\!\!/_{207} = 15.5 \text{ mm}$$

Correcting 635° to 15.5 mm gives 394°F. Partial condenser unit 3 was computed in a similar manner.

Partial Condenser Unit 4. By the time unit 4 is reached, the amount of noncondensable gases (steam) has become relatively so large that a more detailed analysis is necessary. The following tabulation was computed (curve 4, Fig. 17-16) by using the same general principles that were used in studying units 1 and 2.

The pressure drop is very small (1 mm), and hence a constant pressure of 23.5 mm was used throughout the entire unit. Likewise the flash curve 4 is so flat that a temperature of 563°F was used to represent the entire curve.

Per cent vapor remaining	Moles not condensed (approx.)	Partial pressure, mm	Condensation points, °F
11.0	50	8.6	305
7.5	33	6.5	296
5.0	22	4.8	283
3.5	16	3.8	274
1.5	11	2.7	264
1.0	6	1.4	241

The sharply curving tail on the front of the condensation curve shows that all the vapor can never be completely condensed until the steam is condensed. Refiners find that the water leg of the barometric condenser always contains oil and wax stocks, and traps or skimming devices must be installed.

Thermal Duties of the Units. *Unit 1 (47,000 Lb Condensed).* Condensing zone throughout

Btu per hr

Cool vapor.........71,000(490 − 456) × 0.56 = 1,350,000
Cool steam...........1,400(490 − 456) × 0.5 = 23,800

$$\text{Cool}........47,000(490 - 456) \left(\frac{0.68 + 0.55}{2} \right) = 983,000$$

Condense, approx.......47,000 × 92 (Fig. 5-7) = 4,320,000
6,676,800

For the other units the duties are about as follows:

Condenser unit	Lb condensed	Temperature range	Approx. duties, Btu per hr
1	47,000	490–456	6,676,800
2	39,000	456–394	7,213,000
3	20,000	394–323	4,058,000
4	12,000	323–220	2,856,000
Total........	......	....	20,803,800

Transfer Rates, Surfaces, and Temperature Differences.   Crude oil is heated from 140 to 300°F in the first three units, and water is heated from 70 to 120°F in the fourth unit.   The crude oil velocity is 3 ft per sec, and the water 1½ ft per sec.   The temperature ranges are shown in Fig. 17-18.   One-inch tubes were used throughout.

The vapor film rates were considered as consisting of two parts, i.e., condensing and vapor cooling.   The vapor-cooling film rates were obtained by extrapolation of the

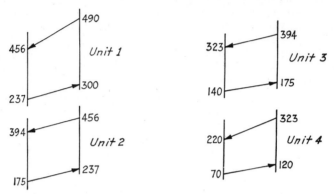

FIG. 17-18. Terminal temperatures for Example 17-11.

TABLE 17-8. COMPUTATIONS FOR SURFACES IN EXAMPLE 17-11

Unit	Duty	Logarithmic mean-temp difference	Mass velocity,[a] lb/ft–sec	h_o	h_i	R_D	H[b]	A[b]
1. Condensing....	5,303,000	204	...	25[d]	190	0.013	16.9	1540
Vapor cooling[c]..	1,373,800	204	1.0	14	190	0.013	11.0	606
Over-all.....	6,676,800	204	...	...	...	.....	15.2	2146
2. Condensing....	5,730,000	219	...	27[d]	130	0.013	17.3	1510
Vapor cooling[c]..	1,483,000	219	0.8	12	130	0.013	9.6	705
Over-all.......	7,213,000	219	...	...	...	.....	14.9	2215
3. Condensing....	3,136,000	196	...	29[d]	100	0.012	17.7	903
Vapor cooling[c]..	922,000	196	0.5	8	100	0.012	6.8	693
Over-all.....	4,058,000	196	...	...	...	.....	13.0	1596
1, 2, & 3 over-all..	17,947,800	243	...	...	...	.....	12.4	5957
4. Condensing....	2,135,000	187	...	32[d]	450	0.011	22.5	507
Vapor cooling[c]..	721,000	187	0.2	5	450	0.011	4.7	820
Over-all.....	2,856,000	187	...	...	...	.....	11.5	1327

[a] Dependent on velocity on the shell side.   The 1 lb per sec per sq ft corresponds to a linear velocity of about 50 ft per sec.

[b] Should be brought to a common basis of surface such as outside surface.

[c] Some liquid cooling also included.

[d] Condensing coefficients are halved for vacuum service.   See pages 560 and 561.

lines of Fig. 17-12 (by almost two logarithmic cycles), and it is believed that somewhat higher rates result from other equations. However, experimental data for high-molecular-weight petroleum vapors are not available. Condensing rates are halved for high-vacuum service. Table 17-8 shows the complete computations.

Note that the logarithmic mean-temperature difference gives confusing results if it is used for the three units together. Its use in this manner shows an over-all rate of heat transfer (12.4) that is lower than the transfer rates in any of the three units.

HEATING COILS FOR TANKS

Storage tanks, tank cars, vessels, and fuel-oil tanks are often equipped with steam coils. The approximate amount of exhaust steam required to heat or maintain temperature in such tanks is approximately

Time of heating	Lb steam per hr per 1,000 bbl per °F difference in air and oil temp (no wind)
1 hr	137–141
5 hr	28–32
10 hr	14–18
Long* (50°F diff.)	5–8
Long* (100°F diff.)	5–10

* Also applies to a tank already hot.

The amount of exhaust-steam-heating surface required for tanks containing semisolid oils such as heavy fuel oil, residuum, heavy topped crude, and heavy asphalt crude oils but not asphalt or waxes is indicated in Fig. 17-19. Similar charts for regular crude oils and lubricating-oil stocks are available.[44] Less surface, by the following percentages, is required if live steam is used.

Pressure, psig	Percentage
Exhaust	100
21	67
63	50
138	33

Example 17-12. Heating Surface for 250-bbl Fuel-oil Tank. A tank of fuel oil is at the air temperature of 50°F, and it is desired to be able to heat it in 7 hr to a temperature of 120°F.

Referring to Fig. 17-19, note the dotted line. Move upward to the capacity (250 bbl), across to the reference line of 50°F, and then follow upward to a temperature difference (oil at 120°F minus air at 50°F) of 70°F and read 520 sq ft surface at the right.

The other dotted line indicates the amount of surface required (225 sq ft) if the tank temperature is to be 80 rather than 120°F.

[44] Nelson, W. L., Heating Coils for Tanks, *Oil Gas J.*, Oct. 7, 1944, p. 103.

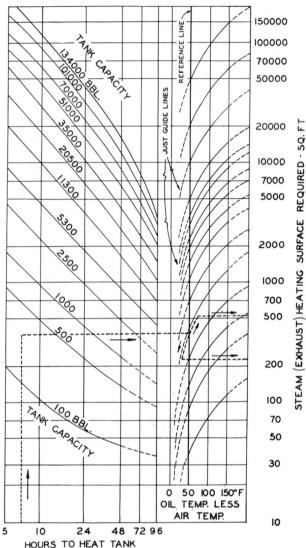

FIG. 17-19. Heating surface (exhaust steam) required for heating semisolid oils in tanks. (*Oil Gas J.*)

COIL-IN-BOX CONDENSERS AND COOLERS

In the past these equipments have been standard, and even today they are used extensively for final cooling before storage. Heat-transfer rates are low in this type of equipment owing (1) to the low velocities that must be used and the low natural-convection rate and (2) to the gradual accumulation of pipe scale and fouled surfaces on the water side. Special cast-iron condenser sections with ribbed outside surfaces, such as the Stirling section of the American Radiator Company, are sometimes used. The main advantage of this condenser section is the large vapor space afforded and the compact arrangement that is possible. To allow for the rapid decrease in vapor volume, coil-in-box condenser coils are usually built as a series of large-diameter pipes connected in parallel to a header, and smaller pipe sizes are used on each of the parallel branches in the liquid cooling zone. For simple cooling, the coils are usually connected in series throughout the entire cooler. The usual inlet vapor velocity is approximately 50 ft per sec, and the outlet liquid velocity is between 0.5 and 2.0 ft per sec. The higher liquid velocity is used for light materials such as gasoline, and the 0.5 velocity for cold tar, wax distillate, etc. In best practice the coils are built in pairs with about 15 in. between pairs to facilitate cleaning and repairs. Using flanged pipe facilitates the removal of pipe, but the coils are not so compact. The Griscom-Russell Company manufactures a "bent-tube" section for coil-in-box service or for cooling by means of water sprays in a cooling tower. These sections consist of two headers with a large number of small tubes between them. The tubes are bowed slightly during manufacture so that by expansion and contraction the accumulation of scale, etc., on the outside of the tubes will be dislodged. For certain scales, the bent-tube section functions properly, but for others the tubes must be cleaned by the usual hand methods.

Coils of standard or extra-heavy steel pipe with double-extra-heavy malleable fittings are used for normal conditions. For hard water, many refiners require the use of genuine wrought-iron pipe. Best practice for long service requires the use of Classes *B* and *C* flanged cast-iron pipe with Class *D* fittings.

The transfer rate inside normal-size pipe cannot be given as for tubular equipments because fouling factors are not available. Owing to the many variables in the design and use of coil-in-box equipment and particularly the wide range of velocity and surface conditions, the rates are not so consistent as for tubular equipment. For natural convection on the outside of pipe coils, the water film rates given on page 559 are suggested, but they must be used with fouling factors in the magnitude of 20 to 30.

Although the water flow in boxes from the bottom to the top is usually considered to be countercurrent with respect to the hot fluid, unsuspected up-currents usually occur at several points[45] so that no clear pattern of flow can be defined. However, the very large fouling factors for such equipments tend to erase any practical effect of type of flow.

[45] Nelson, W. L., Waterflow in Coil-in-box Equipment, *Oil Gas J.*, Dec. 7, 1946, p. 112.

OVER-ALL TRANSFER RATES

Although the use of over-all rates is not recommended, at times the engineer has reason to make very approximate estimations of surfaces, etc. Table 17-9 is a tabulation of over-all rates that were obtained from various authorities in refinery positions and with engineering companies. The discrepancies in the values indicate clearly the difficulties involved in attempting to use over-all rates and why the use of over-all heat-transfer rates is being abandoned.

TABLE 17-9. APPROXIMATE OVER-ALL RATES OF HEAT TRANSFER

Duty	Authority number								
	1	2	3	4	5	6	7	8	Range
Coil-in-box equipment:									
Vapor cooling..................	...	...	7	...	...	...	...	...	7
Condensing and cooling naphtha	15	20	11	18	32	18	26	17	11–32
Cooling naphtha..............	...	...	...	18	20	16	15	...	15–20
Cooling kerosene or gas oil.....	15	15–18	...	16	17	20	21	...	15–21
Cooling wax distillate.........	...	...	...	12	14	12	10	...	10–14
Cooling lubes.................	...	...	...	14	11	12	11	13	11–14
Cooling tars, bottoms, etc.....	12	13	...	10	7	10	...	10	7–13
Condensing kerosene..........	...	...	23	...	26	...	20	15	15–26
Condensing gas oil............	...	...	27	24	23	13	13	12	12–27
Condensing fuel oil and lubes...	...	...	36	...	18	...	...	10	10–36
Tubular equipment:									
Condensing naphtha:									
Water.....................	52	39	55	48	62	60	70	50	39–70
Oil.......................	26	25	...	37	27	27	30	27	25–37
Condensing kerosene:									
Water.....................	...	...	65	31	48	...	...	50	31–65
Oil.......................	...	...	...	25	24	...	...	27	24–27
Cooling naphtha:									
Water.....................	...	...	...	47	54	70	70	...	47–70
Oil.......................	...	...	...	...	20	...	...	...	20
Cooling kerosene or gas oil:									
Water.....................	40	45	...	28	36	35	35	20	20–45
Oil.......................	20	...	...	28	18	...	...	...	18–28
Cooling wax distillate:									
Water.....................	25	25	...	14	24	...	...	25	14–25
Oil.......................	...	...	...	27	16	...	...	...	16–27
Cooling fuel oils and lubes:									
Water.....................	...	...	...	...	19	20	20	...	19–20
Oil.......................	...	...	...	12	9	25	25	...	9–25

CHAPTER 18

TUBESTILL HEATERS

When pipe- or tubestills were first built, the important part that radiation plays in any open-fired heater was not appreciated, and the first stills were purely convection types, consisting of a bank of closely spaced tubes with a combustion space below or to the side. Coke deposited in the tubes that were exposed to radiation and the remaining tubes absorbed little heat. When overheated tubes were removed from the still, other tubes began to overheat, and as the number of radiant tubes was reduced, the situation was aggravated. Finally, designers realized that the radiation from the flame cloud must be distributed over a large surface, and the modern radiant type of still has been the result. If exceedingly mild rates of heating are required, the still may consist almost entirely of tubes that are exposed to radiation.

Shell or batch stills are no longer used except when a single still may be used to rerun or distill several small stocks such as "slops," special naphthas, petrolatum solutions, etc.

Types of Stills. Most modern stills are built with two distinct heating sections: a radiant section which can receive heat directly from the flame. and a convection section which recovers heat from the hot gases traveling to the stack. Figure 18-1 indicates diagrammatically the arrangement of tubes and the direction of liquid flow. Names are not standardized but the several stills of Fig. 18-1 might be called:

(a) Large box-type   (g) Large isoflow (Petrochem)
(b) Separate-convection (Lummus) (h) Small isoflow (Petrochem)
(c) Down-convection   (i) Equiflux (UOP)
(d) Straight-up (Born)   (j) Double-upfired (UOP)
(e) A-frame (Kellogg)   (k) Radiant wall (Selas)
(f) Circular (DeFlorez)

Although all of the stills of Fig. 18-1 are useful for many services, there are certain features in which each excels or may be deficient.

1. *Flame Impingement.* Too large a flame can cause impingement or overheating of certain tubes in nearly all of the stills, but tubes that are vulnerable are those just above the bridgewall in (c) down-convection,

and the lowest tubes of (j) double-upfired or (d) straight-up. The difficulty disappears in stills (d) and (j) when the capacity is large, i.e., the stills can be wider. Note the black tubes in Fig. 18-1.

2. *Hot Tubes.* The rate of heat absorption tends to be high at the entrance to the convection section because heat is delivered by both radiation and convection [black tubes in types (a), (c), (d), (e), and (j)]. The feed, because it is cooler, is sometimes introduced through these tubes (a screen bank), and in some instances steam is superheated or water is heated in the screen bank. Likewise, the tubes situated closest to the flame receive the largest amount of heat [black tubes in (d), (f), (g), (h), and (j)].

3. *Oil Firing.* Oil fuel tends to produce larger flames especially because larger burners are used. Stills (a), (b), (c), and (e) are best suited for oil firing although the larger sizes of the other stills encounter little difficulty.

4. *Heat Distribution.* One phase of poor heat distribution has been mentioned in item (2) above, but in addition the rate of heating varies widely in different parts of the boxes or cavities of such stills as (a) and (c), although most of the other vertical stills can attain a fairly uniform distribution of heat.

5. *Two-coil Heating.* Still (c) is not suited for two-coil flow although by experiment it is possible to use it for two streams. Symmetrical two-coil arrangements can be devised for most of the other stills, but if a different rate of heat input is needed in each coil, the stills with a center bridgewall are most effective.

6. *Control of Rates.* Stills (i) and (k) are eminently suitable for precise control of the rate of heat input and for operation at exceedingly high (1000 to 1500°F) temperatures. Very low rates of heat absorption can be attained in the circular types (f), (g), and (h), and in other types if enough radiant surface is provided.

7. *Capacity.* Stills (c), (d), (h), (i), and (k) can be built for the lowest capacities, and types (a), (b), (e), and (j) are best suited for large capacities.

8. *Stacks.* Stills (a), (b), (c), and (i) require tall stacks, but scarcely any stack (except to release the gas at a high level) is needed with the other stills because the hot furnace itself produces a draft.

9. *Cost.* The roof constructions of types (a), (b), and (c) are expensive. Walls not covered with tubes [see (a), (b), (c), and (e)] tend to overheat and must be of heavier construction. Suspended panel walls are usually cheaper than brick walls, but suspended tile walls are very expensive. The large framework of still (i) is expensive, and the numerous burners of type (k) add to its cost. The A-frame still (e) conserves on structural steel.

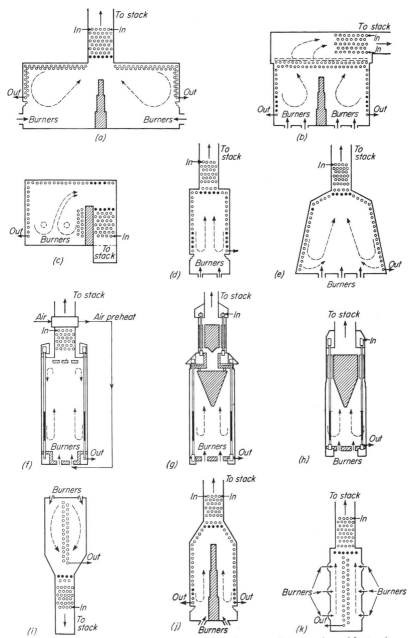

Fig. 18-1. Basic types of pipestill heaters (see text for meaning of letters).

In the isoflow stills (g) and (h), finned tubes are used in the convection section. This greatly reduces the amount of tubing required and results in rates of heat transfer in the convection section as large as or sometimes larger than in the radiant section. In still (h) the upper ends of the tubes are finned and thus there is no distinct convection section. The Selas still (k) employs ceramic burner cups,[1] spaced at about 30 in., which cover both walls.

Gases are cooled by tubes on the walls, and this tends to cause a downward gas flow behind the tubes. Velocities as high as 10 ft per sec have been recorded,[1a] and it is becoming evident that much heat is transferred in the radiant section by convection as well as by radiation. The optimum space between the wall and the tube is about one tube diameter.[1a] In Petrochem heaters (Fig. 18-1g and h) about 13 per cent of the heat absorbed by the radiant tubes is delivered by convection and by internal recirculation.

The actual heat intensity curves for several heaters are presented by H. C. Schutt,[2] when applied to cracking for the production of ethylene.

Air preheat is indicated in Fig. 18-1f (DeFlorez), and it can be employed in any still that is mechanically tight from gas leakage. The recirculation of flue gas through the combustion chamber by means of a fan is not indicated in any of the stills. The flue gas is reheated by the flame, causing a lower flame temperature and thus a milder radiation rate. At the same time the convection-section duty is increased, and a larger convection section must be provided. Thus, flue-gas recirculation is particularly suited to the older convection-type stills. When it is necessary to alter or regulate the rate of radiant absorption, no method other than flue-gas recirculation is available except such expensive methods as the use of large amounts of excess air, a reduction in capacity, or possibly to obtain a fuel which radiates less. Flue-gas-recirculation stills were widely used during the development of thermal cracking processes; but, now that engineers know how to design stills for specific radiant-absorption rates, recirculation stills are no longer installed.

The advantages of a symmetrical arrangement of radiant-heat-absorbing surface are apparent in the stills of Fig. 18-1. The ideal still will be one in which the rate of heat absorption is the maximum (at all points) that can be transferred to the oil without causing coking, discoloration, or decomposition. If two coils are to be heated and properly controlled in a

---

[1] Tate, C. C., A New Development in Radiant Heating, *Oil Gas J.*, May 10, 1951, p. 106.

[1a] Reed, R. D., Radiant Heat Transfer versus Wall-to-tube Spacing, Western Pet. Ref. Assoc., Chicago Meeting, June 18, 1953.

[2] Schutt and Zdonik, Designing a Tubular Pyrolysis Furnace, *Oil Gas J.*, May 14, 1956, p. 149.

single still, some partition arrangement as in Fig. 18-1a, b, d, e, or j must be provided. It is desirable to fire with gas because fuel-oil flames radiate intensely and thus tend to "burn out" or cause local overheating of certain tubes. Part of the advantage of gas lies in the fact that gas burners are relatively cheap and thus several gas burners can be afforded.

FIG. 18-2. A-frame furnace under construction. Open header boxes show radiant return bends and welded convection bends. (*M. W. Kellogg Co.*)

Preheating the air that is used in combustion has an effect that is the reverse of flue-gas recirculation. It tends to increase the absorption rate in the radiant section and to increase the flame temperature. To be most effective, the air should be heated by only the gases that are passing to the stack.

A limiting factor in the design of all direct-fired stills is the tendency of oil to coke or decompose at the wall of the heated tube. This limits the rate of radiant-heat absorption to 6000 to 20,000 Btu per sq ft of outside area, depending on the operation, because if coke is formed the tube-wall temperature rises and the tube softens and fails. An equipment that somewhat overcomes this difficulty is the pebble heater.[3,4] It consists essentially of two vertical cylindrical chambers mounted one above the other. Ceramic-ware pebbles are heated in the upper chamber by direct contact with burning fuel, and the flue gases pass upward in counter-current flow to the incoming pebbles. The hot pebbles flow downward to the lower chamber where they are used to heat air or steam, crack ethane or possibly oil or hydrocarbon gases. The cooled or spent pebbles, along with any accumulation of carbon, are lifted by an elevator or airlift to the heating chamber. An advantage of such a heater is the fact that coke, etc., is deposited on the moving stream of pebbles rather than attaching itself to a direct-fired heating surface.

The efficiency of a process can be increased in two main ways. The loss through the walls and in the stack gas from the furnace can be decreased, or heat can be saved from the products of the process. The use of air-cooled walls, aside from the preservation of brickwork, has often been referred to as an economy but since hot air raises the flame and stack temperature, it is necessary also to add convection surface, or no economy is effected.

The heat that is absorbed by heat exchangers is often credited as a direct saving in heat. Such is not always the case because the efficiency of the still decreases as the temperature of the charge stock is increased by exchangers. As an example, consider a pipestill distillation unit that operates with no exchangers and at a stack gas temperature of 350°F. The stack loss is only about 8.4 per cent (Fig. 14-2). If the charge stock is then heated by exchangers to 300°F, the stack temperature will be about 550°F and the stack loss 14 per cent. In such a case the saving of heat by raising the temperature of the charge stock from 100 to 300 must more than compensate for the decrease in the efficiency of the still. A study of the economics of the complete unit, including both the pipestill and the exchangers, is the only way to determine the amount of heat that is actually saved.

RADIATION

The evaluation of the percentage of radiant absorption that will occur in a particular pipestill, and the distribution of this radiation throughout the furnace cavity, has always been difficult. However, in recent years,

[3] Norton, C. L., Jr., Pebble Heater, *Chem. & Met. Eng.*, July, 1946, p. 116.

[4] Kilpatrick et al., New Pebble Heater Process, *Pet. Refiner*, April, 1954, p. 171.

owing primarily to the efforts of Professor Wohlenberg[5] of Yale and Professor Hottel[6] of the Massachusetts Institute of Technology, a comprehensive theoretical background has been developed by which plant performance can be predicted with some success. Still more recently correlations of the behavior of plant stills have been made available.[7,8]

Stefan's law of radiation is fundamental.

$$Q = bAT^4$$

where A = area of radiating surface, sq ft

T = absolute temperature of the surface, °F

Q = Btu transferred per hr

b = 1.72 × 10^{-9} Btu/(°F diff.)(sq ft)(hr) at black-body conditions

But a surface cannot radiate all this heat to another surface because the cooler surface also radiates heat. For a small body completely surrounded by a hotter body the foregoing statement simplifies to

$$Q = \text{net heat transferred} = Q_2 - Q_1 = bA(T_2^4 - T_1^4) \qquad (18\text{-}1)$$

This expression involves the assumption that all the energy emitted by the hot body is absorbed by the cooler body and that all the energy emitted from the cooler body is absorbed by the hotter body. In practice most materials fail to absorb all the radiant energy that falls upon them, and hence the constant b is different for all materials. (Table 18-1).

TABLE 18-1. RADIATION CONSTANTS

Material	$b \times 10^{-9}$
1. Perfect black body	1.72
2. Brass, matte	0.374
3. Cast iron, rough and highly oxidized	1.57
4. Clay	0.65
5. Copper	0.278
6. Ceramics ware, unglazed	1.34
7. Field soil	0.63
8. Granite, smooth but not polished	0.745
9. Lampblack	1.56
10. Lime mortar, rough	1.51
11. Sheet iron, matte oxidized	1.55
12. Sheet iron, polished	0.466

[5] Wohlenberg and Lindseth, The Influence of Radiation on Boiler Surface and a Simplified Method for Its Calculation, *Trans. ASME*, **48**, 849 (1926).

[6] Hottel, H. C., Radiant Heat Transmission between Surfaces Separated by Non-absorbing Media, *Trans. ASME Fuel Steam Power Division*, **53**, 265 (1931).

[7] Wilson, Lobo, and Hottel, Heat Transmission in Radiant Sections of Tube Stills, *Ind. Eng. Chem.*, **24**, 486 (1932).

[8] Lobo and Evans, Heat Transfer in the Radiant Section of Petroleum Heaters, *Trans. A.I.Ch.E.*, **35**, 743 (1939).

Materials that have a rough or dull-finish surface absorb radiation almost as completely as perfect radiation absorbers (black bodies), but polished surfaces or even clean metallic rough surfaces reflect a large part of the radiation that falls upon them.   Furthermore, surfaces such as a brick wall at incandescent temperatures appear to reflect much of the radiation that falls upon them.

The differences in the fourth powers of the temperature are involved in this formulation, and it becomes apparent that the higher temperature raised to the fourth power may be so large that the lower temperature may be neglected.   In doubling the temperature, the radiation increases sixteenfold.

Another deduction of a qualitative nature but of great value concerns the angle of vision or sight of a point radiation source.   Radiation is a wave phenomenon, and it travels through gaseous materials in a straight line without suffering much of a loss in intensity.   It is unable to penetrate opaque or dark solid materials.   Thus cooling surfaces cast what might be called "radiation shadows" behind them.

Heating by radiation is practiced by allowing combustion to take place in proximity to cooled surfaces.   Radiation from flames and gases cannot be easily handled by Eq. (18-1) because (1) the size of the flame cannot be accurately determined, (2) the flame has a thickness so that radiation from the center of the flame must penetrate the outer layers, and (3) the luminosity of flames varies with different fuels and conditions of combustion.   In nonluminous flames, radiation is found to be dependent to a large extent on the percentage of carbon dioxide and water vapor that is present.   However, radiation from such a flame is not effective, and the presence of partly burned carbon particles (luminous flames) greatly increases radiation.   The mechanism of radiation from flames is further complicated by the convection heat transfer that occurs by the circulation of gases within the furnace box.

The heat energy that is liberated during combustion is confined in such a small space at the start of combustion that either a very high temperature is attained or heat must be dissipated to the surrounding by radiation, convection, or conduction.   No doubt heat is initially used in heating the reactant materials to the flame temperature by conduction. However, if all the heat were utilized in this manner, the theoretical flame temperature would be attained, and experience shows that this temperature is never reached in ordinary combustion reactions.

Radiant-absorption Rate.   Radiation between solid surfaces is dependent upon the fourth power of the temperature difference and upon a constant, the value of which is dependent on the kind of material and the condition of the surface.   Radiation from a flame, as in pipestill or boiler furnaces, is governed by the same laws except that the size of the flame and the conditions within the flame are so difficult to evaluate that empirical relationships have been adopted. The most important factors that affect radiation from flames are (1) percentage of total heat that is absorbed as radiant heat, (2) ratio of air to fuel, (3) arrangement and spacing of absorbing surface, and (4) kind of fuel.

Regarding the first of these, consider a flame burning within a furnace whose walls consist entirely of absorbing surface. Rays of radiation proceed in all directions from the flame; and with the exception of the small amount of heat that is used in heating the intervening gas, all the heat from the flame is absorbed by the cool surface. In this case, a *large percentage* of the heat is transferred by radiation, although the rate of heat absorption per square foot of surface is low. If all the absorbing surface, except a single tube, is removed from such a furnace, the radiation strikes the refractory walls and is reflected or reradiated about the furnace interior so that the single tube receives a relatively larger amount of radiation per unit of surface. Although the single tube absorbs heat at a high rate, it absorbs a relatively small percentage of the total heat liberation.

The ratio of air to fuel is important mainly because it affects the flame temperature. The larger the quantity of air (or products of combustion) that must be heated in the flame the lower will be the resultant flame temperature and the lower the rate of radiation. Thus large quantities of excess air reduce the radiant absorption. For the same reason the recirculation of flue gas reduces the flame temperature, but air preheat increases it. The arrangement of the cooling surfaces also affects the rate of radiant absorption. The closer the surface is to the flame the greater the amount of radiation that falls upon it. Thus corners and ends of furnaces receive less radiation than other surfaces (pages 609 and 611).

These factors have been related by Wilson, Lobo, and Hottel:[7]

$$R = \cfrac{1}{1 + \cfrac{G\sqrt{Q/aA_{cp}}}{4{,}200}} \tag{18-2}$$

where R = fraction of heat liberation (above 60°F) that is absorbed by the cold surfaces in the combustion chamber

G = air-fuel ratio, lb of air per lb of fuel. For flue-gas recirculation: lb of air and recirculated gases per lb of fuel

Q = total heat developed in the flame (above 60°F), Btu per hr. This may consist of the net heating value of the fuel, heat in air or in recirculated gases, and sensible heat in the fuel or atomizing steam

A_{cp} = area of furnace wall that has tubes mounted on it, sq ft

a = a factor by which A is multiplied to obtain the effective cool surface. a = 0.986 for two rows of tubes (Fig. 18-3).

The A_{cp} term requires special consideration. It is simply that portion of the wall area of the still that has tubes in front of it. Thus, A_{cp} has the same value regardless of the number of rows of tubes. However, a single row behaves as if it covered 88 per cent of the wall area ($a = 0.88$ at a center-to-center spacing that is double the tube diameter, Fig. 18-3), whereas two rows behave as if they cover 98.6 per cent of the wall area.

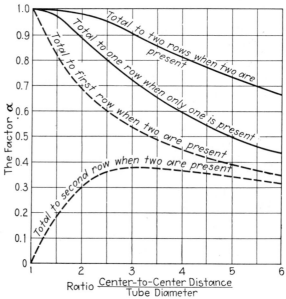

FIG. 18-3. Distribution of radiation to tubes suspended in front of a wall. (*Hottel, Mech. Eng.*)

The area described by A_{cp} or aA_{cp} is not convenient because the designer or operator is primarily interested in the area of the tubes that transfer the radiant heat. The wall area (A_{cp}) in terms of length (L, ft), center-to-center spacing (C, in.), and number of tubes per row (N) is

$$A_{cp} = L \times N \times \frac{C}{12} \qquad (18\text{-}3)$$

and the projected area of the tubes (A) in terms of tube diameter (D in.) and number of rows (n) is

$$A = L \times n \times N \times \frac{D}{12}$$

or

$$A = nA_{cp}\frac{D}{C}$$

or

$$A_{cp} = \frac{A}{n} \times \frac{C}{D}$$

In terms of q, defined as the rate of heat absorption per square foot of projected tube area,

$$RQ = Aq$$

and

$$Q = \frac{Aq}{R} = \frac{nA_{cp}(D/C)q}{R}$$

When these terms are introduced into Eq. (18-2), the following forms are obtained:

$$R = \frac{1}{1 + \dfrac{G\sqrt{\dfrac{q}{R} \times \dfrac{n}{a} \times \dfrac{D}{C}}}{4,200}}$$

and

$$q\left(\frac{D}{C} \times \frac{n}{a}\right) = \frac{(1 - R)^2}{R} \times \frac{17,640,000}{G^2} \qquad (18\text{-}4)$$

The most common commercial case in which $D/C = 0.5$ and $n = 2$ is plotted in Fig. 18-4.

$$1.014q' = \frac{(1 - R)^2}{R} \times \frac{17,640,000}{G^2} \qquad (18\text{-}5)$$

The special q' of Fig. 18-4 can be corrected to the general q which applies to any number of rows of tubes and any tube spacing, as follows:

$$\left(\frac{D}{C} \times \frac{n}{a}\right) q = f(R) = 1.014q'$$

or

$$q = 1.014\left(\frac{C}{D} \times \frac{a}{n}\right) q' \qquad (18\text{-}6)$$

Common center-to-center spacings[9] for tubes and the approximate equivalent lengths of bends (for friction-loss calculations) are indicated in Table 18-2.

TABLE 18-2. MINIMUM SPACING OF TUBES AND EQUIVALENT LENGTH OF BENDS

Tube size, o.d., in.	Minimum spacing, in.				Approx. equivalent length of bends, ft	
	Box type		Streamline			
	Lightest	Heaviest	Lightest	Heaviest	Box type	Streamline
2	3.75	4.87	4.50	5.87	13.3	6.7
3	5.00	6.37	5.75	6.75	20.0	10.0
4	6.00	7.75	6.75	8.25	26.7	13.3
5	7.12	9.25	8.25	9.75	33.3	16.7
6	8.25	10.50	....	....	40.0	20.0

[9] Nelson, W. L., Return Bends, *Oil Gas J.*, Sept. 7, 1946, p. 107.

Equations (18-2) to (18-6) apply to any conventional box-type furnace with radiant tubes any number of rows deep, with or without air preheat or flue-gas recirculation, and with any normal percentage of excess air. The factor a may be obtained from Fig. 18-3[10] but for normal tube arrangements, such as two rows of tubes spaced at a center to center of about twice the tube diameter, the value of a is 0.986.   The relative absorption

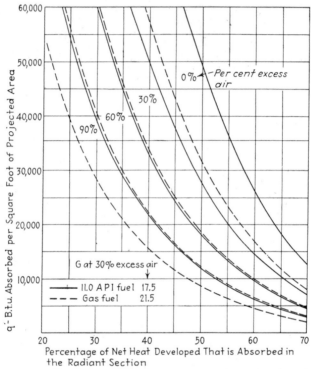

Fig. 18-4. Rate of radiant absorption (Btu per square foot of projected area) for a center-to-center tube spacing that is double the tube diameter, and for two rows of radiant tubes [also see Eq. (18-6)].

rates in the first three rows of tubes, when only three are present, is approximately 7:3:1 so that the third row is of little value.

A study of this equation for the effect of the type of fuel is useful. Table 18-3 is based on the fuel analyses and data given in Chap. 14. The radiant-absorption factors and rates of absorption per square foot of projected area are computed for 30 per cent excess air when half of the heat liberation is absorbed in the radiant section.

The effect of the percentage of excess air is indicated in Fig. 18-4.   The radiation rates for two common fuels, i.e., dry refinery gas (G for 30 per

[10] Hottel, H. C., Radiant Heat Transmission, *Mech. Eng.* **52**, 699 (1930).

cent excess air) and heavy fuel, are shown for 0 to 90 per cent excess air. Other fuels can be represented by lines between these two extremes by referring to Table 18-3. This chart may be used directly in the design of simple furnaces, but it should not be used for furnaces using air preheat or flue-gas recirculation. Note also that it is based on a center-to-center tube spacing that is twice the tube diameter [Eq. (18-5)] and on the use of two rows of tubes. It may be applied to other situations by means of Eq. (18-6). With proper burners and an experienced fireman, it is possible to fire with less than 25 per cent excess air, but the average amounts

TABLE 18-3. COMPARISON OF RADIATION PROPERTIES OF REFINERY FUELS

Fuel	Heating value		Lb flue gas per lb fuel	Btu absorbed per sq ft (proj.)
	Gross	Net		
1. Hydrogen-rich reformer gas......	641	569	26.6	13,200
2. Pure methane................	1,009	909	23.5	17,100
3. Dry natural gas...............	1,160	1,051	23.2	17,700
4. Wet cracked gas..............	2,058	1,893	22.0	19,700
5. Wet natural gas..............	1,360	1,239	21.0	21,600
6. 24.4 API Ky. topped crude......	19,358	18,168	19.7	24,800
7. 9.2 API cracked tar (M.C.)......	18,274	17,324	18.8	27,400
8. 7.6 API resid. fuel oil (Calif.)....	17,970	17,075	18.4	28,600
9. Bituminous coal (Mo.)..........	13,533	13,098	13.6	54,700[a]

[a] Of questionable value because Eq. (18-2) is not for solid fuels.

used are about 35 per cent for gaseous fuels and 50 per cent for oil fuels (Table 14-6).

If a low rate of absorption is not necessary but gas is available and must be burned, a mixture of oil and gas may be fired together. The luminosity or radiating power of such flames appears to be almost as good as for pure oil flames. Hence for such mixed flames the curves in Fig. 18-4 for oil flames may be used. The radiating power of these mixed flames may be explained by considering the carbon particles in an oil flame as radiators. These particles also exist in the mixed flame.

Lobo and Evans[8] have made a complete study of petroleum heaters and the Wilson, Lobo, and Hottel radiation equation [Eq. (18-2)]. They also present a theoretical equation that appears to check well with all types and arrangements of heaters. With regard to Eq. (18-2), they conclude that it may be used for designing the older conventional box-type heaters (Fig. 18-1a, b, c) or other very large stills but subject to the following qualifications:

1. Fuel oil or cracked refinery gas must be used as fuel.
2. Radiant rates must range between 5000 and 30,000 Btu per hr per sq ft based on outside tube area.
3. Percentage of excess air must range between 5 and 80 per cent.
4. Tube skin temperatures must not be closer than 400°F to the temperature of the flue gas leaving the radiant section.
5. Length of radiant beam should be greater than 15 ft.

FIG. 18-5. Straight-up type of still (Fig. 18-1d) showing counterbalanced elevator platforms on the ends for servicing the tubes and bends. (*Born Eng. Co.*)

The theoretical equations developed by them[8] give closer results (maximum 16 per cent deviation), but the use of the equations is complicated, particularly for design purposes.

Various types of elaborate burner systems for the production of more radiation and a better distribution of heat in the combustion chamber have been suggested. Some of these consist of a furnace floor of small gas jets; and although they perform well, they are expensive. A successful artificial-radiation device is the muffle burner of the Alcorn Combustion Company. In this burner the gas fuel is fired through a long muffle which may extend along the entire length of the floor of the still. The muffle becomes hot and acts as a radiator, and the flame that issues from the end of the muffle also contributes to the radiation.

Example 18-1. Rate of Absorption in the Radiant Section. A pipestill uses 7,110 lb per hr of a cracked gas (net heating value 20,560 Btu per lb or 1900 Btu per cu ft). The radiant section contains 1,500 sq ft of projected area, and the tubes (5 in. outside diameter) are spaced at a center-to-center distance of 10 in. There is only one row of radiant tubes, and they are 40 ft long. The ratio of air to fuel is 21.0 (30 per cent excess air). What percentage of the heat liberation is absorbed in the radiant section and how many Btu are absorbed per hour through each square foot of projected area?

$$Q = 7{,}110 \times 20{,}560 = 146{,}000{,}000 \text{ (heat liberation)}$$
$$a = 0.88 \text{ (Fig. 18-3)}$$
$$N = \text{number of tubes} = \frac{1{,}500}{40 \times \frac{5}{12}} = 90$$
$$A_{cp} = 40 \times 90 \times \frac{10}{12} = 3{,}000 \text{ [Eq. (18-3)]}$$
$$aA_{cp} = 0.88 \times 3{,}000 = 2{,}640 \text{ sq ft}$$
$$R = \frac{1}{1 + \dfrac{21.0 \sqrt{\dfrac{146 \times 10^6}{2{,}640}}}{4{,}200}} \text{ [Eq. (18-2)]}$$
$$= \frac{1}{1 + 1.18} = 0.458$$

Heat absorption in radiant section

$$0.458 \times 146 \times 10^6 = 66{,}900{,}000 \text{ Btu per hr}$$

$$\text{Btu absorbed per sq ft projected area} = q = \frac{66{,}900{,}000}{1{,}500} = 44{,}500 \text{ Btu per hr}$$

The results may be checked by means of Fig. 18-4. It applies to two rows of tubes and a spacing of tubes that is twice the diameter of the tubes. At an R value of 0.458, 30 per cent excess air, and an average gas fuel ($G = 21.5$),

$$q = 24{,}000 \text{ (for two rows)}$$

Correcting to one row by Eq. (18-6),

$$q = 1.014 \times 24{,}000 \times \frac{10}{5} \times \frac{0.88}{1.0} = 42{,}800$$

Note, however, that the gas of Fig. 18-4 has a G of 21.5, whereas the fuel used herein has a G of 21. Thus, the line for the particular gas fired in this example should lie about one-eighth of the distance between the gas and the fuel-oil lines, or at about

$$42{,}800 + 1{,}500 = 44{,}300$$

Lobo-Evans Method. The theoretical furnace-design method developed by Lobo and Evans[8] involves so many relationships that a theoretical development cannot be attempted here, but it can be presented by means of a series of charts (Figs. 18-3 and 18-6 to 18-11). It can be applied only to already designed or completed furnaces to see how they behave. It involves a determination of the following factors or relationships:

1. *Effective Surface* (aA_{cp}). This has already been discussed and is defined by Eq. (18-3) and Fig. 18-3.

2. *Mean Length of Radiant Beam* (L). This has been evaluated by Hottel[11] as shown in Table 18-4. The mean length is defined in terms of the ratios of length, width, and height, and in terms of diameter and height.

3. *Partial Pressure of* CO_2 *and* H_2O (P). This is a function of the carbon-hydrogen ratio of the fuel and the percentage of excess air as shown in Fig. 18-10.

4. *Flame Emissivity* (P_F). This is related to PL, the atmosphere-feet of radiating gas cloud, in Fig. 18-9 by means of assumed values of the gas temperature at the bridge wall (t_g) and the tube skin temperature (t_s).

5. *Effective Refractory Area* $(A_R, sq\ ft)$. The effective refractory area is the total wall area less the effective surface (aA_{cp}).

TABLE 18-4. MEAN LENGTH OF RADIANT BEAMS IN VARIOUS GAS SHAPES

Dimensional ratios (length, width, height in any order) or diameter (d), ft	Length of beam (L, ft)
Rectangular furnaces:	
1–1–1 to 1–1–3 and 1–2–1 to 1–2–4	⅔ ∛furnace volume
1–1–4 to 1–1– ∞	1.0 times smallest dimension
1–2–5 to 1–2–8	1.3 times smallest dimension
1–3–3 to 1– ∞ – ∞	1.8 times smallest dimension
Cylindrical furnaces:	
$d \times d$	⅔ times diameter
$d \times 2d$, to $d \times \infty d$	1.0 times diameter

6. *Exchange Factor* (ϕ) The over-all exchange factor is evaluated in Fig. 18-11 in terms of the flame emissivity (P_F) and the ratio of A_R to (aA_{cp}).

7. *Rate of Heat Absorption Factor* $\left(\dfrac{RQ}{aA_{cp}\phi}\right)$. In this term, Q is the total heat liberation per hour and R is the fraction of this heat that is absorbed by the radiant surface. Thus RQ is the Btu absorbed per hour in the radiant section. The term can be evaluated directly by adopting the desired value of RQ or a suitable value of the rate of radiant absorption such as the q value of Eq. (18-5) or Table 18-5.

8. *Check of Gas Temperature* (t_g). At this stage the assumed gas temperature (t_g) of item 4 above can be checked by Fig. 18-6 using $(RQ/aA_{cp}\phi)$ on the right scale. If t_g is in error by more than 100°F, the values of P_F and ϕ (items 4 and 6 above) must be revised.

[11] Perry, J. H. (ed.), "Chemical Engineers' Handbook," 2d ed., p. 1015, McGraw-Hill Book Company, Inc., New York, 1941.

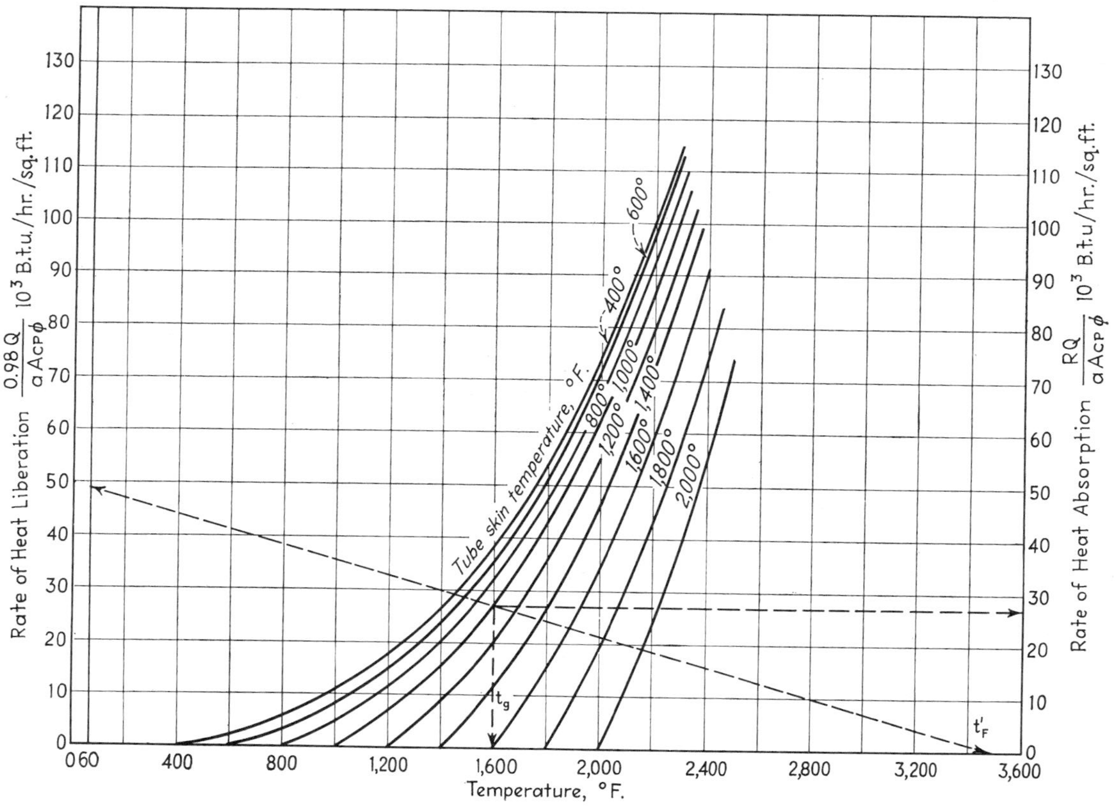

FIG. 18-6. Theoretical radiant equation (high range). (*Lobo and Evans, Trans. A.I.Ch.E.*)

9. *Pseudo Flame Temperature* (t'_F). This temperature can be computed from Fig. 18-7 or 18-8 by using the per cent excess air. Note that if the air is preheated (°F above 60°F) a further correction is necessary on Fig. 18-7 or 18-8.

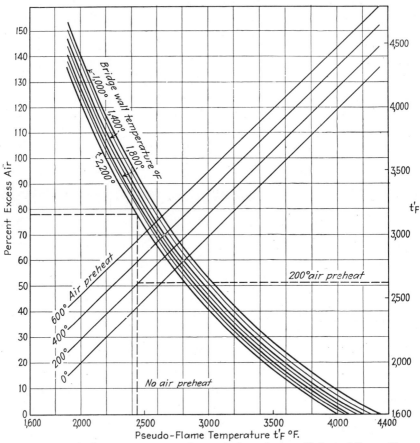

FIG. 18-7. Pseudo flame temperatures for cracked-gas fuels. (*Lobo and Evans, Trans. A.I.Ch.E.*)

10. *Rate of Heat Liberation Factor* $\left(\dfrac{0.98Q}{aA_{cp}\phi}\right)$. This can also be evaluated from Fig. 18-6 by connecting the t'_F with the tube skin temperature (t_s) and reading the rate of heat liberation on the left scale. Since all factors are already known, the value of Q can be computed.

Example 18-2. Rate of Absorption by Lobo-Evans. What is the total heat input required and the radiant absorption for the following still and operating conditions?

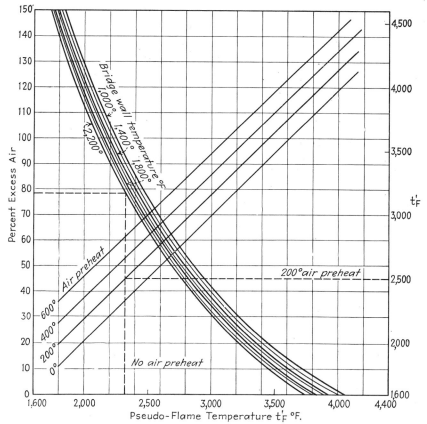

FIG. 18-8. Pseudo flame temperatures for oil fields.   (*Lobo and Evans, Trans. A.I.Ch.E.*)

Still data:

Dimensions of combustion chamber...................... 15 ft × 30 ft × 40 ft
Tube, outside diameter................................ 5 in.
Center-to-center spacing.............................. 10 in.
Number of tubes (arranged in a single row)............ 90
Tube area, outside.................................... 4,710 sq ft
Total wall area, A_T (the opening into the convection section
  is 200 sq ft)....................................... 4,300 sq ft

Operating conditions:

Net heat input to coil.......................... 70,650,000 Btu per hr
Desired radiant rate on outside area............ 15,000 Btu per sq ft-hr
Fuel, cracked gas, net H.V...................... 20,560 Btu per lb
Excess air, per cent............................ 30
Temperature of air leaving preheater............ 460°F
Estimated tube skin temperature................. 1000°F

Calculation of effective surface (aA_{cp}):

a (Fig. 18-3) = 0.88

$$A_{cp} = \frac{LNC}{12} = 40 \times 90 \times \frac{10}{12} = 3,000 \text{ [Eq. (18-3)]}$$

$$aA_{cp} = 0.88 \times 3,000 = 2,640$$

Mean length of radiant beam:

Ratio of dimensions $15\!\!/_{15} \times 30\!\!/_{15} \times 40\!\!/_{15} = 1\text{--}2\text{--}2.67$

L (Table 18-4) = $2\!/_3 \sqrt[3]{15 \times 30 \times 40}$ = 17.5 ft

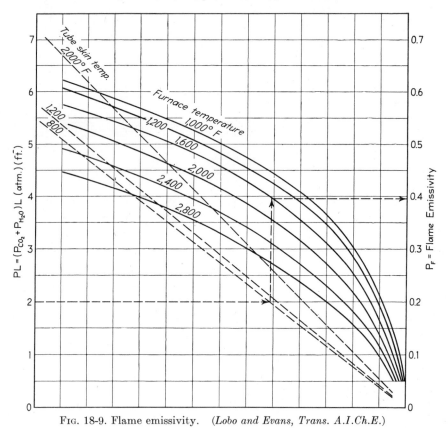

FIG. 18-9. Flame emissivity. (*Lobo and Evans, Trans. A.I.Ch.E.*)

Partial pressure of CO_2 *and* H_2O. Reading upward from 30 per cent excess air on Fig. 18-10, to the cracked gas fuel line, P is found to be 0.22.

Flame emissivity:

$$PL = 0.22 \times 17.5 = 3.84 \text{ (atm)(ft)}$$

Reading across from 3.84 on Fig. 18-9 to a tube skin temperature of 1000°F, then upward to an *assumed* flue gas temperature at the bridge wall (t_g) of 1800°F, and then to the right, P_F, the flame emissivity, is found to be 0.495.

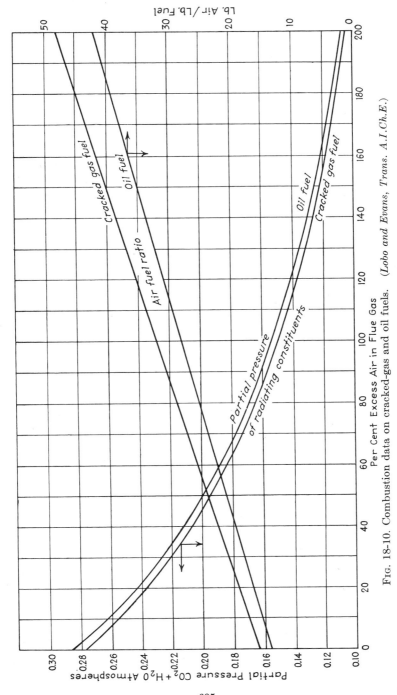

FIG. 18-10. Combustion data on cracked-gas and oil fuels. (*Lobo and Evans, Trans. A.I.Ch.E.*)

605

Effective refractory area (A_R):

$$A_R = A_T - aA_{cp} = 4{,}300 - 2{,}640 = 1{,}660 \text{ sq ft}$$

Exchange factor (ϕ):

$$\frac{A_R}{aA_{cp}} = \frac{1{,}660}{2{,}640} = 0.628$$

According to Fig. 18-11, for a P_F of 0.495, ϕ is 0.56.

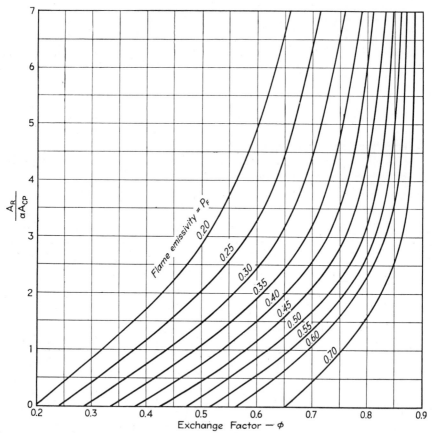

FIG. 18-11. Over-all exchange factor. (*Lobo and Evans, Trans. A.I.Ch.E.*)

Rate of heat absorption factor:

$$RQ = 70{,}650{,}000 = 15{,}000 \times 4{,}710$$

$$\frac{RQ}{aA_{cp}\phi} = \frac{70.65 \times 10^6}{2{,}640 \times 0.56} = 47{,}900 \text{ Btu per hr-}aA_{cp}\phi$$

Check gas temperature (t_g). Using 47,900 on the right scale of Fig. 18-6, the flue gas temperature is found to be 1850°F rather than 1800°F assumed. This is satisfactory.

Pseudo flame temperature (t'_F). Moving from 30 per cent excess air on the left of Fig. 18-7 to 1850°F and then upward to an air preheat of 400°F (460 − 60), the pseudo flame temperature is 3600°F.

Rate of heat liberation factor. Connect 3600°F with a tube skin temperature of 1000°F on Fig. 18-6. The heat liberation factor is 97,000.

$$\frac{0.98Q}{aA_{cp}\phi} = 97,000$$

$$Q = \frac{97,000 \times 2,640 \times 0.56}{0.98} = 146,000,000 \text{ Btu per hr}$$

$$R = \frac{70,650,000}{146,000,000} = 0.484$$

$$q = \frac{70,650,000}{4,710/3.14} = 47,200 \text{ Btu per sq ft projected area}$$

Note that the less exact method of Eq. (18-2) and Example 18-1, which applies to the same still (except with no air preheat) gives the following results: $R = 0.458$ and $q = 44,500$. Had the air preheat been accounted for, the agreement would have been even better.

Commercial Radiant Rates. Although the starting point in any pipe-still design is the radiant rate that can be attained with various feed materials or in various processes, the literature is almost silent on this important matter. A few rates are given by J. H. Rickerman,[12] by H. C. Schutt,[2] and the author has recorded[13] many rates, but it is necessary to infer rates from the rest of the literature.[14,15,16,17,18,19,20,21,22] This is easily understood because precise rates cannot be given because of the many factors that appear in commercial operation. Among these are the wide variety of stocks, the variation in the liquid velocity, and the different temperatures that are used for the different stocks. However, Table 18-5 presents rates that have been used in commercial plants. Doubtless many stills deviate from the recommendations in the table, and the rates cannot be maintained if local overheating occurs. The firing of powdered coke[22] does not seem to alter materially the radiant absorption rate.

Velocity is important primarily because of the pressure drop created by it. In fact, a high cold (60°F) velocity in most instances causes a low velocity in the vaporization zone because it tends to suppress vaporization at the outlet of the still.

[12] Heater Designs for the Petroleum Industry, *Trans. ASME*, **67**, 531 (1945).

[13] Nelson, W. L., Allowable Radiation Rates (First Edition of this book and *Oil Gas J.*, Sept. 21, 1946, p. 305.

[14] McCulloch, C. E., *Oil Gas J.*, May 10, 1934, p. 92.

[15] Leach, T. B., WPRA Meeting, Shreveport, La., Nov. 6, 1936.

[16] Jamison, J. A., *Proc. API*, **19** (III), 1938.

[17] Rickerman et al., *Oil Gas J.*, May 5, 1938, p. 50.

[18] Campbell, O. F., *Pet. Refiner*, January, 1950, p. 109.

[19] Born and Rose, *Oil Gas J.*, Mar. 9, 1953, p. 101.

[20] Naugle, J. M., *Pet. Processing*, December, 1949, p. 1346.

[21] Morrow, R., *Oil Gas J.*, Jan. 21, 1957, p. 88.

[22] Foster Wheeler Corp., Direct Fired Oil Heaters, *Heat Engineering*, November–December, 1956, p. 212.

TABLE 18-5. APPROXIMATE ALLOWABLE RADIATION RATES AND VELOCITIES[a]

Service	Btu per sq ft–hr		Velocity based on volume at 60°F, ft per sec
	On projected area	On outside area	
Simple heating (and topping):			
Reboiling at low temperatures (large vaporization)[12]......	63,000	20,000	
Heating (no vaporization)[12,13].	47,000	15,000	7–10
Natural gasoline plant services[19]................	34,600	11,000	
Heating to 750°F (cracking still with convection soaker)[12,13]................	25,000–50,000	8,000–16,000	5–8
Topping to 600°F[12,13−16,22]....	31,000–47,000	10,000–15,000	2–5
Topping to 800°F (over 60% vaporization)[12,13]..........	28,000	9,000	3–4
Heating to 950°F (catalytic cracking)[21]...............	23,000–56,000	7,000–18,000	1–2
Mild decomposition:			
Vacuum distillation (reduced crude oil)[12,13,20]...........	25,000–31,000	8,000–10,000	0.5–4
Delayed coking[12]............	31,000	10,000	7
Viscosity breaking[12,13]........	31,000–63,000	10,000–20,000	2–6
Cracking and thermal processes:			
Gas oil, reforming and polymerization[12]...............	37,000–50,000	12,000–16,000	5–8
Light oil coil and distilled stocks[15,16,17]...............	27,000–40,000	8,500–13,000	4.7–7.6
Heavy oil coil and residual stocks[14,15,17]...............	25,000–37,000	8,000–12,000	5.6–7.0
Hydrocarbon cracking for ethylene:			
Ethane (50–60% conversion)[2].	23,600–28,250[b]	7,500– 9,000[b]	23–26[c]
Propane (70–85% conversion)[2]	14,100–17,300[b]	4,500– 5,500[b]	26–28[c]
Butane (75–90% conversion)[2].	11,000–14,100[b]	3,500– 4,500[b]	28–32[c]
Naphtha[d] (50–58% conversion)[2]....................	11,000–14,100[b]	3,500– 4,500[b]	24–26[c]
Rerunning sensitive stocks:			
Pressure distillate (acid treated)[13,16]...............	25,000	8,000	3–4
Pressed distillate (light lube)[13].	20,000	6,400	5
Bright stock solution (heavy lube)[13]....................	17,000	5,400	7
Miscellaneous:			
Lube oil—phenol[18]..........	24,000–35,000	7,600–11,000	
Lube oil from reduced crude (vacuum)[13]...............	25,500	8,110	4

[a] Superior numbers in first column refer to same-numbered references in text.

[b] Rates near outlet of coil. In earlier sections of radiant coil, the rates need to be nearly double the values shown here.

[c] Mass velocity, lb per sq ft–sec.

[d] Weight per cent butane and lighter.

Distribution of Radiant Heat. A knowledge of the distribution of radiation in different parts of the radiant section is important. Usually only two rows of radiant tubes are used in the radiant section. If three tubes are used, the third row receives only about 12 per cent as much heat as the first row. Many stills have been built with only one row of tubes.

The first rows of tubes in the convection section absorb heat by radiation from the flame as well as heat by convection. The radiation into the convection section, if the tubes are not screened by superheater tubes or by brickwork, is about as follows: first row, 100 per cent; second row, 56 per cent; third row, 19 per cent; fourth row, 4 per cent; and fifth row, 1.5 per cent. Often the first row of convection tubes absorbs 24,000 Btu per sq ft of outside surface (17,000 Btu by radiation and 7,000 by convection). This is a rate far higher than those suggested in Table 18-5. For this reason the first rows of the convection section are often designed with the same diameter as the radiant tubes or, in other words, for a high oil velocity. Steam superheater tubes are often placed between the radiant and convection sections to protect the first convection tubes. In a superheater the high rate of absorption is desirable if the superheater is constructed of an alloy steel that can withstand high-temperature oxidation.

The rate of radiant absorption varies at different parts of the radiant section. In ordinary stills the exact distribution of radiation is not important; but for (1) heating sensitive stocks such as treated lubricating oils, (2) heating to very high temperatures as in cracking stills, and (3) heating two different stocks in separate coils in the same radiant section, the rate of heat absorption in the different parts of the furnace box becomes very important. Data on several stills have been reported that indicate radiation rates that varied by 400 per cent in different parts of the radiant section. Combustion space[23] is not of direct importance in pipestills.

The following method (Example 18-3) of estimating the distribution of radiant heat is not based on theoretical considerations, but it does give results that were dependable in all instances studied. Radiation proceeds in all directions from point sources within the flame. It proceeds in straight lines and either strikes a cold tube surface and is absorbed or strikes a refractory wall. Upon striking a wall, the radiation first heats the wall; but after the wall reaches a temperature higher than that of the tubes, the wall itself begins to radiate. At the high temperature existing in pipestill walls, the walls act as reflectors so that radiation falling upon the wall is reflected in such a way that the angle of reflection equals the angle of incidence. Each time the radiation is reflected, it becomes less intense, (1) owing to the heat lost through the walls by conduction and (2) because the intervening gas is heated. The intensity of reflected radia-

[23] Nelson, W. L., Combustion Space, and Formula for Boiler Combustion Space, *Oil Gas J.*, Nov. 23, 1946, p. 74, and Feb. 1, 1947, p. 55.

tion, with the heat liberated considered as unity, is somewhat as follows: initial radiation, 0.75; once reflected, 0.68; twice reflected, 0.61; and thrice reflected, 0.54.

Example 18-3. Distribution of Radiation in Radiant Section. A scale drawing of the inside of a commercial furnace is shown in Fig. 18-12. The distribution of radiation can be determined graphically by selecting a source of radiation in about the center of the flame and dividing the total radiation into equal parts. Thirty-five equal units or rays of radiation are used in this example. Only 9 rays are shown in Fig. 18-12 because if 35 are shown, such a maze of lines results that the drawing is not intelligible.

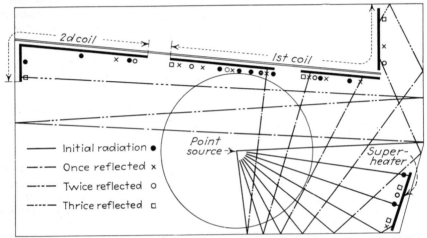

FIG. 18-12. Distribution of radiation in radiant section. Refer to Example 18-3.

The 35 lines or rays were completed as for the 9 shown in Fig. 18-12. Upon the first coil fall 9 rays of initial radiation; 8 rays of once-reflected radiation; 3 rays of twice-reflected radiation; and 3 of thrice-reflected radiation. The total radiation (comparative units only) that is absorbed by the first coil is

$$
\begin{aligned}
\text{Initial}\dots\dots\dots\dots\dots\dots & \ 9 \times 0.75 = \ 6.0 \\
\text{Once reflected}\dots\dots\dots\dots & \ 8 \times 0.68 = \ 5.44 \\
\text{Twice reflected}\dots\dots\dots\dots & \ 3 \times 0.61 = \ 1.83 \\
\text{Thrice reflected}\dots\dots\dots\dots & \ 3 \times 0.54 = \ 1.62 \\
\hline
\text{Total radiation to first coil}\dots\dots\dots & = 14.89
\end{aligned}
$$

There were 88 sq ft in the first coil so that the relative radiation per square foot is

$$
\frac{14.89}{88} = 0.1695
$$

The average relative rate per square foot for all of the radiant surface was 0.126 (see accompanying table), and the actual average absorption rate was 11,000 Btu per sq ft of projected area per hr. Hence the rate in the first coil is

$$
\frac{0.1695}{0.126} \times 11,000 = 14,800 \text{ Btu}
$$

The same computations for each of the three coils are shown in the following tabulation:

	Relative heat units absorbed by		
	First coil	Second coil	Super-heater
Initial radiation (No. rays × 0.75)...............	6	2.25	1.5
Once reflected (No. rays × 0.68).................	5.44	1.36	0.68
Twice reflected (No. rays × 0.61)................	1.83	0.61	0.61
Thrice reflected (No. rays × 0.54)...............	1.62	0	1.08
Total heat units for each coil..................	14.89	4.22	3.87
Surface in each coil (sq ft).....................	88.0	71.0	23.0
Relative absorption rate, heat units per sq ft.......	0.1695	0.0595	0.168

$$\text{Relative avg absorption rate} = \frac{14.89 + 4.22 + 3.78}{88 + 71 + 23} = 0.126$$

$$\text{Actual avg absorption rate} = 11,000 \text{ Btu per sq ft}$$

Actual rates:

$$\text{First coil}............ \quad 11,000 \times \frac{0.1695}{0.126} = 14,800$$

$$\text{Second coil}.......... \quad 11,000 \times \frac{0.0595}{0.126} = 5,100$$

$$\text{Superheater}......... \quad 11,000 \times \frac{0.168}{0.126} = 14,750$$

The accuracy of the method can be improved by repeating the foregoing computations for several planes and for several point sources of radiation.

CONVECTION

The rate of heat absorption in the convection section can be approached with more assurance than for the radiant section. The only troublesome points are (1) the combination of radiation and convection heating that occurs through the first rows of the convection section and (2) the radiation from the hot gas and the walls of the convection section. The first difficulty is often handled by counting these tubes twice; i.e., the first two rows are counted as radiant tubes, and they are also counted as convection tubes. The second difficulty is discussed later.

The empirical equation by Monrad[24] is the only comprehensive formulation of convection transfer rates. For pipestills he suggests

$$h_c = \frac{1.6G^{0.667}T^{0.3}}{D^{0.33}} \tag{18-7}$$

[24] Heat Transmission in Convection Sections of Pipestills, *Ind. Eng. Chem.*, **24**, 505 (1932).

where h_c = pure convection film-transfer rate for flue gas flowing at right angles to staggered tubes (no radiation)

G = mass velocity of gas at minimum cross section, lb per sec per sq ft

T = average gas temperature, °F abs

D = outside tube diameter, in.

Equation (18-7) applies to any conventional arrangement of the convection section. However, the coefficient h_c is the pure convection coefficient and it does not include radiation from the flame, from the hot gas, or from the walls. Monrad[24] has made a study of these factors. The first of these is designated as h_{rg} or the coefficient of heat transfer from the gas by radiation. As an approximation, the value of the gas radiation coefficient may be found by the following relation:

$$h_{rg} = 0.0025t - 0.5$$

where t is the average temperature in degrees Fahrenheit of the flue gas. More exact methods of computing this factor are given in the aforementioned reference.[24]

The second factor, the wall effect, usually ranges in magnitude between 6 and 15 per cent of the sum of the pure convection and the radiation coefficients.

$$\text{Per cent wall effect} = \frac{h_{rb} \times A_w \times 100}{(h_c + h_{rg} + h_{rb})A_t}$$

where h_{rb} = radiation coefficient from walls = $0.00688p(T/100)^3$

p = emissivity of wall surface, usually about 0.95

T = absolute temperature of tube, °R

h_c = pure convection coefficient [Eq. (18-7)]

h_{rg} = gas radiation coefficient

Subscripts w and t refer to the wall and tube respectively. The complete coefficient of heat transfer in the convection section may be computed from the preceding items as follows:

$$h = \left(\frac{100 + \text{per cent wall effect}}{100}\right) \times (h_c + h_{rg}) \qquad (18\text{-}8)$$

The area through which heat is transferred may be considered as the outside area of the tubes because the gas film coefficient controls. The gas velocity can seldom exceed 12 ft per sec in stills that are dependent on a stack for draft. A stack draft of 0.6 in. of water will cause a velocity of about 15 ft per sec, but in the now popular long-tube stills (Fig. 18-1d, e, i, j, k) the velocity ranges downward to 4 ft per sec. In recirculation stills the velocity may exceed 25 ft per sec.

Air preheaters are of many designs. Few data on the transfer rates in

TABLE 18-6. APPROXIMATE CONVECTION COEFFICIENTS

Velocity, ft per sec	Temperature, °F	Size of tube, o.d., in.				
		2	3	4	5	6
4	800	4.7	4.4	4.1	3.9	3.8
4	1100	5.3	5.0	4.7	4.6	4.6
4	1400	6.0	5.7	5.3	5.2	5.2
8	800	6.3	5.8	5.4	5.1	4.9
8	1100	6.8	6.3	6.0	5.8	5.6
8	1400	7.3	7.0	6.5	6.3	6.1
12	800	7.9	7.3	6.7	6.3	6.0
12	1100	8.3	7.7	7.2	6.9	6.6
12	1400	8.7	8.2	7.7	7.5	7.1

air preheaters are available, but the rates are low because two gas films are present and because little radiation occurs.

Pipestill Losses. The heat losses in pipestills, when based on the net heating value, consist mainly of two items: (1) the sensible heat content of the stack gases above 60°F and (2) the losses through the furnace walls, header boxes, roof, floor, etc. Pipestills are usually fired with 25 per cent or more excess air, and hence carbon monoxide is seldom reported in the flue gas, and no loss occurs by incomplete combustion of the fuel. No loss due to the heat contained in the cinder or combustible in the cinder is necessary unless coal is fired.

The brickwork of pipestills and boilers is not usually airtight. The following tabulation shows the flue-gas analysis at two points in a commercial still. Air leaked into the still in the radiant and convection sections

Flue gas	Radiant section	Breeching
Carbon dioxide..........	13.5	7.6
Oxygen...............	0.7	9.4
Carbon monoxide.......	0.3	0.0

and lowered the percentage of carbon dioxide. In this still, radiation occurred at a low percentage of excess air, but the stack loss corresponded to a high percentage of excess air.

The stack loss may be rapidly computed by referring to Figs. 14-2 and 14-3, but the method outlined in Example 14-7 should be used for exact computations. In making a detailed heat balance, the steam that is required to atomize the oil (page 426) is easily forgotten.

Actual heat losses (5.3 per cent) through the walls of one still are reported in the Second Edition of this book. For modern brickwork constructions that are in good condition, the loss from the radiant section is only 2 to 3 per cent and from the convection section about 1 per cent. With some panel or steel-encased designs, the total loss may not exceed 1 to 2 per cent.

PIPESTILL DESIGN

Designing a pipestill involves the computation (or selection) of a (1) flash-vaporization curve of the feedstock to determine the tower vaporizer temperature (Figs. 4-18 and 4-19); (2) sensible and latent heat duty[25] up to the vaporizer temperature, plus, in the case of cracking, the heat of decomposition; (3) radiant-absorption rate suitable for the operation or stock being handled (Table 18-5); (4) tube length and stack-gas temperature that are economically feasible for the type of still and feed temperature employed (Figs. 23-9 and 23-6); (5) radiant-section area and tube length [Eq. (18-2) or Fig. 18-4]; (6) bridgewall temperature (Fig. 14-2 or 14-3); and (7) convection-section area and tube length [Eq. (18-8) or Table 18-6]. The details of these operations can best be explained in an actual example (Example 18-4). Finally, if a precise design is advisable, the still can be redesigned by the Lobo-Evans method (Example 18-2); and if the pressure drop or rate of temperature rise must be accurately determined, an elaborate computation as on page 618 must be undertaken.

Example 18-4.   Design of a Pipestill.   Four thousand barrels per day of a 37 API crude oil similar to that of Fig. 4-4, available at 300°F from exchangers, is being processed for the materials (see Chap. 4) shown in Table 18-7.

Vaporizer Temperature.   A flash-vaporization curve (Figs. 4-18 and 4-19) is drawn. At atmospheric pressure a vaporizer temperature of 655°F is required to vaporize the 63 per cent of products, and for a tower pressure of 10 psig the vaporizer temperature becomes 695°F (Fig. 5-27). If steam were used in the tower it would reduce the vaporizer temperature [Eq. (15-8)].

Heat Duty.   The crude oil will be heated to 695°F.

$$48,900(695 - 300)0.71 \times 1.02 = 14,000,000 \text{ Btu per hr}$$

and each of the stocks (that are vaporized) will be vaporized at 695°F. This requires the total latent heat shown in the last column of Table 18-7. Thus, the total heat duty or heat absorbed is 15,454,000 Btu per hr.

In actuality, vaporization takes place throughout a range of temperature near the outlet of the still, but according to the law of conservation of energy, the heat duty as computed above is almost exactly the same as that computed by following the actual mechanism of heating and vaporization that occurs in the still.[25]

Heat Balance.   Dry cracked gas (No. 12 of Table 14-4) which has a net heating value of 1475 Btu per cu ft will be used, and 30 per cent of excess air can be used.

[25] Nelson, W. L., Pipe-still Duty, *Oil Gas J.*, Aug. 17, 1946, p. 117.

TABLE 18-7. MATERIALS FOR EXAMPLE 18-4

Material	Per cent	Gal per hr	API	Lb per gal	Lb	Mol wt	Moles per hr	Latent heat[a] at 695°F	Total latent heat, Btu per hr
Loss.............	1	.....	.....	....	245	35	7.0	0	0
87-octane gaso.....	12	840	64.5	6.01	5,050	90	56.0	0	0
3rd grade gaso.....	16	1,120	51.0	6.46	7,240	125	58.0	42	304,000
Kerosene.........	6	420	44.0	6.71	2,820	165	17.0	68	142,000
Diesel fuel........	16	1,120	37.3	6.98	7,820	217	36.0	73	571,000
Gas oil...........	12	840	31.5	7.23	6,070	320	19.0	72	437,000
Topped crude.....	37								
Crude oil.........	100	7,000	37.0	6.99	48,900				
Totals.........							193.0		1,454,000

[a] Read from paraffin base curves of Fig. 5-8.

According to Fig. 23-6, a stack temperature of 600°F will be economical. This corresponds to a stack loss of about 15 to 16 per cent (Fig. 14-3). Wall losses for a straight-up-type still (Fig. 18-1d) will be only about 4 per cent (2 per cent in the radiant and 2 per cent in the convection section). In the topping of crude oil, a radiant-absorption rate or q of 35,000 Btu per sq ft of projected area (Table 18-5) is safe, and a velocity of 3 ft per sec will not give a prohibitive pressure drop. According to Fig. 18-4, the percentage of the heat liberation that is absorbed in the radiant section is about 39.4, but since the gas fuel used here is different from the one of Fig. 18-4, an R of 41 will be used. Note that this applies only to radiant sections in which two rows of tubes are used, and for center-to-center spacings that are twice the tube diameter. The heat balance is

Heat absorbed: 15,454,000 Btu per hr
Heat developed (eff. = 100 − 15 − 4 = 81): 19,100,000 Btu per hr

	Per cent	Btu per hr
Radiant absorption..............	41	7,840,000
Radiant wall loss...............	2	380,000
Convection absorption...........	40	7,640,000
Convection wall loss............	2	380,000
Stack loss.....................	15	2,860,000

Heating Surface. According to curve 4 of Fig. 23-9, the approximate economical tube length for such a still is about 20 ft. A cold velocity of 3 ft per sec indicates a tube size of about 4.75 outside diameter. The amount of radiant surface and the number of tubes for an effective tube length of 19 ft are

Surface: $\dfrac{7,840,000}{35,000} = 224$ sq ft projected area

Tubes: $\dfrac{12}{4.75} \times \dfrac{224}{19} = 30$

As the gases enter the convection section they contain 100 − 41 − 2 per cent of the heat liberation, or 57 per cent. This corresponds to a temperature of about 1850°F (Fig. 14-3). Such temperatures are exactly correct according to heat balances; but, for some unknown reason, the temperatures recorded in stills are usually lower. The temperature of the oil leaving the convection section will be

$$300 + \frac{7,640,000}{48,900 \times 0.64 \times 1.02} = 540°F$$

and the logarithmic mean-temperature difference is

$$\frac{1,310 - 300}{\ln 1,310/300} = 684°F$$

The average flue-gas velocity in such a still is only about 4 ft per sec, and the average gas temperature is about 1225°F. Accordingly, the convection coefficient is about 4.8 (Table 18-6), and the surface required is

Surface:
$$\frac{7,640,000}{684 \times 4.8} = 2,325 \text{ sq ft outside area}$$

Tubes:
$$\frac{12}{4.75 \times 3.14} \times \frac{2,325}{19} = 99(98.5)$$

Considering the distribution of tubes between the radiant and convection sections, it would probably cost little more if more tubes were put in the radiant section, and this would be highly advisable because it would reduce the radiant-absorption rate to such low values that no danger of overheating would exist. In addition, the radiant section is so small that only one row of radiant tubes (rather than two) would allow a better arrangement of surface.

Pipestill Outlet Temperature. The outlet temperature of the still is usually higher than the vaporizer temperature because self-evaporation occurs as the oil flows through the transfer line. Also, if steam is present at the vaporizer, a sizable vaporization or flashing occurs at the end of the transfer line, which causes a further decrease in temperature. The situation and pressure drop through the transfer line can be analyzed with relative ease because the heat required for vaporization comes from sensible cooling of the stock flowing in the line. An explanation in words of the computations involved is of little value, and hence Example 18-5 is used to illustrate the principles involved.

Example 18-5. Approximate Pipestill Outlet Temperature. The quantities (pounds) shown in Table 18-7 of Example 18-4 are to dump from the pipestill into a fractionator at 10 psig pressure, but 57 moles of steam (1,026 lb) passes through the vaporizer per hour. The crude oil of Fig. 4-4 does not exactly fit the materials of Table 18-7, but it will be used here.

Sixty-three per cent can be vaporized at atmospheric pressure with no steam present at a vaporizer temperature of 645°F (Fig. 4-4). However, the effective pressure at 10 psig and in the presence of 57 moles of steam is [Eq. (15-8)]

$$(10 + 14.7) \frac{193}{(193 + 57)} = 19.1 \text{ psia}$$

According to Fig. 5-27, the temperature required to vaporize 63 per cent at 19.1 psia is 663°F. This was obtained by raising 645°F to 19.1 psia (Fig. 5-27).

Vaporization by Flashing. However, the pressure at the end of the transfer line, but before coming in contact with the steam, is 24.7 psia (10 psig), and vaporization, therefore, occurs as the material spews into the tower. The amount of vaporization can be computed by a trial-and-error solution.

If 3 per cent vaporization occurs the temperature drop will be about

$$\frac{0.03 \times 7,000 \times 7.18 \times 78}{48,900 \times 0.71} = 3.4°F$$

In this multiplication the 7,000 is the gallons per hour of stock, 7.18 is the pounds per gallon of the 3 per cent of material being vaporized (33 API), the 78 is its latent heat at about 664°F, and the 0.71 is an average specific heat of the stream of vapor and liquid.

This means that the temperature of the material leaving the transfer line is about (663 plus 3.4) or 666.4°F. If our assumption of 3 per cent vaporization is correct, the atmospheric flash temperature of 622°F at (63 − 3) or 60 per cent vaporized when raised to 24.7 psia will be 666.4°F. Our assumption is substantially correct because 622 raised to 24.7 psia (by Fig. 5-27) is about 666°F. A larger scale figure than Fig. 5-27 is necessary if it is to be read with sufficient accuracy for such problems as this.

Vaporization in Transfer Line. A direct way of solving for this vaporization is to adopt a percentage vaporized, determine the drop in temperature that must occur to supply the latent heat for such a vaporization, compute that pressure which must exist at the inlet of such a vaporization zone, and compute the length of the zone from the pressure drop as follows:

Consider a zone in which 10 per cent vaporization occurs. Thus, 50 per cent is in the vapor state at the inlet to the zone and 60 per cent at the outlet (or entrance to tower). Such a material has a gravity of about 34 API (Fig. 4-4) and a latent heat at about 671°F of 77.

$$0.10 \times 7,000 \times 7.12 \times 77 = 48,900 \times 0.72\Delta T$$
$$\Delta T = 10.9°F$$

The inlet temperature to the zone will be 666.4 + 10.9 = 677.3°F.

Raising 553°F (50 per cent vaporized) to 677.3°F by Fig. 5-27 indicates that the pressure at the inlet to the zone must be about 59 psia.

The pressure drop is also related to length [Eq. (13-1)]

$$\Delta P = \frac{0.323 f s u^2 L}{d}$$

For most mixed-phase systems the value of f is about 0.005, and if the inside diameter of the transfer line is 3.5 in.

$$\Delta P = \frac{0.323 \times 0.005 s u^2 L}{3.5} = \frac{s u^2 L}{2,170}$$

In this instance the volume of the liquid will be neglected, but at small percentages vaporized, it becomes an important part of the total volume. The average percentage vaporized (based on crude) is 55, the moles of vapor about 180 (see Table 18-7 or Fig. 4-4), and the average temperature and pressure 42 (41.8) psia and 672°F (671.8).

$$\text{Volume} \ldots \ldots \quad 180 \times 379 \times \frac{1,132}{520} \times \frac{14.7}{42} \times \frac{1}{3,600} = 14.45 \text{ cu ft per sec}$$

$$s = \frac{48,900}{14.45 \times 3,600} \times \frac{1}{62.4} = 0.0151$$

$$u = \frac{14.45 \times 144}{3.5^2 \times 0.785} = 218 \quad \text{and} \quad u^2 = 47,300$$

In addition, the pressure drop caused by the change in kinetic energy content of the stream of fluid [Eq. (13-5)] must be computed. The change in momentum from the entrance to the zone, where the velocity is 218 ft per sec, to the tower vaporizer where the velocity is substantially zero is

$$\Delta P = 0.00673su^2$$
$$= 0.00673 \times 0.0151 \times 47,300$$
$$= 4.8 \text{ psi}$$

Thus, the pressure drop that is available for friction loss is

$$\Delta P = 59 - 4.8 - 24.7 = 29.5$$
$$L = \frac{29.5 \times 2,170}{0.0151 \times 47,300} = 89.5 \text{ ft of equivalent length}$$

If the transfer-line length is greater than 89.5 ft additional zones of vaporization can be computed. For an 89.5-ft equivalent length transfer line the temperature at the outlet of the transfer line (inlet to the transfer line or inlet to our 10 per cent vaporization zone) will be 677°F, and about 50 per cent of the crude oil will have been vaporized in the pipestill.

Tabulations of transfer-line temperature drop, pressure drop, and percentage vaporized have been published[26] for the special case of pipestills discharging at substantially atmospheric pressure.

Pressure Drop in Pipestills. The application of flash-vaporization data to the problem of computing the vaporization that occurs within pipestill tubes is complicated by the constantly changing pressure throughout the entire length of pipestill tubing. However, vaporization occurs mainly throughout the final tubes of the still, because as soon as vaporization starts, the friction loss and the pressure become so high that vaporization tends to be suppressed. In fact a large part of the pressure drop through a pipestill often occurs in the transfer line from the still to the fractionating tower. To shorten this line does little good because the vaporization is simply pushed back into the still. Likewise a larger transfer line decreases the pressure at the outlet of the still so that more vaporization occurs in the tubes.

Pressure drops through stills can be computed in much the same manner as for transfer lines (Example 18-5) except that length affects not only the pressure drop but also the temperature (and indirectly vaporization) of the stock because heat flows through the walls of the tubes. Thus a trial-and-error computation is required for each zone of vaporization. The operations involve

1. Adoption of a zone in which the amount of vaporization is fixed.
2. Assumption of a length for the zone and computation of the amount of heat that enters the oil in this zone.
3. Computation similar to that illustrated in Example 18-5 to determine the length of the zone.

[26] Nelson, W. L., *Oil Gas J.*, Jan. 25, p. 285; Feb. 22, p. 171; and Mar. 8, 1947, p. 101.

4. If the computed length differs from the assumed length, the entire operation must be repeated.

Rickerman[11] suggests a modification of Eq. (13-1) for pipestill pressure-drop computations. It includes a correction for the kinetic energy of motion.

$$\Delta P = \frac{0.005185 f G^2 v L}{d} \left[\frac{1}{1 - (G^2 v / 4{,}637 P)} \right] \qquad (18\text{-}9)$$

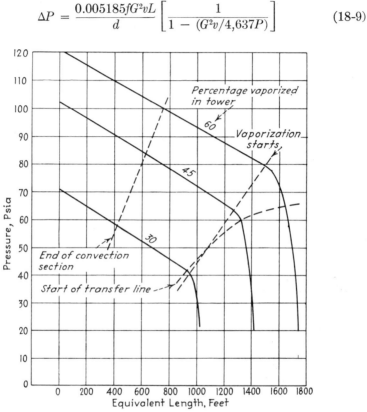

FIG. 18-13. Pressure drop in small-tube-diameter pipestills dumping into atmospheric-pressure towers (2,000 bbl per day, distillation slope 4.0, tubes 2 in. inside diameter). Refer to Fig. 18-14. (*Oil Gas J.*)

in which the symbols are the same as in Eq. (13-1), page 395, and v is specific volume, cu ft per lb.

Figures 18-13 and 18-14 show the relationship among such variables as equivalent length, percentage vaporized at tower (or still outlet), pressure drop, temperature, and percentage vaporized in one still design. There are so many variables that not many such studies[27] have been made. The

[27] Nelson, W. L., *Oil Gas J.*, Aug. 31, 1946, p. 91; July 5, 1947, p. 93; and Nov. 29, 1947, p. 89.

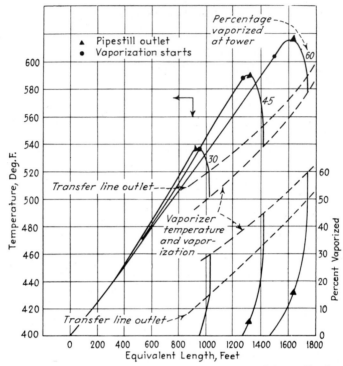

FIG. 18-14. Temperature gradient and percentage vaporized in small-tube-diameter pipestills dumping into atmospheric-pressure towers. Refer to Fig. 18-13. (*Oil Gas J.*)

still and stock considered in Figs. 18-13 and 18-14 were

Slope of distillation curve of feedstock.................	4°F/per cent
Charge stock (mixed-base)...........................	37 API
Mid boiling point..............................	600°F
Charge rate.......................................	2,000 bbl per day
Cold velocity.....................................	4.2 ft per sec
Tube diameter, inside..............................	2.0 in.
Tube length.......................................	15 ft
Return bend, equivalent length.....................	15 ft
Transfer line, equivalent length....................	100 ft
Inlet temperature.................................	400°F
Tower pressure....................................	6 psig
Radiant-absorption rate, per sq ft projected area........	25,000 Btu per hr
Still efficiency...................................	77 per cent

The method outlined here is obviously gross. Nevertheless, the method works reasonably well (see Table 18-8), and the method or modifications of it are used by the major oil companies.

TABLE 18-8. COMPUTED PIPESTILL PRESSURE DROPS

Material	Pressure drop, psi	
	Actual	Computed
Crude oil	198	192
Reduced crude oil	124	115
Bright-stock solution	197	209
Treated cylinder stock solution	85	103
Cracking still	605	563
Cracking still	394	362
Cracking still	238	275
Fat absorption oil	31	33

Mathematical methods[28,29,30] are either exceedingly complicated, or assumptions must be made which cast doubt on the results. However, F. L. Maker[31] has developed a graphical integration method which appears to greatly shorten the tedious trial-and-error method suggested herein.

Small-diameter tubes (a high cold or 60-degree velocity) tend to suppress vaporization (as see Figs. 18-13 and 18-14) except in tubes near the outlet, and thus coking or overheating may tend to occur in the tubes situated back in the still where no vaporization has occurred. Conversely, large-diameter tubes (low cold velocity) tend to permit vaporization to penetrate back into the still giving a high velocity in all of the tubes past the point of initial vaporization. Thus, a still with large tubes may be safer from the standpoint of coking or overheating than a still that contains small tubes, and higher rates of radiant absorption can be used with more confidence.

Vaporization in Pipestills. The amount of vaporization that occurs in a still is intimately related to many processing operations. If the liquid contains high-boiling parts that are sensitive to heat it may be advisable to suppress vaporization. Vaporization concentrates the reactive material into the liquid phase and if this phase becomes very small it moves through the coil very slowly. In the extreme, it sticks to the walls and undergoes chemical reactions which may be completed to the formation of solids such as coke.

When designing a coil for a reaction, computations can be made with more accuracy if the material is totally vaporized or totally liquid. Thus, it is sometimes advisable to suppress vaporization whereas in other situations everything possible is done to encourage vaporization. It is

[28] Dittus and Hildebrand, *Trans. ASME*, p. 185, April, 1942.

[29] Baars, G., *J. Inst. Pet. Tech.*, 1948, p. 417.

[30] Harbert, W. D., *Pet. Refiner*, September, 1947, p. 9.

[31] Flashflow Pressure Drop in Heaters, *Pet. Refiner*, November, 1955, p. 140.

often impossible to maintain a single phase, and in such situations, stratification can be avoided in some degree by the use of a high pressure. At pressures approaching or above the critical pressure, the density of the vapor tends to approach that of the hot low-density liquid. Thus, the larger of the two phases tends to contain enough kinetic energy of motion to move the other phase along at nearly the same velocity as that of the main stream. This is the primary reason for the use of a back pressure in conventional thermal cracking or reforming processes.

Tube Design. The temperature difference that always exists when heat is delivered through a series of resistances is of great importance in the selection of still tubes. Nearly all the radiation that falls upon a tube must be absorbed, regardless of the transfer rate on the inside of the tube. Thus the temperature in the film and tube is higher than in the fluid.

As coke is deposited in the oil film, the temperature in the tube rises, and it continues to rise as coke is deposited until finally the tube attains the temperature of the furnace or it bursts. For normal thicknesses of coke, the amount of heat absorption is not decreased greatly. Partridge and White[32] find that a normal thickness of boiler scale does not decrease the rate of radiant-heat absorption by more than about 3 per cent. In general, coke deposits act in the same manner.

Pipestill tubes often receive radiation at the rate of about 5500 Btu per sq ft per hr of outside surface or a rate of about 9500 Btu per sq ft of inside surface, and the oil film-transfer rate may be 600 Btu per sq ft per hr per deg of temperature difference. Obviously the temperature difference through the oil film, if the tube is clean, is only

$$\frac{9,500}{600} = 15.8°F$$

If the oil temperature is 900°, the temperature at the inside of the wall is (900 + 15.8) or 915.8°F. If the wall is ½ in. thick, the temperature drop in the wall will be

$$\text{Deg drop in wall} = \frac{9,500}{25} \times \frac{0.5}{12} = 15.8°F$$

and the outside of the metal tube is at (900 + 15.8 + 15.8), or 931.6°F (Fig. 18-15).

If a ⅛-in. coke deposit having a conductivity of 0.5 is produced, the tube temperature is increased by

$$\frac{9,500}{0.5} \times \frac{0.125}{12} = 198°F$$

and the outside tube temperature is (Fig. 18-15)

$$900 + 15.8 + 198 + 15.8 = 1129.6°F$$

[32] The Effect of Boiler Scale, *Ind. Eng. Chem.*, **21**, 839 (1929).

A temperature of 1130°F (red heat) is too high for a carbon steel tube because the strength drops to about 1,000 psi (creep strength) and the tube will fail. However, if the pressure is very low so that the coke can be deposited to thicknesses greater than ⅛ in., the tube wall temperature continues to rise with increase in coke thickness and eventually the tube will attain the temperature of the furnace.

The rate of coke deposition is not greatly dependent on the amount of coke already deposited, but the rate can be retarded by increasing the velocity and therefore the transfer rate through the oil film. The rate of

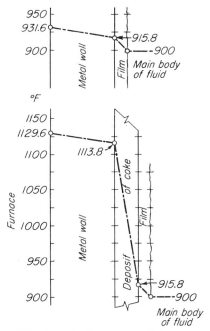

Fig. 18-15. Effect of coke on wall temperature.

depositing coke is directly dependent on the thickness of the oil film because the thicker the film the greater the volume of oil (in the film) that is exposed to the high temperature. Figure 18-16 shows the relative rate of coking for different film-transfer rates and for common rates of total heat absorption. They are based on a rate of unity for a transfer rate of 300 and an absorption rate of 10,000. These conditions are commonly found in cracking plants. The data are only approximate because the velocity and the film-transfer rate cannot be accurately computed.

Figure 18-16 clearly shows why a hot velocity exceeding 13 ft per sec is now commonly used in cracking plants. A higher velocity greatly increases the pressure drop and aids little in decreasing the formation of

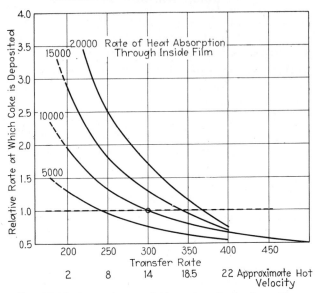

Fig. 18-16. Approximate relative rates of coke formation.

coke.   Tube-wall temperatures have been used as a means of controlling cracking-plant operations.[33]

Minimum tube thicknesses may be computed from[34]

$$t = \frac{RP}{1.2S}$$

where t = wall thickness, in.

    R = external radius, in.

    P = internal pressure, psig

    S = allowable metal stress, psi

The allowable stress (creep strength) was discussed in Chap. 9 (Table 9-5). Thinning by corrosion and oxidation is so vital that strength, as computed above, means little.   Allowances for thinning usually range from 0.1 to 0.25 in. (Chap. 9), but if corrosion is severe special alloy steels must be employed (Chap. 9, page 278).   The stresses in thick-wall cylinders under conditions of creep and while heat is being transferred have been studied.[35,36]   The kinds of alloys used for tube supports are also discussed in Chap. 9.

[33] Nelson, W. L., Coking of Tubes, *Oil Gas J.*, Apr. 19, 1947, p. 130.

[34] Harrington, Northrup, and Rhys, Cracking Coil Tubes at War, *Oil Gas J.*, Nov. 11, 1943, p. 161.

[35] Bailey, R. W., The Utilization of Creep-stress Data . . . , *Proc. Inst. Mech. Engrs.* (*London*), 1935.

[36] Rhys, C. O., Application of Bailey's Theory of Tube Stress Calculations, *Proc. API Refining Division*, 1938, p. 102.

Flue-gas Recirculation Stills. The important advantages of the recirculation still are as follows: (1) The rate of radiant absorption can be controlled by adjusting the quantity of flue gas that is recirculated, and (2) a low rate of radiant absorption can be obtained without building an excessively large radiant section. If the duty of an ordinary still is increased to above its rated capacity, the rate of absorption in the radiant section increases greatly and all out of proportion to the increase in duty. In the recirculation still the rate of absorption can be kept low by increasing the circulation of flue gas. In both types of stills the efficiency may decrease slightly, but the efficiency of pipestill heaters is not of major importance to the refiner. The most real concern of the refiner is to avoid deposits of coke with resulting costly shutdowns and to avoid discoloration of finished stocks by localized overheating. The absorption rate can be regulated in ordinary stills by using different quantities of excess air, but a great loss in the efficiency occurs if the absorption rate is lowered by even a few thousand Btu.

In general, recirculation stills require less surface than simple stills of the same efficiency.[37] However, the saving in the cost of surface must pay for the recirculation equipment, the gastight construction of the still, and the increased operating cost. Thus the initial cost is usually greater for the recirculating still, as well as the operating cost, so that the adoption of a recirculating still rests entirely with the advantage that it affords as a means of controlling the rate of radiant-heat absorption. In the past the design of pipestills for low radiant-absorption rates was not well understood and the recirculation still was widely used. Today the industry has reverted to the use of simple radiant-type stills that are designed for a specific service.

Shellstills and Heated Chambers. The heating of oil in shells or chambers is limited by the amount of heat that can be conducted from the heated surface by means of the boiling oil. In commercial stills the maximum transfer rate is about 6 Btu per sq ft per °F temperature difference per hr, and most stills operate at a transfer rate of about 4. However, if forced circulation is used or internal flues, the rate of transfer may be increased to as much as 12. The temperature difference is the difference between the oil temperature and the gas temperature. Thus the total heat transmission per square foot per hour amounts to about 4000 Btu for an oil at 400°F to as low as 2000 Btu for an oil at 800°F. Shellstills range in capacity from 215 to 2,700 bbl per day and in diameter from 8 to 15 ft.[38]

[37] Nelson, W. L., Modern Pipestill Heater Design, Recirculation, *Pet. Engr.*, June, 1933, p. 23.

[38] Nelson, W. L., Shell-still Heaters, *Oil Gas J.*, July 27, 1946, p. 213.

CHAPTER 19

THERMAL CRACKING AND
DECOMPOSITION PROCESSES

Thermal decomposition or cracking was called to our attention in 1871 by Silliman,[1] and it was practiced commercially as the Burton process during 1910–1920. Modern cracking processes continue to occupy an important position. Catalytic processes are somewhat replacing the older thermal process, but thermal cracking along with topping will continue to be a basic refinery operation. Coking and the viscosity breaking of heavy residues is especially important. Older processes such as the Burton, Fleming, Jenkins, Cross, Gyro, Dubbs, and Holmes Manley are described in First and Second Editions of this book as well as in "Motor Fuels" by E. H. Leslie,[2] and "American Petroleum Refining" by H. S. Bell.[3]

Mechanism of Cracking. Cracking is a phenomenon by which large oil molecules are thermally decomposed into smaller lower-boiling molecules; at the same time certain of these molecules, which are reactive, combine with one another to give even larger molecules than those in the original stock. The more stable molecules leave the system as cracked gasoline, and the reactive ones polymerize, forming cracked fuel oil and even coke. Although gasoline is the primary final product from cracking plants, all the oils having boiling ranges intermediate between fuel oil and gasoline are also produced. These intermediate materials, called "recycle stock," can be kept in the cracking system until they are decomposed, by recycling them in a continuous system or by operating a batch system under a high pressure. The production of intermediate stocks is illustrated by the following general chemical reactions:

Charge stock. . . . . $C_7H_{15} \cdot C_{15}H_{30} \cdot C_7H_{15}$
$\downarrow$ *heavy gas oil*

Cracked stock. . . . . $C_7H_{16} + C_{14}H_{28}:CH_2 + C_6H_{12}:CH_2$
$\downarrow$ *gasoline* + *recycle stock* + *gasoline(antiknock)*

More cracking. . . . .
$\quad$ $C_2H_6 + (C_4H_8:CH_2 + C_8H_{18} + C_6H_{12}:CH_2) + CH_2:CH \cdot CH:CH \cdot CH_3 + C_2H_4$
$\downarrow$ *gas* +   *gasoline*   +   *gum-forming materials*   + *gas*

Polymerization. . . . . $C_2H_6 + (C_4H_8:CH_2 + C_8H_{18}) + C_{12}H_{22} + C_2H_4$
$\quad$ *gas* +   *gasoline*   + *tar or recycle* + *gas*

---

[1] *J. Am. Chem. Soc.*, **2**, 18 (1871–1872).

[2] Reinhold Publishing Corporation, New York, 1923.

[3] 2d ed., D. Van Nostrand Company, Inc., Princeton, N.J., 1930.

Although these exact reactions probably do not take place, they are representative of the over-all reaction that occurs during cracking.

Thus two general types of reactions take place: (1) primary reactions in which decomposition of large molecules into small molecules takes place and (2) secondary reactions by which active products polymerize to form heavy tarry materials. At the same time the products of polymerization may be again decomposed into smaller molecules. The nature of the primary reactions may be illustrated by the experimental work of Hurd and Spence[4] on the decomposition of n-butane at 600°C (1112°F).

$$CH_3 \cdot CH_2 \cdot CH_2 \cdot CH_3 \rightarrow CH_4 + CH_3 \cdot CH : CH_2$$
and $$CH_3 \cdot CH_2 \cdot CH_2 \cdot CH_3 \rightarrow CH_3 \cdot CH_3 + CH_2 : CH_2$$

"At 600 degrees the first of these appears to proceed to the extent of about 55 per cent and the second to 40 per cent. Dehydrogenation reactions into butene or butadiene appear to represent less than 5 per cent of the total." The dehydrogenation reactions referred to are

$$CH_3 \cdot CH_2 \cdot CH_2 \cdot CH_3 \rightarrow H_2 + CH_3 \cdot CH_2 \cdot CH : CH_2$$
and $$CH_3 \cdot CH_2 \cdot CH_2 \cdot CH_3 \rightarrow 2H_2 + CH_2 : CH \cdot CH : CH_2$$

Their work also indicates that the tendency to dehydrogenate, leaving an olefin with the same number of carbon atoms as the original paraffin hydrocarbon, rapidly diminishes as the series is ascended. Thus the production of large amounts of hydrogen by cracking gas-oil stocks should not be expected.

The olefin hydrocarbons are not usually found in raw petroleum stocks, and hence the decomposition of olefins should properly be considered as a secondary decomposition reaction. Both hydrogenation and dehydrogenation may occur during the decomposition of olefins. Diolefins, paraffins, polymers, new olefins, hydrogen, and probably many other materials are produced. As an example of diolefin and paraffin formation, pentene-1 reacts thus:

$$CH_2 : CH \cdot CH_2 \cdot CH_2 \cdot CH_3 \rightarrow CH_4 + CH_2 : CH \cdot CH : CH_2$$
and $$CH_2 : CH \cdot CH_2 \cdot CH_2 \cdot CH_3 + H_2 \rightarrow CH_4 + CH_3 \cdot CH_2 \cdot CH : CH_2$$

The secondary reactions by which polymers are formed may be illustrated thus:
$$CH_2 : CH_2 + CH_2 : CH_2 \rightarrow CH_3 \cdot CH_2 \cdot CH : CH_2 \text{ (dimer)}$$
$$CH_3 \cdot CH_2 \cdot CH : CH_2 + CH_2 : CH_2 \rightarrow CH_3 \cdot CH_2 \cdot CH_2 \cdot CH_2 \cdot CH : CH_2 \text{ (trimer)}$$
or $$RCH : CH_2 + R'CH : CH_2 \rightarrow \text{tars, oils, etc. (polymers)}$$

Frolich and Fulton[5] conclude that the paraffin hydrocarbons are least

[4] J. Am. Chem. Soc., **51**, 3353 (1929).

[5] The Theory of Cracking, "Science of Petroleum," vol. III, p. 2104, Oxford University Press, New York, 1938.

stable and that others follow in the order olefins, diolefins, naphthenes (six carbon ring), naphthenes (five carbon ring), and aromatics. This applies to cracking temperatures of 750 to 1100°F and to compounds of the same molecular weight. At higher temperatures the diolefins become more stable than the naphthenes, and hence the diolefins and their condensation products can be produced at high temperatures.[6]

Properties of Cracked Materials.   The properties of the products that are produced by cracking depend greatly upon the extent of cracking that is practiced.   Sachanen and Tilicheyev[7] have studied the mechanism of cracking by producing recycle stocks that had been cracked once, twice, and several times.   In each cracking test the oil was cracked at 450°C. The fraction boiling between 200 and 350°C was separated by distillation and subjected to another cracking operation at 450°C.   The extent of cracking was not exactly the same for each recycle oil, but the qualitative comparison (Table 19-1) is useful.   Note the 30.6 API 392°F gasoline that was produced from the sixth recycle stock.

The most useful means of estimating the physical properties of cracked materials is the UOP Characterization Factor (pages 81 to 85, Fig. 5-9, and Table 4-2).   In most cases, Characterization Factors are somewhat as follows:

Cracked gasoline (Mid Continent charge)	11.7–12.0
Cracked gasoline (general)	11.5–12.0
Pipestill feed (charge and recycle)	10.5–11.5
Recycle stocks (general)	10.0–11.0
Recycle stocks (light)	10.5–11.0
Recycle stocks (heavy)	10.0–10.5
Cracked gas oil (paraffin charge)	11.6–11.9
Cracked gas oil (naphthenic charge)	11.0–11.3
Residuum (3–12 API)	10.5–11.0
Residuum (under 3 API)	9.5–10.5
Distillates from residuum (12–20 API)	10.3–10.7
Distillates from residuum (2–9 API)	9.9–10.3

In general, the Characterization Factors of cracked materials are lower than those of the parent feed.   Thus coker gas oils normally have factors 0.1 to 0.2 units lower than those of the parent feed,[7a] but when coking most vigorously (much recycling) the factors may be lower by 0.4 to 0.5 units.   Scant information indicates about the same relationship for viscosity-breaker gas oils.

[6] Frolich, Simard, and White, *Ind. Eng. Chem.*, **22,** 240 (1930).

[7] *Oil Gas J.*, Dec. 19, 1929, p. 48.

[7a] Nelson, W. L., Characterization Factor of Coker Gas Oils, *Oil Gas J.*, April 8, 1957, p. 127.

Sydnor and Patterson[8] have studied a Mid Continent gas oil and the cycle oils produced from it in a manner similar to that used by Tilicheyev.[7] The chemical composition of cracked and other gasolines is indicated in Fig. 2-3. Although the residues of cracking are frequently considered as being highly condensed aromatic structures, they must also be highly unsaturated[9] because they exhibit lower Characterization Factors than those of aromatics. However, nearly pure aromatic residue products are produced[10] when cracking saturated gaseous hydrocarbons at very

TABLE 19-1. CRACKING TESTS OF EMBA (RUSSIAN) GAS OIL

No. of opera- tion	Time, min at 450°C	Yield per cent by weight		API gravities			Approximate Characterization Factor	
		Below 200°C (392°F)	Above 350°C (672°F)	Cracking stock and recycle oils	Below 392°F	Above 672°F	Recycle oils	Gaso- lines
1	42	28.7	10.5	30.8[a]	58.2	10.6	11.4[a]	11.9
2	52	21.3	8.6	28.2	52.5	1.05[b]	11.2	11.6
3	75	16.3	7.9	23.8	46.0	1.116[b]	10.9	11.2
4	101	12.1	10.3	19.2	38.4	1.177[b]	10.5	10.8
5	101	3.9	12.4	15.4	37.1	1.157[b]	10.3	10.6
6	160	8.0	19.0	14.5	30.6	1.243[b]	10.2	10.3

[a] Emba gas oil (uncracked).
[b] Specific gravity.

high temperatures. The residue consists almost totally of such condensed aromatic and fluorene structures as phenanthrene (3 rings); pyrene, tryphenylene, 1:2 benzanthracene and chrysene (4 rings); fluoranthene, 1:2 and 2:3 benzfluorene; and naphtho anthracene, picene, and 1:12 benzpyrene. Several of these compounds tend to produce cancer when applied to living animal cells. Likewise, the lighter liquid products of ethane or propane cracking consist almost totally of (mono-cyclic) aromatics.

Cracked gasolines have higher octane numbers than straight-run gasolines from the same parent crude oil (Tables 4-1 and 4-15). The Research

[8] Ind. Eng. Chem., 22, 1237 (1930).

[9] Nelson, W. L., High-boiling Hydrocarbon Analysis, Oil Gas J., July 27, 1953, p. 369.

[10] Borrows et al., Composition . . . Polycyclic Aromatics . . . , Proc. Third World Pet. Congr., sec. V, The Hague, 1951.

method octane number usually ranges from 72 to 82, but from naphthenic charge stocks, such as some from the Gulf Coast, California, the Far East, and Venezuela, the octane number may exceed 86. The corresponding Motor method octane numbers can be estimated from Table 3-3. By high-temperature (1080 to 1250°F) low-pressure vapor phase cracking, octane numbers of 95 or higher (Research) are obtained. The effect of tetraethyllead on octane number can be estimated from Table 3-12, and the behavior of cracked gasoline in blends from Fig. 4-46. The effect of gasoline boiling range on octane number is indicated in Tables 4-16 and 4-17, and the effect of time of cracking in Table 19-13.

TABLE 19-2. APPROXIMATE MOTOR METHOD OCTANE NUMBERS OF REFORMED GASOLINES FROM STRAIGHT-RUN NAPHTHAS[a]

Yield,[a] per cent	Octane number of reformed gasoline for charge stocks of the following octane numbers				
	35	40	45	50	55
60	72.5	73.5	75	77	
75	69	70.5	72	73	75
80	68	69.5	70	71.5	73
85	67	68	69	70	72
90	65	66.5	67	68.5	70
95	....	....	...	66	67.5

[a] Polyforming yields are about 5 per cent larger (Offutt et al., *Pet. Refiner*, November, 1946, pp. 120 and 129).

The octane number of a cracked gasoline can be estimated from the ASTM distillation and the API gravity,[11] but no truly satisfactory means of estimating octane numbers from physical properties has been developed.

In studying the reforming of straight-run naphtha, LeRoi and Ferguson[12] find that the smaller the yield of gasoline and the greater the loss by producing gas the higher the octane number. The relationship between yield and octane number (accuracy ± 4 units) of gasolines produced by thermal reforming of straight-run stocks in a once-through operation is indicated[13] in Table 19-2. Recycling or the reforming of cracked distillates is not very successful because the losses are two or three times

[11] Cox, R. B., Gasoline Octane Rating, *Ref. Nat. Gaso. Mfr.*, Feb. 10, 1940, p. 31; also p. 296 of the Second Edition of this book.

[12] Developments in Naphtha Reforming Practice . . . , 3d Midyear Meeting, API, Tulsa, Okla., May, 1933.

[13] Nelson, W. L., Octane Number of Reformed Naphthas, *Oil Gas J.*, Dec. 13, 1947, p. 118.

larger than when handling straight-run stocks by a once-through operation. Reforming to the extent of producing 90 to 95 per cent yields may be profitable, but greater degrees of reforming probably are not useful unless olefinic gases are desired. Higher yields of a given octane-number product are obtained at higher pressures. An increase of 10 per cent in yield is obtained when the pressure is increased from 250 to 800 psi.[12]

Albright[14] shows that an increase in temperature increases the octane number of the gasoline, if other conditions are kept the same. The Motor method octane number was increased from 69 to 72 by increasing the temperature in a commercial unit from 997 to 1010°F. Turner and LeRoi[15] find that the octane number of reformed naphtha can be computed as a function of the equivalent time at 900°F (see page 663).

Polyforming is a modification of the thermal reforming process which involves the recycling of propane and butane gases.[16] Although the process requires the use of a 1,000 to 1,500 psig pressure on the reaction coil,[17,18] it produces yields about 5 per cent larger (a nomographic chart[17]) than plain reforming (see Table 19-2).

The ever increasing demand for higher octane numbers has led to the thermal reforming of already catalytically reformed gasoline.[19] When reforming 84 to 89 Research octane catalytic reformates, yields of 75 to 93 per cent of 93 to 100 octane finished gasoline are produced.

Sulfur in Products. The distribution of sulfur in cracked products is indicated in Figs. 4-35 and 4-36, Table 4-11 (coke), and on page 130. Typical sulfur balances are indicated[20] in Table 19-3. Most generally, the sulfur compounds in Venezuelan, Californian, and Mexican stocks appear to be most stable, whereas they are least stable in cracking stocks from the Middle East and from the Mid Continent (Oklahoma, Illinois, Kansas, North Texas, Pennsylvania, Texas, and Turner Valley, Canada).

Cracked distillates or diesel fuels have lower pour points (Tables 4-23 and 4-24) than straight-run or catalytically cracked distillates. The

[14] Influence of Temperature in Reforming Naphtha, *Ref. Nat. Gaso. Mfr.*, January, 1933, p. 2.

[15] Octane-number Improvement in Naphtha Reforming, *Ind. Eng. Chem.*, **27**, 1347 (1935).

[16] Ostergaard and Smoley, . . . High Gasoline Yield by Polyform Process, *Oil Gas J.*, Sept. 12, 1940, p. 52.

[17] Offutt et al., 2 articles, Naphtha Polyforming and Naptha Polyform..ng with Outside Gas, *Pet. Refiner*, November, 1946, pp. 120 and 129.

[18] Hirsch, Ostergaard, and Offutt, . . . Operating Variables in the Polyform Process, *Pet. Refiner*, November, 1946, p. 136.

[19] Heinemann et al., High Octanes from "Iso-Plus" via the Thermal Reforming Route, *Pet. Processing*, October, 1955, p. 1570.

[20] Nelson, Thery, and Cordero, *Proc. Fourth World Pet. Congr.*, sec. V, Rome, 1955.

Diesel Indexes of thermally cracked distillates are so low that scarcely any information is available in the literature.

Heat of Decomposition.   Theoretical methods of computing the heat of decomposition are more exact than most experimental determinations, but precise physical data must be employed.   Computations indicate

TABLE 19-3. SULFUR BALANCES WHEN THERMALLY CRACKING TYPICAL STOCKS

Stock	West Texas		Venezuela		Middle East		Mid Continent	
	Percentage of charge sulfur that appears in each product for charge stocks that contain these percentages of sulfur							
	1.0	3.0	0.8	2.4	1.5	4.5	0.5	1.5
32° API gas-oil feeds and 6° API fuel oils (severe cracking):								
Gasoline............	13.6	8.0	8.1	7.9	4.0	3.8	6.6	5.4
Fuel oil............	46.6	33.0	43.7	43.8	39.0	38.9	20.4	20.4
Gas................	39.8	59.0	48.2	48.3	57.0	57.3	73.0	74.2
26° API gas-oil feeds and 5° API fuel oils:								
Gasoline............	11.8	7.0	7.1	6.9	3.4	3.4	5.6	4.7
Fuel oil............	60.9	43.2	57.0	57.0	50.6	50.6	26.6	26.7
Gas................	27.3	49.8	35.9	36.1	46.0	46.0	67.8	68.6
26° API reduced crude feeds and 8° API fuel oils:								
Gasoline............	13.6	6.7	6.8	6.6	3.3	3.2	5.4	4.5
Fuel oil............	66.6	47.3	62.5	62.5	55.5	55.5	29.2	29.2
Gas................	19.8	46.0	30.8	30.9	41.2	41.3	65.4	66.3
20° API reduced crude feeds and 10° API fuel oils (mild cracking):								
Gasoline............	10.0	5.8	4.7	4.6	2.3	2.3	3.8	3.2
Fuel oil............	90.5	64.0	90.6	90.9	80.6	80.6	42.5	42.3
Gas................	....	30.2	4.6	4.5	17.1	17.1	53.7	54.5

clearly that if large amounts of gas are produced, the heat of decomposition is relatively high, and if a process could be operated so that no gas was produced, the cracking reaction would generate rather than require the addition of heat.   The methods also show that the heat of decomposition for heavy fuel oils is higher than for gas-oil or naphtha stocks.   The general situation is indicated by Fig. 20-2.

The magnitude of the heat of decomposition expressed as Btu per pound of 437°F gasoline that is produced is indicated in Table 19-4.[21,22,23]

TABLE 19-4. HEAT OF DECOMPOSITION

Reference	Btu per lb gaso.	Method of determination
Leslie and Potthoff[a]	900	Laboratory measurements
Obryadchikov and Velikanov[b] . .	630	3 commercial heat balances
Weir and Eaton[c] (0–24% gaso.).	808[d]	31 laboratory tests
Weir and Eaton (24% gaso. up).	429	7 laboratory tests
Author.	671	6 commercial heat balances
Author.	1,920[e]	Computed for $C_2H_6 \rightarrow C_2H_4 + H_2$
Author.	1,309[e]	Computed for $C_3H_8 \rightarrow C_3H_6 + H_2$
Author.	659[e]	Computed for $C_3H_8 \rightarrow C_2H_4 + CH_4$
Author.	993[e]	Computed for $nC_4H_{10} \rightarrow C_4H_8 + H_2$
Author.	528[e]	Computed for $nC_4H_{10} \rightarrow C_2H_4 + C_2H_6$
Author.	546[e]	Computed for $nC_4H_{10} \rightarrow C_3H_6 + CH_4$
Author—viscosity breaking.	50–100[e]	Computed

[a] *Ind. Eng. Chem.*, **18**, 776 (1926).

[b] *Neftyanoe Khoz.*, **17**, 370 (1929); and *Chem. Abstracts*, **24**, 1206 (1930).

[c] *Ind. Eng. Chem.*, **29**, 346 (1937).

[d] 410°F ASTM end point.

[e] Btu per pound of feed material.

The heat of decomposition applies to a reaction in which a liquid is decomposed into both gaseous and liquid products, and hence the latent heat of vaporization is contained in the heat of decomposition and does not need to be included in heat balances.

Perhaps the most reliable method of computing the heat of decomposition is by means of heats of combustion and the law of conservation of energy. The difference between the heat of combustion of the cracking stock and the total heat of combustion of the products of cracking is the heat required for cracking. Heats of combustion are normally given at 60°F, and hence it is necessary either to convert all these to the cracking temperature or to convert the computed heat of decomposition at 60°F to the cracking temperature.

Example 19-1. Computation of Heat of Decomposition. One hundred pounds of a gas oil is cracked to produce 17.1 lb of fixed gas, 57.5 lb of pressure distillate, and 25.4 lb of cracked tar which have physical properties as shown below. What is the heat of decomposition at 60 and at 900°F?

[21] Leslie and Potthoff, *Ind. Eng. Chem.*, **18**, 776 (1926).

[22] Obryadchikov and Velikanov, *Neftyanoe Khoz.*, **17**, 370 (1929); and *Chem. Abstracts*, **24**, 1206 (1930).

[23] Weir and Eaton, *Ind. Eng. Chem.*, **29**, 346 (1937).

Basis: 100 lb cracking stock.   A negative sign means heat liberated.

	Character-ization Factor	API	Heat of combustion, Btu per lb (Fig. 5-22)
Cracking stock............	11.8	37	19,600
Fixed gas[a]................	....	...	22,250[a]
Pressure distillate..........	11.8	59	20,130
Cracked fuel oil............	10.8	10	18,450

[a] Gas 17 of Table 14-4.

Energy in stock:

Cracking stock: $100(-19,600) = -1,960,000$ Btu

Energy in products:

Heat in gas: $17.1(-22,250) = -380,475$
Heat in P.D.: $57.5(-20,130) = -1,157,475$
Heat in fuel: $25.4(-18,450) = -468,630$
Subtracting $-2,006,580$ $-(-2,006,580)$
Difference in energy: $+46,580$

Heat of decomposition Btu per pound of gasoline at 60°F $= \dfrac{46,580}{57.5} = 810$

Heat of decomposition at 900°F (the sensible heat contents were computed from Figs 5-1 and 5-2):

Cool stock from 900 to 60°F: $100(-580) =$ $-58,000$
Decomposition at 60°F: $= +46,580$
Heat gas to 900°F: $17.1(655)$ $= +11,200$
Heat P.D. to 900°: $57.5(642)$ $= +36,900$
Heat tar to 900°: $25.4(492)$ $= +12,650$
                                          $+107,330$ $+107,330$
Difference in energy: Heat absorbed (adding) $= +49,330$

Heat of decomposition, Btu per pound at 900 $= \dfrac{49,330}{57.5} = 858$

Although the method outlined in Example 19-1 is correct from the standpoint of theory, it is not satisfactory for practical work unless great care is used.   Very small errors in the heats of combustion or in the yields of products that are assumed will introduce great errors in the computed heat of decomposition.   However, many useful generalizations such as the following tabulation of S. N. Obryadchikov[24] can be computed. The first column is the yield of gasoline in a single cracking operation (or the crack per pass), and the second column shows the heat required to produce a pound of gasoline.

[24] *Ref. Nat. Gaso. Mfr.*, January, 1932, p. 34.

Yield	*Heat of decomposition per lb gasoline, Btu*
5	2,700
10	1,710
15	1,170
20	900
25	865
35	790

Yields by Cracking. The estimation of yields has been difficult because the product is a mixture which cannot be completely analyzed, and because the viscosity of the residue cannot be accurately predicted. Laboratory yields are in many instances worthless because commercial conditions cannot be adequately duplicated by laboratory procedure.

The over-all reaction of cracking involves the decomposition of a heavy oil into gas, light naphtha, and heavy condensation products. In this operation the hydrogen in the stock is concentrated into the light products, and hence the residue material becomes more and more deficient in hydrogen. Thus the larger the percentage of distillate produced the higher will be the specific gravity of the residue that is left [see Fig. 19-1 and Eqs. (19-1) to (19-3)]. Yields would be a simple matter if the gravity or viscosity of the residue could be accurately predicted. Attempts to relate viscosity to yields have not been truly satisfactory,[25,26] and accordingly gravity of the fuel oil is used herein as the basis of correlation, understanding that the fuel oil produced during cracking will be too viscous to meet ASTM No. 6 viscosity specifications. However, the fuel-oil gravities suggested here (Table 19-6, etc.) are the gravities of the final fuel oil after it has been cut back from such viscosities as 1,500 to 30,000 sec Furol at 122°F to the specification viscosity of 300 sec Furol or lower. Fig. 4-44 indicates one such blend. The conversion of viscosities at various temperatures to a temperature of 122°F (Fig. 4-45) is bothersome especially for viscous tars or pitches, and hence Fig. 19-2 covering zero to 100 Viscosity Index materials was prepared.

Two distinct types of material are found in cracked fuel oil: (1) scarcely decomposed straight-run asphaltic material derived from residual feedstocks, and (2) condensation or polymerization materials derived from reactive fragments produced during cracking. In addition, the straight-run asphaltic material is frequently exposed to the mild operation known as viscosity breaking (either in a separate coil or as part of the recirculation in a black-oil coil). The viscosities and gravities of these com-

[25] Mithoff et al., Characteristics of California Crude Oils, *Oil Gas J.*, Nov. 6, 1941, p. 81.

[26] Nelson, W. L., *Oil Gas J.*, June 29, 1950, p. 88; Apr. 13, 1953, p. 143; and Apr. 20, 1953, p. 167.

ponents differ greatly (Table 19-5), and the condensation tars usually contain little material boiling higher than 850°F, whereas the bulk of straight-run tar boils above 900°F. Although very low-gravity fuel oils (below zero API) can be produced from cycle stocks, most refiners choose to operate for gravities of 2 to 7 API because further degradation leads mainly to the production of gas.

TABLE 19-5. INDICATION OF THE VISCOSITIES OF CRACKED RESIDUAL FUEL COMPONENTS

API gravity	Furol viscosity at 122°F		
	Straight run	Condensation products	
		From S.R. feeds	From cat. cycle stock
−5	...	...	100
−2.5	...	...	60
0	...	...	40
2.5	...	100	
5	...	65	
7.5	...	29	
12	800[a]		
14	240[a]		
16	77[a]		

[a] Varies severalfold for different Characterization Factors.

Thus, at one extreme, fuel-oil gravities of 0 to 6 are possible when cracking distilled charge stocks (straight-run or cycle stocks), but gravities of 2 to 12 API are necessary when cracking residual materials. The higher the gravity of the original straight-run residue, the lower the gravity of the cracked fuel oil (Table 19-6) because the ratio of highly fluid condensation tar to straight-run tar is larger. At the other extreme, 6 to 12 API viscosity-breaking charge stocks produce scarcely any condensation tar, and the allowable fuel-oil gravities are high (4 to 12 API). Likewise, the lower the Characterization Factor of the feed, the lower the allowable cracked fuel-oil gravity.

Traces of polymerization or condensation products in the cracking coil feed lead to the rapid formation of coke, and hence a "tar number" has been widely used to judge[27] the coking tendency of charge stock or recycling stocks. It is determined by contacting 100 ml of oil with 10 ml of 66°Bé sulfuric acid in a 4-oz sample bottle, shaking for 1 to 2 min,

[27] Nelson, W. L., Cracking-stock Control, *Oil Gas J.*, Nov. 23, 1946, p. 74.

and allowing to settle for $1\frac{1}{2}$ hr. Another refiner uses a 100-ml pear-shaped centrifuge tube and settles by "spinning" at 1,500 rpm for 20 min. Tar number is the milliliters of tar less 10 (for the acid). Asphaltic materials may be diluted 50:50 with kerosene. A. W. Trusty[28] shows the following tar numbers:

	Tar number
Kerosene	0
Cracked gas oil (30–36 API)	2–4
Straight-run gas oil (30–36 API)	2–6
Topped crude (26 API, East Texas)	26
East Texas crude	16
Fuel oil (14 API)	100

One refiner[27] keeps his cycling stock to a tar number under 5.0 and the overhead from the flash chamber to less than about 11.0. Carbon residue is also used[28] as a measure of coking tendency.

Gasoline yields (400 E.P., 10 R.v.p.) can be obtained from Fig. 19-1[29] or Eqs. (19-1) to (19-3)[30] which apply to somewhat special feedstocks or operations. The symbols refer to the API gravities of the distillate feeds A_D and cracked fuel-oil products A_F, and the gasoline yields are volume per cent. Fig. 19-1 applies to straight-run residual or distilled

Feeds

Thermal distillates:	gaso. $\% = 4 + 2(A_D - A_F)$	(19-1)
Catalytic cycle stocks:	gaso. $\% = 8 + 1.7(A_D - A_F)$	(19-2)
Vapor-phase cracking of distilled S.R. stocks:	gaso. $\% = 23 + 1.4(A_D - A_F)$	(19-3)

feeds. Yields are a little lower than indicated by Eqs. (19-1) to (19-3) when the gravity A_F of the fuel oil is very low. The behavior is similar to that indicated in Fig. 19-1. Straight lines such as Eqs. (19-1) to (19-3) lie across the series of curving lines of Fig. 19-1. In conducting viscosity breaking, i.e., the mild cracking of very heavy residues, the yield of gasoline is usually of little interest (note 5 to 15 per cent, Fig. 19-1). Scarcely any cracked gas oil is produced (other than that required as a cutter stock) when viscosity breaking 5 to 9 API feeds, but 10 to 30 per cent of gas oil is produced when handling 9 to 12 API feeds. Total liquid volume yields are nearly 100 per cent, but cracked gas in the amount of 2.5 to 5 weight per cent is also produced.

The "unaccounted-for loss" on a liquid volume basis is about the same

[28] Laboratory Control Cracking Still Charging Stock . . . , *Oil Gas J.*, Oct. 8, 1931, p. 22.

[29] Nelson, W. L., *Oil Gas J.*, Feb. 25, 1952, p. 183.

[30] Nelson, W. L., *Oil Gas J.*, Oct. 20, 1952, p. 187; Feb. 4, 1952, p. 75; and June 30, 1952, p. 113.

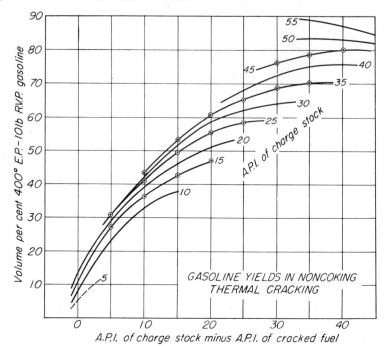

FIG. 19-1. Yields when thermally cracking straight-run materials as a function of the degradation in gravity.

for all types of cracking [Eq. (19-4)] except vapor-phase cracking [the constant of Eq. (19-4) becomes 1.15 rather than 0.5].

$$\text{Liquid volume loss} = 0.5(A_D - A_F) \qquad (19\text{-}4)$$

The gravities of Table 19-6 and the yields of Fig. 19-1 and Eqs. (19-1) to (19-3) cannot be attained except by the most vigorous cracking including the use of downflow vapor reaction chambers (page 683).

Reforming operations are concerned with octane number rather than fuel-oil gravity, and therefore yields are not obtained from Fig. 19-1 but from Table 19-2.

Mithoff et al.[25] present the only satisfactory study relating yields to fuel-oil viscosity. The yield of debutanized gasoline G that is possible from California crude oils in terms of the viscosity V of the feedstock (Saybolt Universal sec at 130°F) and the viscosity of the cracked fuel oil is given by Eq. (19-5). Between the ranges of 31 and 40 per cent of cracked fuel oil and when producing 300 viscosity (Furol) at 122°F fuel oils, the yields of butane-free cracked naphtha (gasoline) are approximately

$$G = 45 - 1.62 \frac{V}{100} \qquad (19\text{-}5)$$

Eq. (19-5) applies particularly to "black-circulation" single-coil operations in which reaction chambers are used. Yields decrease sharply if thinner cracked fuels are produced.

TABLE 19-6. APPROXIMATE MINIMUM GRAVITY OF CRACKED FUEL-OIL RESIDUE (A_F) POSSIBLE BY SEVERE THERMAL CRACKING OF TOPPED (RESIDUAL) CRUDE OILS

Character. Factor of feed	6 to 12 API feedstocks	12 to 14 API feedstocks	14 to 18 API feedstocks	18 to 26 API feedstocks	Higher gravity feedstocks
11.2	4–7	2.0–4.0	0–2.0	−2.0–zero	
11.3		2.5–4.5	1.0–3.0	−1.0 to 1.0	
11.4	5–8	3.0–5.0	1.5–3.5	0 to 1.5	
11.5		4.0–6.0	3.0–4.0	1.0–3.0	−1.0 to 1.0
11.6	6–9	5.0–6.5	3.5–5.0	2.0–3.5	0–2.0
11.7		6.0–7.0	5.0–6.0	3.0–5.0	1.0–3.0
11.8	7–10	7.0–8.0	6.0–7.0	4.5–6.0	2.5–4.5
11.9		8.0–9.0	7.0–8.0	5.5–7.0	3.5–5.5
12.0	9–11	9.0–10.0	8.5–9.0	7.0–8.5	4.5–7.0
12.1	....	10.5–11.0	9.5–10.0	8.0–9.5	6.0–8.0
12.2	....	....	11.0–11.5	9.0–11.0	7.0–9.0
12.3	....	....	12.0–13.0	10.5–12.0	8.0–10.5
12.4	....	....	13.0–13.5	11.5–13.0	9.0–12.0

Not much can be done about the yield of gasoline except to change the gravity of the cracked fuel oil. However, the following conditions are said to slightly affect gasoline yield:

1. A low crack per pass or a high recycle ratio.
2. A relatively low pressure (200 to 300 lb).
3. A relatively low cracking temperature (860 to 900°F), which means a low octane number.

Example 19-2. A 24 API Mid Continent reduced crude oil of 11.9 Characterization Factor is to be cracked. According to Table 19-6, it is possible by the most severe cracking to produce a 6 API fuel oil.

The degradation in gravity is (24 − 6) or 18 units API, and Fig. 19-1 indicates a gasoline yield of 52 per cent. In summary:

$$\begin{aligned} \text{Gasoline (400 E.P., 10 R.v.p.)} &= 52 \text{ per cent} \\ \text{Unaccounted [Eq. (19-4)] } 0.5(24 - 6) &= 9 \text{ per cent} \\ \text{Cracked fuel oil (by difference)} &= 39 \text{ per cent} \end{aligned}$$

If the 24 API feed were a catalytic cycle stock, a fuel gravity of 2 or lower is possible, but most existing plants do not operate for a gravity lower than about 6 [Eq. (19-2)].

$$\text{Gasoline} = 8 + 1.7(24 - 6) = 38.6 \text{ per cent}$$

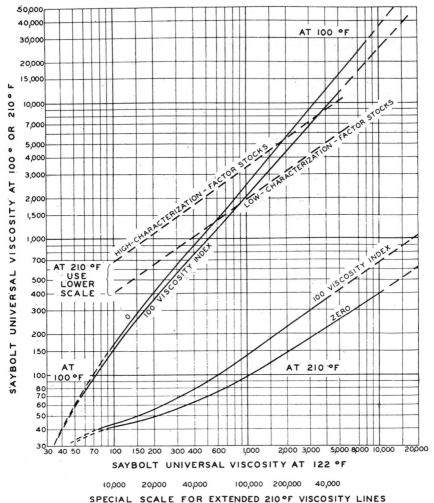

FIG. 19-2. Relation between Saybolt Universal viscosities determined at 100, 210, and 122°F.   (*Oil Gas J.*)

Likewise, the yield by vapor-phase cracking (1050 to 1150°F) of a 24 API distilled straight-run feed would be large [Eq. (19-3)], but the gas loss would be very large:

Gasoline (vapor phase): $23.0 + 1.4(24 - 4) = 51.4$
Unaccounted-for loss: $1.15(24 - 4) = 23.0$
Cracked fuel oil: $= 25.6$

Example 19-3.   Yields by Viscosity Breaking.   A 7 API intermediate-base residue (11.8 Characterization Factor) is to be viscosity broken as severely as possible. Table 19-6 indicates that a fuel-oil gravity of about 9 API is possible.   Note that the lower the gravity of the feed, the higher must be the gravity of the cracked fuel oil (throughout all of Table 19-6).   This increase in gravity of 2 units (i.e., 7 to 9) results in almost no yield (Fig. 19-1) of gasoline (perhaps 3 per cent), it means no unaccounted-for loss [see Eq. (19-4)], and in fact a slight increase in the total liquid yield to perhaps 100.5 per cent.   A material balance on a basis of 100 gal feed shows that a small amount (10 per cent) of cracked gas oil will be produced when producing 300 sec Furol fuel oil.

Feed (7 API): $100 \times 8.509 =$ 850.9 lb
Gaso. (56 API): $3 \times 6.283 = 18.8$
Gas loss (2.5 wt %): $0.025 \times 850.9 = 21.2$
                                            ———
                                            40.0   40.0
    Weight of fuel oil and gas oil (if any)   810.9 lb

The amount of excess gas oil above that required to reduce the viscosity of the fuel oil will be x per cent of, say, 20 API material.

$$810.9 = 7.778x + 8.388(100.5 - 3 - x)$$
$$-0.61x = 810.9 - 817 \qquad x = 10 \text{ per cent}$$

Thus, the yields are:

Gasoline...................   3 per cent
Gas oil (20 API)..........   10 per cent
Fuel oil (9 API)...........   87.5 per cent
    Total liquids............   100.5 per cent

Yields by Coking.   Two general types of coking processes are now employed extensively, delayed coking and fluid coking.   The processes are seldom operated for an ultimate yield of coke but are operated for as much gas oil as possible because it is cheaper to crack the gas oil in thermal or catalytic units than in the coking unit.   However, the yields of gasoline (volume per cent) when coking to the formation of only gasoline and coke (and gas) are about:

$$\text{Gaso. (residual feed) per cent} = 303 - 250d \qquad (19\text{-}6)$$
$$\text{Gaso. (gas oil feed) per cent} = 331 - 300d \qquad (19\text{-}7)$$

The gasoline is 400 E.P., 10 R.v.p. material, and the symbol d refers to the specific gravity of the charge stock.   In such an operation the amount of coke produced (C tons per 1,000 bbl feed) in terms of the API gravity of the feed (A_R) is:

$$C = 99 - 3.4A_R + 0.03(A_R)^2 \qquad (19\text{-}8)$$

The yield of coke is intimately related to the carbon residue (weight per cent) of the feed,[31] and the yields of coke when operating the Delayed and Fluid processes for the production of maximum gas oil are indicated in Table 19-7.   In using this table it is suggested that the remaining material, after deducting the weight of the coke and the gas (see tabulation), be split into gasoline and gas oil of an appropriate gravity.   The amount of gasoline produced when operating in the conventional way

[31] Nelson, W. L., *Oil Gas J.*, Dec. 19, 1955, p. 99.

for a large gas-oil yield ranges from 15 to 25 liquid volume per cent depending upon the amount of recycling that is conducted. Tables or charts could be presented[32] but there are so many variables that numerous charts would be required.

TABLE 19-7. COKE YIELDS, AS A FUNCTION OF CARBON RESIDUE[a]

Carbon residue, per cent	API gravity of feeds		Coke yield, wt per cent			
	Intermediate base	Naphthenic and cracked	High temp oven coke	Fluid process	Delayed coking	Ultimate coking[b]
1	. . . .	. . . .	. . .	. . . .	0	
5	26	22	. . .	3	8.5	22
10	16	14	. . .	11.5	18	37
15	10	8	15	17	27.5	40
20	6	4.5	21	23	35.5	45
25	3.5	2	26	29	42	48
30	2	0	31	34.5		
40	. . . .	−2.5	41	46		

[a] Nelson, W. L., *Oil Gas J.*, Dec. 19, 1955, p. 99.
[b] No gas oil.

The amount of gas produced is related to the coke production somewhat as follows:

API gravity of feed	Ratio of weight of gas to weight of coke*		
	Fluid	Delayed	Ultimate
0	0.27		
5	0.335		
7	0.37	. . . . .	0.20
10	0.43	0.185	0.27
12	0.48	0.21	0.32
15	0.56	0.265	0.405
20	0.725	0.415	0.585
25	0.95	0.61	0.800

* Nelson, W. L., *Oil Gas J.*, Sept. 3, 1956, p. 129.

Only one means of significantly reducing the amount of sulfur in petroleum coke[32a] has been discovered. When finely powdered coke at 1500°F is exposed to ethylene, propylene or butylene, the amount of sulfur is reduced to less than 10 per cent of the amount originally present.

[32] Nelson, W. L., *Oil Gas J.*, Feb. 15, 1954, p. 181; and July 7, 1952, p. 103.
[32a] Sabott, F. K., . . Methods of Removing Sulfur from Petroleum Coke, *Quarterly of the Colorado School of Mines*, vol. 47, no. 3, July, 1952.

Example 19-4. Yields by Coking. Yields when coking a naphthenic 7 API residue will be explored. Such a material would have a carbon residue (Table 19-7) of about 16 per cent. If it were coked by the several available processes, and also to the ultimate production of as much coke as possible, the amounts of coke would be about (Table 19-7):

	Weight per cent	Lb per bbl (feed 358 lb per bbl)	Tons per 1,000 bbl
By high temperature oven processes.......	16	57.1	28.5
By Fluid coking........................	18.6	66.4	33.2
By Delayed coking	29.8	106.5	53.2
Ultimate coking........................	41.2	147.0	73.0

By ultimate coking, the yield of gasoline would be [Eq. (19-6)]

$$\text{Gasoline} = 303 - 250 \times 1.0217 = 47 \text{ per cent}$$

The amount of gas per barrel would be (about 20 per cent of the coke weight)

$$357.5 \times 0.412 \times 0.2 = 29.5 \text{ lb per bbl}$$

which at a molecular weight of 19 would be

$$\frac{29.5}{19} \times 379 = 588 \text{ cu ft per bbl}$$

If coking is conducted by the Delayed process, the yields would be somewhat as follows:

Feed (7 API), weight: 357.5 lb
Coke, weight: 106.5 lb
Gas, weight: $106.5 \times 0.17 = $ 18.1
                               124.6 lb   124.6
  Gasoline and gas oil: 232.9 lb
  Gasoline: $0.20 \times 42 \times 6.385 = $ 53.5
    Weight of gas oil: 179.4 lb

If the gas oil has a gravity of 20 API, the percentage of gas oil will be

$$\frac{179.4}{7.778} \times \frac{1}{42} = 55 \text{ per cent}$$

The amount of gas will be about

$$\frac{18.1}{21} \times 379 = 327 \text{ cu ft per bbl}$$

The yield of gas oil will be changed slightly if a different gas-oil gravity is assumed, and even larger differences will arise if recycling is practiced to the extent of producing 25 per cent of gasoline.

By the Fluid process the gas yield would be slightly larger:

$$\frac{357.5 \times 0.186 \times 0.37 \times 379}{22} = 422 \text{ cu ft}$$

Yields from Hydrocarbons. The thermal cracking of hydrocarbons, especially for the production of ethylene, has become extremely important. At low conversions per pass, ethane and propane decompose about as follows:[33]

Per cent of reaction	Reaction	
100	$C_2H_6 \rightarrow C_2H_4 + H_2$	(19-9)
63.5	$C_3H_8 \rightarrow C_2H_4 + CH_4$	
30.0	$C_3H_8 \rightarrow C_3H_6 + H_2$	
6.5	$2C_3H_8 \rightarrow C_2H_4 + 2C_2H_6$	

The last of these is a bimolecular reaction and it therefore should be affected by pressure. The over-all propane reaction from the above is:

$$100C_3H_8 \rightarrow 30H_2 + 63.5CH_4 + 66.75C_2H_4 + 6.5C_2H_6 + 30C_3H_6 \quad (19\text{-}10)$$

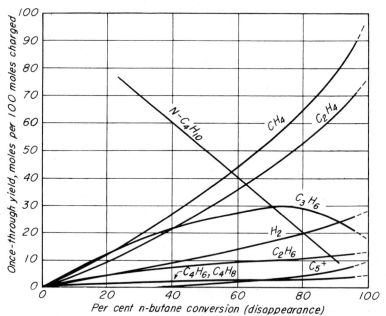

FIG. 19-3. Once-through yields from n-butane pyrolysis for tubular units with exit conditions of 1350–1400°F and 0–20 psig. (*Pet. Refiner.*)

This contemplates decomposition of all of the propane feed, and in practice this is accomplished by recycling any undecomposed propane. The common and economical conversion per pass for propane is about 85 per cent, and accordingly the single pass yields would be about 85 per cent of Eq. (19-10) plus 15 moles of unreacted propane. According to Eq.

[33] Schutt, H. C., *Chem. Eng. Progr.*, **43**, 103 (1947).

(19-10) the ultimate yield of ethylene from propane is 66.75 per cent on a mole basis, or 42.5 weight per cent.

H. C. Schutt[33] also states that the ultimate decomposition (including unavoidable polymerization) of propylene gives the following yields:

$$100C_3H_8 \rightarrow 17H_2 + 45CH_4 + 42C_2H_4 + 4.1C_4H_{6.8}$$
$$+ 26.6C_{5.8}H_{7.15} \quad (19\text{-}11)$$

Thus, additional yields of ethylene, if only ethylene is desired, can be obtained by recycling the propylene produced by Eq. (19-10) in a separate coil under appropriate conditions obtaining the yields of Eq. (19-11). This is not normally a commercially feasible operation.[34]

Once-through typical yields[34] when cracking various charge stocks primarily for the production of ethylene are indicated in Table 19-8. The yield of ethylene is increased for any of the feedstocks of Table 19-8 by subjecting any unreacted feedstock to additional passes through the system, and it may be further increased by the recycling of unwanted products, particularly the saturated hydrocarbons. Thus, in cracking propane, a significant amount of ethane is produced, and it may be cracked by recycling or better by processing it through an ethane cracking coil. The ultimate yields of ethylene in commercial practice are somewhat as follows:

	Weight, %	Conversion, % per pass
From ethane..........................	74–75	60
From propane........................	42–43	85
From propylene......................	26–27	
From butane.........................	38–39*	85–90
From kerosene or gas oil.............	22–23	58†

* When recycling propylene.

† Based on weight per cent production of butanes and lighter.

Somewhat higher once-through and ultimate yields are said[35] to be possible with special heaters such as the pebble heater,[35] and it is evident that heaters must be designed to eliminate, insofar as possible, undesirable side reactions leading to coke or polymerization products.

The general effect of conversion per pass is illustrated in Fig. 19-3 for the high-temperature (1350 to 1400°F) low-pressure (0 to 20 psig) cracking of normal butane in tubular heaters.[36] Dehydrogenation equi-

[34] Schutt and Zdonik, Making Ethylene . . . Part I, *Oil Gas J.*, Feb. 13, 1956, p. 98.

[35] Kilpatrick et al., *Oil Gas J.*, May 10, 1954, p. 162.

[36] Fair et al., Comparing Olefin Unit Feedstocks, *Pet. Refiner*, November, 1955, p. 185.

TABLE 19-8. TYPICAL ONCE-THROUGH YIELDS WHEN CRACKING PRIMARILY FOR ETHYLENE[a]

	Ethane	Propane	Propane propylene[b]	Butane	Nat. gaso. Grade 26-70	Light S.R. distillate (89-215°F)[c]	S.R. naphtha (215-430°F) 52.2 API	Gas oil 36-38 API[d]
Coil outlet, temp °F	1515-1525	1438-1460	1472-1485	1415-1448	1410	1365-1410	1340-1405	1335-1375
Coil outlet pressure, psig	3-31	7.5-10	31-32	6.8	11.6	12.5-15.3	13.6-15	6.5-8.5
Steam to hydrocarbon ratio, mole/mole	0.3-1.1	0.35-0.4	1-1.15	0.28-0.35	2.75	3.05-7.5	3.5-8.2	4-7.9
Conversion, per cent	58.8-62.6	83-87.7	81-82[b]	74.8-90.5				
Expansion	1.5-1.58	1.72-1.75	1.62-1.64	1.9-2.17				
Products, mole per cent:[e]								
Hydrogen	31.1-35.6	12.7-13.5	11.9-13.3	11.2-12.6	14.5	11.2-14.6	10.5-15.5	13.2-15.6
Methane	3.6-9.6	32.4-34	30.3-31.4	29.5-33.6	28.5	29.5-31.4	28.3-28.7	28.5-29.6
Acetylene	0.2	0.1-0.2	0.2-0.3	0.2-0.4	0.2	} 25.2-33	0.1-0.6	0-0.2
Ethylene	31-33.1	25.4-25.7	24.9-25.6	18.4-24.4	27.6	}	26.7-32.4	26.9-32.4
Ethane	22.6-26.7	7.9-10.3	4.7-6.0	5.1-5.7	5.1	5.7-8.5	3.4-9.1	2.9-7.9
Propylene }	0.6-1.9	8.2-8.7	14.1	11.5-14.1	12.5	10.5-14.3	11.7-15.1	11.3-14
Propane }		6.0-9.7	7.9-8.3	1.8-2.9	1.1	0.7-1.2	0.4-1.1	0.6-1.2
Butadiene }	0.2-0.4	} 0.9-1.1	} 0.5-0.7	1-1.4	2.3	2.5	2.4-3.2	2.1-3.8
Butene }				1.2-2.0	5.1	4.3-5.5	3.9-5.8	3.4-5.9
n-Butane }				4-12.2	3.1	0.2	0.2-0.3	0.2-0.3
i-Butane				0.2-0.6				
Butane and lighter					100 (73.5)[e]	100 (70.3-73.8)[e]	100 (57.5-59)[e]	100 (56.5-59.6)[e]
Pentane fraction	0.1-1.3	1.3-1.9	2.5-3.3	2.4-3.6				2.8-4.8[e]
Pentane plus								
Pentane to 375°F, E.P.					21.0[e]	17.8-24.1[e]	30.5-35.2[e]	
Hexane to 375°F, E.P.								16.5-18.0[e]
Fuel oil and carbon					5.5[e]	5.6-8.4[e]	7.3-10.5[e]	19.6-22.6[e]

[a] Schutt and Zdonik, Making Ethylene . . . Part I, Oil Gas J., Feb. 13, 1956, p. 98.
[b] 18.8 to 24.1 per cent propylene in feed. The propylene conversion ranged from 40 to 48 per cent.
[c] 73.2 API.
[d] Characterization Factor of 11.85.
[e] Except liquid products which are weight per cent.

646

librium constants[37,38,39] for ethane, propane, and butane are shown in Fig. 19-4.

The principal reactions in the thermal decomposition of butane and isobutane are:

$$nC_4H_{10} \rightleftharpoons nC_4H_8 + H_2 \tag{19-12}$$
$$nC_4H_{10} \rightarrow C_3H_6 + CH_4$$
$$nC_4H_{10} \rightarrow C_2H_4 + C_2H_6$$
$$2nC_4H_{10} \rightarrow nC_4H_8 + C_3H_8 + CH_4 \tag{19-13}$$
$$2nC_4H_{10} \rightarrow nC_4H_8 + 2C_2H_6 \tag{19-14}$$

$$iC_4H_{10} \rightleftharpoons iC_4H_8 + H_2 \tag{19-15}$$
$$iC_4H_{10} \rightarrow C_3H_6 + CH_4$$
$$iC_4H_{10} \rightarrow C_2H_4 + C_2H_6$$
$$2iC_4H_{10} \rightarrow iC_4H_8 + C_3H_8 + CH_4 \tag{19-16}$$

The reversible equations [(19-12) and (19-15)] are suppressed by pressure, but the bimolecular reactions [Eqs. (19-13), (19-14), and (19-16)] are promoted by pressure.

The extent to which each of the reactions takes place depends upon the temperature and the pressure. Low-pressure operations have been explored above and in Fig. 19-3, but the butanes are also cracked at high pressure, especially if the recovery of butylenes is desirable. The following equations represent the results of Tropsch, Thomas, and Egloff[40] for a temperature of about 1020°F and a pressure of 725 psi.

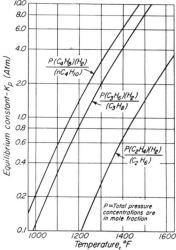

FIG. 19-4. Dehydrogenation equilibria of ethane, propane, and butane with their reaction products. (*Oil Gas J.*)

$$100nC_4H_{10} \rightarrow 19.25C_4H_8 + 33C_3H_6$$
$$+ 30C_2H_4 + 16C_3H_8 + 33.5C_2H_6$$
$$+ 49CH_4 + 1.5H_2 \tag{19-17}$$
$$100iC_4H_{10} \rightarrow 29iC_4H_8 + 43C_3H_6 + 5.5C_2H_4$$
$$+ 22.5C_3H_8 + 5.5C_2H_6 + 65.5CH_4 + 6.5H_2 \tag{19-18}$$

[37] Frey and Huppke, *Ind. Eng. Chem.*, **25**, 54 (1933).

[38] Storch and Kassel, *J. Am. Chem. Soc.*, **59**, 1240 (1937).

[39] Kistiakowsky et al., *J. Am. Chem. Soc.*, **57**, 65 (1935).

[40] Pressure Pyrolysis of Gaseous Paraffin Hydrocarbons, *Ind. Eng. Chem.*, **28**, 324 (1936).

Similar data have been published by various investigators;[41,42,43] and although the exact products that are produced at various pressures and temperatures vary somewhat, the total production of olefins from either normal or isobutane and the total volume of gaseous products are remarkably uniform:

Moles of olefins produced = 80–85 per cent of moles of butanes
Total moles of products = 190 per cent of moles of butanes

Such yields cannot be obtained commercially unless recycling is used, because polymerization consumes part of the yield. In general, short reaction times, a low crack per pass, low pressures, and high temperatures are the best operating conditions, but each of these is limited by economics or practical considerations in commercial practice.

Butadiene and cyclopentadiene appear in small quantities in the products of vapor-phase or gas cracking. The effect of temperature on butadiene production appears to be somewhat as follows:

Cracking temp, °F	% Butadiene	Cracking temp, °F	% Butadiene
1000	0.4	1320	3.07
1080	1.06	1400	3.75
1160	1.73	1740	6.6
1240	2.4		

During World War II several vapor-phase cracking plants operated[44,45,46] primarily for the production of butadiene. The liquid products produced by vapor-phase cracking are rich in aromatic hydrocarbons, and when cracking normally gaseous feedstocks or light naphtha, the liquids are so predominantly aromatic that they can be separated by distillation into pure compounds.[10,47] Yields from a Middle East naphtha in weight per cent are shown at top of page 649.[47]

Although gas cracking is primarily a cracking operation, plants for producing olefins will be discussed in Chap. 20.

[41] Egloff, Thomas, and Linn, Pyrolysis of Propane and the Butanes, *Ind. Eng. Chem.*, **28**, 1283 (1936).

[42] Echols and Pease, Kinetics of the Decomposition of *n*-Butane, *J. Am. Chem. Soc.*, **61**, 208 (1939).

[43] Neuhaus and Marek, Thermal Decomposition of *n*-Butane into Primary Products, *Ind. Eng. Chem.*, **24**, 400 (1932).

[44] Camp, E. Q., Equipment Protection for Cracking Units, *Oil Gas J.*, Nov. 29, 1947, p. 83.

[45] Ralph, H. D., *Oil Gas J.*, Dec. 15, 1945, p. 70.

[46] Masser, H. L., *Oil Gas J.*, Oct. 28, 1943, p. 45.

[47] Catarole Process Produces . . . Olefin Gas and Aromatics, *Pet. Refiner*, July, 1952, p. 154.

Prebenzene	1.8
Benzene	5.3
Nonaromatics in benzene range	0.4
Toluene	6.0
Nonaromatics in toluene range	0.3
m- and p-xylene	3.0
o-xylene and styrene	2.5
Alkyl benzene	7.1
Prenaphthalene	1.2
Refined naphthalene	1.0
Alkyl naphthalenes	5.2
Anthracene cut	3.4
Pyrene-chrysene cut	3.4
Hard pitch, mp 203–338°F	4.8

Rate of Cracking. The yield in a given length of time increases rapidly with temperature; the yield at a fixed temperature increases with time up to a certain point, and then it decreases; and the yield for a given length of time is greater for heavy stocks. Table 19-9 taken from the work of

TABLE 19-9. EFFECT OF TYPE OF CHARGE STOCK ON THE REACTION VELOCITY[a]

Stock	Sp gr	392°F distillate per cent by weight	Reaction[b] velocity constant
Kerosene	.....	4.9	0.0000672
Solar oil	.....	18.6	0.000288
Paraffin oil	0.833	26–30	0.000457
Spindle oil	0.904	28.2	0.000461
Three cylinder oils	0.931	29.5–30.5	0.000498
Paraffin	.....	31.2	0.000518

[a] Sachanen and Tilicheyev, *Oil Gas J.*, June 23, 1927, p. 144.
[b] Computed by author by Eq. (19-19).

Sachanen and Tilicheyev[48,49] indicates the relation of the rate of cracking to the properties of the cracking stock.

Sung, Brown, and White[50] have studied the rates at which products (including gas) of different end point are produced. Their approximate results for 900°F tabulated here do not check the rates shown in Fig. 19-5, which may be due in part to the fact that they extrapolate their experimental data to zero per cent conversion in determining the equilibrium constant, but since scarcely any other such data are available, their study is extremely valuable.

Product	Reaction velocity constant
Gas (only)	0.0039
Gas and up to 200 E.P.	0.0063
Gas and up to 300 E.P.	0.0105
Gas and up to 400 E.P.	0.0160
Gas and up to 500 E.P.	0.0205
Gas and up to 600 E.P.	0.0270

[48] *Oil Gas J.*, June 23, 1927, p. 144.
[49] *J. Inst. Pet. Tech.*, **14**, 761 (1928).
[50] Thermal Cracking of Petroleum, *Ind. Eng. Chem.*, **37**, 1153 (1945).

Most approximately, their results indicate that the rate of gas formation is 15 to 25 per cent of the rate of gasoline formation.

Thus the lighter the cracking stock the longer the time required. In commercial practice the yield from light stocks is obtained not by using a long length of time but by using a higher temperature. As will be shown later, an increase in temperature is very effective in decreasing the time required. Stocks that have already been cracked, such as recycle stock, also require a longer time. In general, stocks that require a relatively long time for a given yield are termed "refractory stocks." Recycle stock, kerosene, naphtha, and gasoline are classed as refractory stocks.

The cracking reaction may be described in a general way as a first-order reaction if the decomposition is limited as in conventional cracking operations to a low conversion per pass (20 to 25 per cent):

$$K_1 = \frac{1}{t} \ln \frac{a}{a-x} \qquad \text{or often} \qquad = \frac{1}{t} \ln \frac{100}{100-x} \qquad (19\text{-}19)$$

where K_1 = reaction velocity constant (Fig. 19-5)

t = time, sec

a = percentage of material in feedstock—for a pure feedstock $a = 100$

x = percentage of material that disappears during the reaction time t

In order to use the equation in designing cracking equipment it is necessary to assume that x represents the percentage of product that is produced. Several different definitions of the term x are used on Fig. 19-5:

1. *Hydrocarbons* (ethane through heptane). The term x is used as mole (or gas volume) percentage, and it refers to the disappearance of the feedstock hydrocarbon.

2. *Cracking stocks* (naphtha through residuum). The term x is used as the liquid volume percentage of 400 E.P. gasoline that is produced.

3. *High-boiling products* (vacuum decomposition). The x refers to liquid-volume percentage of various gravities of products obtained by the vacuum decomposition of asphalt or high-boiling feeds.[51,52] Note especially that these distillate and lubricating-oil products can only be obtained at subatmospheric pressure when decomposing higher-boiling materials than the products desired.

The pressures that apply to each of the lines on Fig. 19-5 are the conventional pressures employed in conducting the processes. Thus, for ethane, propane, and butane, the pressure is very low (0 to 50 psig).

[51] Gunnerson, L., Operating Variables and Reaction Rates in Vacuum Decomposition, master's thesis, University of Tulsa, 1948.

[52] Nelson and Fancher, U.S. Pat. 1,990,664.

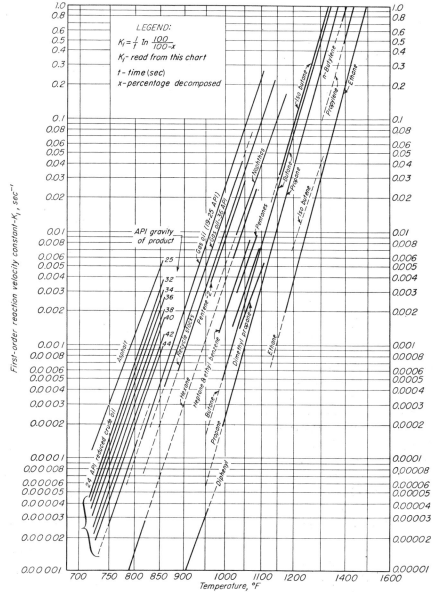

Fig. 19-5. Reaction velocity constants for the decomposition of hydrocarbons and petroleum fractions into various products (see text).

At high pressures (1,500 to 2,500 psig), the reaction velocity constants of propane and isobutane are about 2.0 times larger[53] than shown on Fig. 19-5 and the constants for butane 6 to 9 times larger.

The exact types of reactions that are contemplated in using Fig. 19-5 or the kinds of products that will be produced must be gained from independent sources or reference to the original data.[33,51—55,56] The constants may be used for either liquid- or vapor-phase reactions. R. Rosen[54] presents a digest of a series of articles published abroad by M. D. Tilicheyev on the reaction velocity rates for paraffin, olefin, diolefin, naphthene, aromatic, etc., hydrocarbons. In general, the reaction rates shown by Rosen;[54] Schutt;[53] and Sung, Brown, and White[50] are somewhat higher than the lines shown on Fig. 19-5.

The reaction velocity constant may be related to temperature by the following form of equation:

$$\ln K_1 = \frac{-E}{RT} + C$$

where R = gas law constant = 1.985
T = absolute temperature, °K
E = energy of activation, cal
C = a constant

For gas oil the value of E is about 55,000 and of C about 30.

Effect of Time. In general, the longer the length of time the greater the yield. However, the yield decreases if the time is very long. This is illustrated by the data of Watermann and Perquin[57] (Fig. 19-6) for paraffin wax. As cracking starts, primary decomposition reactions take place; but as the time is increased, the concentration of reactive unsaturated materials increases and polymerization reactions begin to be important. These combination reactions use some of the material that has been formed by decomposition so that the yield of gasoline decreases. In Fig. 19-6 the curve of the cracking rate is nearly linear out to 30 per cent. This shows that only one factor, viz., decomposition, is greatly affecting the yield. But at 30 per cent the effect of polymerization becomes marked; and at 48 per cent the rate at which polymerization is taking

[53] Hepp and Frey, Thermal Pyrolysis of Propane and Butanes at Elevated Pressures, Milwaukee Meeting of ACS, Mar. 30, 1952.

[54] Rosen, R., Kinetics and Chemistry of Cracking of Hydrocarbons, Oil Gas J., Feb. 13 and 20, 1941.

[55] Arnold, P. M., Olefin Production by Thermal Cracking of Isobutane, Oil Gas J., July 7, 1945, p. 87.

[56] Seventeen references shown in the Second Edition of this book, p. 307; 5 references shown on p. 323 of the First Edition of this book; and laboratory tests by the author on viscosity breaking and vacuum decomposition.

[57] J. Inst. Pet. Tech., 11, 36 (1925).

place is more rapid than the rate of decomposition, and the yield becomes less. As the yield becomes less, large amounts of tar are produced and coke may be formed. Hence commercial processes are never operated at times that are greater than the time at the maximum point in the time-yield curve. If recycling is practiced, the conversion per pass must be well below the maximum point of the fresh charge stock, but for once-through operation the conversion per pass may approach the maximum point closely.

Temperature affects the general shape of the time-yield curve. The maximum percentage point is lower for high cracking temperatures

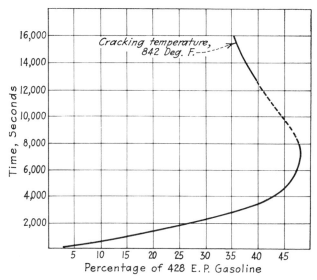

FIG. 19-6. Yield of gasoline vs. time at 842°F. (*Watermann and Perquin, J. Inst. Pet. Tech.*)

and also lower for stocks that have already been cracked. Thus at high temperatures the rate of polymerization is relatively faster than at low temperatures. The maximum points and times for several sets of data are shown in Table 19-10.

The use of reaction chambers and soaking drums is to some extent being abandoned, except when coke is desired, because of the decreased yields at a long length of time. However, in some modern plants, the use of reaction chambers for soaking of only the vapor has resulted in both increased capacity and an increased yield.[58] The maximum points are also the governing factor in determining the recycle ratio that is possible.

[58] Mithoff and Schimansky, Reaction Chambers on Thermal-cracking Units, *Oil Gas J.*, Nov. 6, 1941, p. 135.

TABLE 19-10. TIME FOR MAXIMUM YIELD OF GASOLINE

Temperature, °F	Max yield in once-through operation	Time, sec, at max yield, approx.	Phase	Stock	Reference
700	Negative[a]	20,000+	Liquid	Recycle	59
844	24	5,200	Liquid	Recycle and gas oil	50
894	28	420	Liquid	Recycle and gas oil	50
800	40	14,000	Liquid	Gas oil	60
842	48[b]	7,500	Liquid	Paraffin wax	57
850	35	3,500	Liquid	Light gas oil	50
900	36	1,215	?	Gas oil	50
932	31	1,000	Vapor	Gas oil	61
1076	26	30	Vapor	Gas oil	61
1184	23	3	Vapor	Gas oil	61

[a] Yield decreases with time for recycle stock probably because of polymerization.
[b] Either poor data, or paraffin wax behaves differently from oils.
[59] Leslie and Potthoff, *Ind. Eng. Chem.*, **18**, 776 (1926).
[60] Cross, "Handbook of Petroleum, Asphalt, and Natural Gas," *Bull.* 25, p. 287, 1928.
[61] Geniesse and Reuter, *Ind. Eng. Chem.*, **24**, 219 (1932).

An idea of the lengths of time used in commercial processing may be gained from the following tabulation:

Operation	*Time, sec*
Butane decomposition at 1000°F	380
Reforming (once-through) at 1000°F	300
Cracking (mixed-phase recycling) at 900°F	170
Viscosity breaking (once-through) at 860°F	150
Reforming (recycling) at 980°F	130
Butane decomposition at 1100°F	40
Cracking, vapor-phase (recycling), at 1050°F	3
Ethane and propane (for ethylene) at 1400–1500°F	1
Cracking, vapor-phase (recycling), at 1150°F	0.3

Recycle stocks require more time for a given yield than straight-run stocks. Table 19-11 indicates the refractive nature of these stocks. The figures refer to the ratio of the yield from recycle stock to the yield from fresh stock, if the two are cracked under the same conditions of time, temperature, and pressure.

Recycle stock, regardless of recycle ratio, will consist almost entirely of material that has been cracked once and twice. Hence the currently recycled stock will crack about half as readily as fresh stock.

Although cracking is usually considered to be a decomposition process, mainly because of the interest in producing lower-boiling materials such as gasoline or ethylene, polymerization products such as cracked fuel oil (in viscosity breaking) and polymer gasoline produced by the thermal process often constitute the major product, nor can polymerization or condensation products be entirely avoided during cracking.   Thus, cracking is a process of both decomposition and polymerization.   If the time is sufficiently short and the percentage conversion is low, decomposition reactions predominate, whereas at longer times and more complete conversions polymerization products may predominate.

Recycling in Cracking Plants.   In commercial plants the ultimate yield of cracked naphtha is not produced in a single cracking operation. Recycle stock and gas oil are charged to the cracking heater, and a relatively small percentage yield from this large amount of mixed stock is a large yield when based on the original stock.   As an example, assume that two parts of recycle and one part of fresh stock are cracked giving a

TABLE 19-11. RATE AT WHICH RECYCLE STOCKS CRACK, COMPARED
WITH STRAIGHT-RUN STOCKS

Once cracked	Twice cracked	Current recycling	Thrice cracked	Reference
0.6	0.318	....	0.175	7
0.79	.....	....	.....	7
0.795	0.69	....	.....	8
.....	.....	0.4–0.47	.....	21
.....	.....	0.43	.....	Fig. 19-5

yield, based on the mixture, of 20 per cent, or $0.2 \times 3 = 0.6$ parts of distillate.   Based on the one part of fresh stock, which is all that comes into the plant, the yield of pressure distillate is $0.6 \times 100 \div 1 = 60$ per cent.

Recycling is necessary because coke is deposited and a large gas loss occurs if high yields per pass are produced.   The tarry material and the reactive materials that are produced during cracking seem to be the source of coke.   If the yield is great, the maximum point shown in Fig. 19-6 is approached, and polymerization takes place with the formation of tar and coke.   These products are always produced to some extent, but in the recycling operation they are currently eliminated before they attain reactive concentrations.   The common arrangement is to cycle the cracked material that issues from the pipestill, through a fractionating system.   In the fractionating system the tarry materials are eliminated into the cracked fuel oil; the gas and cracked naphtha pass overhead; and a heart-cut material consisting of fresh gas oil and recycle is withdrawn as a clean distillate which is continuously pumped into the pipestill.   Thus the same quantity of recycle stock and of fresh gas oil or reduced crude oil is charged to the pipestill each hour, and constant quantities of recycle, gas, distillate, and cracked tar issue from the outlet of the still each hour.

The relative quantities handled at various points in a particular type of cracking system are illustrated in Fig. 19-7.   The quantities in the figure are given in barrels and are based on a charge of 100 bbl of a fuel oil charging stock.   The charging stock consists of 80 bbl of gas oil and 20 bbl of straight-run tar.   The charge is heated by exchangers and a heater, if necessary, and is then mixed with the hot cracked material that issues from the pipestill.   In evaporator A everything except the straight-run tar and the cracked tar is vaporized.   In the fractionator B the pressure distillate and gas are eliminated, and the gas oil and recycle stock are separated and returned to the pipestill.

The *recycle ratio* is defined as the barrels of recycle stock per barrel of fresh gas oil.   The recycle ratio for this operation is 175/80, or 2.28, and the *crack per pass* is 48.5/255, or 19 per cent.   The recycle ratio is some-times used as the barrels of recycle divided by the plant charge (100 bbl in this case).   Such a definition of recycle ratio is not logical in the system illustrated because the entire 100 bbl is not exposed to cracking conditions.

The general effect of increasing the crack or conversion per pass is as follows:

1. Lower ultimate gasoline yield.
2. Higher octane number.
3. An increased tendency to produce coke.
4. The production of more gas.
5. An increase in the volatility of the light end of the gasoline.

In most respects it is an advantage to use a low crack per pass or a high recycle ratio, but the cost of the plant is much greater.

If the percentage of distillate that is produced per pass is high, coke will be deposited in the tubes and the entire operation may be prematurely terminated.   Even traces of cracked fuel oil in the cracking still charge stock cause coke deposition.   The tar number (page 637) or carbon residue is used in testing the charge stock.   The crack per pass is definitely related to the maximum points shown in Table 19-10.   The allowable crack per pass for recycling processing is about half of the maximum yield of gasoline that can be produced in a single cracking operation.   Thus the allowable crack per pass for a liquid-phase process operating at 800°F (Table 19-10) is about 40/2, or 20 per cent, and for a vapor-phase process operating at 1184°F about 11 per cent.   For once-through processing systems the crack per pass may be larger.   The reason for the relation between the crack per pass and the maximum yield is the fact that the fresh stock is cracked much more severely than the recycle stock.   Both stocks are in the cracking zone for the same length of time, but the yield from the recycle stock is only about half as large as the yield from the gas oil. Thus the gas oil is being cracked at a yield that is closed to the maximum point, but the recycle stock is being cracked for a yield that is less than the average crack per pass (Example 19-6). At very high cracks per pass the gas oil will be cracked for a time greater than that for the maximum yield, and coke will be formed.

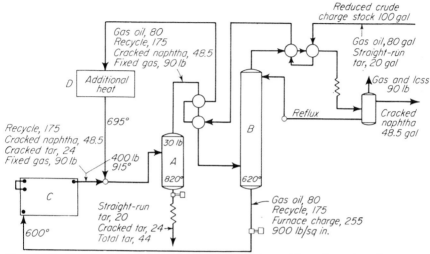

FIG. 19-7. Simple "distilled-circulation" type of cracking plant for illustrating material balance relationships.

According to Smoley, Mekler, and Schutt,[62] the conversions per pass (to gasoline) used in commercial units are:

Stock	Process	Per cent
Viscosity breaking............	Once-through	3–12
Residual stocks...............	Recycling	10–17
Gas oil......................	Recycling	15–21
Naphtha....................	Recycling	18–26

Distilled charge stocks can be cracked at somewhat higher conversions (15 to 21) than black or residual stocks (10 to 17 per cent). The higher the temperature the lower the allowable conversion per pass, and the lower the boiling range the greater the crack per pass. Finally, the higher the carbon content (residual or recycle stocks) the lower the allowable conversion per pass.

Example 19-5. Material Balance and Crack per Pass. A cracking plant such as that shown in Fig. 19-7 is to operate at a coil outlet temperature of 915°F and at 400 psig. The topped crude oil feed of 24 API has a Characterization Factor of 11.8, and it is assumed that 80 per cent of 27.0 API gas oil can be distilled from the topped

[62] Combination Selective Cracking, *Ref. Nat. Gaso. Mgr.*, June, 1937, p. 288; and other sources.

crude oil by exposure to the conditions in vessel A of Fig. 19-7.   Material balances to determine the quantities at all points will be made, and the recycle ratio and crack per pass will be estimated.

Basis: 100 gal topped crude oil.

According to Table 19-6, a fuel-oil gravity of 5 or 6 is possible if the entire residual material is cracked. In this instance the asphaltic part of the topped crude oil escapes from the system through vessel A without undergoing much cracking or viscosity breaking, and a gravity of only about 9 is feasible. The ultimate yields [Fig. 19-1 and Eq. (19-4)] based on the 24 API topped crude oil will be:

Gasoline (24–9 API)............ 48.5 per cent
Unaccounted-for loss............ 7.5
Cracked fuel oil................ 44.0

This may be checked by considering that only the 80 gal of gas oil is vigorously cracked, and thus nearly all of the cracked gasoline comes from the gas oil. The gas oil can be degraded to a 6 API fuel oil and the yields are:

Gasoline (27–6 API)............. $58 \times 0.8 = 46.5$ per cent
Unaccounted-for loss........... $10.5 \times 0.8 = 8.4$
Cracked fuel oil.......... $31.5 \times 0.8 + 20 = 45.2$

This is not a good check but it is reasonably good compared with variations sometimes encountered.[63]   In addition, a small amount of viscosity breaking of the 20 per cent of straight-run fuel oil occurs and this contributes to the gasoline yield.   The production of more gas when cracking distilled feeds, as indicated above, is a common plant experience.

Material balance of fuel oil charging stock:

Material	Per cent or gal	API	Lb per gal	Total lb
Fuel oil, charging stock.......	100	24	7.58	758
Gas oil....................	80	27	7.434	595
Straight-run tar..............	20	...	.....	163

Lb per gal of straight-run tar $^{163}\!/_{20} = 8.15$.

The API corresponding to 8.15 lb per gal is 13.1.

Material balance of plant tar:

Plant tar	Per cent or gal	API	Lb per gal	Total lb
Total tar....................	44	9.0	8.388	369
Straight-run tar..............	20	13.1	8.15	163
Cracked tar..................	24	....	.....	206

Lb per gal of cracked tar $^{206}\!/_{24} = 8.583$.

API of cracked tar is about 5.8.

[63] The author has received proposals from 5 contractors showing variations of plus or minus 20 per cent in gasoline yield (1955).

Recycle ratio:

When cracking at 915°F the allowable crack per pass is about 36 divided by 2 (Table 19-10), or 18 per cent. In general, a little higher value than this is possible, and hence 19 per cent will be used as the crack per pass. The total 48.5 gal of naphtha is 19 per cent of the charge to the furnace. Furnace charge:

$$\frac{48.5}{0.19} = 255 \text{ gal}$$

Material balance of furnace charge:

Material	Per cent or gal	API	Lb per gal	Total lb
Gas oil............................	80	27	7.43	595
Recycle....................	175	17*	7.935	1,390
Furnace charge..............	255	...	.....	1,985

* The API of recycle stock will be over half as much as the API of the gas oil, or about 17 API.

Lb per gal of furnace charge:

$$\frac{1,985}{255} = 7.78 \text{ and its API is } 20.0$$

Recycle ratio:

$$175/80 = 2.28 \text{ parts recycle per part gas oil}$$

Material leaving pipestill:

Material	Per cent or gal	API	Lb per gal	Total lb
Cracked naphtha.............	48.5	59.0	6.18	299
Recycle....................	175.0	17.0	7.93	1,390
Polymer tar................	24.0	5.8	8.58	206
Fixed gas (by difference)......	.....	....	....	90
Furnace charge..............	255.0	20.0	7.78	1,985

Recycling in Butane Plants. The thermal decomposition of butane is practiced in essentially the same manner as cracking. Differences arise only because the feeds and products have boiling ranges different from those encountered in cracking plants. The feed to the pipestill consists of butane feedstock mixed with a recycle stock that consists of propane and some butane. The propane (and excess butane) serves as a diluent in keeping the concentration of the products of decomposition to a low value just as recycle stock keeps the concentration of polymer tar to a low value in a cracking plant. The conversion per pass ranges from 5 to 13 per cent. The primary difference between the two processing schemes lies in the manner of recovering the products or in recovering the recycle stock.

In the butane plant the product is separated as a liquid in the fractionating system (or subjected directly to some process such as polymerization for utilization of the olefins) and the excess butane and propane are separated from the gaseous product to be employed as a recycle stock. Thus, butane plants require fractionating equipment similar to those used in natural gasoline plants and gas recovery systems, whereas separation systems operating at only a few pounds above atmospheric pressure are suitable for cracking plants. The butane decomposition plant shown in Fig. 19-8 should be compared directly with the cracking system shown in Fig. 19-7.

The system shown in Fig. 19-8 is usually employed with other systems such as polymerization, alkylation, etc., and such processes are inferred in

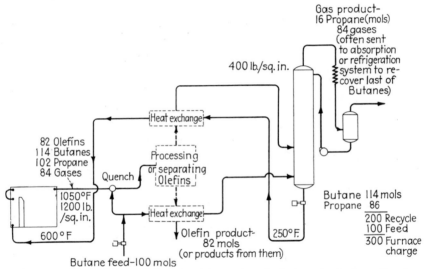

FIG. 19-8. Typical thermal-decomposition system for butane (or hydrocarbons).

the dotted-line operations indicated in the center of the diagram. High temperatures and pressures are necessary in the decomposition zone in order to care for the relatively large volume that is occupied by gaslike materials such as butane. If thermal polymerization is the process contemplated in the center of the diagram, the whole flow diagram is the same as a cracking process except that a long time element is required in the polymerization zone whereas in cracking plants the polymerization of tars, etc., is avoided in every way possible and particularly by cutting the time to a minimum.

The design of coils for the cracking of propane and ethane into ethylene is completely outlined by Schutt.[33]

Effect of Temperature. The temperature at which cracking starts to take place is between 680 and 700°F. This appears to be true even for decomposition at subatmospheric pressures (vacuum), although minor changes in color and viscosity appear at lower temperatures.

According to Fig. 19-5 and numerous investigators, the rate of thermal decomposition is found to increase rapidly with temperature. The approximate number of degrees rise in temperature that will cause the rate of decomposition to double is shown in Table 19-12.

TABLE 19-12. TEMPERATURE INCREASE WHICH CAUSES THE RATE OF CRACKING
TO DOUBLE

Decomposition temperature, °F	Rate doubles for each—	Decomposition temperature, °F	Rate doubles for each—
700	20.0°F	1100	34.5°F
800	22.0°F	1200	39.0°F
900	25.7°F	1300	44.0°F
1000	30.0°F	1700	67.0°F

The general relation among temperature, time, and yield is given by Eq. (19-19) and Fig. 19-5. It must always be recalled that these data do not apply to large yields or to situations in which polymerization (or secondary) reactions occur to such an extent that they undo the results of the primary decomposition reactions. For the usual situation, however, in which temperature varies, equations such as (19-20), (19-21), and (19-22) may be employed or the Soaking Factor method of pages 674 to 678 may be used.

Example 19-6. Temperature, Time, and Yield. The cracking operation presented in Example 19-5 will be continued. Cracking is to occur at about 915°F.

How much time is required to give a crack per pass of 19 per cent?

Basis: 255 gal of furnace charge (or 100 gal of reduced crude).

The recycle stock (155 gal) will produce only 43 per cent as much gasoline as that which accrues from the fresh stock (gas oil). (Table 19-11.)

Rate of cracking gas oil (let x = yield from gas oil):

$$255(0.19) = 80x + 0.43 \times 155x$$
$$x = 33.1$$

Simultaneous yield from recycle = 14.2 per cent

At 915°F the value of K_1 is 0.00296 (Fig. 19-5).

Time at 915°F [Eq. (19-19)]:

$$t = \frac{1}{0.00296} \ln \frac{100}{100 - 33.1} = 337 \ln 1.485 = 133 \text{ sec}$$

Note also that based on recycle stock, or on the mixture, the time is

$$t = \frac{1}{0.00122} \ln \frac{100}{100 - 14.2} = 820 \ln 1.163 = 124 \text{ sec}$$

or

$$t = \frac{1}{0.00165} \ln \frac{100}{100 - 19} = 606 \ln 1.233 = 127 \text{ sec}$$

For cracking at a constant length of time:

$$C_2 = C_0 2^{\left(\frac{T_2 - T_0}{x}\right)} \tag{19-20}$$

And for a constant yield,

$$V_2 = V_0 2^{\left(\frac{T_0 - T_2}{x}\right)} \quad \text{or} \quad = \frac{V_0}{2^{\left(\frac{T_2 - T_0}{x}\right)}} \tag{19-21}$$

where C_2 = yield for a given time at temperature T_2
C_0 = yield for a given time at temperature T_0
V_2 = time for a given yield at temperature T_2
V_0 = time for a given yield at temperature T_0
x = number of degrees required to double the yield

An equation of rate of cracking through a range of temperature can be derived by assuming that the rate of heating is uniform. If the rate of heating is far from uniform in some particular situation, the error can be reduced by considering the heating range as a series of short temperature ranges. The differential of yield with respect to time is

$$\frac{dC}{dt} = C_0 2^{\left(\frac{T - T_0}{x}\right)}$$

where C = yield during heating for time t, per cent
C_0 = yield, per cent per sec at T_0
T = final temperature, °F
T_0 = initial temperature, °F
x = a constant, average number of degrees to double yield

If the heating takes place at a uniform rate,

$$T = T_0 + kt$$

where k = rate of heating, °F per sec
t = total time, sec

$$C = \int_0^t dC = C_0 \int_0^t 2^{\left(\frac{kt + T_0 - T_0}{x}\right)} dt = C_0 \int_0^t 2^{\left(\frac{kt}{x}\right)} dt$$

$$C = C_0 \left[\frac{1}{\ln 2} \frac{x}{k} \times 2^{\left(\frac{kt}{k}\right)} - \frac{1}{\ln 2} \frac{x}{k} \right]_0^t$$

$$C = 1.44 \frac{C_0 x}{k} \left(2^{\left(\frac{kt}{x}\right)} - 1 \right) = 1.44 \frac{C_0 x t}{T - T_0} \left(2^{\left(\frac{T - T_0}{x}\right)} - 1 \right) \tag{19-22}$$

Turner and LeRoi[15] conclude from reforming tests that the octane number of the product is purely a function of time, as shown in Table 19-13.

Times of reaction are so short at 900 to 1300°F that the furnace effluent in commercial plants must be cooled rapidly (quenched). Cracked fuel oil, fresh charge stock, or recycle stock is mixed in the pipestill transfer line with the hot cracked stock, or the cooling agent is introduced into the flash chamber marked A in Fig. 19-7.

Although cracking, in the normal sense, occurs at temperatures exceeding 680°F, other less vital changes take place when oils are heated to lower temperatures. Many untreated lubricating-oil stocks are discolored if they are heated even to 300°F in the presence of air. If they are

TABLE 19-13. EFFECT OF TIME ON OCTANE NUMBER OF REFORMED PRODUCT
(45 OCTANE NAPHTHA)

Equivalent time at 900°F, sec	Octane number, Motor method	Equivalent time at 900°F, sec	Octane number, Motor method
0	45.0	500	68.5
100	55.5	600	70.5
200	60.0	700	72.0
300	63.5	900	73.5
400	66.5	1,200	75.0

heated to higher temperatures for a long time, the viscosity and the gravity are also lowered. In the author's laboratory a paraffin-base lubricating oil was redistilled three times for the purposes of separating the oil into well-fractionated products of short boiling range. During these distillations the temperature in the main body of liquid never exceeded 620°F and the pressure was kept at less than 10 mm. The oil was heated for a total time of 22 hr at 300 to 620°F. The viscosity and gravity dropped as follows:

30°F fractions boiling at these average atmospheric boiling points	Viscosity at 100°F		Sp gr	
	Before	After	Before	After
700	57	56	0.8484	0.8471
800	104	99	0.8636	0.8616
900	245	229	0.8742	0.8729
1000	415	350	0.8825	0.8794

Effect of Pressure. The technical literature offers many conclusions as to the effect of pressure on the cracking reaction, but most of these conclusions are based on experiments in which other variables, such as temperature or time, were not held constant.

The most obvious effect of pressure is the fact that a high pressure suppresses vaporization and tends to produce a liquid phase whereas a low pressure allows a vapor phase to be produced.   Obviously, a gas oil that vaporizes completely at 880°F (760 mm) cannot be cracked at 880°F at atmospheric pressure because it will be vaporized almost completely and will pass into the condenser without allowing time for cracking to occur.   The products from such an operation are tar, gas oil, and a small amount of kerosene or gasoline.   In order to produce mainly gasoline, the pressure must be sufficiently high to keep all materials, other than gasoline and gas, in the liquid phase.

In a similar manner lubricating oils or heavy distillates can be the major products of decomposition if the pressure on the cracking system is less than atmospheric[51,52] (see Fig. 19-5).   As indicated previously, the cracking reaction takes place as a series of decompositions in which the first product is lubricating oil.   At high pressures the lubricating oil remains in the system and in turn is decomposed into recycle stock, cracked kerosene, and finally gasoline and gas.   In other words, the decomposition continues until the decomposition products can vaporize at the temperature and pressure that prevail in the cracking system.   If the pressure is reduced to 30 to 100 mm, the lubricating oils that are produced during the decomposition reactions are vaporized and are automatically withdrawn from the system without decomposing into gasoline.   The fact that decomposition is much more severe when gasoline is produced than when the action is stopped at intermediate stages of decomposition is illustrated by the yields shown in Fig. 19-14.   The tabulation shows the yields when a 10 API Mid Continent straight-run tar is decomposed to produce coke by using different pressures in the equipment.   In each run the products were gas, coke, and the major liquid product shown in Table 19-14.   Thus, if a large molecule is decomposed into relatively small molecules such as those in gasoline, the yield is low; whereas if the decomposition is carried only to the production of molecules such as those found in lubricating oil, the yields are considerably larger.

The important effect of pressure on the phase condition in the reaction coil will be discussed under the next heading.

In addition to the aforementioned purely mechanical effects of pressure, the properties of gasolines produced at a high pressure are somewhat different from those produced at a low pressure.   Sachanen and Tilicheyev[64] report that the amount of unsaturated hydrocarbons found in gasoline produced at moderate cracking conditions decreases by about half as the pressure is increased from 10 to 40 atm.   But at the same time the percentage of naphthene hydrocarbons increases about 12 to 16 per cent. The increase in the percentage of naphthene hydrocarbons is even greater in the cracked kerosene fraction.   They also find that the yield of gasoline

[64] *Oil Gas J.*, Nov. 28, 1929, p. 46.

is slightly less at high pressures.   This may be explained by the decomposition of part of the gasoline into fixed gas by the prolonged time of cracking.[65]   However, Keith, Ward, and Rubin[66] and LeRoi and Ferguson[12] report just the opposite effect of pressure.   Keith finds that the gas loss is three times as much at 100 as at 1,000 psi.   Commercial practice also indicates that the gas loss is less at high pressures.   Most experimenters[12,66] find that the octane number decreases as the pressure is increased if the same amount of cracking is practiced.

Liquid-phase and Vapor-phase Operation.   In general, three phase conditions are recognized in commercial processes.   If the pressure is relatively low, so that a pure vapor phase can be produced at the cracking temperature, the process may be classed as vapor phase.   Vapor-phase processes are not successful unless a vapor that is free from liquid is produced, because coke will be deposited in the tubes.   At higher pressures and lower cracking temperatures a mixed phase results.

TABLE 19-14. YIELDS BY VACUUM DECOMPOSITION OF ASPHALT

Run number	Total liquid product	Per cent total distillate
. . .	Gasoline, computed from Eq. (19-6)........	53
1	Kerosene..............................	63
2	Gas oil (35 API)........................	65
3	Lubricating oil (600 vis. at 100°F).........	69
4	Heavy lubricating oil (93 vis. at 210°F).....	72

The ideal condition, from the standpoint of heating, would be either a pure liquid or pure vapor phase, but commercially it may be necessary to be satisfied with a *pseudo homogeneous phase* condition.   As a mixed phase is heated, it is necessary to avoid segregation of the liquid from the vapor.   This may be accomplished in two ways: (1) by maintaining such a high velocity that the liquid is scoured from the heating walls or (2) by maintaining a pressure that is high enough to cause the density of the vapor to be about as large as the density of the liquid.   Most of the hydrocarbons found in recycle stock and pressure distillate have critical pressures that are less than 500 psi, and hence these materials occupy a relatively small volume even though they are in the form of vapor.   For this reason, a back pressure larger than 350 psig is held on the reaction

[65] The bomb equipment that Sachanen and Tilicheyev used promoted the cracking of gasoline by allowing part of it to condense and drip back into the cracking vessel. In some tests they kept the products of cracking in the cracking still until the test was completed.

[66] The Cracking of M. C. Virgin Gas Oil . . . Range of Temperature and Pressure, *Proc. API, Refining Division,* 1933.

coils of mixed-phase processes.   Nearly all modern processes are mixed-phase processes.   In vapor-phase processes the pressure is normally less than 100 psig and often only 15 or 35 psig.

Volume at Decomposition Conditions.   No single factor is of greater practical importance in cracking-plant design than the computation of volumes of liquids and vapors at cracking-zone conditions.   Volume is directly related to time in the cracking zone and to the friction loss.

Volumes may be computed with reasonable accuracy by the use of Figs. 5-9, 5-12, 5-13, and 5-15, but careful consideration must be given to

TABLE 19-15. PROPERTIES OF THE FURNACE CHARGE STOCKS OF FIG. 19-9

Curve	API	Character- ization Factor	Recycle ratio	Aniline point, °F	Cracking temp, °F	Source
1	24.7	11.05	....	...	.....	Wagner[a]
2	24.7	11.2	....	...	.....	Wagner[a]
3	25.6	11.2	....	...	.....	Wagner[a]
4[b]	20.0[b]	10.75[b]	2.4[b]	...	920	3 plant tests, author
5[b]	19.0[b]	10.6[b]	1.7[b]	...	930	2 plant tests, author
6[c]	20.8[c]	10.85[c]	2.0[c]	...	.....	Commercial vapor phase author[c]
7	24.8	10.9	3.0	...	.....	Huntington & Brown[d]
8	24.5	11.2	....	...	.....	Allen & Duckwall[e]
9[f]	18.7[f]	10.72[f]	....	...	.....	Allen & Duckwall[e]
10	31.4	10.65	4.1	66	1,070	3 vapor phase tests, author
11	21.8	10.7	3.3	67	1,097	5 vapor phase tests, author
12	21.5	10.6	2.58	56	1,100	2 vapor phase tests, author
13[f]	30.6[f]	11.05[f]	....	...	.....	Naphtha reforming

[a] Cracking Recycle Stock, *Oil Gas J.*, Sept. 30, 1943, p. 45.
[b] 745°F evaporator temperature, and pressure distillate end points of 440 to 445°F.
[c] Recycle 2 parts and Mid Continent reduced crude 1 part, a black feed.
[d] *Ind. Eng. Chem.*, **27**, 699 (1935).
[e] *Pet. Refiner*, February, 1945, p. 89.
[f] Pure recycle stock rather than furnace charge.

the physical properties of the stocks.   For example, should the gravity of the recycle stock be assumed to be 15 API, whereas the actual value is 17, the results may be somewhat misleading.   Small errors become very important, because the stocks are at or near their critical points and a small misjudgment may shift the behavior of the material from that of a vapor to that of a liquid.

The extent of vaporization may be estimated by drawing flash-vaporization curves of the stocks (Figs. 4-18 and 4-19) and correcting these curves for pressure by means of Fig. 5-27, but more precise results can be obtained by drawing the phase envelopes of the outlet material and also that of the furnace feed if it is low boiling enough to be vaporized to any extent at cracking conditions. The construction of such phase envelopes is discussed on pages 452 to 461 (Figs. 15-9 to 15-12), and Example 19-8 indicates the general procedure.

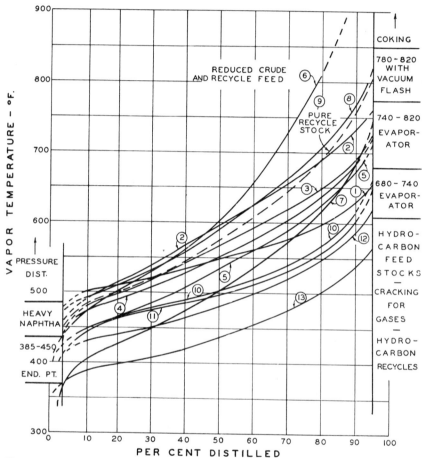

Fig. 19-9. True-boiling-point curves of distilled charge stocks except curve 6, which contains some residual material. (See Table 19-15 for kinds of materials.)

The distillation curves of several distilled furnace feedstocks are indicated in Fig. 19-9 and meager information about them in Table 19-15.[67,68,69,70]

[67] Nelson, W. L., *Oil Gas J.*, Dec. 27, 1951, p. 84.
[68] Wagner, C. R., Cracking Recycle Stock, *Oil Gas J.*, Sept. 30, 1943, p. 45.
[69] Huntington and Brown, *Ind. Eng. Chem.*, **27**, 699 (1935).
[70] Allen and Duckwall, *Pet. Refiner*, February 1945, p. 89.

The front end of the distillation curves is fairly well defined by the end point of the light product, and the high-boiling end by the extent to which recycle stock is vaporized from the cracked fuel oil (or coke). However, if the furnace charge stock contains residual material (topped or reduced crude oil, etc.) the high-boiling end of the distillation curve depends entirely on the distillation curve of the residue material (see curve 6, Fig. 19-9). Inasmuch as high-boiling materials decompose most readily (see Fig. 19-5), such materials are eliminated more completely from the recycle stock (and the furnace charge). Recycle stocks (low Characterization Factor) usually have lower boiling ranges than the parent feed (but see curve 13 of Fig. 19-9). This results in relatively large amounts of low-boiling material in the recycle stock and in the furnace charge stock (Fig. 19-9). The higher the cracking temperature, the lower the boiling range of the furnace charge stock and the lower the Characterization Factor of the recycle stock. Extensive recycling tends to lower the boiling range of the furnace charge stock. Only curves 9 and 13 are pure recycle stocks, nor were the data adequate for an estimation of the distillation curves of other pure recycle stocks.

Example 19-7.   Increase in Volume during Cracking.   Example 19-5 provides data by which the volume increase can be computed. In this example the weight of fixed gas per 100 gal of charging stock was 90 lb. The density of cracked gas, if liquefied and measured at 60°F, would be approximately 3 lb per gal.

$$\text{The volume of fixed gas (liquid)} = {}^{90}\!/_{3} = 30 \text{ gal}$$

The total liquid yield measured at 60° is

Gal

Pressure distillate.............	48.5
Fuel oil (cracked).............	44.0
Fixed gas....................	30.0
	122.5

Thus the charge increased by 22.5 per cent in volume during cracking.

Although the gas cannot be liquefied at 60°F, it may be dissolved in the other parts of the furnace stock at high pressures, and hence the volume as computed above becomes valuable for computing the volume of the cracking stock while it is in the furnace tubes.

Example 19-8.   Cracking Still Design.   The coil conditions necessary to crack the materials studied in Examples 19-5 to 19-7 will be investigated. Cracking will be conducted in the radiant section of a still which delivers 12,000 Btu per sq ft of projected area, and an actual capacity of 3,000 bpd of reduced crude oil rather than 100 gal (Examples 19-5 to 19-7) will be considered. Such a basis is 52.5 times larger.

$$\frac{3{,}000 \times {}^{42}\!/_{24}}{100} = 52.5$$

Basis: 3,000 bpd reduced crude oil. Refer to Table 19-16 for the quantities and properties of the materials.

The distillation and flash vaporization curves were computed for the furnace feed, the effluent, and for the material when it was half cracked, as indicated in Fig. 19-10. In estimating the distillation curves, the mid boiling points of Table 19-16 were used, along with a terminal temperature of 770°F for the recycle stock (see Fig. 19-9), and an initial boiling point of 590°F for the gas oil. It was judged that material boiling up to 1000°F could be vaporized (into the gas oil) by exposure of the reduced crude oil in vessel A of Fig. 19-7.

Phase envelopes were also computed for the feed, the effluent, and the material after the reaction was half complete, as indicated in Figs. 19-11 and 19-12. They are not of much use except in a general way in judging the situation in the coil at various degrees of reaction. However, they were used to raise the atmospheric E.F.V. curves to various coil pressures as indicated for the effluent at 415 psia in Fig. 19-10.

TABLE 19-16. PROPERTIES OF MATERIALS FOR EXAMPLE 19-8

| | Per cent by volume | | Gph | API | Lb per hr | C.F. (UOP) | 50% bp | | Mol. wt | Mole per hr |
	In	Out					Molal	Liq. vol.		
Fixed gas.........	....	10.8	1,575	....	4,720	....	...	...	33	143
Cracked naphtha..	....	17.5	2,545	59.0	15,700	11.7	200	220	90	174
Cracked tar.......	....	8.6	1,260	5.8	10,800	10.6	840	860	350	31
Gas oil..........	31.4	....	4,200	27.0	31,200	11.8	720	780	330	94
Recycle stock.....	68.6	63.1	9,180	17.0	73,000	10.6	575	610	210	348
Furnace charge....	100.0	....	13,380	20.0	104,200	11.0	...	...	...	442
Furnace effluent...	....	100.0	14,560	33.3	104,200	....	...	...	...	696

Figure 4-22 was actually used in raising the E.F.V. curves to various pressures because the scales that are necessary in such figures as 19-11 and 19-12 cannot be precise.

Zone 1. Consider the last tubes of the still. The outlet pressure is 400 psig (415 psia), and a temperature, after much trial and error, of 912°F was selected. According to Fig. 19-10 and the phase envelopes, about 76 per cent is vaporized at the outlet of the still. About half of the cracking will be done in this zone and the pressure drop will be about 190 psi. This indicates scarcely any material will be vaporized at the inlet to the zone. Note that all of these conclusions must be checked by the trial-and-error computations which follow.

The average amount of vaporization is (76 + 0) ÷ 2 = about 38%

At 75% cracked, the gas and naphtha constitute 0.75 × 28.3 = 21.2%

Moles at (100 + 50) ÷ 2 or 75% cracked are:

Fixed gas 0.75 × 143   = 107 moles
Naphtha 0.75 × 174   = 131

Recycle and gas oil $\dfrac{38 - 21.2}{91.4 - 21.2}$ (348 + 23) = $\dfrac{89}{327}$ moles

At an average pressure of 510 psia and at 902°F, the compressibility factor is about 0.37, but note that an average (rather than the 50 per cent) boiling point must be used for such a wide-boiling mixture and also that the pseudo critical point of Figs. 5-9

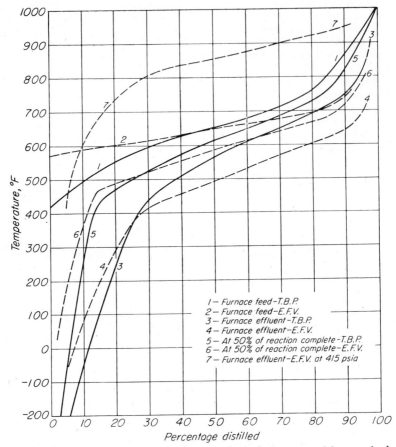

Fig. 19-10. Estimates of distillation and atmospheric-flash curves of furnace feed and effluent of Example 19-8, and the equilibrium-flash-vaporization curve of the effluent at 415 psia.

and 5-12 is used in computing compressibility. The approximate volume is

$$\text{Cu ft per sec } 0.37 \times 327 \times \frac{379}{3600} \times \frac{14.7}{510} \times \frac{1362}{520} = 0.961$$

$$\text{Volume of liquid } \frac{0.61}{3600} \times \frac{5250}{7.48} \times \frac{0.934}{0.6} \qquad = \underline{0.185}$$
$$\overline{1.156 \text{ cu ft per sec}}$$

$$\text{Density } \frac{104,200}{3,600} \times \frac{1}{1.156} = 25 \text{ lb per cu ft}$$

A 3.25 i.d. tube (4.0 o.d.) gives a mass velocity of:

$$G = \frac{104,200}{3,600} \times \frac{1}{0.0575} = 504 \text{ lb per sec per sq ft}$$
$$G^2 = 253,000$$

This is a higher cold velocity (8.4 ft per sec) than those customarily employed (5 to 8 ft per sec), and accordingly, the pressure drop will be relatively high in this design.

Velocity: $1.156 \div 0.0575 = 20.1$ ft per sec

Time of cracking at 904°F $= \ln \left(\dfrac{a}{a-x} \right) \div K$

$$t = \ln \frac{90.5}{90.5 - 9.5} \div 0.00125 = \frac{0.111}{0.00125} = 89.0 \text{ sec}$$

Reaction length: $20.1 \times 89 = 1,785$ ft
Heated length, approx.: $1,785 \times {}^{28}\!\!/_{30} = 1,670$ ft
Equivalent length, approx. (incl. bends): $1,785 \times 1.3 = 2,320$ ft

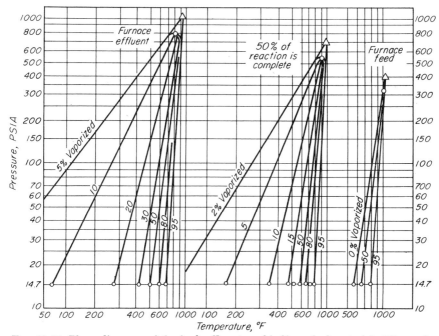

Fig. 19-11. Phase diagrams of the feed, effluent, and half-cracked material of Example 19-8 (also see Fig. 19-12).

At a heat input of 12,000 Btu per hr per sq ft of projected area, the duty of the zone is:

$$1,670 \times {}^{4}\!/_{12} \times 12,000 = 6,680,000 \text{ Btu per hr}$$
less $\quad \Delta H_D = 15,700 \times 0.5 \times 600 = \underline{4,710,000} \text{ Btu per hr}$
$$\overline{1,970,000} \text{ Btu per hr}$$

In this instance no heat of vaporization is needed because the vaporization is taking place at or above the critical temperatures of the components.

Temp rise approx.: $\dfrac{1,970,000}{104,200 \times 0.84 \times 0.96} = 23.5°\text{F}$

Thus, the use of a 902°F average temperature was substantially correct.

$$\Delta P = \frac{2fG^2L}{144gD\rho} = \frac{2 \times 0.005 \times 253{,}000 \times 2{,}320 \times 12}{144 \times 32.2 \times 3.25 \times 25}$$

$$= 2.02 \times \frac{L}{\rho} = 187 \text{ psi}$$

This also is a check on the assumed ΔP of 190 psi.

In summary, at the entrance to the zone:

$$\text{Temp} = 912 - 24 = 888°F$$
$$\text{Pressure} = 415 + 187 = 602 \text{ psia}$$

One-half of the cracking has already occurred.

Vaporization is approximately zero.

Zone 2.   The material is a liquid throughout this zone, and the phase state is not significant because the vapor has nearly the same density as the liquid.   Although Fig. 5-14 can be used in approximating liquid densities, the method which employs Fig. 5-15 is necessary at the high pressures of this operation.

Assume 33.3 per cent conversion in zone 2.   Density of the liquid (Fig. 5-15) at an average temperature of 875°F is about 0.59 or 36.8 lb per cu ft.   At an average reaction temperature of 880°F

$$\text{Time: ln} \frac{96.8}{96.8 - 6.3} \div 0.00065 = \frac{0.0676}{0.00065} = 104 \text{ sec}$$

$$\text{Volume:} \frac{104{,}200}{3{,}600} \times \frac{1}{36.8} = 0.786 \text{ cu ft per sec}$$

$$\text{Velocity:} \frac{0.786}{0.0575} = 13.7 \text{ ft per sec}$$

Travel: $13.7 \times 104 = 1{,}423$ ft
Heated length, approx.: $1{,}423 \times {}^{28}\!\!/\!{}_{30} = 1{,}330$ ft
Equivalent length, approx.: $1{,}423 \times 1.3 = 1{,}850$ ft
Heat input: $1{,}330 \times {}^4\!\!/\!{}_{12} \times 12{,}000 = 5{,}320{,}000$ Btu per hr
Less ΔH_D: $15{,}700 \times 0.33 \times 640 = 3{,}340{,}000$ Btu per hr

For sensible temperature rise $= 1{,}980{,}000$ Btu per hr

$$\text{Temp rise, approx:} \frac{1{,}980{,}000}{104{,}200 \times 0.9 \times 0.96} = 22.1°F$$

This nearly checks the assumed temperature range of 24°F.

$$\Delta P = 2.02 \frac{L}{\rho} = 2.02 \frac{1850}{36.8} = 101.5 \text{ psi}$$

Summarizing zone 2, at the inlet:

$$\text{Temp} = 888 - 22 = 866°F$$
$$\text{Pressure} = 602 + 101 = 703 \text{ psia}$$

$16\frac{2}{3}\%$ of the cracking occurred ahead of this zone.

Zone 3.   The remaining one-sixth of the cracking will be accomplished in this zone.

The density of the cracking stock at an average temperature of 836°F is about 0.66 (Fig. 5-15) or 41.1 lb per cu ft.   However, a temperature of 850°F was used as more nearly the average reaction temperature.

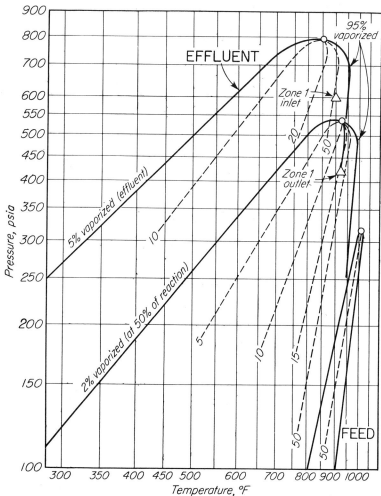

Fig. 19-12. Enlargement of the phase diagrams of Fig. 19-11 (Example 19-8) showing conditions at the inlet and outlet of zone 1.

Time: $\ln \dfrac{100}{100 - 3.2} \div 0.00028 = \dfrac{0.0315}{0.00028} = 112$ sec

Velocity: $\dfrac{104,200}{3,600} \times \dfrac{1}{41.1 \times 0.0575} = 12.25$ ft per sec

Travel: $12.25 \times 112 = 1,385$ ft
Heated length, approx.: $1,385 \times {}^{28}\!\!/_{30} = 1,295$ ft
Equivalent length, approx.: $= 1,800$ ft
Heat input: $1,295 \times {}^{4}\!\!/_{12} \times 12,000 = 5,180,000$ Btu per hr
Less ΔH_D: $15,700 \times 0.167 \times 670 = 1,750,000$ Btu per hr
$\overline{ 3,430,000}$ Btu per hr

Temp rise: $\dfrac{3{,}430{,}000}{104{,}200 \times 0.86 \times 0.96} = 40°F$

$$\Delta P = \frac{2 \times 0.0043 \times 253{,}000 \times 1{,}800 \times 12}{144 \times 32.2 \times 3.25 \times 41.1}$$

$$= 75.7 \text{ psi}$$

Thus, these computations indicate that most cracking occurs after a temperature of 826°F has been attained. Although this is substantially correct, a small amount actually occurs between 680 and 826°F. The situation was checked by assuming only 33 per cent cracking rather than 50 per cent in zone 1, and although the same temperature curve was obtained, this pushed the inlet temperature to zone 3 down to 677°F, which is obviously in error in the opposite way. The zones are summarized in Table 19-17.

TABLE 19-17

	Temp range, °F	Psia	Coil length, ft
Zone 1..........	888–912	415–602	1,785
Zone 2..........	866–888	602–703	1,423
Zone 3..........	826–866	703–779	1,385
Zone 4..........	700–826	779–947	2,740

Examination of the computations of Example 19-8 shows that vaporization is a function almost entirely of the amount of cracking that has occurred, and that pressure drop has little effect on the vaporization. It also clearly indicates that the densities of the vapors are not greatly different from those of the liquids, and this further depreciates the effect of vaporization on the velocity and time in the reaction zones.

Soaking Factor. If the temperature and pressure curves are available, as in an existing plant or in experimental operation, the so-called "Soaking Factor" may be used to compare the effect of various temperatures and capacities (or velocities) on the extent of the cracking. It is of little use in the design of stills, but it is valuable during operations.

$$(\text{S.F.})_{750} = \int_0^V R \, \frac{k_T}{k_{800}} \frac{dV}{F} \tag{19-23}$$

where R = a standard correction for pressures other than 750 psig obtained from Fig. 19-13

k_T/k_{800} = relative cracking reaction velocity at temperature T, obtained from Table 19-18

dV/F = differential reactor coil volume in cu ft per bbl of daily throughput

In words, the Soaking Factor is defined as the equivalent coil volume in cubic feet per daily barrel of charge (60°F) if the reaction occurred at 800°F and at a pressure of 750 psig. In addition, it applies only to the

TABLE 19-18. RELATIVE REACTION VELOCITIES IN THERMAL CRACKING, k_T/k_{800} [FOR USE WITH EQ. (19-23)] FOR ONE-DEGREE INCREMENTS

Temp °F	0	1	2	3	4	5	6	7	8	9
800	1.00	1.03	1.06	1.09	1.12	1.16	1.19	1.23	1.26	1.31
10	1.35	1.40	1.44	1.49	1.53	1.58	1.64	1.69	1.75	1.81
20	1.87	1.94	2.00	2.06	2.13	2.20	2.27	2.35	2.42	2.49
30	2.57	2.65	2.73	2.82	2.90	2.99	3.08	3.18	3.27	3.37
40	3.47	3.57	3.68	3.78	3.90	4.01	4.12	4.25	4.37	4.49
50	4.61	4.74	4.87	5.00	5.13	5.27	5.41	5.55	5.69	5.84
60	6.00	6.17	6.33	6.50	6.68	6.87	7.04	7.24	7.44	7.63
70	7.83	8.03	8.23	8.43	8.64	8.84	9.04	9.25	9.48	9.70
80	9.92	10.15	10.4	10.6	10.9	11.1	11.4	11.7	11.9	12.2
90	12.5	12.8	13.1	13.5	13.8	14.1	14.5	14.9	15.2	15.6
900	16.0	16.4	16.8	17.3	17.7	18.1	18.5	19.0	19.4	19.9
10	20.3	20.8	21.3	21.8	22.3	22.8	23.3	23.8	24.3	24.8
20	25.3	25.9	26.4	27.0	27.5	28.1	28.8	29.4	30.0	30.6
30	31.4	32.1	32.8	33.5	34.3	35.0	35.8	36.6	37.5	38.4
40	39.2	40.0	40.9	41.8	42.7	43.6	44.5	45.4	46.4	47.4
50	48.5	49.5	50.5	51.6	52.6	53.6	54.6	55.6	56.6	57.6
60	58.8	59.8	60.8	61.9	63.1	64.2	65.4	66.6	67.8	69.0
70	70.3	71.6	72.8	74.0	75.3	76.6	77.9	79.2	80.5	81.8
80	83.3	84.6	85.9	87.3	88.7	90.1	91.5	92.9	94.4	95.9
90	97.3	98.8	100	101	103	104	106	108	109	110
1000	112	113	114	116	118	119	121	122	124	125
10	127	129	130	132	134	135	137	139	140	142
20	144	146	148	149	151	153	155	156	158	160
30	161	163	165	167	169	170	172	174	176	178
40	179	181	183	185	187	188	190	192	194	196
50	198	199	201	203	205	207	209	211	213	215
60	217	218	220	222	224	226	228	230	233	235
70	237	239	241	243	245	247	249	251	253	256
80	258	260	262	264	267	269	271	273	275	278
90	280	282	285	287	289	292	294	296	298	301
1100	303	305	308	310	312	315	317	319	321	324

cracking of distillate or gas-oil stocks, and this implies that the material is in the form of a vapor during the reaction.

Note that k/k_{800} is not simply the ratio of the K values read from Fig. 19-5 because it contains a correction for the effect of temperature on the volume of the reacting material. The ratio of k/k_{800} must be read from Table 19-18. Derivation[71] of the Soaking Factor relationship for gases indicates the following:

$$(\text{S.F.})_{750} = \frac{[-\delta x - (1 + \delta) \ln (1 - x)]zs}{14 K_{800} \nu M} \qquad (19\text{-}24)$$

[71] Prof. Paul A. Buthod, Chairman, Dept. Chemical and Refinery Engineering, University of Tulsa.

where δ = moles product minus moles reactant per mole reactant

     x = fraction of original moles (fresh and recycle) reacted (conversion per pass)

     v = fugacity coefficient (often = 1.0)

     K_{800} = reaction velocity constant at 800°F (Fig. 19-5)

     M = molecular weight of feed

     s = specific gravity of feed at 60°F

     z = compressibility factor, average throughout the reaction coil

The Soaking Factor ranges from about 0.03 for viscosity breaking practiced on the lowest gravity pitches (5 to 7 API) to about 1.2 in cracking

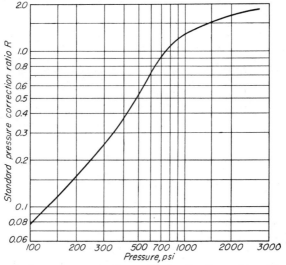

Fig. 19-13. Standard pressure-correction ratios for the thermal cracking of distillate feeds.

light gas oil. The plant studied in Example 19-8 requires a Soaking Factor of about 0.70 (Example 19-9) and this is representative of values for heavy gas-oil cracking. There is some doubt about whether or not the pressure correction factor should be applied to sections of the coil in which nothing but liquid is present (or to viscosity-breaking operations). However, some type of correction is necessary in viscosity breaking if the pressure is very low (100 to 150 psia).

Example 19-9. Soaking Factor. The coil operating conditions of Example 19-8 will be examined to determine the Soaking Factor. Figure 19-14 is a plot of the coil volume versus temperature and pressure for the range above 800°F. The integration is accomplished in Table 19-19 by the graphical or finite increment method. Columns (1) and (2) show increments of coil volume per daily barrel throughput. The average temperatures are shown in column (3) and the values of k/k_{800} from Table 19-18

TABLE 19-19. FINITE INCREMENT INTEGRATION FOR SOAKING FACTOR

(1)	(2)	(3)	(4)	(5)	(6)	(7)
Coil increments	$\dfrac{\Delta V}{F}$	Temp, °F	k/k_{800}	Pressure, psia	Pressure correction (R)	$R \times \dfrac{k}{k_{800}} \times \dfrac{\Delta V}{F}$
0.00–0.01	0.01	816	1.64	790	1.07	0.0175
0.01–0.02	0.01	841	3.57	755	1.01	0.0361
0.02–0.03	0.01	858	5.69	720	0.95	0.0540
0.03–0.04	0.01	871	8.03	683	0.89	0.0715
0.04–0.05	0.01	880	9.92	645	0.83	0.0823
0.05–0.06	0.01	889	12.2	605	0.72	0.0878
0.06–0.07	0.01	896	14.5	565	0.65	0.0941
0.07–0.08	0.01	902	16.8	524	0.57	0.0957
0.08–0.09	0.01	907	19.0	480	0.50	0.0950
0.09–0.098	0.008	911	20.8	435	0.42	0.0700
					Soaking Factor	0.7040

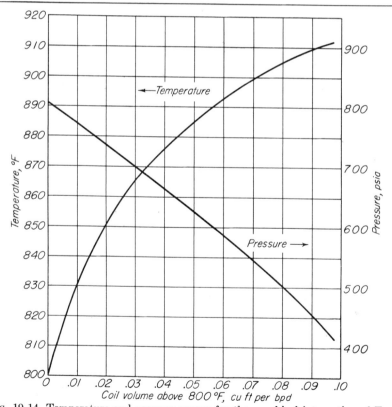

FIG. 19-14. Temperature and pressure curves for the graphical integration of Example 19-9.

in column (4). Likewise, column (5) shows average pressures for each of the coil increments and column (6) the pressure correction factors from Fig. 19-13.   The last column shows the integral (area under the temperature curve of Fig. 19-14).

The application of Eq. (19-24) is confusing on one point, namely, the selection of an average compressibility factor z.   However, the results are as follows:

δ (Table 19-16) $= (696 - 442)/442 = 0.575$
x for the mixture of recycle and gas oil $= 0.19$ (Example 19-6)
$\nu = 1$ (usually)
K for the mixture at 800°F $=$ about 0.00007
M (Table 19-16) $=$ about 250
$s = 0.934$ (20 API)

The value of z was 0.37 for zone 1 of Example 19-8, but the material was a liquid in the other zones.   Thus, an equivalent z might range from 0.6 to 0.9.

$$(S.F.)_{750} = \frac{[-\delta x - (1 + \delta) \ln (1 - x)]zs}{14K_{800}\nu M}$$

$$= \frac{[-0.575 \times 0.19 - (1.575) \ln (1 - 0.19)]0.934z}{14 \times 0.00007 \times 1.0 \times 250}$$

$$= 0.85z$$

Thus, the Soaking Factors for various values of z are:

z	S.F.
0.37	0.314
0.6	0.51
0.825	0.70
0.9	0.765

PRACTICE OF CRACKING

Modern cracking processes are expected to produce a large yield of gasoline, produce little coke, and be able to operate for a long time before cleaning is necessary.   The percentage of time that the unit is in operation is the cycle time efficiency.   The expense of shutdown is so great that it is usually economical to sacrifice some yield rather than suffer a poor cycle efficiency.   This also accounts for the relatively small amount of coking that is practiced.   The yield by cracking is much greater if coke, rather than fuel oil, is produced, but the cost of operating a coking plant is great.

Cracking processes may be generally classified as follows:

1. *Viscosity Breaking.* A short-time decomposition, usually conducted at low cracking temperatures (860–900°F), for the purpose of reducing the viscosity or pour point of a heavy straight-run fuel oil.
2. *Mixed-phase Cracking.* Most of the widely known processes are classed as mixed-phase processes.   The name liquid phase, which is often used, is a misnomer, because in most processes some vapor generation occurs.   The purpose is the production of antiknock gasoline and a greater total yield of gasoline from crude oil.

3. *Reforming.* A high-temperature cracking process that utilizes straight-run gasoline or naphtha as a charging stock. The cracked distillate has a much higher octane number than the charging stock. The feasibility of the process depends upon the market demand for high-octane fuel.

4. *Selective Cracking.* A process in which the charge stock is separated into several parts, each part being cracked separately under the most favorable conditions for that part. Many plants now utilize four cracking coils: one for viscosity breaking, another for reforming, and two other coils to handle light and heavy charge stocks.

5. *Combination Cracking.* A process involving the four processes enumerated above and one that in the extreme might also involve topping of crude oil, gas recovery, and even coking (see Fig. 19-21).

6. *Vapor-phase Cracking.* These processes are usually more expensive than the liquid-phase processes, and although the gasoline has a high octane number it also contains large amounts of gum. No processes for producing gasoline are in operation today.

7. *Coking.* The operation of coking involves nothing more than a cracking process in which the time of cracking is so long that coke is produced as the bottoms product. Special means of collecting and removing the coke must be provided, and a market must be available for the coke.

Cracking Plant Design. In the liquid- or mixed-phase processes, the reaction pressure is usually held above 350 psi, whereas in the vapor-phase processes the pressure is usually held below 50 psi. The importance of a *homogeneous phase* must again be stressed. If any liquid particles are present in the vapor, they will be thrown to the tube walls and cause the formation of coke.

The time of cracking in modern processes ranges from about 1 sec for some vapor-phase processes to about 200 sec for liquid-phase processes, and hence most processes are arranged so that the hot cracked material can be suddenly cooled or *quenched* by means of the charge stock or fuel oil from the process.

Quenching is particularly necessary at the transition condition at and about the dew point.[72] Traces of liquid tend to wet the walls of the line or equipment, and if the temperature is high, decomposition and coking occur. In order to cut the time to a minimum throughout the transition zone, quenching is sometimes conducted to much lower temperatures than would seem to be necessary.

Another factor that is vital in the operation of many cracking systems is the production of a *clean distilled stock.* If a residual product is to be cracked, the gas oil that it contains may be distilled from it in a topping operation; this topping may be conducted in the cracking plant itself, or the system may be arranged so that only straight-run tar is cracked. Although the cracking of a distilled stock is advantageous from the standpoint of a high crack per pass and in some instances the cycle time efficiency, the yield of pressure distillate is usually slightly smaller than when a *residual* or *black stock* is cracked. If a distilled stock is produced from a

---

[72] Smith, J. H., Transeconomizers, *Oil Gas J.,* Aug. 3, 1950, p. 45.

black charging stock, a part of the charging stock is not thoroughly cracked, and therefore the yield is smaller. Likewise, the tar that is produced by cracking only the distilled part of a black charging stock tends to have a high viscosity, and the yield of distillate must be less in order to produce a tar of suitable viscosity. The now well-established Dubbs process was one of the first to avoid serious coking of the tubes when cracking a black stock. In summary, *clean* stocks (distilled or black) contain no *cracked tar*.

The use of a quench stock, the production of a homogeneous phase, the use of recycling, and the cracking of stocks that contain no cracked tar are details that are not easily recognized in flow diagrams of processes, but close inspection reveals that all successful processes utilize these principles. The rate of heat absorption (Table 18-5) in the pipestill usually ranges from 25,000 to 40,000 Btu per sq ft of projected area (8,000 to 13,000 Btu per sq ft outside-diameter surface). These somewhat low rates can be produced in the radiant section by using a large amount of radiant surface, by using flue-gas recirculation, or theoretically by using large amounts of excess air. Part of the convection section may be used for the cracking zone, but the exact location in the convection section cannot be easily determined. Some engineers believe that cracking must take place at a constant or slightly rising temperature, or coke will be deposited. Coke is usually cut from the tubes by mechanical cleaners, but more and more refiners are decoking the tubes by means of steam and air.[73] The method is clean and rapid (6 to 10 hr), and little polishing is necessary during the inspection, but the tubes must be watched carefully throughout the entire heating so that they do not lose their heat-treatment. After regular steamout, the fires are lighted and a temperature of 1150 to 1300°F is maintained. Steam is passed through the tubes, and air is introduced with the steam either continuously or occasionally at such a rate that the red-hot spot never exceeds a medium cherry red. The hot spot moves slowly along the tube coil until finally the entire length of the coil is traversed. Details of the operation and an equipment layout are given in Reference 73.

Selective Cracking. Each stock has particular characteristics that govern the best conditions of temperature, pressure, etc., for cracking the stock. This fact is utilized in selective combination cracking units in which the refractory stocks are cracked for a long period of time or at a higher temperature and the less stable stocks are cracked at lower temperatures. Thus, for a four-coil (or heater) unit operating on Mid Continent stocks, temperatures and pressures[16,62] are about as follows:

[73] Anon., Decoking Heater Tubes with Steam, Air Saves Time . . . , *Pet. Processing*, Aug. 7, 1946, p. R-577.

	Temperature, °F	Outlet pressure, psi
Viscosity-breaking heater............	870–890	230–250
Heavy oil heater..................	920–960	300–500
Light oil heater...................	950–990	500–700
Reforming heater (once-through) or	975–1000	650–800
Polyforming (once-through).........	1000–1125	1,000–2,000

Larger yields are obtained in this manner, and for very large plants the use of selective cracking is always justified. In smaller plants the erection of several pipestills is costly, or the operation of several coils in one furnace is difficult, and hence the position of selective cracking is not clear. Separate evaporators may be used for each stock, but common practice is to use a single evaporator into which all stocks are led (Fig. 19-21).

In wide-boiling-range stocks the refractory low-boiling parts are insufficiently cracked at low temperatures, with the result that they accumulate in the recycle stock—or at high temperatures the high-boiling parts are cracked so violently that coke formation takes place.

Tubestill Processes. Nearly all processes, particularly the Donnelly, the Winkler-Koch, and the Dubbs, discovered at much the same time the possibilities of conducting cracking in the tubes of a pipestill, and hence the general process so evolved is referred to as the tubestill process. Practically all the cracking takes place within the furnace tubes so that no reaction chambers are required. The success of the process is largely due to the production of a clean cracking stock which can be cracked with the production of little or no coke. A small amount of decomposition also takes place in the evaporator (Fig. 19-15) or flash drum, but this decomposition is not important, except as it aids in reducing the viscosity of the pressure-still tar and in producing additional clean recycle stock. The vapor heat exchangers shown in Fig. 19-15 are a source of difficulty, and the use of an additional pipestill heater is a better arrangement.

In order to crack the oil in the short length of time during which it passes through the tubes, a high temperature is necessary. The pipestill outlet temperature is about 890 to 975°F depending on the stock, and the time for cracking is only 2 or 3 min. At these rapid rates of cracking it is necessary to lower the temperature quickly. This is accomplished at the point marked "quench" in Fig. 19-15 by mixing the charging stock with the cracked material from the pressure still. Mixing in this manner is a perfect means of heat exchange, and hence the maximum amount of heat contained in the pressure-still product is recovered and utilized in vaporizing the charging stock.

Continuous operation for periods of 3 months is common, although the operation is occasionally terminated by the formation of coke within the tubes. In maintaining long cycles of operation, the condition of the charge to the furnace is of prime importance. If this stock contains any tar by imperfect separation in the fractionating tower, coking proceeds immediately, and after 6 hr of operation on a dirty charge stock the tubes will often be badly coked and the operation must be halted. A low conversion per pass is necessary in avoiding coke formation. A conversion of 15 to 21 per cent is adequate for clean distilled stocks, but only 10 to 17 per cent can be used with clean but undistilled (black) stocks.

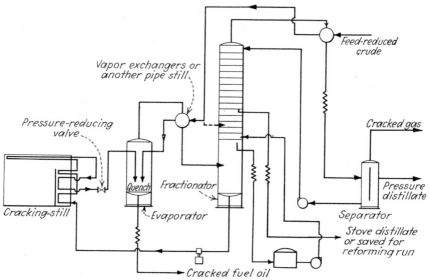

Fig. 19-15. Simplified flow diagram of the tubestill cracking process.

Thus, if reduced crude oil is charged to the cracking furnace, a larger recycle ratio must be used.

Although many of these plants operate on a gas-oil charging stock, it is becoming more and more common to charge a reduced crude stock as shown by the dotted line in Fig. 19-15, or better yet by the two-coil system of Fig. 19-16, which is typical of the Dubbs process. Thus the topping of gas oil from reduced crude oil and the viscosity breaking of the reduced crude oil is accomplished within the cracking plant itself. A vaporizer temperature higher than 820°F will usually cause the deposition of coke in the evaporator.

In the two-coil system of Fig. 19-16 (Dubbs) the amount of heavy or black-oil circulation is about 3.5 to 1.0 of topped crude feed, and the light-oil circulation is about 2.5 to 1.0, when operating on a Mid Continent 24-gravity topped crude oil. The outlet temperature of the heavy-oil coil ranges from 930 to 970°F and the light-oil outlet from 990 to 1050°F. Pressures of 175 to 350 psi are maintained in the reaction chamber and 60 to 130 psi in the evaporator and fractionating tower.

Since about 1935, reaction chambers have been abandoned in all processes except as indicated in Fig. 19-16; and, of course, coke (or reaction) chambers are necessary in coking plants (Fig. 19-19). Vapor reaction

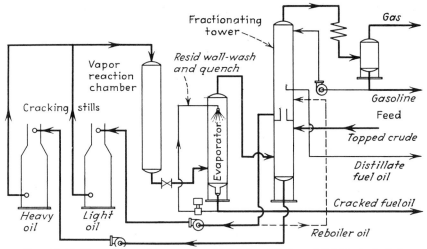

FIG. 19-16. Two-coil cracking system (Dubbs). (*Universal Oil Products Co.*)

chambers (Fig. 19-16) increase the capacity,[58] octane number, and gasoline yield of black-feed units as shown in Table 19-20. Inasmuch as reaction chambers are cheaper than cracking plants, the use of 300 to 400 cu ft of reaction space for each 1,000 bbl of feed is economically sound.

TABLE 19-20. EFFECT OF DOWNFLOW REACTION CHAMBERS ON CAPACITY, ETC.

Ratio of reaction volume (cu ft) to charge rate (thousand bbl per day)	Percentage increase in capacity[a]	Maximum naphtha production		Quality operation	
		Percentage increase in naphtha	Percentage increase in feed rate	Increase in octane number	Decrease in 20 or 50 per cent points, °F
50	0	0	0	0	0
100	8.5	19.0	6.5	2.5	2.5
150	15.5	29.5	11.0	4.5	4.0
200	20.5	36.0	13.0	6.0	5.0
250	24.0	41.0	15.0	7.0	5.5
300	26.5	45.0	16.5	8.0	6.0
350	29.0	47.0	17.5	8.5	6.5

[a] Constant yield and quality of naphtha.

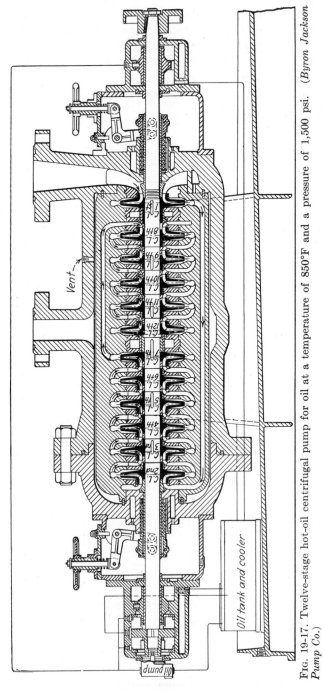

Vent

C.I. 1st
418
73
446
71
440
73
441
71
442
71
445
73
449
73
445
74
447
73
343
74
C.I. 2nd

Oil tank and cooler

Oil pump

FIG. 19-17. Twelve-stage hot-oil centrifugal pump for oil at a temperature of 850°F and a pressure of 1,500 psi. (Byron Jackson Pump Co.)

Outlet pressures of 350 to 700 psi are maintained at the outlet of the pipestill. Lower pressures result in the formation of coke; and though we know little of the phase condition at such temperatures and pressures, it is apparent that a large generation of vapor takes place even at a pressure of 700 psi because vaporization is primarily a function of the critical temperature rather than the pressure. A pressure drop of 300 to 800 psi occurs through the pressure still, so that inlet pressures of 600 to 1,200 psi (as coking occurs) are common. Twin-simplex, compound steam cylinder pumps or crank-and-flywheel steam-engine pumps were once widely used, but multistage centrifugal pumps are now standard practice (Fig. 19-17).

The tubestill process has been used for vapor-phase cracking without fundamentally changing the process. However, the outlet temperature is much higher (1050 to 1250°F), and the outlet pressure must be reduced to 30 to 50 psi so that substantially a pure vapor phase exists in the cracking tubes. Likewise the best known continuous coking processes are like the tubestill process except that coke drums are introduced before the evaporator vessel of the tubestill process (Fig. 19-15).

In processing topped or reduced crude oil, the maximum yield of gasoline is largely dependent upon the properties of the pressure-still tar. If too high an evaporator or vaporizer temperature is used or if the time in the evaporator is too short, the tar may be a solid asphaltic material, which is awkward to handle and cannot be marketed. In processing gas oil, this difficulty seldom arises because the tar consists almost entirely of cracked tar which has a lower viscosity. However, an evaporator temperature of about 820°F cannot be exceeded because coke will be deposited in the evaporator. It is now almost universal practice to avoid these difficulties by flashing the cracked fuel oil or residuum at atmospheric or subatmospheric pressure (Fig. 19-21). This produces an almost solid, very low gravity residuum, which is diluted or cut back with a small amount of light cracked distillate to produce a black fuel oil of suitable viscosity (300 Furol sec at 122°F). The flash characteristics of one 14 API residuum when being adiabatically flashed from 820°F (in evaporator) are indicated in Fig. 19-18.[74] The heavy dashed line shows the percentage of residuum that will be vaporized as the temperature is reduced to various temperatures lower than 820°F. Obviously, the pressure must be reduced to 10 psig to vaporize 45 per cent, or to 200 mm to vaporize 77 per cent. At the evaporator pressure of 65 psig none of the residuum is vaporized. In computing the curve for an adiabatic vaporization (Fig. 19-18), the following operations are necessary:

1. Construct distillation, gravity, and vaporization curves for atmospheric pressure.
2. Assume some percentage vaporized such as 45 per cent.

[74] Nelson, W. L., Flashing Cracking Plant Residuum, *Oil Gas J.*, Aug. 25, 1945, p. 130.

3. By a heat balance compute the decrease in temperature from 820°F that will occur in vaporizing the 45 per cent. This temperature is 774°F.
4. A temperature of only 731°F at atmospheric pressure is required to vaporize 45 per cent, and hence a pressure of 10 psig (Fig. 5-27) is required to raise 731 to 774°F.
5. Repeat for other percentages vaporized.

The flashing and cutback of cracked residuum is highly advantageous because it produces a lower gravity residuum, and by Fig. 19-1 a greater yield of gasoline.

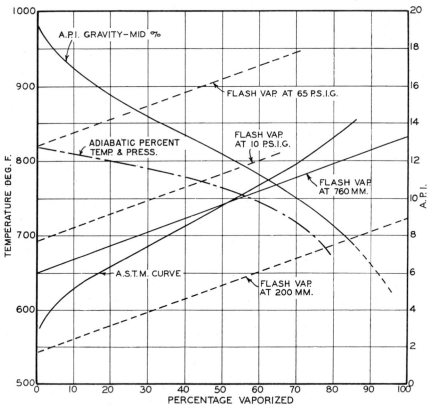

FIG. 19-18. Adiabatic vaporization curve of one 14° API cracked residuum, and the construction curves used in computing the amounts of vaporization.

Yields are so similar from all the processes that Fig. 19-1 and Eqs. (19-1) to (19-8) should be employed rather than scattered data on the various processes.

Coking. The production of coke is accomplished by lengthening the time of liquid-phase cracking (Fig. 19-6) so that polymerization or condensation products are produced. However, only the most degraded carbonaceous high-boiling parts of the cracking reaction are exposed to prolonged time in coking chambers. The semicontinuous Delayed Coking process is basically similar to the tubestill process of Fig. 19-15 except that liquid holdup time is provided in the evaporator or flash chamber, rather than holding the customary low level of only 24 in. or less (in a spool at the bottom of the evaporator). In addition, no quench is employed, and this allows the temperature in the coke drum (the evaporator of Fig. 19-15) to rise above the temperature of 820°F at which coking is encountered. All of these and more features are indicated in Fig. 19-19.[75] All fractionation operations, i.e., removal of straight-run gas oil from the feed and separation of coked products, are accomplished in a single tower. Even more gas oil is removed from the residuum coker charge by flashing at atmospheric pressure. The highly reduced residuum is then cracked as severely as possible in a single-pass operation and admitted to a coke chamber where liquid products remain to form coke, and vaporized products (mainly coker gas oil) proceed to the combination fractionating tower. So much extra heat is available at the fractionator that it is cooled on the side by a waste-heat steam boiler. In this instance (Fig. 19-19) so many coils are used in a single pipestill that independence from the convection section is gained by the circulation of boiler feedwater through the convection section. Polymer tar tends to spray from the top of the coke chambers causing subsequent coking of the pipestill tubes, and accordingly the level in the chambers cannot become too high. Radioactive cobalt has been used[76] to detect the level in the coke drum.

The main purpose of coking, as practiced today, is the production of coker gas oil which is charged to catalytic or thermal crackers. In the earliest coking operations (Dubbs, 1924 to 1930) coke was removed by means of a special steel cable suspended in spiral form from the top to the bottom of the chamber. At the end of the run the cable was pulled through the bottom manhole, cutting through the coke and breaking it so that it could be dropped through the bottom manhole. Much time (8 to 15 hr) and labor was required and the coke contained some wire. Large drills are also used to cut the coke from the chamber. The hydraulic method[77] has recently assumed great importance. It involves drilling a 24- to 38-in. hole down the center of the chamber. A hydraulic cutting assembly, which has horizontal water jets through which water at 1,200 psi is directed, is raised through the chamber. The coke is cut

[75] Lummus Delayed Coking, *Pet. Refiner*, July, 1953, p. 102.

[76] Werstler, Miederstaät, and Lutz, Inside a Coke Drum, *Oil Gas J.*, Aug. 9, 1954, p. 98.

[77] Court, W. F., Hydraulic Decoking of Coke Chamber, *Proc. API, Refining Division*, Chicago Meeting, 1938; also Watson, K. M., Cracking Fuel Oil to Coke, *Ref. Nat. Gaso. Mfr.*, Dec. 1, 1938, p. 652.

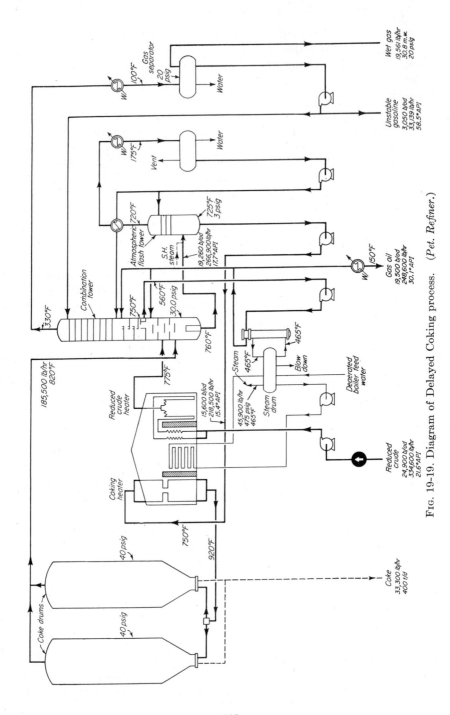

FIG. 19-19. Diagram of Delayed Coking process. (*Pet. Refiner.*)

and broken from the walls and falls into a sluice system for dewatering, drying, and storage.[78]

The Knowles or similar coking ovens that have been used in the coal industry have been used also for petroleum. They involve increased flexibility in operation and produce a uniform high-quality coke.[79] A cracked fuel oil, which has been flashed down to a gravity of 1 to 2 API, is introduced slowly into the oven for about 100 min or until a 10-in. layer of coke is produced. The coke bed is dried by heating for about 3 hr, reaching a final temperature of 1200°F, and is then removed by opening doors at both ends of the oven and ramming the hot coke into a quench car by means of a large mechanical ram.

Almost pure carbon or artificial graphite, which is suitable for carbon electrodes, motor brushes, dry cells, etc., can be made by calcining petroleum coke.[80] In this process, the refinery coke is passed through a 100- to 125-ft cylindrical rotating kiln by which it is heated to a bright red heat.

Completely continuous coking systems (Continuous Contact[81] and Fluid Coking[82]) were developed during 1949 to 1955, and these promise to revolutionize the coking art (over 500,000 bpd capacity, 1956)[83] and possibly the economics of residual fuel production. In these processes, coke is built up on pellets[81] or on fluidized coke particles[82] until a size suitable for removal is attained. Meanwhile, the smaller particles are retained within the system. In the Fluid process[82] shown in Fig. 19-20, about 5 per cent of the coke yield (on feed) is burned in a fluidized coke bed to dry the coke particles and to heat them (1100 to 1200°F) for the reaction chamber which is also maintained in a fluidized state. The reactor operates at 900 to 1050°F, and the pitch-type feed is also introduced and heated in the reactor. Reaction products are separated in a fractionator system situated just above the reactor. Fluidized coke has a gross heating value of about 14,300 Btu per lb and its size distribution[84] is:

Screen size	Cumulative per cent retained
8	5.2
35	11.1
65	48.6
100	80.1
200	95.8

[78] Breese, F., Drier, Cleaner Petroleum Coke, *Pet. Processing*, August, 1953, p. 1170.

[79] Foster, A. L., Lubrite Converts Fuel Oil into More Profitable Products, *Natl. Pet. News*, May 6, 1936, p. 33.

[80] Stockman, L. P., First California Calcining Unit . . . , *Oil Gas J.*, July 4, 1940, p. 36.

[81] Mekler et al., *Oil Gas J.*, Nov. 16, 1953, p. 200.

[82] Anon., Coke and Lighter Products, *Pet. Processing*, March, 1956, p. 135.

[83] Weber, G., *Oil Gas J.*, Aug. 8, 1955, p. 62.

[84] Cornforth and Lee, Fluidized Coke Tested in Rotary Kiln, *Oil Gas J.*, Sept. 12, 1955, p. 137.

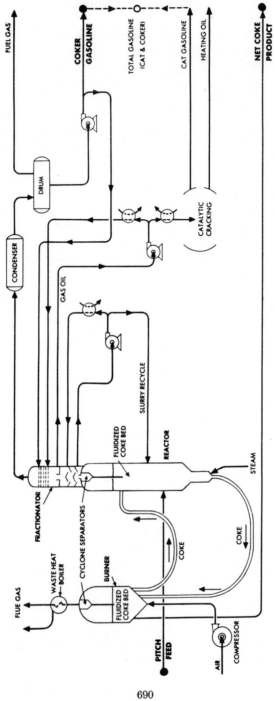

FIG. 19-20. Simplified diagram of the Fluid Coking process. (*Pet. Processing.*)

FUEL GAS

COKER GASOLINE

TOTAL GASOLINE (CAT & COKER)

CAT GASOLINE

HEATING OIL

NET COKE PRODUCT

CATALYTIC CRACKING

DRUM

CONDENSER

GAS OIL

SLURRY RECYCLE

FLUIDIZED COKE BED

REACTOR

FRACTIONATOR

CYCLONE SEPARATORS

STEAM

COKE

COKE

WASTE HEAT BOILER

FLUE GAS

BURNER

FLUIDIZED COKE BED

PITCH FEED

AIR

COMPRESSOR

This is a satisfactory distribution for handling and storage, but it must be ground for use as a power plant fuel.[84] The coke is so free from hydrogen (Table 3-30) that different burners and firing conditions from those used when burning fuel oil or powdered coal had to be developed.

Approximate yields during coking can be obtained from Eqs. (19-6) to (19-8) and Table 19-7.

Combination Cracking Units. The large amount of heat that can be recovered from a cracking plant, the advantages of cracking selected stocks at optimum operating conditions, and the general similarity of such operations as cracking, viscosity breaking, and reforming have led to the development of processes that comprise a combination of operations. Among the operations that have been advantageously combined are the following:

1. Crude-oil topping, using a separate tower for straight-run distillates.
2. Viscosity breaking, usually a once-through operation on straight-run residuum, although admission of black stock to the cracking coil is practical in many plants.
3. Reforming of naphtha, usually as a once-through operation but also as a recycling operation—and sometimes employing a catalyst.
4. Selective cracking of several boiling ranges of stock.
5. Coking of cracked tar.
6. Vacuum flashing of hot cracked tar for asphalt or to produce more recycle stock.
7. Gasoline recovery from the cracked gas.
8. Polymerization of olefin gases and decomposition of saturated gases.
9. Stabilization of gasolines and pressure distillate.

Operations 2, 3, and 4 are so similar in principle that they can be centered about a single evaporator or vaporizer. In each of these processes the cracked stocks must be currently freed from cracked tar if coking of the tubes is to be avoided. Thus in Fig. 19-21 all these stocks are led to a common evaporator vessel, and the commingled vaporized parts proceed to a single fractionating tower. In this tower the several recycle stocks are separated from one another and sent back to their respective cracking coils. If coking is practiced, the evaporator would be replaced by coking chambers much as shown in Fig. 19-19. Operations 7 and 8, viz. gasoline recovery and polymerization, are also similar in principle, and hence the recovery of any gaseous products, either natural or polymer, may be conducted in a common absorption and stabilizing system.

Figure 19-21 has purposely been simplified to permit illustration of the principles that are involved—and it should not be considered as a working flow diagram. In commercial practice many elaborations have been used or found necessary. As illustrations, several evaporator vessels and fractionating towers may be used rather than a single vessel; the polymerization processing may be conducted in a separate evaporator, fractionator, and absorption system; or a pipestill may be used instead of heat exchang-

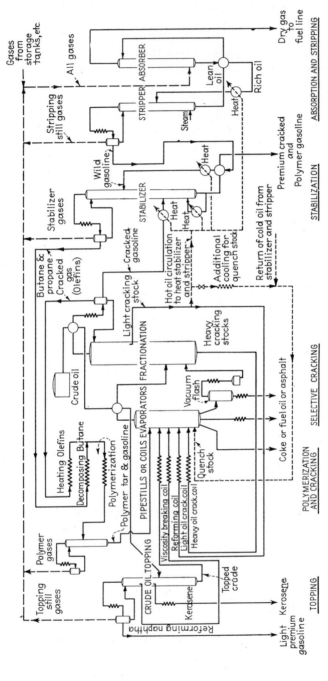

FIG. 19-21. Diagrammatic illustration of the interrelationship between the many operations that can be conducted in a combination cracking plant.

ers. In many instances the complicated processing utilized in actual plants is due to the use of old equipment that by itself is not large enough to handle the combined stocks indicated in Fig. 19-21.

Yields by combination processes are, of course, a summation of the yields from the separate operations (Table 19-21).

TABLE 19-21. YIELDS BY COMBINATION CRACKING PROCESSES

	East Texas crude 39 API	East Texas crude 38.6 API	EastTexas crude		M.C. crude 36.9 API	Michigan crude 39.9 API	M.C. crude 36.9 API		
Straight-run gasoline..............	19.7	....	18.5	18.5	26.8	7.3	33	26	20
Cracked gasoline...............	43.7	....	39.3	39.3	41.5	56.9	36	42	45
Poly gasoline..................	None	....	5.2	....	None	None	None	None	None
Total gasoline.................	63.4	70.6	63.0	57.8	68.3	64.2	69	68	65
Furnace distillate...............	....	....	12.0						
Fuel oil........................	28.9	18.6	20.0	....	25.2	25.1	25.0	25.0	25.0
Gas and loss...................	7.7	10.6	5.0	10.2	6.5	10.7	6.0	7.0	10.0
Fuel oil, API..................	12.4	4.3	....	....	9.2	9.6			
Gasoline (total), Octane No......	69.2	68.0	70.0	....	66.0	63.0	63.0	66.0	70.0

CHAPTER 20

REBUILDING HYDROCARBONS

The development of a chemical industry based upon petroleum as a raw stock is an accomplished fact (see Tables 3-35 and 3-36). Such developments had long been delayed because of the relatively unreactive nature of most petroleum hydrocarbons and because only a few of the many hydrocarbons present in petroleum or even its reaction products can be identified.

Although intense interest in hydrocarbon chemistry is evident and many valuable developments have been made since 1930, as yet the study of hydrocarbon rebuilding has been centered on ascertaining what reactions can be accomplished rather than on details of operation, reaction rates, or engineering considerations. The use of numerous catalysts has also caused confusion in the correlation of engineering design data. All these facts as well as the newness of the developments have made it impossible to present more than a bare introduction to the design of equipment for these processes.

Most rapid advancement took place during World War II. Commercial processes for the manufacture or separation of isopentane, isobutane, butene, 2-2-4-trimethylpentene (Codimer),[1] isopropyl benzene (cumene),[2] butadiene,[3] styrene,[4,5] toluene,[6] 2-2-4-trimethylpentane (alkylate),[7] alcohol,[8] etc., were in operation.

More recently, commercial application of the Fischer-Tropsch process

---

[1] Kunkel, J. H., Bayway Unit Holds Polymer Make Record, *Pet. Eng.*, August, 1945, p. 76.

[2] McAllister et al., Production of Cumene . . . , *Chem. Eng. Prog.*, **43**, 189 (1947).

[3] Van Antwerpen, F. J., Neches Butadiene Unit Opened, *Chem. Eng. News*, **22**, 316 (1944).

[4] Smith, H. H., Los Angeles Styrene Plant, *Chem. Eng Progr.*, **43**, 152 (1947).

[5] Pardee and Dodge, Catalytic Alkylation of Benzene with Ethylene, *Ind. Eng. Chem.*, **35**, 273 (1943).

[6] Hartley, F. L., Commercial Synthesis of Toluene by Hydroforming . . . and Azeotropic Distillation, *Pet. Refiner*, December, 1945, p. 131.

[7] Phillips Petroleum Company, "Hydrofluoric Acid Alkylation," from the Company at Bartlesville, Okla., 1946.

[8] Beamer, C. M., . . . Synthetic Alcohol from Ethylene, *Chem. Eng. Progr.*, **43**, 92 (1947).

or modifications of it[9,10,11] have attracted attention. Although the process is important to the gasoline and chemical markets, it is not very directly related in a technical way to the petroleum industry because it involves the production of carbon monoxide and hydrogen from any materials that may contain carbon or hydrocarbons. The carbon monoxide and hydrogen are then recombined by means of a catalyst into gasolinelike hydrocarbons, diesel fuel, and numerous oxygenated compounds such as alcohols, aldehydes, acids, ketones, etc. The process has been made more economical for conditions in the United States by the use of oxygen[12] for the burning of the natural gas, the development of the reversing-type exchanger,[12] the development of turbine-type compressors, and the application of the fluidized catalyst principle, all on a large scale. Because of its limited relation to the petroleum industry, the process will not be presented here.

Very much of the petrochemical industry is based on low-pressure high-temperature cracking for olefinic hydrocarbons. Figure 20-1 indicates[13] the main raw materials, basic products, intermediate chemicals, and end products. Although vapor-phase cracking was developed before 1932, the process attained little commercial success until World War II. Another basic process, namely, catalytic reforming, not only provides large amounts of raw aromatic stocks but substantial amounts of by-product hydrogen which can be used for large-scale hydrogenation and desulfurization processes.

Types of Reactions. Among the many types of reactions are those referred to as decomposition, dehydrogenation, polymerization, alkylation, isomerization, hydrogenation, aromatization, depolymerization, and dealkylation. Several of the reactions usually take place at the same time, particularly in thermal processes (Table 20-1). The process of *thermal decomposition,* or cracking, occupies a position of primary importance because the process has been used so extensively and because the average boiling range of crude oil is so high that it must be reduced in order to meet the market demands for gasoline.

Decomposition (see pages 626 and 713)

$$CH_3 \cdot CH_2 \cdot CH_2 \cdot CH_3 \xrightarrow{\text{heat}} CH_4 + CH_3 \cdot CH:CH_2$$

$$\quad\;\; \text{n-butane} \qquad\qquad\qquad \text{methane} \qquad \text{propene}$$

[9] Lane and Weil, The Synthine Process, 4 parts, *Pet. Refiner*, August, p. 87; September, p. 97; October, p. 109; and November, 1946, p. 153.

[10] Keith, P. C., Gasoline from Natural Gas, *Oil Gas J.*, June 15, 1946, p. 102.

[11] Roberts and Phinney, . . . Synthetic Gasoline Nearing Commercial Application in U.S., *Oil Gas J.*, Mar. 15, 1947, p. 72.

[12] Rushton and Stevenson, Developments in Oxygen Production, *Chem. Eng. Progr.*, **43,** 61 (1947).

[13] Linden and Reid, *Pet. Refiner*, June, 1956, p. 189.

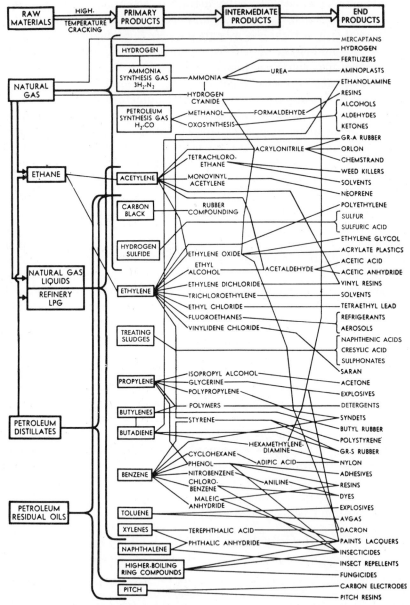

FIG. 20-1. Some of the petrochemicals that can be produced from natural gas, natural-gas liquids, and petroleum. (*Pet. Refiner.*)

The need of converting stable hydrocarbons into reactive ones such as olefins makes *dehydrogenation* occupy a position of primary importance. Such a reaction is the special case of decomposition in which rupture of a carbon-hydrogen bond occurs.

Dehydrogenation (see pages 743 to 748)

$$CH_3 \cdot CH_2 \cdot CH_2 \cdot CH_2 \cdot CH_3 \underset{\text{catalyst}}{\overset{\text{heat or}}{\rightleftharpoons}} CH_3 \cdot CH_2 \cdot CH_2 \cdot CH : CH_2 + H_2$$

n-pentane ⠀⠀⠀⠀⠀⠀ pentene-1 ⠀⠀⠀⠀⠀ hydrogen

Once the paraffin and naphthenic hydrocarbons have been converted into reactive unsaturated hydrocarbons, many chemical reactions or processes are possible. Dehydrogenation may occur during decomposition [see Eqs. (19-9) to (19-12) and (19-15)]. In a general processing scheme dehydrogenation is usually coupled with or followed by other processes such as polymerization or alkylation. Reactions that have been termed *cyclization* or *aromatization* may also be dehydrogenation reactions[14] and may also involve decomposition, as indicated here:

Aromatization (see pages 811 to 815)

$$CH_3 \cdot CH_2 \cdot CH_2 \cdot CH_2 \cdot CH_2 \cdot CH_2 \cdot CH_3 \xrightarrow[\substack{\text{chromium} \\ \text{oxide}}]{\text{heat and}} \quad + \quad 4H_2$$

n-heptane ⠀⠀⠀⠀⠀⠀⠀⠀⠀⠀⠀ toluene ⠀⠀⠀⠀ hydrogen

Polymerization has also been an important reaction because it was the first of the rebuilding reactions (except cracking) to become of commercial importance.

Polymerization (see pages 722 to 735)

$$CH_3 \cdot CH : CH_2 + CH_3 \cdot CH_2 \cdot CH : CH_2 \xrightarrow[\text{catalyst}]{\text{heat or}} CH_2 : CH \cdot CH_2 \cdot CH_2 \cdot \overset{\overset{\displaystyle CH_3}{|}}{CH} \cdot CH_3$$

propene ⠀⠀⠀⠀⠀ butene-1 ⠀⠀⠀⠀⠀⠀⠀⠀ 4 methyl hexene-1

Such reactions permit the manufacture of liquid gasoline from gases and in special instances the production of tetramer (dodecene), nonene, polyethylene, and polybutenes.

Likewise, some unsaturated hydrocarbons may be *depolymerized*.[15,16] Thus, during World War II, isobutene was polymerized to isooctene

[14] Archibald and Greensfelder, Promoted Chromia-alumina Catalyst . . . n-Heptane to Toluene, *Ind. Eng. Chem.*, **37**, 356 (1945).

[15] Doumani, Deering, and McKinnis, Depolymerization of Butadiene Dimer, *Ind. Eng. Chem.*, **39**, 89 (1947).

[16] Reid and Bailey, Thermal Depolymerization of Viscous Isobutylene Polymer, *Ind. Eng. Chem.*, **40**, 349 (1948).

which can be shipped in regular tank cars because it has a low vapor pressure and then depolymerized[17] to isobutene again at destination.

Depolymerization

$$\underset{\text{2,2,4 trimethylpentene}}{CH_3 \cdot \underset{\underset{CH_3}{|}}{\overset{\overset{CH_3}{|}}{C}} \cdot CH_2 \cdot \overset{\overset{CH_3}{|}}{C} : CH_2} \xrightarrow{\text{heat}} \underset{\text{isobutene}}{2CH_3 \cdot \overset{\overset{CH_3}{|}}{C} : CH_2}$$

Reactions by which molecules (other than olefins) are connected are termed *alkylation*—or specifically, *propylation* or *ethylation* if the alkyl radicals of propane or ethane are the reactants. The linking of a paraffin and an olefin hydrocarbon is a common example:

Alkylation (see pages 735 to 743)

$$\underset{\text{ethene}}{CH_2 : CH_2} + \underset{\underset{\underset{CH_3}{|}}{i\text{-butane}}}{CH_3 \cdot CH \cdot CH_3} \xrightarrow[\text{or catalyst}]{\text{heat, pressure,}} \underset{\text{2,2 dimethylbutane}}{CH_3 \cdot \overset{\overset{CH_3}{|}}{\underset{\underset{CH_3}{|}}{C}} \cdot CH_2 \cdot CH_3}$$

Such a process holds an advantage over polymerization because only half as many of the expensive olefin molecules are required.

The reverse of alkylation, or *dealkylation*,[18] may also be practiced.

Isomerization reactions involve rearrangement of the molecular structure of a hydrocarbon, but nothing is added to or taken away from the material.

Isomerization (see pages 750 to 753)

cyclohexane   methylcyclopentane

Not many commercial processes of this type are available, but such reactions probably occur along with other reactions such as cracking, polymerization, and alkylation but cannot be recognized because of the other reactions and because of the difficulty in identifying the hydrocarbon products.

[17] Murphree, Brown, and Gohr, Hydrogenation of Petroleum, *Ind. Eng. Chem.*, **32**, 1203 (1940).

[18] Kutz and Corson, Dealkylation of Dialkylbenzenes, *Ind. Eng. Chem.*, **38**, 761 (1946).

The process of *hydrogenation* may be utilized in adding hydrogen to unsaturated hydrocarbons. For many years it did not find wide application because most oils are already saturated with hydrogen to a sufficient degree. However, during World War II it was applied to isooctene to produce isooctane and more recently it has been used in the desulfurization processes of pages 305 and 332.

Hydrogenation (see pages 748 to 750)

$$\underset{\substack{\text{2,2,3 trimethylpen-}\\\text{tene-4}}}{\text{CH}_3\cdot\overset{\overset{\displaystyle\text{H}_3\text{C}}{|}}{\underset{\underset{\displaystyle\text{H}_3\text{C}}{|}}{\text{C}}}\cdot\overset{\overset{\displaystyle\text{CH}_3}{|}}{\text{CH}}\cdot\text{CH}:\text{CH}_2} + \underset{\substack{\text{hydro-}\\\text{gen}}}{\text{H}_2} \xrightarrow[\text{oxide}]{\text{molybdic}} \underset{\substack{\text{2,2,3 trimethylpentane}}}{\text{CH}_3\cdot\overset{\overset{\displaystyle\text{H}_3\text{C}}{|}}{\underset{\underset{\displaystyle\text{H}_3\text{C}}{|}}{\text{C}}}\cdot\overset{\overset{\displaystyle\text{CH}_3}{|}}{\text{CH}}\cdot\text{CH}_2\cdot\text{CH}_3}$$

It has already been used in connection with thermal decomposition (cracking) as a means of adding hydrogen to the residue of tar that is produced in cracking so that greater yields are possible. When used in this way it is referred to as *destructive hydrogenation*.

Many reactions of hydrocarbons with other agents such as oxygen, water, halogens, nitric acid, etc., are practiced commercially but can hardly be claimed as petroleum refinery operations even though the hydrocarbons came originally from petroleum. Direct *oxidation* has been practiced for many years[19] in the production of aldehydes, ketones, alcohols, and acids. Direct oxidation processes usually produce several products at the same time,[20] but the reaction shown here serves as an illustration.

Oxidation

$$\underset{\text{methane}}{\text{CH}_4} + \underset{\text{oxygen}}{\text{O}_2} \xrightarrow[\text{catalyst}]{\text{heat and}} \underset{\text{formaldehyde}}{\text{CH}_2\text{O}} + \underset{\text{water}}{\text{H}_2\text{O}}$$

The *hydration* of olefins has long been practiced for the manufacture of amyl[21] and isopropyl alcohol,[22] and more recently for ethyl alcohol.[8] Hydration is usually accomplished by a series of reactions involving the chlorides or alkyl sulfates, rather than the direct hydration reaction indicated here.

Hydration

$$\underset{\text{ethylene}}{\text{CH}_2:\text{CH}_2} + \underset{\text{water}}{\text{H}_2\text{O}} \to \underset{\text{ethyl alcohol}}{\text{CH}_3\cdot\text{CH}_2\cdot\text{OH}}$$

[19] Walker and Malakoff, Basic Oxygenated Chemicals from C_1, C_2, and C_3 Paraffins and Olefins, *Oil Gas J.*, Dec. 21, 1946, p. 59.

[20] Linford, H., Oxidation Methods . . . , *Oil Gas J.*, Nov. 12, 1942, p. 71.

[21] Bohall, H. A., Synthetic Amyl Alcohols and Amyl Acetates . . . , *Ref. Nat. Gaso. Mfr.*, August, 1932, p. 438.

[22] Ellis, C., "Chemistry of Petroleum Derivativies," vol. II, chap. 14, Reinhold Publishing Corporation, New York, 1937.

TABLE 20-1. SUMMARY OF

(1)	(2)	(3)	(4)	(5)
Molecular change	Kind of physical or chemical change	Energizer, catalytic or thermal	Commercial name of process	Common feedstock
Disintegration (breaking into parts)	Desulfurization and hydrogenation	Catalyst	**Catalytic desulfurization**	Distillates
		Catalyst	**Catalytic desulfurization**	Gasoline
	Dehydrogenation	Catalyst	**(No common name)**	Butane
	Decomposition	Thermal	**Viscosity breaking**	Residua
Several (both disintegration and synthesis)	Decomposition and adsorption (catalytic cracking or reforming)	Catalyst	**Houdry catalytic cracking**	Gas oil
		Catalyst	**Fluid catalytic cracking**	Gas oil
		Catalyst	**Thermofor catalytic cracking**	Gas oil
		Catalyst	**Cycloversion**	Gas oil
	Decomposition and polymerization (cracking)	Thermal	**Thermal cracking**	Topped crude oil and gas oil
		Thermal	**Reforming**	Heavy gasoline or distillate
		Thermal	**Coking**	Topped crude or fuel oil
	Decomposition, polymerization, and alkylation	Thermal	**Polyforming**	Naphtha and refinery gas
	Dehydrogenation, hydrogenation, and isomerization	Catalyst	**Hydroforming**	Naphtha
		Catalyst	**Catalytic reforming**	Naphtha
	Decomposition and hydrogenation	Catalyst	**Destructive hydrogenation**	Many stocks
	Decomposition, hydrogenation, and desulfurization	Catalyst	**Hydrodesulfurization**	Residua
	Dehydrogenation and rearrangement	Catalyst	**(No common name)**	Heptane and methyl cyclohexane
	Polymerization and decomposition	Thermal	**Thermal polymerization**	Cracking-still gases
Synthesis (uniting)	Alkylation	Catalyst	**HF alkylation**	Iso and normal butane
		Catalyst	**Sulfuric acid alkylation**	Iso and normal butane
		Catalyst	**(No common name)**	Propane and benzene
		Catalyst	**(No common name)**	Ethene and benzene
		Thermal	**Thermal alkylation**	Ethene or propene and isobutane
	Hydrogenation	Catalyst	**(No common name)**	Codiner (trimethylpentene)
	Polymerization	Catalyst	**Phosphoric acid polymerization**	Cracking-still gases
		Catalyst	**Sulfuric acid polymerization**	Cracking-still gases
		Catalyst	**(No common name)**	Isobutene
Rearrangement (of mole structure)	Isomerization	Catalyst	**Isomate**	Naphtha, pentane, or hexane
		Catalyst	**Butane isomerization**	Butane
		Catalyst	**(Several names)**	Pentane or hexane

^a In main reaction.   ^b These are back pressures held in pipestill heaters.

MODERN REFINING PROCESSES

(6) General purpose	(7) Main product	(8) Illustrative reaction	(9) Operating conditions[a]		(10) Catalyst
			Psig	Temp, °F	
Remove sulfur	Distillate	$R(SH) = R + H_2S$	300–700	700–780	Cobalt molybdenum
Remove sulfur	Gasoline	$R(SH) = R + H_2S$	40–70	700–800	Bauxite or clay
Make olefin	Butene or butadiene	$C_4H_{10} = C_4H_8 + H_2 = C_4H_6 + 2H_2$	Low	850–1150	Chromic oxide on bauxite
Reduce viscosity and produce gas oil	Fuel oil	$C_nH_{2n+2} = C_{n/2}H_{n+2} + C_{n/2}H_n$	230–250[b]	860–890	
High octane number	Catalytic gasoline		20–50	800–860	Natural clays, aluminum hydrosilicates, bauxite, etc.
High octane number	Catalytic gasoline		2–15	860–950	
High octane number	Catalytic gasoline		10–15	750–900	
High octane number	Catalytic gasoline		50–100	900–1100	
Make gasoline	Cracked gasoline		300–700[b]	880–950	
Make gasoline	Cracked gasoline		400–800[b]	960–1020	
Eliminate fuel oil	Cracked gasoline		300–500[b]	890–960	
Increase gasoline yield	Gasoline		1,000–2,000[b]	1020–1120	
Aromatics	Solvents		100–300	890–1020	Molybdia
Aromatics	Gasoline		200–750	850–970	Platinum
Paraffinic stocks	Many	$C_nH_{2n+2} + H_2 = 2C_{n/2}H_{n+2}$, etc.	3,000	800–950	Molybdic trioxide
Produce gas oil	Gas oil		700–1,000	750–800	Cobalt molybdenum
Aromatic hydrocarbons	Toluene	$C_7H_{16} = C_7H_8 + 4H_2$	Low	1020	Chromic, molybdic, etc., oxides
Recover gases	Poly gasoline	$C_3H_6 + iC_4H_8 = C_7H_{14}$	1,500–2,000	900–1025	
High-octane gasoline	Alkylate	$iC_4H_{10} + iC_4H_8 = C_8H_{18}$	100–150	70–115	Hydrofluoric acid
High-octane gasoline	Alkylate	$iC_4H_{10} + iC_4H_8 = C_8H_{18}$		30–90	Sulfuric acid
High-octane gasoline	Cumene	$C_6H_6 + C_3H_6 = C_9H_{12}$	100–600	350–550	Phosphoric acid
Needed for styrene and synthetic rubber	Ethyl benzene	$C_6H_6 + C_2H_4 = C_8H_{10}$	15	150–210	Aluminum chloride
Recover gases	Neohexane	$C_2H_4 + iC_4H_{10} = C_6H_{14}$	3,000–8,000	900–1000	
High-octane blending stock	Isooctane	$C_8H_{16} + H_2 = C_8H_{18}$	15–60	320–400	Nickel
Recover gases	Poly gasoline	$2.3(C_nH_{2n}) = C_{2.3n}H_{4.6n}$	300–600	300–450	Phosphoric acid
Recover gases	Poly gasoline	$x(C_nH_{2n}) = C_{xn}H_{2xn}$		70–190	Sulfuric acid
Intermediate stock for isooctane	Codimer	$2iC_4H_8 = C_8H_{16}$	350–650	350–500	Phosphoric acid
High-octane gasoline	Isomate gasoline	$nC_6H_{14} = iC_6H_{14}$	120–200	150–220	Aluminum chloride
Branched-chain hydrocarbons	Isobutane	$nC_4H_{10} = iC_4H_{10}$	200–350	100–210	Aluminum chloride
High-octane gasoline	Isomate	$nC_5H_{12} = iC_5H_{12}$	High	800–900	Platinum, etc.

The *halogenation, chlorination, bromination,* etc., of hydrocarbons[23] has long been practiced, particularly as an intermediate step in the manufacture of other chemicals.   Even kerosene has been chlorinated.[24]

Chlorination

$$CH_3 \cdot CH_2 \cdot CH_2 \cdot CH_2 \cdot CH_3 + Cl_2 \rightarrow$$

pentane   chlorine

$$CH_3 \cdot CH_2 \cdot CH_2 \cdot CH_2 \cdot CH_2Cl + \qquad HCl$$

amyl chloride   hydrochloric acid

The physical and thermal properties of chlorohydrocarbon solvents are completely summarized by E. W. McGovern.[25]

The *nitration* of the paraffin[26] and other hydrocarbons produces nitro-compounds that are valuable solvents, particularly for lacquers.   Nitration reactions do not go completely to the formation of a single product, but they may be illustrated by the direct reaction shown here.

Nitration

$$CH_4 + HNO_3 \rightarrow CH_3NO_2 + H_2O$$

methane   nitric acid   nitromethane   water

Over-all Reactions or Processes.   Some of the more important plant processes are analyzed in Table 20-1 with respect to type of reaction, common feedstock, operating conditions, etc.   In most thermal processes, or even catalytic ones that involve high temperatures, several reactions occur at the same time.   Thus reforming with a platinum catalyst involves thermal decomposition, dehydrogenation, aromatization, isomerization, desulfurization, and hydrogenation.   Most processes are not direct or simple, and hence the purposes [column (6)], main products [column (7)], illustrative reactions [column (8)], etc., must all be considered as generalizations.   Operating pressure in the reaction zone [column (9)] may be of little significance because higher pressures may be encountered in auxiliary equipment.   Many of the processes are a wholesale treatment of a wide-boiling-range of hydrocarbons belonging to many organic series, and hence undesirable as well as desirable products are made.

REACTION VELOCITY

Rates of reaction cannot always be given because experimental data are lacking, and hence it is valuable to know the general kinetic relationships of various types of reactions.   These reactions are not complicated

[23] Egloff and Alexander, The Halogenation of Aliphatic Hydrocarbons, 2 parts, *Oil Gas J.*, Aug. 20, p. 39, and Oct. 22, p. 49, 1942.

[24] Dean and Lieber, Chlorinated Kerosene, *Ind. Eng. Chem.*, **37**, 181 (1945).

[25] Chlorohydrocarbon Solvents, *Ind. Eng. Chem.*, **35**, 1230 (1943).

[26] Hass and Riley, The Nitroparaffins, *Chem. Revs.*, **32**, 373 (1943).

for constant-volume reactions (nearly true for liquids), but they become cumbersome and nearly useless as a means of correlating data if the volume is not constant, as is the case for many gaseous reactions. Fortunately, most reactions are not conducted to completion, and hence at yields per pass of 25 or 50 per cent the failure of the volume to remain constant does not introduce serious errors. In all the derivations that follow, the reaction is assumed to be taking place at a constant temperature. Perhaps the greatest usefulness of the following derivations is to point out the general mathematical forms to use in developing empirical formulas of the rate of reaction.

Rates at Constant Volume. For a unimolecular reaction of which pure decomposition is an example, the rate of reaction is directly dependent on the amount of reactant material that is left at any time during the reaction.

$$A \rightarrow B + D + \cdots$$

The rate at which the concentration of A decreases with time is a constant function of the concentration designated as c_A:

$$\frac{-dc_A}{dt} = k_1 c_A$$

and if the initial concentration of A is designated as a, the amount of A that has reacted during a time t is designated as x, and $(a - x)$ is the concentration of A after a time of t:

$$\frac{-dc_A}{dt} = \frac{-d(a - x)}{dt} = k_1(a - x)$$

and by integration

$$k_1 = \frac{1}{t} \ln \frac{a}{a - x} \tag{20-1}$$

When possible it is best to use the concentration in moles, but liquid volume or weight per cent can be used with fair accuracy (see Fig. 19-5) for first-order, or unimolecular, reactions.

Similarly for bimolecular (second-order) reactions at constant volume, pressure, and temperature

$$A + B \rightarrow D + E + \cdots$$
$$\frac{dx}{dt} = k_2(a - x)(b - x)$$

and

$$k_2 = \frac{1}{t(a - x)} \ln \frac{b(a - x)}{a(b - x)} \tag{20-2}$$

in which a and b are the initial concentrations of A and B in moles per unit volume and x is the number of moles of A and B that react with one another during a time t. In the special case in which A and B are present in stoichiometric proportions or if two molecules of the same material react with one another (polymerization), the second-order equation simplifies to

$$2A \rightarrow D + E + \cdots$$

$$\frac{dx}{dt} = k_2(a - x)^2$$

and

$$k_2 = \frac{1}{t} \frac{x}{a(a - x)} \tag{20-3}$$

Note that pressure enters into the reaction velocity constant for gaseous reactions as an inverse function because the units of a, b, and x are moles per unit volume (or density).

The order of a reaction may be determined by inserting experimental data in the equations and noting which equation gives the most constant value of k. A discussion of other methods of determining reaction order and a discussion of the kinetics of higher order reactions are given in the "Chemical Engineers' Handbook."[27]

Rates at Varying Conditions. In most gaseous reactions the volume does not remain constant and modified equations are required. Note, however, that, if the conversion per pass is low or the system is diluted with some unreactive material such as a recycle stock, the volume change may be so small that the reaction behaves essentially as a constant-volume one.

In the case of a unimolecular reaction at a varying volume[27] the constant is

$$k_1 = \frac{vV}{V_b} \ln \frac{1}{1 - x} - \frac{V}{V_b} (v - 1)x \tag{20-4}$$

where V = volume of gas entering per second at contact conditions
  V_b = entire volume of reaction space
  v = moles of product produced from 1 mole of reactant material
  x = fraction of reactant material that undergoes reaction

The relationships for higher order reactions are extremely complicated, and hence it has become common usage to employ the so-called "space velocity" as a measure of reaction rate or capacity. The space velocity is defined as the ratio of the volume of inlet material (at standard conditions and per unit of time) to the volume of the reaction space. Thus, if no change in volume or temperature occurs during the reaction, the time of reaction is

$$\text{Time} = \frac{\text{reaction space}}{\text{volume feed per unit time}} = \frac{1}{\text{space velocity}}$$

[27] Perry, J. H. (ed.), 3d ed., McGraw-Hill Book Company, Inc., New York, 1949.

However, many different units of time, etc., are employed, and hence, whenever space velocity is mentioned, the particular units must be noted. If the volume or temperature (absolute) is assumed to vary according to a linear function, the time can be approximated by using the average of the inlet and outlet volumes rather than the volume of feed.

In systems in which the temperature varies, the rate can be described approximately by equations such as Eq. (20-3), but the situation can usually be handled more accurately by means of a series of computations each of which embraces a short range of temperature. Each short range of temperature can be handled at a weighted average temperature (refer to Example 19-9).

Effect of Temperature on Rate. The effect of temperature is to double the rate for a rise in temperature of about 10°C. The influence of temperature is, however, a function of the particular reaction. The change in reaction velocity with temperature can usually be described by the Arrhenius equation:

$$\frac{d \ln k}{dT} = \frac{A}{RT^2}$$

or for ranges in temperature through which A is constant:

$$\ln k = \frac{-A}{RT} + B \tag{20-5}$$

or

$$k = Be^{\frac{-A}{RT}}$$

where A = a characteristic constant ($-53{,}500$ cal per g mole for gas oil) referred to as the "energy of activation"

T = absolute temperature, °C

R = the gas law constant (1.987)

B = a constant (about 28.8 for gas oil)

A convenient way of correlating data is to plot the logarithm of the reaction velocity constant vs. the reciprocal of absolute temperature. This yields a substantially straight line (Fig. 19-5) having a slope of $-A/2.303R$.

M. D. Tilicheyev and others[28] have determined the rates of reaction of many hydrocarbons when they are heated. This work has been digested by R. Rosen,[28] and he presents tabulated rates for normal paraffin, olefin, diolefin, indene, styrene, aromatic, alkyl benzene, alkylated polycyclic, and naphthene hydrocarbons.

[28] Anon., Kinetics and Chemistry of Cracking Hydrocarbons, *Oil Gas J.*, Feb. 13 and Feb. 20, 1941.

THERMODYNAMICS OF REACTIONS

Many of the hydrocarbon-conversion processes are still in the development stage, and this is particularly true of the higher-molecular-weight materials, which constitute the bulk of petroleum. For these reasons, it is of primary importance to be able to judge the feasibility of proposed reactions or processes and to compute (or estimate) other thermal factors such as the heat of reaction. These factors can be evaluated by means of thermodynamics, and in time it may be possible to develop processes by which whole series of hydrocarbons can be converted into other series of hydrocarbons in a selective manner or by a number of consecutive processes to convert one series of hydrocarbons after another, until the entire mixture is converted into a single type of material.

Feasibility of a Reaction. The possibility that a reaction may occur can be judged by means of the free energy of the materials that are involved in the reaction. The free energy change may be considered as a measure of the tendency of a reaction to occur. The standard free energy change designated as $\Delta F°$ may be defined as the free energy change of the reaction if each of the materials involved in the reaction is assumed to be at unit activity. Mathematically the free energy, mass-law equilibrium constant, and thermodynamic constants are related by

$$\Delta F° = -RT \ln K = \Delta H - T \Delta S \tag{20-6}$$

where $\Delta F°$ = standard free energy change of reaction
ΔH = heat of reaction (exothermic is negative)
ΔS = entropy change of reaction
T = absolute temperature
K = equilibrium constant (mass law)
R = gas constant = 1.987 cal per mole-deg

If the value of $\Delta F°$ is found to be negative, the value of K will be relatively large and the yield will also be large when and if equilibrium is established. As $\Delta F°$ approaches zero or becomes positive, the value of K and of the yield at equilibrium becomes smaller and smaller. If $\Delta F°$ is negative, the reaction is a promising one; if $\Delta F°$ is zero, the usefulness of the reaction is doubtful but may justify further study; but if the value of $\Delta F°$ is greater than 10,000, in most instances such a process would not be feasible. It will also be noted that temperature exerts an important influence on the value of $\Delta F°$, and hence the foregoing situations may be altered by the use of another temperature.

No idea of the rate at which the reaction will occur is possible from a consideration of free energies, and hence many of the reactions that are found to be thermodynamically feasible do not occur at a practical rate or they may require the use of catalysts or an activating influence in order to cause the reaction to attain equilibrium within a reasonable length of time. Nevertheless, the examination of a process or reaction by these thermodynamic methods will indicate the feasibility of the reaction and thus save time and energy in studying reactions experimentally that hold little promise of success.

The mass-law equilibrium constant of a reaction is designated as

$$aA + bB + \cdots = cC + dD + \cdots$$

$$K = \frac{a_C^c a_D^d \cdots}{a_A^a a_B^b \cdots} \tag{20-7}$$

in which a is the activity. At moderate pressures, however, the activity of a gas is approximately equal to its partial pressure in atmospheres or to mole percentage, so that

$$K = \frac{p_C^c p_D^d \cdots}{p_A^a p_B^b \cdots}$$

Approximate values of the activities or corrected partial pressures of gases at elevated temperatures and pressures are given by Hougen and Watson.[29]

Values of Free Energy. From Eq. (20-6) it appears that $\Delta F°$ can be determined in three general ways, i.e., from entropies and heats of reaction, from equilibrium data, or from correlations of the free energy values of materials that have already been examined experimentally. Only the last method is of much value for the purpose of investigating the feasibility of a reaction, although in some instances it may be possible to compute approximate free energies by computing ΔS and ΔH.

Complete free energy data on all hydrocarbons will probably never be available, but several generalizations[30,31] have been developed.

For n paraffin hydrocarbons:[30]

$$\Delta F_T° = 10{,}550 - 5{,}890n + 25.2nT - 2.2T$$

For olefin-1 hydrocarbons:[30]

$$\Delta F_T° = 20{,}321 - 5{,}835n + 24.52nT - 33.26T$$

For simple naphthene hydrocarbons:[31]

$$\Delta F_T° = 10{,}375 - 8{,}633n + 26.09nT - 15.9T$$

For acetylene hydrocarbons:[31]

$$\Delta F_T° = 70{,}425 - 8{,}633n + 26.09nT - 67.5T$$

[29] "Chemical Process Principles," part 2, John Wiley & Sons, Inc., New York, 1947.

[30] Thomas, Egloff, and Morrell, Thermodynamics in Hydrocarbon Research, *Ind. Eng. Chem.*, **29**, 1260 (1937).

[31] Francis and Kleinschmidt, Application of Thermodynamics to Chemical Reactions of Petroleum Products, *Proc. API* December Meeting, 1929.

A somewhat more useful type of approach[32] involves the use of the free energy change required to produce various bondages (even branch-chain) such as those given in Eqs. (20-8) to (20-11). In all these equations n refers to the number of carbon atoms and T to the temperature in °K.

C—H bonds[32]

$$\Delta F_T^\circ = -3{,}344.5 + 2.97T \ln T - 0.0023T^2 \\ + 0.000000188T^3 - 13.68T \quad (20\text{-}8)$$

C—C bonds[32]

$$\Delta F_T^\circ = 4{,}437 + 0.421T \ln T + 0.0017T^2 - 0.00000062T^3 \\ + 9.53T \quad (20\text{-}9)$$

C=C bonds[32]

$$\Delta F_T^\circ = 28{,}024 + 2.75T \ln T - 0.0014T^2 - 0.00000080T^3 \\ - 24.86T \quad (20\text{-}10)$$

C—CH$_3$ bonds[32]

$$\Delta F_T^\circ = -7{,}624 + 10.42T \ln T \\ - 0.0057T^2 - 0.00000015T^3 - 36.12T \quad (20\text{-}11)$$

Values for particular hydrocarbons are given in Table 20-2.[30,33,34] Tables and equations have also been computed[35] for a large number of hydrocarbons, and the National Bureau of Standards currently collects, analyzes, and calculates thermodynamic data.[36]

In using free energies for examining the feasibility of a reaction, the free energies of the reactants are subtracted algebraically from the free energies of the products of the reaction as in Example 20-1.

Example 20-1. Feasibility of a Reaction. The possibility of making 2,2-dimethyl-pentane from propene and isobutane will be investigated.

$$CH_3 \cdot CH : CH_2 + CH_3 \cdot \underset{\underset{CH_3}{|}}{CH} \cdot CH_3 \rightarrow CH_3 \cdot \underset{\underset{CH_3}{|}}{\overset{\overset{CH_3}{|}}{C}} \cdot CH_2 \cdot CH_2 \cdot CH_3$$

[32] Bruins and Czarnecki, Relation between Structure and Free Energy of Organic Molecules, *Ind. Eng. Chem.*, **33**, 201 (1941).

[33] Pitzer, K. S., Chemical Equilibria, Free Energies and Heat Contents for Gaseous Hydrocarbons, Symposium on Fundamental Chemical Thermodynamics, ACS Cincinnati Meeting, April, 1940.

[34] Parks, G. S., Some Free Energy Data for Typical Hydrocarbons . . . , Symposium on Fundamental Chemical Thermodynamics, ACS Cincinnati Meeting, April, 1940.

[35] Thacker, Folkins, and Miller, Free Energies of Formation of Gaseous Hydrocarbons . . . , *Ind. Eng. Chem.*, **33**, 584 (1941).

[36] API Research Project 44 of the National Bureau of Standards pertains to nearly all important physical and thermodynamic data on hydrocarbons such as boiling point, vapor pressure, critical constants, viscosity, entropy, heat of combustion, etc.

TABLE 20-2. FREE ENERGIES OF FORMATION OF HYDROCARBONS[a]
Cal per g mole

Substance	Formula	$\Delta H_f°$ (heat of formation, 298°K)	$\Delta F°$ at 298°K	$\Delta F°$ at 500°K	$\Delta F°$ at 1000°K
Methane	CH_4	−17,865	−12,300(−12,085)	−8,050(−8,050)	3,450(3,450)
Acetylene	C_2H_2	58,228	50,840(50,034)	48,100(47,160)	41,300(40,850)
Ethylene	C_2H_4	12,556	15,820(16,279)	18,520(18,830)	27,670(26,700)
Ethane	C_2H_6	−20,191	−8,260(−7,787)	1,960(−50)	25,790(24,190)
Propene	C_3H_6	4,956	14,820(14,730)	22,510(20,930)	43,380(40,340)
Propane	C_3H_8	−24,750	−6,220(−5,550)	7,540(5,640)	45,200(41,300)
Butadiene 1-3	C_4H_6	26,865	(33,960)	(40,000)	(60,000)
Isobutene	C_4H_8	−3,205	14,240(14,440)	26,970(25,500)	62,780(58,720)
Butene-1	C_4H_8	383	16,780(16,810)	29,440(27,000)	62,960(58,230)
Butene-2 (cis)	C_4H_8	−1,388	14,860(15,570)	27,440(26,290)	60,800(58,590)
Butene-2 (trans)	C_4H_8	−2,338	14,450(14,800)	27,390(25,640)	61,650(58,240)
Isobutane	C_4H_{10}	−31,350	−4,900(−4,160)	14,670(11,440)	67,350(60,680)
n-Butane	C_4H_{10}	−29,715	−5,000(−3,630)	13,500(11,070)	63,170(58,300)
Pentadiene 1-4	C_5H_8	25,565	40,220	57,000	
Pentene-1	C_5H_{10}	−4,644	17,800	36,000	80,000
Isopentane	C_5H_{12}	−36,671	−4,230(−3,190)	19,850	85,300
n-Pentane	C_5H_{12}	−34,739	−2,570(−1,620)	21,040	85,670
Tetramethyl-methane	C_5H_{12}	−39,410	−4,500(−3,310)	21,180(17,760)	90,950(84,020)
Benzene	C_6H_6	....	30,640	38,700	59,600
Cyclohexene	C_6H_{10}	....	19,400	32,100	
Hexene-1	C_6H_{12}	....	19,200	42,000	99,100
Cyclohexane	C_6H_{12}	....	8,030	34,600	103,500
Methylcyclopentane	C_6H_{12}	....	3,700	21,500	
2-Methylpentane	C_6H_{14}	−41,800	(−1,000)		
n-Hexane	C_6H_{14}	−40,010	−1,500(80)	28,000	103,000
2,2-Dimethylbutane	C_6H_{14}	−44,400	(−2,300)		
Toluene	C_7H_8	....	28,400	41,200	74,200
Heptene-1	C_7H_{14}	....	20,720	48,720	118,400
Ethylcyclopentane	C_7H_{14}	....	8,000		
Methylcyclohexane	C_7H_{14}	....	4,280(l)		
2-Methylhexane	C_7H_{16}	−47,100	−1,300(600)	35,700	
3-Methylhexane	C_7H_{16}	....	−930	36,350	
3-Ethylpentane	C_7H_{16}	....	−130	37,050	
2,2-Dimethylpentane	C_7H_{16}	−49,800	−130(−300)	38,300	
2,3-Dimethylpentane	C_7H_{16}	....	−430	37,100	
2,4-Dimethylpentane	C_7H_{16}	....	370	38,500	
3,3-Dimethylpentane	C_7H_{16}	....	−730	37,300	
2,2,3-Trimethylbutane	C_7H_{16}	....	870	40,000	
n-Heptane	C_7H_{16}	−45,350	190(1,750)	35,000	122,500
Ethylbenzene	C_8H_{10}	....	28,090(l)		
m-Xylene	C_8H_{10}	....	29,660	47,300	92,800
Diisobutene (low bp)	C_8H_{16}	....	21,530	56,090	146,700
Diisobutene (high bp)	C_8H_{16}	....	22,260	58,450	150,200
2,2,4-Trimethylpentane	C_8H_{18}	−56,200	1,570(700)	46,000	
n-Octane	C_8H_{18}	−50,700	1,520(3,400)	40,000	141,600
n-Nonane	C_9H_{20}	....	2,280(l)		
n-Decane	$C_{10}H_{22}$	....	3,490(l)		
2-Methylnonane	$C_{10}H_{22}$	....	2,000(l)		
Decylene-2	$C_{10}H_{20}$	....	24,100(l)		
n-Butylcyclohexane	$C_{10}H_{20}$	....	7,000(l)		
n-Butylbenzene	$C_{10}H_{14}$	....	29,670(l)		
Naphthalene	$C_{10}H_8$	....	47,430(s)(50,400)	62,000	93,500
Undecane	$C_{11}H_{24}$	....	4,310(l)		
Dodecane	$C_{12}H_{26}$	....	6,530(l)		
n-Heptylcyclohexane	$C_{13}H_{26}$	....	9,530(l)		
Anthracene	$C_{14}H_{10}$	....	64,190(s)(72,400)	89,200	135,000
Hexadecane	$C_{16}H_{34}$	....	10,710(l)		
Dotriacontane	$C_{32}H_{66}$	....	31,300(l)		

[a] The free energies are for gases except when followed by (l) and (s), which designate liquids and solids. Parentheses around the numbers indicate that they were determined by statistical mechanics and were taken from K. S. Pitzer, Chemical Equilibria, Free Energies . . . , Symposium on Fundamental Chemical Thermodynamics, ACS Cincinnati Meeting, April, 1940.

From Table 20-2

	ΔF°_{298}	ΔF°_{500}
$C_3H_6(g)$	14,820	22,510
$iC_4H_{10}(g)$	−4,900	14,670
C_7H_{16}	−130	38,300

For the entire reaction:

$$\Delta F^\circ_{298} = -130 - 14,820 - (-4,900) = -10,050$$
$$\Delta F^\circ_{500} = 38,300 - 22,510 - 14,670 = 1,120$$

Thus, the preceding reaction appears to be possible at temperatures of 25 to 227°C but may require the use of a catalyst. The reaction should proceed more completely at low temperatures (free energy is negative), but the rate may be so slow that higher temperatures may be necessary. The application of pressure should assist the reaction because it is a bimolecular one.

The numerical values of K are useful in deciding upon a suitable temperature:

$$\ln K_{298} = \frac{-10,050}{-RT} = \frac{-10,050}{-1.987 \times 298} = 17$$

K_{298} is very large, or the yield approaches 100 per cent.

$$\ln K_{500} = \frac{1,120}{-1.987 \times 500} = -1.128$$
$$K_{500} = \frac{(C_7H_{16})}{(C_3H_6)(iC_4H_{10})} = 0.3236$$

Solving for percentage of C_7H_{16} after establishing equilibrium,

$$A + B \rightleftharpoons C$$

Let x = moles of C (or C_7H_{16}) in reaction products per mole A introduced
Moles $A = 1 - x$ = moles B

At equilibrium and for a pressure of $P = 1$ atm:

$$0.3236 = \frac{x/(2-x)}{(1-x)^2/(2-x)^2} P = \frac{x(2-x)}{(1-x)^2} P$$
$$x = 0.131 \text{ moles}$$

Percentages of C_7H_{16} in products:

$$\text{Total moles after reaction} = (1-x) + (1-x) + x = 2 - x$$
$$\text{Percentage} = \frac{0.131 \times 100}{2 - 0.131} = 7.0 \text{ per cent } C_7H_{16}$$

This is not an economical yield in most instances.

Values at other temperatures may be estimated by assuming that ΔF° is a linear function of temperature; i.e., $\Delta F^\circ = aT + b$. The constants a and b in such an equation may be evaluated thus:

at 298° $-10,050 = 298a + b$
at 500° $1,120 = 500a + b$
subtracting $-11,170 = -202a$
                 $a = 55.3$ and $b = -26,530$
and $\Delta F^\circ = 55.3T - 26,530$

If in this instance a yield of 30 per cent is feasible by practicing recycling, the temperature at which the process can operate can be estimated as follows:

Moles of C_7H_{16} produced when 1 mole of A is processed:

$$30 \text{ per cent} = \frac{100x}{2 - x}$$

$$x = 0.4615 \text{ moles of } C_7H_{16}$$

$$\text{Equilibrium constant} = K = \frac{0.4615(2 - 0.4615)}{(1 - 0.4615)^2} = 2.46$$

Also

$$\ln K = 0.9 = \frac{\Delta F^\circ}{-RT} = \frac{55.3T - 26,530}{-1.987T}$$

and

$$T = 465^\circ \text{ abs or } 192^\circ C$$

Thus it would appear that the alkylation of propene by isobutane is thermodynamically possible in the temperature range of about 200°C and lower. The ultimate yield at 200°C is not large; but since the rate or velocity of the reaction increases rapidly with temperature, it will probably be best to operate at as high a temperature as possible. Should the rate be too slow at 200°C, a catalyst must be found.

From a purely thermodynamic standpoint it might also be possible to make 2,3-dimethylpentane, 2,4-dimethylpentane, 3,3-dimethylpentane, or even 2,2,3-trimethylbutane from propene and isobutane. The values of the free energies for these reactions (computed in the same manner) are

	ΔF°_{298}	ΔF°_{500}
2,3-Dimethylpentane..........	$-10,350$	-80
3,3-Dimethylpentane..........	$-10,650$	120
2,2-Dimethylpentane..........	$-10,050$	$1,120$
2,4-Dimethylpentane..........	$-9,550$	$1,320$
2,2,3-Trimethylbutane........	$-9,050$	$2,820$

Thus it appears that several ractions might take place simultaneously but that the amounts of each of the isomers (at 500°K) would be somewhat in the decreasing order shown in the foregoing tabulation. Even this does not include all the thermodynamic possibilities, because there are many other isomeric seven-carbon-atom hydrocarbons.

When data on ΔF° are not available, they can be computed by means of the ΔH and $T\Delta S$ terms in Eq. (20-6). The heat of reaction, or ΔH, may be computed from heats of combustion[36] (or formation) as discussed later, but the entropy change designated by ΔS presents more difficulty. In a practical way the absolute entropy[36] designated as S consists of the sum of all heat energy inputs involved in heating from absolute zero temperature, each energy quantity being divided by the absolute temperature at which the energy is added. All imputs of energy such as those involved in changes of crystalline state at low temperatures, energy or heat of fusion, and heat of vaporization must be included, as well as the sensible heats of the solid, liquid, and vapor. It is usually necessary to approximate the sensible heat at low temperatures (near absolute zero) by extrapolation and to hope that no changes in the crystalline state of the material are involved in this temperature range.   Such computations are discussed in chemical thermodynamics texts,[29] and particularly by Parks and Huffman.[37]

Heat of Reaction.   The heat of reaction may be computed by determining the algebraic sum of the heats of combustion (or formation) of the materials before and after the reaction as in Example 19-1.   If the products contain more chemical energy than the reactants, the reaction

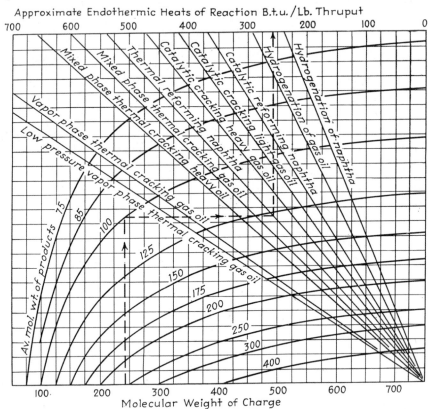

Fig. 20-2. Approximate endothermic heats of reaction.   (*Edmister, Pet. Engr.*)

is endothermic, and vice versa.   Data for heats of combustion (or formation) may be obtained from the National Bureau of Standards[36] (API Research Project 44); or from "Physical Constants of the Principal Hydrocarbons."[38]   The use of generalizations for heating values such as Fig. 5-22 can be misleading[39] if large amounts of aromatic hydrocarbons

[37] "Free Energies of Some Organic Compounds," Reinhold Publishing Corporation, New York, 1932; also R. H. Ewell, *Ind. Eng. Chem.*, **32**, 778 (1940).

[38] Technical and Research Division of the Texas Company, 3d ed., 1942.

[39] Gornowski and Feldbauer, A Method of Estimating Heat Reaction in Catalytic Reforming, ACS Meeting, Dallas, Apr. 8, 1956.

are present, because common criteria such as Correlation Index, Characterization Factor, aniline point, etc., fail to differentiate between aromatic hydrocarbons and mixtures of other hydrocarbons. W. C. Edmister[40] has published Fig. 20-2 by which endothermic heats of reaction can be estimated from the average molecular weights of the feed and the products. Typical heats of reaction are given for particular reactions in the remaining parts of this chapter.

THERMAL CRACKING

Decomposition underlies very much of the petrochemical industry. The gases produced in catalytic cracking (Chap. 21) and thermal cracking (Chap. 19) contain the useful unsaturated hydrocarbons. The amount of reactive gaseous hydrocarbons produced by thermal cracking is greatly increased by the use of vapor-phase conditions of low pressure (50 psig and lower) and high temperature (1150 to 1700°F). Refer to pages 644 to 652 and especially Table 19-8. Some aromatic hydrocarbons, especially high-boiling ones, are produced, but the platinum catalyst reforming processes of pages 810 to 818 are the major source of benzene, toluene, and the xylenes (as well as hydrogen). The numerous products of thermal cracking are indicated[13] in Table 20-3 and also in the tabulation on page 649. The products of Table 20-3 were obtained in an electrically heated tube, and the conditions were selected for the purpose of producing aromatic hydrocarbons rather than ethylene.

The enormous number of by-products that arise during chemical manufacture make it impossible to present the relationships between the many plant operations. Nevertheless, Fig. 20-3 indicates the eminent position of thermal cracking and how one plant operation demands (or rests upon) the installation of other plants. No attempt is made to explore all possibilities (see Fig. 20-1). Thus, chemical developments can occur only in a highly industrialized environment, or inversely, the installation of a single isolated chemical plant is seldom feasible. The industry is one that feeds upon itself; the more diversified it becomes, the easier it becomes to add new processes or plants.

As an illustration, consider a vapor-phase cracking plant (Fig. 20-3) originally installed primarily for ethylene and ethyl alcohol (II). The alcohol plant needs sulfuric acid but not enough to justify the operation of a sulfur or acid plant (III). However the acid could also be used for ammonium sulfate fertilizer (IV), and accordingly the hydrogen from the basic cracking plant is used to manufacture ammonia (V). But even more hydrogen is needed. This is obtained from a catalytic reforming plant (VI). The nitrogen needed for ammonia synthesis calls for an oxygen plant (VII), but to utilize the by-product oxygen an acetylene plant (VIII) is contemplated (which could very well supply acetylene

[40] Hydrocarbon Thermodynamics, Part III *Pet. Engr.*, May, 1946, p. 211.

TABLE 20-3. PRODUCT DISTRIBUTION FOR THERMAL CRACKING OF HYDROCARBONS
Weight, per cent

Feed	Propane	Butane	12-lb R.v.p. natural gasoline	Reduced crude oil
Operating conditions:				
Cracking temperature, °F..........	1500	1400	1400	1470
Total pressure, atm...............	1.00	1.02	1.00	1.02
Residence time, sec...............	4.5	10.9	9.6	2.5
Steam-hydrocarbon feed ratio, lb/lb.	0	0	0	0.15
Product distribution, wt % of feed:				
Methane........................	36.15	28.70	28.28	15.11
Ethane.........................	3.70	6.80	5.18	3.62
Propane........................	0.42	......	0.78	0.21
Isobutane......................	......	......	0.20	
n-Butane.......................	0.28	0.68	......	0.14
Ethylene.......................	28.44	30.11	24.08	17.88
Propylene......................	1.99	4.92	3.41	5.86
Butenes........................	0.27	0.44	0.39	1.06
1,3-Butadiene..................	1.79	1.48	1.33	2.43
Cyclopentadiene................	0.31	0.27	0.24	0.62
Hydrogen.......................	2.26	1.15	1.13	0.79
Acetylene......................	0.49	0.10	......	0.18
Inerts.........................	1.93	1.42	0.25	0.21
Benzene........................	7.71	12.57	9.04⎫	
Toluene........................	1.08	1.91	1.87 ⎪	
Xylenes........................	0.38	0.06	...... ⎪	
Ethylbenzene...................	0.29	0.29	0.64 ⎬	10.01
Styrene........................	0.66	0.71	0.82 ⎪	
C₉ + aromatics in 32–392°F distillate	0.96	0.86	1.60 ⎪	
Olefins in 32–392°F distillate.......	1.40	0.83	1.12 ⎪	
Paraffins in 32–392°F distillate......	0.10	0.67	1.05⎭	
Distillate 392–572°F..............	3.70	1.48	5.77	8.63
Distillate 572–670°F..............	1.22	0.49	2.14	5.07
Pitch..........................	3.82	3.79	10.03	20.79
Carbon.........................	0.75	0.27	0.65	7.39
Total.....................	100.00	100.00	100.00	100.00

to a hydrocyanic acid plant for acrylonitrile plastics such as Orlon). Meanwhile, the olefins of the basic cracking plant call for aromatics separation and for plants for making cumene, phenol, isopropanol, glycerol, acetone, styrene, polyethylene, ethylene glycol, etc. Indeed, the chemical industry continually widens its own horizons. It may have been implied that all of the installations just enumerated are operated by a single organization. This is not necessary if a highly industrialized and competitive enterprise environment is available, but if no such system exists these installations and more must be undertaken by the parent organization, and most of the program during a short period of time.

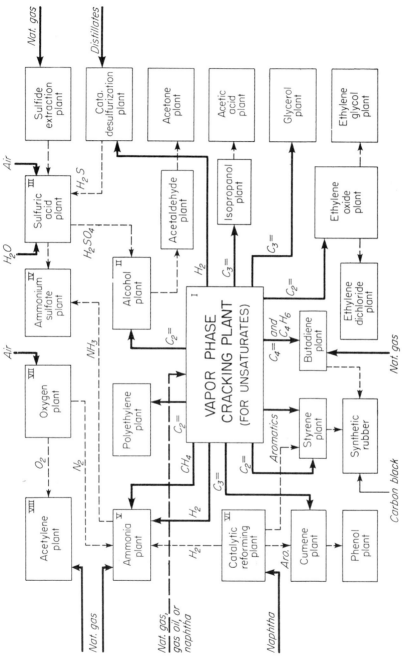

FIG. 20-3. The by-product nature of the petrochemical industry (also see text).

Ethylene Plants. Of the 10 million pounds per day of ethylene produced in the United States during 1956, about half came from the vapor-phase cracking of natural gas hydrocarbons, 15 per cent from the vapor-phase cracking of naphtha or distillates, and less than 35 per cent by extraction from refinery cracking-plant gases. The ethylene in various refinery gases (Table 14-4) is recovered in an ethylene recovery system, and the other gases that are useful as a cracking stock for ethylene manufacture are present in the following amounts:

	Mole %, range	Average
Ethane...............	5.0–28.0	12
Ethylene............	3.3– 8.2	5
Propane.............	7.0–44.0	14
Propylene...........	1.0–36.0	19

Of course, richer gases could be made available or, if the refiner chose to recover the propylene as tetramer or as bottle gas along with propane, the gas would be leaner. Note that a separate feed preparation system is not necessary (Fig. 20-4) because the products of cracking contain the same gases as the feed, and thus both the feed and the products can be processed in a single product recovery system. It is necessary, however, to remove hydrogen sulfide from the incoming gaseous feed.

TABLE 20-4. HEAT OF REACTION OF ETHANE AND PROPANE
Btu per pound mole reacting divided by 1000

Percentage conversion	Ethane		Propane	
	Differential	Cumulative	Differential	Cumulative
0	59	59	41	41
20	52	54.5	37	38.5
40	49.5	53	32.5	36.5
60	48	51.5	28.5	35
70	47.5	50.5	25	33.5
80	....	....	20.5	32
90	....	....	low	30

Approximate yields, conversions per pass, reaction velocity constants, heats of reaction, etc., have already been discussed. Heat of reaction decreases as the reaction becomes more complete[41] as shown in Table 20-4. The temperature heating curve should continue to rise smoothly to the

[41] Schutt and Zdonik, Designing a Tubular Pyrolysis Furnace, *Oil Gas J.*, May 14, 1956, p. 149.

outlet. A sharp increase at the outlet means too high a rate of heat input with high film temperatures and excessive secondary reactions leading to coke, whereas a drop in temperature allows too close an approach to equilibrium and thus a long time for condensation reactions to occur among the heavy products leading to the formation of heavy liquids, tars, and coke. The production of ethylene is primarily a reaction of dehydrogenation, and the equilibrium constants for dehydrogenation are given in Fig. 19-4. Low pressures cause the reaction to go more completely toward dehydrogenation and thus pressures under 50 psig are used at the outlet of the coil, and steam is often introduced to further reduce the partial pressure. The amount of steam ranges from 0.3 mole steam per mole ethane to as high a ratio as 8 when cracking heavy oils (see Table 19-8). Commonly used heat transfer rates and velocities[41] are indicated in Table 20-5.

TABLE 20-5. HEAT TRANSFER RATES IN ZONE OF HIGH CONVERSION[a]

Inside tube diameter, in.	Cracking stock	Mass velocity, lb per sec-sq ft	Range of conversion, per cent[b]	Radiant heating rate, Btu per sq ft projected area[a]
4	Ethane	23–26	50–60	23,600–28,250
4	Propane	26–28	70–85	14,100–17,300
4	Butane	28–32	75–90	11,000–14,100
4.5	Naphtha	24–26	50–58[c]	11,000–14,100

[a] The radiant absorption rate must be larger (sometimes double) in the earlier reaction zones in order to maintain a constantly rising temperature.

[b] The range in the high-conversion zone.

[c] In terms of weight per cent butanes and lighter.

In Fig. 20-4, refinery gas is treated with diethanolamine for the removal of hydrogen sulfide, and it then joins the reaction products for a wash with caustic for the removal of the last traces (below 10 ppm) of hydrogen sulfide, carbon dioxide, or any acidic materials. The reaction products contain small amounts of acetylene (0.2 to 0.5 mole per cent based on C_4 and lighter) especially if the reaction temperature is high and the amount of steam used for partial pressure reduction is large.[42] This must be reduced to 10 ppm to meet ethylene purity specifications. Selective hydrogenation at 50 to 350 psig is the common method of removing acetylene. The gas is then compressed and cooled to as low a temperature as possible without hydrate formation (see Table 22-3) and dried using a solid desiccant such as alumina. The gas is then passed through a series of fractionating towers for the recovery of ethylene and propylene,

[42] Schutt and Zdonik, Compression and Pretreatment of Pyrolysis Product, *Oil Gas J.*, June 25, 1956, p. 92.

the elimination of methane and hydrogen, and the separation of feed-stocks (ethane, propane, and small amounts of the butanes) for the vapor-phase cracking coils. Refrigeration for cooling the feeds and refluxes of the demethanizer and ethylene towers is usually provided by a cascade refrigeration system operating on ammonia and ethylene which

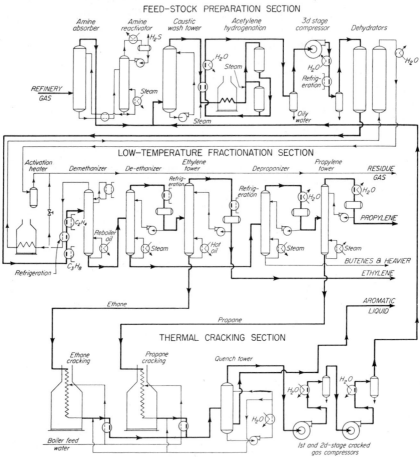

FIG. 20-4. Simplified diagram of ethylene manufacture.   (*Pet. Processing.*)

permits the low temperature of $-150°F$ in the ethylene condenser. Approximate operating conditions for the several towers are indicated in Table 20-6.   In many plants the propylene and propane are not separated nor is a propane cracking coil employed.   In such plants the entire propylene and heavier fraction may be polymerized into gasoline.   Further reaction among the unsaturated products must be arrested at the outlet of the reaction coil to avoid coke formation in the transfer line. This is accomplished by quenching with water to a temperature of 700°F or lower[43] and then cooling to as low a temperature as possible before the compressors by the circulation of a large amount of water through the so-called quench tower.

In manufacturing ethylene from reduced crude oil or residues, the feed is heated and sent to a flash or evaporator chamber to vaporize a gas-oil or distillate fraction, as practiced in the early Gyro Vapor Phase cracking process[44] for the production of ethylene. Steam is used to assist in the vaporization and to reduce the partial pressure in the reaction zone as

TABLE 20-6. APPROXIMATE OPERATING CONDITIONS FOR ETHYLENE RECOVERY SYSTEMS (SEE FIG. 20-4) OF THE REFRIGERATION AND PRESSURE TYPE[a]

	Demethanizer	Deethanizer	Ethylene tower	Depropanizer
Pressure, psia........	425–500	325–450	275–350	150–225
Top temp, °F.	−100 to −150[b]	10–30	0 to −20	75–110
Reboiler temp, °F....	35–65	155–190	10–40	225–275
Plates..............	20–30	30–40	50–65	
Reflux ratio.........	Low	0.8–2.0	3.5–5.2	1.0

[a] Basically the same conditions as those of Gyro Vapor Phase designs of 1932 and used in plants of 1935-1938.

[b] Feed to tower at about −70°F to save refrigeration at top of tower.

practiced now in the so-called Steam Pyrolysis Process[45] of ethylene manufacture. When vapor-phase cracking is practiced on entire crude oils[45] (36.2 API) a significant amount of butylene-butadiene fraction is produced as well as exceedingly high-octane gasoline, and according to Reference 45 the cost of ethylene (corrected for the value of the other products) is lower than when it is produced from most other feedstocks. Yields are somewhat as follows:

	Volume per cent	Weight per cent
Ethylene...............	....	11–17
Propylene..............	16.6–17.3	10.2–10.7
Butene-butadiene........	7.7–8.9	5.7–6.6
Gasoline...............	20.2–29.7	
Heavy fuel oil..........	25.4–30.9	
Fuel gas...............	....	8.9–13.6

[43] The same temperature and method used in the arrestor of the original Gyro Vapor Phase Process in 1928 and thereafter.

[44] Wagner, C. R., Vapor Phase Cracking, *Pet. Engr.*, November, 1929; also see page 487 of the First Edition of this book.

[45] Anon., Steam Cracking Extended to Ethane, Propane Feed Stocks, *Oil Gas J.*, Jan. 2, 1956, p. 113; also *Pet. Processing*, February, 1956, p. 87.

The composition[46] of the B-B (four-carbon-atom) cut from vapor-phase cracking is indicated in Table 20-7, and such a material was produced during World War II in the production of synthetic rubber.[47]

The use of tubular converters, quenching or arresting, and low-temperature high-pressure recovery, as outlined in Fig. 20-4, is most common, but modifications of heating and recovery have also been employed. In addition to tubular heaters such as stills (i), (j), and (k) of Fig. 18-1, as well as two other arrangements analysed by Schutt,[41] the pebble heaters mentioned on page 590 are also used, and, when operating at 2000°F on

TABLE 20-7. COMPOSITION[a] OF VAPOR-PHASE B-B CUTS AND CATALYTIC B-B CUTS FOR COMPARISON,[b] VOLUME PER CENT

	Gas cracking[c]		Heavy stocks cracked for		Fluid process[b]	T.C.C. process[b]
			Gases	Gasoline		
Butadiene.........	38–56	44–52	10–46	13	None	None
Butylenes }	39–53	12–24	37	60	25.6	18.9
Isobutene }		23–37	7–40	25	10.6	12.7
Butane }	2.2–6.7}	1–2.5}	}	2	10.7	12.2
Isobutane }			}		53.1	56.2
Others (acetylenes).	2.1–4.2	0.5	7			

[a] Wagner, C. R., *Ind. Eng. Chem.*, **27**, 933 (1935); Poffenberger et al., *Trans. A.I.Ch.E.*, **42**, 815 (1946); and private communications to the author.

[b] Nelson, W. L., *Oil Gas J.*, Sept. 22, 1949, p. 297.

[c] Two different operators.

normal butane, they are said[48] to produce 50 per cent more ethylene than tubular stills. The use of highly superheated steam (1700 to 1900°F) as the main heating medium[49] is a means of avoiding coking on the surface of tubes, and thus reaction temperatures of 1700 to 1880°F become feasible. Likewise, oxygen or air introduced into the hot (1100 to 1500°F) stream of feed material has been suggested as a means of heating (by combustion) during the reaction, in the autothermic process.[50] Finally, various regenerative methods of heating similar to those used in gas manufacture have been used.[51]

[46] Wagner, C. R., *Ind. Eng. Chem.*, **27**, 933 (1935) relates vapor-phase BB cut produced in 1929; also Poffenberger et al., *Trans. A.I.Ch.E.*, **42**, 815 (1946); and private communications to the author.

[47] Ralph, H. D., *Oil Gas J.*, Dec. 15, 1945, p. 70.

[48] Kilpatrick et al., Phillips Pebble Heater . . . , *Oil Gas J.*, May 10, 1954, p. 162.

[49] King and Warburton, *Oil Gas J.*, Dec. 8, 1950, p. 92; also *Pet. Processing*, November, 1952, p. 1644.

[50] Deanesly and Walkins, *Chem. Eng. Progr.*, March, 1951, p. 134.

[51] Schutt and Zdonik, Processing Scheme—Pyrolysis Methods, *Oil Gas J.*, Apr. 2, 1956, p. 99.

Likewise, several variations in recovery methods have been employed. The gaseous mixture may be highly compressed and chilled as indicated in Fig. 20-5.[52] Expansion of the gases causes refrigeration and condensation of the ethylene and higher-boiling materials which are then fractionated in an ethylene column. Further refrigeration for the top of this column is obtained by using the ethylene product itself as a refrigeration medium. Compression costs are high, but the process has been used in small European plants. Another widely used method employs a fractionator-absorber or absorber-demethanizer for elimination of the methane and hydrogen.[52,53] A large amount of cold (-30 to $+40°F$)

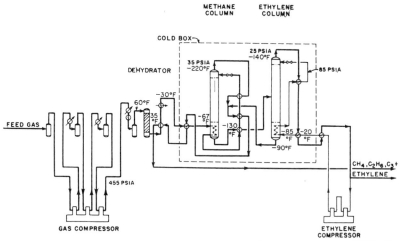

Fig. 20-5. Ethylene purification by the Linde fractionation process. (*Schutt, Oil Gas J.*)

absorption medium of low molecular weight (30 to 72) is used to absorb the ethylene and higher-boiling components. The absorber is held at a high pressure (425 lb or higher), and the temperature is kept low by the use of intercoolers on the side of the absorber. The lowest or stripper part of the equipment is heated for the elimination of absorbed methane so that substantially no methane issues from the bottom of the combination absorber-fractionator. After demethanization, the stream is fractionated in much the same type of system as that of Fig. 20-4. Finally, ethylene may be recovered by adsorption, utilizing the hypersorption process and equipment described on pages 344 and 346 and Table 10-15, but the ethylene must also be purified in an ethylene tower similar to that used in Fig. 20-4.

[52] Schutt and Zdonik, How to Recover Ethylene, *Oil Gas J.*, July 30, 1956, p. 171.

[53] Kniel and Slager, Ethylene Purification by Absorption Process, *Chem. Eng. Progr.*, July, 1947, p. 335.

POLYMERIZATION

This reaction occurs in several ways, i.e., as bimolecular or polymolecular reactions, or as successive reactions that produce dimer, trimer, or polymer products:

$$2C_2H_4 \rightarrow C_4H_8 \qquad 3C_3H_6 \rightarrow C_9H_{18}$$
and
$$C_4H_8 + C_9H_{18} \rightarrow C_{13}H_{26}$$

The polymerization of ethylene in the early stages is bimolecular,[54] but some third-order combinations also take place. In phosphoric acid polymerization, low temperatures[55] (300°F) and high pressures (750 psig and higher) tend to produce true or primary polymers, but at higher temperatures, such as those used commercially (400 to 500°F) in making polymer gasoline the product is a gross mixture indicating that secondary depolymerization reactions also occur. Thermal polymerization at low pressures and high temperatures[56] also indicates the heterogeneous nature of so-called polymerization. When charging a gas containing 35 per cent C_3 and C_4 olefins, the total liquid product was aromatic (gasoline gravity 34.4 API) to the degree of showing distinct plateaus for benzene (about 23 per cent) and toluene (about 12 per cent) in its distillation curve.

The National Bureau of Standards[57] indicates that average Hydrocodimer (hydrogenated isobutylene dimer) contains about 0.7 per cent hexanes, 3.2 per cent heptanes, 85.8 per cent octanes, and 10.3 per cent nonanes or heavier.

The heat of reaction (exothermic) is about 40,000 Btu per lb-mole for each union of two molecules, regardless of the type of molecules. However, the conservative values of 670 Btu per lb propene, or 450 Btu per lb butenes polymerized, are used by some designers.

Thermal Polymerization. Although not as effective as catalytic polymerization, thermal polymerization has been used in many plants[58,59] (about 40,000 b.p.d. during 1955) and especially as a means of utilizing the saturated gases that cannot be directly polymerized catalytically.[60] The process consists essentially of vapor-phase cracking of propane and the butanes followed by prolonged time at 950 to 1100°F for polymeriza-

[54] Russell and Hottel, *Ind. Eng. Chem.*, **30**, 183 (1938).

[55] Langlois, G. E., *Ind. Eng. Chem.*, **45**, 1470 (1953).

[56] Ridgway et al., *Natl. Pet. News*, Nov. 4, 1936, p. 47.

[57] Glasgow et al., Analysis of Alkylates and Hydrocodimers, *Oil Gas J.*, Nov. 16, 1946, p. 236.

[58] Turner and Ruby, *Ref. Nat. Gaso. Mfr.*, September, p. 423, and Ridgway and Maschwitz, *Oil Gas J.*, Oct. 30, 1941, p. 30.

[59] Maschwitz and Henderson, "Progress in Pet. Technology," Polymerization of Hydrocarbon Gases . . . , ACS Meeting, New York, September, 1951.

[60] Smith, J. H., Transeconomizers, *Oil Gas J.*, Aug. 3, 1950, p. 45.

tion and further decomposition, depolymerization, etc., reactions (Fig. 20-6). The original cracking reactions are highly endothermic, but the reactions in the polymerization zone are exothermic. Although the process was developed mainly during 1930–1939, methods of estimating yields[59] were not disclosed until 1951. The method of H. C. Schutt, based on per cent of hydrogen in the feed and products and related to operating temperatures and pressures, is too long to present here, but it is described in detail in Reference 59.

Rate of reaction data are scarce, but Eq. (20-12) represents the general situation.

$$\frac{K_2}{P} = \frac{1}{tP}\frac{x}{a(1-x)} \tag{20-12}$$

where K_2/P = reaction velocity constant divided by pressure (Table 20-8)

t = time, min

p = pressure, psia

x = fraction of olefins reacting during time t

a = fraction of olefins contained in feedstock

The values of K_2/P of Table 20-8[61] cover experimental ranges of pressure up to 3,000 pounds and temperatures of 650 to 850°F and 1400 to 1500°F when handling ethene, propene, and the butenes. According to H. C. Schutt,[59] the preferred range of time for the polymerization zone in commercial thermal polymerization is 50 to 100 seconds.

TABLE 20-8. REACTION VELOCITY CONSTANTS[a] IN THERMAL POLYMERIZATION

Temp, °F	1,000 K_2/P	Temp, °F	1,000 K_2/P
650	0.0048	1,000[b]	0.95
700	0.013	1,100[b]	2.9
750	0.029	1,200[b]	7.5
800	0.063	1,300[b]	17.0
850	0.135	1,400	35.0
900[b]	0.29	1,500	68.0
950[b]	0.56		

[a] From p. 640 of the Third Edition of this book.
[b] Experimental data not available in this range.

Thermal polymerization is so intimately related to the process of thermal decomposition that most commercial flow diagrams show both processes—in fact, the flow diagrams are devoted more to decomposition and product recovery than to polymerization. Propane is seldom used as a feedstock because of the high pressures and temperatures that must be employed, although it usually constitutes a portion of the recycling stream of a polymerization plant.

[61] See p. 640 of the Third Edition of this book for plotted experimental points.

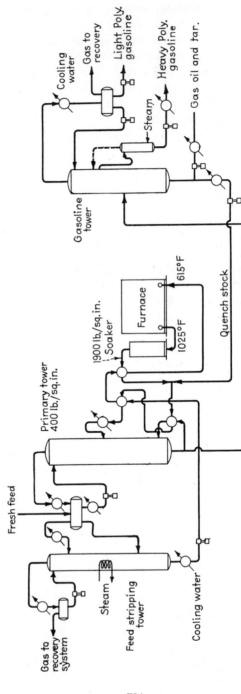

FIG. 20-6. Typical thermal polymerization (and decomposition) plant.

724

The flow diagram shown in Fig. 20-6 shows the essential features of the Baytown plant of the Humble Oil & Refining Co.[58] Analyses of the feed and several stocks are shown in Table 20-9. The capacity of the plant is 10,000 bbl daily, but the amount of material charged to the furnace is

TABLE 20-9. STOCKS AND PRODUCTS OF A THERMAL POLY PLANT[a]

Stock	Fresh feed, mole %	Furnace feed, mole %	Residue gas, mole %	Properties of stock	Light poly gaso.	Heavy poly gaso.	Gas oil and tar
Methane.....	...	....	51.0	Gravity, API	75	44	20
Ethane.......	...	1.5	28.0	I.B.P., °F	90	195	370
Propane......	...	10.5	19.5	F.B.P., °F	245	450	(90% at 660°F)
Isobutane....	20	30.0 ⎫	1.5	Per cent at 158°F	58		
n-Butane.....	80	58.0 ⎭		Per cent at 212°F	95	2–3	
Total......	100	100.0	100.0	Reid v.p., psi	13	2–3	
Unsaturates..	15	14.0	12.0	Octane No. (CFR Motor method)	77.5	75	
				Octane No. (blending value)	87.0		

[a] See Fig. 20-6.

38,000 bbl per day. The yield of gasoline (10 lb Reid) decreases[58] with the conversion per pass somewhat as follows:

	Yield of polymer, weight per cent		
	5% conversion	10% conversion	15% conversion
Propane....	51.7	47.5	
Butane.....	71.6	64.4	56.7

Note that the conversion per pass applies to both the decomposition and polymerization parts of the still. These yields apply to a specific plant, and the method of H. C. Schutt[59] is probably more dependable when considering various operating conditions. Complete operating conditions are given by Ridgway and Maschwitz,[58] and their data on the effect of pressure and recycle ratio on the yields of one plant are indicated in Table 20-10. Yields increase up to even 2,500 psig, but such an operation is not economical. Based on propane and butanes, the ultimate yields of poly gasoline are 62 to 72 per cent by weight, and the tar or residue 5 to 10 per cent.

Feed Preparation. Although propane, butane, etc., may be decomposed or dehydrogenated to produce propylene and butenes (pages 644 to 652), this method is not followed except in thermal polymerization processes because olefinic gases are already available in the gases of thermal or catalytic cracking operations.   Feeds for catalytic polymerization processes must contain less than 10 grains hydrogen sulfide per 100 cu ft, and the moisture content must be adjusted so that the phosphoric acid catalyst is neither dried nor converted to a mud.   The Girbotol process is widely used to remove hydrogen sulfide.   The phosphoric acid process converts sulfide into highly undesirable mercaptans.

TABLE 20-10. EFFECT OF PRESSURE AND RECYCLE RATIO ON THERMAL POLY YIELDS[a]

Pressure, psig	4.5 recycle ratio		7.0 recycle ratio	
	Bbl per year	Percentage based on 500 psig	Bbl per year	Percentage based on 500 psig
500	318,000	100	349,000	110
1,000	358,000	113	387,000	122
1,500	383,000	121	414,000	130

[a] Turner and Ruby, *Ref. Nat. Gaso. Mfr.*, September, 1938, p. 423; and Ridgway and Maschwitz, *Oil Gas J.*, Oct. 30, 1941, p. 30.

The olefins in the cracked gases are handled or concentrated in several ways, depending on the pressure at which the gas is available and how much can be afforded in recovering the olefins.   It is seldom economically feasible to recover or process ethylene for polymer gasoline, and hence the preparation of the feed pertains mainly to the retention of propene and the butenes, or to the segregation of them for selective polymerization or alkylation.

1. *Complete.*   The entire cracked gas is compressed and is sent to the poly plant along with the overhead liquid from the cracked gasoline stabilizer (or debutanizer).   Hydrogen sulfide must be removed before the feed enters the poly plant.   The product from the catalyst chambers contains much gas (and some olefins), and hence this gas is sent through an absorber wherein lean absorption oil from the cracking unit is used to deliver propene and heavier hydrocarbons back to the cracking plant and eventually to the gas separator of the cracking plant.   This is the desired method if the gas pressure is high (50 to 125 psi), and it is always desirable except for the cost of compression.

2. *Low-pressure Separator.*   With low-pressure gas (as in a catalytic cracking unit) less compressor capacity is required if the separator gas is compressed and sent to a high-pressure absorber in which some of the cracked gasoline is used to absorb the propene and heavier hydrocarbons

as shown in Fig. 20-7. The flashing of the gasoline to produce a low-vapor-pressure absorption oil, as shown in Fig. 20-7, is relatively expensive.

3. *Deep Stabilization.* This simplest and widely used method requires no compression because the olefinic feed is only the liquid overhead of the cracked gasoline stabilizer. The cracked gasoline is stabilized as deeply as possible (4 to 7 Reid vapor pressure) without driving pentenes into the stabilizer overhead. Under proper conditions pentenes can be polymerized, but the dienes associated with them harm the catalyst. Since little ethene and only part of the propene are held in the cracked gasoline in the gas separator, some of the olefins never enter the stabilizer, and the yields of poly gasoline are somewhat low.

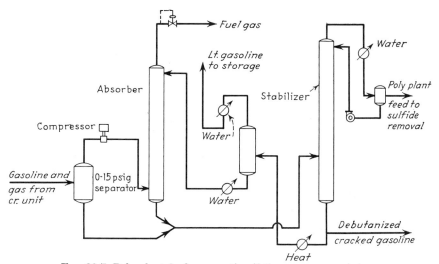

FIG. 20-7. Poly plant feed preparation if the gas pressure is low.

Nonselective polymerization involves the polymerization of propene, the butenes, and about one-fifth of the ethene; whereas *selective* polymerization employs only the butenes or in some cases only isobutene. The gasoline from selective operation is primarily 2,2,4-trimethylpentene or similar branched hydrocarbons (Codimer) which have a high octane number (92 to 103). The Codimer may be hydrogenated to make isooctane. Obviously, special methods of feed preparation or fractionation must be employed for selective operation, and the same applies to alkylation which is frequently applied to only the butylenes and isobutane.

Phosphoric Acid Polymerization. At least three modifications in the use of phosphoric acid as a catalyst are widely used: (1) quartz wetted with liquid acid,[62] (2) acid-impregnated pellets (solid phosphoric acid)

---

[62] Langlois and Walkey, *Pet. Refiner*, August, 1952, p. 79.

in chambers,[63] and (3) solid catalyst pellets packed in tubes surrounded with cooling water in so-called reactors.[63] In addition, copper pyrophosphate[64] is widely used and it seems to produce almost the same results as phosphoric acid except that the reaction temperature is slightly lower.

The properties of polymer gasolines and special polymer products[63] are indicated in Table 20-11. The Reid vapor pressure of pure debutanized polymer is usually less than 3 psia. The octane number of nonselective polymer gasoline is nearly constant for all operations, being 82 to 84 by the Motor method (85 to 87 with 3 cc TEL) or 96 to 99 by the Research method (100 with 3 cc TEL), and in blends 100 to 115 (see Fig. 4-46). The boiling range is slightly raised[64] (15 to 25°F) by increase in the reactor temperature from 340 to 400°F.

TABLE 20-11. PROPERTIES OF PHOSPHORIC ACID GASOLINES AND PRODUCTS

Feed..........	Mixture	Mixture	Mixture	Butenes	Butenes	Butenes	Propene	Propene
Product........	Motor fuel	Motor fuel	Motor fuel	Motor fuel	Codimer[a]	Codimer	Motor fuel	Tetramer[b]
Operation.......	Nonselective	Nonselective	Nonselective	Nonselective	Selective	Selective	Nonselective	Selective
Type of unit....	Chamber	Chamber	Tubular	Reactor	Reactor	Reactor	Reactor	Reactor
Pressure, psig...	250	500	900	1,000	900	1,000	1,000	900
API gravity.....	....	67.3	66.6	64.3	61.3[a]	66.4	62.4	51.0[b]
Initial bp, °F....	102	90	90	78	210	136	144	353
10 per cent...	127	143	146	152	223	207	210	363
50 per cent....	226	225	228	258	228	230	266	371
90 per cent....	372	367	330	379	234	276	330	397
E.P., °F......	486	422	400	416	257	400	402	450
R.v.p., psia.....	10	11	10.9	11.0	....	3.2	4	0

[a] Dimer from nearly equal amounts of i- and n-butene in feed. About 1/16 as much 51.5 API trimer, boiling from 261 to 434°F, also produced.

[b] Some motor fuel and heavy polymer also produced.

Conversion of 88 to 94 per cent of the olefins is common, and for the pyrophosphate process the conversion has been related[64] to reactor temperature, space velocity, and catalyst activity as indicated in Fig. 20-8. The conversion in phosphoric acid plants is a function of the same variables, but it seems that the temperature range is higher in the phosphoric acid process (350 to 450°F), and somewhat higher space velocities (gph per lb catalyst) are used. Likewise, lower temperatures (300 to 400°F) are recommended for the liquid phosphoric acid process.[62]

Rate of reaction cannot be easily defined but Langlois[62] has devised a semiempirical relationship which properly describes behavior in the liquid-acid process. Likewise, Bethea and Karchmer[65] have studied the rate of reaction in polymerizing propene with phosphoric acid. In the widely

[63] Weinert and Egloff, *Pet Processing*, June, 1948, p. 585.

[64] Steffens et al., *Chem. Eng. Progr.*, April, 1949, p. 269.

[65] Propylene Polymerization in a Packed Reactor, *Ind. Eng. Chem.*, **48**, 370 (1956).

used solid-acid process, space velocities of 0.15 to 0.4 have been used. The activity of the catalyst is gradually destroyed and hence extreme catalytic activity occurs during early stages of operation. Low feed temperatures are used during the stage of high catalyst activity, inert gas (butanes) may be recycled, or in the reactor-type process the temperature may be reduced by cooling with water. Inert liquid is also sprayed into the chambers as a means of temperature control. The general effect of

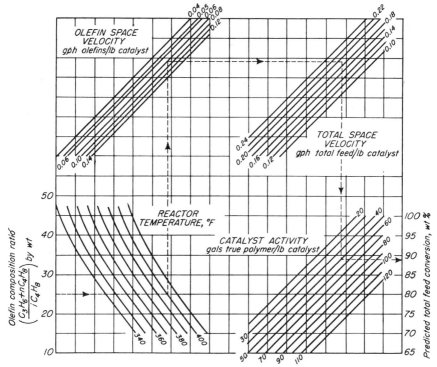

Fig. 20-8. Chart for predicting the conversion of total feed in catalytic polymerization when using copper pyrophosphate as the catalyst. (*Chem. Eng. Progress.*)

reaction temperature on conversion is indicated in Table 20-12. Likewise, the effect of space velocity on olefin conversion in chamber-type solid acid plants,[66] when charging a feed of 35 to 40 per cent olefins, and for pyrophosphate plants[64] is indicated in Table 20-13.

Orthophosphoric acid is the kind of acid desired in the phosphoric acid process. It tends to lose water and form inactive metaphosphoric acid at temperatures above about 450°F. Vaporization of water may be suppressed somewhat by the use of 2 to 10 per cent steam or water in the olefin feedstock, but larger amounts will cause the formation of

[66] Shanley and Egloff, *Ref. Nat. Gaso. Mfr.*, June, 1939, p. 227.

alcohols. Solid forms of phosphoric acid catalysts[67] may consist of admixtures of kieselguhr, starch, magnesia, alumina, zinc chloride, zinc oxide, etc., calcined at 180 to 250°C. In reactor-type plants (900 psig) as much as 160 gal of polymer gasoline have been produced per pound of catalyst. At such "makes" the catalyst can be discarded after it is spent. When operating in a selective manner for maximum octane number, or in

TABLE 20-12. EFFECT OF TEMPERATURE ON OLEFIN CONVERSION, PER CENT

Catalyst, temp °F	Copper pyrophosphate[a]	Solid acid[b]
330	70.5	
350	75.5	
370	81.0	
390	86.5	
410	91.0	77.0
420	....	79.5
430	....	90.5
450	....	95.0

[a] Steffens et al., *Chem. Eng. Progr.*, April, 1949, p. 269.
[b] Shanley and Egloff, *Ref. Nat. Gaso. Mfr.*, June, 1939, p. 227.

TABLE 20-13. OLEFIN CONVERSION VERSUS SPACE VELOCITY

Space velocity, gph per lb catalyst	Per cent olefin conversion	
	Pyrophosphate plants	Solid acid plants[a]
0.1	97.5	
0.15	92.5	
0.2	88.0	93
0.4	....	86
0.6	....	77

[a] 400 to 500°F reaction temperature and 500 psig.

high-pressure chamber-type plants, polymer production is usually under 100 gal per lb. At low pressures (150 to 200 psig) the make is only 10 to 50 gal per lb, and in such plants it pays to regenerate the catalyst. Regeneration is conducted by passing air (650°F) into the chamber at such a rate that the temperature does not exceed 950°F (hot spots cause volatilization of the acid) and then hydrating the catalyst by maintaining an atmosphere of steam for 10 to 16 hr at approximately 500°F. The

[67] Nash and Howes, "Principles of Motor Fuel Preparation and Application," 2d ed., vol. I, p. 438, John Wiley & Sons, Inc., New York, 1938.

conversion of propene and butene to polymer gasoline amounts to about 90 per cent or a yield of about 16 gal per thousand cu ft of pure olefin gases.

The reactor type of plant (Fig. 20-9) consists essentially of a heater and tubular reactors. The temperature at the heater output ranges from 300 to 400°F, and typical operating conditions are shown in Table 20-14.

TABLE 20-14

	Chamber type		Reactor type	
	Low pressure regenerative[a]	High pressure	Non-selective	Selective
Pressure, psig	250	500	900	900
Operation	Nonselective			Selective
Catalyst temperature, °F:				
Inlet	400	375	340	310
Outlet	475	450	380	350
Olefin conversion	80	85–90	92	90–95
Octane No.—Motor method	75–80	82–83	82–84	93–95
Catalyst life, gal per lb	50	75+	120–150	130–150

[a] No longer being installed.

Higher temperatures dry and reduce the activity of the catalyst and promote the formation of cokelike deposits. Water in the amount of about 5 per cent by volume of the feed keeps the catalyst in the form of orthophosphoric acid. Larger amounts of water may cause the catalyst to cake into a mud and become highly corrosive. Pressures of 500 psig are advantageous because such a pressure reduces the volume of gas that must be handled, increases the rate of reaction, and provides sufficient pressure in the depropanizer to easily condense propane reflux. The reaction vessels[68] are of two general types. They may be constructed like a heat exchanger with the catalyst packed inside of large tubes, or they may be a plain chamber having several spiders for introducing inert gas. Thus cooling can be accomplished by passing water through the shell as indicated in the auxiliary steam generation system of Fig. 20-9, or by inert gas. Some recirculation of butanes (handled as a liquid) is practiced, particularly if the chambers are not water-cooled, so that the general reaction rate can be regulated. In some plants the catalyst is washed and somewhat cooled by the introduction of poly gasoline or butanes.

Catalyst life is greatly reduced by even 0.002 mole per cent oxygen in the feed, by the formation of varnishlike substances. Likewise, nitrogen

[68] Armistead, G., Jr., Nonselective Catalytic Polymerization . . . , *Oil Gas J.*, Apr. 6, 1946, p. 131.

compounds (0.5 per cent ammonia) rapidly destroy the catalyst.   A wash with water removes most undesirable nitrogen compounds.   At reaction temperatures exceeding about 500°F water must be continuously added, whereas at temperatures below 300°F moisture must be eliminated from the feed.

Armistead[68] indicates the production of olefins by thermal and catalytic cracking operations, and the approximate yields of 10-lb poly gasoline obtained with average Mid Continent crude oil, as in Table 20-15.   The

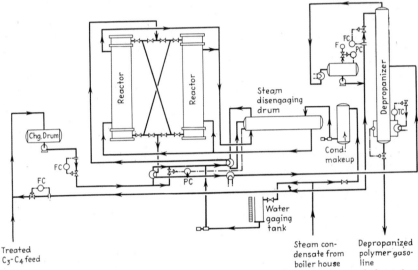

Fig. 20-9. Large phosphoric acid polymerization plant employing water-cooled catalyst cases.   (*Oil Gas J.*)

production of a total of 60 per cent of gasoline is contemplated in Table 20-15.

In general, the yield of 10-lb (Reid vapor pressure) polymer from processing the total gas from topped crude thermal cracking operations will be 4 to 4.5 per cent of the cracking unit charge, but when processing only the stabilizer gas (with an absorber operating at 70 to 90 psig) the yield is only 3 to 3.5 per cent of the charge.   The ratio of absorber gas to stabilizer overhead is approximately 2 to 1.   Catalytic cracking produces more propylene and butylenes than thermal cracking, and the amount of butane-free poly gasoline is 10 to as much as 14 per cent of the debutanized gasoline, whereas for thermal cracking on the same basis, the percentage is only 6 to 7 per cent.

Much of the foregoing applies to the liquid phosphoric acid process as well as the solid-acid process.   Figure 20–10 shows only the reaction chambers proper of a liquid-acid plant because in other respects such a

TABLE 20-15. APPROXIMATE OLEFIN AND POLY GASOLINE PRODUCTION FROM
A MID CONTINENT CRUDE OIL[a]

Type of operation	Self-contained processing of Mid Continent crude		
	All thermal[b]	Catalytic thermal[c]	
Catalytic cracking-plant conditions:			
Temperature, °F	. . .	850	900
Conversion, per cent	. . .	55	65
Yields, volume per cent basis crude:			
Propylene	2.1	2.9	4.3
Propylene polymer at 65 per cent recovery (10 lb R.v.p.)	1.1	1.4	2.1
Butylene[d]	3.1	3.4	4.0
Butylene polymer at 90 per cent recovery (10 lb R.v.p.)	2.5	2.8	3.2
Total 10-lb polymer	3.6	4.2	5.3

[a] Armistead, G., Jr., Nonselective Catalytic Polymerization . . . , *Oil Gas J.*, Apr. 6, 1946, p. 131.

[b] Reforming heavy straight-run naphtha, thermal cracking of 56 per cent reduced crude to ultimate yield of gasoline.

[c] Reforming heavy straight-run naphtha, single-pass catalytic cracking of virgin gas oil (40 per cent of crude), and thermal cracking of virgin residuum (16 per cent of crude) and catalytic cycle oil to ultimate yield of gasoline.

[d] Total production.

plant is similar to other catalytic polymerization plants. The chambers are filled with sized quartz to provide a large area for film contact between the acid and the olefinic feed. After the acid becomes spent a chamber is cut off from the system, and fresh acid is pumped up into the chamber and drained back through the catch-pot into the acid storage drum. A complete turn-around for a reactor requires about 24 hours,[62] and regeneration is required at 2- or 3-month intervals:

Release pressure and vent reactor	1 hr
Fill with cold water and drain twice	3 hr
Fill with hot water (280 to 300°F) and continue to pump through the reactor to the sewer	4 hr
Pressure with steam to 120 psig draining condensate as it forms	4 hr
Release reactor to atmospheric pressure to evaporate most of the condensate wetting the hot quartz	1/2 hr
Evacuate to 4 psia to complete the evaporation of condensate	2 hr
Fill with 75 per cent phosphoric acid	3 hr
Drain acid back to storage	5 hr
Return reactor to service	1 1/2 hr
	24 hr

During operation, a small amount of acid may drip into the catch-pot where it can be periodically drained to the acid-storage drum. Acid consumption usually amounts to less than a pound (75 per cent acid) per 140 gal[62] of polymer product. Loss in acid arises mainly by carry-over into the knockout drum which contains limestone for neutralization of

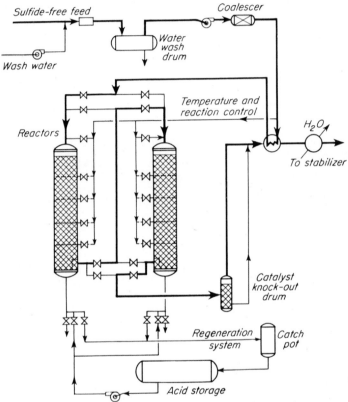

FIG. 20-10. Liquid phosphoric acid polymerization plant.

the acid. The moisture content of the feed is adjusted by the temperature (about 100°F) in a water-wash drum which is also needed for dissolving nitrogen compounds from the feed. The process is said to be more economical than the solid-acid process.

Other Processes. Numerous catalysts have been employed for polymerization, including highly stable silica-alumina (Phillips Pet. Co.), aluminum chloride,[69] boron trifluoride, and activated bauxite.[70]

The *hot* and the *cold* sulfuric acid polymerization processes were once

[69] Waterman et al., *Rec. trav. chim.*, **53**, 699 (1934).
[70] Heinemann et al., *Ind. Eng. Chem.*, **40**, 1224 (1948).

widely used.[71] At lower temperatures only isobutylene is absorbed by 67 per cent acid, and hence the cold-acid process may be used (along with hydrogenation) for the manufacture of isooctane (2,2,4-trimethylpentane). In the hot-acid process, mixed butylenes are polymerized to the extent of 85 to 90 per cent by absorption into 67 per cent acid at a temperature of about 80°C. Polymerization is so rapid at this temperature that the butylenes are scarcely absorbed before polymers are formed. The plant consists of a reaction tower followed by vessels for prolonging the time, and acid settlers. The acid is recycled through this part of the system along with the feedstock and is not consumed except by mechanical entrainment or losses. The polymerized material along with unaffected hydrocarbons is neutralized with caustic soda and sent to a stabilizing column for the separation of raw polymer gasoline and gas. The contact time is between 10 and 15 min. Plain steel and iron equipment is used for the part of the system that is in contact with acid. Excessive corrosion does not take place. The sulfuric acid process was used early in World War II, but few plants are being installed now.

ALKYLATION

Although alkylation of isobutane with olefins is theoretically preferable to polymerization as a means of utilizing cracking-still gases because it consumes only one molecule of valuable olefin, rather than two, to produce a molecule of gasoline, the cost of alkylate is about $1\frac{1}{3}$ times that of poly gasoline. However, now that 100 octane number motor gasoline is being sold, it is necessary not only to practice cracking, polymerization, and catalytic reforming but to alkylate and to isomerize. Butylenes are the preferred olefins (see Fig. 6-5), but isobutylene and propylene are used up to whatever amount is needed to alkylate all of the isobutane available to the refiner. This may sometimes be accomplished by polymerizing at a low temperature and a high space velocity to consume most of the propylene and isobutylene, and this also causes some isomerization of butene-1 to butene-2. The remaining unreacted stream may then contain enough olefins to match the available isobutane. The hydrofluoric acid process is better able to utilize propylene, and the thermal process is excellent for ethylene. Meanwhile, alkylation occupies a unique position in the production of alkyl aromatics such as cumene,[72] ethyl benzene[4,5] or cresols.[73]

[71] McAllister, S. H., The Catalytic Polymerization of Butylenes by Sulfuric Acid, *Ref. Nat. Gaso. Mfr.*, November, 1937, p. 493.

[72] McAllister, Anderson, and Bullard, Production of Cumene by . . . Alkylation Processes, *Chem. Eng. Progr.*, **43**, 189 (1947).

[73] Weinrich, W., Alkylated Cresols from Refinery Gases, *Ind. Eng. Chem.*, **35**, 264 (1943).

Alkylation is the union of an olefin with an aromatic or paraffinic hydro-carbon.   Common operations are

$$C_2H_4 + iC_4H_{10} \rightarrow 2,2 \text{ dimethylbutane (neohexane)}^{74}$$
$$C_2H_4 + iC_4H_{10} \rightarrow 2,3 \text{ dimethylbutane (diisopropyl)}^{75,76}$$
$$C_4H_8 + iC_4H_{10} \rightarrow 2,2,4 \text{ trimethylpentane (isooctane)}$$
$$C_3H_6 + C_6H_6 \rightarrow \text{isopropylbenzene (cumene)}^{72,77}$$
$$C_2H_4 + C_6H_6 \rightarrow \text{ethyl benzene}^{4,5}$$

The National Bureau of Standards[57] found that early World War II alkylates contained primarily octanes (60 to 92 per cent) but that the process was sometimes operated for heptanes (41 to 66 per cent) or for nonanes and heavier (48 to 61 per cent).

In most processes recirculation of the stable feed hydrocarbon is maintained and the reactive olefin is fed into the recycling stream some-times at several points.   Thus, the concentration of olefin is always low and polymerization reactions are minimized.   The alkylation reaction is favored by high pressures and low temperatures.   However, in order to accomplish the reaction without catalysts, temperatures of 900 to 975°F are required.[74]   Polymerization also occurs rapidly at such temperatures, and hence the olefin concentration must be kept low.   Thermal alkylation is conducted at 3,000 to 8,000 psig, whereas by means of catalysts such as sulfuric acid, boron fluoride,[76,78] aluminum chloride,[75,79] double halides of alkali metals with aluminum,[80] and hydrogen fluoride, pressures less than 500 psi and temperatures ranging from 450°F down to below zero may be employed.   Sulfuric acid was widely used early in World War II as a catalyst in commercial installations,[81] and a revival of interest has occurred since 1951.   The process operates at 30 to 50°F for butenes and at substantially atmospheric pressure.   The hydrofluoric acid process also proved during World War II to be a highly successful process, but only

[74] Oberfell and Frey, Thermal Alkylation and Neohexane, *Oil Gas J.*, Nov. 23 and 30, 1939, p. 50.

[75] Alden et al., The Story of Diisopropyl, *Oil Gas J.*, Feb. 9, 1946, p. 70; and Holloway and Bonnell, Pilot Plant Production of 2,3-Dimethylbutane, *Ind. Eng. Chem.*, **38**, 1231 (1946).

[76] Axe and Schulze, Diisopropyl from . . . Alkylation in Presence of BF_3-H_2O-HF Catalyst Systems, *Ind. Eng. Chem.*, **39**, 1273 (1947).

[77] O'Donnell, J. P., . . . Cumene Process Has Speeded Aircraft-fuel Program, *Oil Gas J.*, Feb. 24, 1944, p. 73.

[78] Egloff and Morrell, Alkylation of Hydrocarbons, Symposium on Role of Catalysts . . . , ACS Baltimore Meeting, April, 1939.

[79] Ipatieff et al., *J. Am. Soc.*, **58**, 913 (1936).

[80] Blunck and Carmody, Catalytic Alkylation of Isobutane with Gaseous Olefins, *Ind. Eng. Chem.*, **32**, 328 (1940).

[81] Birch, Dunstan, Fidler, Pim, and Tait, Condensation of Olefins with Isoparaffins in Sulfuric Acid, *Oil Gas J.*, June 23, 1938, p. 49; also Nov. 17, 1939, p. 104.

about 18 per cent of the alkylation capacity is handled by the HF process (1955).

The acid alkylation process works most successfully on the higher molecular weight olefins (such as the butenes), whereas thermal alkylation attacks ethene most readily. Acid alkylation is limited to the isoparaffin hydrocarbons (isobutane and isopentane), but the thermal process handles either the iso or the normal compounds.

The composition of depentanized alkylate from mixed butenes was determined[82] in API Project 6, and although the HF alkylate contains more 2,2,4-trimethylpentane both of the alkylates have much the same octane number:

	H_2SO_4 process	HF process
Hexanes	6.8 vol. %	2.1 vol. %
Heptanes	7.0	4.5
2,2,4-Trimethylpentane	26.7	41.7
2,2,3-Trimethylpentane	1.3	2.9
2,3,3-Trimethylpentane	13.5	10.0
2,3,4-Trimethylpentane	14.3	9.4
Dimethylhexanes	11.2	19.6
Nonanes	6.4	3.4
Heavier	12.8	6.4

Table 20-16 indicates the laboratory properties of alkylates. The heat of reaction,[83] Btu per lb of alkylate, is about as follows:

Butylenes–isobutane............ 315
Pentenes–isobutane............. 250
Propylene–isobutane............ 350

Hydrofluoric Acid Process (HF). This highly successful process[7,84,85,86,87] for combining isobutane and isobutene, as shown in Fig. 20-11, involves the recirculation of about 6 parts of isobutane to 1 part of isobutene. A temperature of 75 to 105°F and a pressure of 100 to 150 psig is maintained on the reaction contractors. The acid is currently dried (kept

[82] Draeger et al., *Pet. Refiner*, August, 1951, p. 71.

[83] Mrstik et al., Commercial Alkylation of Isobutane, "Progress in Petroleum Technology," ACS Meeting, New York, September, 1951.

[84] Benson, R., Safety in . . . Hydrogen Fluoride Alkylation Plants, *Pet. Refiner*, December, 1943, p. 116.

[85] Shanley and Nebeck, Numerous Improvements in HF Alkylation . . . , *Oil Gas J.*, Dec. 1, 1945, p. 94.

[86] Kunkel, J. H., HF Alkylation Unit on Stream in Record Time, *Pet. Engr.*, September, 1944, p. 80.

[87] Scott and Cooper, Economic . . . Operation at HF Alkylation Plant, *Oil Gas J.*, Mar. 30, 1946, p. 204.

TABLE 20-16. PROPERTIES OF ISOBUTANE ALKYLATES

Property	Sulfuric acid as catalyst						Hydrofluoric acid as catalyst			
	Propylene feed	Butene feed	Pentenes feed	50:50 propene-butenes feed	Aviation grade	Heavy	Propene-butene feed	Butene feed	Propene-butene-pentene feed	Light
API Gravity.......	72.3–73.7	69.0–72.4	66.5	73	69.7	52.3	74.0	72.8	70.2	71.0
Reid v.p., psia.....	3.5–5.8	3.0–5.8	1.5	5.8	4	.....	8.6	....	2.0	3.0
I.B.P., °F........	108–143	110–145	124	114	125	353	94	....	139	138
10 per cent.......	163–179	158–197	227	161	177	360	138	136	181	182
50 per cent.......	195–196	213–224	247	206	212	374	215	212	204	210
90 per cent.......	239–246	258–261	281	251	236	483	237	239	239	238
E.P., °F..........	338–360	335–360	360	340	320	579	314	309	327	334
Octane ratings:										
F-1 clear[a].......	88.2–91	91.8–96	90–91	90	98	98	....	....	....	92
F-3 with 4 cc TEL	102.2–106	105–108	103–107	103.6	.....	.....	+0.56[b]	+1.15[b]	+0.79[b]	
F-4 with 4 cc TEL	122	151	127	+2.0[b]	.....	.....	+2.2[b]	+3.2[b]	+2.4[b]	
Performance No.:										
F-3.............	....	....	....	......	.....	.....	117	128	122	119–120
F-4.............	135–145	153–161	145–150	......	.....	.....	140	148	142	140–142
Yield, % on olefin consumed......	170–178	165–172	155–172							
Cat. consumption, lb per bbl.......	84–140	25–40	42–80							

[a] Motor method octane numbers are 0 to 0.8 units lower.
[b] Cc of TEL added to isooctane.

at 2 per cent moisture or less), about 6 per cent of heavy oil or tarlike material is removed, and 0.3 to 0.8 lb acid per barrel of alkylate is consumed or lost.   The octane number of the alkylate depends mainly upon the kind of olefin involved

$$iC_4H_{10} + iC_4H_8 \rightarrow \text{isooctanes (92–94 Oct. No.)}$$
$$iC_4H_{10} + iC_5H_{10} \rightarrow \text{isononanes (90–92 Oct. No.)}$$
$$iC_4H_{10} + C_3H_6 \rightarrow \text{isoheptanes (89–91 Oct. No.)}$$

Plain carbon steel is used throughout except that some rundown lines are constructed of Monel metal.   All lines are jacketed and connected to a "blowdown" or water spray pump so that the gaseous acid will be caught if a break occurs.   Much of the operation is by remote control; and, when the operator must approach the unit, face masks and rubberized clothing are worn.   The cycle time efficiency is said to be 96 per cent.

Sulfuric Acid Process.   This process has been applied primarily to isobutane and butenes.   The absorption of the olefin hydrocarbon occurs at a rate several hundred times as fast as the absorption of paraffins, and hence in order to maintain the proper concentration of the two hydrocarbons in the acid it is necessary to recycle a large excess of the saturated hydrocarbon through the system as indicated in Fig. 20-12.   The higher the ratio of isoparaffin to olefin in the feedstock, the greater the yield, the higher the octane number, and the smaller the acid consumption,[88] and hence this ratio is always held at 5:1 or at even 8:1 in producing the very

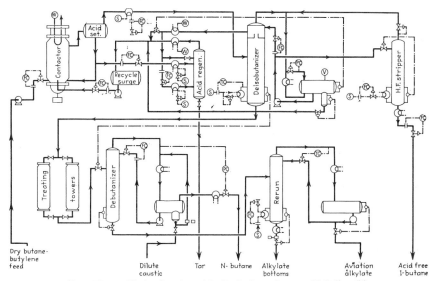

FIG. 20-11. Hydrofluoric acid alkylation plant.   (*Oil Gas J.*)

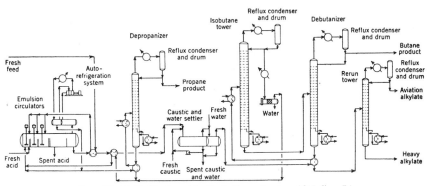

FIG. 20-12. Sulfuric acid alkylation plant.   (*Oil Gas J.*)

highest octane number alkylate.   Contact times of about 5 min appear to be satisfactory, but commercial plants are operating at 20 to 40 min.   An acid strength of 98 per cent is used, but it becomes diluted during processing to about 90 per cent.   The dilution, however, is by absorption of unactive hydrocarbons and certain oxidation products rather than by

[88] Mackenzie, K. G. (read by), High Octane Aviation Fuel by . . . Alkylation Process, *Ref. Nat. Gaso. Mfr.*, November, 1939, p. 494.

water. Thus, the spent acid that is currently removed from the process is not destroyed chemically and may be recovered by standard methods or may be used in acid treating other refinery stocks such as lubricating oils. The make-up acid amounts to 1 to 3 lb of acid per gal of product, but if a recovery plant is available, only 0.1 to 0.4 lb acid is lost per gal of alkylate. From one to two parts of acid are circulated per part of hydrocarbon. Agitation is accomplished by means of jets or baffles. Temperatures of 32 to 50°C are employed, and a temperature above 70°C results in excessive acid replacement and a decreased yield of gasoline.

TABLE 20-17. OCTANE NUMBERS OR QUALITY OF SULFURIC ACID ALKYLATE IN TERMS OF THE CORRELATION FACTOR OF EQ. (20-13)

	Correlation factors of Eq. (20-13)				
	4	10	20	40	200
Research o.n. when alkylating:					
Propylene	88.0	88.8	89.6	90.3	92.0
Pentenes (thermal)	....	88.0	89.1	90.4	93.0
Pentenes (catalytic)	89.6	90.7	91.6	92.5	94.4
Butylenes	94.2	94.8	95.3	95.8	97.0
F-3 blending o.n. with 4 cc TEL per gal:					
Propylene	102.6	103.0	103.2	103.5	104.2
Pentenes	102.0	102.5	102.9	103.3	104.3
Butylenes	105.4	105.8	106.2	106.4	107.0
F-4 blending o.n. with 4 cc TEL per gal:					
Propylene	110	118	123	129	141
Pentenes (thermal)	112	118	124	130	144
Pentenes (catalytic)	126	131	135	138	147
Butylenes	149	151	153	155	158

Octane number is especially significant in alkylation because it is the reason for conducting such an expensive process. A relationship between the various operating conditions and a correlating or operating factor F based on impeller-type reaction systems has been devised by Mrstik, Smith, and Pinkerton.[83]

$$F = \frac{I_E(I/O)_F}{100(SV)_0} \qquad (20\text{-}13)$$

where I_E = liquid volume per cent isobutane in reaction effluent

$(I/O)_F$ = volumetric isobutane-olefin ratio in feed

$(SV)_0$ = olefin space velocity, volumes per hour per reactor volume

A large F factor indicates improvement in the alkylate quality (see Table 20-17), and it ordinarily ranges in value from 10 to 40.

The acid consumption[89] when handling propylene is about three times as much as when using butylenes, but if the liquid volume percentage in

[89] Oden et al., Propylene, a Valuable Feed . . . , *Pet. Refiner*, April, 1950, p. 103.

the mixture is kept below about 30 per cent, little if any increase in acid consumption is noted.[90]   Alkylation of pentenes requires slightly more acid than butenes.   Low acid consumption is attained[90] by keeping the propylene below 30 per cent in the mixture, using a high ratio (6:1 or more) of isobutane to olefin, low space velocities, and low reaction temperatures (40°F).

Thermal Alkylation.   Whereas sulfuric acid alkylation operates most successfully on isobutylene, the butenes, and propylene, thermal alkylation acts most readily on ethylene followed by propylene, butenes, and

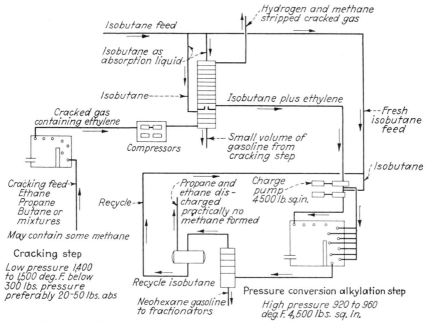

Fig. 20-13. Thermal alkylation (neohexane pilot plant).   (*Oil Gas J.*)

isobutylene in the order named.   A temperature of about 950°F and a pressure of 3,000 to 5,000 psi[74] are required.   The olefin-rich charge stock may be produced by a hydrocarbon decomposition process operating at 1200 to 1425°F and at nearly atmospheric pressure.   Such conditions are favorable for ethylene formation.   The ethylene is absorbed in isobutane for introduction into the alkylation plant.   The alkylation furnace handles a recycling stream of isobutane, and the ethylene-isobutane solution is introduced at 10 points in the soaking zone of the furnace.   Little tar or material boiling above gasoline is produced because of the low concentration of ethylene in the reaction zone.   A general flow diagram of the process is shown in Fig. 20-13.   Times of 2 to 7 sec are required at

[90] Borthick et al., *Oil Gas J.*, June 4, 1956, p. 88.

950° F, depending largely on the hydrocarbons being treated and the amount of isobutylene recirculated.

The yield of liquid products, including all hydrocarbons in the boiling range of gasoline as well as neohexane, is approximately 70 per cent by weight of the net consumption of ethane-propane and isobutane consumed during decomposition and alkylation. As the normally liquid hydrocarbon content of the coil effluent is increased from 20 to 35 per cent by weight (conversion per pass), the neohexane content of these liquids decreases from about 40 to about 30 per cent.

Other Alkylation (and Dealkylation). Phosphoric acid acts as a catalyst in uniting propylene with benzene to form isopropyl benzene or

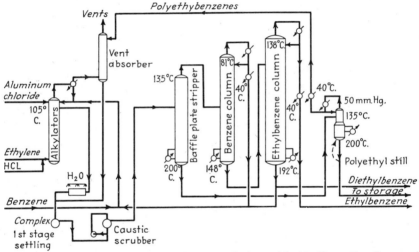

FIG. 20-14. Production of ethyl benzene by alkylation. (*Smith, Chem. Eng. Progress.*)

cumene. The regular solid phosphoric acid polymerization plant equipment (Fig. 20-9) may be used,[91] and much cumene was made in this way in petroleum polymerization plants early in World War II. A large ratio (6 or more) of benzene to propylene is maintained, and yields of 96 volume per cent of cumene are common[91] (the remaining 4 per cent being heavier alkylated aromatics).

The alkylation of benzene with ethylene to produce ethyl benzene is widely practiced in the manufacture of styrene. The ethyl benzene is subsequently dehydrogenated to styrene. Aluminum chloride in the presence of anhydrous hydrochloric acid is the catalyst. The reaction is conducted[4] at the boiling point of the alkylate (about 105°C), and evaporation of benzene from the reactor removes the heat of reaction. Granu-

[91] Universal Oil Products Co., Phosphoric Acid Condensation, *Oil Gas J.*, Mar. 19, 1956, p. 172.

lar aluminum chloride is fed continuously to the reactor by means of a variable-speed screw conveyor. Figure 20-14 indicates the series of fractionators for separating recycle benzene, 99 per cent purity ethyl benzene, diethyl benzene, and polyethyl benzenes. The reaction of ethene with benzene takes place to 95 to 97 per cent of what is indicated by theory.[5]

Dealkylation of the higher aromatics is a somewhat similar reaction. Benzene can be produced by demethylating toluene and the xylenes or by deethylating ethyl benzene.[92] Several chemical methods are available, but the type of catalyst used in catalytic cracking is also effective.[92]

DEHYDROGENATION

The main practice of dehydrogenation in the petroleum industry is the manufacture of ethylene (and propylene) by vapor-phase cracking, and the multireaction processes of catalytic reforming. Ethylene plants were discussed in detail in Chap. 19, and equilibrium constants (Fig. 19-4), reaction velocity constants (Fig. 19-5), and heats of reaction are given. The Hydroforming and platinum catalyst reforming processes are discussed on pages 810 to 818. A major reaction in reforming processes is the dehydrogenation of cyclic compounds to aromatics, but other compounds undergo isomerization, decomposition, and hydrogenation.

Dehydrogenation equilibrium constants for the thermal decomposition of ethane, propane, and butane are given in Fig. 19-4, and the percentage of dehydrogenation that takes place at various temperatures can be estimated from Table 20-18.

TABLE 20-18. PERCENTAGE COMPLETION OF DEHYDROGENATION REACTION
AT EQUILIBRIUM

Temperature, °F	Ethane	Propane	n-Butane	Isobutane
801 (427°C)	1.6	6.4	11.0	12.2
932 (500°C)	5.4	18.6	29.2	31.9
1112 (600°C)	19.5	53.6	69.8	72.1
1341 (727°C)	57.5	89.8	95.2	95.2

Note that a dehydrogenation of 95 per cent as shown for 1341°F does not mean an olefin yield of 95 per cent. According to the dehydrogenation reaction the analysis of product gas would be 5 per cent unreacted paraffin hydrocarbon and 47.5 per cent each of the olefin and the hydrogen gases.

Catalytic methods of dehydrogenation have received attention because

[92] Nager, M., Dealkylation of Ethylbenzene, *Ind. Eng. Chem.*, **49**, 39 (1957).

of the extremely high temperatures required for plain thermal decomposition (see Fig. 19-5) and because undesirable reactions also occur [see Eqs. (19-12) to (19-16)] when propane or larger molecules are cracked. Two general types of catalysts have been employed: (1) ferric oxide supported on magnesia with potassium oxide (carbonate) as a promotor for the elimination by the water gas reaction[93] of carbon deposition, and (2) chromia-alumina[94] modified with alkali, zinc compounds, or beryllia. The first type was used extensively during World War II (Type 1707 composition) for the dehydrogenation of ethyl benzene to styrene, 2-methyl 2-butene to isoprene, and butene to butadiene, and these are stated in the decreasing order of reactiveness. Kearby[93] finds that the best promotors are potassium, cesium, and rubidium carbonates or oxides, the best dehydrogenators are iron and chromium oxides, and the best support materials are magnesium, iron, zinc, copper, or beryllium oxides.

TABLE 20-19. COMPOSITION OF SOME DEHYDROGENATION CATALYSTS[a]

	Related to Type 1707			Alumina-chromia type		
MgO...............	72.4	80				
Al₂O₃.............	....	....	....	59.25	50	80
Fe₂O₃.............	18.4	....	20			
Cr₂O₃.............	....	20	....	40	40	20
K₂O...............	4.6	1.5	5	0.75		
CuO...............	4.6	....	5			
Others............	....	....	80 ZnO	.....	10 BeO	

[a] Kearby, K. K., Catalytic Dehydrogenation of Butenes, *Ind. Eng. Chem.*, **42**, 295 (1950), and Pitzer et al., Improved Butane Dehydrogenation Catalysts, *Ind. Eng. Chem.*, **46**, 1541 (1954).

Several analyses are indicated in Table 20-19. The other type of catalyst,[94] i.e., chromia-alumina, appears to be most useful for the dehydrogenation of propane and the butanes. Alumina prepared by calcining specially crystallized alumina trihydrate is used at 600 to 650°C for propane or isobutane. Chromium oxide in the form of its active gel is highly selective in its action but is destroyed by temperatures exceeding 500°C. If alumina is used as the carrier for 10 to 20 per cent chromium oxide, the dehydrogenation reaction proceeds at even 50 to 70°C but the life of the catalyst is short. Both the activated alumina and the alumina-chrome catalysts may be regenerated by careful oxidation of the impurities in a

[93] Kearby, K. K., Catalytic Dehydrogenation of Butenes, *Ind. Eng. Chem.*, **42**, 295 (1950).

[94] Pitzer et al., Improved Butane Dehydrogenation Catalysts, *Ind. Eng. Chem.*, **46**, 1541 (1954).

stream of air (diluted with nitrogen) for as many as 200 regenerations.[95] The life of the catalyst is greatly improved by introducing small amounts of water vapor. For the dehydrogenation of isobutane using alumina, 0.1 mole per cent of water vapor is the optimum. Iron, cobalt, nickel, and some other metals promote the formation of carbon and hydrogen at temperatures of 300 to 700°C, but these metals are being used in commercial cracking equipment, etc., without causing destructive decomposition. Steam is used with either type of catalyst to decrease the rate of carbon formation.

Complete thermodynamic data on the dehydrogenation of ethyl benzene to styrene have been obtained by Wenner and Dybdal[96] for two catalysts. The average heat of dehydrogenation (for the several reactions) is about 60,000 Btu per lb-mole of styrene. Temperatures of 1000 to 1100°F with very large amounts of steam are used. Flow diagrams of these operations are presented by Smith.[4] Isopropyl benzene (cumene) is dehydrogenated to methyl styrene in much the same manner.[97] These reactions, not being limited by the low equilibrium concentrations of the lower olefins, take place readily at 1000 to 1050°F with large conversions per pass (about 45 per cent for styrene and 60 to 65 per cent for methyl styrene).

Butadiene and Butylenes. Although the first commercial butadiene was obtained as a by-product in the manufacture of ethylene (Tables 20-3 and 20-7) and much of the butadiene produced during the rubber crisis of World War II was obtained in this manner or from alcohol, later in the war butadiene was made by the catalytic dehydrogenation of butenes.

The dehydrogenation of butane to butene and of butene to butadiene are similar operations:

	Butane to butylene	Butylene to butadiene
Temperature.	1100–1125°F	1125–1250°F
Pressure.	10–20 psig	5 in. Hg to atmospheric
Partial pressure (using steam).	low	0.1 atm
Conversion, per cent.	30–40	11*–28
Ultimate yield.	70–80	60–80

* Houdry process which employs automatically operated short cycles of only 8 to 10 minutes onstream.

[95] Williams, E. C., Dehydrogenation in Petroleum Industry, ACS Baltimore Meeting, April, 1939.

[96] Catalytic Dehydrogenation of Ethlybenzene, *Chem. Eng. Progr.*, April, 1948, p. 275.

[97] Lassiat and Parker, *Oil Gas J.*, Nov. 18, 1944, p. 229.

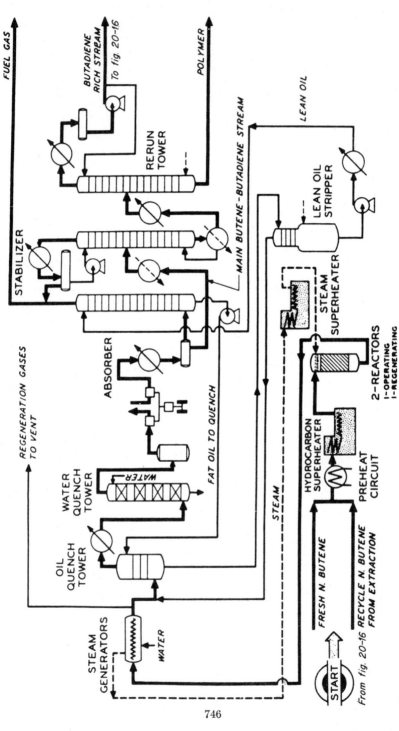

FIG. 20-15. Production of butadiene by the dehydrogenation of butylenes. (*Standard Oil Development Co.*) See feed preparation and butadiene purification in Fig. 20-16.

746

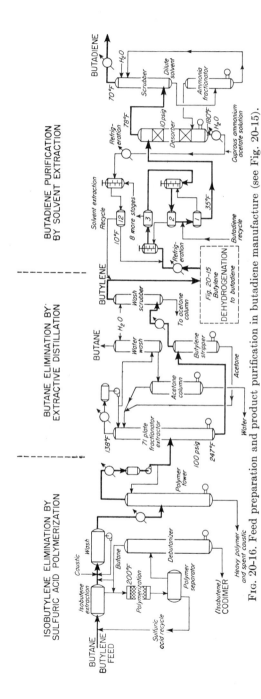

ISOBUTYLENE ELIMINATION BY
SULFURIC ACID POLYMERIZATION

BUTANE ELIMINATION BY
EXTRACTIVE DISTILLATION

BUTADIENE PURIFICATION
BY SOLVENT EXTRACTION

Fig. 20-16. Feed preparation and product purification in butadiene manufacture (see Fig. 20-15).

747

Both the magnesium oxide (Type 1707) and chromia-alumina catalysts are used. The life of Type 1707 is long (5,000 hr) but the other catalysts must be regenerated frequently. Regeneration is accomplished by controlled burning or oxidation with air, flue gas, and steam. The dehydrogenation reaction is highly endothermic (about 725 Btu per lb butenes converted to butadiene), and thus the temperature drops 60 to 70°F during passage (0.2 sec) through the reactor. Figure 20-15 indicates how the processes are conducted in the Standard Oil Company type of plant[98] using Type 1707 catalyst. Butene-rich (50 per cent or more) feed is heated to about 1000°F in a tubular heater and then mixed with superheated steam (1300°F) to attain the reaction temperature of 1125 to 1150°F.

The manufacture of butadiene appears from the foregoing to be simple, but in actual practice many purification operations for both the feed and the raw butadiene products are necessary.[99] Accordingly, Fig. 20-16 showing feed preparation and product recovery should be examined along with Fig. 20-15. In the Shell Chemical Co. government-owned plant at Torrance, Calif. (Fig. 20-16), isobutylene is removed by the sulfuric acid (cold-acid) polymerization process. Butane is then removed from the normal butylenes by extraction (71 plates) with aqueous acetone, and more recently (1956) in this plant, with acetonitrile. After the butylenes are dehydrogenated as in Fig. 20-15, the raw butadiene is purified (98 per cent) by the Standard Oil Co. of New Jersey's aqueous cuprous ammonium acetate extraction process consisting primarily of a 12-stage extraction at 10°F. Raffinate butylene is recycled back to the dehydrogenation operation.

Furfural has also been extensively used in the purification of butadiene.

HYDROGENATION

The only extensive use of hydrogenation in the industry is in connection with the desulfurization of naphthas, distillates, and most recently residual materials (see Fig. 10-13). These processes employ cobalt molybdenum catalysts supported on bauxite. Dozens of plants have been installed since 1953. During this same period, large amounts of by-product hydrogen became available from catalytic reforming processes.

The hydrogenation of animal and vegetable oils at relatively low pressures by the use of activated nickel, platinum, or palladium catalysts involves direct union with hydrogen. In the case of mineral oils or coal, it is also usually advisable to decompose or crack the oil to some extent as

[98] Hatch, L. F., *Pet. Refiner*, September, 1954, p. 311.

[99] Anon., How to Make Butadiene, *Chem. Eng.*, September, 1954, p. 306, and February, 1957, p. 146.

well as to hydrogenate, in order to make lower boiling products (gasoline) or to rebuild the structure of the molecule. Thus, cracking temperatures (800 to 950°F) and high pressures (3,000 lb up) are employed, and special catalysts that are not poisoned by sulfur are necessary. Such processes are called "destructive hydrogenation."

A common method of producing hydrogen is by the reaction of steam and methane to give hydrogen and carbon monoxide. Newman and Jacob[100] find the equilibrium to be as follows:

$$\log K = \log \frac{P_{CO} \times P_{H_2}^3}{P_{CH_4} \times P_{H_2O}} = \frac{-10{,}300}{T} + 4.87 \log T$$
$$+ 0.000066T - 0.000000081T^2 - 3.04$$

in which partial pressures are in atmospheres and T is temperature, degrees Kelvin. In order to obtain good yields at temperatures below 1000°C, catalysts are necessary. Nickel or cobalt catalysts promoted by alumina[101] and supported on some refractory such as fire clay or magnesia brick are good catalysts, but they are somewhat sensitive to hydrogen sulfide.

The destructive hydrogenation[17] of crude petroleum stocks as referred to above permits products that have almost any desirable properties such as high octane number, high Viscosity Index, or high solvency power (naphthas), but the process is so expensive that it cannot be widely used at the present time. The real usefulness of hydrogenation at our present stage of development is as an adjunct to other processes such as polymerization. As an example, one method of producing high-octane fuels is by catalytic dehydrogenation of gaseous paraffin hydrocarbons into olefins, polymerization of the olefins into hydrocarbons of the gasoline range, followed by catalytic hydrogenation to produce a stable final product. During World War II isobutene was polymerized to diisobutene (Codimer) and then hydrogenated to isooctane (Hydrocodimer). For such operations the activated nickel catalyst[102] mentioned above can be used because sulfur can be removed from the incoming gases. Such a catalyst[102] may be prepared by impregnating porcelain with hydrated nickel nitrate. The nitrate is then converted into the oxide by heating and reduced in a stream of hydrogen to elemental nickel. It must be kept in an atmosphere of hydrogen when not in service. If stocks that contain

---

[100] *Z. Elektrochem.*, **30**, 557 (1924).

[101] Fischer and Tropsch, *Brennstoff-Chem.*, **9**, 39 (1928); Marek and Hahn, "Catalytic Oxidation of Organic Compounds in the Vapor Phase," p. 27, Chemical Catalog Company, Inc., New York, 1932; and Hawk, Golden, Storch, and Fieldner, *Ind. Eng. Chem.*, **24**, 23 (1932).

[102] Anon., Catalytic Hydrogenation of Octenes to Octanes, *Oil Gas J.*, May 26, 1938, p. 50.

sulfur must be handled, recourse must be had to such catalysts as molybdic trioxide, molybdic acid, or chromium oxides supported on charcoal or pumice.[103] Catalysts of this nature are said to be used in the destructive hydrogenation of crude petroleum stocks.

Thermodynamic relationships[17] favor a low temperature, but at 0 to 150°C the reaction rate is low. Commercial operations have been conducted at 180 to 190°C and at 1 to 4 atmospheres pressure[104] using a nickel catalyst. Sulfide-resistant catalysts require higher temperatures, and at such temperatures depolymerization of diisobutylene to isobutene occurs rapidly unless the pressure is high.[17]

Catalytically cracked gasolines contain more olefinic hydrocarbons than are desirable, and hence methods[105] of hydrogenating the olefins without hydrogenating the aromatics are being studied.

Supported nickel sulfide catalysts are remarkably selective in the range of 200 to 300°C in hydrogenating diolefins to monoolefins without hydrogenating monoolefins to paraffins.[106] Diolefin removal is necessary when alkylating B-B (four-carbon-atom) cuts from vapor-phase or thermal cracking operations.

In the manufacture of ethylene small amounts of acetylene are produced (Table 19-8) and the specifications for ethylene allow only 10 ppm. Larger amounts are produced if regenerative type refractory furnaces are used.[42] Selective catalytic hydrogenation is used (Fig. 20-4) to eliminate the acetylene.[107] Temperatures of 400 to 550°F, pressures of 50 to 350 psig, and space velocities of 500 to 1,000 may be used. Enough hydrogen for the reaction is usually present in the ethylene stream. In connection with Fig. 20-4, it is necessary to provide an auxiliary pipestill for regeneration of the catalyst with air, hydrogen, and steam.

ISOMERIZATION

Although isomerization processes have developed slowly because of the cost of handling corrosive catalytic agents and the cost of separating the isomers of hydrocarbons that contain five or more carbon atoms, the increasing need for high-octane-number fuels will require a more extensive use of isomerization processes. Branched-chain compounds have much

[103] Nash and Howes, "Principles of Motor Fuel Preparation and Application," 2d ed., vol. I, p. 337, John Wiley & Sons, Inc., New York, 1938.

[104] Edlund, K. R., Proc. 8th Midyear Meeting API sec. 3, 87, 1938.

[105] Voorhies, Smith, and Hemminger, Hydrogenation of Catalytically Cracked Naphthas . . . , *Ind. Eng. Chem.*, **39**, 1104 (1947).

[106] Anderson et al., Conversion of Diolefins in Alkylation Feedstocks . . . , ACS Meeting, Chicago, Apr. 19, 1948.

[107] Fleming et al., Selective Hydrogenation, *Pet. Refiner*, September, 1953, p. 138.

higher octane numbers than straight-chain compounds (Table 5-9, p. 212). Refiners are now (1957) almost completely utilizing all available cracked gases by polymerization and alkylation, and low-octane gasoline is being upgraded by catalytic reforming. Thus, other means of upgrading octane number, notably isomerization, will be explored in an effort to upgrade pentane and hexane. Isomate when blended with catalytic reformate is said to have a blending octane number about 9 per cent higher than its Research octane number, and it is especially useful because it increases the road (or performance) octane number. All commercial processes prior to 1956 employed anhydrous aluminum chloride as catalyst, but combination cracking (silica alumina) and hydrogenation catalysts[108] such as nickel-silica-alumina or platinum-silica-alumina[110] or a similar catalyst which contains a precious metal,[111] and other highly stable catalysts[109,112,113] which may need little or no regeneration,[112] are being offered.

The main commercial applications during World War II and in a limited way thereafter were the isomerization of butane to isobutane,[114,116] of pentane to isopentane,[115,117,118] and of naphtha or normal hexane fraction into isohexanes[119,120] (or a naphtha of higher octane number). In these processes aluminum chloride is used in several ways, (1) with anhydrous hydrochloric acid[114,119,120] as a liquid slurry or complex, (2) on a granular alumina or bauxite support,[115,116] or (3) dissolved in molten antimony trichloride.[117] In all processes the feed must be dried so that moisture is not carried into the acid zone, but corrosion may be severe.[121]

The isomerization of butane into isobutane is important in connection

[108] Ciapetta and Hunter, *Ind. Eng. Chem.* (3 papers), **45**, 147–165 (1953).

[109] Anon., New Process Expands High Octane Pool, *Oil Gas J.*, Apr. 30, 1956, p. 86.

[110] Anon., Pentafining, *Oil Gas J.*, Mar. 19, 1956, p. 183.

[111] Anon., Here's How New Iso-Kel Works . . . , *Oil Gas J.*, Jan. 7, 1957, p. 76.

[112] Anon., Super Octane Spread, *Oil Gas J.*, June 18, 1956, p. 138.

[113] Anon., Penex—Platforming of Naphthas, *Oil Gas J.*, July 23, 1956, p. 96.

[114] Chenicek et al., Butane Isomerization, *Chem. Eng. Progr.*, **43**, 210 (1947).

[115] Perry, S. F., Isomerization of Light Hydrocarbons, *Trans. A.I.Ch.E.*, **42**, 639 (1946).

[116] Cheney and Raymond, . . . Vapor-phase Isomerization . . . Isobutane, *Trans. A.I.Ch.E.*, **42**, 595 (1946).

[117] Galstaun, L. S., 60 Per Cent Yield in Liquid-phase Isomerization of Pentane, *Oil Gas J.*, Jan. 5, 1946, p. 56.

[118] Armistead G., Jr., Isomerization and Isoforming—Pentane, *Oil Gas J.*, Oct. 5, 1946, p. 80.

[119] Evering et al., *Oil Gas J.*, Oct. 28, 1944, p. 77.

[120] Swearingen et al., The Isomate Process, *Trans. A.I.Ch.E.*, **42**, 573 (1946).

[121] Fragen et al., Corrosion in Isomerization of Light Hydrocarbons, *Ind. Eng. Chem.*, **40**, 1133 (1948).

TABLE 20-20. TYPICAL COMMERCIAL PROCESS DATA FOR BUTANE ISOMERIZATION

	Vapor-phase processes		Liquid-phase processes		
	Shell	AIOC-Jersey	UOP	Indiana-Texas	Shell
Catalyst form................	Impregnated bauxite	Sublimed on bauxite	Complex on quartz chips	Liquid complex	Dissolved in SbCl₃
Catalyst life, gal isobutane per lb AlCl₃.....................	200	200	50–120	50–120	50–120
HCl concentration, wt %.......	2–14	4	5	4	5
Once-through conversion, %....	40	35	38	38	45
Reactor conditions					
Temp, °F..................	210–300	270	200	205	180
Pressure, lb/sq in...........	200	235	235	365	300
Space velocity, vol./hr/vol...	0.5–1.0	0.5–1.0	0.5	1.0	2.5
Reactor material.............	Carbon steel		Hastelloy B or gunite cement		Nickel
No. of U.S. plants (1951).......	7	8	14	3	2

with alkylation processes based on isobutane, and with the manufacture of butyl rubber. Although five processes are mentioned (two vapor-phase and three liquid-phase), the operations are much alike (see Table

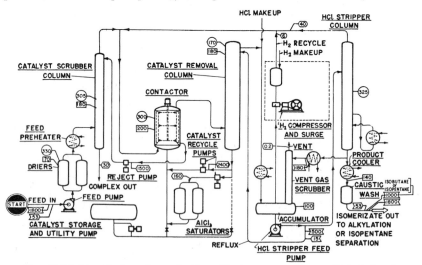

FIG. 20-17. Liquid-phase isomerization of butane or pentane. (*Pet. Refiner.*)

20-20).[122]   As one illustration, the Shell liquid-phase process is shown in Fig. 20-17.   The feed is dried, heated to 180°F, and fed through a packed

[122] Gunness, R. C., Isomerization, "Progress in Pet. Technology," ACS Meeting, New York, September, 1951.

catalyst-scrubber into the contactor. The valuable active catalyst introduced in the scrubber passes back with the butane into the contactor, whereas an inactive $AlCl_3$ hydrocarbon complex formed by side reactions collects at the bottom of the scrubber for periodic removal. Time in the contactor is 10 to 15 minutes and this effects a conversion of 50 per cent or more for butane[123] and 55 to 60 per cent for pentane. Catalyst is recovered from the isomerized stream by fractionation, and the condensed product is stripped of hydrochloric acid. The final product is caustic washed.

In isomerizing butane with aluminum chloride, only a small amount of catalyst-hydrocarbon complex is formed, but pentane and especially hexane produce more complex. Both pentane and hexane tend to crack during treatment and this is the cause of the extensive side reactions.[124] The formation of sludge is inhibited in pentane isomerization by the use of 0.3 to 1.3 weight per cent benzene, and in hexane isomerization, hydrogen is used as an inhibitor.

In the isomerization of naphtha[119] using aluminum chloride, the Research octane number in a once-through operation is increased from 65 to 80. Further increase in octane number occurs with recycling (91 at 2:1 recycle ratio), but the economy of recycling is doubtful because of difficulties with fractionation. When processing mixed hexanes[125] operating conditions are

Reactor temperature	240–250°F
Reactor pressure	700–850 psig
Space velocity*	1–2
Catalyst depth	20–25 ft
Hydrogen added, std. cu ft per bbl reactor charge	50–180
HCl weight per cent of reactor charge	4–8
$AlCl_3$ injection rate per bbl reactor charge	0.5–1.0

* Volume charge per hour per volume catalyst.

Ultimate yields are almost 100 per cent, and the conversion to isoparaffins is 50 to 60 per cent on a once-through basis.

The use of hydrogenation cracking catalysts[108–113] for isomerization is so new that processes cannot be described here. However, it is probable that such processes will displace the aluminum chloride processes except for the isomerization of butane. The platinum catalyst reforming processes cause some isomerization of straight-chain paraffins, and continued developments may lead to cheap means of isolating straight-chain materials for recycling through such processes. It is obvious that iso-

[123] Shell Development Co., *Pet. Refiner*, September, 1954, p. 205.

[124] Evering et al., *Ind. Eng. Chem.*, **45**, 582 (1953).

[125] Armistead, G., Jr., Isomerization . . . Hexane, *Oil Gas J.*, Sept. 28, 1946, p. 43.

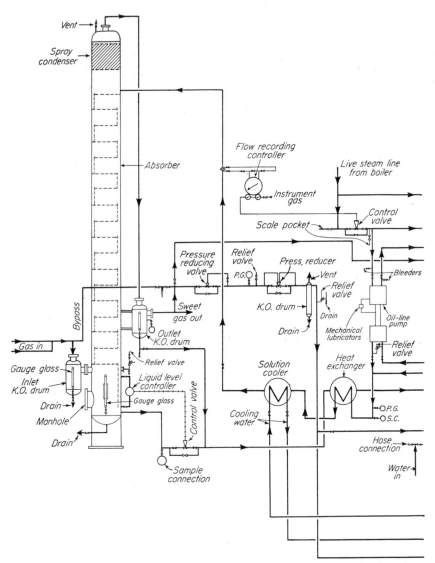

FIG. 20-18. Desulfurization of gas

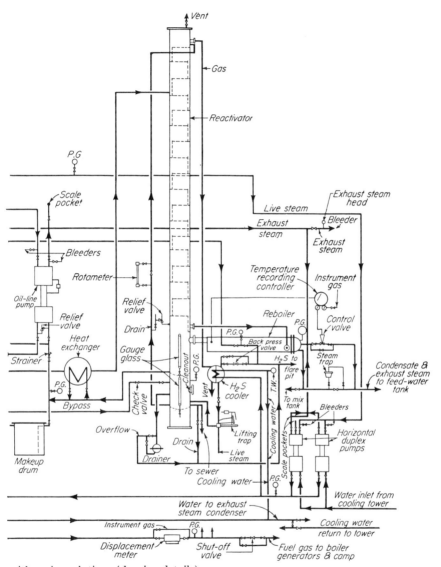

with amine solutions (showing details).

merization of pentane and of hexane, plus catalytic reforming of the heptane plus fraction of a naphtha, leads to high motor fuel octane numbers:[113]

	Total yield, per cent	Octane numbers (F-1)			
		Catalytic reforming (Platforming)		Catalytic reforming plus isomerization (Penex)	
		Clear	With 3 cc TEL	Clear	With 3 cc TEL
Natural gasoline..........	93.5	76.5	95.0	86.5	100
Arabian straight-run......	81.5	85.5	96.5	91.0	100
Wyoming straight-run.....	84.5	84.5	96.5	91.5	100

GAS DESULFURIZATION AND SULFUR MANUFACTURE

The recovery of hydrogen sulfide from natural and refinery gases, and its conversion into sulfur or sulfuric acid, is being conducted extensively. In Wyoming oil and gas fields alone, the available sulfur is estimated[126] to be 5,678,400 long tons (1950), in Arkansas sour gas fields (1942) at least 1,500,000 long tons, and in the Permian Basin of West Texas and southeastern New Mexico a daily production of at least 400 long tons[126] (1950).

Hydrogen sulfide is first removed from the gas by one of the many conventional regenerative gas desulfurization processes. Amine solutions are the most widely used desulfurization agent. They remove carbon dioxide as well as hydrogen sulfide:

$$RNH_2 + H_2S \rightleftharpoons RNH_3HS \qquad (20\text{-}14)$$

or $\qquad RNH_2 + CO_2 + H_2O \rightleftharpoons RNH_3HCO_3$

Absorption of hydrogen sulfide occurs at 100°F or lower (120°F for CO_2) and rejection of sulfide is active at 240°F (300°F for CO_2). Solution strengths of 15 to 20 per cent monoethanolamine (MEA) in water or 20 to 30 per cent diethanolamine (DEA) are used, and these are easily able to reduce the sulfide content of the gas stream to below 0.25 grains per 100 cu ft.

DEA causes a little more dehydration than MEA, and for even more dehydration diethylene glycol (DEG) may be added to the solution (25 to 35 per cent). Triethanolamine and methyldiethanolamine

[126] Espach, R. H., *Ind. Eng. Chem.*, **42**, 2235 (1950); also Cunningham, **42**, 2238 (1950).

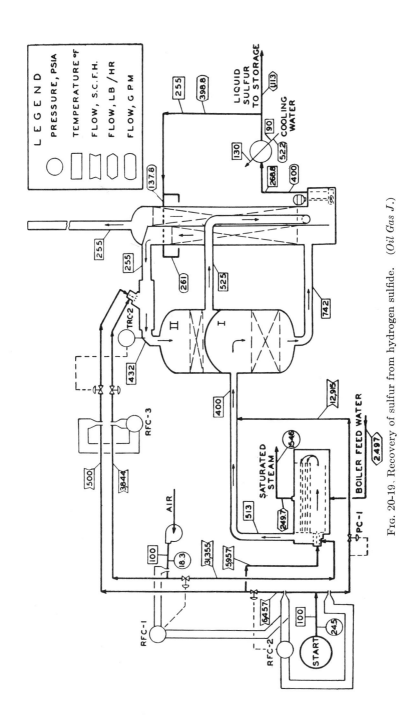

LEGEND

PRESSURE, PSIA

TEMPERATURE °F

FLOW, S.C.F.H.

FLOW, LB/HR

FLOW, GPM

Fig. 20-19. Recovery of sulfur from hydrogen sulfide. (*Oil Gas J.*)

757

(MDEA)[127] are selective in absorbing hydrogen sulfide rather than carbon dioxide. Consumption of amine ranges from 0.5 to 2 lb per million cubic feet of gas depending mainly on the pressure. Most of the loss occurs by entrainment, but in addition small amounts of thiosulfates are formed by reactions with oxygen. These can be converted to sodium thiosulfate by the addition of soda ash, but eventually the concentration becomes so high that a current elimination of the thiosulfates is necessary. This is usually done by rejecting a portion of the solution after steaming it for the recovery of useful amine.

The plant equipment is basically simple, only an absorber (usually 20 plates), a rectifier or regenerator (also 20 plates), exchangers, a cooler for the amine solution, and a reboiler at the base of the rectifier for supplying heat to the process. Thus, this is an opportunity to introduce the details that are necessary in actual plant operations (Fig. 20-18),[128] by showing a more complete type of flow diagram.

The sulfide-rich gas is then processed for sulfur as indicated in Fig. 20-19 which is a somewhat "package-type plant.[129] In the presence of bauxite (and many surface active materials) hydrogen sulfide burns directly to sulfur and water. However, this reaction is so highly exothermic that sulfur is usually produced in two steps as follows:

$$H_2S + 1\frac{1}{2}O_2 \rightarrow SO_2 + H_2O \qquad (20\text{-}15)$$

$$3H_2S$$

$$2H_2S + SO_2 \rightarrow 3S + 2H_2O \qquad (20\text{-}16)$$

In addition, the final reaction [Eq. (20-16)] is conducted in two stages (see converters I and II, Fig. 20-19). One-third of the sulfide is burned as fuel in a boiler and then contacted with substantially the remaining two-thirds of sulfide for reaction in the first and major converter. The gas which still contains a small amount of sulfide and sulfur dioxide is cooled, the sulfur is condensed, and it is then reheated by burning the last of the sulfide gas in a final converter (II, Fig. 20-19). This eliminates the last traces of sulfide and sulfur dioxide, so that only sweet flue gases pass to the atmosphere. Over 90 per cent of the sulfur in the hydrogen sulfide is collected as sulfur.

[127] Miller and Kohl, Selective Absorption of Hydrogen Sulfide, *Oil Gas J.*, Apr. 27, 1953, p. 175.

[128] Anon., *Oil Gas J.*, May 19, 1945, p. 123.

[129] Vlcek and Graff, Globe Solves Pressing Air-pollution Problem . . . , *Oil Gas J.*, July 6, 1953, p. 64.

CHAPTER 21

CATALYTIC CRACKING AND REFORMING

Since 1938, the development of methods of applying or handling catalysts in the production of gasoline has become fundamentally important to all chemical industry as well as to the petroleum industry. The approximate capacities of such plants during 1955 were:[1]

Cracking bpd		Reforming (cat.) bpd		Desulfurization or hydrogenation, bpd	
Fluid (F.C.C.)	2,621,000	Platinum cat	748,000	Unifining	192,000
Thermofor (T.C.C.)	730,000	Hydroforming	105,000	Hydrofining	114,000
Houdriflow	186,000	Houdriforming	41,000	Hydrotreating	15,000
Houdry	55,000	Thermofor	24,000	Hydrodesulfurization	97,000
Cycloversion	23,000	Others	9,000	Diesulforming	1,000

Catalytic cracking constitutes about 60 per cent of all cracking capacity, and catalytic reforming about 70 per cent of all reforming capacity.

Catalytic cracking is practiced primarily on distilled gas-oil charge stocks, although the moving-bed processes are experimenting with residual charge stocks, and the hydrogenation-desulfurization processes (see Chap. 10) may lead to the handling of residual feeds. Average yields (1955) are 40 to 45 per cent of gasoline and 40 to 45 per cent of catalytic cycle oil. The process was first economically feasible because it decreased the yield of residual fuel oil produced from crude oil, i.e., the thermal process produces about twice as many pounds of fuel oil as the pounds of coke burned (and residual fuel oil produced) in catalytic cracking. At the same time the octane number of the catalytic gasoline was higher, with the result that catalytic cracking is now absolutely necessary in meeting octane number requirements. The large volume of olefinic gases produced in catalytic cracking requires extensive gas recovery and purification systems, and requires the conversion of these gases into salable products such as polymer gasoline, alkylate gasoline, synthetic rubber, liquefied petroleum gases, etc. The position of catalytic cracking

[1] Turner, LaWanda, Refining Capacity Presses 9 Million Barrels, *Oil Gas J.*, Mar. 19, 1956, p. 213.

with respect to the entire processing scheme of a refinery is illustrated in Figs. 6-3 and 6-5.

Theory. Porous adsorbent catalysts of the silica alumina type are widely used. The fact that one or more hydrous metallic oxides are present in all successful catalysts suggests that water in some way is important in this type of catalysis.[2] Nevertheless, completely satisfactory explanations of the mechanism of catalytic cracking have not been presented. Greensfelder and associates[3] have studied the cracking of dozens of paraffinic, naphthenic, and aromatic hydrocarbons. They find that

1. Paraffins crack preferentially at such linkages that fragments containing three or four carbon atoms are produced. Normal paraffins tend to crack at the gamma carbon-carbon bonds or still nearer the center of the molecule so that yields of methane and two-carbon-atom gases are low. Long chains tend to crack simultaneously at several places.
2. Naphthenes also tend to yield fragments of three or four carbon atoms, and they crack both in the ring and in the chain especially if the chain contains more than three carbon atoms.
3. In substituted aromatics the link to the ring is selectively attacked, leaving in the extreme a bare aromatic ring. Such a reaction is extensive if the substituted groups contain more than three carbon atoms.
4. Olefins react as the paraffins, except much more readily. In addition, many secondary and auxiliary reactions occur. The rate of cracking is extremely rapid,[3] being 1,000 times as fast as thermal cracking when cracking naphthenes at 500°C.

Undoubtedly, the over-all mechanism involves at least four types of reactions: (1) thermal decomposition, (2) primary catalytic reactions at the catalyst surface, (3) secondary catalytic reactions between the primary products, and (4) removal of polymerizable products from further reaction by adsorption of them on the surface of the catalyst as coke. The last of these, adsorption, is of great practical significance because it permits large conversions without encountering mechanical difficulties with coke formation on the surfaces of tubes in heaters. Adsorption of polymerizable compounds allows the decomposition reactions to be completed to an extent never possible in commercial thermal cracking. This almost totally eliminates the need of the recycling practiced so extensively in thermal cracking.

Large amounts of gaseous molecules are produced, and the four-, five- and six-carbon-atom fractions are rich in olefins and in branched-chain hydrocarbons.[4] Relatively little ethylene is produced, but propene in the C_3 cut is 60 to 70 per cent, butenes in the C_4 cut 35 to 40 per cent, and

---

[2] Hansford, R. C., A Mechanism of Catalytic Cracking, *Ind. Eng. Chem.*, **39**, 849 (1947).

[3] *Ind. Eng. Chem.*, **37**, 514, 983, 1038, and 1168 (1945).

[4] Bates et al., Composition of Catalytically Cracked Gasolines, *Ind. Eng. Chem.*, **34**, 147 (1942).

pentenes in the C_5 cut 20 to 30 per cent.[5]   The higher the temperature the greater the olefin production.[5]   Figure 2-3 shows the general composition of catalytic gasolines.   They contain less olefins than thermally cracked or Fischer-Tropsch gasolines.

Catalyst Handling.   Four main ways of using catalysts have been explored (Fig. 21-1):

1. Fixed-bed: Houdry and Cycloversion catalytic cracking, platinum catalyst reforming, the original Hydroforming installations, and the desulfurization processes are examples.
2. Moving-bed: Thermofor cracking with bucket elevators, and the Thermofor Catalytic cracking (T.C.C.) and Houdriflow air-lift processes are examples.
3. Fluidized-bed: the Fluid and recent Hydroforming plants are examples as well as many (at least 20) chemical applications.[6]
4. Once-through: the Suspensoid catalytic cracking process once attracted attention.[7,8]

In the *fixed-bed* processes (Fig. 21-1c) a series of chambers are employed, some being onstream and others in process of cleaning, regeneration, etc. Molten salt is circulated through tubes in Houdry cases or converters, acting as a cooling agent during regeneration and as a heating agent during the endothermic cracking reaction.   The activity of Houdry catalyst decreases rapidly during a 9- to 15-min useful cycle whereas with Cycloversion catalyst useful runs of many hours are possible.   Regeneration is accomplished by steaming remnants of oil from the catalyst; sometimes evacuating the last traces of oil vapor by applying a vacuum; burning carbon from the catalyst by a controlled composition of hot air, flue gas, and sometimes steam; and removing the last traces of air by steaming or vacuum.

In *moving-bed* catalyst systems (Fig. 21-1b) such as those of the T.C.C. and Houdriflow processes, catalyst moves through the oil zone causing reaction and then through a regeneration zone where air continuously burns the coke deposits from the catalyst.   Catalyst in the form of beads or pellets is lifted by air, or in older plants by bucket elevators, to a high position so that it can flow downward by gravity through the reaction and regeneration zones.

In *fluidized* systems, finely powdered catalyst is lifted into the reaction zone by the incoming oil which immediately vaporizes upon contact with the hot catalyst (Fig. 21-1a), and after reaction is complete it is lifted into the regeneration zone by air.   In the reaction and regeneration zones, the catalyst is held in a suspended state by the passage of gases through the

[5] Olsen and Sterba, Effect of Reactor Temperature . . . Fluid Cat. Cracking, *Chem. Eng. Progr.*, November, 1949, p. 692.

[6] Nelson, W. L., *Oil Gas J.*, Jan. 28, 1952, p. 369.

[7] Purvin, R. L., Suspensoid Catalytic Cracking, *Pet. Processing*, May, 1947, p. 328.

[8] Anon., Suspensoid Catalytic Cracking, *Oil Gas J.*, Mar. 22, 1947, p. 154.

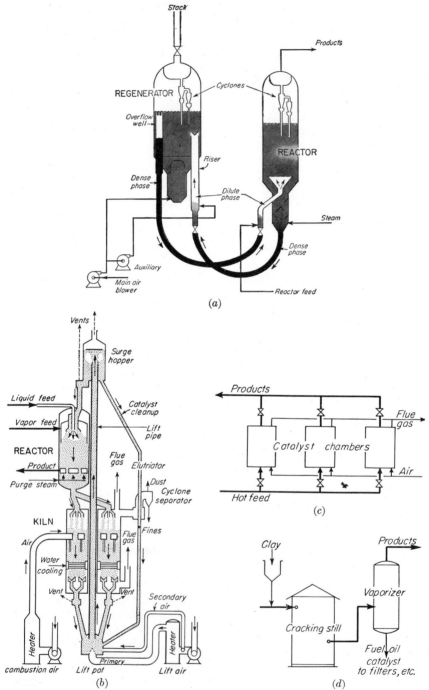

FIG. 21-1. Basic ways of handling catalysts. (a) Fluidized catalyst; (b) airlift (T.C.C. and Houdriflow); (c) fixed bed (Houdry and Cycloversion); and (d) suspended in oil (Suspensoid).

762

catalyst dust, and a small amount of catalyst is currently moved from the reactor to the regenerator and vice versa. Oil tends to saturate the enormous volume of pulverized catalyst in the reactor and hence the catalyst must be carefully stripped by means of steam before it enters the regenerator.

In the circulation processes, the residual heat in the regenerated catalyst is a major source of heat for the incoming oil, supplying not only the heat of reaction but much of the sensible heat.

TABLE 21-1. SINGLE-PASS PERCENTAGE CONVERSIONS, VOLUME PER CENT, WHEN CRACKING 11.8 TO 12.0 CHARACTERIZATION FACTOR STRAIGHT-RUN FEEDS BY THE MOVING-BED PROCESSES[a]

Space velocity	Cat. temp	Reactor temp[b]	Single-pass percentage conversion				
			760°F Inlet	800°F Oil-inlet temperature			880°F Inlet
			Cat./oil ratio 3	Cat./oil ratio 3	Cat./oil ratio 4	Cat./oil ratio 5	Cat./oil ratio 5
3.5	1020	860–920	To 31.5[c]	29–33	33–42	36–45	
	1080	930–960	....	.....	36–45	40–48	41–49
2.1	960	850–880	29–37	32–40			
	1020	875–920	....	36–44	41–49	44–51	
	1080	930–960	....	.....	45–54	47–55	48–56
1.0	960	860–875	40–48	42–53	49–56		
	1020	870–955	....	43–55	52–56	55–62	58–65
	1080	940–955	....	.....	.....	59–65	60–67

[a] Range indicates catalyst activities of AI 25 to AI 31.

[b] The temperature ranges apply to only the ranges of conversions shown in the tabulation.

[c] For 31 catalyst activity (Cat. A method).

Obviously, the large amount of heat contained in the hot flue gases (1000 to 1200°F) from the regeneration operation must be recovered by heat exchange or the use of waste-heat boilers. In addition, the Houdry process employs these gases to drive the air turbine.

Only one *once-through* process (Fig. 21-1d), the Suspensoid process, has been applied commercially. The catalyst (spent lubricating-oil clay) passes through the cracking furnace along with the oil and is removed from the fuel oil by an Oliver precoat filter.[8]

Yields. The accurate prediction of yields is difficult not only because of the effect of legitimate operating variables, but also because of great variations in the unsaturation and cleanliness of charge stocks. Entrainment of asphaltic material into the charge stock during preparation of the feed, contributes almost quantitatively to coke deposition and at the same time has little direct effect on the yields of gasoline and other products. Likewise, sulfur, nitrogen, etc., act mildly as inhibitors to the cracking reaction. These factors cannot be easily assessed, and they lead to variations in yield, especially in the percentage of coke.

Yields depend more directly on "percentage conversion" than on any other common factor. Percentage conversion is defined as 100 minus the amount of catalytic distillate or cycle stock, but corrected for any gasoline contained in the feed material. The gravity of the cycle stock is usually almost the same as that of the charge stock, and hence the conversion is almost the same on either a liquid volume or a weight basis. In turn, the percentage conversion is a function of at least the type of feed material, reaction temperature, catalyst-to-oil ratio, space velocity, and catalyst activity. Table 21-1 indicates the ranges of these variables for the T.C.C. process. Increasing severity is encountered as one moves to the right and downward in the table toward higher temperatures, higher ratios of catalyst to oil, and lower space velocities. The catalyst-to-oil ratio is on a volume basis, i.e., cu ft catalyst (about 45 lb per cu ft) per cu ft of liquid oil (60°F), and the space velocity is the volume per hour of liquid oil (60°F) per volume of catalyst bed. The activity index used in Table 21-1 is the standard Cat. A method used in testing T.C.C. catalyst.[9] Table 21-1 also appears to represent fairly accurately the behavior of the Houdriflow process.[10] The effect of recycling is somewhat as follows:

Single-pass conversion	Conversions at these recycle ratios*				
	0.25	0.5	1.0	1.5	2.0
40	47.5	56.0	67.0	75.0	84.0
45	53	61.5	73	83	91.5
50	59	67.5	80.5	91.5	
55	64	73	88	99.0†	
60	70	79	94.0†		
65	75.5	85.5			

* Cycle oil over fresh feed.

† Meaningless. Only for interpolation purposes.

[9] Alexander and Shimp, *Natl. Pet. News*, **36** (31), R-537 (1944).

[10] Maerker et al., Moving Bed Recycle Catalytic Cracking Correlations, *Chem. Eng. Progr.*, February, 1951, p. 95.

In analyzing the Fluid process, a so-called "severity factor" has been extensively used:[11]

$$\text{Severity} = \frac{\text{cat./oil ratio, lb/lb}}{\text{space velocity, lb oil per hr/lb cat. in bed}} \qquad (21\text{-}1)$$

Various exponents (from 0.5 to 1.5) for the space-velocity term have been proposed, but since agreement has not been reached, an exponent of 1.0 is used herein. At the somewhat standardized conditions of a reactor temperature of 900°F, a carbon content on the regenerated catalyst of 0.5 per

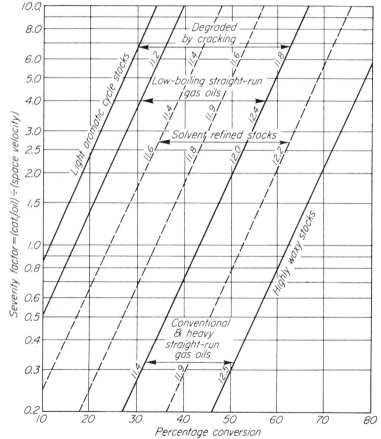

Fig. 21-2. Indication of single-pass severity factors [Eq. (21-1)] for 900°F reaction, 0.5 weight per cent carbon on catalyst, and a Jersey "$D + L$" activity of 30.0. (See Table 21-2 for effect of operating variables.)

[11] Oden and Granberry, Propane Deasphalted Gas Oil . . . Cracking Feed Stock, *Ind. Eng. Chem.*, **44,** 896 (1952).

cent, and a Jersey "$D + L$" activity[12] of 30, severity is related to conversion somewhat as indicated in Fig. 21-2.[11,12a] The lines on Fig. 21-2 have various Characterization Factors depending on the kind of feedstock. Characterization Factor of the feed is basic, but in addition higher conversions are obtained with straight-run materials, and lower conversions with low-boiling (below 600°F) materials. Solvent refined feeds occupy an intermediate position and the lowest conversions of all are obtained with light low Characterization Factor cycle stocks. The general effect[11] on conversion, of reaction temperature, carbon on catalyst, and catalyst activity or poisoning is indicated in Table 21-2. Three separate corrections can be read from this table.

TABLE 21-2. EFFECT OF OPERATING VARIABLES ON THE PERCENTAGE
CONVERSION OF FIG. 21-2[a]
(Read 3 separate corrections)

Catalyst activity[b]	Reactor temperature	Carbon on regenerated catalyst	Correction to conversion of Fig. 21-2, %
15	...	...	−18
20	...	...	−11
25	...	...	− 5
27.5	875	...	− 2.6
28.5	885	0.8	− 1.6
....	892	0.6	− 0.7
30	900	0.5	0
....	907	0.4	+ 0.7
32	915	0.3	+ 1.5
33	925	0.2	+ 2.5
36	950	...	+ 5.2
38	975	...	+ 8.0
40	...	...	+10.0
45	...	...	+14.0

[a] Standard severity is 900°F, 30 activity, 0.5 residual carbon.
[b] Volume per cent distillate, plus loss, of the Jersey fluid testing method.

Change in severity by changing (primarily) the catalyst-to-oil ratio while maintaining a constant reaction temperature results in a different distribution among the gaseous products and coke (see Table 21-3).

[12] Conn and Connolly, Testing of Cracking Catalysts, *Ind. Eng. Chem.*, **39**, 1138, (1947).

[12a] Based on many scattered references but especially on Oden and Perry, *Oil Gas J.*, Mar. 22, 1954, p. 164; Shelley and Rackley, *Pet. Processing*, December, 1952, p. 1772; Davidson et al., *Oil Gas J.*, June 4, 1956, p. 81; and Wunderlich et al., *Oil Gas J.*, Oct. 17, 1955, p. 121.

Greater severity leads to larger amounts of coke but smaller amounts of the various gaseous components especially the hydrogen.

A study of yields as a function of conversion for the two major types of processes indicates for entrainment-free stocks the general relationships of Figs. 21-3 to 21-5. Materials having a Characterization Factor of 11.8 to 12.0 have been most completely studied, and the relationship of yields to conversion for such stocks is shown in Fig. 21-3.[5,10,13,14,15,16,17] Conversions under recycling conditions are indicated in Fig. 21-3 in terms of single-pass conversion capacity as well as recycle ratio (cycle oil

TABLE 21-3. GENERAL EFFECT OF CATALYST-TO-OIL RATIO (OR SEVERITY) ON PRODUCT DISTRIBUTION

Cat./oil ratio (wt)	Severity[a]		Yields relative to the yield for a cat./oil ratio of 10 and a severity of 1									
			Coke		C_3's and C_4's		C_2's		Methane		Hydrogen	
	Nat.	Syn.	Nat.	Syn.	Nat.	Syn.	Nat.	Syn.	Nat.	Syn.	Nat.	Syn.
5	0.9	0.72	85	84	105	107	116	115	128	120	187	150
7.5	0.96	0.88	94	93	...	...	107	106	111	108	130	118
10	1	1	100	100	100	100	100	100	100	100	100	100
15	1.08	1.21	111	110	...	...	93	93	88	90	70	79
25[b]	1.17	1.55	127	126	95	92	84	84	74	80	45	59

[a] Note that the space velocity as well as the cat./oil ratio was changed to obtain these severities.

[b] Extrapolated.

over fresh feed). Thus, a plant which is able to accomplish only a 47 per cent single-pass conversion does not respond as well to recycling as a plant that can crack to a 62 per cent single-pass conversion. The average amount of recycling in United States plants during 1956 was about 18 per cent in Fluid process plants, and 25 per cent in moving-bed plants. Recycling is not entirely effective because coke and gas production increase more rapidly than gasoline production. In total recycling, yields appear to approach 61 per cent gasoline, 27 per cent B-B cut (less by the Fluid process), 12 to 14 per cent coke, and 13 to 15 per cent dry gas. Cycle oil is rich in aromatics and hence higher operating temperatures are required when recycling is practiced. Much cycle oil is ther-

[13] Schall et al., *Chem. Eng. Progr.*, December, 1949, p. 746.

[14] Schwarzenbek et al., Factors Affecting Octane Number, *Proc. Third World Pet. Congr.*, sec. IV, The Hague, 1951.

[15] Nelson, W. L. (many references given), *Oil Gas J.*, Jan. 14, 1957, p. 126.

[16] Oden and Perry, *Oil Gas J.*, Mar. 22, 1954, p. 164.

[17] See page 672 of the Third Edition of this book for additional references.

mally cracked by using somewhat high cracking temperatures, but yields are low [Eq. (19-2)]. Although the total yield of liquid product is about the same for all of the processes, the Fluid process somewhat dominates in the United States. The Fluid process, when compared with the moving-bed processes at the same percentage conversion, produces smaller

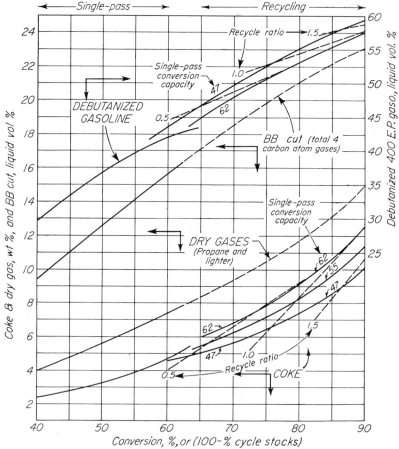

FIG. 21-3. Approximate yields in the catalytic cracking of 11.8–12.0 Characterization Factor feeds.

amounts of B-B cut and more coke and gas than the moving-bed processes. Figure 21-3 is an average for the major processes. A method of comparing the efficiency of catalytic cracking is

$$\text{Efficiency} = \frac{\text{per cent gasoline}}{\text{per cent conversion}} \times 100$$

Cracking efficiency seldom exceeds 80 per cent.

In general, the moving-bed processes, at a particular conversion, produce less coke (7 to 10 per cent), and the Fluid process[5,10-17,18,19] more coke (11 to 14 per cent) than the values indicated in Fig. 21-3. Nearly the same amount of gasoline is produced by all processes, but the Fluid-process gasoline has a slightly higher octane number (mainly because of the higher reaction temperature). Likewise the amount of dry gas (propane and lighter) in the moving-bed processes is lower than indicated in Fig. 21-3 by about 6 to 9 per cent (and by the Fluid process the same amount higher).[5,10-19] The Fluid process produces a B-B cut (all 4-carbon-atom materials) that is richer in olefins, but 7 to 14 per cent less B-B is produced, whereas in the moving-bed processes 7 to 12 per cent more B-B is produced.[5,10-19] The cost of catalyst or its replacement is usually larger for the moving-bed processes. All of these comparisons are for the same percentage conversion. In practice, a different conversion or severity is used in each process, and after such adjustments and after having utilized the gases, the total liquid yield by all of the processes is about the same. The composition of the dry gas and B-B cut can be estimated from Table 21-4. The higher the reaction temperature, the larger the unsaturation of the gases.

TABLE 21-4. COMPOSITION OF CATALYTIC GASES

		Range
B-B cut:		
Butenes, vol. %..........	40 (Fluid)	21–49
	35 (T.C.C.)	17–42
Isobutane, vol. %........	52 (Fluid)	42–68
	51 (T.C.C.)	
Propane-propene cut:		
wt % of dry gas..........	68 (Fluid)	61–85
	66 (T.C.C.)	62–76
	68 (Houdriflow)	65–78
Propene in C_3 cut, %......	71 (Fluid)	60–76
	62 (T.C.C.)	54–65

Example 21-1. Yield from 30 API East Texas Gas Oil. In a Fluid-process plant, the space velocity is 3 and the catalyst-to-oil ratio is 8. This is a severity factor of 8 ÷ 3 or 2.67. According to Fig. 21-2, the standard conversion for a conventional 11.9 Characterization Factor feed is about 63 per cent, and this applies to operations

[18] Moorman, J. W., How Conversion Level Affects Product Distribution, *Oil Gas J.*, Jan. 4, 1954, p. 76.

[19] Nelson, W. L., p. 673 of the Third Edition of this book and *Oil Gas J.*, Aug. 30, 1947, p. 67.

at 900°F, a residual carbon of 0.5 on the catalyst, and a catalyst activity of 30. The plant is actually operating at 925°F, the catalyst has an activity of only 25, and it bears 0.7 per cent carbon. According to Table 21-2, the conversion will be lower by 5 per cent because of the low activity, the reactor temperature increases the conversion by about 2.5 per cent, and the high carbon reduces the conversion by about 1.1 per cent, so that the actual conversion is about 63 − 5 + 2.5 − 1.1, or 59.4 per cent.

Figure 21-3 indicates the following average or basic yields and, in the second column of the tabulation, the somewhat different yields of the Fluid process at this conversion (note that this does not necessarily mean that the Fluid process is inferior).

	Basic yields		Fluid yields	
	Vol. %	Wt %	Vol. %	Wt %
Coke...........................	....	4.6	....	5.15
Dry gas.......................	....	7.3	....	7.9
B-B cut.......................	15.5	...	14.0	
Debutanized gasoline...........	41.7	...	41.7	
Cycle stock (100–59.4).........	40.6	...	40.6	

The amounts of various gaseous components (Table 21-4) for the Fluid yields of 7.9 per cent dry gas and 14 per cent B-B cut are about:

$$\text{Propane-propylene} \ldots \ldots \quad 7.9 \times 0.68 = 5.4\%$$

		Vol. %	Wt %
Ethane and lighter.......	7.9 − 5.4 =		2.5
Propylene..............	5.4 × 0.71 =		3.8
Propane...............	5.4 − 3.8 =		1.6
Isobutane..............	14 × 0.52 =	7.3	
Butylenes..............	14 × 0.40 =	5.6	
Butane................	14 × 0.08 =	1.1	
		14.0	7.9

If this plant (59.4 per cent conversion) were used by recycling 0.5 of cycle stock to 1.0 of fresh feed, the conversion would be raised (Fig. 21-3) to about 70. This was obtained from the dashed line for 0.5 recycle ratio and among the 3 lines at 59.4 per cent conversion.

The general effect of type of charge stock is partly indicated in Fig. 21-2, but the conversions indicated from Fig. 21-2 should not be used with Fig. 21-3 unless the Characterization Factor is in the range of 11.8 to 12. For other Characterization Factor stocks, the percentage conversion of Fig. 21-2 or Table 21-1 should be transferred to Fig. 21-4 to estimate the yield of coke and the yield of gasoline. These yields are then used in Fig. 21-5 to estimate the yield of dry gas and B-B cut. The simple relationship of Fig. 21-4 cannot be perfect, but it is the result of extensive study,[16,20,21,22,23,24,25] and no specific method of handling the situation appears in the literature. The yields of Figs. 21-4 and 21-5 are affected by the type of process in the same way as those of Fig. 21-3, giving larger or smaller coke, etc., yields depending on the kind of cracking process. Coke yields (Figs. 21-3 and 21-4) are least dependable because of variations in the entrainment of asphaltic materials into the feed.

Finally, no way to account completely for the boiling range of the stock was devised. The information given herein (Figs. 21-3 to 21-5 and Table 21-1) applies to full-boiling-range straight-run feedstocks, and for cracked feedstocks of the boiling range ordinarily encountered in refinery practice. In general, the conversion for low-boiling-range feeds (400 to 600°F) at the same severity appears to be 15 to 30 per cent less than the conversions obtained with full-boiling-range feeds, whereas material boiling above 700°F cracks very easily. Undoubtedly part of the poor behavior ascribed to stocks that have been degraded by cracking is due to their relatively low boiling range rather than to the kinds of hydrocarbons contained in them.

Example 21-2. Effect of Kind of Stock on Catalytic Yields. Example 21-1 will be repeated except to consider an 11.7 Characterization Factor stock which was produced by viscosity breaking.

According to Fig. 21-2, the conversion for an 11.7 C.F. stock at a severity of 2.67 will be about 47.6 per cent. If this is corrected as in Example 21-1 for the operating conditions, it becomes a conversion of 44.0 per cent. According to Fig. 21-4, the percentage of carbon will now be about 3.8 and the amount of gasoline about 32 per cent. The dry gas and the B-B yields are obtained from Fig. 21-5.

Dry gas	6.4 wt per cent
B-B cut	10.4 vol. per cent

Yields by the Fluid process would be smaller than these average yields.

These low yields compared with the results of Example 21-1 leave the impression that the viscosity broken stock is very inferior, whereas in actuality, a greater severity and a higher temperature could be used to crack the stock more thoroughly. However, these changes in conditions are expensive, or result in reduced capacity.

Another way to compare the two stocks is to burn the same amount of carbon, i.e., 4.6 per cent as in Example 21-1. This would require a greater conversion (see Fig.

[20] Ardern et al., Catalytic Cracking in Fixed and Moving Bed Processes, "Progress in Pet. Technology," ACS Meeting, New York, September, 1951.

[21] Bergstrom et al., Recent Developments in T.C.C. Cracking, *Proc. Fourth World Pet. Congr.*, Sec. III, Rome, 1955.

[22] Hamilton et al., Catalytic Cracking in Airlift T.C.C. Units, *Pet. Engr.*, August, 1952, p. C-5.

[23] Noll and Luntz, T.C.C. Processing . . . , *Oil Gas J.*, Jan. 15, 1948, p. 81.

[24] Shelley and Rackley, Better Yields from Cat. Cracking, *Pet. Processing*, December, 1952, p. 1772.

[25] Duval and Holmes, How Charge Stock Properties Affect . . . , *Pet. Refiner*, August, 1952, p. 109.

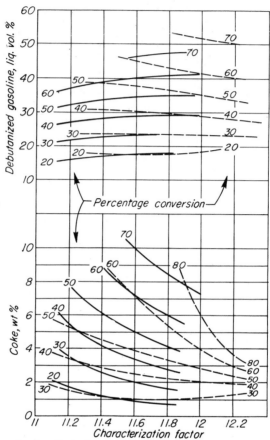

FIG. 21-4. Approximate effect of type of charge stock on catalytic-cracking yields. Dashed lines are for straight-run feeds and solid lines for materials degraded by previous thermal or catalytic cracking. (See Fig. 21-5 for yields of gas or B-B cut.)

21-4), i.e., about 50 per cent, but the gasoline yield would rise to about 35 per cent. Such a change would, of course, require a large adjustment in the severity.

In catalytic reforming, only the platinum catalyst processes (Platforming,[26] Catforming,[27] Sinclair Baker,[28] Ultraforming,[29] Powerforming,[30] Sovaforming,[31] etc.[32]) are sufficiently well defined to allow the prediction of yields[33] (see Table 21-24). The approximate maximum

[26] Haensel, Vladimir, *Oil Gas J.*, Mar. 30, 1950, p. 82.
[27] Fowle et al., *Oil Gas J.*, May 26, 1952, p. 181.
[28] Decker and Stewart, *Oil Gas J.*, July 4, 1955, p. 80.
[29] Gumaer and Raiford, *Oil Gas J.*, Aug. 8, 1955, p. 119.
[30] Anon. (Std. Oil N.J.), *Oil Gas J.*, Mar. 5, 1956, p. 62.
[31] Backensto et al., *Pet. Refiner*, August, 1956, p. 165.
[32] Sittig and Warren, *Pet. Refiner*, September, 1955, pp. 230–280.

yields of debutanized reformed gasoline as a function of octane number and the properties of the parent stock are shown in Fig. 21-6. The process operates differently during each stage of degradation of the catalyst, and each stock must be processed at somewhat different operat-

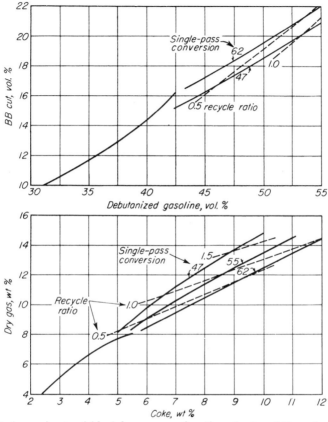

FIG. 21-5. Approximate yield of dry gas as a function of coke yield, and of B-B cut as a function of gasoline yield.

ing conditions, but Fig. 21-6 is based on the optimum or best operating conditions for each feed material. The effect of boiling range on the octane number of reformer charge stocks (see Fig. 21-6) has recently been published.[33a] About 12 to 17 per cent of butane can be added to the debutanized material to produce 10 R.v.p. motor gasolines, making total yields of about:

[33] Nelson, W. L., Yields by Platinum Catalyst Reforming, *Oil Gas J.*, Jan. 3, 1955, p. 117; also *Oil Gas J.*, Nov. 12, 1956, p. 211.

[33a] Nelson, W. L., *Oil Gas J.*, Nov. 18, 1957, p. 246.

Characterization Factor	Approx. percentage		Illustration of charge stock
	Pentane plus	10 R.v.p.	
11.6	90.7	104.3	Coastal
11.7	89.1	102.5	Venezuela
11.8	87.7	101.0	Texas
11.9	86.4	99.4	Mid Continent
12.0	85.0	97.7	Pennsylvania
12.1	83.3	95.8	Middle East

Yields of propane (including propene) are about the same by all of the platinum reforming processes (Fig. 21-6) but the Sinclair-Baker[28] and Powerforming[30] processes appear to produce less butanes (and butylenes) than the Atlantic[27] process, and the Powerforming,[30] Platforming, and Ultraforming[29] processes produce an intermediate amount. The ratio of iso to normal compounds for butanes produced by the Catforming process is 1.1 (only 0.71 by Platforming), and for the pentanes the ratios are 1.7 and 1.94. Debutanized reformate usually has a Characterization Factor of 11.35–11.50.

Products. The major products of catalytic cracking are (1) olefinic gases that are useful for polymerization or alkylation, (2) cracked gasoline, and (3) catalytic cycle oil. The latter is produced in amounts about equal to the amount of residual fuel oil produced in thermal cracking, and its disposal is requiring a revision of the specifications of distillate and diesel fuel oils to accommodate such materials.

Catalytic 390 end point debutanized gasoline has a Characterization Factor of about 11.5 regardless of the Characterization Factor of the feedstock or the percentage conversion. Apparently the cracking reaction produces the same type of organic molecules from any charge stock. Thus, the gravity of debutanized gasoline is 51 to 53 API, and with butanes to 10 Reid vapor pressure, 55 to 57.5 API. Heavy naphthas (300 to 400°F) or gasolines have Characterization Factors of about 11.3 from highly paraffinic charge stocks down to about 10.8 from naphthenic feeds.

The octane number of the gasoline is affected by the reactor temperature (Table 21-5) but scarcely at all by other operating conditions. It increases only 0.5 to 1.0 units (sometimes none) for an increase in the conversion of 10 per cent (in the range of 50 to 80 per cent) and it increases only slightly with catalyst-to-oil ratio. However, low Characterization Factor feeds produce gasolines of slightly higher (1 to 3 units) octane numbers, and Table 21-5 is based primarily on Mid Continent feeds such

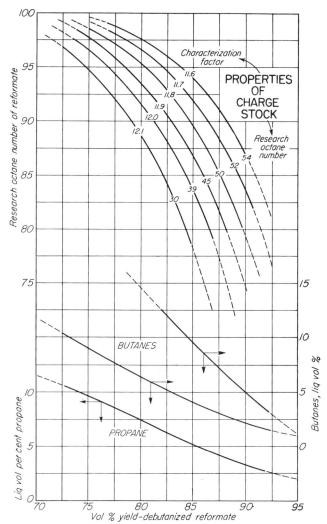

Fig. 21-6. Approximate relation of octane number to yield of reformate by platinum-catalyst reforming of 200–400°F naphthas (also yields of propane and butane). See reference 33a for the effect of boiling range on the octane number of charge stocks.

as those from East Texas. Natural catalyst produces slightly lower octane numbers, but the yield of gasoline is slightly higher. High catalyst activity reduces slightly the octane number, and a high sulfur content or a high-boiling-range feed has the same effect.[14]

Cycle stocks normally have the same or a lower gravity than the feedstock, and the greater the conversion the lower the gravity. The boiling range usually falls within the limits shown in Table 21-6, and the more the conversion the lower the Characterization Factor, and to a small degree the boiling range. More detail on Characterization Factor is

TABLE 21-5. APPROXIMATE OCTANE NUMBERS OF CATALYTIC GASOLINES FROM MID CONTINENT CHARGE STOCKS, AS A FUNCTION OF REACTOR TEMPERATURE

Reactor temp, °F	Motor method numbers				Research method numbers			
	Clear		3 cc TEL		Clear		3 cc TEL	
	Syn.	Nat.	Syn.	Nat.	Syn.	Nat.	Syn.	Nat.
800	79	76	86	86	88	81	95	92
850	80	77	86.5	86	92	87	96.5	95
900	81.5	80	86.5	87	95	92	98.5	98
950	82	82	86.5	87	96	94	99	99

available in Table 21-7, and Schall, Dart, and Kirkbride[13] indicate the following gravities for Houdriflow cycle oil from East Texas gas oil (these gravities are lower than those found in most of the literature):

Conversion	API	Conversion	API
80	17.9	60	24.3
75	20	50	26.5
70	21.7	40	28
65	23.2	0	28.9

The ignition quality or Diesel Index[34] of cycle oils is indicated in Table 21-8 for once-through operations. When recycling, the Characterization Factors of Table 21-7 are lower (occasionally by 0.3 units) and the Diesel Indexes (Table 21-8) are correspondingly lower. The general effect of boiling range on pour point and on Diesel Index is indicated in Tables 4-23 and 4-24 and Figs. 4-50 and 4-51. The effect of furfural refining on the properties of cycle stocks is indicated in Table 11-4.

TABLE 21-6. APPROXIMATE DISTILLATION RANGES OF TOTAL CYCLE STOCKS
Range °F

ASTM—I.B.P............	400–450
10%............	445–520
50%............	515–635
90%............	580–760
E.P............	630–820

[34] Nelson, W. L., Properties of Catalytic Cycle Stocks, *Oil Gas J.*, Dec. 14, 1953, p. 157.

TABLE 21-7. APPROXIMATE CHARACTERIZATION FACTORS OF CYCLE STOCKS
FOR THESE CONVERSIONS

Characterization Factor of feed	40%	50%	60%	70%	80%
11.2	10.7[a]	10.5[a]	10.1[a]		
11.4	11.0	10.85	10.6	10.1[a]	
11.5	11.2	11.05	10.8	10.3	
11.6	11.35	11.25	11.05	10.65	
11.7	11.45	11.4	11.2	10.9	10.2
11.8	11.6	11.5	11.3	11.1	10.6
11.9	11.7	11.55	11.4	11.2	10.85
12.0	11.75	11.6	11.5	11.3	11.0
12.2	11.8	11.7	11.55	11.35	11.1

[a] Extrapolation of data.

TABLE 21-8. APPROXIMATE DIESEL INDEXES OF CYCLE STOCKS FROM
ONCE-THROUGH OPERATIONS

Conversion	Diesel indexes for feeds of these C.F.'s and D.I.'s								
	11.4 42	11.5 46	11.6 49	11.7 53	11.8 57	11.9 61	12.0 65	12.1 68	12.2 72
40%	31	33.5	38.5	44	49.5	53.5			
50%	26.5	31	35.5	40.5	45	50	52		
60%	23	27	31.5	36	39.5	43	45.5	47.5	49
70%	....	....	25	29.5	34	37.5	39.5	41	42
80%[a]	....	....	....	....	23.5[a]	27.5[a]	30.5[a]	32.5[a]	33.5[a]

[a] Based mainly on recycling operations.

The average composition of cracked gases has been indicated in Table 21-4 under the topic of Yields. The analyses of B-B cuts were also indicated in Table 20-7 and for gases, Table 14-4.

Example 21-3. Weight and Volume Per Cent Yields. Example 21-1 will be continued to determine the weight and volume per cent yields. In addition, the yield of poly gasoline and finished 10 R.v.p. gasoline will be estimated.

Table 21-9 is a material balance of the Fluid-process yields of Example 21-1. The gravity of the debutanized gasoline from an 11.9 Characterization Factor stock will be about 52.5 API. The weight of the cycle stock was obtained by difference, and its gravity checks reasonably well with Table 21-7.

The total liquid volume recovery including the propane and propylene is 105.3 per cent. However, the butylenes and part of the propylene would be recovered as polymer gasoline (or alkylate), and this decreases the total liquid yield by nearly 5 per cent.

TABLE 21-9. MATERIAL BALANCE OF CATALYTIC YIELDS
(Examples 21-1 and 21-3) Basis 100 gallons

	API	Lb per gal	Wt %[a]	Vol. %[a]	Wt per 100 gal	Volume %
Coke........................	....	.....	5.15	....	37.6	
Ethane and lighter..........	....	.....	2.5	....	18.2	
Propylene...................	....	4.35	3.8	....	27.6	6.30
Propane.....................	....	4.24	1.6	....	11.7	2.72
Butylenes...................	....	5.00	......	5.6	28	5.60
Isobutane...................	....	4.7	......	7.3	34.2	7.30
Butane......................	....	4.86	......	1.1	5.3	1.10
Gasoline....................	52.5	6.402	......	41.7	267.0	41.70
Cycle stock.................	28.1	7.38	41.9[b]	40.6	300.0[b]	40.6
Feed gas oil................	30.0	7.296	100	....	729.6	100.0

[a] Yields obtained in Example 21-1.

[b] Obtained by difference.

Information is not complete enough for the use of the polymerization chart (Fig. 20-8), but for an olefin composition ratio of 2.0, a reactor temperature of 380°F, an olefin space velocity of 0.08, a total space velocity of 0.18, and a catalyst activity of 50, the total conversion of olefins by weight will be about 90 per cent (this is a high total conversion). On such a basis, and if 90 per cent of the olefins are exposed to polymerization, the yield of polymer gasoline per 100 gal will be about:

$$\frac{0.9 \times 0.9(27.6 + 28.0)}{6.15 \text{ lb/gal}} = 7.33 \text{ gal (or per cent)}$$

The final gasoline, a debutanized total of 41.7 + 7.33 or 49.0 per cent, will have a vapor pressure of only about 5 psia. Butane will be added to produce a total gasoline of 10 R.v.p. Most approximately the amount of mixed butanes required will be a little more than the difference in vapor pressures, namely, 5 to 6 per cent, but more specifically, using the true vapor pressures of Table 4-12, and a mole basis:

$$5 \times 1.07(100 - x) + 63 \times 1.4x = 100 \times 1.07 \times 10$$
$$x = 6.5 \text{ mole per cent}$$

This corresponds approximately to a liquid volume per cent of

$$\frac{\dfrac{6.5 \times 58}{4.77} \times 100}{\dfrac{93.2 \times 100}{6.249} + \dfrac{6.5 \times 58}{4.77}} = 5.0 \text{ per cent}$$

Thus, the total yield of gasoline is about

$$\frac{49.0}{1 - 0.05} = 51.5 \text{ per cent}$$

The percentage of sulfur in catalytically cracked products can be estimated from Figs. 4-37 and 4-38. Material balances indicate that very much of the feed sulfur appears in the flue gases and cracked gases.

Charge Stocks and Feed Preparation. Theoretically it is possible to process almost any material including light distillates, which require a high severity, and very heavy gas oils,[35,36,37,38] which deposit so much carbon that various means of eliminating high-boiling or high-carbon parts of the feedstock are usually adopted. Part of the feed to the T.C.C. process is a liquid (5 to 25 per cent), and experiments have been made with the charging of residual stocks[38] directly to the reactor if they have no higher carbon residue than 4 per cent. In 1955, the Houdry Process Corp.[39] announced the processing of reduced crudes and residues (see page 808) by its Houdresid process.

In the T.C.C. and Houdriflow processes, reduced or topped crude oil is heated to 780 to 860°F vaporizing material boiling up to about 850°F as a vapor feed. Three major means of obtaining additional charge stock from the residual feed have been used (see Fig. 21-7):

1. Recycling of cycle stock through the topped crude oil furnace in amounts equal to or larger than the fresh feed permits vaporization of substantially all useful material (up to 920°F). This remarkably simple method of operation accounts for the larger amount of recycling practiced in moving-bed types of plants.

2. Vacuum flashing of the residuum from the primary atmospheric flash. This is satisfactory if no recycling is practiced but ineffective with recycling because the primary flash leaves a very high-boiling feed for the vacuum unit.

3. Viscosity breaking the residue from the primary flash and after having distilled the low-boiling materials, subjecting the residue to vacuum flashing.

In a few plants, the entire crude oil has been cracked by introducing it into the system of Fig. 21-7, but the passage of straight-run gasoline through the reactor produces little reforming and it requires a much larger reactor. Recycling is highly useful in the moving-bed processes because not only does it increase the yield but it assists in causing the vaporization of the highest-boiling parts of the charge stock.

There is no true feed preparation for the Fluid process because only distilled feedstocks in the form of a liquid are charged to the process.

[35] M. W. Kellogg Co., special edition of the *Kelloggram*, 1945.

[36] Simpson et al., Liquid-charge Technique in T.C.C. Cracking, *Oil Gas J.*, Nov. 24, 1945, p. 119.

[37] Mateer and Haney, . . . Fluid Catalytic Units Form Heart of Refinery, *Oil Gas J.*, July 8, 1944, p. 87.

[38] Simpson, T. P., T.C.C. Unit Announces Liquid Processing, *Oil Gas J.*, May 12, 1945, p. 88.

[39] Dart et al., Houdresid Converts Crude Residua . . . , *Oil Gas J.*, May 9, 1955, p. 123.

However, the customary operations of topping, vacuum distillation,[40] propane decarbonizing (deasphalting),[41,42] coking,[43] viscosity breaking,[16] and furfural treating[44] have all been employed in an effort to obtain carbon-free and hydrogen-rich charge stocks. Substantially all of the carbon found by the carbon residue test appears during cracking as

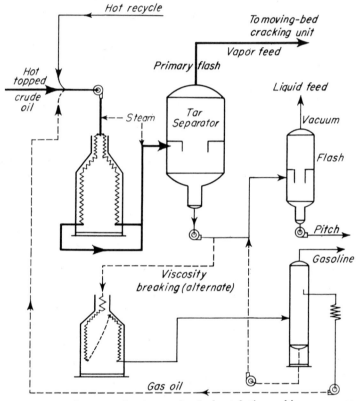

Fig. 21-7. Feed preparation for moving-bed catalytic cracking processes.

coke deposit, in addition to the coke produced by the reaction. Furfural has been used to upgrade cycle stocks before they are returned to the reactor,[44] and if the treating is sufficiently extreme, the raffinates so produced are nearly equal to parent charge stocks of the same Characterization Factor. The solvent processes are particularly useful[41,42] in

[40] Hirsch, R. W., Tidewater's Special Unit . . . , *Pet. Refiner*, June, 1945, p. 93.

[41] M. W. Kellogg Co., Propane Decarbonizing, *Pet. Refiner*, September, 1954, p. 223.

[42] Johnson et al., Recovery of . . . Stock by Solvent Fractionation, *Ind. Eng. Chem.*, **47**, 1578 (1955).

[43] Blau-Knox, Decarbonizing Process (Coking), *Oil Gas J.*, Mar. 22, 1954, p. 132.

[44] Carter, R. T., Furfural Refining Scores on Four Points, *Oil Gas J.*, Mar. 22, 1954, p. 157.

eliminating the metallic contaminants or catalyst poisons that are found in trace but extremely harmful amounts in many oils. In vacuum distillation, every effort is made to eliminate entrainment of carbonaceous material, and by the use of wire-mesh mist-extractor pads or blankets the carbon residue of the catalytic charge stock can often be kept to below 0.2 per cent.

The use of boron trifluoride ether (BF_3—$C_2H_5OC_2H_5$) as a precipitant for asphaltenes has been studied experimentally.[44a] When 2.5 to 4 per cent of this dense (1.125 sp gr) liquid is mixed with Kuwait crude oil, it settles at room temperature along with about 8 per cent (based on crude oil) of the asphaltenes and higher aromatic hydrocarbons. The tar

TABLE 21-10. EFFECT OF CHARGE STOCK ON CARBON BURNOFF[a]

	Approx. Characterization Factor	Percentage gasoline			
		20	30	40	50
Mid Continent...............	12.0	...	2.0	4.0	
Mixed base..................	11.6	0.9	1.5	2.7	
Coastal.....................	11.2	0.5	0.9	1.7	4.1
Highly naphthenic............	10.9	...	...	1.2	2.15

[a] Ardern et al., Catalytic Cracking in Fixed and Moving Bed Processes, Progress in Pet. Technology, ACS Meeting, New York, September, 1951.

layer is then distilled to recover the boron compound (bp 258°F). The metals content of the crude oil is reduced by about half and the percentage of carbon residue by about 30 per cent.

Carbon burnoff is of vital importance to the economics of catalytic cracking. This explains the superiority and need for low-boiling, light-colored (under 5 NPA), low-carbon-residue, metal-free distilled stocks. Material balances or the yields of Figs. 21-3 to 21-5 indicate clearly that high API gravity stocks yield more gasoline by being able to conduct operations at larger percentage conversions. However, for a fixed gasoline yield, the somewhat low-gravity naphthenic stocks produce less carbon on the catalyst than paraffinic stocks[20] (Table 21-10), at least by the Houdry process. Figure 21-4 indicates the opposite relationship. In the extreme, kerosene, naphtha, or even gasoline may be cracked by the catalytic processes.[45,46] The Houdry[47] and particularly the Cyclo-

[44a] Anon. (C. D. Shiah), Pet. Processing, October, 1956, p. 55.

[45] Saegebarth, E. O., Catalytic Reforming Process of . . . , Pet. Engr., May, 1946, p. 95.

[46] Greensfelder, Archibald, and Fuller, Catalytic Reforming . . . Molybdenum-alumina and Chromia-alumina Catalysts, Chem. Eng. Progr., 43, 561 (1947).

[47] Peterkin, Bates, and Broom, Catalytic Reforming for . . . Aviation Gasoline, Ref. Nat. Gaso. Mfr., November, 1939, p. 126.

version,[48] Platforming,[26–32] and Hydroforming[49] processes have been used for reforming.

The use of Characterization Factor in Figs. 21-2 and 21-4 takes into account the major differences in charge stocks. However, the boiling range, degradation by previous cracking, entrained carbonaceous material, metallic contaminants, high percentage of nitrogen,[50] or extremely high percentages of sulfur[51] are extra factors all of which influence the yields.

Trace amounts of metals (vanadium, nickel, iron, copper, etc.) are not particularly harmful[21] to the catalyst in moving-bed processes because contamination occurs mainly on the surface of the beads and the contaminant is ground off by natural erosion. In the Fluid process about half[52] of the metal contaminant pervades the catalyst dust causing a sharp decrease in catalytic activity,[52,53] increased carbon and gas formation, and a decrease in gasoline yield. Only one extreme illustration can be given. As the ferric oxide in the catalyst rose to 1.1 per cent, the yields[54] changed as follows:

Coke increased from	3.1 to 5.9%
Dry gas increased from	8.0 to 10.6%
Gasoline decreased from	48 to 28.5%
Gas sp gr decreased from	1.6 to 0.56

Only 0.18 per cent copper had much the same effect on the coke yield but a lesser effect on the other yields.

If the sum in the feedstock of the parts-per-million of iron and vanadium, plus ten times the ppm of nickel and copper, is above 5 to 10, rapid replacement of catalyst (in the Fluid process) will be necessary. Thus, a gas oil that contains 0.5 ppm V, 1.0 ppm Fe, 0.3 ppm Ni, and 0.1 ppm Cu results in a sum of 5.5, and rapid contamination of the catalyst will occur. Another authority[55] has mentioned the following limits for a satisfactory feed: Fe, 1.0; V, 0.4; Ni, 0.15; and Cu, 0.1 ppm. Although this is a fairly good feed according to the formulation given just above (total = 3.9, which is under 5), it would be classified as bad by the

[48] Daniels and Conn, Perco Cycloversion, *Pet. Processing*, May, 1947, p. 391.

[49] Swift et al., Aromatics Recovery by Hydroforming . . . , *Pet. Processing*, January, 1953, p. 81.

[50] Schall and Dart, Cat. Cracking of High Nitrogen Charge Stock, *Pet. Refiner*, March and April, 1952.

[51] Thomas, E. J., Fluid . . . High Sulfur Stocks with Natural Catalysts, *Oil Gas J.*, Mar. 23, 1950, p. 221; also Carney et al., *Oil Gas J.*, Nov. 4, 1948, p. 49.

[52] Duffy and Hart, Metal Poisoning . . . , *Chem. Eng. Progr.*, July, 1952, p. 344.

[53] Rothrock et al., Fluid Cracking Catalyst Contamination, ACS Meeting, Dallas, Apr. 8, 1956.

[54] Mills, G. A., Aging of Cracking Catalysts, *Ind. Eng. Chem.*, **42**, 182 (1950).

[55] Eckhouse and Keightley, *Pet. Engr.*, April, 1954, p. C-96.

contamination index of still another authority which states that the sum of the Fe, V, and Cu plus 5 times the Ni (all in ppm) should not exceed about 1.0. Finally, the American Cyanamid Co. once used a contamination index based on the catalyst (weight per cent), which is:

$$C.I. = 1,000(Fe + 4V + Cu + 14Ni)$$

New catalyst has a contamination index of about 75, fairly clean equilibrium catalyst 150, fairly badly contaminated 750, and heavily contaminated 900 to 1,500.

Metallic contaminants are found to be concentrated in the highest-boiling parts of petroleum, and hence metals can appear in charge stocks by plain mechanical entrainment along with carbonaceous material. However, there are clear indications[56] that at least some of the metallic contaminants are vaporizable. Apparently about half of the metal compounds in a parent stock appears in the overhead distillate when a temperature of 950°F has been attained, and as distillation continues, substantially all of the original metal appears in the overhead product. Some of the metals, as they become part of the catalyst, appear to cause the catalyst to become a dehydrogenation catalyst.

Catalysts. There are two main types of catalysts: (1) synthetic silica-alumina[56a] and (2) natural[56a] silica-alumina compositions, treated bentonite clay, Super Filtrol, fuller's earths, aluminum hydrosilicates, and bauxite (see Tables 10-4 and 10-5). In addition, little used synthetic catalysts such as silica-magnesia,[57] alumina-boria,[58] and silica-zirconia[58] have been suggested. The alumina-molybdia,[46,59] chromia-alumina,[46] and platina-alumina[26] catalysts used in catalytic reforming operations are not included in the present discussion. The main catalysts are available in either the pellet (bead) or powdered form. The bead form is obviously required in the T.C.C. process, and very hard synthetic beads are particularly valuable. Likewise, the ease of handling and freedom from plugging of the bead form are advantageous in even the fixed-bed processes.[60] Attrition of even powdered catalysts is significant with respect to dusting losses, and hence a "micro-sphere" (MS) form of Fluid

[56] Gamble and Jones, Determination of Trace Metals . . . , *Anal. Chem.*, **27**, 1456 (1955).

[56a] Heinemann and Heinemann, Adsorbents and Catalysts, *Pet. Refiner*, June, 1954, p. 159.

[57] Anderson and Sterba, Simplified Catalytic Cracking . . . Smaller Refiners, *Oil Gas J.*, Dec. 22, 1945, p. 77.

[58] Webb and Ehrhardt, Properties of Cracking Catalysts, *Pet. Processing*, January, 1947, p. 5.

[59] Webb, Smith, and Ehrhardt, . . . Properties of Alumina-molybdenum Oxide Catalysts . . . , *Pet. Processing*, November, 1947, p. 834.

[60] Hornberg, Keiper, and Chesney, Use of Bead Catalyst . . . Houdry Units, *Oil Gas J.*, July 26, 1947, p. 214.

process catalyst[61] has been developed.　The size distribution of some fluid catalysts is shown in Table 21-11.[62]

One of the latest Houdriflow catalysts is kaolin.[62a]　It is relatively cheap, quite erosion-resistant, and because of its stability at high temperatures, the kiln can operate at a higher carbon-burning capacity.

TABLE 21-11. VARIATIONS OF PARTICLE DISTRIBUTION IN TYPICAL F.C. CATALYSTS[a]

Particle size, microns[b]	Cumulative weight per cent of each size for these catalysts											
	A	B	C	D	E	F	G	H	I	J	K	L
0–10	75	60	0	5	12	1	1	...	...	...	4	6
0–20	95	85	0	15	22	5	3	10	1	13	15	19
0–40	100	95	50	25	41	30	17	25	12	24	33	44
0–80	...	100	100	75	71	75	56	50	48	40	55.8	71
0–125	...	...	...	...	84	93	...	...	71	...	....	...
0–180	...	...	...	100	93	99	95	...	86	...	....	...
0–500	...	...	...	...	100	100	100	100	100	100	....	...

A and B—commercially available, but expensive.
　　C—theoretically desirable, but expensive.
　　D—commercially available at moderate expense.
　　E—average of commercially available at average cost.
　　F—used catalyst, similar to D sample, when new.
G, H, and J—samples cited in the literature.
　　I—used catalyst, similar to E, when new (now too coarse).
　　K—used synthetic.
　　L—used natural.
　[a] Nelson, W. L., What Is a Good Catalyst, *Oil Gas J.*, Apr. 28, 1949, p. 120; see also Mar. 17, 1949, p. 162.
　[b] 1,000 microns = 1 mm.

In general a good catalyst should not lose its activity during operation, and the loss by attrition should be small.　Natural catalysts are softer and are therefore destroyed more rapidly than most synthetic catalysts. Obviously, the catalyst for the Fluid process must exhibit such a size distribution that it fluidizes properly.　For a natural catalyst, the percentage of 0 to 80 microns material should be kept above 50 (preferably 75) and the 0 to 40 microns material above 15 per cent (preferably 25). Cyclone separators often behave erratically, but will usually retain particles larger than 10 microns in both reactor and regenerator service. Natural fluid catalyst contains some particles that are oblong rather

　[61] Thornton, D. P., Jr., Fluid Cat . . . Use New MS Catalyst, *Pet. Processing*, March, 1947, p. 173.
　[62] Nelson, W. L., What Is a Good Catalyst, *Oil Gas J.*, Apr. 28, 1949, p. 120; see also Mar. 17, 1949, p. 162.
　[62a] Beyler et al., *Oil Gas J.*, June 3, 1957, p. 95.

than round, and hence the average-size particle that passes through a screen has an average diameter that is about 20 per cent larger than the screen opening.

New catalyst is offered in various grades, depending on particle size, as 50/60 (light) or 75/85. Catalytic activity is vital, but in addition all cracking catalysts are strongly adsorptive. Tables 10-4 to 10-6 show the physical properties of common catalytic and adsorptive materials.

Catalytic activity is measured by determining the behavior of the catalyst in laboratory-scale equipment at standardized conditions for each test method, measuring especially the production of gas and distillate, although carbon deposition and other results are also noted in most methods. Of the numerous methods[63] (at least 14), the Houdry Cat. A, Jersey $D + L$, and UOP activity rating are probably the most widely used. The approximate relation between these is indicated in Table 21-12.

The amount of distillate and gas loss $(D + L)$ is reported in several tests, and this amounts simply to the conversion for the standard conditions of the test. Stabilizing and deactivation treatments using high temperature steam are employed prior to the evaluation of fresh catalyst. Pore volume, pore radius, and surface area measurements are useful in following the changes that occur in a catalyst during use,[64] but such measurements are not a substitute for activity determinations nor studies of the selectivity of the catalyst. Catalysts of the same activity often behave differently with regard to selectivity, i.e., the proportions among gaseous components (especially the hydrogen), amount of coke, gasoline, etc.

Centrifugal separators (cyclones) are most widely used to retain the powdered catalyst in the regenerator and reactor, but electrostatic precipitators (Cottrell) are also used, especially in older plants. The sizes of particles handled by various entrainment separators are approximately as follows:[65]

Micron size

Electrostatic precipitators	0.01–20 (smoke and fume)
Scrubbers	0.6–200 (mist and spray)
Packed beds	0.5–100
Cyclones	4–1,000 (dust and spray)
Gravity settling chambers	80–10,000

The behavior of cyclones is erratic, but Montross[65] outlines theoretical design methods of estimating the smallest-size retention, the range of

[63] Sittig, M. (A review of catalytic cracking), *Pet. Refiner*, September, 1952, pp. 265–316.

[64] Mills and Shabaker, *Pet. Refiner*, September, 1951, p. 97.

[65] Montross, C. F., Entrainment Separation, *Chem. Eng.*, October, 1953, pp. 213–236.

particle sizes that are retained, effect of velocity, and gas and solid densities. Percentage efficiency curves (percentage of each particle size retained) vary widely because of the many operating variables such as size distribution, velocity, etc., but behavior is somewhat as shown in Table 21-13. Regenerator cyclones behave less well than reactor cyclones because of the lower density of the gases. Thus with coarse catalyst

TABLE 21-12. APPROXIMATE RELATIONSHIP BETWEEN VARIOUS CATALYST
ACTIVITY RATINGS[a]

	Activity ratings corresponding to these AGC[a] weight activities[b]								
	10	15	20	25	30	35	40	50	60
Shell surface area, m²/g:									
25% Al₂O₃, fresh	38	.....	77	.....	116				
25% Al₂O₃, equilibrium	43	.....	86	.....	128				
13% Al₂O₃, fresh	50	.....	100	.....	150				
13% Al₂O₃, equilibrium	53	.....	107	.....	158				
UOP weight activity	19.5	24	28	33	37.5	42	46.5	55.5	65
Texas $D + L$ activity	13	17	20	23	25.5	27.5	29.5	33	35.5
Jersey $D + L$ activity:									
0.4 bulk density	13.5	17	20.5	23	25.5	27	29.5	33	35.5
0.6 bulk density	16.5	21	25	28	31	33	35	39	42
0.8 bulk density	21	25.5	29	32.5	35.5	38.5	40.5	44	47
Cat. A Houdry activity	20.5	25.5	29.5	32.5	36	38	40	43	
Indiana relative activity	0.12	0.19	0.26	0.34	0.42	0.505	0.59	0.77	0.97
Phillips conversion	36	41.5	46	50	54	57.5	60.5	65.5	69
UOP volume activity:[c]									
0.4 bulk density	16	19	22	26	30	34	37	44	52
0.6 bulk density	23	29	34	40	45	50	56	67	78
0.8 bulk density	31	38	45	53	60	67	74	89	
Atlantic $D + L$ activity	49	57	63	67.5	71.5	74.5	77	82	

[a] The letters AGC of the American Cyanamid Co. mean "activity, gas, and coke."
[b] Mainly from American Cyanamid Co. release of May, 1957, entitled "Activity of Synthetic Fluid Cracking Catalyst," but other sources used for Cat. A Houdry method.
[c] Volume activity = 2 times UOP wt activity times bulk density.

(65 per cent over 40 microns) a reactor cyclone may recover 99 per cent of the catalyst, whereas a regenerator cyclone only 57 per cent (and with fine catalyst containing 95 per cent under 20 microns, the recoveries are only 63 and 51 per cent). Saving of catalyst is important, but cyclones and precipitators should also retain a distribution of catalyst that fluidizes properly, and this means mainly the retention of so-called fines. Thus, an effort is made to retain catalyst even if some is later discarded in-order to maintain catalyst activity. In a few plants, elutriation methods have been used to eliminate too coarse particles, and in at least one plant[66] the

[66] Viland, C. K., Gravity Separation of Inactive Catalyst, *Oil Gas J.*, Nov. 30, 1950, p. 74.

heavy, coarse particles have been separated by a gravity-classification system.

The common catalysts lose most of their activity at the following temperatures[58]: Super Filtrol natural, 1400°F; silica-alumina synthetic, 2000°F; silica-magnesia, 1400°F; and silica-boria, 1400°F. However, in practice, regeneration temperatures are kept below 1000 to 1100 or 1150°F[67,68,69,70] except bauxite which may be regenerated at even 1300°F without appreciable loss in activity. All catalysts lose some activity upon long use. The decline is particularly noticeable with natural catalyst processing sour stocks[51,52] and even the excellent catalyst cases of the Houdry process allow some decline in activity over a period of a

TABLE 21-13. EFFICIENCY OF RECOVERY BY CYCLONES

Particle size, microns	Electrical precipitator	Percentage efficiency		
		Single-stage cyclones		2-stage cyclone (design)
		Design	Commercial[a]	
5	. . . .	Up to 82	49–66	92
10	99.5	77–93	72–85	99 −
20	99.2	97–99	93–99	99 +
30	99.45	. . . . .	99–100	

[a] Three commercial units; the lowest values for a regenerator.

year.[60] In the fixed-bed processes, the catalyst is removed at intervals, and in the circulation-type systems, a portion of the catalyst is currently replaced with new catalyst to maintain an optimum activity of catalyst. In the T.C.C. process the mechanical loss of clay catalyst may not exceed 0.15 lb per bbl handled,[70] but attritions of 0.2 to 0.4 are more common[21] (the average for all units during 1956 except newly installed ones was 0.27 lb per bbl feed). Thus, a plant operating at a recycle ratio of 1.5:1 might consume 0.4 lb catalyst per bbl fresh feed. The smallest or most worn pellets are the least active, and hence it is possible to discard only the least effective catalyst. Contamination by metallic poisons is not as troublesome in the moving-bed processes[71] as in the Fluid process

[67] Newton and Shimp, The Design . . . of Houdry Fixed Bed Catalytic Cracking Units, *Trans. A.I.Ch.E.*, **41**, 197 (1945).

[68] Snuggs, J. F., Regeneration of Spent Catalyst in Fluid Catalytic Cracking, *Oil Gas J.*, Mar. 15, 1947, p. 88.

[69] Hagerbaumer and Lee, Combustion of (T.C.C.) Coke Deposits . . . , *Oil Gas J.*, Mar. 15, 1947, p. 76.

[70] Bland and Smith, Earnings—A Function of Catalyst Activity, *Pet. Engr.*, August, 1946, p. 55.

[71] McEvoy et al., Distribution of Metal . . . , ACS Meeting, Dallas, Apr. 8, 1956.

because the metals are found in the outermost layer of the bead.   Thus much of the contaminated catalyst is eliminated as dust.   During early development of the Fluid process, elaborate equipment was installed to ensure a small loss to the regenerator flue gas.   Most plants now employ only cyclones but in two and sometimes more stages.   Losses in the Fluid process are not as vital as once thought because a makeup of 0.3 to 0.6 lb per bbl fresh feed is usually necessary for maintenance of activity.   Loss of fine catalyst from the reactor appears in the small

TABLE 21-14. COMPARISONS[a] OF FLUID CATALYSTS IN ONCE-THROUGH OPERATIONS AT 60 PER CENT CONVERSION[b]

	Silica alumina	Activated natural	Silica magnesia	Synthetic		Natural	
				13% alumina	Silica magnesia	Grade 53	S.R.
Conversion.............	60	60	60	60	60	60	60
Temperature...........	975	975	975	930	930	930	930
Cat. to oil ratio.........	9–12	7–10	6–10				
Gaso., 10 R.v.p., vol. %.	45.5	47.8	56.2	46.9	57.2	49.3	49.0
Carbon, wt %..........	2.9	3.1	2.9	3.4	3.4	3.6	3.4
Dry gas, wt %.........	9.0	8.7	6.2	6.4	5.0	7.0	6.8
Butanes, vol. %........	7.0	4.8	3.6	9.0	5.1	6.9	7.8
Butenes, vol. %........	9.0	9.2	6.4	7.0	4.9	7.1	6.3
Oct. No.—10 R.v.p.:							
F-1 Clear.............	95	93.6	91.5	93.7	90.3	89.9	92.8
F-2 Clear.............	81.6	79.8	79.2	81.0	78.6	79.2	80.5

[a] Gohr, E. J., Advances in Fluid Cat. Cracking, *Proc. Fourth World Pet. Congr.,* sec. III, Rome, 1955; and E. V. Murphree, Fluid Cat. Cracking Process, "Progress in Pet. Technology," ACS Meeting, New York, September, 1951.

[b] Feedstock 29–29.4 API, ASTM 50% at 701°F.

heavy portion of cycle oil known as slurry oil.[72]   This is often returned to the reactor because the fine catalyst is valuable, but the low-gravity slurry oil tends to cause a larger carbon deposition.   The fixed-bed processes can operate with extremely low physical losses of catalyst (under 0.1 lb per bbl), the circulation processes lose more catalyst (0.15 to 0.7 lb), and, of course, all of the catalyst in the Suspensoid process is rejected (2 to 3 lb).[7]

Natural catalysts are the cheapest (under $100 per ton, as against $300 or more for synthetic types), they cause a slightly larger carbon deposit,[57] and the gasoline produced by them has a lower octane number (1 to 4 units).   Yields are, however, slightly larger with natural catalyst.

[72] Moorman, J. H., Slurry Recycle and Slurry Settling, *Oil Gas J.,* Aug. 22, 1955, p. 128.

Synthetic catalyst produces gasolines of slightly lower boiling range (5 to 8°F at 50 per cent point) and gasolines whose lead susceptibility is slightly better. The less used silica-magnesia type of catalyst behaves somewhat like natural catalyst (see Table 21-14)[73,74] with respect to octane number, but it produces very large gasoline yields.

Regeneration. The amount and kind of carbon deposited on the catalyst is highly important with respect to operation and particularly the economy of the process. However, a very low carbon deposition is not altogether advantageous, because the deposit must contain at least enough heating value to burn or regenerate the catalyst properly. The specific heat of the catalyst varies somewhat but is generally of the magnitude of 0.25 Btu per pound per degree Fahrenheit (see Table 10-5). Likewise, the so-called "carbon" on the catalyst is not pure carbon, but may contain 7 to 15 per cent hydrogen (about 10 per cent for design purposes) in Fluid process deposits,[68] or 2.5 to 8 per cent (average 5 per cent) in moving-bed deposits.[68,75] This indicates gross heating values for the carbon laydown of 16,000 to 18,000 Btu per lb, but under regenerator combustion conditions the deposit is seldom burned completely to carbon dioxide and water, and hence only the heating values given by Eq. (21-2) are possible.[69]

$$\text{Net H.V.} = 4,100 + 10,100 \left(\frac{CO_2}{CO_2 + CO} \right) + 3,370 \ (H/C) \qquad (21\text{-}2)$$

The H/C ratio is the atomic ratio (12 times the weight ratio), and the CO_2 and CO refer to the relative volumes of these gases in the flue gas. Equation (21-2) was obtained from experimental heat balance data and it does not check precisely with the following computed net heating values:[69,75]

CO_2/CO mole ratio	Heat of regeneration, Btu/lb deposit for these percentages of hydrogen		
	4.3[75]	8[69]	12[69]
0	7,200		
1	12,450	12,440	14,140
2	14,000	13,840*	15,480*
4	15,300		
10	16,350		

* Ratio of 1.85 rather than 2.0.

[73] Gohr, E. J., Advances in Fluid Cat. Cracking, *Proc. Fourth World Pet. Congr.*, sec. III, Rome, 1955.

[74] Murphree, E. V., Fluid Cat. Cracking Process, "Progress in Pet. Technology," ACS Meeting, New York, September, 1951.

[75] Dart and Oblad, Heat of Cracking and Regeneration . . . , *Chem. Eng. Progr.*, February, 1949, p. 110.

The ratio of CO_2/CO is widely used rather than $CO_2/(CO_2 + CO)$ and the corresponding values are:

CO_2/CO	$CO_2/(CO_2 + CO)$
0.5	0.334
1.0	0.5
2.0	0.667
3.0	0.75
4.0	0.80
6.0	0.856
10.0	0.91

The ratio of CO_2 to $(CO_2 + CO)$ in Fluid units ranges[68] between 0.5 (synthetic) and 0.65 (natural), and Hagerbaumer and Lee[69] for T.C.C. operation (apparently with average carbon deposits of 1.5 to 3.0 per cent of catalyst) present the data of Table 21-15. The catalyst during regen-

TABLE 21-15. APPROXIMATE CARBON DIOXIDE, CARBON MONOXIDE RATIOS IN T.C.C. FLUE GAS[a]

Mean catalyst tempera-ture	The ratio $CO_2/(CO_2 + CO)$ for these air rates (cu ft per min, per cu ft of 43.6 lb catalyst)				
	1	2	4	8	12
800	0.685	0.670	0.645	0.635	0.630
900	0.679	0.647	0.615	0.590	0.567
1000	0.672	0.624	0.585	0.545	0.504
1100	0.665	0.600	0.555	0.500	0.440

[a] Hagerbaumer and Lee, Combustion of (T.C.C.) Coke Deposits . . . , Oil Gas J., Mar. 15, 1947, p. 76.

eration is not entirely freed of deposit. At low carbon deposits (2 to 4 per cent) about 25 per cent of the carbon remains after burning and it is recycled with the catalyst. However, the carbon so cycled seems to age and tends to destroy the catalyst activity, and so an effort is made to keep the residual carbon below 0.9 per cent (the average is probably not higher than 0.5 per cent). A minimum temperature of 900°F is required to burn T.C.C. catalyst,[76] and regeneration temperatures usually range from 1000 to 1150°F.

The amount of air required is related to the $CO_2/(CO_2 + CO)$ ratio somewhat as shown in Table 21-16.

The specific gravity of bead catalyst is about 2.37 to 2.42 (Table 10-4) and fluidized catalyst 1.3 to 1.8, the higher value being for used or nearly spent catalyst. The bulk density of bead catalyst ranges from 40 to

[76] Newton, Dunham, and Simpson, The T.C.C. Catalytic Cracking Process . . . , Oil Gas J., June 2, 1945, p. 84.

TABLE 21-16. AIR REQUIRED FOR REGENERATOR COMBUSTION

Ratio $CO_2/(CO_2 + CO)$	Hydrogen in deposit		Combustion air, lb per lb deposit
	Weight, per cent	Atomic H/C	
50	4	0.50	10.92
50	8	1.04	12.05
50	12	1.63	13.18
65	4	0.50	11.82
65	8	1.04	12.92
65	12	1.63	14.02

50 lb per cu ft and the bed density of fluidized catalyst is somewhat a function of the average particle size:[77]

Avg diameter, microns	Bed density, lb per cu ft, for these particle specific gravities	
	2.0	1.5
25	22	15
40	28	19
60	35	24
80	41	27

Such bed densities are obtained at velocities of 1 to 2 ft per sec.[68] The depth of fluidized bed is usually limited to 15 ft[77] so that the load on the cyclones is not excessive but the real limit is the disengaging space, which should be about 15 ft or more. The pounds of dust per cubic foot of exit gas according to Brown and Wainright[77] remains constant at about 0.002 at bed velocities up to a critical velocity of 1.5 ft per sec, whereupon it rises rapidly at higher velocities to 0.01 lb dust at 1.8 ft per sec. Another refiner has a limiting velocity of 2.2 ft per sec. In the moving-bed processes, the total carbon burnoff is limited to some extent by the rate of heat removal through the water cooling tubes[67] and by the maximum allowable rate of catalyst circulation.

Air preheat temperatures vary widely depending on the amount of catalyst recirculation and the carbon laydown. If the laydown is very large or the catalyst to oil ratio is large (8 to 20 lb catalyst per lb oil), the air may require little or no preheat whereas at low recirculations (2 to 5) the air must be heated to 700 to 1100°F. Catalyst to oil ratios

[77] Brown and Wainright, Synthetic Fluid Cracking Catalyst, *Oil Gas J.*, Dec. 1, 1952, p. 133.

in the Fluid process range from 6 to 16 (as high as 25 in some World War II plants) and in the moving-bed processes from 2 to 5.

The pressure in regenerators is always low (0 to 10 psig) and especially low in the largest regenerators of the Fluid process.[78] In the Houdry fixed-bed process, the pressure can be as high as 40 psig, in the Houdriflow process 1 to 3 psig, and in the highest pressure Fluid regenerators, about 10 psig.

The coke deposition can be obtained from Figs. 21-3 to 21-5, but the average depositions are about as shown in Table 21-17.

The heat of adsorption (or desorption) of water on T.C.C. catalyst is stated by Newton et al.[76] to be 1,580 Btu per pound of water, but per pound of catalyst the heat of desorption (Table 10-6) is very small.

TABLE 21-17. AVERAGE CARBON DEPOSITION
Weight per cent of feed

Percentage conversion	Cycloversion[a]	Fluid	Houdry[a]	Moving-bed
40	1.0	2.5	4.0	2.2
50	1.2	3.7	4.8	3.1
60	1.9	5.3	5.5	4.3
70	3.3	7.2	6.2[b]	5.9
80	...	10.0	....	7.7

[a] Nelson, W. L., p. 673 of the Third Edition of this book, and Oil Gas J., Aug. 30, 1947, p. 67.
[b] Extrapolated beyond data.

Example 21-4. Regenerator Heat Balance. Example 21-1 will be continued by determining the heat balance of the regenerator. If the 5.15 weight per cent of carbon is to be burned to produce a flue gas containing one part of CO_2 per one part of CO, and it contains 10 per cent of hydrogen, it will have a net heating value [Eq. (21-2)] of:

$$\text{Net H.V.} = 4,100 + 10,000 \left(\frac{1}{1+1}\right) + 3,370 \frac{10/1}{90/12} = 13,650$$

As a check, using the heating values of Table 14-5:

$$
\begin{array}{rcl}
0.45 \times 14,600 &=& 6,560 \\
0.45 \times 4,400 &=& 1,980 \\
0.1 \times (61,400 - 1\frac{8}{9} \times 1058) &=& 5,190 \\
\hline
&& 13,730
\end{array}
$$

Thus, the heat available for heating the air and catalyst per 100 lb of feedstock is:

$$5.15 \times 13,650 = 70,300 \text{ Btu}$$

[78] Murphree et al., Improved Fluid Process . . . , Trans. A.I.Ch.E., **41**, 19 (1945).

The amount of air required (Table 21-16) is about:

$$5.15 \times 12.61 = 65 \text{ lb per } 100 \text{ lb feed}$$

If the air is not preheated (60°F), reaction is conducted at 925°F, and regeneration at 1160°F:

Heat available (total)	$= 70,300$ Btu
Heat air $\dfrac{65}{28.8}(7,300 - 200)$	$= 16,000$ (Fig. 14-1)
Available to heat catalyst (neglecting losses)	$= 54,300$ Btu

(Catalyst equilibrium) circulation $\dfrac{54,300}{1/.993(1160 - 925)0.25} = 918$ lb per 100 lb oil feed

This is a cat./oil ratio of 9.18, and the total weight of carbon (including the 0.7% of residual carbon) on the equilibrium or carbon-laden catalyst is:

$$100 \left(\frac{0.0515 \times 100 + 9.18 \times 0.007}{918} \right) = 1.26 \text{ per cent}$$

The circulation of pure catalyst is lower than 9.18 by the amount of carbon recycled on the catalyst or $9.18 - (0.007 \times 9.2) = 9.12$
The heat of desorption of steam was neglected in this balance.

The large amount of combustible carbon monoxide in the flue gases sometimes leads to after-burning in the disengaging space and cyclones of Fluid regenerators. Such fires are put out by means of steam or water, and the best safeguard seems to be to keep the excess air low (oxygen below 0.5 to 1 per cent in the flue gas), and to keep the regenerator temperature low (below about 1130°F). Adjustment of the regenerator temperature is also accomplished by the introduction of steam or water, and by circulation of the catalyst through a heat exchanger. In moving-bed kilns, water may be circulated through tubes.

The large amount of sensible heat as well as carbon monoxide in regenerator gases has led to the installation of special waste-heat boilers in which the dilute flue gas is burned by the aid of oxidation catalysts.[79]

Reactor Operation. The heat in the regenerated catalyst assists in supplying the heat of reaction and the heat required to raise the temperature of the incoming feedstock to the reaction temperature.

Octane number is probably affected more by the reaction temperature than by any other variable. The trend of octane number is indicated in Table 21-5 for a fixed percentage conversion. Similar data are given for the Fluid process alone by Murphree and associates,[78] and for the T.C.C. process alone by Noll and associates.[80] Table 21-5 does not apply directly to Cycloversion, Suspensoid, or Hydroforming operations, but the general trend is the same.

The Houdry process generally operates at 830 to 900°F, the Fluid

[79] Campbell and Pennels, CO Boiler . . . , *Oil Gas J.*, Feb. 22, 1944, p. 132.
[80] Noll et al., Thermofor Cat. Cracking, *Oil Gas J.*, May 10, 1947, p. 64.

process at 900 to 960°F, the T.C.C. process[69] at 830 to 930°F, and the Cycloversion process at 980 to 1020°F. The yield of 10 Reid vapor pressure gasoline is not greatly altered by reactor temperature[80] because the yield of propylene and butylenes increases rapidly thus increasing the yield of poly gasoline, but at about 875°F the T.C.C. process is most economical.[80]

The effect of percentage conversion on yields has already been mentioned under the heading of Yields. In addition, octane numbers are higher by one or two units when raising the once-through conversion from 55 to 65 per cent. Schulze and Helmars[81] discuss the effect of percentage conversion on the Cycloversion process.

Computed heats of reaction are not adequate because of the great accuracy required in yields and in the properties of the products. Thus, in Example 21-5 the computed heat of decomposition is 623 Btu per lb of gasoline and lighter materials, a value apparently 100 per cent high. Furthermore, had the Characterization Factor of the gasoline been assumed as 11.7 and the heat of combustion of the feedstock 19,450, the computed heat of reaction would then have been the impossibly high value of 825. It is therefore necessary to rely on approximations from the literature and especially the carefully conducted experiments of Dart and Oblad[75] on the Houdriflow process. Their smoothed data and a few suggestions and computations[82] from the literature are shown in Table 21-18. However, it must be mentioned that commercial T.C.C. operations appear to substantiate lower heats of reaction than those of Dart and Oblad. If computations of heats of reaction are undertaken, the following average heats of combustion (Btu per lb) may be useful:[83]

	Ethane and lighter	Propane and lighter	B-B cut
Fluid process..........	24,130	21,922	21,069
Houdry..............	......	21,912	21,186
T.C.C...............	......	22,112	21,101
Average.............	......	21,940	21,140

Although the same basic method of computing heats of reaction can be used for the Hydroforming[84] and platinum catalyst processes, it is not possible from the data given in this book to estimate properly the heating values of the highly aromatic products of these processes. The formation

---

[81] Gas Oil Cracking by the Cycloversion Process, *Oil Gas J.*, Apr. 13, 1944, p. 225.

[82] Nelson, W. L., *Oil Gas J.*, Jan. 26, 1950, p. 355; and Nov. 10, 1949, p. 376.

[83] Nelson, W. L., *Oil Gas J.*, Sept. 22, p. 297, and Sept. 29, p. 90, 1949.

[84] Gornowski and Feldbauer, . . . Heat of Reaction in Catalytic Reforming, ACS Meeting, Dallas, Apr. 8, 1956.

of aromatics is an endothermic reaction whereas hydrocracking reactions are exothermic. This leads[84] to heats of reaction ranging from about 125 Btu per lb feed for the least severity (80 Research o.n.) to as high as 400 Btu for the most severe operations (96 Research o.n.).

TABLE 21-18. APPROXIMATE HEAT OF REACTION
Btu per pound gasoline and lighter materials

Percentage conversion	Dart and Oblad[a]	Others
35	300	
40	285	
....	...	245[b]
50	250	
56	222	95[c] and 100[c]
....	...	90–120[d]
59.1	205	221[e]–399[d]
60	200	
70	135	
80	55	
....	...	112[d]

[a] *Chem. Eng. Progr.*, February, 1949, p. 110.
[b] Computed in Third Edition of this book.
[c] Used by two Fluid plant operators.
[d] Nelson, W. L., *Oil Gas J.*, Nov. 10, 1949, p. 376.; and Jan. 26, 1950, p. 355.
[e] Fluid process (computed).

Example 21-5. Heat of Reaction. The charge stock and yields of Examples 21-3 and 21-1 will be used to compute the heat of reaction (at 60°F).

The Characterization Factor of the gasoline will be 11.5 and of the cycle oil, 11.4 (see Table 21-7). Heats of combustion may then be read from Fig. 5-22, which possibly gives too high values because Characterization Factor does not properly account for the aromatic hydrocarbons in these materials. Other heats of combustion may be read from the tabulation on page 794 or Tables 5-2 and 5-3. The heat of combustion of the coke deposit can be computed from Table 14-5. The energy contents of the feed and the products are computed in Table 21-19.

Thus, the products contain about 330 more Btu of energy than the feed, leading to a heat of reaction based on gasoline and lighter materials of:

$$330 \div 0.53 = 623 \text{ Btu per lb gasoline and lighter}$$

This is apparently over twice as large as it should be (see Table 21-18), and the error arises because the properties (and yields) of the products are not precise.

Fluid reactor beds operate much as regenerator beds. The linear gas velocity is 1 to 2 ft per sec with a critical velocity past which large amounts of dust escape to the cyclones. The density of the fluidized bed ranges from 20 to 40 lb per cu ft and depths up to about 30 ft are maintained. A disengaging space of about 15 ft is employed.

The hot catalyst furnishes some heat to the oil charge; but unless the rate of catalyst recirculation is large, the feedstock must be heated. If the catalyst has been contacted with steam, it contains adsorbed water which requires about 1,580 Btu per lb for removal. Newton et al.[76] indicate about 78.3 lb adsorbed water per ton of catalyst.

TABLE 21-19. COMPUTATIONS FOR EXAMPLE 21-5.

Material	Weight per cent	API	UOP factor	Gross heat of combustion, Btu per lb	Gross H.V., Btu per lb feed	
Coke..............	5.1	....	....	19,270	983	983
Ethane and lighter..	2.5	....	....	24,130	603	
Propylene.........	3.8	....	....	21,060	800	
Propane..........	1.6	....	....	21,690	347	
Dry gas...........	7.9	....	....	21,922	1,750	1,732
Butylenes.........	3.8	....	....	20,690	786	
Isobutane.........	4.7	....	....	21,290	1,001	
Butane..........	0.7	....	....	21,340	149	
B-B cut............	9.2	....	....	21,140	1,936	1,945
Gasoline...........	35.9	52.5	11.5	19,830	7,119	7,119
Cycle stock.........	41.9	28.1	11.4	19,210	8,049	8,049
Total products...	.....	....	....	......	19,837	19,828
Feed..............	100.0	30.0	11.9	19,500		

Example 21-6. Reactor Heat Balance. The stock of Examples 21-3 and 21-1 will be cracked. The amount of recirculation was found to be 9.18 in Example 21-4 and this is different from the original assumption of 8 which was used in Example 21-1 in determining yields. A heat of reaction of 200 (Table 21-18) will be used. The size of the reactor will not be computed, and the heat loss through the walls (under 0.5 per cent) will be neglected.

Basis: 100 lb feed.

Heat delivered by catalyst = 918(1160 − 925)0.25 = 54,000 Btu per hr
Heat of reaction = 53 × 200   = 10,600
    Available for heating feed   = 43,400 Btu per hr

The heat content (Fig. 5-3) of the feed at 925°F is 665 Btu per lb and the content at the inlet temperature to the reactor is:

$$\frac{43,400}{100} = (665 - x) \qquad x = 231 \text{ Btu per lb}$$

This corresponds to a feed temperature of about 432°F.

The handling of bead catalyst through orifices, etc., of the Thermofor process is discussed by Newton et al.[76] and Hagerbaumer and Lee.[69] The rate at which powdered catalysts settle through a rising stream of gas, as in the regenerator or the reactor of the Fluid process, is apparently more rapid than indicated by Stokes's law for the free settling of particles.[77,78] Murphree et al.[78] state that 0.5 per cent of the catalyst recirculation should be lost in commercial operations to maintain a proper activity. This indicates that particles of about 10-micron diameter must be retained. The average particle size usually ranges from 45 to 70 microns. Parent, Yagol, and Steiner[85] find that fluidization occurs at lower velocities (one-third and even one-thirty-eighth) than the "free-fall" velocity of the finest particles in the mixtures. Cyclones, Cottrell precipitators, and scrubbers are used to recover the fine particles carried out with the gas stream. Fluid-process reactors are normally held at 8 to 12 psig.

TABLE 21-20. FLOW RATES AND DENSITIES IN FLUIDIZED SYSTEMS

Location	Density, lb per cu ft	Gas velocity, ft per sec
Dense phase (beds)..............	13–40[a]	1–2
Standpipes (downflow)..........	15–30	2–7
Risers........................	1.5–5	15[b]–40
Handling......................	0.2–1.0	30–40
Vapor lines...................	....	90–115

[a] See page 791 for effect of average particle size.
[b] 15 ft per sec is frequently called a minimum.

The catalyst is saturated with oil during the reaction, and this must be removed by stripping with superheated steam or hot flue gas. Little specific information on stripping appears in the literature, but it is vital, particularly in the Fluid process.

The rate of carbon formation[86] is somewhat less rapid in Fluid catalyst cracking than in fixed-bed cracking, and the rate with synthetic catalyst is slower than with natural catalyst. During 10 min Fluid catalyst accumulated 0.8 to 1.3 per cent carbon whereas fixed-bed catalyst accumulated 1.7 to 2.2 per cent carbon.

Fluidization Mechanics. Regenerators and reactors behave very much the same, and common flow rates and densities are indicated in Table 21-20. Fluidization may be maintained (see Fig. 21-1) at velocities of 1 to 2 ft per sec, but at some limiting velocity (1.5 to 2.2) fine catalyst tends suddenly to be carried upwards out of the bed to the cyclones. If downward movement is desired as in standpipes, a higher gas velocity is maintained (2 to 7) so that packing of the catalyst does

[85] Fluidizing Processes, *Chem. Eng. Progr.*, **43**, 429 (1947).

[86] Voorhies, A., Carbon Formation in Catalytic Cracking, *Ind. Eng. Chem.*, April, 1945.

not occur, and to care for the greater pressure toward the foot of the standpipe. If the downward movement is appreciable (2 ft per sec) the aeration medium tends to move downward with the catalyst and be compressed.[87] This is offset by aeration at several levels to maintain a fluidized state even though the gas is constantly shrinking in volume. At very low rates of downward flow, the gas tends to pass upward through the catalyst giving variations in density. Aeration is, however, held to a minimum because erosion in the standpipe and slide valves is thought to increase in proportion to the third power of velocity.

The lowest point in the standpipe-riser system is the point of greatest pressure (or tendency toward movement). Referring to Fig. 21-1a the dense phase in the regenerator standpipe stands at such a level that it more than balances the weight of the dilute phase in the riser, the part of the reactor bed above the riser outlet, and the greater pressure (usually) in the reactor vapor space. Flow is permitted by opening or closing of the slide valve, while always maintaining by aeration the proper densities in each part of the system. In the riser, a high aeration velocity (15 to 40 ft per sec) must be maintained so that no parts of the catalyst can fall back through the gas stream. The minimum velocity to avoid slump back, slugging, or even plugging is about 15 ft per sec. A pressure differential of 3 to 6 psi (or more) is maintained across the slide valve, and two valves are usually installed so that operation can be continued after one valve becomes worn.

The carrier medium moves at a higher velocity than the catalyst particles and thus a slip factor that cannot easily be evaluated must be introduced. Some allowance in the density must be made, and usual design practice is to set the slip at 2:1, i.e., double the density calculated from the amount of gas and catalyst flowing. Densities in the carrier or riser lines are usually held under 5 lb per cu ft (neglecting slip).

PROCESSES

Only the barest process information can be given here because of the numerous improvements that are still occurring. The Fluid process dominates the domestic installed capacity, but the T.C.C. process is used almost as much as the Fluid process in foreign plants. Thermal cracking has rapidly been relegated to the position of a secondary process used for the viscosity breaking and coking of residual materials, and to some extent the cracking of catalytic cycle stocks. Approximate operating conditions for the major processes are indicated in Table 21-21 (see Table 21-24 for reforming processes).

[87] Nelson, W. L., Circulation Control in Fluid Process, *Oil Gas J.*, Apr. 14, 1949, p. 120.

TABLE 21-21. APPROXIMATE OPERATING CONDITIONS FOR THE MAJOR CATALYTIC CRACKING PROCESSES

	Houdry	T.C.C.	Houdri-flow	Fluid	Cyclo-version
Reactor temp, °F	840–900	780–950	850–925	885–975	980–1050
Reactor (top) pressure, psig	7–30	10–15	5–10	9–18	35–100
Cat. to oil ratio		2–5	3–7	8–20	
Space velocity, V/V-hr	0.75–1.5	1–3.5	1.5–4	1–3	2–4
Average recycle ratio, (1955)		0.25		0.18	
Regenerator, temp, °F	850–900	960–1080	700–1100	1050–1150	1200
Regenerator, pressure, psig	20–50	Atm. to 1	Atm.	5–10	
Regenerator, air temp, °F	700–800	Atm. to 1000			800–850
Onstream time	10 min	Continuous	Continuous	Continuous	3–10 hr
Catalyst shape	Beads	Beads	Beads	300-mesh powder	Beads
Hydrogen, % of coke	2–7	2.5–8	2.5–8	7–15	
Catalyst replacement and loss, lb per bbl processed	0.3–0.5	0.15–0.5	0.2–0.5	0.2–0.6	Nil

Houdry Fixed-bed. Although this process has now been replaced to a large extent, it was the first (1937) truly successful process and it illustrates the full development of a fixed-bed type of process (Fig. 21-8).

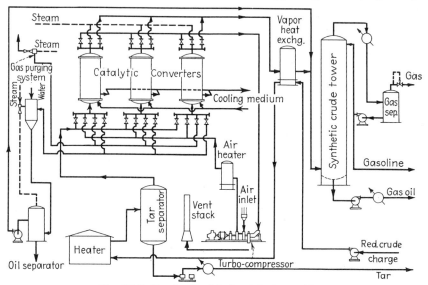

FIG. 21-8. Houdry fixed-bed catalytic cracking.

Vapor from the tar separator or a vaporizer is mixed with steam and is admitted to the reaction chambers at 840 to 860°F. Passage through the chamber is continued for about 10 minutes. By this time the pores and surfaces of the catalyst have been covered with a thin film of carbon, and the catalyst must be regenerated. The entire cycle is about as follows:

1. Onstream—10 min.
2. Oil and vapor purge by venting to a condenser and steam-jet evacuation system—5 min.
3. Regeneration with preheated air—10 min.
4. Air purge by steam-jet ejectors—5 min.

All operations are automatic, even to the opening and closing of valves.[88] Air is supplied by a centrifugal multistage compressor directly coupled to a gas turbine.[89] Compressed air (350°F) at 50 lb gauge pressure is preheated to 700 to 800°F and admitted to the chambers. The flue gases issue from the chamber at 850 to 950°F, having absorbed enough heat energy to operate the gas turbine used in compressing the air.

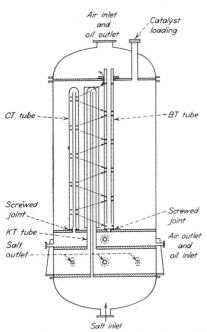

During this cycle the heat of reaction must be provided during the onstream phase and the heat generation during regeneration or burning with air must be removed. These conditions are met by recycling a mixture of molten salts which tends to keep the reaction temperature up to about 850°F and the regeneration temperature down to 950°F. The net result is an excess of heat which may be used to produce high-pressure superheated steam. The chamber or case[90] indicated in Fig. 21-9 contains bayonet-type salt tubes (K.T.) and regenerating tubes (C.T.), and B.T. tubes for conducting air into the bed or delivering cracked vapors to the outlet. Holes are provided in the outer C.T. and B.T. tubes for distributing air or oil throughout the length of the case. Catalyst surrounds the tubes, and metal fins on the K.T. and C.T. tubes extend to within about ½ in. of any part of the

FIG. 21-9. Longitudinal section of a modified design of Houdry reactor. (*Oil Gas J.*)

[88] Tuttle, R. B., Houdry Cycle-timing System, *Oil Gas J.*, Feb. 24, 1945, p. 120.
[89] Evans and Lassiat, Combustion-gas Turbine . . . , *Pet. Refiner*, November, 1945, p. 135.
[90] Lassiat and Thayer, Improved Design of Houdry Reactor . . . , *Oil Gas J.*, Aug. 3, 1946, p. 84.

catalyst mass. Cases hold about 34,000 liters of catalyst weighing about 21 tons.

Regular Houdry clay pellets have lasted more than 18 months.[90] Newer catalysts[60] contain some high-thermal-conductivity material to assist in heat flow, and T.C.C. beads are being used because of their mechanical stability. Catalyst costs are less than 2 cents per barrel processed. New catalyst is very active, and hence process steam is introduced and then reduced in amount as the run proceeds. Increase in pressure from the usual 10 psig to 70 psig increases the gasoline yield, but the yields of gas and coke increase even more rapidly.

Yields are generally in agreement with Figs. 21-3 to 21-5, being similar to those of the moving-bed processes, i.e., lower coke deposits (8 to 11 per cent) and more gasoline (1 to 4 per cent) than shown in Fig. 21-3. The process was also used during World War II for the dehydrogenation of butane, isobutane, and butene.[91]

Fluid Catalytic Cracking (F.C.C.). The Model IV design of Fig. 21-1a is used for most large plants, but Fig. 21-10 which is discussed here, illustrates the smaller Orthoflow[92,93] type. It was designed to charge 8,350 bpd of 30 API West Kansas gas oil plus 31 per cent (2,589 bpd) of recycle, giving the following yields:

	Weight, %	Volume
Dry gas	7.8	
Coke	8.5	
Debutanized gasoline	...	36.4
Naphtha	...	13.6
Cycle and decanted oil	...	30.0
B-B cut	...	15.6

In actual operations[94] the gas and B-B production were closer to those of Fig. 21-3 than the design yields tabulated above. Some design operating conditions were:

Catalyst to oil ratio, lb/lb	16.7	Catalyst holdup, tons:	
Space velocity	1.35	In reactor	44.2
Catalyst circulation rate, tons	14.8	In stripper	14.4
Settled slurry oil, bpd	250	In regenerator	96.4
Steam—to cat. stripper, lb per hr	8,900	Carbon on regenerated catalyst	0.5
Steam—to reactor, lb per hr	1,400	Conversion, vol. %	67
Steam—generated, lb per hr	27,260	Catalyst in slurry, %	0.5
Total blower air, lb per hr	114,900		

[91] Lassiat and Parker, Butane Dehydrogenation . . . Houdry Process, *Oil-Gas J.*, Nov. 18, 1944, p. 229.

[92] Reidel, J. C., First Orthoflow . . . in U.S.A., *Oil Gas J.*, Mar. 24, 1952, p. 200.

[93] Degnen and Skelly, Design and Operation . . . , *Pet. Engr. Ref. Annual*, 1953, p. C-7.

[94] McGrath, R. V., *Pet. Engr.* December, 1953, p. C-5.

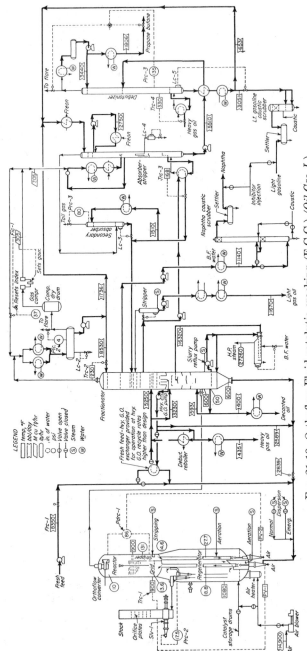

FIG. 21-10 Orthoflow Fluid catalytic cracking (F.C.C.) (*Oil Gas J.*)

Fresh feed (often heated to 600 to 700°F) lifts hot regenerated catalyst into the reactor as the feed vaporizes. Cracked material leaves the reactor through cyclone separators and is fractionated into products. Clay fines accumulate in small amounts (0.5 lb per gal) at the bottom of the fractionator, and they (as slurry oil amounting to 3 to 10 per cent of feed charge) are usually returned to the reactor. Spent catalyst overflows into the stripper where it is stripped by steam. The spent catalyst is lifted into the regenerator by preheated air. Catalyst (above about 10 microns) is held in the system by cyclone separators (and sometimes Cottrell precipitators), but scrubbers utilizing the incoming fresh feed have been used in one plant.[95] Heat may be removed from the regenerator catalyst by

TABLE 21-22. OVER-ALL HEAT BALANCES

Carbon or fuel burned, weight per cent of feed	Cracking temperatures for these feed temperatures		
	700°F	400°F	100°F
3	800		
4	915		
5	995	800	
6	. . .	905	
7	. . .	980	825
8	. . .	. . .	925

recycling the catalyst through a "solids" heat exchanger against water and by the operation of waste-heat boilers on the flue gas.

The mechanism of fluidization and the settling of catalyst were discussed on pages 797 to 798. Catalyst is aerated at various points, and transfer occurs at velocities of about 30 ft per sec. Difficulty is encountered with erosion of lines, standpipes, etc., but runs of 677 days have been accomplished.[96]

According to Voorhies[86] the residence time of catalyst appears to be 1.5 to 10 min in the reaction zone. Residence times of 10 to 20 min in the regenerator are employed, and the depth of bed ranges from 10 to 15 or even 30 ft. Over-all and regenerator balances[78] are indicated in Tables 21-22 and 21-23, and complete charts have been published by J. W. Moorman.[97] An air preheat temperature of 200 to 300°F is probably

[95] Anon., . . . Features of the Smallest (Frontier) Fluid . . . Unit, *Pet. Engr.*, May, 1945, p. 135.

[96] Johnson, R. L., New Cat Cracking Record, *Pet. Engr.*, April, 1951, p. C-50.

[97] What is the Effect of Feed Preheat, Part 5, *Oil Gas J.*, Jan. 10, 1955, p. 68.

employed in Table 21-23.   In such complicated systems, maintenance[98] and instrumentation[99,100] are extremely important.

Product properties and yields may be determined from the information on pages 763 to 779.   Carbon laydown and dry-gas production is larger than shown in Figs. 21-3 to 21-5, and B-B production is smaller.

Even though feedstocks are separated into shorter boiling ranges in order to conduct selective cracking of each part at optimum conditions, overcracking of the most reactive part of the feed occurs, and as the time is prolonged in order to adequately convert the more refractory parts of the feed, some of the gasoline already produced is overcracked or

TABLE 21-23. REGENERATOR HEAT BALANCES FOR A 950°F
REACTOR TEMPERATURE

Catalyst to oil weight ratio	Regenerator temperatures for these percentages of carbon on the catalyst			
	3	4	5	6
5	1125	1190[a]		
10	1040	1080	1115	1150
20	995[a]	1015	1035	1055
30	.....	995[a]	1005	1020
40	.....	.....	....	1000

[a] Extrapolated.

destroyed.   This has been cured in part by the development of a two-stage system[101] which produces less coke and more gasoline (tending to approach the yields of Fig. 21-3).   The feed is first contacted with hot regenerated catalyst for a few seconds in an upflow riser reactor at a high temperature (1000°F).   The partially cracked material is separated from the catalyst, and the gasoline is removed in a fractionator.   The remaining partially cracked feed, along with recycle, is then cracked in a conventional bed type reactor for a longer period, using the still hot catalyst (without regeneration) from the first or riser reactor stage.

Thermofor (T.C.C.) and Houdriflow Processes.   These processes[20-24] during early stages were developed jointly by the Socony Mobil Oil Company and the Houdry Process Corporation.[102]   In many respects

[98] Foster, A. L., Maintenance of Fluid Cat. Cracker, *Oil Gas J.*, Oct. 25, 1947, p. 86.

[99] MacDonald, M., Automatic Control of a Fluid Catalytic . . . , *Pet. Refiner*, October, 1946, p. 87.

[100] Anon., Instrumenting the Fractionator . . . , *Pet. Processing*, September, 1946, p. 52.

[101] Heldman et al., Two-stage Fluid Cat. Cracking, *Oil Gas J.*, May 21, 1956, p. 230.

[102] Now that differences of opinion over the ownership of certain features have been settled (*Pet. Week*, Dec. 23, 1955, p. 21) the processes are rapidly assuming a greater importance.

they are similar but each has its own features of reactor and kiln design. Figure 21-1b is based on the T.C.C. process and Fig. 21-11 shows the Houdriflow process.[103,104] Before 1951, the bucket elevator rather than the air-lift method of lifting catalyst (as in Fig. 21-12) was used.[105] Hot regenerated catalyst beads are lifted with hot air or elevators to the reaction zone where the major amount of the feed and recycle in the form of a vapor is introduced. In addition, a small amount (10 to 20 per cent) of feed may be introduced as a liquid[36,38] at the top of the reactor, but the Conradson Carbon test of the feed should be kept below about 4 per cent. Most plants do not superheat the vapor feed as shown in Fig. 21-12. Ratios by volume of catalyst to oil, up to 7, are employed but commonly range from 3 to 5. Steam or flue gas is employed at a slight pressure to sweep hydrocarbon vapor from the spent catalyst as it flows to the lift mechanism. Regeneration of the catalyst occurs as it flows downward through the regenerator countercurrent to preheated air (400 to 900°F). The pressure is substantially atmospheric in the kiln. Flue gas is circulated through cooling coils in the kiln to control the rate of combustion of the coke[69] and to provide a means of saving excess heat from the process by means of a waste-heat boiler. Additional heat is usually recovered at the base of the main fractionator by a waste-heat boiler, although Fig. 21-12 shows this heat being used to heat crude oil. A part of the regenerated catalyst is currently cleaned of "fines" and small particles by means of a stream of air in what is called an elutriator. Much of the catalyst that is poisoned by metal contaminants is found on the surface of the beads, and thus much of the deactivated catalyst leaves the system as dust (about 4 times as much metal in the dust as in the beads[21,71]). Catalyst loss by attrition is usually under 0.6 per cent of the circulation although values up to 2.5 per cent have been mentioned for clay beads.[103,104] Little catalyst need be added to maintain catalyst activity.

Recycling is advantageous not only because of the increase in yields but also because it assists in the vaporization of additional fresh feed from the primary residual feed (see Fig. 21-7). Nearly all plants conduct some recycling (average ratio is 0.25), and many plants operate at a ratio of recycle to fresh feed of 0.5 (several plants at 1.2). Yields may be estimated from Table 21-1 and Figs. 21-3 to 21-5, but smaller yields of coke and dry gas are produced than indicated in the figures, and the yield of B-B cut is larger.

The superiority of the moving-bed systems in tolerating metal contamination has been put to test in the installation of a commercial plant

[103] Barton, P. D., Sun's New Houdriflow Unit, *Oil Gas J.*, Mar. 29, 1951, p. 232.

[104] Noll et al., The Houdriflow Catalytic Process Today, *Proc. Fourth World Pet. Congr.*, sec. III, Rome, 1955.

[105] Socony Vac. Oil Co., Test Run . . . T.C.C. Commercial Plant, *Pet. Refiner*, September, 1950, p. 115.

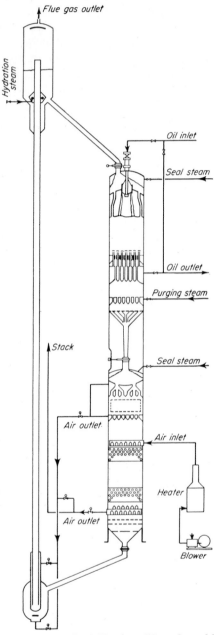

FIG. 21-11. Basic arrangement of Houdriflow gas-lift and cracking equipment.   Also see Fig. 21-1*b*.   (*Oil Gas J.*)

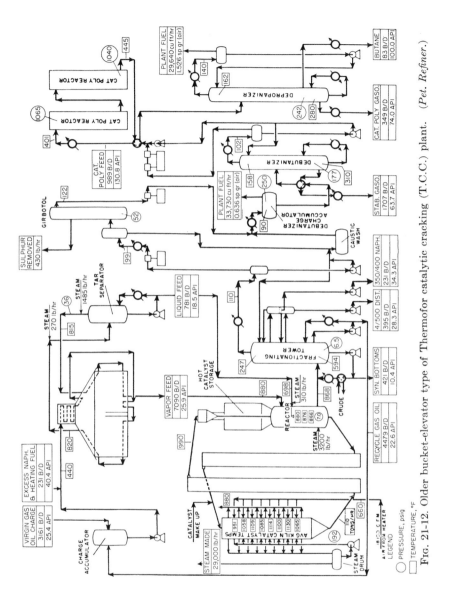

FIG. 21-12. Older bucket-elevator type of Thermofor catalytic cracking (T.C.C.) plant. (*Pet. Refiner.*)

807

(Houdresid process).[106]   Although the upper economic limit of catalyst contamination has been reported to be about 200 ppm of nickel and vanadium[54] on the catalyst, such a supposedly poisoned catalyst was used in the commercial operations.   After more than a million barrels of reduced crude oil (Ni, 4.6; Va, 6.1; and Fe, 9.4 ppm) had been processed, the activity of the catalyst had dropped from 26 to only 23.6 by the Cat. A activity test, but scarcely any addition of catalyst, other than to replace the attrition of 0.4–0.5 lb per bbl of feed, was necessary.   Meanwhile, the iron had risen and stabilized at 1.4 per cent of the catalyst, and the nickel and vanadium to over 400 ppm each.   At the conversion of about 68 per cent, yields were nearly the same as those indicated in Fig. 21-3, except that the coke yield was somewhat high (7 to 8.2 per cent rather than 5.5 to 6.5), and the B-B cut was smaller (12 to 15 per cent rather than 18).

Although Fig. 21-12 shows an older type bucket elevator plant, it was used here because of the complete operating data.   The feed of 3,161 bpd of 25.4 API virgin gas oil (about 1.18 per cent sulfur) plus 231 bpd of 40.4 API naphtha, plus 4,479 bpd of 22.6 API recycle stock, produced the following products:

	Vol. %	Wt %
Debutanized 400 E.P. gaso.............	57.5	47.0
B-B cut..............................	16.1	10.5
Cycle oil—400–500°F.................	11.6	11.5
Cycle oil—synthetic bottoms...........	12.4	13.9
Total liquids.....................	97.6	
Propylene and lighter.................	....	9.6
Coke.................................	....	7.5
		100.0

Small packaged T.C.C. units in which the tall structure is supported by an oil-well derrick have been built.[107]

Other Cracking Processes. Although (1) the amount of coke produced by the Cycloversion process is only about half of that produced by other processes, (2) the cycle of useful operation is very long, and (3) the equipment is relatively simple, it has not been widely installed because of the relatively low leaded octane number of the gasoline product.   Any distilled charge stock of 5 or less NPA color is suitable, even gas oils from viscosity breaking or coking operations.   Gasoline yields are slightly lower than by other processes (except the Fluid process), and gas losses

[106] Dart et al., New Catcracking Process Solves Residuum Problems, *Pet. Engr.*, June, 1955, p. C-43.

[107] Jacobs, W. O., First "Packaged" T.C.C. Unit . . . , *Oil Gas J.*, Jan. 21, 1952, p. 92.

are somewhat larger than by all but the Fluid process. The catalyst, bauxite, is mechanically strong[108] and may be regenerated at 1275°F (even 1400°F) rather than the customary 1050 to 1125°F used for other catalysts. The catalyst does not appear to lose its activity,[109] but about 15 per cent is lost per inspection. Cracking cycles of 2 to 10 hr are possible before regeneration is necessary and even 24 to 36 hr when reforming naphthas. The octane number of the gasoline from Texas Panhandle gas oil is 76 to 77 ASTM (86 Research),[109] but with 3 cc TEL, octane numbers of only 81 to 82 ASTM are obtained because of the high olefinic content. The charge stock is heated[48] to 980 to 1020°F (even 1050°F in reforming) and admitted to one of the two catalyst chambers at 70 to 90 psig (200 psig in reforming). Meanwhile the spent-catalyst chamber is purged with steam, and the carbon is burned by a mixture of superheated steam and air.

The same process and equipment are widely used for straight-run gasoline reforming (980 to 1050°F)[110] and for catalytic desulfurization (650 to 850°F). When employed for desulfurization, 5,000 to 15,000 bbl can be processed per ton of catalyst,[48] and hence the catalyst may be discarded.

A flow diagram of the Suspensoid process[7] is not shown here (except see Fig. 21-1d) because the process consists simply of introducing a slurry of catalyst in cycle oil into the cracking stock, and then removing the spent catalyst from the residual fuel by means of an Oliver Precoat Rotary filter.[8] The oil and catalyst are heated to about 1050°F and an outlet pressure of 400 psig is maintained. The main effect of the clay catalyst is to allow a higher cracking temperature and to assist, perhaps mechanically, in keeping coke from accumulating on the walls of the tubes. Temperatures up to 1105°F increase the yields of excess butanes and gas at the expense of heating and fuel oils,[111] but erosion becomes severe. Although gas-oil charge stocks can be employed, a mixture of heavy straight-run naphtha and gas oil is advantageous because the low-octane naphtha can be reformed along with the cracking of the gas oil with total yields that are greater than when each operation is conducted separately.[7] New or synthetic catalyst produces slightly larger gasoline yields (but of lower octane number) than the used Super Filtrol (from lubricating-oil contact treating) now employed, but since only 2 lb used-catalyst per barrel of oil is required, the use of expensive catalyst is not

[108] Buell and Waddill, Cycloversion Process, *Pet. Refiner*, October, 1944, p. 83.

[109] Buell and Skinner, Cracking Texas Panhandle Gas Oil . . . Cycloversion, *Oil Gas J.*, May 5, 1945, p. 87.

[110] Goldtrap and Skinner, Refinery Conversion for Premium Fuels, *Pet. Engr.*, April, 1945, p. 174.

[111] Burk, C. F., Suspensoid Catalytic Cracking, *Oil Gas J.*, Oct. 12, 1946, p. 100.

justified.   More catalyst accomplishes little.   Yields are given on page 702 of the Third Edition of this book.

CATALYTIC REFORMING

Although the development of catalytic cracking was a momentous achievement, especially in developing methods of handling and regenerating catalysts, the crowning achievement in refinery catalytic processing was the development of Platforming by Haensel[26] and the Universal Oil Products Co. in 1947–1949.   In catalytic cracking, the catalyst needs regeneration after 10 to 20 min and after 3 to 14 gal of oil has been processed per pound of catalyst.   In Platforming and some of the related platinum catalyst processes, 253 bbl[112] of oil has been processed per pound of catalyst before regeneration or replacement was necessary.   This is accomplished by concurrently hydrogenating certain molecules, especially carbonaceous materials, while dehydrogenating other molecules, and adjusting conditions to minimize cracking types of reactions.   Platforming used mainly by smaller independent refiners, and the platinum catalyst processes used by larger refiners, now dominate in the field of gasoline reforming and the production of aromatics, although other processes especially Hydroforming are also used (Table 21-24).   Space is available for a discussion of only the platinum catalyst processes and Hydroforming.

In both platinum and molybdenum reforming the major types of reactions are:[7]

1. *Naphthene Dehydrogenation*

$$\text{cyclohexane} \rightleftharpoons \text{benzene} + 3H_2 \qquad (21\text{-}3)$$

2. *Naphthene Dehydroisomerization*

$$\text{1,2-dimethylcyclopentane} \rightleftharpoons \text{methylcyclohexane} \rightleftharpoons \text{toluene} + 3H_2 \quad (21\text{-}4)$$

[112] Eckhouse, J. G., *Pet. Engr.*, April, 1954, p. C-26.   (The average Platformer throughput up to 1954, including the early plants and the many which had only been started, was 65 bbl.)

TABLE 21-24. APPROXIMATE OPERATING CONDITIONS OF REFORMING PROCESSES (1956)

Process	Thermal reforming	Molybdenum catalysts			Platinum catalysts			Other catalysts	
		Hydroforming		Hyperforming moving-bed, Union Oil Calif.	Platforming nonregenerative, UOP	Occasionally regenerative[a]	Cyclically regenerative[b]	Thermofor moving-bed, Socony	Cycloversion fixed-bed, Phillips
		Fixed-bed, M. W. Kellogg Co.	Fluidized bed, Esso and Std. Ind.						
Capacity, bpd, Jan., 1956[c]	394,000	41,000	69,000	1,000	500,000	93,000	141,000	24,000	8,200
Refineries conducting[d]	57	4	5	1	76	18	11	2	4
Catalyst:									
Composition	None	10% MoO₃ on Al₂O₃	10% MoO₃ on Al₂O₃	Cobalt molybdate	Pt plus halogen on Al₂O₃	0.5% Pt on Al₂O₃[e]	Pt on Al₂O₃	Chromia and alumina	Bauxite
Life	....	9–12 months	0.1 lb/bbl	....	60–250 bbl /lb	20–100 bbl /lb	40–200 bbl /lb	5 bbl/lb	....
Cost, $/lb (1956)	....	$0.90	$0.60	$0.90–1.50	($9.00–14.00 but $4.00 replacement)		....	....	$0.08–0.11
Reaction:									
Temp, °F	970–1060	950–1020	890–940	870	850–960	875–950	850–970	950–1000	950–1000
Press, psi	250–900	150–200	100–300	400	200–700	200–600	200–400	100–200	50–57
Space vel., lb/lb-hr	....	0.5–0.6	0.3–1.0	1.0	1–4	1–5	1–5	0.7	1–2
Contact time, sec	10–20	15	....	0.05	....				
Cat./oil ratio	....	....	0.5–1.0	....					
Gas recirculation, cu ft/bbl[f]	....	2000–4000	4000–6000	3600					None
Regeneration:									
Type	None	Cyclic	Separate	Separate	None	Occasional	Cyclic	Separate	Cyclic
Temp, °F	....	1050–1100	1100	950	....	1050	....	800–1000	....
Press, psi	....	170	200	415	....	250–300	....	....	15
Time between regenerations	....	4–16 hr	Continuous	Continuous	Years	2–5 months	7.5 bbl/lb	Continuous	18–36 hr

[a] Catforming (Atlantic Ref. Co.), Houdriforming (Houdry Process Corp.), Powerforming (Esso Research & Eng.), and Sovaforming (Socony-Mobil).
[b] Ultraforming (Std. Oil Ind.) and Sinclair-Baker-Kellogg.
[c] Turner, L., Oil Gas J., Mar. 19, 1956, p. 213.
[d] Not units or plants because some refineries have several units of the same process.
[e] Catforming uses SiO₂, Al₂O₃, and platinum.
[f] Rich in hydrogen (50–95%).

3. Paraffin Dehydrocyclization

$$H_3C-\underset{\overset{|}{H_2}}{C}-\underset{\overset{|}{H_2}}{C}-\underset{\overset{|}{H_2}}{C}-\underset{\overset{|}{H_2}}{C}-CH_3 \rightleftharpoons \text{benzene} + 4H_2 \qquad (21\text{-}5)$$

n-hexane   benzene

4. Paraffin Isomerization

$$H_3C-\underset{\overset{|}{H_2}}{C}-\underset{\overset{|}{H_2}}{C}-\underset{\overset{|}{H_2}}{C}-\underset{\overset{|}{H_2}}{C}-\underset{\overset{|}{H_2}}{C}-CH_3 \rightleftharpoons 1 \text{ methylhexane, etc.} \qquad (21\text{-}6)$$

5. Paraffin Hydrocracking

$$C_{10}H_{22} + H_2 \rightleftharpoons H_3C-\underset{\overset{|}{H_2}}{C}-\underset{\overset{|}{H_2}}{C}-\underset{\overset{|}{H_2}}{C}-CH_3 + H_3C-\underset{\overset{|}{H_2}}{C}-\underset{\overset{|}{CH_3}}{C}-CH_3 \qquad (21\text{-}7)$$

n-decane   pentane   isopentane

6. Olefin Hydrogenation

$$C_5H_{10} + H_2 \rightleftharpoons C_5H_{12} \qquad (21\text{-}8)$$

pentenes   pentanes

7. Hydrodesulfurization

$$\text{thiophene} + 4H_2 \rightarrow C_4H_{10} + H_2S \qquad (21\text{-}9)$$

thiophene   butanes

Dehydrogenation of naphthenes [Eq. (21-3)] occurs very rapidly, and the isomerization of paraffins and naphthenes [Eqs. (21-4) and (21-6)] also occurs rapidly. Thus these reactions predominate, and the slower cyclization and hydrocracking reactions [Eqs. (21-5) and (21-7)] become significant mainly at severe conditions of low space velocity, high pressure, and high temperature. Equilibrium relations for the several reactions have been surveyed by Sittig and Warren.[32] Hydrocracking, as against the dehydrogenation and isomerization reactions, is usually undesirable because it leads in the extreme to the deposition of coke, a decrease in hydrogen production, and lower liquid yields. However, with paraffin-rich stocks, it is necessary to conduct hydrocracking vigorously. Low pressure encourages the dehydrogenation and cyclization reactions but mildly suppresses the hydrocracking reactions. Operation at 900 psi causes about twice as much hydrocracking[26] as does operation at 500 psi. Although more hydrogen is produced at low pressures, the partial pressure of the hydrogen is relatively lower, and this leads to a tendency for the hydrocracking reactions to produce coke.

In summary, the most useful operating conditions for most purposes are (1) low pressure, (2) high temperature, (3) low space velocity, and (4) a high rate of gas or hydrogen recirculation, because liquid yields are larger, the vapor pressure of the reformate is lower (allowing the addition of more butane in attaining a vapor pressure of 10 R.v.p.), and the hydrogen production is larger. However, this leads to coke deposition or deactivation of the catalyst, and the need for a regenerative, more expensive type of plant. Only the Platforming process is nonregenerative, and it therefore must operate at higher pressures (500 to 700 psi) than the other processes (200 to 500 psi—and 100 to 300 psi in Hydroforming).

Yields. Figure 21-6 indicates approximate yields when operating at favorable conditions for each type of feed material. Naphthene-rich stocks (low Characterization Factor) are best, but somewhat comparable yields (Fig. 21-6) are obtained from paraffinic stocks by the use of operating conditions that favor the hydrocracking reactions, i.e., high-pressure and greater severity.[26,113] The low vapor pressure (2.2 to 3.6 R.v.p.) of reformates (pentanes plus) permits the addition of 10 to 17 per cent of butanes in producing a 10 R.v.p. product. This results in final yields of 90 to even 106 liquid volume per cent. Reformate normally has an end point 15 to 30°F higher than that of the feedstock.

The regenerative processes can operate at the low pressures which produce larger yields but more deactivation of the catalyst.[114] Such superiority is not fully evident in the literature, but the yields relative to those of Fig. 21-6 or nonregenerative (Platforming) operation are thought to be[114] about:

Regenerative processes: 3–4% larger (C_5-plus material)
                             5–10% larger (10 R.v.p. material)
Fluid Hydroforming: 1% smaller (C_5-plus)
                             2–3% smaller (10 R.v.p.)

The regenerative processes also[114] produce more hydrogen and a lower-vapor-pressure less volatile gasoline. The hydrogen production ranges from as low as 400 cu ft per bbl for mild operations on highly paraffinic feeds, to as much as 2,200 cu ft when operating for aromatics on highly naphthenic feeds. The off-gas consists mainly of hydrogen (see Table 14-4, gas No. 27).

Material boiling below about 200°F is not usually included in the re-

[113] Haensel and Donaldson, How Paraffin Content Affects Quality . . . , *Pet. Processing*, February, 1953, p. 236.

[114] Steel et al., Factors in Selecting . . . Process, *Pet. Engr.*, February, 1955, p. C-25.

former feed because it already has a relatively high octane number and because it contains only a small amount of the hydrocarbons that can be converted (see Table 21-25). Material boiling above about 400°F is

TABLE 21-25. COMPOSITIONS (VOLUME PER CENT) OF A FEW
STRAIGHT-RUN NAPHTHAS

	Ponca, Okla.	East Texas	Brad-ford, Pa.	Green-dale, Mich.	Cali-fornia[a]	Wink-ler, Texas	Mid-way, Calif.	Con-roe, Texas
Feed fraction (140–185°F) for benzene								
Feed, per cent naphtha[b]...............	13	16	15	18	..	10	12	14
Paraffins.............................	60	62	78	77	10	78	44	39
Methylcyclopentane...................	20	23	9	9	...	15	34	21
Cyclohexane.........................	16	12	12	11	...	6	21	31
Benzene.............................	4	1	1	3	3	1	1	9
Total naphthenes....................	36	35	21	20	87	21	55	52
Feed fraction (185–200°F) for toluene								
Feed, per cent naphtha[b]...............	23	25	24	23	...	15	20	27
Paraffins.............................	47	38	52	66	34	65	20	23
1,1-Dimethylcyclopentane..............	2	2	2	2	...	4	3	2
trans. 1,3-Dimethylcyclopentane........	15	16	6	3	...	10	26	6
trans. 1,2-Dimethylcyclopentane........	5	6	6	1	...	8	10	1
Methylcyclohexane...................	21	27	24	18	...	10	30	36
Ethylcyclopentane[c]..................	3	4	4	3	...	1	5	5
Toluene.............................	7	7	6	7	4	2	6	27
Total naphthenes....................	46	55	42	27	62	33	74	50

[a] Select naphthas, Decker, W. H., *Pet. Engr.*, April, 1954, p. C-30.
[b] Per cent of pentane—360°F gasoline.
[c] Estimated.

not included because of greater coke deposition or deactivation of the catalyst. When operating for aromatic hydrocarbons, short-boiling-range stocks (Table 21-25) of about 150 to 225°F (for benzene and toluene), and 150 to 270°F if xylenes are also desirable, are used as feeds.[115,116] Straight-run feeds are used almost exclusively, but cracked or coker distillates are suitable except for their tendency to produce coke. If such stocks are first hydrogenated (desulfurized) by the processes described on pages 305 and 332, they are said to equal the straight-run feeds.[117] At the same time, poisonous arsenic is completely removed during the desulfurization.

[115] Forziati et al., *Pet. Refiner*, November, 1943, p. 22.
[116] Haensel, V., Aromatics Production by . . . Platforming, *Oil Gas J.*, Aug. 9, 1951, p. 80.
[117] Anon. (J. F. Walter), Catalytic Reforming Problems, *Pet. Processing*, June, 1956, p. 76.

The lead susceptibility of reformates is shown in Table 3-12, the relationship (spread or sensitivity) between Research and Motor method octane numbers in Table 3-3, and the blending octane number in Fig. 4-46.

Aromatics and Hydrogen. During 1955, reformer capacity devoted (in part) to aromatics production[118] was 181,200 bpd, of which 148,000 employed platinum catalyst processes. The aromatic production of such plants if fully utilized would, however, probably not exceed 80,000 bpd. Over half of the nation's need for benzene and toluene was produced from such plants, and much more can be produced as the need arises. In aromatics production the most useful feed hydrocarbons are such naphthenes as methylcyclopentane, cyclohexane, dimethylcyclopentanes, etc. (see Table 21-25), but aromatics are also produced in smaller amounts by cyclization [Eq. (21-5)] of paraffins. Higher-boiling aromatics such as 1,2,4- and 1,3,5-trimethylbenzene, and 1,2,4,5- and 1,2,3,5-tetramethylbenzene are also produced by reforming, but there has thus far been no need of recovering them as pure products. About 90 per cent of the possible yield of aromatics (based on naphthenes) can be readily accomplished by operations at low pressure (200 to 400 psi), low space velocity (2 to 4), and moderate temperatures.

Narrow-boiling-range feeds (150 to 225°F, see Table 21-25) are processed, and the reformate seldom contains more than 50 per cent of aromatics. The aromatics are recovered and purified by processes of adsorption (Arosorb or silica gel), extractive distillation (phenol), azeotropic distillation, or solvent extraction (Udex, diethylene glycol, or sulfur dioxide).

The reforming processes are a valuable source of by-product hydrogen, and the availability of this hydrogen has been a great incentive in the development of the hydrodesulfurization processes. The amount of hydrogen produced is so much a function of the feed composition that no means of approximation is possible. However, the amount is substantial (400 to 1,200 cu ft per bbl)—and quite large (1,500 to 2,200 cu ft) from special naphthene-rich stocks used for the production of aromatic hydrocarbons.

Platinum Reforming. The regenerative processes[27-31] differ from the nonregenerative[26,113,116] Platforming process mainly by the addition of regenerative equipment (and usually an extra reactor). Thus, it is possible to show a single basic diagram (Fig. 21-13) for all processes. The fixed-bed Hydroforming process is also basically the same except that regeneration must be practiced so frequently (about 8 hr) that the use of a waste-heat boiler is justified. In some plants, a single still with several coils is used rather than the 3 heater stills shown in Fig. 21-13. A prefractionator is not required if the regular topping equipment of the refinery can separate a large well-fractionated (200 to 400°F) Platformer feed. A

[118] Guthrie, V. B., *Pet. Processing*, August, 1955, p. 1159.

small high-pressure (600 psi) drum is used to store hydrogen for startup. When the catalyst is new and active, the first of the three reactors is held at a temperature about 5°F higher than the second, etc., but as the catalyst becomes deactivated all of the reactors are allowed to come up to full temperature.

Naphthas have been encountered which contain as much as 350 parts per billion of arsenic, and this must be removed because it quantitatively unites with the platinum causing deactivation of the catalyst. Most feeds (over 80 per cent) contain little or no arsenic, and need not be treated. Filtration through fuller's earth is highly successful in reducing

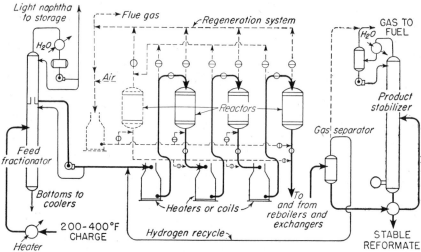

Fig. 21-13. Platinum catalyst reforming processes (regenerative and nonregenerative.)

the arsenic to below 10 ppb and usually 5 ppb. Little clay is used (6,000 to 28,000 bbl per ton) unless the naphtha contains abnormal amounts of water which is also adsorbed. A relatively simple method of determining these trace amounts of arsenic has been devised,[119] and it is mentioned that about 90 per cent of the arsenic, during a distillation, stays with the residue. Clay filtration also removes traces of lead.

Large amounts of sulfur tend to deactivate the catalyst temporarily or to utilize the active surface. Many plants desulfurize the feedstock, and catalytic desulfurization (hydrogenation) not only removes all arsenic but upgrades cracked materials so that they can be reformed. Sulfide corrosion is normally severe, necessitating the use of 12 and 16 per cent chromium steels (18–8 chrome nickel is even better).[31]

Three to five pounds of catalyst per barrel charge stock is required to fill the reactors, and a fresh charge of catalyst must be readily available.

[119] Jay and Dickson, *Pet. Processing*, March, 1954, p. 374.

The service charge for replacing spent catalyst with new is about $4.00 (1956), and the cost of new catalyst ranges from $9.00 to $14.00 per lb.

Yields were indicated in Fig. 21-6.

In an effort to obtain even higher octane numbers, the Universal Oil Products Co.[120] has devised a combination solvent extraction (aqueous diethylene glycol) and Platforming system which permits the recycling of

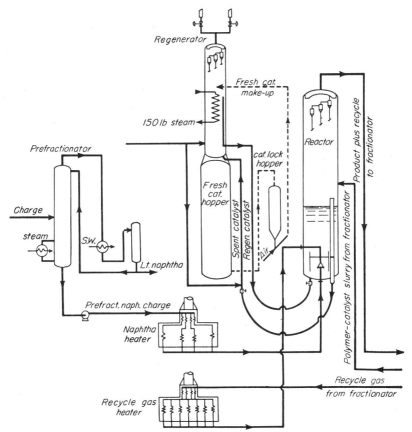

Fig. 21-14. Basic diagram of a Fluid Hydroformer.   (*Pet. Refiner.*)

paraffinic raffinate through the reactors of the Platformer process. This prolonged treatment of paraffins results in more complete conversion of them, and a yield of final product from Mid Continent feed of about 78 per cent of 100 Research octane number reformate.

Hydroforming.   The fixed-bed version of this process was the original (1941) aromatization process used during World War II for the production of toluene, and later for the production of aromatic solvents and

[120] First Rexformer Goes on Stream, *Oil Gas J.*, Aug. 3, 1956, p. 106.

naphthas. The fixed-bed process was conducted in equipment similar to that of Fig. 21-13. The catalyst is relatively cheap molybdenum oxide (MoO_3) supported on alumina, and it must be regenerated at 4 to 16 hour intervals for the removal of coke.

All recent installations have been of the fluid catalyst type indicated in Fig. 21-14.[121] The plant operates on 12,500 bpd of 220 to 355°F Middle East naphtha. Gas is recycled at the rate of about 4,000 cu ft per bbl of feed. Coke laydown with the 12.1 Characterization Factor feed has been 1.3 to 1.9 per cent of feed, and the yields of 5 R.v.p. reformate range from 66 per cent of 94 Research octane number to 75 per cent of 87.5 octane number. Catalyst losses amount to only 0.03 to 0.05 lb per bbl feed. The preferred catalyst size is about 5 to 10 per cent finer than 20 microns, more than 20 per cent between 20 and 40 microns, and less than 30 per cent coarser than 80 microns. Viscosity-broken feeds and coker distillate can be processed, but the carbon laydown is larger.

Additional operating information is given in Table 21-24.

[121] Jaggard and Johnson, Aramco's Fluid Hydroformer . . . , *Pet. Refiner*, August, 1956, p. 157.

CHAPTER 22

NATURAL AND REFINERY GASES

Casinghead gasoline first attracted commercial attention in about 1904 in Pennsylvania. By 1955, proven natural gas reserves of the United States exceeded 230,000,000,000,000 cu ft, and natural gas liquids (propane and heavier) 5,600,000,000 bbl. Nearly 10 trillion cu ft of natural gas was marketed during 1956. The low boiling range of natural and distillate (field) gasolines or their tendency to vaporize easily makes them highly useful for cold-weather operation when ordinary gasolines fail to vaporize rapidly. For some years, natural gasoline has constituted 6 to 8 per cent of the total gasoline (Table 6-3) and butanes (mainly from refinery operations) about 5 per cent.

Natural gas is used primarily as a fuel, but it is also processed for the liquid hydrocarbons that it contains, it is partly burned or oxidized into carbon black, and plants have been built[1] for burning the gas to carbon monoxide and hydrogen so that these gases can be synthesized mainly into gasoline but also into numerous chemical products such as methyl, ethyl, propyl, butyl, and amyl alcohols, acetaldehyde, acetic acid, acetone, and methyl ethyl ketone. Gas is such a convenient fuel that the reforming of high-heating-value refinery gases (1,600 Btu per cu ft) into low-heat city or manufactured gas (550 to 1,000 Btu per cu ft) has been proposed.[2] Winter demands for natural gas as a fuel are so great that pipelines are seldom large enough. This situation was solved by one gas-distribution system by the installation of a gas-liquefaction plant and storage[3] tanks for liquid natural gas (at $-250°F$) at the terminal. More recently,[4] gas (mainly methane) has been liquefied and transported in heavily insulated atmospheric-pressure tanks on barges and ocean-going vessels. Gas that evaporates is used as fuel to drive the vessel. Atmospheric-pressure storage has also been explored for the transportation of propane,

[1] Lane and Weil, The Synthine Process, 4 parts, *Pet. Refiner*, August, p. 87; September, p. 97; October, p. 109; and November, 1946, p. 153.

[2] Bevan, R. L., Reforming Refinery Still Gases . . . , *Oil Gas J.*, Aug. 19, 1943, p. 52.

[3] Elliott et al., . . . Investigation of the Fire at the Liquefaction, Storage and Regasification Plant . . . , *U.S. Bur. Mines Rept. Invest.* 3867, February, 1946.

[4] Nelson, W. L., Natural Gas to Move by Barge, *Oil Gas J.*, Mar. 22, 1954.

but pressure tanks are the common method of storage. Although enormous amounts of butane, propane, and ethane are available and very cheap (butane valued at only 1 cent per gal when sold as part of natural gasoline),[5] the lack of a cheap method of accumulating and transporting these high-vapor-pressure materials has been a great deterrent to widespread use or the development of chemical projects. Underground storage in natural or man-built caverns (1.8 trillion cu ft of gas,[6] and over 16 million bbl liquefied gases[6]) is aiding in stabilizing winter and

TABLE 22-1. MARKETED PRODUCTION OF LIQUEFIED PETROLEUM GASES[a]
(1,000 gallons)

Year	Total sales	Domestic and motor fuel[b]	Industrial and misc.[c]	Gas manu- facture	Chemical manu- facture	Rubber compo- nents
1922	233[d]					
1928	4,523	2,600	400	1,500		
1938	165,201	57,832	62,694	12,386	32,299	
1948	2,736,801	1,473,289	275,883	237,638	524,350	225,641
1952	4,477,379	2,636,736	338,959	259,697	870,990	370,997
1954	5,125,533	3,174,012	401,615	191,932	1,050,239	307,735
1956	6,997,000	4,068,000	614,000	234,000	1,642,000	439,000

[a] Does not include gases used by producer. Figures not entirely consistent because classifications were changed at various times. See *Oil Gas J.*, Jan. 21, 1956, p. 52.

[b] Household plus irrigation pumping, tractor fuel, flame weeding, chicken brooding, and similar uses; also sales of domestic distributors for industrial uses; also internal-combustion fuels after 1950.

[c] Including fuel for internal-combustion engines during years to 1951.

[d] Sales confined mainly to bottle gas prior to 1928.

summer operations, but only a few (5) major L.P.G. (liquefied and petroleum gas) lines, all in Texas, have been proposed or built. Chemical developments at distant points are usually situated on a major natural-gas pipeline, and the ethane, propane, etc., are separated at the point of use.

The lighter hydrocarbons, such as propane, isobutane, butane, and the corresponding olefins, removed from natural gasoline and refinery gases, are widely used as so-called "bottle gas" (Table 3-5). The enormous growth[7] of the liquefied petroleum gas (L.P.G.) industry is indicated in Table 22-1.

[5] Nelson, W. L., Relative Prices of Various Grades of Natural Gasoline, *Oil Gas J.*, Sept. 28, 1953, p. 149.

[6] Underground Gas Storage Still Rising, *Oil Gas J.*, Apr. 23, 1956, p. 68; and L.P.G. Storage Hits New Peak, *Oil Gas J.*, Aug. 1, 1955, p. 60.

[7] L. P. G. Chalks Up Record Gain in '55, *Oil Gas J.*, Jan. 21, 1956, p. 52.

The use of L.P.G. for chemical manufacture grew rapidly between 1938 and 1948, but since 1950 the most rapid gain has occurred in its use as an engine fuel for busses, trucks, tractors, diesel-electric locomotives, tankers, and barges. As much as 15 per cent propylene does not harm propane fuels for bus services.[8] Propane (and propene) constitutes nearly 70 per cent of the total L.P.G. marketed. During 1956 the demand for L.P.G. (excluding that used in gasoline) was:

	Millions bbl	Per cent
Propane (incl. C_3H_6)............	90.6	56.2
Butanes (incl. C_4H_8)............	29.7	18.4
Butane-propane mixes..........	17.5	10.8
Other mixes*.................	23.4	14.6

* Probably gross mixtures used mainly for chemical manufacture including some isobutane, ethane, and possibly some ethylene.

Natural gas is still the major source of carbon black (Table 22-2), but increasing amounts of oil are being utilized. About 94 per cent of the carbon black used in the United States is compounded into rubber goods. Synthetic rubber requires much more black (Table 22-2) than natural rubber. Most of the rest of the black is used for printer's ink and paint.

TABLE 22-2. CARBON BLACK STATISTICS

Year	Millions lb, by process[a]			Millions lb by raw material source		Lb per 100 lb rubber[b]
	Total production	Channel	Furnace	Gas	Oil[b]	
1925	178	144	34	178	...	12
1935	353	316	37	353	...	18
1945	1,053	539	514	983	70	37
1950	1,382	617	765	1,042	340	33
1953	1,611	454	1,157	938	673	35

[a] Chemical Economics Handbook, Stanford Research Institute.
[b] Strasser, D. M., Pet. Refiner, December, 1954, p. 177.

The drying of gases and volatile liquids was discussed briefly on pages 233 to 235, the solubility of water in liquids is indicated in Fig. 5-24, and the properties of the adsorbents used in drying are indicated in Tables

[8] Ebinger et al., Propane Motor Fuel with 15% Propylene . . . , SAE Journal, January, 1955, p. 34.

10-4 to 10-6.   The formation of hydrates with carbon dioxide and with hydrocarbons such as:[9]

| Methane | $CH_4 \cdot 7H_2O$ | Propane | $C_3H_8 \cdot 18H_2O$ |
| Ethane | $C_2H_6 \cdot 8H_2O$ | Carbon Dioxide | $CO_2 \cdot 7H_2O$ |

is troublesome in high-pressure gas lines and particularly in low-temperature fractionating equipment.   The temperatures and pressures for hydrate formation[10] are indicated in Table 22-3.

TABLE 22-3. APPROXIMATE PRESSURES FOR HYDRATE FORMATION
Pounds per square inch absolute

Temp, °F	Specific gravity			
	0.55 (methane)	0.7	0.8	0.9
35	430	120	100	
40	600	165	140	110
45	800	230	192	150
50	1,100	320	265	230
55	1,500	450	380	330
60	2,100	680	580	500
65	2,950	1,000	890	780
75	....	3,100	2,600	2,200

Hydrogen sulfide is an acidic material and it can be removed by the many agents indicated in Table 22-4 as well as nickel oxide (NiO), sodium

TABLE 22-4. HYDROGEN SULFIDE REMOVAL PROCESSES

Name	Reaction	Regeneration
Caustic soda....	$2NaOH + H_2S \rightarrow Na_2S + 2H_2O$	
Lime..........	$Ca(OH)_2 + H_2S \rightarrow CaS + 2H_2O$	
Iron oxide......	$FeO + H_2S \rightarrow FeS + H_2O$	Partly by air
Seaboard.......	$Na_2CO_3 + H_2S \rightleftharpoons NaHCO_3 + NaHS$	Air blowing
Thylox.........	$Na_4As_2S_5O_2 + H_2S \rightarrow Na_4As_2S_6O + H_2O$	$Na_4As_2S_6O + \frac{1}{2}O_2 \rightarrow$ $Na_4As_2S_5O_2 + S$
Girbotol........	$2RNH_2 + H_2S \rightleftharpoons (RNH_3)_2S$	Steaming
Phosphate......	$K_3PO_4 + H_2S \rightleftharpoons KHS + K_2HPO_4$	Steaming
Phenolate......	$NaOC_6H_5 + H_2S \rightleftharpoons NaHS + C_6H_5OH$	Steaming
Vacuum carbonate..........	$Na_2CO_3 + H_2S \rightleftharpoons NaHCO_3 + NaHS$	Vacuum steaming

[9] Frost and Deaton, Gas Hydrate Compositions and Equilibrium Data, *Oil Gas J.*, July 27, 1946, p. 170.
[10] Schutt and Zdonik, Compression and Pretreatment of Pyrolysis Products, *Oil Gas J.*, June 25, 1956, p. 92.

bichromate and zinc sulfate, potassium permanganate, and alkacid ($RCHNH_2COONa$). In handling large volumes of gas, the regenerative processes such as the soda ash, phenolate, tripotassium phosphate, and aqueous amine processes (Table 22-4) are widely used.[11,12] The Girbotol process is described briefly on pages 754 to 756 along with Figs. 20-18 and 20-4 and the conversion of hydrogen sulfide to sulfur is indicated in Fig. 20-19. Carbon dioxide is also removed by the amines as well as small amounts of water. Monoethanolamine (MEA) is used for sulfide (also triethanolamine), and diethanolamine (DEA) if carbon dioxide is also present. If diethylene glycol is also added to the solution and low temperatures are employed, dehydration can be accomplished along with desulfurization.[13]

GENERAL PROCESSING

Natural gas is processed mainly for the recovery of liquid hydrocarbons useful in gasoline, pure hydrocarbons as butane, propane, ethane, or mixtures of them, hydrogen sulfide (and sulfur or sulfuric acid), and carbon black; but significant amounts of gas are also converted into ammonia, synthesized by the Fischer-Tropsch reaction, or oxidized into chemical products such as formaldehyde. Conventional operations, however, consist of mainly two operations, viz., recovery of liquids (absorption, etc.), and purification of the liquid.

1. *Wet* natural (or refinery) gas or a gas containing significant amounts of compounds higher in molecular weight than propane is processed to produce *dry* natural (or fuel) gas, and raw, or *wild*, natural gasoline. Separation of raw gasoline from the gas can be accomplished in many ways as (a) absorption in mineral oil or in high-boiling gasoline, (b) compression, often with refrigeration, (c) adsorption by charcoal in fixed beds or continuously (see Hypersorption), and most often by (d) combinations of several of these such as low-temperature high-pressure absorption.

2. Purification may amount only to stabilization or fractionation of the liquid mixture, but if absorption is used, a preliminary separation of the absorption oil from the recovered oil in various types of stripping stills is practiced. Raw gasoline (or naphtha) contains 10 to 30 per cent methane, ethane, and propane, and these dissolved gases cause the gasoline to be so highly volatile (often completely evaporates if exposed to atmospheric pressure) that they must be removed in producing a stabilized product that can be shipped and marketed. Stabilization is nothing more than high-pressure fractionation for the separation of hydrocarbons lighter than the butanes. Since the top of the fractionator must be cooled or refluxed with nearly pure liquid propane or butane, and water allows cooling to only 80 to 100°F, stabilization must be conducted at a high pressure.

[11] Reed, R. M., *Oil Gas J.*, Mar. 30, 1946, p. 219; also *Pet. Processing*, December, 1947, p. 907.

[12] Culbertson and Connors, *Oil Gas J.*, Aug. 11, 1952, p. 114.

[13] Chapin, W. F., High Purity Natural Gas by the Glycol-amine Process, *Pet. Refiner*, June, 1947, p. 109.

The removal of gases from any stock by high-pressure fractionation (Chaps. 7 and 16), whether it be wild natural gasoline, casinghead (or drip) gasoline, cracked naphthas, or the products from hydrocarbon conversion processes (Chap. 20), is referred to as "stabilization." When a single hydrocarbon is removed, the operation is called deethanization, debutanization, etc. (refer to Figs. 7-13 and 20-4).

The chemical treatment of finished products consists primarily of sweetening with copper chloride (Fig. 10-7) and caustic washing of the bottle gases. Reforming with platinum catalysts is being practiced in several gasoline plants to improve the relatively low octane number (Table 22-9) of most natural gasolines.

Natural Gasoline. A simplified flow diagram of absorption, stripping, and stabilization operations is given in Fig. 22-1. The compressors that

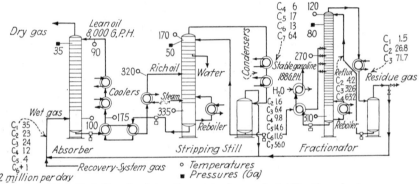

Fig. 22-1. Simple absorption, stripping, and stabilization plant.

are used to create the pressure in the absorption tower are not shown. Figure 8-2 presents much the same arrangement except that control instruments are shown. The wet gas is compressed and admitted to an absorber column. This column and also the stripper and stabilizer are of the bubble-plate or other conventional type of construction, although the tray spacing is usually not over 18 in. In the absorber the wet gas flows countercurrently to an absorption oil and leaves the top as a dry natural or refinery gas. The rich absorption oil flows through exchangers in which heat is exchanged with the hot lean absorption oil, through a steam heater, and into the stripping column. Some fractionation as well as stripping may be accomplished in the stripper or still, and hence heat is supplied at the bottom by a steam reboiler and reflux is used at the top. Wild, or raw, natural gasoline and steam pass overhead, and some of the light constituents cannot ordinarily be condensed. These are cycled back into the absorber. The wild gasoline is pumped through heat exchangers to the stabilizer (fractionator or rectifier), and stable natural gasoline and dry gas are produced. The stabilizer is a typical fractionating column with a steam reboiler. Sometimes it is more economical to allow some gasoline hydrocarbons to escape in the residue gas from the stabilizer and cycle this gas through the absorber than to do an exact job of fractionation in the stabilizer.

When handling large amounts of gas, exceedingly elaborate plants such as the 350,000,000 cu ft plant[14] shown in Fig. 22-2 are justified. This plant handles the six gases shown in Table 22-5. The absorbers operate at 2,250, 1,250, 500, 150, and 50 psig; the rich absorption oil is stage

TABLE 22-5. GAS FEEDS TO PLANT OF FIG. 22-2

Volumes of feeds[a]	207	100	12	20	4	3
Pressures of feeds, psig	2,250	1,250	500	150	50	Vacuum
Analysis (mole per cent):						
Methane	90.83	91.27	91.81	89.33	68.51	56.43
Ethane	5.04	4.96	4.50	5.52	13.73	8.90
Propane	1.90	1.80	1.86	2.46	10.20	15.35
Isobutane	0.52	0.43	0.50	0.59	2.21	6.48
Butane	0.57	0.57	0.52	0.60	2.52	5.60
Isopentane	0.18	0.18	0.20	0.36	1.00	3.76
Pentane	0.20	0.19	0.21	0.23	0.63	1.98
Hexane plus	0.78	0.60	0.39	0.91	1.20	1.50
Gal per 1,000 cu ft	0.807	0.700	0.636	0.969	5.598	6.570

[a] Million cu ft per day.

stripped[15] at pressures of 185, 50, and 5 psig; the rich oil is heated in direct-fired pipestill heaters; and the liquid product is fractionated into deisopentanized gasoline, kerosene, propane, isobutane, butane, and isopentane. Stage stripping or stage separation is the same general operation as the successive flashing shown in Fig. 15-15 except that vaporization is accomplished by reduction in pressure rather than increase in temperature. Such an operation assists in holding gaseous or low-boiling materials in the liquid, and hence this operation is also useful in the separation of gas from crude oil.[16,17]

Although steam is used for heat in many small and older plants, direct-

[14] Anon., Process Improvements Mark Design and Operation . . . , Oil Gas J., Dec. 15, 1945, p. 88.

[15] Wade, H. N., Multistage Weathering of Saturated Absorption Oil, Oil Gas J., Mar. 10, 1945, p. 57.

[16] Kimmel et al., Stage Separation of Oil-gas Mixtures, Oil Weekly, Oct. 17, 1938.

[17] Huntington and Schmidt, Problems in Condensate Type Production, Pet. Engr., February, 1941.

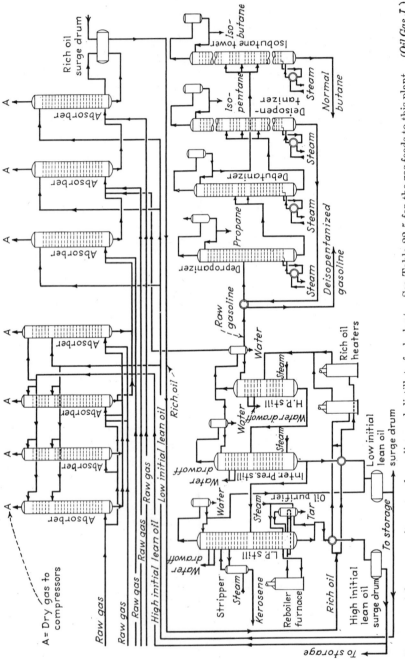

FIG. 22-2. A large-capacity natural-gasoline and distillate-fuel plant. See Table 22-5 for the gas feeds to this plant. (*Oil Gas J.*)

fired pipestill heaters are being more and more widely used.[18] These are used not only to heat the rich oil but to produce a stream of the hot oil which is used to heat all of the reboilers and sometimes to generate enough steam for stripping. Some plants are so completely automatic that they shut themselves down in an emergency.[18] Water is often scarce and in such plants air-cooled condensers are used.[19] One operator finds[19] that plants operated entirely without water (or steam) cost only slightly more than conventional plants. In the extreme, gas can be used to drive reciprocating pumps or by means of gas engines, and the stripping of rich oil can be accomplished with gas,[20] or high-pressure fractionation can be used rather than a steam-stripping still. Carryover of absorption oil is expensive and it tends to befoul the beds of desiccant type driers. It may be alleviated[20] by (1) admitting the oil two or three trays from the top of the absorber, (2) using higher-molecular-weight (210 to 230) absorption oil of a nonaromatic type, and (3) using various types of mist extractors in the top of the absorber and in the dry-gas line, especially the wire-mesh type of extractor. Small plants [2 to 5 million standard cu ft per day (MMscfd)] are becoming economically feasible,[21] and some small plants complete with drying and treating equipment are mounted on skids so that they can easily be set at a new location.

Distillate Plants. The gas in some fields is at such extremely high pressures (2,000 to 6,000 psia) that it dissolves some of the heavy liquids with which it is associated. It is so dense that it behaves somewhat as a liquid. Note in Table 22-5 that the hexane-plus content of the gases is large in the 2,250-lb gas, that it decreases down to 500 lb, and then increases again at low pressure. Thus the highest-pressure gases dissolve hexane somewhat as if the gas is a liquid whereas the hexane gets into the lowest-pressure gases simply by exerting its vapor pressure. Upon reducing the pressure of high-pressure gases, a region of liquid formation is encountered as indicated by the isothermal line of Fig. 15-6 (see also Fig. 15-8) and then upon further reduction in pressure the material becomes totally gaseous again. This type of condensation is referred to as *retrograde condensation*. For this reason, distillate gases are usually processed by reducing the pressure to 1,500 to 2,250 psia and passing them through a separator for the removal of some liquid. The gas may then be forced back into the field by compressors, or it may be sent through high-pressure absorbers before being sent back to the field. Each gas

---

[18] Sutherland and Swindell, One-man Operation . . . , *Oil Gas J.*, Apr. 18, 1955, p. 180.

[19] Lane, R. L., Dry Distillation, Two-still System, *Oil Gas J.*, Jan. 2, 1956, p. 80.

[20] Lane and Thompson, Hydrocarbon Stripping, *Oil Gas J.*, May 5, 1952, p. 174.

[21] Symposium, Midget Plants—and How They Grew, *Pet. Refiner*, June, 1956, pp. 145–156.

behaves differently, so that experimental tests are still necessary.   However, progress is being made on determining the equilibrium ratios (or constants) of hydrocarbons at high pressures and in various mixtures.   Obviously it behooves the producer to maintain a high field pressure because reduction of the pressure to 2,500 lb or lower will cause the "distillate" (hexane-plus hydrocarbons) to be lost as a liquid in the gas sand.   Almost any flow diagram would be misleading because distillate plants are so large and elaborate that no two are alike.   Figure 22-2 at least the part pertaining to high-pressure absorption and the general recovery and separation system, is typical of many recycling or distillate plants. Examples are available of plants that utilize (1) the retrograde condensation mentioned above,[22] (2) simple cooling and pressure maintenance with compressors, (3) stage separation,[22] (4) high-pressure absorption somewhat as in Fig. 22-2, and particularly combinations of these operations.

Refinery and Chemical Plant Gas Recovery.   It is becoming increasingly useful to recover substantially all of the propane and even ethane (or ethylene).   Higher absorber pressures and larger circulations of oil may be used to capture the propane or ethane, but it is also necessary to use refrigeration if ethane is to be recovered.   The Tennessee Gas Transmission Co.[23] cools the entire gas stream (750 $MMscf$) to minus 96°F with temperatures of minus 121°F at some points.   The plant can be operated so that substantially only methane is returned to the company pipeline. A somewhat similar operation is shown in the gas recovery part of Figs. 20-4 and 20-5 under the discussion of Ethylene Plants (Chap. 20).

Although true gases such as propane and ethane can be captured in absorption oil or into a liquid by refrigeration, the retention of them in the liquid state so that they can be purified by fractionation requires the use of high pressures and low temperatures.   As a compromise, one method of deethanization and retention of propane involves elimination of the main bulk of methane and ethane by means of a primary absorber.   Dissolved ethane is then completely flashed from the rich oil, carrying with it much propane which is captured again at high oil-circulation rates in a smaller reabsorber.   Much the same is accomplished in the catalytic cracking plant gas-recovery system[24] of Fig. 22-3.   This involves use of the gasoline product itself as part of the absorption liquid (it is able to hold additional gas because of the higher pressure in the absorber) but at the very top

[22] Reid and Huntington, Recent Developments in Distillate Recovery, *Ref. Nat. Gaso. Mfr.*, May, 1940, p. 69.

[23] King and Mertz, Hydrocarbon Extraction by Refrigeration, *Oil Gas J.*, Mar. 10, 1952, p. 95.

[24] Gilmour and Bauer, Refinery-Gas Extraction Plants, *Oil Gas J.*, Nov. 29, 1951, p. 84.

of the absorber, a heavy gasoline recycle oil is used to absorb the last of the propane (up to about 90 per cent). The highly wild gasoline is then processed in a combination fractionator-absorber (rich oil deethanizer of Fig. 22-3) which vaporizes unwanted methane and ethane into the upper absorber part where it is met with heavy gasoline absorption oil.

About the simplest system for the recovery of large amounts (60 to 75 per cent) of propane and propene is a plain fractionator operated at a pressure so high (300 to 360 psia with catalytic cracking gases) that the entire

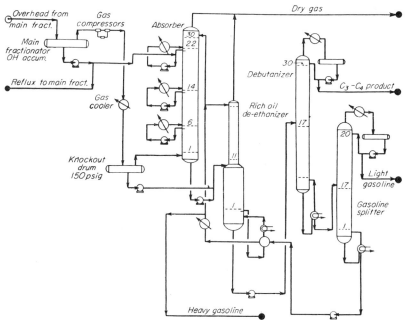

FIG. 22-3. Gas-recovery system, utilizing rich-oil deethanization, for a catalytic-cracking plant. (*Oil Gas J.*)

cracking-plant gas and gasoline stream can be admitted at the top without losing significant amounts of butane. Dissolved ethane and ethylene are eliminated from the bottom product by heating the bottom of the fractionator with a reboiler. If the recovery of even more propane is feasible an absorber operating on light cycle oil from the cracking-plant fractionator (and returning to it) can be used on the gases from the fractionator. The disadvantage of such a simple system is the cost of compression.

A small amount of refrigeration (water refrigeration to about 55°F or propane, etc., refrigeration to 0 to 10°F) is sometimes economical in recovering propane (Fig. 21-10), and in the case of ethane or ethylene recovery it is necessary to refrigerate to about minus 100°F or lower because the critical temperature of ethane is minus 89°F.   Although systems basically similar to those described for propane recovery can be used for ethane, it is usually advisable to condense all of the desired materials by refrigeration (see Figs. 20-4 and 20-5) and then separate the several hydrocarbons by a series of fractionators.   As an extreme, the Phillips Co. at Borger, Texas, separates 12 hydrocarbons (propane through isooctane) as well as 5 mixtures, using a total of 24 fractionating towers.

Carbon Black.   The three main processes of manufacture[25] in the order

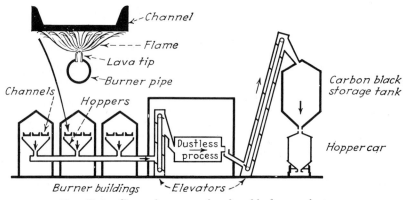

Fig. 22-4a. Channel process of carbon-black manufacture.

of importance are the Furnace[26] (Fig. 22-4b), Channel[27] (Fig. 22-4a), and Thermal[28] (Fig. 22-4c) processes.   In the *Channel* process incomplete combustion occurs in the presence of steel channels that chill the gas flame.   The *Furnace* process also involves incomplete combustion, but mixtures of gas and oil are burned (gas furnace process) and more recently oil alone.   The *Thermal* process is a cyclic process in which hot checker-brick is used to decompose the gas thermally.   Yields are large by the Thermal process, but the carbon-black particles are too large for many applications.   The carbon and gases are cooled with water (no cooling is needed in the Channel process); and the carbon is separated by Cottrell

[25] Nelson, W. L., all in *Oil Gas J.*, Furnace, May 11, 1946; Thermal, June 8, 1946, p. 95; and Channel, July 20, 1946, p. 123.

[26] Swaminathan, V. S., Britain Gets "Sootless" . . . Plant, *Oil Gas J.*, Jan. 11, 1951, p. 75.

[27] Kiddoo, G., Carbon Black . . . Natural Gasoline Industry, *Oil Gas J.*, Apr. 5, 1951, p. 81.

[28] Paulsen, D. C., Cyclic, Yet Continuous, *Instrumentation* (Minneapolis-Honeywell Regulator Co.), vol. 6, no. 6, p. 35 (1952).

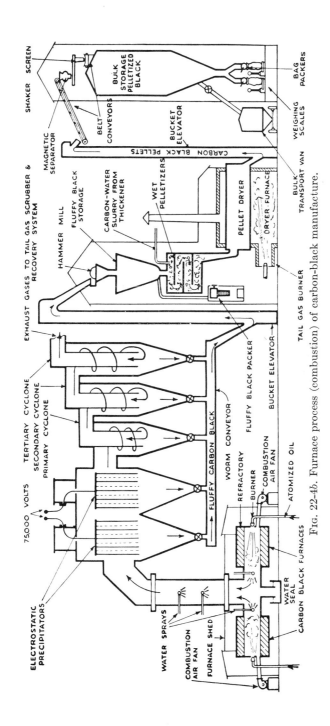

Fig. 22-4b. Furnace process (combustion) of carbon-black manufacture.

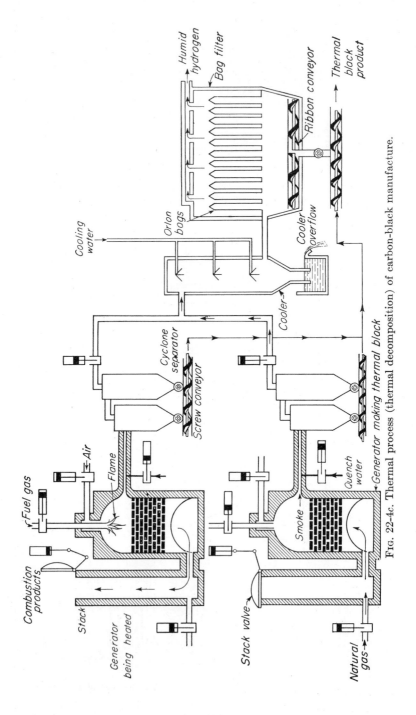

FIG. 22-4c. Thermal process (thermal decomposition) of carbon-black manufacture.

precipitators, cyclones, or bag filters and finally is consolidated into tiny beads[29] which can be handled without excessive dusting.

GAS AND PRODUCTS

Almost all field and refinery gases are of such a composition that they can be profitably processed for the manufacture of natural gasoline. Prior to 1915 a gas containing less than 7 gal of stable natural gasoline per thousand cubic feet was called a "dry gas" and in general was not considered suitable. Since that time the value of natural gasoline has increased and the methods of recovering the gasoline have been so improved that almost all natural gas containing more than 2 gal of gasoline per thousand cubic feet is being processed and gases that contain only 0.3 gal per thousand cubic feet may be economically handled. Tables 22-5, 22-6, 14-4, and 19-8 show analyses of various natural and refinery gases.

In estimating the gasoline or liquid content of a wet gas (Example 22-1), Table 22-7 will be useful. In general, the olefin hydrocarbons produce less liquid by about 7 per cent, but exact values can be computed from the specific gravities of Tables 5-2 and 5-3.

Liquids. The general composition of raw and stabilized gasolines, bottle gases, and distillates (or condensates) is shown in Table 22-6 and of pressure distillates in Table 7-2. Similar information about crude oils is shown in Table 4-5. The compositions of distillates or condensates from cycling plants (items 21 to 25, Table 22-6) are of little significance because of the wide range of pressure and temperature maintained, and because the liquid recovery is often reported as several products such as hydrocarbon liquids, distillate, and even kerosene.

The specifications of natural gasoline and the system by which it is graded are given in Fig. 3-2, and the somewhat standard grades of liquefied petroleum gases are shown in Table 3-5. The approximate relationship among the composition, properties, and grades of natural gasolines is given in Fig. 22-5. It is not generally applicable to the olefin-bearing liquids produced in refineries, but it may be used as an approximation. The butane content of many gasolinelike products is closely related to their vapor pressures (Table 22-8). In natural gas, the butanes fraction contains about 31.9 per cent (22 to 49) of isobutane, and the pentane fraction 53.7 per cent (19 to 70) of isopentane.

For statistical purposes, the U.S. Bureau of Mines and the Natural Gasoline Association of America (NGAA)[30] use the following factors (multipliers) to obtain the equivalent volume of Grade 26–70 natural gaso-

[29] Strasser, D. M., From Hydrocarbons to Carbon Black, *Pet. Refiner*, December, 1954, p. 177.

[30] Nelson, W. L., Volume Equivalent . . . , *Oil Gas J.*, July 13, 1953, p. 149; and Relative Prices . . . , *Oil Gas J.*, Sept. 28, 1953, p. 149.

TABLE 22-6. HYDROCARBON ANALYSES OF GASES AND LIQUIDS

Material	From	Gaso.,[a] gal per Mscf	API gravity	Reid v.p., psia	CH$_4$[b]	C$_2$H$_6$	C$_3$H$_8$	iC$_4$H$_{10}$	C$_4$H$_{10}$	iC$_5$H$_{12}$	C$_5$H$_{12}$	C$_6$H$_{14}$+
1. Dry natural gas	Stabilizer	0.0			77.9	10.0	8.61	2.60	0.85			
2. Dry natural gas	440-lb absorber	0.13			86.4	8.7	3.92	0.36	0.47			
3. Dry natural gas	52-lb absorber	0.06			60.8	19.8	17.12	1.21	0.97		0.2	
4. Dry natural gas	18-lb absorber	0.0			18.7	27.2	45.10	6.00	3.00			
5. Dry natural gas	Average of 45[c]	0.10			84.3	6.3	7.74	0.78	0.69	0.10		
6. Dry cracked gas[d]	Gyro plant	1.48			38.8	13.2	3.68		6.43		0.16	
7. Dry cracked gas[g]	Gyro absorber				44.4	10.3	2.95				2.47	
8. Wet refinery gas	Raw gaso. tanks				7.2	15.2	34.72	10.88	23.16	4.29	3.02	1.55
9. Wet natural gas	2,400-lb well	4.87			88.6	4.8	2.11	0.61	0.63	0.49	0.24	2.56
10. Wet natural gas	Average of 45[c]	2.13			79.8	6.5	6.22	1.35	2.33		2.97	
11. Raw natural gasoline	Absorber	1.78	94.5		0.1	1.5	12.12	8.76	29.33		48.2	
12. Raw natural gasoline	High press. abs		92.2	60.0	0.1	2.3	17.29	9.38	23.33		47.7	
13. Raw natural gasoline	High press. abs		92.2	50.0	0.1	1.8	16.03	8.81	26.95	5.54	12.24	28.61
14. Raw natural gasoline	High press. abs		91.8	51.0		1.9	17.08	10.23	25.54		45.25	
15. Raw cracked naphtha	150–200 lb separator				0.9	3.1	6.71	8.74		8.36		72.2
16. Raw cracked naphtha	25-lb sep.					0.7	3.16	6.06		6.36		83.69
17. Natural gasoline	Stabilizer		78.7	17.2				1.73	16.13	11.58	19.33	51.23
18. Natural gasoline	175-lb stabilizer		77.0	18.4				2.67	19.17	18.80	13.27	46.09
19. Commercial butane	245-lb stabilizer			62.0[f]				58.20	41.20	0.60		
20. Commercial propane	440-lb stabilizer			216.0[f]		0.2	99.4	0.40				
21. Distillate	522-lb separator				15.3	4.6	5.63	3.58	5.74	6.42	3.68	54.94[g]
22. Distillate	Stabilizer		63.7	8.9			0.13	2.87	4.45	6.72	4.38	81.45
23. Distillate, separator fluid[h]	1,250-lb, zero °F				43.7	9.4	11.55	3.80	10.30	2.45	3.90	14.85
24. Distillate flash tank[h]	400-lb, −12°F				16.7	12.0	17.10	5.80	15.85	3.75	5.90	22.90
25. Distillate low-pressure flash[h]	−50°F				1.6	2.5	8.90	3.94	14.81	7.16	8.30	52.80

[a] Approximate, Grade 26–70.
[b] N$_2$, CO$_2$, O$_2$, etc. usually included in CH$_4$.
[c] The wet gases of 10 yielded the dry gases of 5.
[d] Also 20.31% ethylene and 13.5% propene.
[e] Also 30.35% ethylene and 12.0% propene.
[f] At 105°F to simulate true vapor pressure.
[g] Heptane plus 42.14%.
[h] All from the same plant.

line, and the price factors (multipliers) used by industry during 1933–1956 are also shown:

	Volume	Price
12 R.v.p. and lower..........	1.470	
14 R.v.p...................	1.362	1.36 (and 1.30)
18 R.v.p...................	1.258	1.20
22 R.v.p...................	1.129	1.10
26 R.v.p...................	1.000	1.00
30 R.v.p. and above..........	0.896	

TABLE 22-7. RELATIONSHIP BETWEEN LIQUID AND GAS VOLUMES

	Gal liquid per 1,000 standard cu ft pure component	Standard cu ft pure component per gal liquid		Gal liquid per 1,000 standard cu ft pure component	Standard cu ft pure component per gal liquid
Methane.......	16.9[a]	59.1[a]	Hexane.......	41.1	24.3
Ethane........	25.2	39.7	Heptane......	46.4	21.6
Propane.......	27.4	36.5	Pentanes and		
Isobutane......	32.4	30.9	heavier.....	41.5	24.1
Butane........	31.6	31.6	Hexanes and		
Pentanes......	36.4	27.5	heavier.....	45.0	22.2

[a] NGAA Standard 2145, apparent values if dissolved (60°F).

TABLE 22-8. BUTANE CONTENT VERSUS VAPOR PRESSURE

Reid vapor pressure	Material	Approx. liq. vol. per cent butanes
8	400 E.P. motor gasoline	6.6
10	400 E.P. motor gasoline	10.0
12	400 E.P. motor gasoline	14.0
14	Nat. gaso. (20% evapo. at 140°F)	14.0
18	Nat. gaso. (50% evap. at 140°F)	18.0
22	Nat. gaso., Grade 22–55	15–24
26	Nat. gaso., Grade 26–70	24–33
30	Nat. gaso., Grade 30–70	33–42

Natural gasoline prior to 1931 usually fell in Grade 26–70, and such a basis is still retained in statistics, but shortly after 1931 during the development of the Oklahoma City field, great surpluses led to the sale of mainly Grade 22–70, and most gasoline during 1956 had a vapor pressure of only about 18 pounds. The volume factors tabulated above are simply the ratios of the butane-free parts of the gasolines (see Fig. 22-5). Thus if butanes had no value at all, the volume factors could be used as price factors (actually so used during 1931), but the price factors in use during 1956 imply a butane value (when sold in natural gasoline) of about one cent per gal and lower.

Example 22-1. Gasoline Content of Natural Gas. A wet gas contains 30 per cent butanes, 5 per cent pentanes, and 2 per cent hexanes and heavier.

Basis: 1,000 cu ft of the natural gas. See Table 22-7.

$$\text{Gasoline from butanes} = \frac{30}{100} \times 1,000 \times \frac{31.9}{1,000} = 0.3 \times 31.9 = 9.57 \text{ gal}$$

$$\text{Gasoline from pentanes} = 0.05 \times 36.4 = 1.82 \text{ gal}$$
$$\text{Gasoline from hexane plus} = 0.02 \times 45.0 = .90 \text{ gal}$$
$$\text{Pentanes plus} = 2.72 \text{ gal}$$

The percentage of butanes in 26–70 grade gasoline is about 32 (Fig. 22-5).

$$\text{Yield of 26–70 grade gasoline} = \frac{2.72}{0.68} = 4.00 \text{ gal per 1,000}$$

Some excess butanes would be available for bottle gas, etc.

Example 22-2. Relation of Composition and Physical Properties of Natural Gasoline (Fig. 22-5). A natural gasoline has a Reid vapor pressure of 16; it contains no propane; and 50 per cent of it distills at 140°F. What are its approximate composition, its gravity, and the percentage evaporated at 100°F?

The percentage evaporated at 140 deg is located along the base line, and the vapor pressure is located among the Reid vapor pressure axes on the right, using the 0 per cent propane axis. These two lines cross at the circle point on the diagram. This intersection point is then located with respect to the other axes in the figure, giving properties as follows:

API gravity.................... 79.2 (curved lines reading along base and to right)
Per cent evaporated at 100°F... 18.5 (rather flat curving lines reading to right)
Per cent butanes and lighter.... 13.5 (horizontal lines reading at left)
Per cent pentanes in pentanes and
 heavier.................... 35.5 (converging straight lines reading at top)

ANALYSIS

Propane...............	0.0	Pentanes (35.5%)......	30.7
Butanes...............	13.5	Hexanes + (100 − 35.5)	55.8
Pentanes +...........	86.5		86.5

Products that are to be vaporized out of the presence of air, such as bottle gas, must be substantially free from water vapor (10 ppm) because the water (or hydrate) freezes and clogs the vaporizing equipment. All products must be noncorrosive (mainly free from hydrogen sulfide), and most products must be sufficiently free from mercaptan sulfur compounds to produce a "sweet" or acceptable odor. One company's gases[31] at the

[31] Powell, J. S., Experience with Odor and Deodorization . . . , *Pet. Engr. Ref. Annual*, 1949, p. C-30.

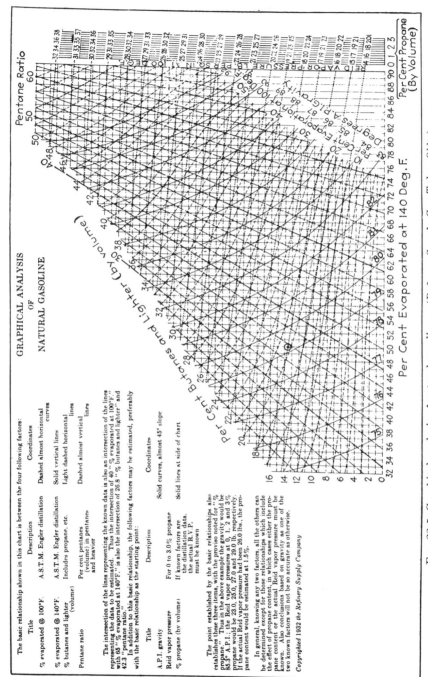

Fig. 22-5. Graphical analysis of natural gasoline. (*Refinery Supply Co., Tulsa, Okla.*)

837

field, and after passing through desulfurizers and gasoline plants, contained the following grains of sulfur per 100 cu ft:

	Mid Continent*		California
	At field	Finished	Finished
Hydrogen sulfide..........	30–650	0.25	0.30
Mercaptan...............	1.5–7.0	0.5–1.0	None
Residual organic..........	0.1–0.4	Under 0.1	None†

* Mainly West Texas–New Mexico.
† Organic sulfur added to 0.4 grains.

Air introduced into the line (within 100 miles of destination) quantitatively oxidizes the mercaptans to disulfides.[31] However, the disulfides will be reduced again to mercaptans after the oxygen is used up, in passing through additional line in which the scale is wet with slightly acid water. Natural gas and bottle gases are odorized with such stenches as ethyl mercaptan, amyl mercaptan, etc., so that gas leaks can be quickly detected. Methods of introducing stenches are discussed completely by Roy W. Parker.[32] The NGAA[33] has Tentative Standards for Liquefied Petroleum Gas, Specifications and Test Methods, and Standard Factors for Volume Correction and Specific Gravity Conversion of LPG Gases and Volatile Gasolines. The hazards of handling volatile liquids are emphasized by Pamphlet 58 of the National Board of Fire Underwriters.[34]

Conventional low-temperature analyses methods are too complicated for plant control purposes, and hence numerous approximate tests have been developed such as the absorption and weathering test of the California National Gasoline Association,[35] which is primarily for detecting losses of isobutane and heavier hydrocarbons in absorber residue gases. Generally, the test consists of passing a measured quantity of gas through a standard hydrocarbon solvent at $-44°F$ (for pentanes plus) or $-110°F$ (for isobutane plus), and then weathering the contacted solvent to a prescribed end point temperature. If the absorption factor for the commercial absorber and the composition of the inlet gas are known, the split between iso and normal butane may be estimated. Empirical boil-away

[32] Survey of Odorizing Practice in Gas Transmission, *Pet. Engr.*, Midyear, 1941, p. 114; also Anon., Inexpensive Burette Dispenses LPG Odorant, *Natl. Pet. News*, July 3, 1946, p. R-498.
[33] Kennedy Building, Tulsa, Okla.
[34] 85 John St., New York.
[35] Liljenstein and Schaufelberger, A Rapid Test for Isobutane (+) Fractions . . . , *Pet. Refiner*, April, 1946, p. 129; and CNGA Tent. Standard Methods of Test for L.P. Gases, *Bull.* T.S. 441 (1945), Los Angeles, Calif.

or controlled evaporation tests for the purity of isopentane[36] and of iso-butane[37] have also been devised. One refiner uses the following boil-away test for estimating the composition of mixed butanes (B-B cut): 100 ml of sample is run into a 100-ml graduate containing a thermometer (-20 to 120°F), everything being chilled to a temperature below the boiling point of the sample. This specimen is rejected, and the graduate is immediately refilled to 100 ml. Evaporation occurs at room temperature, and for control purposes the evaporation to 0 to 5°F is taken as propane, that

TABLE 22-9. APPROXIMATE OCTANE NUMBERS (F-1)[a] OF NATURAL GASOLINES[b]

Reid vapor pressure, psia	Lowest, clear	Average		Highest, clear
		Clear	With 3 cc TEL	
I.B.P. of 160°F............	35	44	67.5	57
Butane-free.............	56	62	80.3	69
10	60	66.5	83.3	73.5
12	62	68.5	84.3	74.5
14	63.5	70	85.1	76
16	65	71.5	85.8	77.5
18	66.5	72.5	86.3	78
20	67.5	73.5	86.7	78.5
22[c]	69	74	86.8	79.0
26[c]	70.5	75.5	87.2	80.5
30[c]	73.0	77	86.3	

[a] Motor octane numbers (F-2) are 2 to 5 units lower (Table 3-3).

[b] Empirical. The effect of vapor pressure (or percentage butanes) is greater than computations indicate.

[c] Somewhat hypothetical because cannot test by standard methods.

between 5 and 40°F as B-B cut, and the remaining material as pentane. No claims of accuracy are made, but similar split temperatures may be developed that will reasonably duplicate the performance of any commercial plant.

Natural gasoline usually has a higher octane number than normal straight-run gasoline, primarily because of the high butane content. Table 22-9 shows the approximate relationship between octane number and Reid vapor pressure for Mid Continent and Texas natural gasolines. The lowest octane numbers are associated with the highest Characterization Factor stocks, and the low values for gasolines with many side-chain

[36] Hachmuth and Tooke, Determination of the Composition of Commercial Isopentane, Natl. Pet. News, May 1, 1940.

[37] Tooke and Roberts, Determination of the Composition of Commercial Isobutane, Oil Gas J., Apr. 7, 1945, p. 98.

hydrocarbons (slightly lower C.F.).   Distillates from condensate fields
have slightly lower octane numbers because of the higher-boiling materials
(between 300 and 400°F) associated with them.   The excellent susceptibility to TEL is substantially that shown for straight-run materials in
Table 3-12.   Natural gasolines, with respect to octane number, behave
generally like straight-run gasolines in blending.

   Blending of Natural Gasoline.   The composition of natural gasoline
greatly affects its vapor pressure (Figs. 3-2 and 22-5).   The reason for the

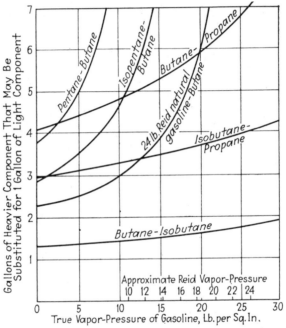

FIG. 22-6. Amount of a natural-gasoline component that can be substituted for
another component without changing the vapor pressure of the gasoline. (*Kremser,
Oil Gas J.*)

powerful effect of composition on vapor pressure is the great differences in
the vapor pressures of the low-boiling components.   The vapor pressure
of propane is very high, and hence a small amount of propane will greatly
increase the total vapor pressure.   If butane is substituted for propane
(by good fractionation), the resulting gasoline has a much lower vapor
pressure.   These relations are given graphically by Kremser.[38]   Figure
22-6 shows the gallons of a heavier hydrocarbon component that may be
substituted for a gallon of a lighter component without changing the vapor
pressure of the total material.   For each gallon of propane that is present
in a 14-lb gasoline, about 5.35 gal of butane or 3.5 gal of isobutane may

   [38] Midyear Meeting, API, Tulsa, June 3, 1932.

be substituted for the propane without changing the vapor pressure. Stated in the reverse, this means that the total yield of 14-lb gasoline can be increased by about 4.35 and 2.5 per cent respectively by substituting butane or isobutane for propane. However, butane and isobutane must be available in sufficient quantity in the raw gasoline. Thus a thorough elimination of the lightest component of a raw gasoline by good fractionation in the stabilizer is a profitable operation. For summer blending requirements a high-pentane-content gasoline is desirable but during the winter a high-butane gasoline is used.

The boiling range of naphtha and natural-gasoline blends can be closely approximated by averaging the material boiling up to a given temperature, in the ratio of the quantity of each blending agent that is used. The method is exact for fractionating distillations, but it is not perfect for distillations such as the ASTM distillation. If the entire distillation range is desired, the calculations can be more easily accomplished by graphical methods. The curve of the blend will be spaced from the curves of the two blending stocks by a distance along the percentage axis that is inversely proportional to the amount of each blending agent.

Example 22-3. Boiling Range of Blends. A naphtha contains 18 per cent of material boiling to 200°F, and a natural gasoline, 70 per cent. If the two stocks are blended 20:80, i.e., 20 volumes of natural gasoline to 80 volumes of naphtha, how much of the blend will distill at 200°F?

Per cent

$$0.80 \times 18 = 14.4$$
$$0.20 \times 70 = \underline{14.0}$$

Material boiling to 200° = 28.4

An illustration of the graphical method is not justified, but the following equations will clarify the operation to be followed in a graphical solution.

$$\text{Per cent in blend, boiling to } 200° = 18 + {}^{20}\!/_{100}(70 - 18) = 28.4$$
or $$\text{Per cent in blend, boiling to } 200° = 70 - {}^{80}\!/_{100}(70 - 18) = 28.4$$

The vapor pressure of blends can be estimated in much the same manner except that mole percentages rather than volume percentages must be used. The method is accurate when true vapor pressures are used, but it is not exact when using the Reid vapor pressure. The Reid vapor pressure is lower than the true vapor pressure because evaporation of light components from the liquid takes place during the Reid test.[39] The kinds of products produced in 1928 showed[40] that the true vapor pressure was 5 to 9 per cent higher than the Reid vapor pressure. However, the range of liquid compositions now being produced is so great that there is little

[39] Nelson, W. L., Relation of Reid to True Vapor-pressure, *Oil Gas J.*, May 10, 1947, p. 84; Recording Vapor-pressure, Sept. 27, 1947, p. 92; and June 21, 1954, p. 179.

[40] Oberfell, Alden, and Hepp, Comparison of Vapor-pressure Testing Methods, 8th Ann. Meeting API, 1928.

relation between true and Reid vapor pressures (Table 4-12).[39] The inconsistencies of Table 4-12 indicate clearly that Reid vapor pressures cannot be accurately computed.

In computing vapor pressures, the vapor pressure of the heaviest or hexane plus fraction is always troublesome. In estimating its vapor pressure, boiling point is the most accurate basis, specific gravity is fairly accurate, and molecular weight means little. The approximate relationship between the true vapor pressure and the specific gravity of "hexane plus" fractions is

Specific gravity	API gravity	Vapor pressure
0.66	83.0	6.5
0.68	76.6	3.0
0.70	70.6	1.6

Example 22-4. Vapor Pressure of Blends. Naphtha and natural gasoline are to be blended. The properties of the stocks are

Stock	Reid vapor pressure	API	Lb per gal	Molecular weight
Naphtha..............	6	57	6.25	119
Natural gasoline.........	18	72	5.79	90

What is the Reid vapor pressure of a 20:80 liquid volume blend?

According to Table 4-12 the true vapor pressure might range as follows:

Naphtha or gasoline 1.03 to 1.17 times 6 R.v.p.
Natural gasoline 1.03 to 1.14 times 18 R.v.p.

Basis: 1 gal of blend.

Mole %

Moles naphtha 0.8 × 6.25/119 = 0.042   76.5
Moles nat. gaso. 0.2 × 5.79/90 = 0.0129   23.5

Partial vapor pressure of naphtha 0.765 × 6 × 1.07 = 4.91
Partial vapor pressure of natural gasoline 0.235 × 18 × 1.085 = 4.60

True vapor pressure of blend = 9.51 psia

Reid vapor pressure of blend 9.51 ÷ 1.075 = 8.85 psia

In this instance the correction for true vapor pressure was not significant but when poorly fractionated materials (crude oils, some bottle gas, etc.) are blended, the results are greatly affected.

Note in pumping the material that the true vapor pressure of 9.51 psia must be used in computing suction conditions.

In blending very light components (ethane, propane, or the butanes) with heavier materials, the light component behaves as if it occupies a smaller volume (see Fig. 4-40). This results in slightly smaller total volumes and slightly higher densities than those obtained by plain weighted averages. When two similar materials such as natural gasoline and straight-run gasoline are blended, the octane number of the blend is the weighted arithmetic average, but when blending with cracked or most other high-octane materials the resultant octane number is higher than one would expect (Fig. 4-46).

Carbon Black. All blacks consist of minute carbon particles having hydrogen adsorbed on the surface, and the channel blacks are also thought

TABLE 22-10. KINDS OF CARBON BLACK

	Main base	Average particle diameter, millimicrons	Percentage of U.S. production (1953)	Price, relative to channel[a]	Yield, per cent of carbon in main fuel
Channel:					
HCC, high color.......	Gas	5–10		To 22[b]	
MCC, medium color...	Gas	9–17			
LCC, low color[c]........	Gas	17–25			
MPC, medium processing (rubber)	Gas	25–30	28.2	1.0[d]	1–6
EPC, easy processing (rubber)	Gas	30–33			
Furnace (rubber):					
HAF, high abrasion....	Oil	33–35	28.6	0.7–1.85	20–65
FEF, fast extruding....	Oil	45	13.2		
HMF, high modulus...	Gas	55–65	6.6	0.6–0.9	10–30
SRF, semireinforcing..	Gas	70–90	16.8		
Thermal:					
FT, fine..............	Gas	150–200	6.6	0.5–0.75	20–40
MT, medium.........	Gas	250–500			
Lamp black............	Oil	70–200	....	1.5–6.0	20–60

[a] Carload lots, f.o.b. plant, are cheaper by 0.25–0.4 cents per lb.

[b] Up to 22 times or about $1.60 per lb.

[c] Similar to HPC, hard processing (rubber) black.

[d] About 7.25 (7.1–7.4) cents per lb., 1954.

to consist of highly complex oxides of carbon. Channel black contains only about 90 per cent carbon. Particle size is fundamentally related to the uses of carbon black. Channel blacks contain the smallest particles (Table 22-10), and the particle size of the thermal blacks is so large that they cannot be used for most purposes.[41] High-color channel (HCC) black has the best tinting power but EPC (easy processing channel) also

[41] Gallie, J. F., Carbon Black Manufacture, *Pet. Processing*, November, 1946, p. 197; also Carbon Black, 2 parts, *Pet. Refiner*, March, p. 97, and April, p. 115, 1944.

has a fair tinting power.   EPC black for many years was the main black
for compounding with natural rubber.   During World War II the high
modulus furnace (HMF) black was found to be superior for use in synthetic (Buna S) rubber, and this accounts for the large increase in the
use of furnace blacks in recent years (Table 22-2).

To obtain good yields, the Characterization Factor of the oils used in
carbon black manufacture should be at least as low as 10.8 and a really

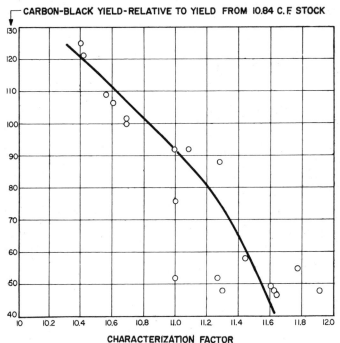

Fɪɢ. 22-7 General effect of Characterization Factor on yield of furnace black (in
one plant).   (*Oil Gas J.*)

superior oil will have a factor of 10.1[42] (Fig. 22-7).   Such oils are scarce (in
large quantity) and refiners cannot always afford to separate such small
and necessarily uniform-quality stocks.   The oil furnace processes require
that the oil vaporize completely in a fraction of a second, and although
temperatures of 2200 to 3000°F are attained, the oils cannot have a final
boiling point much above 750°F.   Common mid boiling points are 550°F
max if fed as a vapor to the carbon black furnace or burner, and 675°F if
the oil is only partially vaporized before the burner.   The yields of Fig.
22-7 apply to a furnace in which the oil is completely vaporized before
it is burned.[43]

[42] Nelson, W. L., Chemical Composition of Oils Used in Carbon Black Manufacture,
Oil Gas J., Mar. 28, 1955, p. 145; and June 20, 1955, p. 117.
[43] Nelson, W. L., Carbon Black Yields . . . , *Oil Gas J.*, Dec. 13, 1954, p. 148.

Ordinary aromatic hydrocarbons do not have the low Characterization Factors of 10.1 to 10.8 although the coal-tar distillate cut between creosote and pitch (anthracene oil) is used widely in England and Germany.[44] The aromatics must be polynuclear aromatics and if any side-chains are present, these must be unsaturated. Almost ideal polynuclear aromatics are produced in the vapor-phase cracking of gases, but the amount is very small (Table 20-3). The main sources of superior carbon black oils are:[42,44]

	Characterization Factor
Sulfur dioxide extracts (Table 11-3)	10.1–10.3
Furfural extracts of cycle oil[42]	10.2–10.5
Thermal tar (when cracking cycle oil)	10.1–10.4
Catalytic cycle stocks (Table 21-7):	
11.4 C.F. feed, 50–70% conversion	10.1–10.9
11.0–11.3 C.F. feeds	10.1–10.9
11.0–11.8 C.F. feeds, 70–90% conversion	10.0–11.1
Ethylene tar	below 10

DESIGN AND OPERATION

Three general methods of separation or concentrating the components of gases are employed: (1) absorption into a low-vapor-pressure liquid, (2) adsorption on activated clays or carbon, and (3) high-pressure low-temperature fractionation. Combinations of these operations are also employed, particularly absorption and fractionation as shown in Figs. 21-10 and 22-3. Demethanization is accomplished in Fig. 22-3 by operating the top of the tower as an absorber (with refrigeration and intercoolers) for ethylene and heavier hydrocarbons, but the bottom of the tower is heated so that it acts as a fractionator for the elimination of any methane that may have been absorbed into the oil. Much the same principles have long (1934) been employed in refinery recovery systems as the Burrell-Mase absorber-fractionator, and more recently in the deethanization of absorption oil.[45]

Absorption is the most important method of gas recovery (Figs. 22-1 and 22-2), and hence the stripping or distilling of the absorbed material from the rich oil is also important. The so-called "stripping still" in absorption plants (Fig. 22-1 or the three strippers of Fig. 22-2) involves both fractionation and stripping. The top part of the still is a fractionator, and any part of the gasoline not removed at the vaporizer section is removed in the lower part of the still by steam stripping. Reduction of the pressure in several steps or stages[15] is somewhat more effective than stripping at one pressure (see Fig. 22-2).

[44] Beede and Stokes, Carbon Black, *Pet. Processing*, September, 1954, p. 1410.
[45] Whistler, A. M., Fat-oil Deethanization, *Oil Gas J.*, Oct. 26, 1946, p. 105.

Raoult's and Dalton's laws (pages 439 and 441 and Example 15-1) are the basis for most absorption and stripping computations. At high pressures Raoult's law is not valid, and the equilibrium constants of Fig. 15-4, etc., must be used.

Basic Absorption and Stripping. The process of absorbing parts of a gas into a substantially nonvolatile liquid is in many respects similar to fractionation. Like fractionation, it depends upon obtaining equilibrium between a liquid and a gas [Eq. (15-1), page 440]. Hence it can also be practiced in a countercurrent manner in bubble towers or packed columns. It differs from fractionation because the temperature is substantially constant and because the liquid and gas do not exchange places. Only the component in which we are interested is transferred from one medium to the other.

In the petroleum industry, absorption processes are usually conducted in a bubble column, and hence the discussion that follows will be limited to this type of equipment. Envelope I (Fig. 22-8) gives the following material-balance equation:

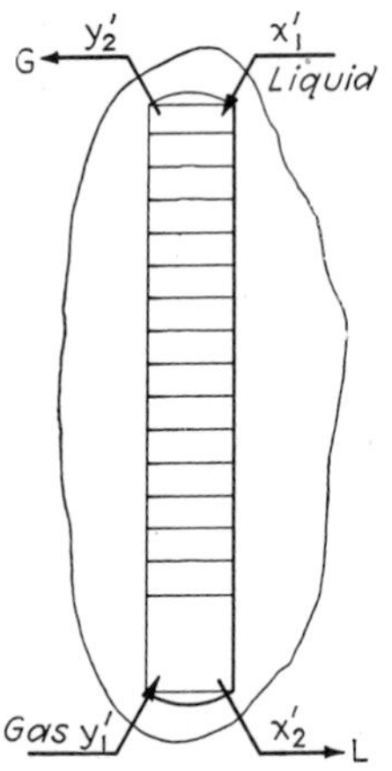

$$G(y'_1 - y'_2) = L(x'_2 - x'_1)$$
$$\frac{L}{G} = \frac{y'_1 - y'_2}{x'_2 - x'_1}$$

where L = moles of pure absorbent liquid
G = moles of pure inert gas
x'_1 and x'_2 = moles of component per mole of L
y'_1 and y'_2 = moles of component per mole of G

Note that x' and y' are defined differently in the study of fractionation. Here, x' refers to the moles of component per mole of absorbent liquid, whereas in fractionation x referred to mole fraction or the moles of component per total moles of liquid and component. A pound basis as well as a mole basis can be used.

FIG. 22-8. Absorption tower.

The ratio L/G corresponds to the ratio R/V that was used in fractionation [Eq. (16-12), page 503]. The ratio is a constant at all points in an absorbing column and is the slope of the operating line. The operating line has terminals at (x'_2, y'_1) and (x'_1, y'_2) and is shown in Fig. 22-9 as line AB. The transfer of the component from the gas to the liquid is a diffusion phenomenon, and hence the rate of transfer depends upon the difference in concentration of the component in the gas and in the liquid. The transfer of material occurs only when a difference in concentration exists, and hence transfer stops when equilibrium is attained. The minimum amount of absorption liquid that can be used can be determined by noting that the outgoing gas is in equilibrium with the incoming absorbent. The operating line for this condition would intersect the equilibrium line at y_2'. Such conditions would require an infinite number of plates but a minimum amount of oil. In Fig. 22-9 and in commercial practice more than the minimum amount of oil is utilized. The number of perfect plates is determined by the stepwise process as indicated in Fig. 22-9.

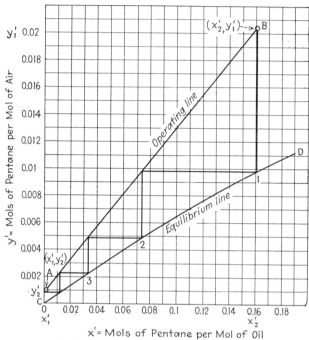

Fig. 22-9. Absorption diagram for Example 22-5.

Example 22-5. Absorption of Pentane in Gas Oil. Air from a solvent plant contains 2 per cent n-pentane. The pentane concentration is to be reduced to 0.1 per cent by contacting the gas, at 80°F and 147 psia, with 6,950 lb per hr of an absorption oil that contains 0.05 per cent pentane by weight; 100,000 cu ft of the gas, measured at 60°F, is handled per hour. The molecular weight of the oil is 220. Raoult's law and Dalton's law are assumed to be valid at these conditions.

Basis: 1 hr. Construction of operating line:
  Gas entering:

$$\text{Moles air} = \frac{100,000 \times 0.98}{379} = 259$$

$$\text{Moles pentane} = \frac{100,000 \times 0.02}{379} = 5.28$$

$$y_1' = \frac{5.28}{259} = 0.0204$$

Gas leaving:

$$\text{Moles pentane} = 259\,\frac{0.1}{99.9} = 0.26$$

$$y_2' = \frac{0.26}{259} = 0.001$$

Liquid entering:

$$\text{Moles oil} = \frac{6{,}950 \times 0.9995}{220} = 31.6$$

$$\text{Moles pentane} = \frac{6{,}950 \times 0.0005}{72} = 0.05$$

$$x_1' = \frac{0.05}{31.6} = 0.00158$$

Liquid leaving:

$$\text{Moles pentane} = (5.28 - 0.26) + .05 = 5.07$$

$$x_2' = \frac{5.07}{31.6} = 0.161$$

These points are plotted as line AB in Fig. 22-9.

Construction of equilibrium line [see Eq. (15-1), page 440]:

$$y = \frac{P}{\pi}\,x$$

where y = mole fraction in vapor
x = mole fraction in liquid

But y' and x' are moles per mole of carrying agent,

$$y' = \frac{y}{1-y} \qquad \text{and} \qquad x' = \frac{x}{1-x}$$

The vapor pressure of pentane at 80°F is 532 mm (Fig. 5-27).   The relation between x' and y' can be computed as follows (where $x = 0.01$):

$$y = \frac{532}{7{,}600}\,0.01 = 0.0007$$

$$x' = \frac{0.01}{1-0.01} = 0.0101$$

$$y' = \frac{0.0007}{1-0.0007} = 0.0007$$

x	y	x'	y'
0	0	0	0
0.01	0.0007	0.0101	0.0007
0.02	0.0014	0.0204	0.0014
0.03	0.0021	0.031	0.0021
0.04	0.0028	0.0416	0.0028
0.05	0.0035	0.0525	0.00351
0.07	0.0049	0.0752	0.00492
0.09	0.0063	0.099	0.00635
0.10	0.0070	0.111	0.00705
0.15	0.0105	0.177	0.0106
0.20	0.0140	0.25	0.0142

The number of plates can be computed by the stepwise method (Fig. 22-9).   About 3.9 perfect plates are required.

The process of stripping a component from a liquid by means of a gas may be considered as the reverse of absorption.   In absorption the concentration in the gas is high enough to drive the component into the liquid, whereas in stripping the concentration in the liquid is high and the component is transferred from the liquid to the gas.   The equilibrium line lies above the operating line (Fig. 22-10).

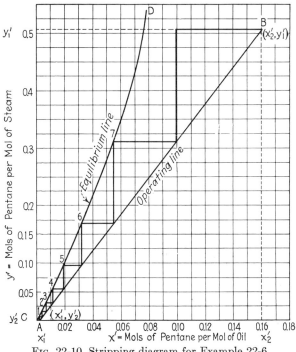

Fig. 22-10. Stripping diagram for Example 22-6.

Example 22-6.   Stripping Hexane from Absorption Oil with Steam.   A rich absorption oil of the same composition as that produced in Example 22-5 but containing hexane is to be heated to 267°F and contacted with 180 lb per hr of steam.   The tower operates at substantially 267°F.   The pressure in the stripper is 1 psig (812 mm).   The vapor pressure of hexane at 267°F is 3,800 mm.

Basis: 1 hr.   Construction of operating line:

$$x_1' = 0.00158 \text{ (liquid leaving stripper)}$$
$$x_2' = 0.161 \text{ (liquid entering stripper)}$$
$$y_2' = 0 \text{ (pure steam)}$$
$$y_1' = \frac{5.07}{180/18} = 0.507 \text{ (gas leaving stripper)}$$

These points are used to draw the line AB (Fig. 22-10).

Construction of equilibrium line: The equilibrium relation will be computed in a different way from that in Example 22-5 to illustrate another conception.

$$\text{Partial pressure} = p = Px$$

$$x = \frac{x'}{1 + x'}$$

$$\text{Partial pressure hexane} = p_p = 3,800 \frac{x'}{1 + x'}$$

$$\text{Partial pressure steam} = p_s = 812 - 3,800 \frac{x'}{1 + x'}$$

$$y' = \frac{p_p}{p_s} = \frac{3,800 \dfrac{x'}{1 + x'}}{812 - 3,800 \dfrac{x'}{1 + x'}}$$

$$y' = \frac{x'}{0.214 - 0.786x'}$$

This equation is plotted as line CD (Fig. 22-10). About $7\frac{1}{2}$ perfect plates are required.

Multicomponent Absorbers and Strippers. The performance of absorbers can be most easily understood by means of a mathematical study.[46] In an equilibrium plate the relation between the composition of the vapor leaving the plate and the liquid overflowing from the plate may be expressed as follows:

$$y_n = Kx_n \tag{15-4}$$

where y_n is the mole fraction of a particular component in the vapor leaving any plate or the nth plate; x_n is the mole fraction in the overflow liquid; and K is an equilibrium ratio that may be determined from Fig. 15-4 or if necessary from Raoult's law.

By a material balance around any tray

$$L(x_n - x_{n-1}) = V(y_{n+1} - y_n) \tag{22-1}$$

where L is the total moles of pure absorber oil; V is the total moles of dry gas; the subscript $n - 1$ refers to the plate above the nth plate; and $n + 1$ to the plate below.

Substituting $\dfrac{y_n}{K}$ for x_n, and $\dfrac{y_{n-1}}{K}$ for x_{n-1},

$$\frac{L}{KV}(y_n - y_{n-1}) = y_{n+1} - y_n \tag{22-2}$$

The factor L/KV is commonly referred to as the "absorption factor." Let

$$A = \frac{L}{KV} = \text{absorption factor} \tag{22-3}$$

[46] Souders and Brown, *Ind. Eng. Chem.*, **24**, 519 (1932).

Solving Eq. (22-2) for y_n and substituting Eq. (22-3),

$$y_n = \frac{y_{n+1} + Ay_{n-1}}{1 + A} \qquad (22\text{-}4)$$

For a *single-plate absorber*:

$$y_1 = \frac{y_2 + Ay_0}{1 + A} \qquad (22\text{-}5)$$

where y_1 is the mole fraction of the component in the gas that leaves the top plate of the absorber and y_0 is the mole fraction of the component in the gas that is in equilibrium with the entering oil (or the oil flowing from the hypothetical zero plate which is above the top plate).

For a *two-plate absorber:*

$$y_2 = \frac{y_3 + Ay_1}{1 + A}$$

Substituting the value of y_1 and solving for y_2,

$$y_2 = \frac{y_3(A + 1) + A^2 y_0}{A^2 + A + 1}$$

For a *three-plate absorber,*

$$y_3 = \frac{y_4(A^2 + A + 1) + A^3 y_0}{A^3 + A^2 + A + 1}$$

or

$$y_3 = \frac{\dfrac{(A^3 - 1)}{(A - 1)} y_4 + A^3 y_0}{\dfrac{(A^4 - 1)}{A - 1}}$$

or

$$y_3 = \frac{(A^3 - 1)y_4 + A^3(A - 1)y_0}{A^4 - 1}$$

For an *absorber with* n *plates,*

$$y_n = \frac{y_{n+1}(A^n - 1) + A^n(A - 1)y_0}{A^{n+1} - 1} \qquad (22\text{-}6)$$

and because $y_n = Kx_n$,

$$x_n = \frac{y_{n+1}(A^n - 1) + A^n(A - 1)y_0}{K(A^{n+1} - 1)} \qquad (22\text{-}7)$$

A material balance over the entire absorber gives

$$A(y_n - y_0) = y_{n+1} - y_1 \qquad (22\text{-}8)$$

Solving Eq. (22-8) for y_n and setting it equal to y_n from Eq. (22-6),

$$y_1 = y_{n+1}\left(\frac{A - 1}{A^{n+1} - 1}\right) + y_0 \frac{(A^{n+1} - A)}{(A^{n+1} - 1)} \qquad (22\text{-}9)$$

in which y_{n+1} is the mole fraction of the component in the entering rich gas or gas arising from the hypothetical plate below the bottom or n plate.

This is a general statement of the absorption equation that was derived by Kremser,[47] although the formulation herein given was published by Brown.[46] The equation may be arranged in a more convenient form thus:

$$\frac{A - 1}{A^{n+1} - 1} = 1 - \frac{A^{n+1} - A}{A^{n+1} - 1}$$

Rearranging Eq. (22-9),

$$\frac{y_1 - y_{n+1}}{y_0 - y_{n+1}} \quad \text{or} \quad \frac{y_{n+1} - y_1}{y_{n+1} - y_0} = \frac{A^{n+1} - A}{A^{n+1} - 1} \tag{22-10}$$

where $(y_{n+1} - y_1)$ = actual change in composition of gas
$(y_{n+1} - y_0)$ = maximum change in composition of gas that would occur if an infinite number of plates were used or if the gas leaving the top of the absorber were in equilibrium with the lean oil

An equation for stripping can be derived in a similar manner:

$$\frac{x_e - x_n}{x_e - x_{n+1}} = \frac{S^{n+1} - S}{S^{n+1} - 1} \tag{22-11}$$

where x_n = mole fraction of component in liquid leaving stripper (lean)
x_e = mole fraction of component in liquid entering stripper (rich)

$$S = \frac{KV}{L} = \frac{1}{L/KV} = \frac{1}{A} \tag{22-12}$$

If steam is used for stripping, as is the case in gasoline plant strippers, $x_{n+1} = 0$ and Eq. (22-11) reduces to

$$\frac{x_e - x_n}{x_e} = \frac{S^{n+1} - S}{S^{n+1} - 1} \tag{22-13}$$

These two fundamental equations [Eqs. (22-10) and (22-11)] are expressed graphically in Fig. 22-11. The figure may be used by determining the value of the factor $(y_{n+1} - y_1)/(y_{n+1} - y_0)$, or $(x_e - x_n)/x_e$, and noting the value of A (or S). Greater accuracy can be attained in such charts if the reciprocal of A and S is used. The quantity of absorption oil or steam may be obtained from A or S as explained in the following paragraph.

Absorption and Stripping Factors. The common method of expressing the amount of absorption oil is gallons of oil per thousand standard cubic feet of gas (60°F, 14.7 lb). With these units the absorption factor can be expressed as follows:

$$A = \frac{L}{KV} = \frac{3.156dG}{KM} \tag{22-14}$$

[47] *Natl. Pet. News*, May 21, 1930, p. 43.

or if Raoult's law holds

$$A = \frac{3.156 dG\pi}{PM} \tag{22-15}$$

where d = sp gr of absorption oil
G = gal of absorption oil per 1,000 cu ft of gas
K = equilibrium ratio or constant (Fig. 15-4, page 441)
M = molecular weight of absorption oil
P = vapor pressure of component, psia
π = total pressure in absorption tower, psia

The stripping factor may be expressed in a similar manner.

$$S = \frac{1}{A} = \frac{KV}{L} = \frac{KWM}{150d} \quad \text{or} \quad \frac{PWM}{150d\pi} \tag{22-16}$$

where W = lb steam per gal oil

In determining the oil-to-gas ratio for an absorber, it is necessary to decide how much of a certain low-boiling component (usually butane) can be allowed in the final gasoline and to compute the absorption factor and the oil circulation for this component. The other components will also be absorbed and to varying extents, depending upon their vapor pressures or equilibrium constants. The amount of absorption is inversely proportional to the vapor pressure [Eqs. (22-14) and (22-15)]. Thus the absorption factor is different for each component even though the oil circulation is the same for all. For several components, i.e., 1, 2, 3, etc.,

$$A_1 : A_2 : A_3 = \frac{1}{K_1} : \frac{1}{K_2} : \frac{1}{K_3} \tag{22-17}$$

After the A for the governing or key component is determined, the values of A and the amount of absorption of each of the other components can be obtained from Eq. (22-17). The reverse is true of stripping; i.e., the amount of stripping is directly proportional to the vapor pressure of the component in question. For an absorption factor of 1 ($A = 1$) for normal butane, the factors for other components in a low-pressure absorber are about as follows:

Component	Absorption factor A
C_3H_8	0.25 of factor for butane
iC_4H_{10}	0.67 of factor for butane
C_4H_{10}	1.0 of factor for butane
iC_5H_{12}	2.67 of factor for butane

This relation is only approximate because it varies with temperature.

The full significance of the factor $(y_{n+1} - y_1)/(y_{n+1} - y_0)$ in Fig. 22-11 may be overlooked. The expression $y_{n+1} - y_1$ is nearly equal to the amount of component that is removed from the gas; i.e., it is the difference between the concentration in the incoming and outgoing gas.[48] The expression in the denominator, $y_{n+1} - y_0$, represents the maximum amount of component that could be removed if the outgoing gas were in equilibrium with the incoming lean oil. If the absorption oil contains none of the component under consideration, i.e., $x_0 = 0$ (therefore $y_0 = 0$), the factor $(y_{n+1} - y_1)/(y_{n+1} - y_0)100$ is nearly[48] equal to the percentage recovery of the component in the absorber. For practical purposes, it may be considered as the fraction of the component that

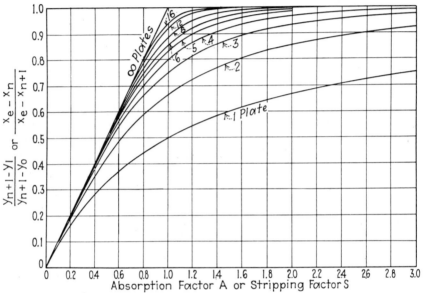

FIG. 22-11. Relation of number of equilibrium plates to absorption and stripping factors. (*Brown, Ind. Eng. Chem.*)

is absorbed.   Likewise, $(x_e - x_0)/x_e$ is nearly[48] equal to the fraction of the component that is removed from the oil by the stripper.   Thus if we desire to absorb 99 per cent of the isopentane from a gas, the value of $(y_{n+1} - y_1)/(y_{n+1} - y_0)$ is nearly 0.99, if the lean oil contains no isopentane.   Or if we wish to strip 99 per cent of a component from the oil with steam, the value of $(x_e - x_n)/x_e$ is nearly 0.99.   The application of Fig. 22-11 to the design or analysis of an absorber is by no means as complicated as the mathematical derivation herein presented.   The use of Fig. 22-11 can be most ably presented by means of the examples which follow this discussion.

[48] It is not exactly equal to the amount of component removed because the total number of moles of gas changes as it passes through the absorber. If the compositions were given as moles of component per mole of dry gas, then the expression would exactly represent the moles of component removed per mole of dry gas.

An examination of Fig. 22-11 also shows the relation between absorption factor and the percentage of component that is absorbed. Consider the line for five theoretical plates. This line approaches the line for infinite plates as the absorption factor is decreased, until at 50 per cent absorption, or $(y_{n+1} - y_1)/(y_{n+1} - y_0)$, the value of A is nearly 0.5 (about 0.505). The number of plates that are used also affect the location of the point at which A is substantially equal to the percentage absorbed. Likewise the number of plates is related to the absorption factor that must be used to absorb substantially all of a component.

The optimum value of the absorption factor A for any particular plant is primarily a function of the value of gasoline and the cost of recirculating oil. The absorption factor (or oil recirculation) increases rapidly as large percentages of the key component are absorbed. In most situations the economical amount of key component to absorb in gasoline plants is between 90 and 95 per cent[49] rather than the 99 per cent value that is so frequently employed. The economical recovery of key component may be as low as 60 to 70 per cent in small refinery installations, if the price of gasoline is low, or if the cost of oil recirculation exceeds about 4 cents. (See page 885.)

Example 22-7. Oil Rate for Low-pressure Absorber. A 26–70 grade of finished gasoline is to be produced from a gas of the following composition:

Component	Volume per cent
C_3H_8	7.15
iC_4H_{10}	1.39
C_4H_{10}	2.55
iC_5H_{12}	1.34
$C_5H_{12}+$	1.98

The absorber is to operate at 90°F and at a pressure of 50 psia. The absorption oil has a specific gravity of 0.83 and a molecular weight of 160. The oil is completely stripped of isopentane, but it contains 0.0005 mole fraction of pentane plus. The absorber has 16 actual plates.

How much oil should be recirculated, and what will be the approximate composition of the raw gasoline?

A 26–70 grade of gasoline will contain about 33 per cent butanes and lighter. If 99 per cent of the isopentane is absorbed, enough butanes will be absorbed to provide the 33 per cent that is required in the finished gasoline (Fig. 22-5).

Considering isopentane (key component),

$$y_1 = \text{mole fraction in residue gas} = \frac{0.01 \times 0.0134}{(1 - 0.0134) + 0.01 \times 0.0134} = 0.000136$$

$$\frac{y_{n+1} - y_1}{y_{n+1} - y_0} = \frac{0.0134 - 0.000136}{0.0134 - 0} = 0.9898$$

[49] Nelson, W. L., Economy in Natural Gasoline Plant Operation, *Ref. Nat. Gaso. Mfr.*, May, 1936, p. 167.

For practical calculations it is customary to use the value of $(y_{n+1} - y_1)/(y_{n+1} - y_0)$ as the percentage absorbed, or in this case 99 per cent.

If the plate efficiency is 50 per cent, the column will behave as if it consisted of eight theoretical plates. The absorption factor, to recover 99 per cent of a component, when eight plates are used, is about 1.5 (Fig. 22-11). The equilibrium constant for isopentane at 90°F and 50 lb is about 0.37 (Fig. 15-4).

$$\text{Gal oil per } 1,000 = \frac{AKM}{3.156d} = \frac{1.5 \times 0.37 \times 160}{3.156 \times 0.83} = 33.8$$

The equilibrium constant for butane is about 0.9 (Fig. 15-4), and hence the absorption factor for butane is

$$A_{\text{butane}} = 1.5 \frac{0.37}{0.9} = 0.615$$

and the absorption of butane (Fig. 22-11) is about 61 per cent. The gallons of butane absorbed per 1,000 cu ft are

$$0.0255 \times 31.6 \times 0.61 = 0.492$$

All the components were studied in the same manner, as shown in Table 22-11.

TABLE 22-11

Component	Mole fraction	Gal per 1,000 cu ft[a]	Equi. constant at 90°F and 50 lb	Ab- sorp- tion factor	Percentage of each component that is absorbed (Fig. 22-11)	Gal ab- sorbed per 1,000 cu ft	Per- centage compo- sition of raw gasoline
C$_3$H$_8$...........	0.0715	1.96	2.8	0.2	20	0.39	16.2
iC$_4$H$_{10}$.........	0.0139	0.45	1.2	0.46	46	0.21	8.7
C$_4$H$_{10}$.........	0.0255	0.8	0.9	0.615	61	0.49	20.4
iC$_5$H$_{12}$.........	0.0134	0.5	0.37	1.5	99	0.49	20.4
C$_5$H$_{12}+$........	0.0198	0.82	0.24	2.3	100	0.82	34.3
						2.40	100.0

[a] Table 22-7.

The analysis of the raw gasoline is not exact because some of the propane and butanes will be lost in the stripper and a little ethane (neglected) will be present in the raw gasoline.

The approximate analysis of the finished stable gasoline can be estimated as follows:

Gal of pentanes and heavier............ $0.49 + 0.82 = 1.31$

Gal of butanes...................... $1.31 \times \dfrac{0.33}{0.67} = 0.645$

Excess butanes............ .... $(0.21 + 0.49) - 0.645 = 0.055$ gal

ANALYSIS OF STABLE GASOLINE

Component	Gal	Percentage, liq vol.
Butanes.............................	0.645	33.0
Isopentane........................	0.490	25.1
Pentanes+.........................	0.820	41.9
Recovery of 26–70 gasoline..........	1.955	100.0

Gasoline plant strippers or stills are primarily fractionators, and the design methods are those of Chaps. 15 and 16. In general, the rich-oil feed would be flashed at the feed plant conditions, and then the equilibrium liquid that travels down the stripping part of the tower would be stripped using computations similar to those of Example 22-7. The capacity of a stripper or stripping section is generally lower than that of most fractionators, and absorbers have especially low capacities (Fig. 16-13 and Table 16-7). The newer perforated types of plates operate at larger capacities.[50] Cracked and high-boiling oils tend to foam more than light straight-run oils, and aromatic or pyrolytic products appear to be the worst foamers.[51] This may further contribute to a low capacity (Fig. 16-13). Example 16-12, page 509, indicates the general procedure in designing 3-component fractionators.

The plate efficiency in absorbers is usually low, being only 8.7 to 18.4 per cent for low-pressure absorbers (under 100 psia) and 38 to 56.4 per cent for absorbers at higher pressures.[52] Similar results, but slightly higher, were obtained by H. E. O'Connell.[53] The low efficiency is exactly what should be expected because of the high viscosity of the absorber oil, [see Eq. (16-10), page 498, and Fig. 16-14]. Likewise, the lower viscosity of the oil when in a stripper (a higher temperature) leads to higher plate efficiencies, i.e., 49 to 64 per cent.

Finally, the theoretical derivation of absorption and stripping introduced heretofore [Eqs. (22-1) to (22-11)] is not perfect.[54,55] The derivation employed mole fraction as if it were moles component per mole of inert gases (or oil), nor can the inert material be defined with certainty in

[50] Kelley, R. E., Perforated Plates vs. Bubble Plates, *Pet. Refiner*, May, 1955, p. 188.

[51] Schutt, H. C., Foaming a Factor in Absorber Design, *Pet. Refiner*, July, 1945, p. 93.

[52] Drickamer and Bradford, Overall Plate Efficiency . . . Function of Viscosity, *Trans. A.I.Ch.E.*, **39**, 319 (1943).

[53] Plate Efficiency . . . Columns and Absorbers, *Trans. A.I.Ch.E.*, **42**, 741 (1946).

[54] Ragatz and Richardson, Absorber Operating Efficiency, *Oil Gas J.*, Nov. 23, 1946, p. 89.

[55] Maass, R., Operation of Central Gas Plant at . . . , *Pet. Engr.*, December, 1944, p. 178.

multicomponent systems. In addition, it has been assumed by almost all designers that theoretical plates can be converted to actual plates by a single plate efficiency divisor whereas there is some indication that the efficiency cannot be applied in this simple manner.[54] Most troublesome of all is the inaccuracy of analysis methods, particularly the "splits" between iso and normal compounds of the same number of carbon atoms. These several difficulties force designers to rely upon the theoretical derivation presented here [Eqs. (22-10) and (22-11)], although at least one complicated correction method is available.[54,56]

High pressure is advantageous because less oil recirculation is required and because a smaller diameter absorber may be used. However, these advantages must pay for the cost of compression and the cost of high-pressure equipment. Compression above about 150 psig in absorbing butanes is not usually justified, and hence high-pressure absorbers are used only if the gas is already available at a high pressure, as from a high-pressure field or from a high-pressure fractionator (or processing) operation. In absorbing highly volatile components, e.g., ethylene or propane, higher pressures are economical. Ordinarily little or no rise in temperature occurs in an absorber; but, if the amount absorbed is very large i.e., when the gas is very rich or the pressure is relatively high, a temperature rise of 10 to 20°F may occur. The heat of absorption is apparently about equal to the latent heat of vaporization of the material at the same temperature. Obviously, intercoolers are helpful in maintaining a low absorber temperature and in increasing the efficiency of absorption.[57] The condensation that takes place during compression may be computed by Eq. (15-9) or (15-10) as in Example 22-8.

The use of crude oil as an absorption oil is sometimes economical.[58] The success of the operation depends upon the substitution (see Fig. 22-6) of butanes and pentanes in the crude oil for propane (and ethane) by high-pressure absorption followed by fractionation.

Example 22-8. Condensation during Compression. A lean natural gas is to be compressed from 30 to 500 psia and cooled to 80°F before it enters the absorber. The analysis of the gas is

CH_4	78.8	C_4H_{10}	2.3
C_2H_6	6.5	iC_5H_{12}	1.6
C_3H_8	6.2	$C_5H_{12}+$	3.2
iC_4H_{10}	1.4		

[56] Ragatz, E. G., Straight-line Chart Determination of Absorber-Extraction Efficiency, *Oil Gas J.*, Feb. 12, 1948, p. 78.

[57] Jackson and Sherwood, Performance of Refinery Gas Absorber . . . , *Trans. A.I.Ch.E.*, **37**, 959 (1941).

[58] Gordon, J. A., Crude Oil Absorption Clicks with Union, *Oil Gas J.*, Nov. 8, 1954, p. 172.

What is the final composition of the gas and condensate and the amount of condensate?

Basis: 100 moles or volumes of gas.

Equation (15-9) must be solved by trial and error because V (or L) is not known until the computation is complete.

A value of V is assumed; L is found from V; and Eq. (15-9) is filled in. The solution of the equation gives the actual V; and if it is not the same as the assumed value, a new assumption must be made.

As an example, the values for methane in the table will be computed:
Assume $V = 96$, then $L = (100 - V)$ or 4.

$$\frac{L}{V} = \frac{4}{96} = 0.0416$$

K_1 for CH_4 at 80°F and 500 lb (Table 15-1) is about 6.5.

$$K_1F_1 = 6.5 \times 78.8 = 512.2$$
$$\frac{L}{V} + K_1 = 0.0416 + 6.5 = 6.542$$
$$\frac{K_1F_1}{(L/V) + K_1} = \frac{512.2}{6.542} = 78.29 \text{ volumes of } CH_4 \text{ uncondensed}$$

The condensation of other hydrocarbons was computed in a similar manner as shown in Table 22-12.

TABLE 22-12. TRIAL-AND-ERROR SOLUTION FOR EXAMPLE 22-8

(1)	(2)	(3)	(4)	Assume $V = 96$, $\frac{L}{V} = 0.0416$		(7)
				(5)	(6)	
Component	Values of F, moles	Values of K at 500 lb and at 80°F[a]	$K \times F$, (2) $\times$ (3)	$\frac{L}{V} + K$	Values of V, (4) ÷ (5)	Moles gaso. (2) − (6)
CH₄...........	78.8	6.5	512.2	6.542	78.29	0.51
C₂H₆..........	6.5	1.2	7.8	1.242	6.27	0.23
C₃H₈..........	6.2	0.46	2.85	0.502	5.68	0.52
iC₄H₁₀........	1.4	0.22	0.31	0.262	1.18	0.22
C₄H₁₀.........	2.3	0.16	0.368	0.202	1.82	0.48
iC₅H₁₂........	1.6	0.071	0.114	0.113	1.01	0.59
C₅H₁₂+.......	3.2	0.052	0.166	0.094	1.77	1.43
Total........	....	.....	....	.....	96.02	3.98

[a] Read from another source than Fig. 15-4, hence slightly different values.

Upon totaling the volumes of each of the hydrocarbons, column (6), the total is 96.02 rather than 96 as assumed. A second solution would have been necessary had the sum been in error by more than about 0.1 per cent.

The compositions of the residue gas and the condensate are as follows:

Component	Moles, or volume per cent	
	Residue gas	Condensate gasoline
CH_4.	81.53	12.80
C_2H_6.	6.53	5.78
C_3H_8.	5.91	13.08
iC_4H_{10}.	1.23	5.53
C_4H_{10}.	1.91	12.06
iC_5H_{12}.	1.05	14.82
$C_5H_{12}+$.	1.84	35.93

The residue gas, as shown above, is the material that would be processed in a 500-lb absorber.

Liquefied Petroleum Gases. The recovery of such materials involves first the absorption and retention of propane as well as butane and, second, the fractionation of the wild natural gasoline into propane, butane (or mixtures of them), and stable gasoline (see Fig. 22-2). Means of increasing the absorption of propane are, (1) use more plates in the absorber (24 to 36), (2) refrigerate the absorption oil and perhaps the rich gas, (3) use lighter absorption oil, and (4) increase the pressure. Increasing the number of plates is effective only if the absorption factor is between about 0.6 and 2.0[59] Refrigeration to temperatures less than about 50°F is difficult because of the formation of gas hydrates throughout the system. Increase in pressure is effective, but the cost of compression is high.

Once the propane has been absorbed, it still presents a problem because it tends to vaporize or escape from the stripping-still receiver. The gas that escapes from the receiver can be recycled back into the absorber as indicated in Fig. 22-1 or 22-2, but this may overload the absorber unless a very high pressure is maintained in the stripping still. F. W. Bell[59] proposes the circulation of stabilized gasoline through the stripping-still receiver as a "sponge" or absorption medium to hold the propane (also see Fig. 15-16). A combination stripping and absorbing still as indicated in Fig. 22-3 is effective in deethanizing the rich oil. Of course, the stripper-still separate gas can be compressed into the stabilizer or fractionator system, but this requires the use of a high-pressure low-

[59] Increasing Propane Recovery in Existing . . . Plants, *Oil Gas J.*, May 19, 1945, p. 114.

temperature fractionator (deethanizer) because ethane will be the overhead product (and reflux) of the fractionator (Fig. 20-4). The retention of
propane is somewhat more effective if two or more stages of pressure
reduction are used in the stripper system, as indicated in Fig. 22-2. This
permits a relatively lean stripping-still gas to be sent back to the absorber;
and the smaller quantities of gases produced from the lower pressure
stages can be compressed, refrigerated, or handled by any of the methods
suggested above.

Finally, the propane can be recovered by adsorption (Hypersorption) as
discussed on pages 342 to 346, and Fig. 10-17.

Stabilizer or Fractionator Design. Entirely satisfactory methods of
determining the number of plates in a stabilizer or fractionator are not
available. However, Chap. 16 discusses the general theory, and Examples 16-9 to 16-12 explain the behavior of two-component and three-
component systems. Commercial reflux ratios and the corresponding
number of plates for separations between common pairs of components
(propane-isobutane, etc.) are indicated in Table 16-10. All methods
involve trial-and-error computations (Example 16-12 p. 509), and to a
large extent they are mathematical exercises because of doubtful assumptions that must be made and especially because of the inadequacy of
equilibrium ratios. Perhaps the safest way to approach the design is to
employ reflux ratios and numbers of plates that have been used commercially, relying, of course, upon a knowledge of the basic relationships.
An illustration of one of the proposed methods of design would consume
20 pages of this book and would arrive at an approximation of the minimum reflux and minimum number of plates but no answer for a practical
reflux ratio.

In designing a stabilizer, the conditions at the top (Example 22-9) and
at the bottom are computed, the number of plates and reflux ratio are
adopted from examining commercial operations (Table 16-10), and means
are provided to condense the reflux at the top and to supply reboiler heat
at the bottom.

Example 22-9. Stabilizer Pressure and Composition of Reflux. A raw gasoline
has the following composition:

CH_4.............	0.03	iC_4H_{10}.........	9.38
C_2H_6...........	2.27	C_4H_{10}.........	23.33
C_3H_8...........	17.29	iC_5H_{12+}........	47.77

A 26–70 grade of gasoline is to be produced. The temperature of the cooling water
is 83°F, and hence the condenser temperature can be about 90°F. What is the approximate fractionator pressure?

A 26–70 grade of gasoline contains about 30 per cent butane. The moles and mole fractions of the components in the residue gas are about as follows:

Component	Moles	Approximate mole per cent in residue gas
CH$_4$...................	0.03	0.09
C$_2$H$_6$.................	2.27	7.1
C$_3$H$_8$.................	17.29	54.21
i and n C$_4$H$_{10}$..........	12.3*	38.6
Total...............	31.89	100.0

* i and n C$_4$H$_{10}$ = (9.38 + 23.33) − (47.7 × $^3\!\%_0$).

If the top reflux ratio is 4 to 1, the total material which comes to the gas separator is 5 parts, and the composition of the 4 parts of reflux must be assumed. As a first approximation, the composition of the dew point liquid can be used. The dew point of the gas occurs when summation of the y/K's for each component (i.e., x's) equals 1.0 [Eqs. (15-3) to (15-7), page 441]. The temperature is fixed but the pressure can be altered as indicated in Table 22-13.

TABLE 22-13. DEW POINT COMPOSITION OF LIQUID IN EXAMPLE 22-9

(1) Component	(2) Vapor y	Assume 100 psia		Assume 65 psia	
		(3) K at 90°	(4) (2) ÷ (3)	(5) K at 90°F	(6) (2) ÷ (5)
CH$_4$................	0.0009	30			
C$_2$H$_6$..............	0.0710	5	0.0142	8	0.009
C$_3$H$_8$..............	0.5421	1.5	0.361	2.3	0.236
C$_4$H$_{10}$.............	0.3860	0.5	0.773	0.71	0.544
Total............			1.1482		0.789

The pressure so obtained is substantially correct, and it will be used although it is obvious that a higher pressure will finally be needed. However, the reflux composition is very wrong. It should be much leaner in ethane and slightly richer in the other components, somewhat as indicated in column (3) of Table 22-14. In a balanced state of operation, the composition of the reflux liquid in the gas separator drum is exactly the same as that of the reflux vapor leaving the top plate (along with the gas product). Accordingly, four parts of reflux and one part of gas, when brought to equilibrium at 90°F at 65 psia and when condensing 80 per cent, should result in a liquid (reflux) composition that is identical with that assumed. Such computations are indicated in Table 22-14 [see Eq. (15-9)], and although the computed reflux composition checks reasonably well with the assumed reflux composition, the reflux ratio is 0.7605/0.2395 or 3.18 rather than 4. Accordingly, Table 22-15 indicates similar and final computations but arriving at a pressure of about 80 psia.

The check is still not perfect but it is obvious that a slight adjustment will make the arithmetic check. Certainly no more detail is necessary because the answers found here, regardless of their detail, are only an indication of the situation. Also, it is still necessary to use enough plates in the stabilizer to accomplish the separation with a reflux ratio of only about 3.2.

TABLE 22-14. REFLUX COMPOSITION AT 65 PSIA FOR EXAMPLE 22-9

(1)	(2)	(3) Reflux	(4) Reflux	(5)	(6)	(7)	(8)	(9)	(10)	(11) Reflux	(12) Reflux
Component	Gas com-position	Assumed	$4 \times (3)$	Separator feed $(2) + (4)$	Mole fraction $(5) \div 5.0$	K at 90°F, 65 psia	$L/V + K$ $4 + (7)$	$\dfrac{K}{L/V + K}$ $(7) \div (8)$	$\dfrac{Kx}{L/V + K}$ $(6) \times (9)$	Mole $(6) - (10)$	Mole fraction
CH$_4$........	0.0009	....	....	0.0009	0.0002	45	49	0.92	0.00018		
C$_2$H$_6$........	0.0710	0.01	0.04	0.111	0.0222	8	12	0.667	0.0148	0.0074	0.0097
C$_3$H$_8$........	0.5421	0.31	1.24	1.782	0.3564	2.3	6.3	0.366	0.1305	0.2259	0.2970
C$_4$H$_{10}$........	0.3860	0.68	2.72	3.106	0.6212	0.71	4.71	0.151	0.0940	0.5272	0.6933
Total......	1.0000	1.00	4.00	5.000	1.0000				0.2395	0.7605	1.0000

The bottom temperature can be computed in a manner similar to that used in Example 22-9.   For this situation, however, the sum of the *partial vapor pressures* (atmospheres) or Kx's should be equal to 1.0.   The temperature is varied until the Kx's are such that the sum is equal to 1.0.   In

TABLE 22-15. ADJUSTING TO PROPER PRESSURE IN EXAMPLE 22-9

(1)	(2)	(3)	(4)	(5)	Reflux		
Component	K at 90°F and 80 psia	$\dfrac{K}{4+K}$	Separator feed, mole fraction[a]	$\dfrac{Kx}{L/V+K}$ (3) × (4)	(6) Mole (4) − (5)	(7) Mole fraction	(8) Assumed
CH$_4$........	40	0.91	0.0002	0.00018	0.00002		
C$_2$H$_6$......	6.3	0.612	0.0222	0.0136	0.0086	0.0109	0.100
C$_3$H$_8$......	1.9	0.322	0.3564	0.1150	0.2414	0.3050	0.310
C$_4$H$_{10}$.....	0.60	0.130	0.6212	0.0810	0.5402	0.6841	0.680
Total....				0.20978	0.79022	1.0000	

[a] Based on same assumption as Table 22-14.   Same as column (6) of Table 22-14.

fact, the same general type of computation may be used at many points such as the gas separator vessel, the top plate, or the feed plate, and may even be used in working from plate to plate throughout the tower to determine the number of plates that are required.   At many points in the tower, however, the method is very complicated, because reflux, whose composition is basically unknown, constitutes a part of the material at each plate.

CHAPTER 23

ECONOMICS OF DESIGN

Engineers tend to become businessmen because of their constant association with economic problems, and this association accounts for the large proportion of engineers found in executive positions. Engineers are also called upon to make decisions and to act, even though technical information is lacking or inadequate. In this respect they differ from pure scientists whose interest usually pertains to the obtainment of scientific facts regardless of the immediate need. Economic considerations pervade every detail of engineering design, and hence only a few illustrations can be introduced here.

COSTS OF PROCESSING

Operating costs vary widely from plant to plant because of numerous factors such as:

1. Type of plant—modern or obsolete, simple or elaborate.
2. Type of management—corporate or personal.
3. Location—cost of fuel, labor, etc.
4. Feedstock quality—gravity, octane number of gasoline, etc.
5. Capacity of plant.

Complete costs can seldom be assembled at a particular date, and hence cost indexes such as those of Table 23-1 must be employed. Indexes are especially useful if they are kept up to date in readily available publications. The ENR (Engineering News Record) index of construction costs has been used since 1913 and it is published each month. Likewise the Nelson Refinery Construction Cost Index is published in the first issue each month of *The Oil and Gas Journal.*[1] Refinery wages and the productivity of refinery labor can be obtained (or computed) from information in the monthly magazine entitled *Survey of Current Business* (U.S. Department of Commerce) or from quarterly issues (January, April, July, and October) of *The Oil and Gas Jouranl* (Itemized Cost Indexes). There is no truly satisfactory way to state an operating cost index because the value of fuel varies widely from plant to plant, and the fuel cost

[1] Nelson, W. L., . . . How it is Computed, *Oil Gas J.*, Oct. 1, 1956, p. 110.

changes frequently in terms of the value of cracking-still gases (bottle gases) and No. 6 fuel oil. However, except for uncertainty about the cost of fuel, the index[2] used in Table 23-1 is logical. The fuel (and power) cost

TABLE 23-1. CONSTRUCTION AND OPERATING COST INDEXES
Basis 1946[a]

Year	ENR construction[b]	Nelson refinery construction			Refinery wages[a]	Productivity (bbl per man)[a]	Operating cost	
		Material	Labor[a]	Total			Refinery[a,c]	Plants[d]
1926	60	88	61	72	57	121	69	86.5
1932	45	68	49	57	49	138	38.5[e]	47
1939	68	83	73	77	71	140	65.5[e]	74
1942	80	86	82	84	82	125	74.5[e]	80.5
1946	100	100	100	100	100	100	100	100
47	119	122	113	117	109	105	122.5	115.5
48	133	139	128	132	126	109	149	138
49	138	144	137	140	133	125	156.5	141
50	147	149	144	146	138	125	170.5	152
1951	157	164	152	157	149	126	180	163
52	164	164	163	164	155	132	185.5	169
53	173	172	174	174	165	135	160	143.5
54	181	175	183	180	170	142	149.5	142
55	191	176	190	184	177	149	176.5	172
56	200	190	198	195	192	145	184.5	181
57 est.	209	202	209	206	198	149	191	187

[a] 1946 basic values are—Nelson index, common labor $1.033 per hr, skilled $1.80 per hr; refinery wages $56.75 per week; productivity 26.7 bpd per employee (total); and operating cost 52 cents per bbl.

[b] 25 cwt building steel; 1,088 fbm specified lumber; 6 bbl cement; and 200 hr common labor.

[c] For complete refineries based on 15%, wage index corrected for productivity; 35% six-year running average of Gulf Cargo Bunker prices plus 20% if price is rising or less 20% is falling, relative to $1.30 for 1946; 30% Nelson Construction Index (maintenance); and 20% cc TEL per gal relative to 1.1 cc during 1946.

[d] Same as complete refinery index except TEL factor is left out.

[e] Estimated.

of the operating index of Table 23-1 is a six-year running average plus 20 per cent if the price is rising and less 20 per cent if it is falling. Although the productivity index of Table 23-1 is a satisfactory average, major refiners during 1955 employed 2 to 3 times as many men per barrel

[2] Nelson, W. L., Operating Cost Index, *Oil Gas J.*, July 13, 1950, p. 98. (A correction for productivity should be applied to the labor cost.)

throughput as independent refiners (in plants of 10,000 to 30,000 bpd capacity). Very large refineries (300,000 bpd) employ about the same number of employees per barrel as do small (10,000 bpd) independent refiners.[3]

These many influences cause wide variations in operating costs. The costs recorded here were taken in many instances from actual plant records for plants situated all over the country and from sources too numerous to list here. The costs for sales, advertising, research, general administration expense, depreciation, taxes, and profit are not included in the general operating costs, but the depreciation and taxes are included in the complete refinery operating costs (except when noted otherwise).

Refinery Operations. The operating costs of refineries usually fall within the following ranges (1956):

Cents per bbl (range)

Topping	35 (13–58)
Topping and thermal cracking	56 (23–95)
Cat. and thermal cracking, polymerization, etc	70 (40–105)
Cat. cracking, coking, polymerization, etc	78 (52–110)
Complete processing	95 (68–135)

Costs may be stated in three major ways: (1) in terms of the labor, utilities, TEL and chemicals, etc. (Table 23-2), (2) in terms of departments or units (Table 23-3), or (3) in terms of the properties of crude oil that affect

TABLE 23-2. TOPPING AND CRACKING, CENTS PER BARREL FEEDSTOCK (1945)[a]

	Topping		Cracking		Topping and cracking	
	10,000[b]	1,000[b]	10,000[b]	2,000[b]	15,000[b]	3,000[b]
Fuel	0.9–6.0	1.1–7.0	2.8–14.0	2.8–14.0	2.8–14.4	2.8–15.4
Water	0.3	0.4	0.7–2.0	0.8–1.6	0.4–1.0	0.5–1.4
Steam and power	0.1–1.7	0.1–2.8	0.4–4.5	0.5–4.9	0.5–4.4	0.4–5.7
Chemicals and TEL	0.1–4.8	0.1–4.9	0.2–9.3	0.2–10.1	0.2–10.4	0.2–11.0
Royalty			To 3.0	To 3.0	To 1.8	To 1.8
Labor	0.5–2.0	1.7–5.1	1.6–5.4	2.6–8.2	1.3–5.2	3.0–10.0
Maintenance and insurance	0.3–1.6	0.5–1.8	0.7–5.0	1.0–5.4	0.6–4.6	1.0–5.0
Depreciation, obsolescence, and paid-up royalty	0.4–0.8	0.5–2.6	1.6–4.2	2.6–6.0	1.2–3.3	1.8–6.2
Supervision	0.6–1.3	3.0–6.6	0.2	0.2–0.8	0.6–1.4	2.8–7.1
Total	7–17	11–28	12–40	14–48	11–39	15–50

[a] Nelson, W. L., Profit per Barrel of "Extra" Throughput, *Oil Gas J.*, May 5, 1945, p. 113.

[b] Capacity, barrels per day.

[3] Nelson, W. L., How is Productivity of Refinery Labor Changing? *Oil Gas J.*, Sept. 24, 1956, p. 157.

operating costs (Table 23-4). The operating costs for a few crude oils, using the same method as that used in Table 23-4, are plotted in Fig. 23-1.

Gulf Coast plants of an average capacity of 30,000 bpd (12,000 bpd for small refiners and 200,000 bpd for major refiners), which conduct both thermal and catalytic cracking, are examined in Table 23-4

TABLE 23-3. APPROXIMATE OPERATING COSTS OF 5,000 BBL PER DAY
COMBINATION UNITS (1946)[a]

	Cents per bbl crude			Percentage		
	Ther-mal	T.C.C. (vis. br.)	T.C.C. (vac-uum)	Ther-mal	T.C.C. (vis. br.)	T.C.C. (vac-uum)
Crude distillation.............	6.0	6.0	6.0	16.9	15.0	14.8
Vacuum reduction.............	....	....	1.8	.....	.....	4.3
T.C.C. cracking...............	....	13.4	12.2	.....	33.5	30.1
Thermal reforming............	3.4	2.9	2.9	9.6	7.2	7.1
Thermal cracking.............	8.0	....	....	22.7		
Debutanization...............	0.3	0.4	0.4	0.8	1.0	1.0
Catalytic polymerization........	2.3	3.1	3.1	6.5	7.7	7.6
Gasoline inhibitor.............	0.1	0.1	0.1	0.3	0.2	0.2
Taxes, interest, insurance (incre-mental)....................	0.4	2.7	3.1	1.1	6.7	7.6
Royalty:						
T.C.C......................	....	2.4	2.5	.....	6.0	6.1
Thermal...................	1.7	....	....	4.8		
Poly......................	0.4	0.7	0.7	1.1	1.7	1.7
TEL to 79 (F-2)..............	12.8	8.4	7.9	36.2	21.0	19.5
Total (1946)................	35.4	40.1	40.7	100.0	100.0	100.0
Total (1956), approx.........	67.0	74.0	75.0			

[a] Noll, Bergstrom, and Holdom, New Integral T.C.C. Unit Makes Catalytic Cracking Available to Small Refiners, *Oil Gas J.*, Apr. 6, 1946, p. 110.

and Fig 23-1.[4] The product yields are based on the needs of world trade, which means that the operating costs should be larger (5 to 8 per cent) in supplying the large gasoline needs of the United States or Canadian market. The solid points of Fig. 23-1 indicate the production of modest amounts of lubricating oil or wax (10 to 50 per cent of the potential yield).

The operating cost items of Table 23-4 are aimed at distinguishing between the various types of crude oils. Basic investment does not include the cost of most of the processing equipment such as that required

[4] Nelson, W. L., Effect of Gravity on Refinery Operating Cost, *Oil Gas J.*, Nov. 26, 1956, p. 99.

for thermal or catalytic cracking, polymerization, catalytic reforming, etc., nor for power generation, or the corrosion due to sulfur. Thus, additional investment charges are included in such items as sulfur penalty, sourness, fuel, cracking, and gasoline upgrading. Likewise, the general labor item does not include processing labor, power plant labor, or that

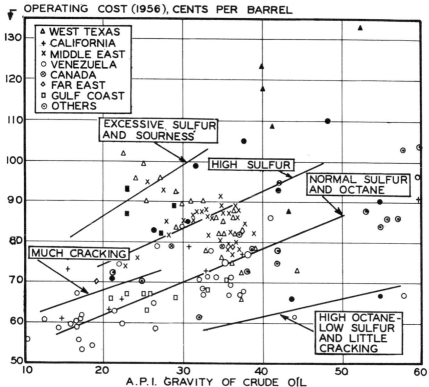

FIG. 23-1. Variations in refinery operating costs (1956) as a function of crude-oil gravity, sulfur, sourness, octane number, and amount of cracking. Gulf Coast 30,000 bpd refineries. (Solid points indicate the production of lubricants or wax.) (*Oil Gas J.*)

part of maintenance labor that is used to combat sulfur corrosion. The item labeled "Gasoline upgrading" consists of the cost of tetraethyl-lead or catalytic reforming or both, for upgrading of the total gasoline to a Research octane number of 90 (1956). "Taxes" are taken as two per cent of the gross value of the refinery products, and they are considered to be about equal to the average profit of refinery operations. The "Miscellaneous" item is simply a factor (5 per cent of other operating costs) which makes costs by the Standard Realization method equal to the average costs of refining of the United States and the world. Each of the operating cost items except the basic investment is related to the properties of the crude oil, i.e., its Characterization Factor, the amount of cracking stock available for processing, the octane number of the

TABLE 23-4. STANDARD REALIZATION METHOD[a] REFINERY OPERATING COSTS FOR A FEW TYPICAL OILS (GULF COAST 1956)

	Crude Oils							
	Bach-aquero, Vene.	Hend-rick, W. Texas	Middle East	Tia Juana 102, Vene.	East Texas	Wax crude, Vene.	South-ern Okla.	Penn-sylvania
Gravity API	16.4	29.7	31.6	25.8	38.5	41.8	32.0	43.9
Sulfur, percentage	2.02	1.49	2.52	1.65	0.33	0.2	0.82	0.1
Octane No. of S.R. gaso.	64	52	41.5	55	57	63	39	46
UOP C.F. at 750°F	11.2	11.5	11.8	11.6	12.0	12.2	11.9	12.45
Cracking stock, %	31.6	33.5	28.4	5	29.8	27.6	18.7	7.9
Yields, %:								
Unaccounted	2.4	3.0	3.5	0.9	3.2	3.0	1.6	1.5
S.R. gaso.	7.8	25.3	27.7	20.2	33.2	40	25.5	35
Cracked and poly gaso.	18.6	20	17	2.8	18.3	17.1	11.2	4.7
Kerosene	.....	.....	.....	.....	13.6	.....	.....	12.7
Diesel fuel	.....	.....	.....	25.5	.....	.....	30	.....
No. 2 distillate	10.8	15.9	13.2	.....	5.1	15.5	.....	4.8
No. 3 distillate	5.5	5.9	5.0	0.9	5.2	4.8	3.3	1.4
Wax	.....	.....	.....	.....	.....	3.9		
Lube oil, low C.T.	.....	.....	.....	10				
Lube oil, paraffinic	.....	.....	.....	.....	.....	.....	.....	30.2
Lube oil, others	.....	.....	.....	.....	3.3			
Bunker C fuel	54.9	29.4	33.6	39.7	18.1	15.7	28.4	9.7
Costs, cents/bbl:								
Basic investment[b]	4.8	4.8	4.8	4.8	4.8	4.8	4.8	4.8
General labor[b]	8.5	13.3	12.6	11.4	15.5	15.9	13.7	17.2
Sulfur penalty	13.4	12.3	16.8	10.1	.....	.....	5.0	
Sourness penalty	.....	6.1						
Fuel, power, and water[b]	7.9	12.4	11.6	10.5	14.3	14.8	12.6	15.8
Cracking[c]	13.5	14.4	12.2	2.1	12.8	11.8	8.0	3.4
Gasoline upgrading	2.0	13.3	16.9	8.7	19.0	16.8	8.1	30.8
Miscellaneous	2.5	3.8	3.7	2.4	3.3	3.2	2.6	3.6
Taxes	5.9	7.1	6.9	6.7	7.8	8.2	6.5	10.3
Total	58.5	87.5	85.5	56.7[d]	77.5[d]	75.5[d]	61.3	85.9[d]
Total incl. specialties	.....	.....	.....	81.7	86.5	91.5	.....	176.4

[a] Devised by author for use in comparing the value of world competitive crude oils.
[b] Part of these costs is included in other items.
[c] Half thermal and half catalytic.
[d] Add cost of producing lubricating oils or waxes.

straight-run gasoline, amount of sulfur, etc. The cost of producing specialty products such as lubricating oil and wax is not included in the operating cost, but such costs have been accounted for by deducting the cost of processing from the sales value of the specialty products (see Table 23-5).

TABLE 23-5. STANDARD REALIZATIONS OF A FEW CRUDE OILS BASED ON GULF
CARGO OR CARIBBEAN PRODUCT PRICES DURING AUGUST 1956
(see Table 23-4)

Oils		Value of products, $ per bbl	Operating cost,[b] $ per bbl	Posted price of crude oil, $ per bbl	Delivery of crude oil to Gulf,[c] $ per bbl	Net profit or loss, $ per bbl
Name	API					
Bachaquero.........	16.4	2.97	0.585	1.90	0.05[d]	0.44
West Texas.........	29.7	3.53	0.875	2.55	0.24	−0.13[e]
Kuwait...........	31.6	4.14[f]	0.929[f]	1.72	1.91[f]	−0.42[f]
South Oklahoma....	32.0	3.54	0.613	2.56		
Tia Juana 102	25.8	3.34[a]	0.567[a]	2.62	0.10[d]	0.05
Far East (light).....	37.0	4.03	0.832	2.60	2.34	−1.74
East Texas.........	38.5	3.89[a]	0.775[a]	2.90	0.16	0.06
Wax crude (Vene.)..	41.8	4.12[a]	0.775[a]	3.04	0.10[d]	0.22
West Texas.........	43.3	3.94[a]	0.79[a]	2.90	0.24	0.01
Pennsylvania.......	43.9	5.47[a]	0.859[a]	4.50		

[a] Cost of manufacturing waxes and lubricating oils already deducted from the value of the product. The low of Gulf Cargo prices for 90-octane gasoline, 48–52 D.I. diesel fuel, and conventional products of Table 23-4.

[b] See Table 23-4 for product yields.

[c] Gathering, pipeline, ocean transport, import duty, etc., to the Gulf or Caribbean area as applicable. USMC tanker rates used, although actual rates were higher during August 1956 by plus 25 to plus 45 per cent and although breakeven rates are minus 25 to minus 40 per cent.

[d] Sold in Caribbean rather than at U.S. Gulf ports, but import duty (as crude oil) to U.S. included.

[e] Profitable when purchased as part of a mixture of 33 or 36 API oils.

[f] Product prices, operating costs, and delivery costs for New York harbor.

MISCELLANEOUS OPERATING COSTS AND FACTORS

Losses during processing:

Topping distillation............... 0.7–1.7 per cent
Pressure gasoline treating.......... 0.3–4.0 per cent
Gasoline, straight-run, treating..... 0.2–1.0 per cent
Kerosene treating................. 0.2–1.0 per cent
Solvents, used in treating.......... 0.2–0.5 per cent
Acid treating of
Nonviscous neutral oil........... 2.8–4.9 per cent
Viscous neutral oil.............. 3.5–12.0 per cent
Residual cylinder stock.......... 18.5–40.0 per cent
Overhead cylinder stock.......... 11.0–18.0 per cent

Major distillation or refinery operations:*

Alkylation...................... 77–112 cents per bbl alkylate (1955)

* Can be estimated for other years by the operating cost index of Table 23-1.

MISCELLANEOUS OPERATING COSTS AND FACTORS (*Continued*)

Aromatics adsorption (benzene) ....   30–40 cents per bbl feed (1956)
Asphalt manufacture..............   26 cents per bbl asphalt (1945)
Coking.........................   25–46 cents per bbl reduced crude (1956)
Cracking (thermal) and gas recovery   16–40 cents per bbl reduced crude (1956)
Cracking (catalytic) and gas recovery   28–50 cents per bbl gas oil (1956)
Cracked (pressure) distillate rerun-
    ing ....   6–18 cents per bbl distillate (1956)
Desalting, electrical...............   0.4–1.3 cents per bbl (1956)
Drying, gases (gasoline plant).......   0.1–0.5 cent per Mcf (1956)
Ethylene manufacture............   2.4–3.3 cents per lb C_2H_4 (1956)†
Gas recovery (catalytic cracking)...   10–14 cents per bbl gas oil (1956)
Hydrogen sulfide removal (gasoline
    plant).........................   13.7 cents per Mcf H_2S (1953)
L.P.G. manufacture...............   34 cents per bbl L.P.G. (1941)
Polymerization (thermal)...........   1–1.4 cents per gal gasoline (1938)
Polymerization (catalytic).........   50–87 cents per bbl gasoline (1949)
Reforming, bauxite catalytic.......   10–15 cents per bbl gasoline (1947)
Reforming, catalytic...............   33–57 cents per bbl feed (1956)
Reforming, thermal...............   24–45 cents per bbl feed (1956)
Stabilizing, natural gasoline........   4–9 cents per bbl (1940)
Stripping, rich absorption oil......   1.2–5 cents per bbl oil (1940)
Sulfur manufacture (20–160 tons per
    day) ....   \$3.50–11.00 per ton sulfur (1956)
Topping, distillation...............   6–15 cents per bbl (1953)
Topping and delayed coking........   10–19.5 cents per bbl crude (1956)
Topping and catalytic cracking.....   25–53 cents per bbl crude (1946)‡
Topping and thermal cracking......   13–60 cents per bbl crude (1956)
Vacuum, distillation...............   15–25 cents per bbl feed (1956)
Vacuum, flashing.................   7.5–18 cents per bbl feed (1956)
Viscosity breaking and gas recovery.   12–28 cents per bbl feed (1956)

† Large credit for other products can be subtracted from this cost.
‡ 5,000 bpd and larger.

Approximate royalties:*

Alkylation........................   20 cents per bbl alkylate (1956)
Benzene recovery from reformate...   1 cent per gal (1955)
Cracking, catalytic................   5 cents per bbl charge (1955)
Cracking, thermal.................   3 cents per bbl charge (1955)
Reforming, catalytic...............   5–7 cents per bbl charge (1956)
Polymerization, catalytic...........   0.5 cent per gal product (1955)
Sweetening, tannin solutizer........   0.3–0.5 cent per bbl product (1947)

* Paid-up royalty is often three years' worth of unit royalty.

Treating light oils:

Acid treating, complete............   1.7–4.5 cents per bbl (1940)
Sweetening, doctor................   0.8–3.0 cents per bbl (1951)
Sweetening, copper...............   2.7–4.5 cents per bbl (1950)
Clay, vapor-phase.................   0.5–1.2 cents per bbl (1940)

Miscellaneous Operating Costs and Factors (Continued)

Sulfur dioxide extraction............ 4.6–5.5 cents per bbl (1940)
Inhibitor, handling only............ 0.15–1.0 cent per bbl (1940)
Catalytic desulfurization........... 6.0–8.0 cents per bbl (1947)
Cracked naphtha (complete)........ 26 cents per bbl (1956)

Chemicals:*

Amyl nitrate (diesel additive)....... $3–3.55 per gal (1953)
Clay, contact.................... $30–60 per ton (1956)
Clay, percolation................. $15–30 per ton (1956)
Catalyst, platinum reforming....... $9–14 per lb ($4 replacement) (1956)
Catalyst, Hydroforming........... $0.59–0.89 per lb (1955)
Catalyst, cracking (synthetic)..... $240–340 per ton (1956)
Catalyst, cracking (natural)....... $140–220 per ton (1956)
Catalyst, desulfurization.......... $0.90–1.50 per lb (1956)
Catalyst, polymerization.......... $0.12–0.15 per lb (1956)
Desalting agents................. $1.50–2.50 per gal (1954)†
Fuel-oil additive................. $0.60–0.63 per lb (1955)
Lube-oil additives................ $1.30–2.40 per gal (1955)
Inhibitors, gasoline............... $1.00–2.00 per lb (1953)
Pour-point depressants........... $0.15–0.41 per lb (1954)
Tetraethyllead fluid.............. $0.218 cent per cu cm (1956)

* For regular chemicals see *Chem. Eng. News Quarterly Report on Current Prices.*
† 500–800 bbl per gal.

The costs for processing heavy oils such as neutral oils and cylinder stock are even less consistent. The great variation in these costs is due to the inherent differences in lubricating-oil stocks and the variety of treating and dewaxing operations that may be used.

Heavy oils:

Rerunning, complete .... 4.1–6.2 cents per bbl charge (1932)
Acid treating, complete .... 11–43 cents per bbl treated (1932)

Percolation (1932):

Nonviscous neutral............... 7.2–36.2 cents per bbl
Viscous neutral.................. 15.4–48 cents per bbl
Wax........................... 19.4–36.4 cents per bbl
Average of straight filtering........ 44–90 cents per bbl (1953)
Solution filtering................. 27–75 cents per bbl of stock
Clay contacting.................. 52–100 cents per bbl charge (1953)
Clay contacting.................. 10 cents per bbl plus clay (1943)

Clay:

Steaming, discharge, and loading.... $5 per ton (1940)
Burning, wedge-type burner........ $1.22–4.13 per ton (1932)
Burning, rotary-type burner........ 50–92 cents per ton (1932)
Loss during burning.............. 1.5–2.0 per cent (1932)

MISCELLANEOUS OPERATING COSTS AND FACTORS (*Continued*)

Dewaxing:

Pressing and sweating............ 13.6–46.8 cents per bbl distillate (1932)
Sweating........................ 41.7–125.0 cents per bbl sweated wax (1932)
Barreling and molding wax........ 7.6–106 cents per bbl finished wax (1932)
Centrifuging.................... 31.9–164 cents per bbl bright stock (1932)
Refrigeration*.................. 46.3–316 cents per ton refrigeration (1932)
Propane dewaxing and deresining... 80–100 cents per bbl (1956)
MEK dewaxing.................. 60–80 cents per bbl (1956)

* One ton refrigeration is 288,000 Btu per 24 hr

Solvent treating:

Furfural........................ 9–20 cents per bbl (1945)
Chlorex......................... 27–33 cents per bbl (1940)
Nitrobenzene.................... 23–42 cents per bbl (1938)
Phenol.......................... 17 cents per bbl (1945)
Propane deasphalting............. 8–14 cents per bbl (1947)

The cost of fuel or power and, to some extent, labor is important in many of the costs or factors listed below. Average refinery wages in 1946 were about $1.42 per hour, common labor $1.00, and skilled construction labor $1.80. (See Table 23-1 for indexes based on 1946. Indexes are published currently in *The Oil and Gas Journal*.)

Steam generation:

Live steam, 100 psig.............. 25–75 cents per 1,000 lb (1956)
Live steam, 400 psig.............. 26–80 cents per 1,000 lb (1956)
Exhaust or low pressure........... 8–12 cents per 1,000 lb (1956)

Steam consumption:

Alkylation (HF).................. 700 lb per bbl (1953)
Coking.......................... 45 lb per bbl (1951)
Cracking, thermal................ 35–60 lb per bbl (1945)
Cracking, catalytic.............. 17–25 lb per bbl feed (1953)
Dewaxing, pressing............... 20–40 lb per bbl (1944)
Dewaxing, centrifuging........... 20–50 lb per bbl (1944)
Dewaxing, solvent................ 337 lb per bbl (1953)
Distillation, 2-stage............ 20.9 lb per bbl (1953)
Gasoline, cracked................ 30 lb per bbl gasoline (1953)
Gasoline, reformed............... 12 lb per bbl feed (1951)
Natural-gasoline stripping........ 1.7 lb per gal gasoline
Percolation filtration........... 150–200 lb per bbl (1940)
Percolator steaming.............. 25,000 lb per 100 cu ft filter (1940)
Propane deasphalting............. 136 lb per bbl (1953)
Refinery, topping and thermal cracking......................... 60–127 lb per bbl (1939)
Refinery, complete............... 144–525 lb per bbl (1956)
Stripping of stocks.............. (see pages 229 to 232)

MISCELLANEOUS OPERATING COSTS AND FACTORS (*Continued*)

Solvent treating................... 38–150 lb per bbl (1953)
Topping......................... 40–172 lb per bbl (1939)

Fuel required:

Topping and skimming (equivalent
 of)........................... 7–13.5 per cent crude (1940)
Complete processing (equivalent of). 15–23 per cent crude (1940)
Heat, topping.................... 65,000–240,000 Btu per bbl (1945)
Heat, general.................... 419,000–1,190,000 Btu per bbl (1940)

Water:

Cost of, filtered only.............. 0.3–1.0 cent per 1,000 gal (1956)
Cost of, recirculation or cooling..... 0.6–2.0 cents per 1,000 gal (1956)
Cost of, treated.................. 3–15 cents per 1,000 gal (1956)
Cost of, large consumption......... 2–8 cents per 1,000 gal (1955)
Topping........................ 4.0–18.0 bbl per bbl crude (1938)
Topping and cracking.............. 13.0–44.0 bbl per bbl crude (1938)
Complete processing.............. 15–52 bbl per bbl crude (1956)
Windage loss, spray pond.......... 10% of circulation (1951)
Windage loss, natural draft tower... 1% of circulation (1951)
Windage loss, mechanical draft tower 0.4% of circulation (1951)

Power:

Gas engine (20 cents per Mcf)...... 0.3 cent per brake hp
Electric motors (1 cent per kw)..... 0.9 cent per brake hp
Diesel engine (14 cents per gal)..... 0.87 cent per brake hp
Gasoline engine (20 cents per gal)... 2.32 cents per brake hp
Steam pumps, small (20-cent gas)... 4.51 cents per brake hp
Steam pumps, small ($2.25 fuel oil).. 8.32 cents per brake hp
Ammonia refrigeration, 150-ton plant $1.10–2.85 per ton (1955)
Ammonia refrigeration, 1,000-ton
 plant......................... $0.71–2.31 per ton (1955)
Electric power................... 0.6–1.1 cents per kw (1956)

Electrical requirements:

Alkylation (HF)................... 5.8 kw per bbl (1953)
Coking, delayed.................. 0.6 kw per bbl (1951)
Cracking, catalytic............... 0.27–1.2 kw per bbl (1953)
Cracking, thermal (also reforming).. 0.52–0.56 kw per bbl (1953)
Distillation, 2-stage.............. 0.6 kw per bbl (1953)
Dewaxing, solvent................ 2.8 kw per bbl (1953)
Dewaxing, centrifuging............ 0.48–0.6 kw per bbl (1945)
Deasphalting, propane............ 1.05 kw per bbl (1953)
Illumination, buildings............ 0.8–1.0 kw per 1,000 sq ft (1945)
Illumination, process............. 0.5–1.0 kw per bbl (1945)
Illumination, yard................ 0.3–0.4 kw per acre (1945)
Polymer gasoline................. 0.34 kw per bbl gasoline (1951)
Refinery, topping................ 0.05–1.57 kw per daily bbl (1938)

MISCELLANEOUS OPERATING COSTS AND FACTORS (*Continued*)

Refinery, topping and thermal crack-
    ing............................ 0.14–2.8 kw per daily bbl (1938)
Refinery, complete................ 1.67–5.3 kw per daily bbl (1938)
Treating......................... 0.03–0.05 kw per bbl (1945)
Treating, solvent................. 0.7–1.2 kw per bbl (1943)
Air, process...................... 1–3 cents per 1,000 cu ft (1946)
Air, filtered and dried for instruments. 3–7 cents per 1,000 cu ft (1946)

REALIZATION OF CRUDE OILS

The most economical "breakup" of products varies day by day because of fluctuations in the market prices and in market specifications. During one season a plant may be most economically operated for the production of maximum yields of gasoline by topping and cracking, whereas at another time the manufacture of a maximum yield of kerosene, distillates, or fuel oil may be advantageous.

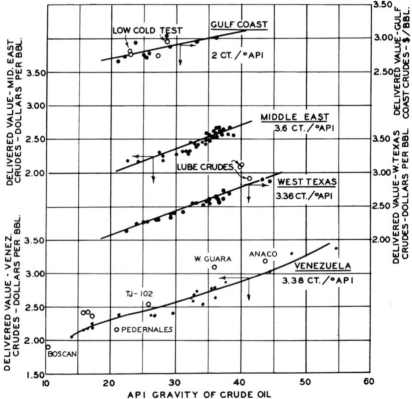

FIG. 23-2. Crude-oil value vs. gravity for various types of crude oils, based on Gulf Coast cargo product prices of June 23, 1954. (*Oil Gas J.*)

Table 23-5 shows the realizations of a few important and widely different (see Table 23-4) crude oils. In marketing crude oils, the price is usually increased by 2 cents for an increase of 1.0 in the API gravity, but the true or correct differential in price based on product value during recent years should have been 3 to 4 cents per degree API (see Fig. 23-2).[5] The proper differential per degree API is a function primarily of the relative prices of gasoline and residual fuel oil, and it may be estimated from Eq. (23-1) in which G, D, and B are the prices respectively of gasoline, distillate, and Bunker C fuel oil, and C is the operating cost, all on a barrel basis.[6]

$$\text{Differential} = \frac{2G + D - 3B - 3C}{150} \tag{23-1}$$

COST OF REFINERY EQUIPMENT

In estimating the cost of refinery equipment, the preferred procedure is to prepare a so-called process design to obtain the approximate capacities, sizes, and types of basic process equipment, such as stills, stacks, vessels, towers, contactors, exchangers, coolers, pumps, compressors, rundown storage, etc., and then obtain the costs[7] of each item of major process equipment. Such costs or prices can be brought to date by cost indexes (Table 23-1) for each general type of equipment.[7,8] Other costs for auxiliary process equipment (piping, instruments, etc.), field expenses, home office expenses, profit and contingencies, off-site facilities, and numerous additional costs for complete refineries can then be estimated by means of average ratios or percentages of the total costs.[9] Space is not available here for presentation of such a method of cost estimation, but much less precise over-all costs are indicated in Fig. 23-3.[10] The approximate costs of Fig. 23-3 may be brought to date by dividing by 195.3 (the Nelson Index for 1956) and multiplying by the current value of the Nelson Construction Cost Index.[1] Note that the cost of small plants on a per barrel basis is greater than the cost of large plants. Although the effect of capacity on cost is often nearly a function of the

---

[5] Nelson, W. L., *Oil Gas J.*, Nov. 8, 1954, p. 191.

[6] Nelson, W. L., *Oil Gas J.*, Aug. 15, 1955, p. 183.

[7] One such source is the "Costimating" series of articles, W. L. Nelson, *Oil Gas J.*, First Series, Oct. 28, 1948 through Dec. 29, 1949, and Second Series Nov. 7, 1955 through Sept. 2, 1957.

[8] Nelson, W. L., Itemized Cost Indexes published in the first issue each quarter (January, April, July, and October) in the *Oil Gas J.* Also, for an explanation see issues of Apr. 11, 1955, p. 132; July 4, 1955, p. 122; and Oct. 3, 1955, p. 146.

[9] Nelson, W. L., Summary for Quick Cost Estimates, *Oil Gas J.*, Jan. 2, 1956, p. 120.

[10] Numbers 26–30 of Second Costimating Series, March-May, 1957, *Oil Gas J.*

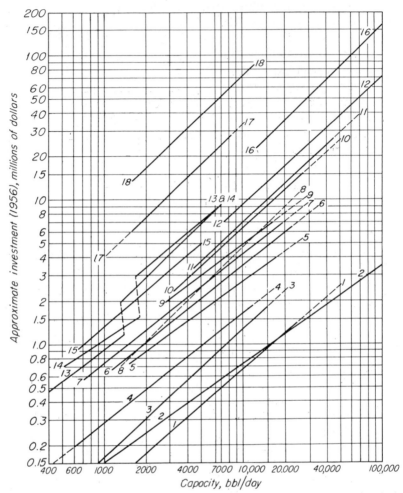

Fig. 23-3. Approximate construction costs of refineries and process units (1956). The Nelson Index for 1956 is 195.3 (based on 1946).

Process units:
1. Vacuum flashing
2. Topping and atmospheric distillation
3. Desulfurization of gasoline (catalytic)
4. Vacuum distillation (lubes)
5. Cracking (thermal)
6. Coking (Delayed or Fluid)
7. Solvent extraction or deasphalting
8. Reforming (platinum catalyst)
10. Catalytic cracking—including feed preparation, gas recovery, and polymerization
*13. Polymerization (catalytic)
*14. Alkylation

15. Solvent dewaxing
*17. Benzene and toluene recovery (large plants)
*18. Lubricating-oil manufacture (complete)
Complete refineries:
9. Topping and asphalt manufacture
11. Topping, thermal cracking, catalytic reforming, and polymerization
12. Topping, catalytic cracking, catalytic reforming, and polymerization
16. Complete for all products
* Per barrel finished product rather than feed.

0.6 power when construction conditions are similar, as indicated in Eq. (23-2), the effectiveness of large organizations in building plants is often inferior and this usually leads to actual exponents nearer to 1.0 than 0.6.

$$\frac{\text{Cost}_A}{\text{Cost}_B} = \left(\frac{\text{capacity}_A}{\text{capacity}_B}\right)^{0.6} \qquad (23\text{-}2)$$

Thus, some of the lines of Fig. 23-3 consist actually of two lines each having exponents near 0.6, but the line for large plants built by major refiners tends to lie above the line for small plants built by small operators.

The approximate costs of other types of plants or equipments are indicated in Table 23-6. Such general costs as these must be used with extreme care. The higher of the two costs is due mainly to the small size of the plant rather than to other factors. In prosperous times the costs will all be higher, and during times of business depression "sacrifice" prices may prevail.

Financial Charges. At one time the concept of depreciation was a simple one; it referred to funds laid aside for replacement of equipment because in time it would be worn out. More recently it has come to mean little more than a percentage of total investment that can by Federal tax regulations[11] be withheld each year from income. Taxation and inflation are requiring a completely new concept of financial charges.

Financial charges (as percentage of investment) may be considered under four general classifications:

1. Interest on investment or borrowings, or dividends paid to stockholders.
2. Depreciation, maintenance, and equipment insurance. Depreciation in the sense of wearing out is of little significance, because a refinery that is kept in proper working order by maintenance or replacement of dangerous equipment is substantially as useful after 10 to 15 years as when new. Thus maintenance and insurance against disaster are the real costs of preserving an operable plant.
3. Retirement or obsolescence, and inflation. Replacement of a plant or the complete retirement of an investment at the present rates of inflation is never necessary unless the process equipment becomes totally obsolete or the plant environment becomes unsatisfactory. However, obsolescence is not usually a large cost because most of the advances of the last 30 years have required additions to the refinery rather than replacement, and almost all discarded equipment can be utilized for new services. To further confuse the situation, inflation during the decade 1946–1956 has averaged 9 per cent per year, so that properly maintained equipment purchased in 1946 would be worth more during 1956 than its original purchase price. Thus, a proper financial charge under these conditions would be one that cares for additions rather than the retirement of investment. Only if inflation should halt, would retirement or repayment of debt be necessary.
4. Taxes and profits. Corporate taxes in the United States during recent years have amounted to about 40 per cent of the gross profit before taxes. Thus, after having laid aside funds for about 9 to 14 per cent of investment (depending on the degree

[11] Income Tax Depreciation and Obsolescence . . . , *Bur. Internal Revenue Bull. F*, January, 1942; also see Nelson, W. L., *Oil Gas J.*, Apr. 23, 1956, p. 141.

of inflation) for items 1 to 3 above, a gross profit before taxes of 5 to 10 per cent must be earned to show a real profit of 3 to 6 per cent on investment.

In summary, financial charges based on investment must be set aside for 3 to 5 per cent per year of interest or dividends, 1 to 3 per cent for maintenance and insurance (no depreciation), 0 to 5 per cent for additional modern equipment (inflation supplies an additional 0 to 9 per cent), and 5 to 10 per cent for taxes and profit, making total financial charges of at least 16 per cent.

TABLE 23-6. APPROXIMATE COST OF MISCELLANEOUS PLANTS OR EQUIPMENT

Type of plant	Capacity	Cost (labor and material), 1956
Acid-treating equipment.................	....	$37–76 per daily bbl
Acid-treating and P.D. rerun..............	15,000 bpd	$119 per daily bbl
Ammonia plants, anhydrous..............	50–300 tons per day	$45,000–54,000 per daily ton
Ammonia plants, incl. HNO₃ or urea........	100–300 tons per day	$74,000–78,000 per daily ton
Asphalt, loading and storage..............	600 bpd	$17.70 per daily bbl
Asphalt processing.......................	1,500–5,000 bpd	$263–390 per daily bbl
Butadiene manufacture..................	83–320 tons per day	$26–210 per yearly ton
Carbon black...........................	30–150 tons per day	$1,070–2,350 per yearly ton
Clay burning...........................	66 tons per day	$3,100 per daily ton
Clay treating (percolation)...............	300–3,000 bpd	$730–2,000 per daily bbl
Clay treating (contact)...................	300–3,000 bpd	$370–1,100 per daily bbl
Coal (hydrogenation)....................	300 tons per day	$4,300 per daily ton
Coal (synthetic gasoline).................	2,000–27,000 bpd	$21,000–23,000 per daily bbl
Copper sweetening, liquid................	1,000–10,000 bpd	$10–37 per daily bbl
Cumene manufacture....................	500 bpd	$1,870 per daily bbl
Dehydration of gases....................	10–100 MMscf per day	$2–5 per Mscf per day
Desalting of crude oil....................	2,000–100,000 bpd	$3.50–16 per daily bbl
Desulfurization of gases..................	20–200 MMscf per day	$1.10–4.50 per Mscf per day
Desulfurization of gas oil.................	1,000–10,000 bpd	$195–314 per daily bbl
Dewaxing (filter press)..................	400–1,200 bpd	$410–550 per daily bbl
Dry-ice manufacture.....................	100 tons per day	$8,400 per daily ton
Ethylene manufacture....................	50–300 tons per day	$4,600–7,800 per daily ton
Extractive distillation...................	420 bpd	$7,800 per daily bbl
Fischer-Tropsch for gasoline..............	10,000–30,000 bpd	$16,200–17,500 per daily bbl
Gasoline (natural) plants[a]..............	10–70 MMscf per day	$173–292 per daily Mscf
Gasoline and kerosene treating............	2,000–30,000 bpd	$45–200 per daily bbl
Gray vapor-phase treating................	....	$27–62 per daily bbl
Hydrogen manufacture...................	200 Mscf per day	$1,470 per daily Mscf
Hydrogen sulfide removal.................	20–200 MMscf per day	$1.10–4.50 per daily Mscf
Hypersorption..........................	2–100 Mscf per day	$15,600–146,000 per Mscf
Inhibitor injection......................	....	$0.49–4.90 per daily bbl
L.P.G. bottling.........................	3,500 gal per day	$26.70 per daily gal
L.P.G. recovery........................	100–1,000 bpd	$370–780 per daily bbl
Lube oil (solution rerun).................	1,000–5,000 bpd	$107–200 per daily bbl
Oxygen separation......................	50–500 tons per day	$6,300–14,000 per daily ton
Polymerization (thermal).................	100–600 bpd	$1,000–1,750 per daily bbl
Shale oil (foreign)......................	3,000–40,000 bpd	$11,700–15,600 per daily bbl
Sulfur or sulfuric acid[b].................	20–200 tons per day	$4,000–9,000 per daily ton
Synthetic rubber.......................	125–1,100 tons per day	$2,160–9,550 per yearly ton
Tetraethyllead blending.................	1,000 bpd	$37 per daily bbl

[a] 50 per cent propane recovery.
[b] 50 per cent H₂S in gas.

ECONOMICS OF UNIT OPERATIONS

The economy of several of the most useful operations will be discussed as illustrations. The most successful way to effect economies is to study independently each phase or operation of the complete processing scheme. By this manner of approach, savings of such magnitude that they may be unnoticed in the total processing cost are forcefully brought to attention. Only a few illustrations can be given here, but almost all phases of design may be studied by means of economic balances of income vs. cost of equipment or its operation. Among such studies are (1) the optimum relation between tower diameter and tray spacing for a bubble tower, (2) the optimum thickness of heat insulation, (3) the optimum cost of protective coatings for pipelines, etc., (4) the optimum dimensions of a storage tank or pressure vessel, (5) the optimum spacing between a series of structural beams, (6) the most economical relation between amount of steam and vacuum to use in a vacuum plant (Fig 7-24), (7) balance of investment for storage vessels vs. loss of light ends by evaporation,[12] (8) gravity of crude oil vs. cost of processing (Fig 23-1), (9) separate topping and cracking vs. combination operation[13], (10) investment in natural-gasoline plant vs. oil-gas ratio,[14] (11) cost of cracking plant vs. gravity of charge stock,[15] (12) life of corrosion-resistant materials (tubing) vs. cost (Table 9-3), (13) coking vs. cracking as a means of disposing of residues,[16] (14) optimum residual fuel gravity vs. its price,[17] and (15) waste heat recovery.[18]

Reduced Capacity. It is highly profitable and nearly necessary to operate a plant at its full rated capacity. Although such costs as those for tetraethyllead, treating, utilities, fuel, and part of the maintenance (wear) are a function of the number of barrels processed, the cost of labor (and its burdens) and investment continues at a nearly fixed total cost regardless of how much is processed. Much the same applies to the effect of cycle-time efficiency except that additional costs for inspection and repair are generated by shutdowns. This results in greatly increased costs of operation at reduced capacity[19] as indicated in Fig. 23-4. A corresponding decrease in operating cost occurs at high capacities and though it may be small, it results in very large profits because nearly

[12] Franklin, W. B., Storage of Light Ends, *Ref. Nat. Gaso. Mfr.*, June, 1937, p. 277.

[13] Chamberlain, N. F., *Ref. Nat. Gaso. Mfr.*, December, 1937, p. 571.

[14] Nissan, A. H., *J. Inst. Pet. Tech.*, **24**, 69 (1938).

[15] Nelson, W. L., *Oil Gas J.*, Apr. 6, 1939, p. 55.

[16] Colquette and Peters, To Coke or Not to Coke . . . , *Oil Gas J.*, Apr. 14, 1952, p. 156.

[17] Gertz, M. H., *Pet. Processing*, January, 1948, p. 41.

[18] Stewart, L. D., *Oil Gas J.*, July 13, 1950, p. 70.

[19] Nelson, W. L., *Oil Gas J.*, Dec. 17, 1956, p. 146.

all of the saving goes directly into profits (and taxes).   Individual units
or plants behave in much the same way.[19]

Economics of Heat Exchange.   The net saving effected by the recovery
of waste heat approaches a definite limit in any plant equipment.   The
value of the heat saved, less the cost of the equipment and the cost of
operating the equipment, is the net saving.   This approaches a high value
for a particular set of conditions and decreases if any of the conditions are
changed.

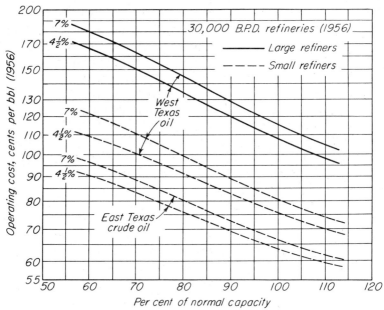

FIG. 23-4. Effect of operation at reduced capacity (or of cycle-time efficiency) on
operating cost (1956).   The percentage figures are the financial charges allowed for
obsolescence, taxes, and profit as percentage of investment.   (*Oil Gas J.*)

In selecting heat exchangers an important consideration is the most
economical "approach" or difference in temperature between the incoming large medium and the outgoing small medium.   The maximum recovery of heat occurs if these two streams are at the same temperature, but in
practical heat-exchange equipment a difference in temperature must
exist.

For liquid-to liquid exchangers, the relationship among the value of heat,
cost of surface, magnitude of the heat-transfer rate, and the several other
variables that govern the most economical approach is extremely complicated—but for a particular refinery situation all the variables have fixed
values and the relationship is reasonably simple.   For the following values

of variables the most economical approach[20] behaves as indicated in Fig 23-5:

Difference in temperature between the 2 incoming fluids........... 200°F
Cost of heat-exchanger surface................................ $2.66 per sq ft*
Interest rate... 6 per cent
Cost of upkeep and repair for each million Btu.................. $160 per year*
Value of fuel, per million Btu................................. 17 cents*
Heat-transfer rate... 25

* Corresponding 1956 costs are, $7.50 per sq ft surface; $450 upkeep; and 48 cents per MM Btu.

In this figure, the most economical approach is given in degrees Fahrenheit and the factor labeled R is the ratio of the weight of the smaller of the two fluids to the weight of the larger quantity fluid. Similar studies have been made for water coolers[21] and condensers.[22]

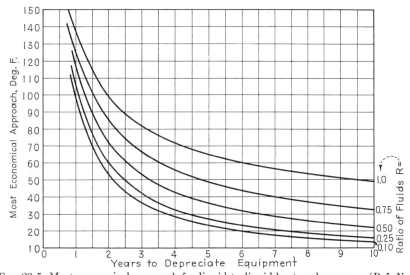

FIG. 23-5. Most economical approach for liquid-to-liquid heat exchangers. (*Ref. Nat. Gaso. Mfr.*)

Finally, an area smaller than 200 sq ft is so expensive that exchangers cannot be justified unless small standard double-pipe or fin-tube units are employed. In general, it is usually economical to bring the temperature of the feedstock by exchange to within about 40°F of the temperature of the hottest stock available.

[20] Nelson, W. L., Economics of Heat Exchanger Design, *Ref. Nat. Gaso. Mfr.*, August, 1936, p. 293.

[21] Douglass and Adams, *Ind. Eng. Chem.*, **33**, 1082 (1941).

[22] Colburn, A. P., Standards of Tubular Exchanger Manufacturers Association, 366 Madison Ave., New York.

Cost of Pipestill Heat. The over-all economy of installing exchangers involves other parts of the plant equipment as well as the exchangers themselves. If exchangers are installed in conjunction with a pipestill, a smaller still may be required because less heat is absorbed in the still, but the flue gases will leave at a higher temperature and hence more heat will be lost in the gas. At the same time, less cooling surface and less cooling water will be required for the condensers and coolers of the plant, because the products are partly cooled by heat exchange. The particular amount of heat exchange that is economical may be determined by comparing the total costs of absorbing heat in the pipestill and exchangers and then removing it again in the coolers. The cost (1956) of absorbed heat in a 20,000,000-Btu simple pipestill distillation unit is approximately as follows:

Pipestill	Cents per million Btu	Saving, dollars per year
Without exchangers...........	66.5	
With exchange to 300°F........	49.3	20,600
With exchange to 500°F........	39.9	39,400
With exchange to 550°F........	41.6	37,600

In this particular case it is not economical to heat the oil by exchangers to a temperature higher than about 500°F.

In general, the efficiency for a pipestill should not be so high as for a boiler. Oil is usually at 300 to 500°F before it enters the pipestill, but the feed water for a boiler may enter the economizer at a temperature as low as 60°F. Thus a pipestill operates most economically at an efficiency of 70 to 75 per cent, but a boiler may operate at 80 to 85 per cent.

The flue gases should leave the pipestill at a temperature about 330°F higher than the charge stock temperature. A closer approach requires a much larger convection section, and a larger approach allows such a large heat loss to the stack that the expenses again rise. These relations are illustrated in Fig. 23-6. The figure was computed for a radiant type of pipestill absorbing about 10,000,000 Btu per hr, fuel cost $2.00 per bbl, and depreciation in 6 years at an interest rate of 6 per cent.

The optimum velocity for flue gases in the convection section of a still can be computed in a similar manner. As the velocity is increased, the surface in the convection section becomes smaller but the friction loss becomes greater, and a taller stack must be provided. These factors affect the cost of the convection section and stack as indicated in Fig. 23-7. However, note that tubes can seldom be spaced close enough to attain such velocities.

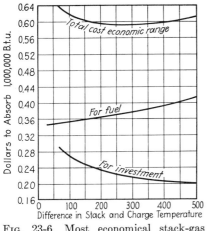

Fig. 23-6. Most economical stack-gas temperature for a pipestill.

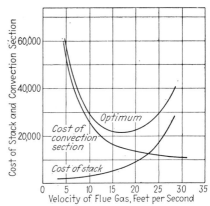

Fig. 23-7. Most economical flue-gas velocity in convection section of pipestill (if such a velocity is geometrically feasible.)

Practical Recovery for Absorption Plant. The yield of natural gasoline that is produced in a gasoline plant is directly related to the pentane-plus content of the gas and to the amount of pentane plus that is recovered.

TABLE 23-7. LOSS BY OPERATION AT 99 PER CENT RECOVERY OF PENTANE[a]

Pressure, psi	Pentane plus, per cent	Grade of gasoline	Gasoline price, cents per gal	Most economical recovery, per cent	Loss, cents per 1,000 cu ft by operating at 99 per cent recovery
50[b]	7	22–70	4	94.25	1.287[b]
50	3	30–70	2	89.8	0.821
50	3	30–70	4	94	0.577
50	3	14–55	4	92	0.455
50	9	14–55	4	96.2	0.286
50	9	30–70	4	97.4	0.227
400	3	14–55	4	96.4	0.117
400	3	30–70	4	97.5	0.068
400	9	30–70	4	98.9	Nil

[a] Although based on 1936 prices and conditions, the conclusions will be the same for 1957.

[b] Refinery conditions, oil recirculation cost of 0.1 cent per gal.

Thus, designers have tended to build plants that would recover 99 per cent of the pentane contained in the gas. This practice, however, is not usually economical, because the cost of operation mounts rapidly as more than 85 per cent of the pentane is recovered, so that in general it may cost twice as much to recover 99 per cent as to recover 85 per cent of the pentane.

The variables such as cost of oil recirculation, value of the gasoline product, and cost of stabilizing the gasoline are related[23] in such a way that the loss involved in recovering 99 per cent of the pentane is somewhat as shown in Table 23-7. Note that the most economical recovery is also given in the table. In computing Table 23-7, the cost of oil circulation was used as 0.05 cents per gal oil, and the cost of stabilization 0.13 cents per gal.

The same basic economic situation will arise with respect to other key components, such as butane or propane, as well as pentane.

Octane Improvement. The extremely complicated problem of octane number improvement is a constantly changing situation, and it is intimately related to the particular environment of each refinery operation. However, the situation during 1956 was somewhat as indicated[24] in Fig. 23-8. The base scale shows the octane number of the original material or gasoline "pool" of the refinery, and the ordinate (cents per R.o.n. per bbl) is defined as the cost of the improvement divided by "the volume of improved-quality gasoline times the difference in the octane numbers of the original and the improved material."[24] On such a basis, cracking, polymerization, and alkylation are not solely improvement processes because they produce gasoline from non-gasoline feedstocks, but they can be compared on a "cents per R.o.n. per bbl" basis by assuming a value for the feedstock. (In Fig. 23-8, the value of feed for polymerization and alkylation was assumed to be 2 cents per gallon above a breakeven value.) The dashed line of Fig. 23-8 indicates the values placed on octane number by the Gulf Coast market for the date of January, 1956. At "pool" octane numbers below about 95 it is not profitable to raise the octane number by isomerization or the

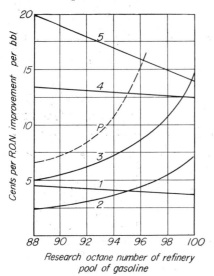

Research octane number of refinery pool of gasoline

FIG. 23-8. Illustration of approximate cost of octane improvement by various methods. (1) Catalytic reforming (mild); (2) alkylation; (3) polymerization; (p) market values (January, 1956) of various-octane gasolines; (4) catalytic reforming, aromatics extraction, and reforming of raffinate—or catalytic reforming plus thermal reforming plus polymerization—or isomerization; (5) severe catalytic reforming.

[23] Nelson, W. L., *Ref. Nat. Gaso. Mfr.*, May, 1936, p. 167.

[24] Kersten and Warren, *Oil Gas J.*, July 30, 1956, p. 176.

complicated combination operations generally designated by curve 4. Although polymerization and alkylation appear in Fig. 23-8 to be profitable, higher feedstock prices can cause the "cents per octane number barrel" to rise to such unprofitable values as 15 to 20 cents. In some situations alkylation is more profitable than polymerization.[24] Note especially in Fig. 23-8 that the original pool materials already contain a normal or average amount of tetraethyllead (for example, 2.25 ml per

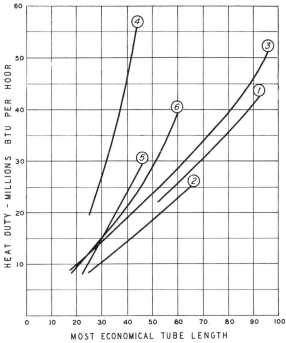

FIG. 23-9. Most economical tube lengths for some common arrangements of pipestills.

gal for the 88 R.o.n. pool). At these high levels of octane number and with 2 or more ml of TEL already present, the use of additional TEL is not usually profitable.

Dimensions of Pipestills. Immature designers are usually confused in deciding what should be the dimensions of a pipestill, whereas experienced designers have become accustomed to using certain arrangements that in some instances may be needlessly expensive. The economic relationship among the costs of tubes, bends, tube supports, roof, walls, et.., is exceedingly complicated. Nevertheless, cost equations can be derived for any conventional type of still such as down-convection, A-frame, etc., stills. Figure 23-9 shows the most economical tube length[25,26] vs. the total cost

[25] Nelson, W. L., *Oil Gas J.*, May 11, 1939, p. 63; and June 1, 1939, p. 34.
[26] Nelson, W. L., *Oil Gas J.*, Nov. 2, 1946, p. 91.

of pipestills.   In general, the high cost of return bends as against the cost of tubing, supports, walls, etc., calls for longer tubes than have commonly been used.   This tendency is becoming evident in stills designed during the last few years.

The types of stills shown in Fig. 23-9 and the major dimensions of the stills are

1. Down convection as in Fig. 18-1c but with two rows of tubes on the roof, and with tubes on the floor.   (Applies only to large stills.)
2. Down convection with only roof tubes and for smaller stills.
3. Down convection as in Fig. 18-1c.
4. Straight-up (Fig. 18-1d) with half the tubes in the convection section, with two rows of tubes on each wall (large stills), and with a width that is one-fourth the length.
5. Straight-up (Fig. 18-1d) with one row of radiant wall tubes and a width of 10 center-to-center tube spacings.   Two-thirds of the tubes are in the convection section.
6. Overhead convection with two rows of radiant tubes.

CHAPTER 24

TYPICAL DESIGN CALCULATION

The design of petroleum equipment is made difficult by the complex composition of petroleum oils. Many features of a design defy exact computation, and such cases must be met by the judgment and experience of the design engineer.

These are the facts concerning the design of petroleum equipment. However, successful equipment can be designed, even though the calculations are not perfect, because a well-designed plant can be operated to overcome the inadequacies in the design information.

Outline of Computations. In this chapter the basic features of a continuous pipestill topping plant will be investigated. A more complicated plant would be more interesting to many engineers, but the calculations would be so involved that they would be almost useless to most readers.

The Mid Continent crude oil shown in Fig. 24-1 is to be topped for the production of gasoline, kerosene, gas oil, and reduced crude oil, as shown in Table 24-1. Its Characterization Factor is 11.8 to 11.9.

TABLE 24-1. YIELDS AND PROPERTIES OF PRODUCTS

Material	Per cent	API	Notes
Loss[a]	0.5	....	About 7 cu ft of gas per bbl
Gasoline	31.0	60.2	ASTM end point about 400 (Fig. 4-25)
Kerosene	10.0	43.0	ASTM end point about 506 (Fig. 4-25)
Gas oil	26.0	34.9	By difference
Reduced crude	32.5	22.5	Viscosity at 210°F, about 107 (Fig. 24-1)
Crude	100.0	38.6	Fig. 24-1

[a] Consider as a gas which has a molecular weight of 45.

Obviously, the selection of products depends upon the market demands and sales opportunities that are available. Although products having particular specifications must be produced in the unit, the designer has little need for more detailed specifications than the general information given in Table 24-1. However, the designer can build a flexible plant and

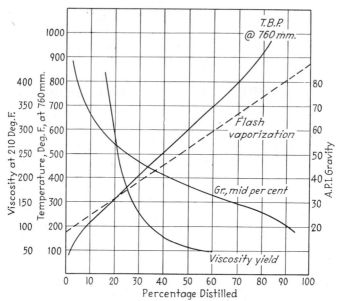

FIG. 24-1. Mid Continent 38.6 API crude oil.

thus permit the plant operator to produce any reasonable specifications that may be desired.

The design computations can be organized somewhat as follows:

1. Estimate the market possibilities of each product including variations therein, and adopt average yields (see Chap. 3).
2. Obtain a comprehensive laboratory evaluation of the stock (see Appendix B). An analysis, such as shown in Fig. 24-1 is satisfactory, but if possible the desired products should be produced in the laboratory and examined by routine tests. This is not always convenient, because many combinations of products may be contemplated. Information about B. S. W., salt and sulfur, or corrosiveness, is particularly useful (Chap. 4).
3. Analyze the evaluation curves of the stock for the yields of products, and if possible produce and examine the products in the laboratory (Chaps. 3 and 4).
4. Prepare a table of the quantities, weights, and oft-used properties of the several stocks (Table 24-2).
5. Prepare a tentative flow diagram of the process. This may be modified as the design progresses to meet unforeseen conditions (Fig. 24-2).
6. Determine the vaporizer temperature at atmospheric pressure required to at least vaporize all the overhead products of item 3.
7. If the vaporizer temperature is so high that it will cause decomposition (usually over 700°F) or discoloration, steam is used to reduce the partial pressure in the vaporizer section [Eq. (15-8), page 442].
8. Next design the fractionating tower because the temperature of the various side-draw products must be known to design the steam strippers and the heat-exchange system.

9. Strippers are designed next because the steam further reduces the temperatures of the side-draw products to the exchangers, and the steam becomes a part of the overhead product.

10. Such exchangers as are needed for heating the crude oil to a proper salt-settling temperature are designed. No salt settler is shown in Fig. 24-2, but one should be installed after the crude oil attains 260°F in the gasoline condensers, or if the crude oil is corrosive or dirty the settling might be done after a temperature of 200°F is attained.

11. Design heat-exchange system by an economic study of each exchanger (Fig. 23-5). Compute the temperature of the stock as it arrives at the pipestill.

12. Design the pipestill.

13. Design the condensers, coolers, stripper, etc.

14. Estimate steam, water, and power requirements.

TABLE 24-2. USEFUL QUANTITIES AND PROPERTIES
10,000 barrels per day

Material	Per cent	API	Lb per gal	Gal per hr	Lb per hr	50 per cent boiling point, °F	Molal[a] average boiling point, °F	Molecular weight[b]
Loss............	0.5	....	0.119[c]	85	350[d]	...	...	45
Gasoline.........	31.0	60.2	6.14	5,425	33,300	258	218	101
Kerosene........	10.0	43.0	6.75	1,750	11,800	460	450	185
Gas oil..........	26.0	34.9	7.08	4,550	32,250	635	615	270
Reduced crude...	32.5	22.5	7.65	5,690	43,550			
Crude..........	100.0	38.6	6.93	17,500	121,250			

[a] Fig. 5-4, approx.
[b] Fig. 5-9.

[c] Density, pound per cubic foot at 60°F.
[d] $\dfrac{10,000 \times 7}{379} \times \dfrac{45}{24} = 350$

The general conditions are as follows:

Capacity..................... 10,000 bbl per day
Temperature of crude oil....... 90°F (avg)
Temperature of cooling water... 75°F (avg) to 95°F (max)
Steam pressure............... 150 psig; saturation temperature, 366°F
Corrosion................... The crude is classed as a sweet oil and contains only 0.2 per cent sulfur

A tentative flow diagram of the process is shown in Fig. 24-2. This diagram shows only the major items of equipment, and it is not intended to indicate anything concerning the size or mechanical design of the equipment. The temperatures and pressures shown are computed or selected as the design proceeds.

FRACTIONATOR SYSTEM

The design of the fractionation system may be outlined as follows:

1. Draw the flash-vaporization curve of the crude oil unless this curve is included in the laboratory analysis (Figs. 4-18 and 4-19).
2. Estimate the amount of steam required for stripping (pages 229 to 232).
3. Estimate the temperatures and pressures at all important points in the tower. Adopt the number of plates to be used between cuts (page 527).
4. Compute a heat balance, and determine the amount of reflux.
5. Compute the diameter of the tower.

The flash-vaporization curve (Fig. 24-1) was computed as follows (Figs. 4-18 and 4-19):

$$70 \text{ per cent on T.B.P. curve} = 798°F$$
$$10 \text{ per cent on T.B.P. curve} = 214°F$$
$$\overline{584°F}$$
$$\text{Slope of T.B.P. curve } ^{584}\!/_{60} = 9.73$$
$$\text{Slope of flash curve (Fig. 4-18)} = 6.85$$
$$50 \text{ per cent on T.B.P.} = 598°F$$
$$50 \text{ per cent on flash curve (Fig. 4-19) } 598 - 80^* = 518°F$$
$$100 \text{ per cent on flash curve } 518 + 50 \times 6.85 = 861°F$$
$$0 \text{ per cent on flash curve } 518 - 50 \times 6.85 = 176°F$$

* Extrapolated.

This curve is plotted as a straight-line vaporization curve in Fig. 24-1. With freak stocks, the curvature of the flash curve should be computed as explained in Example 4-6 (page 119).

The amount of steam required to strip the kerosene, gas oil, and reduced crude oil can be estimated from the figures given on page 229. Table 24-3 summarizes the steam quantities.

TABLE 24-3. STEAM FOR STRIPPING

Material	Lb steam per gal	Gal per hr of material	Lb steam per hr
Kerosene............	0.3	1,750	525
Gas oil.............	0.5	4,550	2,275
Reduced crude.......	0.5	5,690	2,845
Total.............	...	.....	5,645

The number of plates can be estimated from Table 16-13. The following number of plates will be used:

No. of
plates

Gasoline to kerosene.................... 6
Kerosene to gas oil.................... 5
Gas oil to vaporizer.................... 3
No. of plates above vaporizer........... 14
Stripping plates....................... 4
    Total no. of plates................... 18

The pressure at the top of the topping tower is seldom more than 4 psig. The pressure drop per plate is discussed on page 448.   The pressures in the

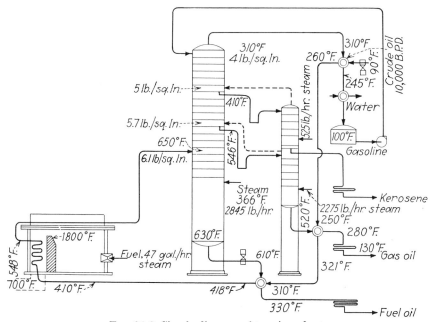

Fig. 24-2. Simple diagram of topping plant.

tower and the amount of steam at various points will be approximately as follows:

Position	Pressure,* psi	Lb steam
At top plate...............	4	5,645
At kerosene plate..........	5	5,120
At gas oil plate............	5.7	2,845
At vaporizer...............	6.1	2,845

* Top velocity approximately 3 ft per sec (see computed velocity, page 896).

Vaporizer Temperature.   The vaporizer temperature, as obtained from the flash curve at 760 mm, must be corrected for the tower pressure and for the effect of steam.   The gasoline, kerosene, gas oil, and loss amount to 67.5 per cent.

Vaporizer temperature at 760 mm (flash curve): 646°F

$$\text{Pressure at vaporizer: } 760 + \frac{6.1}{14.7} \times 760 = 1{,}075 \text{ mm}$$

If the moles of gas are neglected

$$\text{Moles of gasoline (Table 24-2): } \frac{33{,}300}{101} = 330.0$$

$$\text{Moles of kerosene: } \frac{11{,}800}{185} = 63.8$$

$$\text{Moles of gas oil: } \frac{32{,}250}{270} = 119.5$$

Total moles vapor:	513.3
Moles steam: 2,845/18	= 158.0
Total moles vapor and steam:	671.3

$$\text{Partial pressure of oil } \frac{513.3}{671.3} \times 1075 = 821 \text{ mm}$$

Vaporizer temperature at tower conditions, by correcting 646°F to 821 mm by means of Fig. 5-27, is 650°F.

Tower Temperatures.   This tower, the stock that is being processed, and the quantities of steam are all normal.   Under these conditions, the side-draw temperatures and top temperature may be estimated from Fig. 16-4.   In cases in which the conditions are not normal, the method outlined in Example 16-4 (page 474) must be used.

The tower temperatures and the corresponding latent heats are approximately as follows:

	°F	Latent heat[a]
Top temperature	310[b]	120
Kerosene draw plate	410	108
Gas-oil draw plate	546	95
Bottoms product	630	

[a] Estimated from Fig. 5-7.   Latent heat can be computed from Figs. 5-5 and 5-6.
[b] Assumed temperature.   The temperature is checked on p. 896.

The bottoms temperature cannot be estimated as accurately as the other temperatures [Eqs. (16-1) and (16-2)].   However, it is not of great importance because it does not properly belong in the tower balance and is included here only as a factor of safety.

According to Fig. 7-4 the 0.5 lb of steam used for stripping the reduced crude oil will remove about 3 per cent of material.   At the vaporizer the reduced crude (see Fig. 7-9) will have a 0 to 10 per cent boiling range of about 230 to 620°F, and after stripping the average boiling point of the 0 to 10 per cent range will be about 530°F. Equation (4-6a), page 131, indicates an approximate open-cup flash point of

$$\text{Flash point} = 0.64 \times 530 - 100 = 240°F$$

The bottom temperature may be estimated from Eq. (16-2):

$$\Delta T = 1.2P + 35 \frac{D}{B} (T - Ta) + 0.65 \frac{S}{B} (T - Ts)$$

For an estimated tower diameter D of about 9 ft, an air temperature Ta of 40°F, and a steam temperature Ts of 366°F,

$$\Delta T = 1.2 \times 3 + 35 \frac{9}{43,550} (650 - 40) + 0.65 \frac{2,845}{43,550} (650 - 366)$$
$$= 3.6 + 4.4 + 12.1 = 20.1°F$$

Thus the bottoms temperature is approximately 650 − 20, or 630°F. For some unknown reason, actual bottoms temperatures are usually lower than anything that can be computed.

HEAT BALANCE OF TOWER TO TOP PLATE

Temperature datum, vaporizer temperature or 650°F (see Figs. 5-1 and 5-2)

Btu per hr

Cooling gasoline (vapor)............	33,300(650 − 310)0.57 =	6,450,000
Cooling kerosene (vapor)............	11,800(650 − 410)0.58 =	1,640,000
Cooling gas oil (vapor).............	32,250(650 − 546)0.61 =	2,050,000
Cooling reduced crude* (liq)........	43,550(650 − 630)0.76 =	665,000
Cooling steam*...................	5,645(366 − 310)0.5 =	158,000
Total sensible heat....................................		10,963,000
Condense kerosene...............	11,800 × 108 = 1,275,000	
Condense gas oil................	32,250 × 95 = 3,065,000	
	4,340,000	4,340,000
		15,303,000

* Actually, these heats have in part been accounted for in the computation of the bottoms temperature, but most textbooks and designers include them as a factor of safety.

With reflux available at 100°F, the amount of cold or external reflux (or pumparound) for the top of the tower is

Lb cold reflux: (using Fig. 5-3) $\dfrac{15,303,000}{(294 - 50)} = 62,700$ lb per hr

Gal cold reflux: $\dfrac{15,303,000}{244} \dfrac{1}{6.14} = 10,220$ gal per hr

Check on top temperature:

Moles internal reflux and product: $\dfrac{62,700 + 33,300}{101} = 950$

Moles steam: $\dfrac{5,645}{18} = 313$

Total moles: $1,263$

Partial pressure: $\dfrac{950}{1,263}\left(760 + \dfrac{4 \times 760}{14.7}\right) = 727$ mm

The 100 per cent or dew point on the flash-vaporization curve of the gasoline is approximately 324°F. When corrected to 727 mm (Fig. 5-27) the temperature is about 318°F. However, the computed top temperature is usually about 3 per cent too high (page 471), resulting in an actual top temperature of about $0.97 \times 318 = 309$°F. This checks with the assumed temperature of 310°F. The temperature in the liquid of the plate is, theoretically, slightly higher because a larger amount of internal reflux is present, but in practice it is lower because of the large amount of cold reflux.

Diameter of Tower. The allowable mass velocity of the vapors at the top of the tower can be computed from Eq. (16-8). The constant K can be obtained from Fig. 16-13. At a tray spacing of 22 in. and when using conventional bubble plates (curve 3), the value of K is 730 or higher.

The density ρ_L of the gasoline at 310°F can be obtained from Fig. 5-14:

Sp gr at 60°F $= 0.738$ and   at 310°F $= 0.615$

$\rho_L = 0.615 \times 62.4 = 38.4$ lb per cu ft

The density ρ_V of the vapor at 310°F and 4 psig will be computed by the perfect gas laws:

		Moles	*Lb*
Internal reflux.........	$\dfrac{15,303,000}{120 \times 101} =$	1,263	127,700
Gasoline product...............	$=$	330	33,300
Steam....................	$\dfrac{5,645}{18} =$	313	5,645
Total at top...................		1,906	166,645

Volume at top $= 1,906 \times 379 \times \dfrac{770}{520} \times \dfrac{14.7}{18.7} = 840,000$ cu ft per hr

$\rho_V = \dfrac{166,645}{840,000} = 0.198$ lb per cu ft

Mass velocity $w/a = 730[0.198(38.4 - 0.2)]^{0.5} = 2,020$ lb per sq ft per hr

Cross-sectional area of tower.......... $\dfrac{166,645}{2,020} = 82.5$ sq ft

Use a diameter of 10 ft 0 in. This corresponds to a linear velocity of $830,000/(78.5 \times 3,600) = 2.94$ ft per sec.

HEAT-EXCHANGE SYSTEM

The number of products that may be used to heat the charge stock is an economic problem. It usually pays to install condensing exchangers for the overhead product and reflux, because of the large quantity of heat that is available in these materials and because the transfer rate is relatively high in condensing equipment. In the case of kerosene, an exchanger may not be economical because the kerosene stream is small and the cost per unit of surface rises. Heat exchangers are generally used on the gas-oil stream and other high-boiling distillate streams because of the high temperature. The same holds true for the bottoms product, except that the viscosity may be so high that an exchanger is not economical and because such stocks often contain suspended solid matter. Bottoms exchangers are not usually used for viscous stocks unless a pump is provided for the bottoms product.

In general, the exchangers are purchased from manufacturing companies, and these companies are asked to design the exchange system. However, the plant engineer must not depend entirely on the computations from these manufacturers. For this reason, the following approximate design of the heat-exchange system is suggested.

The feedstock should be routed in a countercurrent manner:

1. Gasoline and reflux condenser exchanger.
2. Kerosene exchanger.
3. Gas-oil exchanger.
4. Reduced crude-oil exchanger.

The temperatures in these exchangers will be developed during the computations and are shown in Fig. 24-3.

Gasoline Condensing Exchanger. The pounds of reflux and gasoline are 33,300 plus 62,700 or 96,000 lb, and 5,645 lb of steam must also be handled. Using an approach of 50°F on the hot end of the exchanger, the heat absorbed by the crude oil between 90 and 260°F (Fig. 5-3) is:

$$121,250(130 - 42) = 10,680,000 \text{ Btu per hr}$$

This amount of heat will condense about 60 per cent of the gasoline and reflux, and require an outlet temperature, for the gasoline, of about 245°F.

Cool 60 per cent of vapor and the condensate from it:

$$0.6 \times 96,000(310 - 245) \left(\frac{0.64 + 0.49}{2} \right)^* = 2,115,000$$

Cool vapor that does not condense: $0.4 \times 96,000(310 - 245)0.48 = 1,013,000$
Cool steam: $\qquad\qquad\qquad\qquad 5,645(310 - 245)0.5 = 155,000$
Condense 60 per cent of vapor: $\qquad 0.6 \times 96,000 \times 128\dagger = \underline{7,370,000}$
$$\qquad\qquad\qquad\qquad\qquad\qquad\qquad\qquad\qquad\qquad 10,653,000$$

* Average specific heat of vapor and liquid.
† Higher boiling than the entire gasoline.

This is sufficiently close for checking the temperature of 245°F.

Transfer Coefficients. The crude oil will pass through the tubes, and a mass velocity of 210 lb per sq ft-sec (about 4.5 ft per sec) will be possible because of the pressure that is available.

The average temperature of the crude oil will be about 175°F and its viscosity at this temperature is about 2.4 (Fig. 4-43). Film-transfer rate for crude oil according to Fig. 17-11 is about 160.

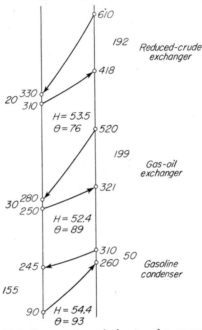

FIG. 24-3. Temperatures in heat-exchange system.

The gasoline, reflux, and steam will be cooled on the outside of the tubes, and the condensing coefficient will be about 140 (Table 17-7). The approximate fouling conditions are as follows:

Crude in tubes (wet)............ 4.0 (Fig. 17-8)
Gasoline in shell................ 1.0 (Fig. 17-9)
    Total fouling factor......... 5.0

Over-all Coefficient (neglecting differences in inside and outside area).

$$H = \frac{1}{\frac{1}{160} + \frac{1}{140} + 0.005} = \frac{1}{0.0184} = 54.4$$

Larger temp diff. (see Fig. 24-3) = about 155
                Smaller temp diff. = about 50
Log mean-temperature diff. (Fig. 17-3) = 93°F

$$\text{Surface} = \frac{10,680,000}{93 \times 54.4} = 2,110 \text{ sq ft}$$

Kerosene Exchanger. Although this exchanger is small it is still economical if a 3 or 4 per cent return on investment is adequate. Our refiner has a better use for the money, and accordingly no kerosene exchanger will be installed. The two following exchangers will assume the heat load and they will operate at better mean-temperature differences if the kerosene exchanger is not installed.

Gas-oil Exchanger

Oil	Lb	Approx. temp after stripper, etc.
Gas oil..........	32,250	520
Crude..........	121,250	250

Using an approach of 30°F (Fig. 23-5) the amount of heat that is exchanged is about as follows:

$$\underset{\text{Gas oil}}{32,250(520 - 280)0.645} = \underset{\text{Crude oil}}{121,250(321 - 250)0.58} = 5,000,000 \text{ Btu}$$

Log mean-temperature difference = 89°F

The transfer-rate conditions will be about as follows:

Oil	Fluid temp	Viscosity*	Side	Mass velocity	Film rate†	Fouling factors
Gas oil..................	400	0.6	Shell	50‡	120	2
Crude (wet)..............	285	1.0	Tube	160	210	4

* Fig. 4-43.
† Figs. 17-11 and 17-12.
‡ Low velocity because no pump is used.

$$H \text{ for gas-oil exchanger} = \frac{1}{\frac{1}{120} + \frac{1}{210} + 0.006} = 52.4$$

$$\text{Surface} = \frac{5,000,000}{89 + 52.4} = 1,072 \text{ sq ft}$$

Bottoms Exchanger

Oil	Lb	Approx. temp
Reduced crude.........	43,550	610
Crude.................	121,250	310

Using an approach of 20°F, the duty of the exchanger would be

$$43,550(610 - 330)0.67 = 121,250(418 - 310)0.625 = 8,180,000$$

Log mean-temperature difference (Fig. 17-3) = 76°F
The transfer-rate conditions will be about as follows:

Oil	Fluid temp	Vis-cosity	Side	Mass velocity	Film rate	Fouling factors
Reduced crude.............	470	1.5	Shell	100*	135	4
Crude.....................	364	0.55	Tube	130	235	3

* Pump on reduced crude oil.

$$H = \frac{1}{\frac{1}{135} + \frac{1}{235} + 0.007} = 53.5$$

If the reduced crude oil were not handled by a pump, the over-all rate would be only about 40.

$$\text{Surface} = \frac{8,180,000}{76 \times 53.5} = 2,015 \text{ sq ft}$$

Water Coolers and Condensers. The design of these equipments is much the same as for the exchangers, and hence only one cooler, the gas-oil cooler, will be designed.   A tubular type of cooler will be used.

The gas oil is available at 280°F from the exchanger, and it will be cooled a few degrees in the transfer line.   However, the cooling will be neglected and considered as a further factor of safety.   The flash point of the gas oil will be above 160°F, and hence it need not be cooled to lower than about 130°F.   The water will be sent through the tubes.   It will not be heated to over 125°F because scale may be deposited.

Duty of Gas-oil Cooler.

$$32,250(280 - 130)0.53 = W(125 - 95)1.0 = 2,560,000 \text{ Btu}$$
$$\text{Gas oil} \qquad\qquad \text{Water}$$

$$W = \text{lb water} = 85,500$$

$$\text{Gal water} = \frac{85,500}{8.33} = 10,280 \text{ gal per hr}$$

Transfer-rate conditions will be as follows:

	Fluid temp	Vis-cosity	Side	Mass velocity	Film rate*	Fouling factor
Gas oil.....................	205	2.8	Shell	48	77	3
Water (spray pond).........	...	...	Tube	260	1,100	3†

* Fig. 17-12 and Fig. 17-11.
† Fig. 17-8.

$$H = \frac{1}{\frac{1}{77} + \frac{1}{1100} + 0.006} = 50.3$$

Log mean-temperature diff. = 81

$$\text{Surface} = \frac{2,560,000}{50.3 \times 81} = 630 \text{ sq ft}$$

PIPESTILL HEATER

Crude oil arrives at the pipestill at a temperature of about 410°F. It must be heated to a temperature sufficiently high to vaporize, by flash vaporization, 67.5 per cent of the crude oil. This requires a temperature of about 650°F at the vaporize at a pressure of 6.1 psig (page 894).

The temperature at the outlet of the still will be somewhat higher than 650°F because of the adiabatic vaporization that occurs in the transfer line to the tower. The outlet temperature can be computed with fair accuracy, but it is not important in this case.

Pipestill Duty. In computing the heat that will be absorbed in the pipestill, it is not necessary to know the pressure in the still or the outlet temperature, because nearly the same amount of heat is required by any heating route, if the initial and final conditions are the same for each route.

Assume that the crude oil is heated to the vaporizer temperature of 650°F and that vaporization of the products occurs at that temperature. Sensible and latent heats can be used, but enthalpies will be used here to illustrate the use of Fig. 5-3.

Btu per hr

Heat gas.	350(650 − 410)0.655* =	55,000
Heat and vaporize gasoline.	33,300(498 − 238) =	8,650,000
Heat and vaporize kerosene.	11,800(481 − 228) =	2,985,000
Heat and vaporize gas oil.	32,250(472 − 220) =	8,130,000
Heat reduced crude oil.	43,550(376 − 210) =	7,220,000
Pipestill duty	=	27,040,000

* Use the propane line of Fig. 5-2.

Heat Balance of Still. The approach between the temperature of the stack gas and the temperature of the feedstock should be about 290°F (Fig. 23-6). The stack-gas temperature would then be 410 + 290, or 700°F.

The furnace could be fired with 25 per cent excess air, but general operation is nearer 40 per cent excess air. With 40 per cent of excess air and burning some of the reduced crude oil as a fuel, the loss due to the temperature of the stack gases amounts to about 18 per cent (Fig. 14-2).

The heating operation is not a difficult one, and hence the radiant section can be designed for a radiant-absorption rate of about 35,000 Btu per sq ft of projected area per hr (Table 18-5).

According to Fig. 18-4, which applies to the use of two rows of tubes in the radiant section and a center-to-center spacing of the tubes of 2.0, the percentage of the heat liberation that is absorbed in the radiant section with 40 per cent excess air is about 44 per cent. Should other tube arrangements be used, Eq. (18-6), page 595, can be employed; or, if the arrangement of the still is not normal, the Lobo-Evans method of Example 18-2 (page 602) can be used.

The losses through the walls, etc., of the still amount to about 3 per cent from the radiant section and 2 per cent from the convection section. The efficiency of the still is $100 - 18 - 5 = 77$ per cent.

The heat balance of the furnace is about as follows:

Heat quantity	Per cent of net H.V.	Heat, Btu per hr
Heat input $27,040,000 \div 0.77$	100	35,150,000
Wall losses	5	1,760,000
Stack loss	18	6,320,000
Radiant absorption	44	15,450,000
Convection absorption (by diff.)	33	11,620,000

Convection Section. If none of the gasoline is vaporized in the convection section, the oil is at approximately 548°F as it leaves the convection section:

$$121,250(x - 410)0.7 = 11,620,000$$
$$x = 548°F$$

The flue gas that enters the convection section still contains $100 - 44 - 3$, or 53 per cent of the net heating value of the fuel. Figure 14-2 shows that the temperature of the gas at the bridge wall will be approximately 1800°F. The furnace temperature that is recorded in plant operation is lower than this, but it is usually measured at another point.

$$\text{Larger temp diff.} = 1800 - 548 = 1252$$
$$\text{Smaller temp diff.} = 700 - 410 = 290$$
$$\text{log mean-temperature diff.} = \frac{1252 - 290}{\ln \dfrac{1252}{290}} = 667°F$$

The convection section will be designed for an average flue-gas velocity of 8 ft per sec. With tubing that has an outside diameter of 6 in. and with an average flue-gas temperature of about 1250°F, the over-all convection coefficient is about 5.9 (Table 18-6).

$$\text{Convection surface} = \frac{11,620,000}{5.9 \times 667} = 2,955 \text{ sq ft outside surface}$$

Radiant Section.

$$\text{Radiant surface} = \frac{15,450,000}{35,000} = 441 \text{ sq ft projected area}$$

In computing the tube diameter, the information given in Tables 9-5 and 18-5 and on page 624 will be useful.

Fuel Required. The net heating value of a 22.5 API fuel is about 17,800 Btu (Fig. 5-22 and Table 14-3).

Fuel
$$\frac{35,150,000}{17,800} = 1975 \text{ lb per hr}$$

or
$$\frac{1975}{7.65} = 258 \text{ gal per hr}$$

Two burners could be used, but six small ones would be more satisfactory. Steam for atomizing (page 426),

$$1,975 \times 0.3 = 593 \text{ lb per hr}$$

WATER REQUIRED

The several products leave the coolers at almost the same temperature as the crude oil enters the plant, and hence the heat that must be removed by cooling water is almost equal to the heat added to the oil in the pipe-still. When the water is at its maximum temperature of 95°F,

$$\text{Approx. gal of cooling water} = \frac{27,040,000}{(125 - 95)8.33} = 108,000 \text{ gal per hr}$$

This is a maximum figure because some of the heat is lost through the insulation of the equipment.

STEAM REQUIRED

Reciprocating steam pumps would be used for the charge stock and the reduced crude oil. The steam required for these pumps would be guaranteed by the pump manufacturers, but simple approximations can be had, as follows:

The charge pump will operate at a pressure sufficiently high to force the oil through the exchangers and the pipestill and into the fractionating tower. The charge pressure will be about 160 psig. If a conventional duplex pump is used, its steam consumption according to Eq. (13-11), page 413, will be about:

$$S = (0.058\ C + 1)(P - p)$$

$$= \left(0.058\ \frac{17{,}500}{60} + 1\right)(160 - \text{zero}) = 2{,}860\ \text{lb per hr}$$

In a similar manner the steam required for the bottoms pump when pumping at 40 psig is about:

$$S = \left(0.058\ \frac{5690}{60} + 1\right)(40 - \text{zero}) = 260\ \text{lb per hr}$$

Approximate steam requirements:

For two pumps.....................	3,120 lb per hr
For stripping (process steam).........	5,645
For burners.......................	593
	9,358
Misc., contingencies, etc.............	3,120
	12,478 lb per hr

With feedwater at 130°F and with saturated 150 psig steam, the boiler horsepower corresponding to 12,478 lb per hr is about 410.

Summary. The design as herein presented is inadequate in many respects. However, each design depends greatly upon the particular plant conditions that are encountered and upon a multitude of practical details. Refer particularly to Chap. 23 on Economics. These details cannot be presented without becoming involved in a hopelessly tedious discussion.

DENSITIES AND SPECIFIC VOLUMES AS A FUNCTION OF API GRAVITY

Material or API 60/60°F	Sp gr 60/60°F	Lb/gal	Lb/bbl	Lb/ cu ft	Lb/hr for 1,000 bpd	Bbl/ long ton	Bbl/ metric ton	Cubic meters/ long ton	Cubic meters/ metric ton
Ethene	0.338	2.8149	118.23	21.10	4,926	18.95			
Ethane	0.374	3.1147	130.82	23.35	5,451	17.12			
Propene	0.522	4.3472	182.58	32.59	7,608	12.27			
Propane	0.509	4.2390	178.04	31.78	7,418	12.58			
i-Butene	0.600	4.9968	209.87	37.46	8,744	10.68			
n-Butene-1	0.601	5.0051	210.21	37.52	8,759	10.66			
i-Butane	0.563	4.6887	196.93	35.15	8,205	11.43			
n-Butane	0.584	4.8636	204.27	36.46	8,551	10.97			
i-Pentane	0.625	5.2050	218.61	39.02	9,109	10.25			
n-Pentane	0.631	5.2550	220.71	39.39	9,196	10.15			
−10.0	1.1646	9.6988	407.35	72.71	16,973	5.50			
− 9.5	1.1600	9.6602	405.73	72.42	16,904	5.52			
− 9.0	1.1553	9.6217	404.11	72.13	16,834	5.54			
− 8.5	1.1507	9.5831	402.49	71.84	16,766	5.57			
− 8.0	1.1461	9.5446	400.87	71.55	16,698	5.59			
− 7.5	1.1414	9.5060	399.25	71.26	16,631	5.61			
− 7.0	1.1368	9.4674	397.63	70.97	16,564	5.63			
− 6.5	1.1322	9.4289	396.01	70.68	16,498	5.66			
− 6.0	1.1276	9.3903	394.39	70.39	16,432	5.68			
− 5.5	1.1229	9.3518	392.77	70.10	16,367	5.70			
− 5.0	1.1183	9.3123	391.15	69.82	16,302	5.73			
− 4.5	1.1141	9.2779	389.68	69.55	16,238	5.75			
− 4.0	1.1098	9.2427	388.20	69.29	16,174	5.77			
− 3.5	1.1056	9.2075	386.72	69.02	16,111	5.79			
− 3.0	1.1014	9.1723	385.24	68.76	16,048	5.81			
− 2.5	1.0971	9.1370	383.76	68.50	15,986	5.84			
− 2.0	1.0929	9.1018	382.28	68.23	15,924	5.86			
− 1.5	1.0887	9.0666	380.80	67.97	15,863	5.88			
− 1.0	1.0845	9.0314	379.32	67.70	15,802	5.91			
− 0.5	1.0802	8.9962	377.84	67.44	15,742	5.93			
0	1.0760	8.962	376.40	67.18	15,682	5.95			
0.5	1.0720	8.928	375.00	66.93	15,623	5.97			
1.0	1.0679	8.895	373.60	66.68	15,564	6.00			
1.5	1.0639	8.861	372.20	66.43	15,505	6.02			
2.0	1.0599	8.828	370.79	66.18	15,447	6.04			
2.5	1.0560	8.795	369.39	65.93	15,390	6.06			
3.0	1.0520	8.762	368.04	65.68	15,333	6.09			

Material or API 60/60°F	Sp gr 60/60°F	Lb/gal	Lb/bbl	Lb/ cu ft	Lb/hr for 1,000 bpd	Bbl/ long ton	Bbl/ metric ton	Cubic meters/ long ton	Cubic meters/ metric ton
3.5	1.0481	8.730	366.68	65.44	15,276	6.11			
4.0	1.0443	8.698	365.33	65.20	15,219	6.13			
4.5	1.0404	8.666	363.98	64.96	15,163	6.15			
5.0	1.0366	8.634	362.63	64.72	15,108	6.18			
5.5	1.0328	8.602	361.32	64.48	15,053	6.20			
6.0	1.0291	8.571	360.01	64.25	14,998	6.22			
6.5	1.0254	8.540	358.70	64.02	14,944	6.25			
7.0	1.0217	8.509	357.39	63.79	14,890	6.27			
7.5	1.0180	8.478	356.08	63.55	14,836	6.29			
8.0	1.0143	8.448	354.82	63.33	14,783	6.31			
8.5	1.0107	8.418	353.56	63.11	14,730	6.34			
9.0	1.0071	8.388	352.30	62.88	14,678	6.36			
9.5	1.0035	8.358	351.04	62.66	14,626	6.38			
10.0	1.0000	8.328	349.78	62.43	14,574	6.4041	6.3030	1.01729	1.00123
10.5	0.9965	8.299	348.56	62.21	14,523	6.4265	6.3250	1.02085	1.00472
11.0	0.9930	8.270	347.34	62.00	14,472	6.4490	6.3472	1.02443	1.00825
11.5	0.9895	8.241	346.12	61.78	14,422	6.4717	6.3695	1.02803	1.01180
12.0	0.9861	8.212	344.90	61.56	14,371	6.4946	6.3920	1.03166	1.01537
12.5	0.9826	8.183	343.69	61.34	14,321	6.5176	6.4146	1.03532	1.01897
13.0	0.9792	8.155	342.52	61.14	14,271	6.5400	6.4367	1.03887	1.02246
13.5	0.9759	8.127	341.35	60.93	14,222	6.5625	6.4588	1.04245	1.02599
14.0	0.9725	8.099	340.18	60.72	14,173	6.5852	6.4812	1.04606	1.02954
14.5	0.9692	8.071	339.02	60.51	14,125	6.6080	6.5037	1.04969	1.03311
15.0	0.9659	8.044	337.85	60.30	14,077	6.6302	6.5255	1.05321	1.03657
15.5	0.9626	8.016	336.71	60.10	14,028	6.6534	6.5483	1.05689	1.04020
16.0	0.9593	7.989	335.58	59.90	13,981	6.6758	6.5704	1.06046	1.04371
16.5	0.9561	7.962	334.45	59.70	13,934	6.6985	6.5927	1.06406	1.04725
17.0	0.9529	7.935	333.31	59.50	13,887	6.7213	6.6151	1.06768	1.05081
17.5	0.9497	7.909	332.18	59.29	13,841	6.7434	6.6369	1.07119	1.05427
18.0	0.9465	7.882	331.08	59.10	13,794	6.7665	6.6596	1.07486	1.05788
18.5	0.9433	7.856	329.98	58.90	13,748	6.7889	6.6816	1.07841	1.06138
19.0	0.9402	7.830	328.88	58.71	13,703	6.8114	6.7038	1.08199	1.06490
19.5	0.9371	7.804	327.78	58.51	13,657	6.8341	6.7262	1.08560	1.06845
20.0	0.9340	7.778	326.68	58.31	13,612	6.8569	6.7487	1.08923	1.07202
20.5	0.9309	7.752	325.61	58.12	13,566	6.8799	6.7712	1.09288	1.07562
21.0	0.9279	7.727	324.54	57.93	13,522	6.9022	6.7932	1.09642	1.07910
21.5	0.9248	7.701	323.48	57.74	13,477	6.9255	6.8161	1.10012	1.08274
22.0	0.9218	7.676	322.41	57.55	13,433	6.9481	6.8383	1.10370	1.08627
22.5	0.9188	7.651	321.34	57.36	13,389	6.9708	6.8607	1.10731	1.08982
23.0	0.9159	7.627	320.32	57.18	13,347	6.9927	6.8823	1.11079	1.09325
23.5	0.9129	7.602	319.29	57.00	13,304	7.0157	6.9048	1.11445	1.09684
24.0	0.9100	7.578	318.27	56.82	13,262	7.0379	6.9268	1.11797	1.10032
24.5	0.9071	7.554	317.24	56.63	13,220	7.0603	6.9488	1.12153	1.10381
25.0	0.9042	7.529	316.22	56.45	13,177	7.0837	6.9718	1.12525	1.10748
25.5	0.9013	7.505	315.22	56.27	13,134	7.1064	6.9941	1.12885	1.11102
26.0	0.8984	7.481	314.22	56.09	13,092	7.1292	7.0166	1.13247	1.11458
26.5	0.8956	7.458	313.22	55.91	13,052	7.1512	7.0382	1.13596	1.11802
27.0	0.8927	7.434	312.22	55.73	13,010	7.1742	7.0609	1.13963	1.12163
27.5	0.8899	7.410	311.22	55.55	12,968	7.1975	7.0838	1.14332	1.12526
28.0	0.8871	7.387	310.26	55.38	12,927	7.2199	7.1059	1.14688	1.12877
28.5	0.8844	7.364	309.30	55.21	12,887	7.2424	7.1281	1.15046	1.13229
29.0	0.8816	7.341	308.35	55.04	12,847	7.2651	7.1504	1.15407	1.13584
29.5	0.8789	7.318	307.39	54.87	12,807	7.2880	7.1729	1.15770	1.13941
30.0	0.8762	7.296	306.43	54.70	12,768	7.3099	7.1945	1.16119	1.14285
30.5	0.8735	7.273	305.49	54.53	12,728	7.3331	7.2172	1.16486	1.14646

Material or API 60/60°F	Sp gr 60/60°F	Lb/gal	Lb/bbl	Lb/ cu ft	Lb/hr for 1,000 bpd	Bbl/ long ton	Bbl/ metric ton	Cubic meters/ long ton	Cubic meters/ metric ton
31.0	0.8708	7.251	304.55	54.36	12,689	7.3553	7.2391	1.16839	1.14994
31.5	0.8681	7.228	303.61	54.20	12,650	7.3787	7.2622	1.17211	1.15360
32.0	0.8654	7.206	302.67	54.03	12,611	7.4012	7.2843	1.17569	1.15712
32.5	0.8628	7.184	301.73	53.86	12,573	7.4239	7.3067	1.17929	1.16066
33.0	0.8602	7.163	300.82	53.70	12,535	7.4457	7.3281	1.18275	1.16407
33.5	0.8576	7.141	299.91	53.54	12,497	7.4686	7.3507	1.18639	1.16765
34.0	0.8550	7.119	299.01	53.37	12,459	7.4917	7.3734	1.19006	1.17126
34.5	0.8524	7.098	298.10	53.21	12,422	7.5139	7.3952	1.19359	1.17473
35.0	0.8498	7.076	297.19	53.05	12,384	7.5372	7.4182	1.19729	1.17838
35.5	0.8473	7.055	296.32	52.89	12,347	7.5597	7.4403	1.20085	1.18189
36.0	0.8448	7.034	295.44	52.74	12,310	7.5822	7.4625	1.20444	1.18541
36.5	0.8423	7.013	294.57	52.58	12,273	7.6049	7.4848	1.20804	1.18896
37.0	0.8398	6.993	293.70	52.43	12,237	7.6266	7.5062	1.21150	1.19237
37.5	0.8373	6.972	292.82	52.27	12,201	7.6496	7.5288	1.21515	1.19596
38.0	0.8348	6.951	291.97	52.12	12,164	7.6728	7.5516	1.21882	1.19957
38.5	0.8324	6.930	291.11	51.96	12,128	7.6960	7.5745	1.22251	1.20320
39.0	0.8299	6.910	290.25	51.81	12,093	7.7183	7.5964	1.22605	1.20669
39.5	0.8275	6.890	289.40	51.66	12,058	7.7407	7.6184	1.22961	1.21019
40.0	0.8251	6.870	288.54	51.51	12,023	7.7632	7.6406	1.23319	1.21371
40.5	0.8227	6.850	287.71	51.36	11,988	7.7859	7.6629	1.23679	1.21726
41.0	0.8203	6.830	286.88	51.21	11,953	7.8087	7.6854	1.24041	1.22082
41.5	0.8179	6.810	286.04	51.06	11,918	7.8316	7.7079	1.24405	1.22441
42.0	0.8155	6.790	285.21	50.91	11,883	7.8547	7.7306	1.24772	1.22801
42.5	0.8132	6.771	284.38	50.76	11,849	7.8767	7.7523	1.25122	1.23146
43.0	0.8109	6.752	283.58	50.62	11,815	7.8989	7.7741	1.25474	1.23492
43.5	0.8086	6.732	282.77	50.48	11,781	7.9224	7.7972	1.25847	1.23859
44.0	0.8063	6.713	281.96	50.33	11,748	7.9448	7.8193	1.26203	1.24210
44.5	0.8040	6.694	281.16	50.19	11,715	7.9673	7.8415	1.26561	1.24562
45.0	0.8017	6.675	280.35	50.05	11,681	7.9900	7.8638	1.26921	1.24917
45.5	0.7994	6.656	279.57	49.91	11,648	8.0128	7.8863	1.27284	1.25274
46.0	0.7972	6.637	278.79	49.77	11,615	8.0358	7.9088	1.27648	1.25632
46.5	0.7949	6.618	278.01	49.63	11,582	8.0588	7.9316	1.28015	1.25993
47.0	0.7927	6.600	277.23	49.49	11,550	8.0808	7.9532	1.28364	1.26336
47.5	0.7905	6.582	276.44	49.35	11,518	8.1029	7.9749	1.28715	1.26682
48.0	0.7883	6.563	275.67	49.21	11,485	8.1264	7.9980	1.29087	1.27049
48.5	0.7861	6.545	274.90	49.08	11,453	8.1487	8.0200	1.29443	1.27398
49.0	0.7839	6.526	274.13	48.94	11,421	8.1724	8.0434	1.29819	1.27769
49.5	0.7818	6.509	273.35	48.81	11,390	8.1938	8.0644	1.30158	1.28103
50.0	0.7796	6.490	272.58	48.67	11,358	8.2178	8.0880	1.30539	1.28478
50.5	0.7775	6.473	271.84	48.54	11,327	8.2394	8.1092	1.30882	1.28815
51.0	0.7753	6.455	271.10	48.40	11,296	8.2623	8.1318	1.31247	1.29174
51.5	0.7732	6.437	270.36	48.27	11,265	8.2854	8.1546	1.31614	1.29536
52.0	0.7711	6.420	269.26	48.14	11,235	8.3074	8.1762	1.31963	1.29879
52.5	0.7690	6.402	268.88	48.01	11,204	8.3307	8.1992	1.32334	1.30244
53.0	0.7669	6.385	268.16	47.88	11,174	8.3529	8.2210	1.32686	1.30591
53.5	0.7649	6.368	267.44	47.75	11,144	8.3752	8.2429	1.33040	1.30939
54.0	0.7628	6.350	266.72	47.62	11,114	8.3990	8.2663	1.33418	1.31310
54.5	0.7608	6.334	265.99	47.49	11,084	8.4202	8.2872	1.33755	1.31642
55.0	0.7587	6.316	265.27	47.36	11,054	8.4442	8.3108	1.34136	1.32017
55.5	0.7567	6.300	264.57	47.24	11,025	8.4656	8.3319	1.34476	1.32353
56.0	0.7547	6.283	263.88	47.12	10,995	8.4885	8.3544	1.34840	1.32711
56.5	0.7527	6.266	263.18	46.99	10,966	8.5115	8.3771	1.35206	1.33071
57.0	0.7507	6.249	262.48	46.87	10,937	8.5347	8.3999	1.35574	1.33433
57.5	0.7487	6.233	261.79	46.74	10,908	8.5566	8.4215	1.35922	1.33775
58.0	0.7467	6.216	261.10	46.62	10,878	8.5800	8.4445	1.36294	1.34141

Material or API 60/60°F	Sp gr 60/60°F	Lb/gal	Lb/bbl	Lb/ cu ft	Lb/hr for 1,000 bpd	Bbl/ long ton	Bbl/ metric ton	Cubic meters/ long ton	Cubic meters/ metric ton
58.5	0.7447	6.199	260.41	46.50	10,849	8.6035	8.4677	1.36667	1.34509
59.0	0.7428	6.184	259.72	46.37	10,821	8.6244	8.4882	1.36999	1.34835
59.5	0.7408	6.167	259.03	46.25	10,792	8.6482	8.5116	1.37377	1.35207
60.0	0.7389	6.151	258.34	46.13	10,764	8.6707	8.5338	1.37734	1.35559
60.5	0.7370	6.135	257.68	46.01	10,736	8.6933	8.5560	1.38093	1.35912
61.0	0.7351	6.119	257.01	45.89	10,708	8.7160	8.5784	1.38454	1.36268
61.5	0.7332	6.103	256.35	45.77	10,680	8.7389	8.6009	1.38817	1.36625
62.0	0.7313	6.087	255.69	45.66	10,653	8.7618	8.6235	1.39182	1.36984
62.5	0.7294	6.072	255.02	45.54	10,626	8.7835	8.6448	1.39526	1.37322
63.0	0.7275	6.056	254.37	45.42	10,598	8.8067	8.6676	1.39895	1.37685
63.5	0.7256	6.040	253.71	45.30	10,571	8.8300	8.6906	1.40265	1.38050
64.0	0.7238	6.025	253.06	45.19	10,544	8.8520	8.7122	1.40614	1.38394
64.5	0.7219	6.010	252.40	45.07	10,517	8.8741	8.7339	1.40965	1.38739
65.0	0.7201	5.994	251.75	44.96	10,490	8.8978	8.7573	1.41342	1.39109
65.5	0.7183	5.979	251.12	44.84	10,463	8.9201	8.7792	1.41696	1.39458
66.0	0.7165	5.964	250.49	44.73	10,437	8.9425	8.8013	1.42053	1.39809
66.5	0.7146	5.949	249.86	44.62	10,411	8.9651	8.8235	1.42411	1.40162
67.0	0.7128	5.934	249.23	44.51	10,385	8.9878	8.8458	1.42771	1.40516
67.5	0.7111	5.919	248.60	44.39	10,358	9.0105	8.8682	1.43132	1.40872
68.0	0.7093	5.904	247.98	44.28	10,332	9.0334	8.8908	1.43496	1.41230
68.5	0.7075	5.889	247.35	44.17	10,306	9.0564	8.9134	1.43861	1.41590
69.0	0.7057	5.874	246.73	44.06	10,280	9.0796	8.9362	1.44229	1.41951
69.5	0.7040	5.860	246.11	43.95	10,255	9.1013	8.9575	1.44574	1.42290
70.0	0.7022	5.845	245.49	43.84	10,229	9.1246	8.9805	1.44945	1.42655
70.5	0.7005	5.831	244.89	43.73	10,204	9.1465	9.0021	1.45293	1.42998
71.0	0.6988	5.817	244.28	43.63	10,179	9.1685	9.0237	1.45642	1.43342
71.5	0.6970	5.802	243.68	43.52	10,154	9.1922	9.0471	1.46019	1.43713
72.0	0.6953	5.788	243.07	43.41	10,129	9.2145	9.0689	1.46372	1.44060
72.5	0.6936	5.773	242.47	43.30	10,103	9.2384	9.0925	1.46752	1.44435
73.0	0.6919	5.759	241.88	43.20	10,078	9.2609	9.1146	1.47109	1.44786
73.5	0.6902	5.745	241.29	43.09	10,054	9.2834	9.1368	1.47468	1.45139
74.0	0.6886	5.731	240.70	42.99	10,030	9.3061	9.1591	1.47828	1.45493
74.5	0.6869	5.718	240.11	42.88	10,006	9.3273	9.1800	1.48164	1.45824
75.0	0.6852	5.703	239.53	42.78	9,982	9.3518	9.2041	1.48554	1.46207
75.5	0.6836	5.690	238.96	42.68	9,958	9.3732	9.2251	1.48893	1.46541
76.0	0.6819	5.676	238.38	42.57	9,933	9.3963	9.2479	1.49260	1.46903
76.5	0.6803	5.662	237.81	42.47	9,909	9.4195	9.2708	1.49629	1.47266
77.0	0.6787	5.649	237.24	42.37	9,886	9.4412	9.2921	1.49974	1.47605
77.5	0.6770	5.635	236.67	42.27	9,862	9.4647	9.3152	1.50346	1.47972
78.0	0.6754	5.622	236.11	42.17	9,838	9.4865	9.3367	1.50694	1.48314
78.5	0.6738	5.608	235.54	42.07	9,814	9.5102	9.3600	1.51070	1.48684
79.0	0.6722	5.595	234.98	41.97	9,791	9.5323	9.3818	1.51421	1.49030
79.5	0.6706	5.582	234.42	41.87	9,768	9.5545	9.4036	1.51774	1.49377
80.0	0.6690	5.568	233.86	41.77	9,744	9.5785	9.4273	1.52155	1.49752
80.5	0.6675	5.556	233.31	41.67	9,722	9.5992	9.4476	1.52484	1.50076
81.0	0.6659	5.542	232.76	41.57	9,699	9.6235	9.4715	1.52869	1.50455
81.5	0.6643	5.529	232.22	41.48	9,676	9.6461	9.4938	1.53229	1.50809
82.0	0.6628	5.516	231.67	41.38	9,653	9.6688	9.5161	1.53590	1.51164
82.5	0.6612	5.503	231.13	41.28	9,630	9.6917	9.5386	1.53953	1.51521
83.0	0.6597	5.491	230.60	41.19	9,608	9.7129	9.5595	1.54289	1.51852
83.5	0.6581	5.477	230.07	41.09	9,586	9.7377	9.5839	1.54683	1.52240
84.0	0.6566	5.465	229.54	41.00	9,564	9.7591	9.6049	1.55023	1.52575
84.5	0.6551	5.453	229.01	40.90	9,542	9.7805	9.6261	1.55364	1.52910
85.0	0.6536	5.440	228.48	40.81	9,520	9.8039	9.6491	1.55736	1.53276
85.5	0.6521	5.427	227.95	40.71	9,498	9.8274	9.6722	1.56109	1.53643

Material or API 60/60°F	Sp gr 60/60°F	Lb/gal	Lb/bbl	Lb/ cu ft	Lb/hr for 1,000 bpd	Bbl/ long ton	Bbl/ metric ton	Cubic meters/ long ton	Cubic meters/ metric ton
86.0	0.6506	5.415	227.42	40.62	9,476	9.8492	9.6936	1.56455	1.53984
86.5	0.6491	5.402	226.89	40.53	9,454	9.8729	9.7170	1.56831	1.54354
87.0	0.6476	5.390	226.36	40.43	9,432	9.8949	9.7386	1.57180	1.54698
87.5	0.6461	5.377	225.83	40.34	9,410	9.9188	9.7621	1.57560	1.55072
88.0	0.6446	5.365	225.32	40.25	9,389	9.9410	9.7840	1.57913	1.55419
88.5	0.6432	5.353	224.81	40.16	9,368	9.9633	9.8059	1.58267	1.55767
89.0	0.6417	5.341	224.30	40.07	9,347	9.9856	9.8279	1.58622	1.56117
89.5	0.6403	5.329	223.78	39.98	9,326	10.0081	9.8501	1.58979	1.56469
90.0	0.6388	5.316	223.27	39.88	9,305	10.0326	9.8742	1.59368	1.56851
90.5	0.6374	5.305	222.78	39.79	9,284	10.0534	9.8946	1.59699	1.57176
91.0	0.6360	5.293	222.28	39.71	9,263	10.0762	9.9171	1.60061	1.57533
91.5	0.6345	5.281	221.79	39.62	9,242	10.0991	9.9396	1.60424	1.57891
92.0	0.6331	5.269	221.29	39.53	9,221	10.1221	9.9622	1.60790	1.58250
92.5	0.6317	5.257	220.79	39.44	9,200	10.1452	9.9850	1.61157	1.58612
93.0	0.6303	5.246	220.31	39.35	9,180	10.1665	10.0059	1.61495	1.58944
93.5	0.6289	5.234	219.82	39.26	9,160	10.1898	10.0289	1.61865	1.59309
94.0	0.6275	5.222	219.33	39.18	9,139	10.2132	10.0519	1.62237	1.59675
94.5	0.6261	5.210	218.85	39.09	9,118	10.2367	10.0750	1.62611	1.60042
95.0	0.6247	5.199	218.36	39.00	9,098	10.2584	10.0964	1.62955	1.60381
95.5	0.6233	5.187	217.87	38.92	9,077	10.2821	10.1197	1.63332	1.60752
96.0	0.6220	5.176	217.40	38.83	9,058	10.3040	10.1412	1.63679	1.61094
96.5	0.6206	5.164	216.92	38.75	9,037	10.3279	10.1648	1.64059	1.61468
97.0	0.6193	5.154	216.44	38.66	9,018	10.3479	10.1845	1.64377	1.61781
97.5	0.6179	5.142	215.96	38.58	8,999	10.3721	10.2083	1.64761	1.62159
98.0	0.6166	5.131	215.49	38.49	8,979	10.3943	10.2302	1.65114	1.62506
98.5	0.6152	5.120	215.02	38.41	8,960	10.4167	10.2521	1.65469	1.62856
99.0	0.6139	5.109	214.55	38.33	8,941	10.4391	10.2742	1.65825	1.63206
99.5	0.6126	5.098	214.08	38.24	8,921	10.4616	10.2964	1.66183	1.63558
100.0	0.6112	5.086	213.61	38.16	8,901	10.4863	10.3207	1.66575	1.63944

TRUE-BOILING-POINT CRUDE-OIL ANALYSES

Yields. Untreated stocks of the following T.B.P. cut points:

Materials	Boiling range, °F	Notes
Loss	Below 80	Mainly gas
300° gasoline	80–300	ASTM end point about 307°F
400° gasoline	80–400	ASTM end point 382–391°F
450° gasoline	80–450	ASTM end point about 427°F
Jet fuel	80–550	275–450°F mid boiling point
Kerosene or distillate	375–500	ASTM end point about 480°F
Diesel fuel or distillate	400–700	Mid boiling point about 550°F
Cracking stock (distilled)	400–900	
Cracking stock (residual)	550 and up	
Lube stock	700–900	Also other boiling ranges
Residue	Above 900	Usually low-penetration asphalt

Quality. The full boiling ranges indicated above must have superior properties if the quality is to be good or excellent, and the percentage yield must be normal. Good products can also be obtained from crude oils not designated as containing superior products but at a sacrifice in yield or by expensive treatment. To be classified as good, the properties must be:

300° Gasoline....... leaded octane number above 83 (Motor method).

or 400° Gasoline.... leaded octane number above 78 (Motor method).

Jet fuel............ gravity above 40 API and Characterization Factor below 11.8 to 12.0.

Kerosene........... sulfur below 0.13%; smoke point above 17; gravity above 39 API.

Diesel fuel......... 50 Diesel Index and 0 pour point (with some credit for exceptionally high Diesel Index or very low pour point); sulfur below 0.5.

Cracking stock...... cracked-gasoline octane number above 71 if crude oil contains 1 to 2% sulfur, but only 69 if crude oil contains under 1% sulfur.

Lube stocks........ Characterization Factor at 550°F above 12.0, and at 750°F above 12.1, or pour point below zero and Viscosity Index above 25.

Name, state, and country	Boscan, Zulia, Venezuela	Kern River, Calif., U.S.	Quitman, Miss., U.S.	Tia Juana, Zulia, Venezuela	Gato Ridge, Calif., U.S.	Bachaquero, Zulia, Venezuela
Gravity, API	9.5	10.7	12.7	13.3	13.8	14.0
Sulfur, %	5.25[a]	1.23	3.85	2.66	5.21	2.64
Viscosity, SSU at 100°F	......	6,000+	....	452 at 210	6,000+	
Date	3-3-48	......	11-49	4-12-48	......	1942–1950
Characterization factor:						
at 250°F	12.20	......	11.9	......	11.62	11.75
at 450°F	11.60	11.13	12.1	11.40	11.28	11.40
at 550°F	11.40	11.15	11.85	11.40	11.20	11.15
at 750°F	11.40	11.15	11.55	11.30	11.20	11.30
Average	11.65	......	11.85	11.40[a]	11.32	11.40
Base	I	N	I	N	N	N
Loss, %	......	0	0	......	1.5	
Gasoline:						
% to 300°F	1.6	0	6.0[a]	0.4	6.3[a]	2.4
Oct. No., clear	......	......	....	......	......	72.4
Oct. No., 3 cc TEL	......	......	....	......	......	86.5
% to 400°F	3.8	1.2[a]	9.4[a]	1.4	11.3[a]	5.0
Oct. No., clear	42.0[b]	......	42.5[b]	62.0[b]	67.0[b]	68.0
Oct. No., 3 cc TEL	66.0[b]	......	....	80.0[b]	......	83.0
% to 450°F	5.2	2.2[a]	11.4[a]	2.9	14.2[a]	7.5
Quality	......	......	....	......	......	Good
Jet stock:						
% to 550°F	10.0	6.1[a]	17.9[a]	8.7	20.7[a]	15.0
API gravity	44.5[a]	29.5[b]	51.0	40.0	37.5	39.5
Quality	Good	......	....	Good		
Kerosene-distillate:						
% 375–500°F	4.1	2.7[a]	5.9[a]	4.2	7.5[a]	7.0
API gravity	39.2	32.5[a]	45.0	36.2	33.9	35.0
Smoke point	19.2[a]	13.0[b]	29.0[b]	15.7[b]	14.5[b]	16.0
Sulfur, %	3.0[b]	0.38[b]	0.75	0.56[b]	2.25[b]	0.56[b]
Quality						
Distillate or diesel fuel:						
% 400–700°F	16.0	19.7[a]	21.0[a]	21.3	20.0[a]	22.5
Diesel index	26.0	30.0[b]	48.0[a]	39.0[a]	32.0[b]	33.0
Pour point	−35.0	−30.0[b]	3.0[a]	−40.0[b]	−30.0[b]	−35.0
Sulfur, %	3.3[b]	0.8[b]	1.7	1.3[b]	3.1[b]	1.1
Quality						
Cracking stock (distilled):						
% 400–900°F	28.8	41.8[a]	38.6[a]	44.5	34.8[a]	41.5
Oct. No. (thermal)	73.0[b]	75.6[b]	71.0[b]	73.5[b]	75.1[b]	75.0[b]
API gravity	21.0	20.0	26.5	22.5	20.4	21.5
Quality	......	Good				
Cracking stock (residual):						
% above 550°F	90.0	93.9[a]	82.1[a]	91.3	77.8[a]	85.0
API gravity	6.5	9.1	6.5	11.3	7.0	10.0
API cracked fuel	......	......	....	4.5	......	6.6
% gasoline (on stock)	......	......	....	26.0	......	19.8
% gasoline (on crude oil)	......	......	....	23.7	......	16.8
Lube distillate (undewaxed):						
% 700–900°F[c]	12.8	22.2[a]	17.6[a]	23.2	14.8[a]	19.0
Pour point	55.0	......	....	−5.0[b]	......	−10.0
Viscosity index	25.0[a]	......	37.0[b]	−20.0	−19.0[b]	−17.0
Sulfur, %	4.3[b]	1.5[b]	2.65	2.30[a]	4.5[b]	2.25
Quality						
Residue, % over 900°F	67.4	57.0[a]	52.0[a]	53.5	52.5[a]	53.5
Asphalt quality	Excell.	Excell.	Good	Excell.	Excell.	Excell.

Name, state, and county	Vermilion, Canada	Qaiyarah, Iraq	Santa Maria, Calif., U.S.	Tia Juana (heavy), Zulia, Venezuela	Lagunillas (heavy), Zulia, Venezuela	Tucupita, D. Amacuro, Venezuela
Gravity, API	14.0	14.4	15.4	16.1	16.5	16.0
Sulfur, %	2.03	7.35	4.63	2.21	2.22	1.01
Viscosity, SSU at 100°P	.....	.....	368			
Date	9-19-42	1-28-37	8-2-54	1937–1950	1935–1950	1945–1947
Characterization factor:						
at 250°F	.....	12.10	11.90	11.65	11.55	11.65
at 450°F	11.27	11.75	11.42	11.35	11.35	11.40
at 550°F	11.28	.....	11.29	11.38	11.30	11.35
at 750°F	11.42	11.40	11.11	11.40	11.48	11.51
Average	.....	11.71[a]	11.48	11.45	11.42	11.47
Base	N	IN	IN	N	N	N
Loss, %	0	.....	0			
Gasoline:						
% to 300°F	0	4.0[b]	7.0	1.1	4.0	2.0
Oct. No., clear	.....	48.0[b]	......	66.0	70.9	62.0[b]
Oct. No., 3 cc TEL	.....	70.0[b]	......	85.0	84.7	81.0[b]
% to 400°F	1.8	12.1	13.2	4.0	8.5	5.0
Oct. No., clear	.....	38.0	59.8[g]	61.5	65.8	52.0
Oct. No., 3 cc TEL	.....	61.5[b]	70.3[g]	81.0	80.6	76.3
% to 450°F	4.0	.....	17.0	7.0	10.0	7.2
Quality	.....	.....	......	Good	Good	
Jet stock:						
% to 550°F	14.2	.....	25.0	13.4	17.9	14.0
API gravity	31.8	.....	43.0	38.8	38.0	38.8
Quality	.....	.....	Good			
Kerosene-distillate:						
% 375–500°F	7.8	12.3	8.5	6.2	8.0	6.5
API gravity	33.8	42.6	34.5	35.2	35.0	36.4
Smoke point	14.5[b]	19.5[b]	......	15.0	17.0	16.0[b]
Sulfur, %	High	1.6	1.8[a]	0.41	0.41	0.18
Quality						
Distillate or diesel fuel:						
% 400–700°F	29.9	.....	23.8	25.5	24.2	25.0
Diesel index	35.0[b]	.....	33.0	37.0	38.0	38.0[b]
Pour point	Low	.....	−3.0	−30.0[h]	−25.0[h]	−40.0[h]
Sulfur, %	High	.....	2.5[a]	1.09	1.04	0.45[b]
Quality						
Cracking stock (distilled):						
% 400–900°F	53.0	.....	39.8	43.0	44.3	46.6
Oct. No. (thermal)	73.0[b]	.....	75.6[a]	73.3[b]	74.5[b]	72.5[b]
API gravity	23.5	.....	22.8	23.0	24.2	25.0
Quality	.....	.....	......	Good	Good	Excell.
Cracking stock (residual):						
% above 550°F	85.8	.....	75.0	86.6	82.1	86.0
API gravity	11.3	.....	8.0	13.1	12.4	12.7
API cracked fuel	6.1	.....	8.0	4.4	5.5	5.6
% gasoline (on stock)	23.7	.....	15.0	33.0	29.7	30.5
% gasoline (on crude oil)	20.3	.....	11.0	28.6	24.4	26.2
Lube distillate (undewaxed):						
% 700–900°F[c]	23.1	.....	16.0	17.5	20.1	21.6
Pour point	0	.....	......	−5.0	9.0	55.0
Viscosity index	35.0	.....	......	15.0	17.0	17.0
Sulfur, %	High	.....	......	2.10	1.98	1.02
Quality	Lube					
Residue, % over 900°F	45.0	.....	47.0	53.0	47.2	48.4
Asphalt quality	Excell.	Good[b]	Excell.	Excell.	Excell.	Excell.

Name, state, and country	Baxter-ville, Miss., U.S.	Lloyd-minster, Canada	Quiri-quire, Monagas, Venezuela	Miss. Mixture, Miss., U.S.	Lost Hills, Calif., U.S.	Tarakan, Kali-mantan, Indonesia
Gravity, API	16.2	16.2	17.2	17.8	18.4	18.0
Sulfur, %	2.82	3.6	1.33	2.09	0.99	0.13
Viscosity, SSU at 100°F	2,661	......	453	1,527	500	
Date	9-27-50	9-8-48	...,....	6-29-51	......	1956
Characterization factor:						
at 250°F	12.02	11.40	11.40[b]	12.22	11.60	
at 450°F	11.70	11.30	11.30	11.75	11.10	10.95
at 550°F	11.68	11.30	11.08	11.68	11.10	11.0
at 750°F	11.58	11.39	11.10	11.60	11.10	10.8[a]
Average	11.75	11.35	11.22	11.81	11.20	
Base	I	N	N	PI	N	N
Loss, %	0.1	0	1.3	0.8	0	0
Gasoline:						
% to 300°F	2.3	7.0	1.0	4.7	0.6[a]	0
Oct. No., clear	......	......	70.5			
Oct. No., 3 cc TEL	......	......	85.0			
% to 400°F	5.9	11.7	4.6	9.3	14.4[a]	2.1
Oct. No., clear	40.0[a]	67.0[b]	65.0	36.5[a]	66.5[b]	
Oct. No., 3 cc TEL	......	......	81.0			
% to 450°F	8.1	14.9	8.2	12.3	19.3[a]	8.1
Quality	.....	.....	Good	.....	Good[b]	
Jet stock:						
% to 550°F	15.2	22.7	21.3	20.0	29.1[a]	32.7
API gravity	43.3	42.0	36.7	47.4	36.1	28.0
Quality	Good	Good				
Kerosene-distillate:						
% 375–500°F	6.2	8.0	11.1	8.1	12.3[a]	19.0
API gravity	39.6	33.8	32.4	40.8	31.3[a]	29.0
Smoke point	18.8[b]	15.0[b]	14.0	19.8[b]	17.5[b]	17.0
Sulfur, %	0.20	High	0.22	0.23	0.28[b]	0.02
Quality						
Distillate or diesel fuel:						
% 400–700°F	25.2	24.6	38.9	25.3	28.6[a]	63.6
Diesel index	52.0[b]	39.0	30.0	32.0[b]	28.0[b]	28.0
Pour point	−6.0[a]	−40.0[b]	35.0	3.0[a]	−35.0[b]	−5.0
Sulfur, %	0.88	High	0.67	1.06	0.61[b]	0.06
Quality	Good	......	......	Good		
Cracking stock (distilled):						
% 400–900°F	47.6	43.3	59.1	46.7	45.0[a]	87.7
Oct. No. (thermal)	70.9[b]	74.9[b]	76.9	70.8[b]	75.5[b]	78–79
API gravity	26.5	22.8	19.5	25.8	20.0	17.6
Quality	.....	......	Excell.	.....	Excell.	Excell.
Cracking stock (residual):						
% above 550°F	84.7	77.3	77.4	79.2	70.9[a]	67.3
API gravity	12.0	10.0	11.2	10.8	12.2	13.3
API cracked fuel	6.3	7.0	4.8	7.7	2.4	Zero[a]
% gasoline (on stock)	25.8	18.5	31.5	20.2	34.5	45.0[a]
% gasoline (on crude oil)	21.7	14.3	24.4	16.0	29.4	30.2[a]
Lube distillate (undewaxed):						
% 700–900°F[c]	22.4	18.7	20.2	21.4	16.4[a]	24.1[a]
Pour point	91.0[b]	30.0	0[b]	66.0[b]	−60.0[b]	Low
Viscosity index	59.0[b]	0	−60.0	43.0[b]	−60.0[b]	
Sulfur, %	2.09	High	1.4[b]	2.58	1.32[b]	
Quality						
Residue, % over 900°F	46.4	45.0	35.0	43.2	40.6[a]	10.2[a]
Asphalt quality	Good	Good	Excell.	Good	Excell.	Excell.

Name, state, and country	Klamono, New Guinea	Placerita, Calif., U.S.	Smack-over, Ark., U.S.	Casabe, Antioquia, Colombia	Langs-dale, Miss., U.S.	Coaligna (East), Calif., U.S.
Gravity, API.................	18.0	19.8	20.5	20.5	20.8	20.7
Sulfur, %....................	0.93	1.25	2.30	1.06	4.1	0.51
Viscosity, SSU at 100°F.......	....	243	270	660	833	178
Date.......................	1956	11-28-51	4-3-39	2-50	11-49	
Characterization factor:						
at 250°F..................	....	11.47	11.62	.....	12.50	
at 450°F..................	11.3	11.23	11.48	11.41	11.90	11.28
at 550°F..................	11.2	11.25	11.47	11.42	11.30	11.20
at 750°F..................	11.1^a	11.27	11.55	11.41	11.35	11.23
Average..................	11.2	11.30	11.53	11.48^a	11.76	
Base.......................	N	N	I	N	PN	N
Loss, %.....................	0	0.6	0	0.8	0.8	3.0
Gasoline:						
% to 300°F...............	1.0	7.8	6.0	3.3	9.1^a	1.2^a
Oct. No., clear..........	82.0^g	76.2	73.2^e	.....	47.0^a	
Oct. No., 3 cc TEL.......	89.8^g	87.5	89.0^e			
% to 400°F...............	8.0	15.7	11.0	7.4	16.3^a	9.6^a
Oct. No., clear..........	69.0^g	74.2	66.0^b	66.0^b	38.0^a	67.0^b
Oct. No., 3 cc TEL.......	82.0^g	82.2	....	.....	62.0^a	
% to 450°F...............	13.3	20.4	14.4	10.5	20.8^a	15.6^a
Quality..................	Fair	Excell.	Good^b	.....	.....	Good^b
Jet stock:						
% to 550°F...............	27.6	29.4	24.1	20.3	29.8^a	29.3^a
API gravity..............	34.7	39.5	41.9	37.6	45.5	36.9
Quality..................	.....	.....	Good			
Kerosene-distillate:						
% 375–500°F..............	14.3	11.0	9.5	9.8	11.0^a	16.0^a
API gravity..............	34.2	32.8	38.0	34.9	38.5	34.0^a
Smoke point.............	19.0	19.0	16.0^b	15.9^b	22.0^b	14.5^b
Sulfur, %................	0.10	0.40	0.29^b	0.2^b	0.55	0.14^b
Quality.................	Fair					
Distillate or diesel fuel:						
% 400–700°F..............	42.2	29.7	29.2	31.9	26.8^a	38.4^a
Diesel index.............	33.2	33.0	43.0^b	40.0	44.0	33.0^b
Pour point...............	0	Low	0^b	−30.0^b	25.0	−25.0^b
Sulfur, %................	0.62	0.67	0.82^b	0.47^b	2.28	0.35^b
Quality.................						
Cracking stock (distilled):						
% 400–900°F..............	65.5^a	54.7	48.2	55.4^a	41.0^a	59.4^a
Oct. No. (thermal)........	76.0^b	74.1^b	71.4^b	73.0^b	73.5^b	
API gravity..............	21.0	27.0	25.7	23.2	24.5	22.3
Quality.................	Excell.	Excell.	.....	Excell.	.....	Excell.
Cracking stock (residual):						
% above 550°F............	72.4	70.0	75.9	78.9	69.4^a	67.7^a
API gravity..............	12.5	12.6	14.7	15.8	10.8	11.0
API cracked fuel...........	3.2	3.8	4.8	2.8	6.5	4.2
% gasoline (on stock)........	38.0	34.0	35.5	40.8	21.6	27.5
% gasoline (on crude oil).....	27.5	23.8	27.0	32.1	15.0	18.6
Lube distillate (undewaxed):						
% 700–900°F^c.............	23.3^a	25.0	19.0	23.5^a	14.2^a	13.0^a
Pour point...............	.....	10.0				
Viscosity index..............	Low	−69.0^a	37.0^b	20.0^b	11.0^b	
Sulfur, %.................	.....	1.37	2.45^b	1.2^b	3.46	0.67^b
Quality..................						
Residue, % over 900°F........	26.5^a	29.0	40.8	36.4^a	42.0^a	28.0^a
Asphalt quality..............	Excell.	Excell.	Good	Excell.	Excell.	Excell.

Name, state, and country	Cabimas (medium), Zulia, Venezuela	Pedernales, D. Amacuro, Venezuela	Eucutta and Yellow Creek, Miss., U.S.	Tatums, Okla., U.S.	Temblador, Monagas, Venezuela	Naranjos, Mexico
Gravity, API	21.0	21.0	21.7	22.1	21.9	21.6
Sulfur, %	1.95	2.72	3.92	1.67	0.84	3.37
Viscosity, SSU at 100°F			478	410		462
Date	1941–1950	1938–1950	9-27-50		1938–1947	1953
Characterization factor:						
at 250°F	11.87	11.90	12.27	11.80	11.65	
at 450°F	11.53	11.60	11.87	11.69	11.40	12.10
at 550°F	11.50	11.60	11.83	11.65	11.40	11.79
at 750°F	11.62	11.60	11.58	11.62	11.54	11.68
Average	11.63	11.70	11.89	11.69	11.50	11.90[a]
Base	I	I	PI	I	I	I[a]
Loss, %	0.7	0.5	0.8	1.7		1.0
Gasoline:						
% to 300°F	6.5	10.1	12.2	8.6[a]	7.0	5.3
Oct. No., clear	64.0	59.0	54.0[a]		72.0	56.0
Oct. No., 3 cc TEL	84.0	75.0	78.9[a]		85.2	76.5[b]
% to 400°F	13.5	16.7	18.8	15.4[a]	13.5	12.0
Oct. No., clear	56.0	51.0	43.0[a]	62.0[b]	66.0	38.6
Oct. No., 3 cc TEL	77.0	67.0			81.0	64.8
% to 450°F	15.7	20.2	22.1	19.3[a]	18.0	16.7
Quality	Fair				Good	
Jet stock:						
% to 550°F	24.0	28.0	28.9	27.3[a]	30.0	26.2
API gravity	43.0	43.8	56.7	52.0	41.0	56.1
Quality	Good	Good		Good	Good	
Kerosene-distillate:						
% 375–500°F	9.0	8.7	8.4	9.7[a]	12.0	11.8
API gravity	38.0	39.2	42.9	40.0	36.0	45.5
Smoke point	19.0	18.0	21.5[b]	18.5[b]	16.0	28.0[b]
Sulfur, %	0.33	0.61[b]	0.29	0.34[b]	0.22[b]	0.58
Quality						
Distillate or diesel fuel:						
% 400–700°F	23.5	23.0	22.7	24.7[a]	33.4	27.3
Diesel index	44.0	48.0	57.0[b]	50.0[b]	43.0	58.3
Pour point	−22.0	10.0	18.0[b]	0[b]	−40.0[h]	9.0
Sulfur, %	1.00	1.70	1.42	0.71[b]	0.35	1.5
Quality			Good	Good		
Cracking stock (distilled):						
% 400–900°F	42.5	35.5	39.5	41.9[a]	54.4	42.1
Oct. No. (thermal)	71.5[b]	71.0[b]	70.4[b]	70.7[b]	72.2[b]	69.5
API gravity	27.6	27.2	27.3	27.8	26.0	31.1
Quality	Good				Excell.	
Cracking stock (residual):						
% above 550°F	75.3	71.5	70.3	71.0[a]	70.0	72.8
API gravity	14.1	13.3	9.8	11.2	14.9	11.2
API cracked fuel	5.1	5.3		7.3	4.6	7.6
% gasoline (on stock)	32.9	30.5		22.5	36.2	22.3
% gasoline (on crude oil)	24.8	21.8		16.0	25.4	16.2
Lube distillate (undewaxed):						
% 700–900°F[c]	19.0	12.5	16.8	17.2[a]	21.0	14.8[a]
Pour point	15.0	75.0	81.0		10.0	
Viscosity index	39.0	40.0	49.0[b]	46.0[b]	30.0	53.0[b]
Sulfur, %	2.05	2.35	3.57	1.7[b]	0.90	
Quality	f				Lube	
Residue, % over 900°F	48.3	47.3	40.9	41.0[a]	32.1	44.9[a]
Asphalt quality	Good	Excell.		Good	Good	Good

Name, state, and country	Wilmington, Calif., U.S.	Loma Novia, Tex., U.S.	Fuhrman Mascho, Tex., U.S.	Goose Creek, Tex., U.S.	Miranda, Tex., U.S.	Kalimantan (nonwaxy), Kalimantan, Indonesia
Gravity, API	21.7	23.5	22.5	22.8	22.5	23.0
Sulfur, %	1.46	0.10	4.17[i]	0.2	0.25	0.07
Viscosity, SSU at 100°F	....	44.0	110	117	65	
Date	....	....	....	....	1954	1956
Characterization factor:						
at 250°F	11.58	....	11.62	....	....	11.4
at 450°F	11.38	11.05	11.57	11.07	11.10	10.96
at 550°F	11.40	10.96[a]	11.44	11.02	11.20	10.8
at 750°F	11.48	11.10[a]	11.64	11.36	11.08	10.8[a]
Average	11.46		11.57	11.15	11.13	11.0
Base	I or IN	N	I	N	N	N
Loss, %	0.5	0	1.2	0	0.2	0.1
Gasoline:						
% to 300°F	11.0	....	8.5	0	....	11.0
Oct. No., clear	....	73.0[b]	65.0[a]	73.0[b]	....	75[a]
Oct. No., 3 cc TEL	....	....	79.0[a]	89.0[b]	....	85.5[a]
% to 400°F	18.5	8.1[a]	16.8	5.2	7.5	27.0
Oct. No., clear	65.6	68.0	53.0	67.5[b]	....	71[a]
Oct. No., 3 cc TEL	80.0	87.0[b]	68.0[a]	86.5[b]	....	82.8[a]
% to 450°F	22.5	20.0[a]	21.7	12.4	11.4	36
Quality	Good	Excell.[b]	....	....	Good	Excell.
Jet stock:						
% to 550°F	31.0	55.0[a]	32.4	35.7	25.8	55.3
API gravity	48.5	28.4	43.0	30.0	29.7	32.0
Quality	Good	....	Good			
Kerosene-distillate:						
% 375–500°F	10.0	36.0[a]	12.3	20.1	12.0	23.3
API gravity	35.5	29.0	38.0	30.8	30.1	29.0
Smoke point	18.0	12.5[b]	16.0[b]	Low	....	11.0
Sulfur, %	0.32	Low	1.35[b]	Low	0.08	0.02
Quality						
Distillate or diesel fuel:						
% 400–700°F	27.3	70.9[a]	33.2	53.8	52.3	50.5
Diesel index	39.0	23.0[b]	42.0[b]	24.0[b]	....	21.4
Pour point	....	−70.0[b]	−28.0[b]	Low	−65.0[h]	Zero[h]
Sulfur, %	0.85	Low	2.1[b]	....	Low	0.07
Quality						
Cracking stock (distilled)						
% 400–900°F	46.8	81.9[a]	54.2	74.4	80.0	67.0[a]
Oct. No. (thermal)	72.0[a]	76.0[b]	71.0[b]	74.0[b]	76+[b]	78+[b]
API gravity	23.5	24.0	26.5	21.5	23.0	16.3
Quality	Good	Excell.	....	Excell.	Excell.	Excell.
Cracking stock (residual):						
% above 550°F	68.5	45.0[a]	64.4	64.3	74.0	44.6
API gravity	13.3	17.8	12.7	19.2	19.2	12.8
API cracked fuel	4.5	2.0[b]	6.3	1.0	Zero	Zero[a]
% gasoline (on stock)	32.5	48.4[b]	28.0	49.0	51.5	43.0[a]
% gasoline (on crude oil)	22.3	21.8[b]	18.6	31.4	38.1	19.2
Lube distillate (undewaxed):						
% 700–900°F[e]	19.5	11.0[a]	21.0	20.6	27.7	16.5[a]
Pour point	....	Low	....	Low	Zero	
Viscosity index	....	Negative	....	Fair	−150[h]	Low
Sulfur, %	....	Low	....	....	Low	
Quality	....	....	....	Lube		5.9[a]
Residue, % over 900°F	34.2	10.0[a]	27.8	20.4	12.3	
Asphalt quality	Excell.	....	Good	Good	Excell.	Excell.

Name, state, and country	Refugio, Tex., U.S.	Talco, Tex., U.S.	Wafra, Neutral Zone, Middle East	Thompsons, Tex., U.S.	Placedo, Tex., U.S.	Santa Barbara. Monagas, Venezuela
Gravity, API	23.6	24.4	24.2	25.3	25.2	24.6
Sulfur, per cent	0.22	2.82	3.12[i]	0.32	0.14	0.92
Viscosity, SSU at 100°F	58	657	......	85	50	
Date	10-4-51	4-1-49	3-54	1954	......	3-42
Characterization factor:						
at 250°F	11.09	12.10	12.05			
at 450°F	11.16	11.92	11.78	11.28	11.32	11.30
at 550°F	11.16	11.88	11.63	11.26	11.14	11.40
at 750°F	11.24	11.87	......	11.58	11.22	11.60
Average	11.16	11.94	......	11.37	......	11.48[a]
Base	N	I	I	NI	N	N
Loss, %	0.2	0.4	......	0.4	1.0	
Gasoline:						
% to 300°F	2.1	12.0	8.0	......	1.4[a]	4.0
Oct. No., clear	70.0[e]	......	68.0	......	70.0[a]	66.0[b]
Oct. No., 3 cc TEL	88.0[e]	......	81.5	......	88.0[a]	84.0[b]
% to 400°F	6.8	19.0	13.5	7.4	8.5[a]	12.3
Oct. No., clear	65.7[a]	48.0	61.0	69.2	64.0	62.0[b]
Oct. No., 3 cc TEL	80.2[a]	......	74.0	83.9	84.0[a]	79.0[b]
% to 450°F	15.1	21.6	16.5	11.9	19.6[a]	17.0
Quality	Excell.[a]	......	......	Excell.	Excell.[a]	Good[b]
Jet stock:						
% to 550°F	48.7	29.0	24.5	30.4	54.0[a]	28.5
API gravity	31.0	54.3	50.1	32.4	33.5	40.0
Quality	......	......	......	......	......	Good
Kerosene-distillate:						
% 375–500°F	26.8	7.4	8.5	14.1	33.4[a]	12.3
API gravity	31.0	43.8	42.3	32.3	33.0	34.7
Smoke point	13.5[b]	23.0[b]	......	17.0	15.0[b]	15.0[b]
Sulfur, %	0.05	0.28	0.414	Low	Low	0.165[b]
Quality						
Distillate or diesel fuel:						
% 400–700°F	67.1	23.3	24.5	47.2	68.0[a]	32.2
Diesel index	30.5[b]	58.0	50.2	34.7	......	39.0[b]
Pour point	−35.0[h]	17.0	10.0	−80.0[h]	......	−40.0[b]
Sulfur, %	0.13	0.90	1.6	Low	Low	0.44[b]
Quality	......	Good				
Cracking stock (distilled):						
% 400–900°F	86.2	39.0	45.0	72.2	80.0[a]	54.0[a]
Oct. No. (thermal)	74.8[b]	67.9[b]	69.0	71.0[b]	74.6[b]	72.0[b]
API gravity	25.5	24.3	25.1	25.7	24.2	26.5
Quality	Excell.	......	......	Excell.	Excell.	Excell.
Cracking stock (residual):						
% above 550°F	51.1	70.6	75.5	69.2	45.0[a]	71.5
API gravity	16.9	14.3	16.1	21.5	14.7	19.4
API cracked fuel	2.0[b]	8.0	4.6	3.0	2.0[b]	3.7
% gasoline (on stock)	47.0[b]	29.6	36.5	50.0	42.4[b]	46.7
% gasoline (on crude oil)	24.0[b]	20.9	27.5	34.5	19.1[b]	33.4
Lube distillate (undewaxed):						
% 700–900°F[c]	19.1	15.7	20.5	25.0	12.0[a]	21.8[a]
Pour point	0	78.0	......	−15.0	......	40.0[b]
Viscosity index	11.0[b]	108.0	......	25.0	......	44.0[b]
Sulfur, per cent	0.25	2.65	......	Low	Low	1.1[b]
Quality	......	......	......	Lube		
Residue, % over 900°F	6.8	41.6	41.5	20.0	10.0[a]	33.0[a]
Asphalt quality	......	Good	......	......	......	Excell.

Name, state, and country	Leona (Tigre), Anzoat., Venezuela	La Rosa (Cabimas), Zulia, Venezuela	Tia Juana (102), Zulia, Venezuela	Tia Juana (medium), Zulia, Venezuela	Brook-haven, Miss., U.S.	Limau, Sumatra, Indonesia
Gravity, API	24.7	25.3	25.8	26.3	26.0	26.0
Sulfur, %	1.24	1.76	1.65	1.55	0.61	0.12
Viscosity, SSU at 100°F					159	
Date	5-20-42	1935–1942	1947–1950	1942–1951	11–49	1956
Characterization factor:						
at 250°F	11.85	11.93	12.00	12.05	12.1	11.57
at 450°C	11.60	11.63	11.62	11.65	11.73	11.4
at 550°F	11.60	11.57	11.50	11.50	11.75	11.4
at 750°F	11.70	11.70	11.63	11.70	11.91	11.6[a]
Average	11.69	11.70	11.69	11.72	11.89	11.5
Base	I	I	I	I	I	I
Loss, %				0.7	0.8	0.2
Gasoline:						
% to 300°F	10.6	11.9	12.0	13.7	6.2[a]	8.0
Oct. No., clear	64.0[b]	59.1	64.0	63.0	65.0[a]	69.0[g]
Oct. No., 3 cc TEL	84.0[b]	78.0[b]	82.3	81.5		89.5[g]
% to 400°F	19.4	19.3	20.2	21.5	11.8[a]	15.0
Oct. No., clear	55.0[b]	49.1	55.0	52.0	56.0[a]	59.5[g]
Oct. No., 3 cc TEL	79.0[b]	72.0[b]	75.0	75.0	74.2[a]	79.6[g]
% to 450°F	24.3	23.0[a]	24.5	26.0	13.6[a]	21.2
Quality	Good[b]					Excell.
Jet stock:						
% to 550°F	33.3	32.0	33.0	34.0	25.4[a]	34.0
API gravity	46.0	46.1	45.2	46.9	43.0	37.0
Quality	Good	Good	Good	Good	Good	
Kerosene-distillate:						
% 375–500°F	11.7	10.0	10.3	9.7	8.5[b]	13.8
API gravity	39.2	39.9	39.6	40.3	41.0	34.3
Smoke point	17.9[b]	18.5[b]	20.0	19.0	19.0[b]	13.0
Sulfur, %	0.22[b]	0.32[b]	0.33[b]	0.21	0.03	0.02
Quality					Good	
Distillate or diesel fuel:						
% 400–700°F	28.8	25.0	25.5	25.0	39.2[a]	41.4
Diesel index	50.0[b]	49.0	46.0	51.0	56.0	41.8
Pour point	5.0[b]	0[h]	−20.0[h]	−25.0	35.0[a]	35.0
Sulfur, %	0.57[b]	0.73	0.85	0.78	0.31	0.06
Quality	Good	Good	Good	Excell.		
Cracking stock (distilled):						
% 400–900°F	51.0[a]	43.0	40.5	40.0	60.2[a]	63.5[a]
Oct. No. (thermal)	70.4[b]	70.6[b]	71.3[b]	71.0[b]	68.5[b]	72.0[b]
API gravity	28.0	27.8	27.2	29.0	29.5	25.7
Quality	Good		Good	Good		Excell.
Cracking stock (residual):						
% above 550°F	66.7	68.0	67.0	65.3	73.8[a]	65.8
API gravity	16.1	17.3	18.0	16.4	19.4	20.6
API cracked fuel	5.5	5.2	4.3	5.2	6.6	3.0
% gasoline (on stock)	37.3	40.2	42.9	38.1	42.8	48.8
% gasoline (on crude oil)	24.9	27.4	28.7	24.9	31.6	32.1
Lube distillate (undewaxed):						
% 700–900°F[c]	22.2[a]	18.0	15.0	15.0	21.0[a]	22.1[a]
Pour point	75.0[b]	30.0	−15.0[b]	68.0		
Viscosity index	55.0[b]	53.0	40.0	65.0	79.0[b]	Low
Sulfur, %	1.35[b]	1.75[a]	1.65	1.6	0.75	
Quality			Lube			
Residue, % over 900°F	30.0[a]	37.7	39.3	37.8	28.2[a]	21.3[a]
Asphalt quality	Fair	Good	Good	Good		

Name, state, and country	Qatif, S. Arabia	Morel, Kan., U.S.	Clear Lake, Tex., U.S.	Steamboat Butte, Wyo., U.S.	Talang Djimar, Sumatra, Indonesia	Amelia (low cold), Tex., U.S.
Gravity, API	27.4	27.3	27.1	28.0	28.0	28.2
Sulfur, %	2.54[i]	0.67	0.17	2.15	0.08	0.28
Viscosity, SSU at 100°F	75	130	67	76	54	56
Date	4-23-52	.....	....	5-5-52	1956	1954
Characterization factor:						
at 250°F	12.18	11.88	11.83	12.00	11.64	11.47
at 450°F	11.95	11.66	11.33	11.78	11.4	11.34
at 550°F	11.82	11.67	11.35	11.63	11.4	11.44
at 750°F	11.71	11.82	11.58	11.61	11.3[a]	11.80
Average	11.92	11.76	11.52	11.76	11.43	11.51
Base	PI	I	I	I	IN	NI
Loss, %	0.7	0.8	0.6	1.3	0.9	0.3
Gasoline:						
% to 300°F	9.7	9.0[a]	4.4[a]	12.0	11.2	8.0
Oct. No., clear	45.0[a]	....	69.5[a]	53.5[a]	70.0[a]	
Oct. No., 3 cc TEL	.....	....	88.0[b]	73.6[a]	85.6[a]	
% to 400°F	20.3	18.2[a]	12.4[a]	21.7	20.3	17.0
Oct. No., clear	31.5[b]	59.0[b]	63.5	45.0[a]	62.0[a]	70.0
Oct. No., 3 cc TEL	55.5[b]	....	84.0[a]	.....	80.9[a]	83.2
% to 450°F	25.6	23.3[a]	18.3[a]	27.0	27.1	22.8
Quality	.....	....	Good[b]	.....	Excell.	Excell.
Jet stock:						
% to 550°F	36.4	33.3[a]	36.2[a]	38.0	43.8	36.3
API gravity	50.9	47.5	38.5	50.0	38.0	37.0
Quality	.....	Good	....	Good		
Kerosene-distillate:						
% 375–500°F	13.4	21.9[a]	17.3[a]	13.4	17.8	14.8
API gravity	44.3	42.3	33.8	41.3	35.7	34.0
Smoke point	23.6[b]	18.0[b]	15.0[b]	19.8[b]	14	
Sulfur, %	0.30	0.13[b]	Low	0.50	0.02	0.10
Quality	.....	Good				
Distillate or diesel fuel:						
% 400–700°F	32.4	30.6[a]	48.7[a]	33.9	44.5	40.7
Diesel index	56.2	51.0[b]	38.0[b]	49.1	44.4	
Pour point	17.0[a]	15.0[b]	−45.0[b]	3.0[a]	30.0	−80.0[h]
Sulfur, %	1.59	0.28[b]	Low	1.70	0.04	Low
Quality						
Cracking stock (distilled):						
% 400–900°F	53.7	49.1[a]	70.2[a]	52.8[b]	65.0[a]	67.0
Oct. No. (thermal)	69.5[b]	69.4[b]	72.0[b]	71.0	73.5[b]	69.0[b]
API gravity	29.5	29.6	26.0	28.5	23.6	29.5
Quality	.....	Good	Excell.	.....	Excell.	Excell.
Cracking stock (residual):						
% above 550°F	62.9	65.9[a]	63.2[a]	60.7	55.3	63.4
API gravity	15.6	17.7	20.3	15.2	19.5	24.6
API cracked fuel	5.5	6.3	3.2	4.6	0.5	4.5
% gasoline (on stock)	35.9	39.3	48.9	36.3	50.0	54.2
% gasoline (on crude oil)	22.6	25.9	30.9	22.0	27.6	34.3
Lube distillate (undewaxed):						
% 700–900°F[c]	21.3	18.5[a]	21.5[a]	18.9	20.5[a]	26.3
Pour point	90.0	.....	....	88.0	....	−25.0
Viscosity index	56.0[b]	69.0[b]	41.0[b]	60.5[b]	Low	40.0
Sulfur, %	3.05	0.81[b]	Low	2.61	....	Low
Quality	.....	.....	....	.....	....	Lube
Residue, % over 900°F	25.3	31.9[a]	27.8[a]	24.7	13.8[a]	15.7
Asphalt quality	.....	....	Good	Good	Good	

Name, state, and country	Howard-Glasscock, Tex., U.S.	Sugar-land, Tex., U.S.	Mara, Zulia, Venezuela	Poza Rica, Mexico	Ventura Avenue, Calif., U.S.	Elk Basin, Wyo., U.S.
Gravity, API	29.1	28.6	29.5	30.7	30.6	31.5
Sulfur, %	1.64[i]	0.3[i]	2.0	1.67	0.9	1.72[i]
Viscosity, SSU at 100°F	65	105	....	67.9	54	47
Date	......	.....	1942–1950	6-20-52	7-22-54	
Characterization factor:						
at 250°F	......	11.84	12.15	12.20	11.87	11.82
at 450°F	11.54	11.27	11.95	11.92	11.57	11.63
at 550°F	11.58	11.24	11.85	11.81	11.58	11.60
at 750°F	11.70	11.52	11.98	11.88	11.58	11.50
Average	......	11.47	11.98	11.95	11.66	11.64
Base	I	NI	PI	PI	I	I
Loss, %	2.0	0.6	0.9	0.4	0	1.3
Gasoline:						
% to 300°F	14.1[a]	9.1	12.7	15.4	22.8	18.7[a]
Oct. No., clear	68.0[a]	70.5[b]	56.5	49.5[a]	68.2	67.0[b]
Oct. No., 3 cc TEL	82.0[a]	88.5[b]	76.0	71.6[a]	86.7	
% to 400°F	22.4[a]	19.1	22.0	25.2	33.5	29.7[a]
Oct. No., clear	57.0	64.0[b]	44.0	40.0[a]	61.2	61.0[b]
Oct. No., 3 cc TEL	72.0[a]	84.5[b]	65.5	....	79.3	
% to 450°F	27.0[a]	25.8	27.0	30.0	38.0	33.9[a]
Quality	Good[a]	Excell.[b]	....	....	Good	
Jet stock:						
% to 550°F	37.0[a]	43.1	36.5	39.5	47.5	44.0[a]
API gravity	50.6	40.6	50.7	54.8	50.2	48.5[a]
Quality	Good	....	....	....	Good	Good
Kerosene-distillate:						
% 375–500°F	19.5[a]	18.2	11.7	12.1	11.0	12.0[a]
API gravity	38.0	33.9	44.0	43.7	37.5	39.5
Smoke point	17.0[b]	15.0[b]	23.0	22.5[b]	18.0	18.0[b]
Sulfur, %	0.64[b]	Low	0.46	0.29	0.28	0.64[b]
Quality						
Distillate or diesel fuel:						
% 400–700°F	30.4[a]	44.5	28.0	28.6	27.8	30.6[a]
Diesel index	48.0[b]	33.0[b]	58.0	56.0[b]	49.0	48.5[b]
Pour point	−5.0	Low	5.0	12.0[a]	15.0[b]	5.0[b]
Sulfur, %	1.15[b]	....	1.15	1.11	0.65	1.15[b]
Quality						
Cracking stock (distilled):						
% 400–900°F	47.6[a]	65.9	47.0	46.0	46.5	50.0[a]
Oct. No. (thermal)	69.4[b]	72.0[b]	68.0[b]	69.0	71.0[a]	71.4[b]
API gravity	28.0	24.0	34.3	31.2	25.0	25.9
Quality	......	Excell.	....	....	Good	Good
Cracking stock (residual):						
% above 550°F	61.0[a]	56.3	62.6	60.1	52.5	54.7[a]
API gravity	15.8	21.3	18.1	17.6	16.5	17.8
API cracked fuel	5.6	1.9	8.1	7.0	3.8	3.4
% gasoline (on stock)	36.3	53.0	38.2	38.3	40.2	44.2
% gasoline (on crude oil)	22.2	29.8	23.9	23.0	21.1	24.2
Lube distillate (undewaxed):						
% 700–900°F[c]	17.2[a]	21.4	19.0	17.4	18.7	19.4[a]
Pour point	......	Low	85.0	90.0		
Viscosity index	......	Fair	90.0	77.0[b]	....	31.0[b]
Sulfur, %	1.92[b]	....	1.95	1.70	....	1.65[b]
Quality	......	Lube				
Residue, % over 900°F	28.0[a]	16.1	30.1	28.4	20.0	19.0[a]
Asphalt quality	......	Good	....	....	Good	Good

Name, state, and country	Coaligna, Calif., U.S.	Kuwait, Kuwait	West Texas (composite), Tex., U.S.	Jusepin, Monagas, Venezuela	Lago Mar, Zulia, Venezuela	Big Valley, Alberta, Canada
Gravity, API	31.1	31.4	32.5	32.4	31.5	31.5
Sulfur, %	0.31	2.59[i]	1.72[i]	1.03	1.41	0.99[i]
Viscosity, SSU at 100°F	48	....	46	....	67.4	58
Date	....	10–52	1-30-42	1940–1948	1956	7-17-52
Characterization factor:						
at 250°F	11.5	12.30	11.91	11.90	12.1	11.98
at 450°F	11.53	11.92	11.72	11.65	11.94	11.73
at 550°F	11.59	11.78	11.65	11.70	12.00	11.79
at 750°F	11.72	11.70	11.70	11.85	12.16	11.86
Average	11.58	11.93	11.75	11.80	12.05	11.84
Base	I	PI	I	I	I	I
Loss, %	1.1	1.6	0.5	1.1	1.1	0.9
Gasoline:						
% to 300°F	21.6[a]	16.7	20.7	15.7	17.9	17.0
Oct. No., clear	72.0[b]	52.6	65.1	64.5	58.0[b]	62.2[a]
Oct. No., 3 cc TEL	....	75.8	76.0	83.4	78.5[b]	78.3[a]
% to 400°F	31.6[a]	26.8	31.7	26.0	26.9	26.6
Oct. No., clear	66.7[b]	40.8	54.4	57.0	43.0[b]	53.2[a]
Oct No., 3 cc TEL	....	....	67.0	77.5	66.0[b]	69.4[a]
% to 450°F	35.6[a]	31.5	37.1	31.0	31.2	31.2
Quality	Excell.[b]	....	....	Good		
Jet stock:						
% to 550°F	46.2[a]	41.3	45.0	42.0	40.2	40.9
API gravity	46.0[a]	55.9	48.1	47.7	55.0	51.4
Quality	Good	....	Good	Good	......	Good
Kerosene-distillate:						
% 375–500°F	11.0[a]	12.1	13.2	12.5	11.1	11.7
API gravity	37.8	43.7	40.6	40.3	43.9	40.6
Smoke point	17.0[b]	22.5[b]	19.0	20.0	24.0[b]	19.1[b]
Sulfur, %	0.06[b]	0.35	0.59	0.18	0.25[b]	0.32
Quality						
Distillate or diesel fuel:						
% 400–700°F	28.0[a]	28.0	30.5	30.0	27.7	29.5
Diesel index	48.5[b]	57.0	50.0	53.0	64.0[b]	55.7[a]
Pour point	20.0[b]	18.0[a]	5.0	−10.0	10.0[b]	12.0[a]
Sulfur, %	0.27[b]	1.36	1.17	0.55	0.61[b]	0.67
Quality	....	....	....	Excell.	Excell.	Good
Cracking stock (distilled):						
% 400–900°F	45.6[a]	42.6	44.3	48.6	46.0	50.4
Oct. No. (thermal)	70.4[b]	69.4[b]	69.8[b]	69.0[b]	Low	68.3[b]
API gravity	28.0	30.7	30.8	33.0	34.5	30.1
Quality	Good					
Cracking stock (residual):						
% above 550°F	52.7[a]	57.4	54.5	56.9	58.7	58.2
API gravity	18.2	16.2	20.8	21.1	16.9	18.8
API cracked fuel	5.0	5.5	4.0	5.8	10.5	6.4
% gasoline (on stock)	42.2	38.9	47.9	46.7	33.0	41.3
% gasoline (on crude oil)	22.2	22.3	26.1	26.6	19.4	24.0
Lube distillate (undewaxed):						
% 700–900°F[c]	17.6[a]	14.6	13.8	18.6	18.3	20.9
Pour point	....	....	80.0	95.0	....	95.0[b]
Viscosity index	58.0[b]	55.0[b]	73.0	55.0	105.0[b]	74.0[b]
Sulfur, %	0.43[b]	3.0	1.87	1.25	....	1.06
Quality	....	....	....	......	Good	
Residue, % over 900°F	21.7[a]	29.0	23.5	24.3	26.0	22.1
Asphalt quality	Good	....	Good			

Name, state, and country	Santa Barbara, Monagas, Venezuela	Southern Oklahoma, Okla., U.S.	Monument, N.M., U.S.	Kalimantan (waxy), Kalimantan, Indonesia	So. Cuyama Valley, Calif., U.S.
Gravity, API	32.0	32.0	32.1	32.0	32.4
Sulfur, %	0.9	0.82	1.39[i]	0.07	0.44
Viscosity, SSU at 100°F	....	....	54	....	46
Date	1942–1950	1952	......	1956	2-20-53
Characterization factor:					
at 250°F	11.88	11.94	11.85	11.3	11.78
at 450°F	11.63	11.88	11.51	11.1	11.56
at 550°F	11.66	11.86	11.4	11.35	11.67
at 750°F	11.78	11.93	11.49	11.65[a]	11.62
Average	11.76	11.90	11.56	11.35	11.66
Base	I	I	I	NI	I
Loss, %	0.8	1.0	1.7	0.2	1.0
Gasoline:					
% to 300°F	13.6	16.0	20.0[a]	22.5	24.2
Oct. No., clear	64.7	63.0	68.0[b]	70.0[g]	
Oct. No., 3 cc TEL	83.6	79.0	81.5[b]	83.7[g]	
% to 400°F	23.9	25.5	31.1[a]	37.4	35.0
Oct. No., clear	58.0	39.0	61.7[b]	62.0[g]	61.3
Oct. No., 3 cc TEL	80.0	60.0	75.0[b]	79.0[g]	80.5
% to 450°F	28.6	30.1	36.1[a]	43.6	39.0
Quality	Good	....	......	Excell.	Good
Jet stock:					
% to 550°F	40.2	40.7	46.3[a]	59.4	49.0
API gravity	46.9	54.9	48.5[a]	38.5	50.2
Quality	Good	Good	Good	....	Good
Kerosene-distillate:					
% 375–500°F	13.5	11.9	12.7[a]	18.7	12.0
API gravity	39.5	42.9	38.0	32.4	38.5
Smoke point	18.0	22.4[b]	16.5[b]	13.0	18.0
Sulfur, %	0.18	0.14[b]	0.55[b]	0.02	0.17
Quality					
Distillate or diesel fuel:					
% 400–700°F	34.0	30.0	30.5[a]	42.1	29.0
Diesel index	52.0	58.0[b]	40.0[b]	37.3	49.0
Pour point	12.0	10.0[b]	−40.0[b]	30.0	15.0[b]
Sulfur, %	0.65	0.37[b]	0.94[b]	0.06	0.31
Quality	Good	Good			
Cracking stock (distilled):					
% 400–900°F	53.5	48.7[a]	45.7[a]	57.0[a]	46.5
Oct. No. (thermal)	69.0[b]	67.5	72.2[b]	72.0[b]	70.7[a]
API gravity	32.1	31.0	25.5	25.7	25.0
Quality	Good	....	Good	Excell.	Good
Cracking stock (residual):					
% above 550°F	59.0	58.3	52.0[a]	40.4	50.0
API gravity	22.1	17.6	17.1	22.5	16.5
API cracked fuel	4.8	7.6	3.5	3.1	4.2
% gasoline (on stock)	49.7	37.7	42.9	52.0	39.5
% gasoline (on crude oil)	29.4	22.0	22.3	21.0	19.8
Lube distillate (undewaxed):					
% 700–900°F[c]	19.5	18.7[a]	15.2[a]	14.9[a]	17.5
Pour point	73.0	....	......	High	
Viscosity index	70.0	82.0[b]	88.0[b]	Low	
Sulfur, %	1.1	0.99[b]	1.55[b]		
Quality	....	....	......	Wax	
Residue, % over 900°F	21.8	24.8[a]	21.5[a]	5.4[a]	17.5
Asphalt quality	....	....	Good	....	Good

Name, state, and country	El Cubo (Los Manueles), Zulia, Venezuela	Bahrein	Oficina, Anzoat., Venezuela	South Louisiana, La., U.S.	San Joaquin Valley, Calif., U.S.
Gravity, API	32.7	32.9	33.0	33.3	33.6
Sulfur, %	0.86	2.08	0.95	0.26	0.32
Viscosity, SSU at 100°F	......	.....	49.2	49.2	
Date	2-12-46	1953	1940–1950	4-24-51	
Characterization factor:					
at 250°F	12.20	12.25	11.78	11.93	11.62
at 450°F	11.85	11.90	11.57	11.77	11.53
at 550°F	11.85	11.85	11.60	11.81	11.64
at 750°F	12.10	11.80	11.73	11.98	11.83
Average	12.00	11.95	11.67	11.87	11.66
Base	PI	I	I	I	I
Loss, %	......	1.2	1.2	0.5	0
Gasoline:					
% to 300°F	17.1	18.0	20.0	10.6	24.0
Oct. No., clear	63.0[b]	57.0	65.0	61.0[b]	70.0[a]
Oct. No., 3 cc TEL	81.0[b]	.....	83.7	82.5[b]	83.7[a]
% to 400°F	27.6	28.6	31.2	20.8	34.3
Oct. No., clear	50.0[b]	46.0	56.8	51.8[a]	61.2
Oct. No., 3 cc TEL	73.0[b]	68.5	77.0	74.0[b]	80.3[a]
% to 450°F	32.5	33.6	36.1	27.2	39.0
Quality	......	.....	Good	.....	Excell.
Jet stock:					
% to 550°F	40.3	43.4	46.3	41.3	49.6
API gravity	50.5	51.5	46.2	47.0	49.5
Quality	Good	.....	Good	Good	Good
Kerosene-distillate:					
% 375–500°F	11.9	12.6	13.7	16.4	12.0
API gravity	42.9	44.0	38.4	40.8	38.0
Smoke point	22.6[b]	24.0	18.0	19.5[b]	23.0
Sulfur, %	0.15[b]	0.21	0.11	0.04	0.05
Quality	Good[b]	.....	......	Good	
Distillate or diesel fuel:					
% 400–700°F	26.1	28.7	30.5	41.3	32.0
Diesel index	57.0[b]	56.0	50.5	56.5[b]	48.6
Pour point	5.0[b]	10.0	5.0	5.0[a]	25.0[b]
Sulfur, %	0.38[b]	1.1	0.62	0.08	0.18
Quality	Excell.	.....	Good	Excell.	
Cracking stock (distilled):					
% 400–900°F	52.0[a]	46.0	48.3	64.7	48.0
Oct. No. (thermal)	67.0[b]	68.9[b]	70.0[b]	67.2[b]	69.0
API gravity	33.5	32.3	31.5	32.3	31.2
Quality	......	.....	Good	.....	Good
Cracking stock (residual):					
% above 550°F	59.7	55.4	52.5	58.2	50.4
API gravity	22.5	17.7	21.3	24.0	20.5
API cracked fuel	8.7	6.2	3.3	6.9	4.8
% gasoline (on stock)	47.2	39.5	48.6	51.3	46.5
% gasoline (on crude oil)	28.2	21.9	25.5	29.8	23.4
Lube distillate (undewaxed):					
% 700–900°F[c]	25.9[a]	17.3	18.0	23.4	16.0
Pour point	105.0[b]	.....	100.0	85.0	100.0
Viscosity index	100.0[b]	.....	64.0	87.0[b]	82.0[a]
Sulfur, %	1.05[b]	.....	1.2	0.26	0.58
Quality	Lube				
Residue, % over 900°F	20.0[a]	24.2	19.4	14.0	18.5
Asphalt quality	......	Good	......	.....	Fair

Name, state, and country	Paconsib, Zulia, Venezuela	Barco (heavy), Colombia	Mulata, Monagas, Venezuela	Ain Dar, S. Arabia	Coastal B-2, U.S.	El Dorado, Kan., U.S.
Gravity, API	33.5	33.8	34.0	34.1	33.7	34.4
Sulfur, %	1.2	0.89	0.75	1.6[i]	0.18	0.27[i]
Viscosity, SSU at 100°F	....	57.3	....	....	44	44
Date	10-55	5-56	1942–1950	....	1-10-46	
Characterization factor:						
at 250°F	12.1	11.88	11.80	12.25	11.84	12.12
at 450°F	12.0	11.9	11.60	12.04	11.70	11.86
at 550°F	11.95	12.0	11.70	11.93	11.70	11.78
at 750°F	12.0	12.03	11.83	11.92	11.89	11.78
Average	12.01	11.95	11.78	12.03	11.78	11.88
Base	PI	I	I	PI	I	PI
Loss, %	1.0	0.5	1.1	1.3	0.7	0.9
Gasoline:						
% to 300°F	14.5	16.9	17.2	19.5	10.9	15.4[a]
Oct. No., clear	52.0	64.2	67.3	42.0	63.6[a]	54.5[b]
Oct. No., 3 cc TEL	72.5	86.5	82.8	64.0	84.0[a]	
% to 400°F	25.5	27.8	28.2	28.5	21.3	28.2[a]
Oct. No., clear	41.0	49.0	58.6	34.0	50.2[a]	46.0[b]
Oct. No., 3 cc TEL	64.5	69.9	77.6	58.0	73.5[b]	
% to 450°F	31.0	31.8	33.8	33.0	28.8	35.3[a]
Quality	....	....	Good			
Jet stock:						
% to 550°F	43.0	40.8	45.1	43.2	50.3	48.9[a]
API gravity	53.0	53.0	46.8	52.6	44.3	51.0
Quality	....	Good	Good	....	Good	Good
Kerosene-distillate:						
% 375–500°F	13.8	12.4	13.5	13.0	21.9	17.7[a]
API gravity	45.0	43.3	39.0	43.2	39.0	43.0
Smoke point	28.0	30.0	18.0	20.0	18.8[b]	21.5[b]
Sulfur, %	0.18	0.085	0.15	0.26	0.035	0.08[b]
Quality	....	Excell.	....	....	Good	Good
Distillate or diesel fuel:						
% 400–700°F	32.0	26.8	34.3	30.0	48.4	38.7[a]
Diesel index	63.0	62.0	53.0	58.0	54.9	55.0[b]
Pour point	5.0	20.0	10.0	25.0	−3.0[a]	15.0[b]
Sulfur, %	0.55		0.68	1.05	0.11[b]	0.15[b]
Quality	Excell.	....	Good	....	Excell.	Good
Cracking stock (distilled):						
% 400–900°F	51.0	45.8	50.5	46.0	65.1	56.2[a]
Oct. No. (thermal)	67.0	66.5[b]	69.0[b]	67.5	68.2[b]	68.9[b]
API gravity	34.5	32.5	32.8	31.5	33.0	32.0
Quality	....	....	Good	....	....	Good
Cracking stock (residual):						
% above 550°F	56.0	58.7	53.8	55.5	49.0	50.2[a]
API gravity	22.0	22.3	23.0	20.0	22.7	19.0
API cracked fuel	7.5	7.4	5.3	7.0	6.0	5.5
% gasoline (on stock)	46.6	47.1	50.9	43.2	49.8	43.1
% gasoline (on crude oil)	26.1	27.6	27.4	24.0	24.4	21.6
Lube distillate (undewaxed):						
% 700–900°F[c]	19.0	19.0	16.5	16.0	16.7	17.5[a]
Pour point	95.0	High	92.0	85.0	78.0	
Viscosity index	97.0	....	73.0	80.0	71.0	65.0[b]
Sulfur, %	1.28	....	1.12	2.15	Low	0.39[b]
Quality						
Residue, % over 900°F	22.5	26.7	20.2	24.2	12.9	14.7[a]
Asphalt quality	....	....	....	....	....	Fair

Name, state, and country	Healdton, Okla., U.S.	West Texas, (composite), Tex., U.S.	Redwater, Alberta, Canada	Hobbs, N.M., U.S.	Cowden North, Tex., U.S.	Dammam, S. Arabia
Gravity, API.................	33.6	34.2	34.3	34.6	35.0	34.9
Sulfur, %.....................	0.77	1.76[i]	0.54[i]	1.45[i]	1.66[i]	1.4[i]
Viscosity, SSU at 100°F........	58	44.8	48.1	42	42	
Date.......................	.....	5-14-47	9-20-50			
Characterization factor:						
at 250°F...................	11.90	11.96	12.06	11.88	11.82	12.03
at 450°F...................	11.77	11.72	11.71	11.66	11.73	11.90
at 550°F...................	11.84	11.70	11.74	11.58	11.71	11.83
at 750°F...................	12.02	11.80	11.81	11.60	11.70	12.0
Average...................	11.88	11.80	11.83	11.68	11.74	11.94
Base.......................	I	I	I	I	I	I
Loss, %.....................	1.4	1.4	2.0	1.8	1.9	Stab.
Gasoline:						
% to 300°F................	16.2[a]	20.5	20.2	23.9[a]	24.1[a]	18.0
Oct. No., clear............	60.0[b]	58.4[a]	63.4[a]	62.5[b]	63.0[a]	50.5
Oct. No., 3 cc TEL........	.....	67.3[a]	78.4[a]	.....	78.5[a]	72.5
% to 400°F................	26.2[a]	32.2	31.6	35.1[a]	35.3[a]	30.5
Oct. No., clear............	53.0[b]	49.3[a]	54.4[a]	55.0[b]	51.0	41.0
Oct. No., 3 cc TEL........	.....	64.0[b]	70.8[a]	69.0[b]	66.5[a]	66.0
% to 450°F................	30.7[a]	37.3	36.5	40.2[a]	40.1[a]	37.0
Quality...................						
Jet stock:						
% to 550°F................	40.5[a]	48.8	46.2	50.1[a]	49.4[a]	47.4
API gravity...............	50.0	52.5	53.3	49.0	49.0	50.8
Quality...................	Good	Good	Good	Good	Good	
Kerosene-distillate:						
% 375-500°F..............	11.9[a]	14.6	12.3	12.8[a]	11.8[a]	14.7
API gravity...............	41.3	40.8	40.3	40.0	41.0	43.1
Smoke point..............	20.0[b]	19.2[b]	19.1[b]	18.0[b]	19.0[b]	21.0
Sulfur, %.................	0.17[b]	0.53	0.18	0.56[b]	0.64[b]	0.15
Quality...................						
Distillate or diesel fuel:						
% 400-700°F..............	28.7[a]	30.2	29.7	28.9[a]	28.0[a]	34.3
Diesel index..............	58.0[b]	53.0[b]	54.5[b]	48.0[b]	53.0[b]	59.0
Pour point................	20.0[b]	−6.0[a]	13.0[a]	−3.0[b]	5.0[b]	35.0
Sulfur, %.................	0.34[b]	0.70[b]	0.39	0.98[b]	1.12[b]	1.13
Quality...................	Good	Excell.	.....	Good		
Cracking stock (distilled):						
% 400-900°F..............	45.6[a]	46.3	47.7	43.8[a]	43.3[a]	51.0
Oct. No. (thermal)..........	67.2[b]	69.1[b]	68.8[b]	70.9[b]	70.0[b]	67.5[b]
API gravity...............	32.0	30.7	30.5	28.2	31.3	32.8
Quality...................	.....	.....	Good	Good		
Cracking stock (residual):						
% above 550°F............	58.1[a]	49.8	51.8	48.1[a]	48.7[a]	52.6
API gravity...............	21.5	17.1	17.3	19.4	19.8	23.0
API cracked fuel............	7.8	6.2	6.3	3.7	4.4	7.3
% gasoline (on stock)........	45.8	38.2	38.5	46.7	46.1	49.0
% gasoline (on crude oil)......	26.6	19.0	19.9	22.5	22.5	25.8
Lube distillate (undewaxed):						
% 700-900°F[c]..............	16.9[a]	16.1	18.0	14.9[a]	15.3[a]	16.7
Pour point................	.....	79.0	90.0	.....	.....	80.0
Viscosity index.............	91.0[b]	68.0[b]	68.0[b]	43.0[b]	55.0[b]	85.0
Sulfur, %.................	0.92[b]	.....	0.62	1.63[b]	1.95[b]	2.1
Quality...................						
Residue, % over 900°F........	26.8[a]	20.1	18.7	19.3[a]	19.5[a]	18.5
Asphalt quality...............	.....	.....	Fair	Good	Good	

Name, state, and country	Fadhili, S. Arabia	Duhamel, Alberta, Canada	Burbank, Okla., U.S.	Seria (waxy), Brunei, Borneo	Golden Spike, Alberta, Canada	Agha Jari, Khuzistan, Iran
Gravity, API	35.4	35.5	35.8	36.0	35.6	36.0
Sulfur, %	1.11[i]	0.79[i]	0.21	0.05	0.2	1.36[i]
Viscosity, SSU at 100°F	42.1	42.5	48	....	....	45
Date	3-24-49	7-16-52	.....	1956	1956	2-50
Characterization factor:						
at 250°F	.....	11.90	11.97	11.74	12.03	11.82
at 450°F	11.99	11.70	11.83	11.48	11.6	11.86
at 550°F	11.92	11.71	11.86	11.4	11.74	11.82
at 750°F	11.97	11.79	12.00	11.4	.....	11.75
Average	.....	11.78	11.91	11.5	.....	11.81
Base	I	I	I	I	I	I
Loss, %	0.05	1.4	0.7	1.4	0.9	4.7
Gasoline:						
% to 300°F	15.4[a]	21.1	14.3[a]	26.0	24.2	20.0
Oct. No., clear	40.0[b]	63.4[a]	.....	65.0[g]	67.0	50.0[b]
Oct. No., 3 cc TEL	.....	80.3[a]	.....	81.9[g]	78.7	70.0[b]
% to 400°F	28.0[a]	32.4	26.9[a]	41.6	35.1	30.4
Oct. No., clear	29.7	53.3[a]	48.5[b]	56.0[g]	60.5	38.0[b]
Oct. No., 3 cc TEL	54.7	69.9[a]	.....	74.2[g]	70.7	61.0[b]
% to 450°F	34.7	38.0	32.6[a]	49.6	40.2	35.0
Quality	.....	.....	.....	Good		
Jet stock:						
% to 550°F	48.2[a]	48.9	44.3[a]	66.5	50.2	44.3
API gravity	52.8	52.0	50.4	43.0	51.4	57.0
Quality	.....	Good	Good	Good	Good	Good
Kerosene-distillate:						
% 375–500°F	16.7[a]	14.1	14.5[a]	21.1	12.9	11.6
API gravity	43.0[a]	40.0	42.0	36.1	38.5	42.2
Smoke point	26.0	18.8[a]	21.0[b]	17.0	23.0	21.3[b]
Sulfur, %	0.16[a]	0.28	0.08[b]	0.02	0.04	0.24[b]
Quality	.....	.....	Good	Fair	Fair	
Distillate or diesel fuel:						
% 400–700°F	36.2[a]	32.0	35.2[a]	43.4	29.3	27.8
Diesel index	58.7	53.0[b]	59.0[b]	42.3	55.0	55.3
Pour point	30.0	17.0[a]	High	25.0	15.0	15.0[a]
Sulfur, %	1.04	0.62	0.15[b]	0.06	0.13	0.82[b]
Quality	.....	.....	.....	.....	Fair	Good
Cracking stock (distilled):						
% 400–900°F	53.5[a]	50.6	55.4[a]	54.8[a]	44.0	44.2[a]
Oct. No. (thermal)	66.7[b]	69.3[b]	67.5[b]	73.0[b]	.....	69.4[b]
API gravity	33.0[a]	30.1	32.2	24.4	31.6	30.3
Quality	.....	Good	.....	Excell.		
Cracking stock (residual):						
% above 550°F	51.8[a]	49.7	55.0[a]	32.1	48.9	51.0
API gravity	21.7	19.8	24.6	20.2	20.5	14.7
API cracked fuel	7.3	5.4	7.0	1.0	.....	6.2
% gasoline (on stock)	44.4	44.6	52.2	50.2	.....	32.7
% gasoline (on crude oil)	23.0	22.2	28.7	16.1	.....	16.7
Lube distillate (undewaxed).						
% 700–900°F[c]	17.3[a]	18.6	20.2[a]	11.4[a]	14.7	16.4[a]
Pour point	.....	97.0	.....	.....	85.0	
Viscosity index	.....	66.0[b]	89.0[b]	Low	80.9	61.0[b]
Sulfur, %	2.1[b]	0.95	0.37[b]	.....	0.35	2.02[b]
Quality	.....	.....	Lube			
Residue, % over 900°F	18.5	15.6	18.0[a]	2.2[a]	20.0	20.7[a]
Asphalt quality	.....	Fair	.....	Good	.....	Good

Name, state, and country	New Norway, Alberta, Canada	West Texas, Tex., U.S.	Salt Creek, Wyo., U.S.	Abqaiq, S. Arabia	Talang Akar Pendopo, Sumatra, Indonesia	Oklahoma City, Okla., U.S.
Gravity, API	36.4	36.3	36.2	36.5	36.5	37.3
Sulfur, %	0.82[i]	1.31[i]	0.17	1.36[i]	0.10	0.11[a]
Viscosity, SSU at 100°F	42.7	41.4	46	.....	45.5	
Date	7-16-52	3-25-47	.....	.....	1937–1953	11-14-29
Characterization factor:						
at 250°F	11.97	11.85	11.76	12.30	11.71	12.05
at 450°F	11.74	11.86	11.73	12.01	11.7	11.97
at 550°F	11.73	11.85	11.81	11.91	11.83	12.02
at 750°F	11.87	11.88	12.02	11.80	12.32	12.22
Average	11.83	11.86	11.83	12.00	11.89	12.06
Base	I	I	I	PI	I	IP
Loss, %	1.8	0.9	1.2	0	2.0	1.0
Gasoline:						
% to 300°F	22.8	22.8	19.1[a]	19.7	20.7	17.0
Oct. No., clear	62.6[a]	55.2[a]	66.5[b]	44.5		
Oct. No., 3 cc TEL	78.2[a]	65.7[a]	.....	68.5		
% to 400°F	34.0	33.5	29.8[a]	31.8	30.8	26.3
Oct. No., clear	52.2[a]	45.4[a]	60.5[b]	36.0	58.0[a]	44.0[b]
Oct. No., 3 cc TEL	69.5[a]	64.0[a]	.....	63.2		
% to 450°F	39.3	39.5	35.1[a]	37.8	35.8	31.3
Quality	.....	.....	.....	.....	Good	
Jet stock:						
% to 550°F	50.5	51.8	45.7[a]	49.9	46.0	42.8
API gravity	52.5	53.3	49.5	54.2	51.3	55.6
Quality	Good	Good	Good	.....	Good	
Kerosene-distillate:						
% 375–500°F	13.5	14.7	13.3[a]	15.3	12.8	13.3
API gravity	40.6	42.5	41.0	44.9	40.2	44.0
Smoke point	19.1[b]	21.5[b]	19.0[b]	24.0	19.0[a]	24.0[b]
Sulfur, %	0.37	0.27	Low	0.16	Low	0.03
Quality	.....	.....	Good	.....	Good	Excell.
Distillate or diesel fuel:						
% 400–700°F	30.9	33.7	30.7[a]	34.3	30.0	33.0
Diesel index	52.7	58.0[b]	57.0[b]	60.0	62.0[a]	68.0[b]
Pour point	15.0[a]	3.0[a]	.....	25.0	High	High
Sulfur, %	0.71	0.39	Low	1.16	Low	0.15
Quality	.....	Excell.				
Cracking stock (distilled):						
% 400–900°F	50.0	49.5	49.7[a]	50.2	47.5	52.9
Oct. No. (thermal)	68.4[b]	68.4[b]	67.8[b]	67.9[b]	63.0[b]	66.0[b]
API gravity	30.5	32.6	32.0	32.5	35.7	34.0
Quality						
Cracking stock (residual):						
% above 550°F	47.7	47.3	53.1[a]	50.1	52.0	57.2
API gravity	19.2	19.2	24.4	21.7	21.9	26.7
API cracked fuel	6.5	6.6	7.2	5.1	11.3	9.3
% gasoline (on stock)	42.2	42.1	51.8	48.6	42.8	54.2
% gasoline (on crude oil)	20.1	19.9	27.5	24.3	22.2	31.0
Lube distillate (undewaxed):						
% 700–900°F[c]	19.1	15.8	19.0[a]	15.9	17.5	19.9
Pour point	96.0	84.0	.....	85.0	High	
Viscosity index	76.0[b]	77.0[b]	91.0[b]	65.0		110.0[b]
Sulfur, %	1.01	1.52	Low	High	.....	0.26
Quality	.....	.....	.....	.....	Wax	Good
Residue, % over 900°F	14.2	16.1	19.3[a]	18.0	19.7	19.8
Asphalt quality						

Name, state, and country	Kirkuk, Kirkuk, Iraq	Graham, Kan., U.S.	Mexia, Tex., U.S.	Malmo, Alberta, Canada	Sprayberry, W. Tex., U.S.	Illinois, Ill., U.S.
Gravity, API	36.6	37.0	37.4	37.2	37.2	37.5
Sulfur, %	1.93[i]	0.47[i]	0.18[a]	0.58[i]	0.18[i]	0.22
Viscosity, SSU at 100°F	42	47	.....	40.1	44	43.3
Date	2-50	.....	1937	7-16-52	1-7-52	11-1-49
Characterization factor:						
at 250°F	12.00	11.98	.....	11.92	11.78	12.10
at 450°F	11.95	11.88	11.86	11.72	11.72	11.84
at 550°F	11.93	11.88	11.95	11.80	11.88	11.82
at 750°F	11.79	12.00	12.02	11.95	12.00	12.01
Average	11.92	11.93	.....	11.85	11.85	11.94
Base	I	I	I	I	I	PI
Loss, %	0.2	2.0	1.2	1.5	1.5	1.0
Gasoline:						
% to 300°F	24.2	23.4[a]	20.5	23.2	25.2	21.1
Oct. No., clear	50.0[b]	.....	.....	61.3[a]	64.4[a]	57.2[a]
Oct. No., 3 cc TEL	72.0[b]	.....	.....	76.7[a]	83.7[a]	84.5[a]
% to 400°F	38.1	34.0[a]	33.3	34.5	35.3	33.7
Oct. No., clear	39.0[b]	46.5[b]	.....	51.9[a]	58.4[a]	51.2[a]
Oct. No., 3 cc TEL	62.0[b]	.....	.....	67.6[a]	79.6[a]	
% to 450°F	42.3	39.0[a]	39.1	40.2	40.7	40.0
Quality	.....	.....	.....	.....	Good	
Jet stock:						
% to 550°F	52.7	48.8[a]	50.8	51.4	50.5	50.7
API gravity	58.6	52.0	50.5	52.1	53.0	53.7
Quality	.....	.....	Good	Good	Good	
Kerosene-distillate:						
% 375–500°F	14.3	12.4[a]	15.3	14.0	13.1	15.4
API gravity	43.3	43.0	42.9	41.0	40.7	42.5
Smoke point	23.1[b]	21.5[b]	21.5[b]	19.5[b]	19.1[b]	21.1[b]
Sulfur, %	0.32[b]	0.12[b]	Low	0.23	0.03	0.07
Quality	.....	Good	Good	....	Good	Good
Distillate or diesel fuel:						
% 400–700°F	29.3	29.0[a]	34.5	32.4	28.2	30.6
Diesel index	60.8	60.0[b]	62.0[b]	56.4	58.3	57.0[b]
Pour point	20.0	High	High	16.0[a]	0[a]	11.0[a]
Sulfur, %	0.99[b]	0.21[b]	Low	0.47	0.07	0.13
Quality	Fair	.....	.....	Good	Excell.	Good
Cracking stock (distilled):						
% 400–900°F	44.7[a]	46.0[a]	52.5	48.5	40.4	44.8
Oct. No. (thermal)	69.0[b]	67.2[b]	66.7[b]	67.8[b]	67.2[b]	67.2[b]
API gravity	33.7	32.5	33.4	31.3	34.0	33.1
Quality						
Cracking stock (residual):						
% above 550°F	47.1	49.2[a]	49.2	47.1	48.0	48.3
API gravity	16.7	21.1	27.3	20.7	20.9	21.5
API cracked fuel	6.1	7.6	6.7	7.1	7.7	7.7
% gasoline (on stock)	36.2	45.0	56.8	44.5	44.3	45.5
% gasoline (on crude oil)	17.1	22.2	28.0	21.0	21.3	22.0
Lube distillate (undewaxed):						
% 700–900°F[c]	15.4[a]	17.0[a]	18.0	16.1	12.2	14.2
Pour point	.....	.....	.....	95.0	87.0	80.0
Viscosity index	66.0[b]	89.0[b]	91.0[b]	84.0[b]	76.0	89.0[b]
Sulfur, %	2.47[b]	0.6[b]	Low	0.77	0.24	0.35
Quality	.....	.....	Lube			
Residue, % over 900°F	17.0[a]	18.0[a]	13.0	15.5	22.8	20.5
Asphalt quality	Good					

Name, state, and country	Conroe, Tex., U.S.	East Texas, Tex., U.S.	Kettle-man, Calif., U.S.	Guara (light), Anzoat., Venezuela	Buckeye Pipeline, Ohio, U.S.	Qatif, Zone D, S. Arabia
Gravity, API.................	37.8	38.4	37.5	37.7	38.0	38.6
Sulfur, %....................	0.12	0.33	0.32	0.54	0.54	1.4[i]
Viscosity, SSU at 100°F........	35	40	......	......	42	
Date........................	......	3-3-42	......	1946–1948	8-2-51	
Characterization factor:						
at 250°F....................	11.25	11.92	11.70	11.90	11.98	12.04
at 450°F....................	11.40	11.72	11.61	11.60	11.89	12.04
at 550°F....................	11.56	11.85	11.68	11.70	11.94	11.97
at 750°F....................	12.00	12.05	11.70	11.82	12.01	11.97
Average....................	11.55	11.89	11.67	11.75	11.96	12.0
Base........................	NI	I	I	I	I	PI
Loss, %.....................	0.2	0.9	1.2	1.2	1.9	5.3
Gasoline:						
% to 300°F.................	23.5[a]	24.1	28.8	25.0	22.4	20.7
Oct. No., clear............	71.3[e]	64.5	......	66.0	58.1[a]	55.0[a]
Oct. No., 3 cc TEL.	88.0[e]	.....	.....	83.0	78.2[a]	69.5[a]
% to 400°F.................	39.6[a]	35.8	40.0	36.5	33.3	31.9
Oct. No., clear............	59.0	57.0	58.0[b]	58.0	50.3[a]	44.8
Oct. No., 3 cc TEL........	80.5[a]	78.0	......	78.0	72.0[a]	62.5
% to 450°F.................	48.4[a]	40.5	45.8	44.3	38.3	37.2
Quality....................	Excell.[b]	.....	Good	Good	.....	.....
Jet stock:						
% to 550°F.................	65.8[a]	50.8	54.8	56.5	48.6	47.7
API gravity...............	44.2	50.0	47.2	48.7	54.5	52.9
Quality....................	Good	Good	Good	Good	Good	
Kerosene-distillate:						
% 375–500°F...............	22.4[a]	12.5	12.0	15.5	12.3	14.7
API gravity...............	36.0	40.7	40.0	39.5	43.6	43.0
Smoke point...............	15.5[b]	20.0	18.5[b]	18.0	22.0	24.0
Sulfur, %..................	Low	0.05	0.06	0.12	0.12	0.30
Quality....................	......	Good	Good	Good	Good	
Distillate or diesel fuel:						
% 400–700°F...............	45.2[a]	29.5	28.5	33.5	31.1	30.4
Diesel index..............	47.0[b]	58.0	53.0	52.0	60.5	60.0
Pour point................	−10.0[b]	15.0	−4.0	−10.0	12.0[a]	25.0
Sulfur, %..................	Low	0.19	0.19	0.35	0.33	1.15[a]
Quality....................	Good	Good	Excell.	Excell.	Good	
Cracking stock (distilled):						
% 400–900°F...............	55.3[a]	44.5	40.8	49.00	47.2	45.1
Oct. No. (thermal).........	67.8[b]	67.0[b]	68.6	69.0[b]	66.9[b]	67.3
API gravity...............	31.8	35.6	30.8	32.8	34.9	33.8
Quality....................	......	.....	......	Good		
Cracking stock (residual):						
% above 550°F.............	34.0[a]	48.3	44.0	42.4	49.5	47.0
API gravity...............	26.0	26.1	25.0	22.7	21.3	20.4
API cracked fuel............	6.8	7.3	3.2	5.2	7.8	7.5
% gasoline (on stock).......	55.0	54.7	56.0	50.4	45.1	43.7
% gasoline (on crude oil)....	18.7	26.4	24.7	21.3	22.3	20.6
Lube distillate (undewaxed):						
% 700–900°F[c].............	10.1[a]	15.0	12.3	15.5	16.1	14.7
Pour point................	......	80.0	95.0	100.0	87.0	85.0
Viscosity index............	89.0[b]	.....	102.0	72.0	89.0[b]	92.0
Sulfur, %..................	Low	.....	0.36	0.8	1.08	2.2
Quality....................	Wax[b]	Lube	.....	......	Lube	
Residue, % over 900°F........	4.9[a]	18.8	18.0	13.3	17.6	17.7
Asphalt quality..............	......	.....	Good			

Name, state, and country	Louden, Ill., U.S.	Fitts, Okla., U.S.	Mid Cont. Pipeline, U.S.	Leduc, Alberta, Canada	Guëre, Anzoat., Venezuela	Panhandle Fullerton, Tex., U.S.
Gravity, API.................	38.8	39.0	38.4	40.4	38.1	39.9
Sulfur, %....................	0.26	0.18	0.37	0.29[i]	0.45	0.78[i]
Viscosity, SSU at 100°P.........	45	42	40	37.8	.....	40
Date........................	.....	......	3-9-50	2-15-51	1951	4-20-49
Characterization factor:						
at 250°F....................	11.94	11.72	11.95	11.94	11.76	11.97
at 450°F....................	11.80	11.85	11.85	11.76	11.69	11.92
at 550°F....................	11.86	11.96	11.86	11.79	11.76	12.02
at 750°F....................	11.90	12.13	12.08	11.88	12.03	12.22
Average....................	11.84	11.92	11.94	11.84	11.81	12.03
Base........................	I	I	I	I	I	IP
Loss, %.....................	2.1	2.9	2.0	3.8	2.3	1.8
Gasoline:						
% to 300°F.................	24.6[a]	22.8[a]	23.9	24.9	25.0	23.0
Oct. No., clear.............	60.0[a]	.....	57.5[a]	65.0[a]	68.5[b]	55.2
Oct. No., 3 cc TEL..........	81.0[b]	.....	78.3[a]	83.0[a]	85.5[b]	77.0
% to 400°F.................	35.7[a]	34.0[a]	35.2	37.9	35.0	35.2
Oct. No., clear.............	51.5[b]	55.0[b]	51.6[a]	55.8[a]	58.0[b]	45.8
Oct. No., 3 cc TEL..........	.....	.....	72.4[a]	75.6[a]	77.5[b]	64.5
% to 450°F.................	40.7[a]	39.1[a]	39.7	43.6	39.9	40.2
Quality....................	.....	......	.....	.....	Good	
Jet stock:						
% to 550°F.................	50.0[a]	49.1[a]	53.1	54.6	49.6	49.4
API gravity................	50.5	50.5	51.7	53.9	55.0	54.3
Quality....................	Good	Good	Good	Good	Good	
Kerosene-distillate:						
% 375-500°F...............	12.6[a]	12.9[a]	15.0	14.4	12.3	12.6
API gravity................	42.0	42.3	42.0	41.1	40.0	43.7
Smoke point...............	20.0[b]	21.0[b]	21.2[b]	19.6[b]	18.5[b]	22.5[a]
Sulfur, %..................	0.06	Low	0.15	0.07	0.08[b]	0.21
Quality....................	Good	Good	Good	Good	Good	
Distillate or diesel fuel:						
% 400-700°F...............	28.5[a]	30.4[a]	26.6	31.7	29.8	28.5
Diesel index...............	60.3	63.0[b]	60.5[b]	56.5[b]	55.0[b]	62.5
Pour point.................	20.0[b]	25.0[b]	17.0[a]	13.0[a]	8.0[b]	12.0[a]
Sulfur, %..................	0.18[b]	0.14[b]	0.33	0.27	0.22[b]	0.3
Quality....................	Good[a]	......	Good	Good	Good	Good
Cracking stock (distilled):						
% 400-900°F...............	43.3[a]	47.4[a]	43.0	48.1	47.3	44.3
Oct. No. (thermal)..........	67.8[b]	66.2[b]	67.5[b]	68.3[b]	67.5[b]	67.6[b]
API gravity................	32.2	34.2	34.9	31.7	31.0	35.7
Quality....................						
Cracking stock (residual):						
% above 550°F..............	47.9[a]	48.0[a]	44.9	41.6	48.1	48.8
API gravity................	24.6	24.2	21.5	19.0	20.4	25.2
API cracked fuel...........	5.8	8.7	8.6	6.7	8.2	8.8
% gasoline (on stock).......	53.3	50.3	44.8	41.6	42.9	52.0
% gasoline (on crude oil)......	25.5	24.1	20.1	17.3	20.6	25.4
Lube distillate (undewaxed):						
% 700-900°F[c]..............	14.8[a]	17.0[a]	16.4	16.4	17.5	15.8
Pour point.................	.....	......	96.0	97.0	.....	83.0
Viscosity index.............	78.0[b]	101.0[b]	97.0[b]	76.0[b]	91.0[b]	93.0[a]
Sulfur, %..................	.....	......	0.73	0.47	.....	0.45
Quality....................	.....	Lube	Lube	.....	Wax	Good
Residue, % over 900°F........	18.9[a]	15.7[a]	19.8	10.2	15.4	18.7
Asphalt quality..............						

Name, state, and country	Gwinville, Miss., U.S.	Santa Elena, etc., Ecuador	Michigan, Mich., U.S.	Mid Continent, Okla., U.S.	Sweden, Tex., U.S.	New Ulm, Tex., U.S.
Gravity, API	39.9	41.0	40.2	40.9	41.0	41.2
Sulfur, %	0.14	0.05	0.20	. . . . .	0.11	0.10
Viscosity, SSU at 100°F	44.2	. . . .	38	. . . . .	32	37
Date	2-10-45	1937	1-10-37	11-8-29	7-12-52	1-18-51
Characterization factor:						
at 250°F	11.99	12.00	12.27	11.95	11.76	11.84
at 450°F	12.14	11.83	12.05	11.95	11.66	11.81
at 550°F	12.18	11.82	12.28	11.98	11.68	11.78
at 750°F	12.55	11.98	12.05	12.13	11.67	12.32
Average	12.22	11.91	12.16	12.00	11.70	11.94
Base	IP	I	P	I	I	IP
Loss, %	0.7	0	2.0	0	0.4	1.1
Gasoline:						
% to 300°F	2.9	25.5	19.5	25.1	26.1	26.1
Oct. No., clear	40.0[b]	65.0	35.5	54.0[b]	66.6[a]	60.8[a]
Oct. No., 3 cc TEL	. . . . .	. . . .	. . . .	. . . . .	86.8[a]	84.7[a]
% to 400°F	7.0	41.0	33.0	37.8	44.8	36.8
Oct. No., clear	27.0[a]	54.0	22.0	46.0[b]	53.3[a]	54.3[a]
Oct. No., 3 cc TEL	. . . . .	. . . .	. . . .	. . . . .	79.0[b]	81.0[b]
% to 450°F	10.7	48.2	39.5	44.1	54.0	42.9
Quality	. . . . .	. . . .	. . . .	. . . . .	Good[b]	Good[b]
Jet stock:						
% to 550°F	25.3	61.5	51.0	56.0	72.9	57.6
API gravity	48.6	. . . .	58.5	53.6	47.2	51.7
Quality	. . . . .	Good	. . . .	Good	Good	Good
Kerosene-distillate:						
% 375–500°F	10.6	18.0	16.0	15.5	23.4	15.7
API gravity	45.7	42.1	45.0	43.8	39.7	41.3
Smoke point	29.4[b]	21.0[b]	27.0[b]	23.0[b]	18.5[b]	20.5[b]
Sulfur, %	0.02	0.03	0.21[b]	. . . . .	0.02	0.02
Quality	Excell.	Good	Good	Good	Good	Good
Distillate or diesel fuel:						
% 400–700°F	66.3	38.0	33.0	32.2	46.2	36.0
Diesel index	74.0[b]	57.0[b]	77.0[b]	63.0[b]	52.0[b]	57.4
Pour point	39.0[a]	High	High	25.0[b]	0[a]	3.0[a]
Sulfur, %	Low	Low	0.32[b]	. . . . .	0.06	0.05
Quality	. . . . .	. . . .	. . . .	. . . . .	Good	Excell.
Cracking stock (distilled):						
% 400–900°F	86.0	. . . .	46.0	49.2	55.0	57.6
Oct. No. (thermal)	61.5[b]	67.0[b]	65.0[b]	66.2[b]	68.2[b]	64.8[b]
API gravity	38.5	. . . .	39.0	35.0	33.0	34.5
Quality						
Cracking stock (residual):						
% above 550°F	74.0	38.5	47.0	44.0	26.7	41.2
API gravity	36.3	. . . .	20.7	27.1	24.0	25.6
API cracked fuel	11.4	. . . .	8.5	8.2	3.0	10.8
% gasoline (on stock)	66.3	. . . .	43.7	55.8	54.5	51.3
% gasoline (on crude oil)	49.0	. . . .	20.5	24.6	14.6	21.2
Lube distillate (undewaxed):						
% 700–900°F[c]	19.7	. . . .	13.0	17.0	8.8[a]	21.6[a]
Pour point	82.0	. . . .	68.0	. . . . .	96.0	
Viscosity index	140.0[b]	. . . .	93.0[b]	102.0[b]	52.0[b]	
Sulfur, %	. . . . .	. . . .	0.38[b]	. . . . .	0.25	
Quality	Good	. . . .	Good	Good	. . . .	Wax
Residue, % over 900°F	. . . . .	. . . .	19.0	13.0		
Asphalt quality						

Name, state and country	Willistan (Devonian), N.D., U.S.	Rincon Largo, Anzoat., Venezuela	San Joaquin, Anzoat., Venezuela	San Roque, Anzoat., Venezuela	Cranfield, Miss., U.S.
Gravity, API	41.4	40.6	40.6	41.0	40.6
Sulfur, %	0.153	0.10	0.15	0.01	0.15
Viscosity, SSU at 100°F	......	......	......	......	39.2
Date	1955	1942–1950	1940–1949	8-15-49	3-7-45
Characterization factor:					
at 250°F	12.18	11.75	11.72	11.70	11.88
at 450°F	11.94	11.65	11.58	11.70	11.92
at 550°F	12.02	11.70	11.72	11.80	12.00
at 750°F	12.35	12.45a	12.40	12.30a	12.16
Average	12.12	11.89	11.85	11.88	11.99
Base	P	IP	IP	IP	I
Loss, %	1.5	......	......	......	1.7
Gasoline:					
% to 300°F	20.2	25.2	24.7	30.0	20.3
Oct. No., clear	......	66.0	68.0b	66.0b	64.3a
Oct. No., 3 cc TEL	......	84.0	86.0	84.0b	83.0a
% to 400°F	30.5	37.0	34.7	40.3	31.5
Oct. No., clear	49.6g	56.0	60.5	58.0b	50.7a
Oct. No., 3 cc TEL	72.9	78.5	80.5	80.0b	
% to 450°F	35.5	42.1	39.4	44.7	37.1
Quality	......	Good	Good	Goodb	
Jet stock:					
% to 550°F	47.2	53.5	51.4	57.4	48.3
API gravity	50.6	49.3	50.3	49.8	53.2
Quality	Fair	Good	Good	Good	Good
Kerosene-distillate:					
% 375–500°F	13.5	13.1	13.0	12.9	14.0
API gravity	43.5	40.0	38.7	40.7	43.5
Smoke point	24.0b	19.0b	16.5	19.5b	22.5
Sulfur, %	......	Low	Low	Low	0.02
Quality	Excell.	Good	......	Good	Good
Distillate or diesel fuel:					
% 400–700°F	33.0	31.5	31.7	29.3	36.1
Diesel index	65.5b	51.5b	51.5	55.0b	64.0b
Pour point	High	5.0b	32.0	20.0b	25.0a
Sulfur, %	Low	0.1	0.14	0.05b	0.04b
Quality	......	Good			
Cracking stock (distilled):					
% 400–900°F	51.0d	49.0a	52.4	46.2a	57.0
Oct. No. (thermal)	63.0b	66.0b	66.2b	66.2b	65.6b
API gravity	34.3	35.0	35.5	35.5	34.5
Quality					
Cracking stock (residual):					
% above 550°F	51.3	46.5	48.6	42.6	50.0
API gravity	31.5	32.1	31.7	30.1	27.1
API cracked fuel	10.2	11.0	10.6	9.6	8.5
% gasoline (on stock)	60.4	61.7	61.5	59.5	55.2
% gasoline (on crude oil)	31.0	28.7	29.9	25.3	27.6
Lube distillate (undewaxed):					
% 700–900°Fc	18.0d	17.5a	20.7	16.9a	20.9
Pour point	110.0a	130.0b	125.0	115.0b	96.0
Viscosity index	121.0b	132.0b	127.0	118.0b	104.0b
Sulfur, %	......	0.25b	0.23	0.15b	0.26b
Quality	Good	Wax	Wax	Wax	Good
Residue, % over 900°F	17.0d	14.0a	12.9	14.0a	9.8
Asphalt quality					

Name, state, and country	Turner Valley, Alberta, Canada	Edmond (West), Okla., U.S.	Southwest Oklahoma, Okla., U.S.	Williston (Madison), N.D., U.S.	Scurry Co., Tex., U.S.
Gravity, API	41.7	41.5	42.0	42.0	42.0
Sulfur, %	0.33	0.14	0.22	0.32	0.33[i]
Viscosity, SSU at 100°F	33.7	39	....	....	40
Date	2-15-51	....	1952	1955	9-14-50
Characterization factor:					
at 250°F	11.83	11.92	11.96	11.76	11.83
at 450°F	11.75	11.87	11.85	11.80	11.67
at 550°F	11.71	11.92	11.88	11.73	11.82
at 750°F	11.97	12.10	12.09	11.86	12.07
Average	11.82	11.95	11.95	11.79	11.85
Base	I	I	I	I	I
Loss, %	1.0	2.1	2.0	1.5	3.1
Gasoline:					
% to 300°F	28.6	24.1[a]	25.0	28.5	30.1
Oct. No., clear	59.1[a]	56.5[b]	61.5	....	64.0
Oct. No., 3 cc TEL	75.3[a]	....	80.5	....	82.8
% to 400°F	43.0	35.3[a]	40.2	43.0	41.9
Oct. No., clear	51.1[a]	47.0	45.0	53.9[g]	55.5
Oct. No., 3 cc TEL	69.4[a]	....	68.0	73.8	75.2
% to 450°F	49.3	40.9[a]	46.2	49.5	47.5
Quality	....	....	....	....	Good
Jet stock:					
% to 550°F	62.1	50.9[a]	57.1	62.0	57.8
API gravity	52.9	53.0	55.2	49.8	54.8
Quality	Good	Good	Good	Good	Good
Kerosene-distillate:					
% 375-500°F	16.1	13.7[a]	15.2	17.0	14.0
API gravity	41.1	43.0	42.4	41.4	40.5
Smoke point	19.7[a]	21.5[b]	22.2[b]	20.0[b]	22.0
Sulfur, %	0.11	Low	0.08	....	0.07
Quality	Good	Good	Good	Excell.	Good
Distillate or diesel fuel:					
% 400-700°F	36.2	30.9[a]	31.0	34.0	29.0
Diesel index	53.0[b]	61.0[b]	59.0	53.5[b]	56.5
Pour point	14.0[a]	25.0[b]	12.0	....	2.0
Sulfur, %	0.26	Low	0.11	....	0.29
Quality	....	....	Good	....	Excell.
Cracking stock (distilled):					
% 400-900°F	52.0	47.9[a]	45.6[a]	48.0[d]	43.0
Oct. No. (thermal)	68.2[b]	66.2[b]	66.5	68.0[b]	66.2[b]
API gravity	31.4	33.3	34.0	30.7	33.2
Quality					
Cracking stock (residual):					
% above 550°F	36.9	47.0[a]	40.9	36.5	39.1
API gravity	23.3	26.7	22.4	27.0	20.5
API cracked fuel	6.9	7.9	8.5	4.9	8.2
% gasoline (on stock)	49.9	55.3	46.7	57.8	43.0
% gasoline (on crude oil)	18.4	26.0	19.1	21.1	16.8
Lube distillate (undewaxed):					
% 700-900°F[c]	15.8	17.0[a]	14.6[a]	14.0[d]	14.0
Pour point	95.0	....	....	87.0[b]	83.0
Viscosity index	86.0[b]	98.0[b]	97.0[b]	75.0[b]	65.0[a]
Sulfur, %	0.55	Low	0.36[b]	....	0.55
Quality	....	Lube			
Residue, % over 900°F	4.0	14.7[a]	12.2[a]	8.0[d]	12.0
Asphalt quality					

Name, state, and country	Farmers Valley (composite), Pa., U.S.	Magallanes, Chile	El Cubo (W. Tarra), Zulia, Venezuela	Rodessa, La. U.S.	Seneca Pipeline, Olean, N.Y., U.S.
Gravity, API...................	42.4	41.9	42.3	42.8	43.9
Sulfur, %......................	0.09	0.04	0.06	0.28	0.10
Viscosity, SSU at 100°F.........	40	37.4	......	......	40
Date...........................	10-31-49	12-55	1948	1952	11-29-49
Characterization factor:					
at 250°F....................	12.04	11.82	12.00	12.06	11.99
at 450°F....................	12.12	11.85	11.95	12.21	12.05
at 550°F....................	12.20	11.92	12.00	12.22	12.22
at 750°F....................	12.45	12.30	12.30	12.40	12.50
Average....................	12.20	12.0	12.06	12.22	12.19
Base........................	P	IP	IP	P	P
Loss, %.......................	1.72	1.0	......	0.3	1.41
Gasoline:					
% to 300°F.................	21.28	23.8	28.0	19.2	24.79
Oct. No., clear.............	54.1[a]	69.0	68.0[b]	....	53.5[a]
Oct. No., 3 cc TEL..........	74.7[a]	85.0	85.0[b]	......	75.6[a]
% to 400°F.................	33.98	35.1	38.0	32.7	37.49
Oct. No., clear.............	44.3[a]	43.0	49.0	36.5	45.8
Oct. No., 3 cc TEL..........	67.7[a]	65.0	78.0[b]	......	66.0
% to 450°F.................	38.98	40.7	47.0	39.7	42.59
Quality.....................	......	....	Good[b]		
Jet stock:					
% to 550°F.................	49.08	51.3	58.0	53.0	52.49
API gravity.................	55.1	52.8	54.0	56.5	57.0
Quality.....................	......	Good			
Kerosene-distillate:					
% 375–500°F................	12.7	14.0	18.7	17.2	12.7
API gravity.................	46.1	43.8	44.4	47.2	45.9
Smoke point................	29.0	32.0	25.4[b]	33.0[b]	29.0
Sulfur, %...................	0.06	0.005	......	Low	0.07
Quality.....................	Excell.	Excell.	Excell.	Excell.	Excell.
Distillate or diesel fuel:					
% 400–700°F................	29.9	32.9	33.5	37.4	28.9
Diesel index................	72.1	69.0	67.0	......	70.6
Pour point..................	15.0[a]	20.0	10.0[b]	45.0	15.0[a]
Sulfur, %...................	0.08	0.013	0.07	......	0.08
Quality.....................	Good	Good	Good	......	Good
Cracking stock (distilled):					
% 400–900°F................	46.2	48.9	49.0[a]	52.5	46.0
Oct. No. (thermal)...........	63.3[b]	64.0[b]	65.3[b]	63.0[b]	63.2[b]
API gravity.................	37.6	34.6	37.5	40.8	37.9
Quality.....................					
Cracking stock (residual):					
% above 550°F..............	49.2	47.7	42.0	46.7	46.1
API gravity.................	28.4	33.3	28.4	28.9	28.8
API cracked fuel............	11.8	9.2	10.0	11.2	11.9
% gasoline (on stock)........	55.1	64.2	56.5	56.5	55.4
% gasoline (on crude oil).....	27.1	30.6	23.7	26.4	25.4
Lube distillate (undewaxed):					
% 700–900°F[c]...............	16.3	16.0	15.5[a]	15.1	17.1
Pour point..................	95.0	High	115.0[b]	103.0	87.0
Viscosity index.............	105.0[b]	125.0[a]	118.0[b]	110.0	107.0[b]
Sulfur, %...................	0.10	....	0.15[b]	......	0.14
Quality.....................	Excell.	....	Lube	Excell.	Excell.
Residue, % over 900°F........	18.1	15.0	13.0[a]	14.5	15.1
Asphalt quality..............					

Name, state, and country	Santa Rosa, Anzoat., Venezuela	Anaco (wax blend), Anzoat., Venezuela	Atlanta (limestone), Ark., U.S.	Djambi (NIAM), Sumatra, Indonesia	Grass Creek, Wyo., U.S.
Gravity, API	44.2	43.7	44.5	46.0	45.8
Sulfur, %	0.08	0.08	0.48[i]	0.03	0.10
Viscosity, SSU at 100°F	.....	.....	35	.....	34
Date	1942–1947	1945–1950	.....	1956	
Characterization factor:					
at 250°F	11.70·	11.70	11.82	11.96	11.62
at 450°F	11.62	11.55	12.05	11.58	11.72
at 550°F	11.70	11.65	12.08	11.9	11.81
at 750°F	12.35[a]	12.20	12.25	11.8[a]	12.08
Average	11.84	11.76	12.05	11.8	11.81
Base	IP	IP	IP	I	I
Loss, %	.....	.....	1.5	2.9	1.6
Gasoline:					
% to 300°F	35.8	34.4	25.2[a]	40.6	38.7[a]
Oct. No., clear	69.0	66.0	.....	61.5[g]	.....
Oct. No., 3 cc TEL	86.7	88.0	.....	81.5[g]	
% to 400°F	46.0	48.5	39.2[a]	61.2	52.1[a]
Oct. No., clear	60.5	60.0	48.5[b]	51.5[g]	59.0[b]
Oct. No., 3 cc TEL	80.0	82.5	.....	74.7[g]	
% to 450°F	51.8	54.0	45.3[a]	68.4	57.7[a]
Quality	Good	Excell.			
Jet stock:					
% to 550°F	63.4	64.5	56.3[a]	79.9	68.4[a]
API gravity	48.5	48.5	57.4	49.5	51.4
Quality	Good	Good	.....	Good	Good
Kerosene-distillate:					
% 375–500°F	13.4	14.5	15.0[a]	18.2	13.9[a]
API gravity	39.4	38.4	46.0	39.5	40.4
Smoke point	18.2[b]	17.3[b]	27.0[b]	18.0	19.Q[b]
Sulfur, %	Low	Low	0.06[b]	0.02	Low
Quality	Good	.....	Excell.	Good	Good
Distillate or diesel fuel:					
% 400–700°F	28.8	35.5	35.0[a]	30.5	28.3[a]
Diesel index	52.3	52.0[b]	76.0[b]	57.8	56.0[b]
Pour point	3.0[b]	10.0[b]	High	25.0	20.0[b]
Sulfur, %	0.07	0.08[b]	0.15[b]	0.04	Low
Quality	Good	Good	.....	.....	Good
Cracking stock (distilled):					
% 400–900°F	41.4	43.5	51.4[a]	35.9[a]	38.8[a]
Oct. No. (thermal)	67.0[b]	67.2[b]	64.5[b]	68.3[b]	67.8[b]
API gravity	35.0	34.0	35.5	30.4	34.0
Quality					
Cracking stock (residual):					
% above 550°F	36.6	35.5	42.2[a]	17.2	30.0[a]
API gravity	36.8	35.2	27.1	24.6	29.7
API cracked fuel	9.1	7.4	9.6	5.2	7.1
% gasoline (on stock)	68.1	67.4	54.9	54.2	60.1
% gasoline (on crude oil)	24.9	24.0	23.2	9.3	18.0
Lube distillate (undewaxed):					
% 700–900°F[c]	12.6	8.0	16.4[a]	5.4[a]	10.5[a]
Pour point	115.0	111.0[b]	.....	.....	
Viscosity index	135.0	108.0[b]	113.0[b]	Low	97.0[b]
Sulfur, %	0.16	0.25[b]	0.8[b]	.....	Low
Quality	Wax	Wax	Excell.	.....	Lube
Residue, % over 900°F	12.6	8.0	7.9[a]	.....	7.5[a]
Asphalt quality					

Name, state, and country	Cumarebo, Falcón, Venezuela	Chase, Kan., U.S.	Luby, Tex., U.S.	Barco (light), Colombia	Coldwater, Mich., U.S.
Gravity, API	47.7	48.1	48.8	48.7	49.7
Sulfur, %	0.07	0.26[i]	0.10	0.10	0.30[i]
Viscosity, SSU at 100°F		34		31.9	37
Date	1944			5-56	
Characterization factor:					
at 250°F	12.10	11.92	11.91	11.88	12.12
at 450°F	11.95	11.94	11.74	12.1	12.28
at 550°F	12.00	11.86	11.68	12.08	12.22
at 750°F	12.20	11.92	11.73	12.1	12.30
Average	12.06	11.91	11.77	12.04	12.25
Base	P	I	I	P	P
Loss, %		3.4	2.9	3.0	2.9
Gasoline:					
% to 300°F	37.5	40.6[a]	41.7[a]	36.0	28.3[a]
Oct. No., clear	64.9		62.0[b]	64.0	
Oct. No., 3 cc TEL	82.4		84.5[b]	83.7	
% to 400°F	51.3	51.6[a]	59.5[a]	51.0	44.1[a]
Oct. No., clear	56.5	49.0[b]	53.0	55.5	28.0[b]
Oct. No., 3 cc TEL	75.9		76.0[a]	77.0	
% to 450°F	57.4	56.9[a]	66.8[a]	57.0	51.8[a]
Quality			Good[b]		
Jet stock:					
% to 550°F	70.0	67.4[a]	78.8[a]	66.5	65.1[a]
API gravity	54.7	54.0[a]	51.8	56.3	57.3[a]
Quality		Good	Good	Good	
Kerosene-distillate:					
% 375–500°F	15.8	13.3[a]	18.3[a]	13.6	18.8[a]
API gravity	44.3	43.7	41.6	45.0	49.0
Smoke point	21.0	23.0[b]	19.5[b]	30.0	40.0[b]
Sulfur, %	Low	Low	Low	0.02	0.15[b]
Quality	Excell.	Good	Good	Excell.	Good
Distillate or diesel fuel:					
% 400–700°F	34.4	27.3[a]	29.6[a]	25.5	33.5[a]
Diesel index	66.0	58.0[b]	52.0[b]	67.0	78.0[b]
Pour point	20.0	15.0[b]	0[b]	20.0	35.0[b]
Sulfur, %	0.09	Low	Low	0.076	0.26[b]
Quality	Good	Good	Good		
Cracking stock (distilled):					
% 400–900°F	43.3	37.1[a]	35.6[a]	37.0	45.5[a]
Oct. No. (thermal)	65.0[b]	67.8[b]	70.0[b]	66.0[b]	64.5[b]
API gravity		34.0	33.2	34.0	39.0
Quality			Good		
Cracking stock (residual):					
% above 550°F	30.0	29.2[a]	18.3[a]	30.5	32.0[a]
API gravity	34.0	25.8	24.6	26.6	28.8
API cracked fuel	7.7	5.9	3.7	7.9	10.0
% gasoline (on stock)	65.9	55.4	55.1	55.1	57.1
% gasoline (on crude oil)	19.8	16.2	10 1	16.8	18.3
Lube distillate (undewaxed):					
% 700–900°F[c]	8.9	9.8[a]	6.0[a]	11.5	12.0[a]
Pour point	85.0			High	
Viscosity index	100.0+	81.0[b]	59.0[b]		118.0[a]
Sulfur, %	0.23		Low		0.35[b]
Quality	Excell.				Excell.
Residue, % over 900°F	5.4	7.9[a]	2.0[a]	9.0	7.5[a]
Asphalt quality					

Name, state, and country	Caico Seco, Anzoat., Venezuela	Pegasus, Tex., U.S.	Camiri, Bolivia	El Roble, Anzoat., Venezuela	Santa Anita, Bolivia
Gravity, API	49.7	52.3	54.7	54.6	57.0
Sulfur, %	0.13	0.04	0.02	0.09	0.02
Viscosity, SSU at 100°F	......	33	......	......	30.2 at 70°
Date	10-1-46	3-15-50	1941	1945–1950	1955
Characterization factor:					
at 250°F	12.05	12.34	12.35	11.75	12.10
at 450°F	12.10	12.41	12.04	11.55	12.06
at 550°F	12.10	12.34	11.98	11.80	12.02
at 750°F	12.20	12.47	12.18	12.25[a]	12.15
Average	12.11	12.39	12.14	11.85[a]	12.08
Base	P	P	PI	IP	PI
Loss, %	......	2.9	0.5	......	2.8
Gasoline:					
% to 300°F	34.3	31.1	44.7	56.5	50.9
Oct. No., clear	64.0[b]	36.6[a]	58.1	69.7	52.0
Oct. No., 3 cc TEL	83.0[b]	61.9[a]	......	86.5	76.6
% to 400°F	55.3	46.2	64.5	69.2	69.6
Oct. No., clear	52.0[b]	12.8[a]	44.8	64.2	39.2
Oct. No., 3 cc TEL	74.0[b]	46.0[b]	......	83.2	69.0
% to 450°F	68.0	53.8	72.3	73.7	76.6
Quality	......	......	......	Excell.	
Jet stock:					
% to 550°F	91.0	68.2	83.8	81.0	87.5
API gravity	56.2	61.0	59.4	56.8	58.4
Quality	......	......	......	Good	
Kerosene-distillate:					
% 375–500°F	30.5	19.0	18.7	10.4	17.7
API gravity	46.0	49.5	45.4	38.2	46.7
Smoke point	33.2[b]	45.2[b]	High	17.0[b]	30.0
Sulfur, %	0.04[b]	0.03	0.02	Low	0.021
Quality	Excell.	Excell.	Excell.	....	Excell.
Distillate or diesel fuel:					
% 400–700°F	41.5	37.0	28.8	20.5	23.6
Diesel index	68.0[b]	81.5	High	53.0	70.0
Pour point	20.0[b]	28.0[a]	25.0	15.0	10.0
Sulfur, %	0.11[b]	0.04	0.04	0.17	0.031
Quality	Good	......	......	......	Excell.
Cracking stock (distilled):					
% 400–900°F	42.2[a]	47.5	33.4	26.8	26.5
Oct. No. (thermal)	65.0[b]	62.5[b]	65.5	66.5[b]	65.0[b]
API gravity	38.0	44.9	38.1	37.5	31.0
Quality	......	......	......	......	
Cracking stock (residual):					
% above 550°F	2.5	28.9	15.7	19.0	9.7
API gravity	......	26.7	31.0	45.7	32.3
API cracked fuel	......	12.4	8.0	6.2	7.4
% gasoline (on stock)	......	52.5	62.0	80.3	64.3
% gasoline (on crude oil)	......	15.2	9.7	15.3	6.2
Lube distillate (undewaxed):					
% 700–900°F[c]	0.7[a]	10.5	4.6	6.3	2.9
Pour point	110.0[b]	63.0	High	120.0	98.0
Viscosity index	110.0[b]	115.0	High	113.0[b]	111.0
Sulfur, %	0.30[b]	Low	......	0.24	0.09
Quality	Excell.[a]	Excell.	......	Wax	Good
Residue, % over 900°F	Trace	3.4	1.6	4.0	0.7[a]
Asphalt quality					

N, naphthene base; I, intermediate base; P, paraffin base.
[a] Approximated from data on other fractions of same oil.
[b] Estimated from general correlations.
[c] Properties of various cuts 700–900°F, 700–930°F, 740–880°F, 700–970°F, and 710–870°F, all T.B.P.
[d] Estimated from U.S. Bureau of Mines Hempel analyses and other sources.
[e] Simply aviation gasoline, not always 300°F cut point.
[f] One sample has a pour point of minus 25°F and a Viscosity Index of 63.
[g] Research method octane number.
[h] Below the temperature shown.
[i] Sour oils, i.e., oils containing over 0.5 cu ft hydrogen sulfide per 100 gal before stabilization.

INDEX